X 51 $\frac{50}{N}$ EC

W9-CRB-275

# VACANCIES AND INTERSTITIALS IN METALS

*(International Conference on)*

# Vacancies and Interstitials
# in Metals

Proceedings of the International Conference held at Jülich, Germany,
23 - 28 September 1968

Editors:

## A. Seeger
*Max-Planck-Institut für Metallforschung, Institut für Physik, Stuttgart, Germany*

## D. Schumacher
*Dornier System GmbH, Friedrichshafen, Germany*

## W. Schilling
*Institut für Festkörper- und Neutronenphysik der Kernforschungsanlage Jülich, Germany*

## J. Diehl
*Max-Planck-Institut für Metallforschung, Institut für Sondermetalle, Stuttgart, Germany*

1970

NORTH-HOLLAND PUBLISHING COMPANY – AMSTERDAM

© North-Holland Publishing Company, Amsterdam, 1970

*All Rights Reserved. No part of this publication may be reproduced, stored in a retrieval system, or transmitted, in any form or by any means, electronic, mechanical, photo copying, recording or otherwise, without the prior permission of the Copyright owner.*

SBN 7204 0154 2

PUBLISHERS:

NORTH-HOLLAND PUBLISHING COMPANY — AMSTERDAM

SOLE DISTRIBUTORS FOR THE WESTERN HEMISPHERE:
WILEY INTERSCIENCE DIVISION
JOHN WILEY & SONS, INC. — NEW YORK

PRINTED IN THE NETHERLANDS

TN690
I58
1968
chem

# PREFACE

The International Conference on Vacancies and Interstitials in Metals was organized with the intention of giving a general survey of our present knowledge on point defect phenomena in metals. Although the rapid development in this field that took place in the early sixties appears to have slowed down in recent years, some of the most fundamental questions have not yet been answered in a definite way. This applies particularly to the problems associated with defect identification and the interpretation of the annealing stages.

It became evident that substantial further progress in solving these problems could only be expected from the development and application of experimental techniques which give more direct information on the nature and the properties of the individual defects. It also appeared essential to achieve a more integrated evaluation of different types of experiments, e.g., quenching, particle irradiation, plastic deformation, and measurements involving the equilibrium concentration of the defects. The outcome of the discussions at the conference has fully endorsed this view-point, and it is hoped that the publication of the conference proceedings will help to stimulate research in these directions.

The organizers felt that the aims outlined above could best be achieved if authoritative reviews of the various aspects of the field and of a number of recent and promising techniques were presented, if ample time for discussion of these reviews was made available, and if it was ensured that important new results were presented at the conference.

The response to these plans was such that the time allotted for the conference had to be extended to a full six-day week. Even during this period not all contributed papers that were accepted could be presented orally. The full texts of the contributed papers were published before the conference as a Report of the Kernforschungsanlage Jülich * and were available to all participants at the time of the conference. For a limited number of contributed papers time was available for oral introduction by the author and subsequent discussion, whereas the majority of the contributed papers were assigned to the invited speakers for inclusion in their reviews. They were discussed together with the review papers.

---

* Report Jül-Conf-2 (Vols. I, II) 1968. Additional copies may be obtained from Zentralbibliothek der Kernforschungsanlage Jülich, Jülich, Germany.

1290

The invited speakers were asked to give a general coverage of the field assigned to them, with some emphasis on their own work or on that of their groups. The organizers and editors would like to express their thanks to the invited speakers, who responded most willingly to these requests and to whom the lion's share in making the conference a success is due. The deadline for submission of the final manuscripts of the reviews was deliberately set well after the end of the conference. This was done to enable the authors to take into account fully the contributed papers presented at the conference as well as the outcome of the discussions. The editors are of the opinion that the resulting delay in the publication of the proceedings is more than compensated for by the better balance of views achieved in this way and by the general usefulness of this volume as a "state of the art" review of the field of vacancies and interstitials in metals.

The highlight of the conference was a panel discussion on what was clearly the most controversial problem at the conference, i.e., the interpretation of the annealing stages in fcc metals. Details on this discussion are given in the text. D.Schumacher acted as conference secretary. The editors would like to acknowledge the help of Drs. H.Blythe, W.Frank and H.Mehrer in condensing the discussion, which lasted several hours, to a — as we hope — faithful written record.

The present volume contains the full texts of the reviews, the introductions to the panel discussion by J.W.Corbett, J.S.Koehler and A.Seeger, and the record of the panel discussion. Discussion remarks, which were very extensive, have only been included if they were submitted in written form and if they had not been taken into account in the final version of the papers. Contrary to the original intention, the abstracts of the contributed papers could not be included. The reason for this was the overlengths of several review papers (which were not completely compensated for by the fact that some authors did not make full use of the allotted space). As a consequence we had also to leave out the discussion remarks pertaining to contributed papers.

The conference was organized by the Kernforschungsanlage Jülich in collaboration with the Arbeitsgemeinschaft Metallphysik (Deutsche Physikalische Gesellschaft, Deutsche Gesellschaft für Metallkunde, Verein Deutscher Eisenhüttenleute). It was sponsored by the International Union of Pure and Applied Physics and the Bundesministerium für wissenschaftliche Forschung. Organizers and editors would like once again to thank these organizations and institutions for their support and collaboration. Particular thanks are due to the directors and technical staff of the Kernforschungsanlage for their efforts in making this conference a success. The editors are indebted to the publishing company for the excellent cooperation throughout the whole production period.

Last but not least the great help of the scientific advisory committee in setting up the program of the conference is gratefully acknowledged. Members of this committee were: R.S.Barnes (who also successfully chaired the panel discussion), L.M.Clarebrough, D.Dautreppe, J.S.Koehler, S.Okuda and F.W.Young, Jr.

Less than a year after the meeting it is already evident that the conference and
its discussion has stimulated the research in the field of vacancies and interstitials
in metals to focus more sharply on the outstanding open questions. An essential
contribution  have been the many clarifying discussion remarks which are reflected
in the review papers. May the present publication make the outcome available to
the wider scientific community and, in this way, contribute to the further development of the field!

Stuttgart, Friedrichshafen, Jülich                                    A.Seeger
August 1969                                                           D.Schumacher
                                                                      W.Schilling
                                                                      J.Diehl

# LIST OF CONTRIBUTORS

Alefeld, G., 959
Anthony, T.R., 935
Baldwin, T.O., 619
Balluffi, R.W., 125
Beukel, A.van den, 427
Burger, G., 255
Chik, K.P., 183
Corbett, J.W., 377
Dederichs, P.H., 619
Diehl, J., 739
Friedel, J., 787
Galligan, J.M., 575
Gonser, U., 649
Hehenkamp, Th., 91
Hoch, M., 81
Isebeck, K., 255
Koehler, J.S., 169, 989
Kraftmakher, Ya.A., 59
Kronmüller, H., 667
Leibfried, G., 803

Lie, K.H., 125
Mehrer, H., 1
Müller, E.W., 557
Nelson, R.S., 637
Nihoul, J., 839
Schilling, W., 255
Schmatz, W., 589
Schumacher, D., 889
Seeger, A., 1, 999
Seidman, D.N., 125
Siegel, R.W., 125
Sosin, A., 729
Strelkov, P.G., 59
Thomas, G.J., 531
Venables, J.A., 531
Wenzl, H., 255, 363
Wilkens, M., 485
Wollenberger, H., 215
Young, Jr., F.W., 619

# CONTENTS

# PART 1

# DIFFUSION ·AND EQUILIBRIUM MEASUREMENTS

# ANALYSIS OF SELF-DIFFUSION AND EQUILIBRIUM MEASUREMENTS

A.SEEGER and H.MEHRER

*Max-Planck-Institut für Metallforschung, Institut für Physik, Stuttgart,*
*and Institut für theoretische und angewandte Physik der Universität Stuttgart, Germany*

## 1. Introduction

The simultaneous measurements of thermal expansion and of lattice parameters at high temperatures have demonstrated that in a number of metals (Al [1–4], Cu [5], Ag [6], Au [7], Pb [8,9], Na [10,11], Cd [12]) vacancies and not interstitials are the dominant point defects in thermal equilibrium. This is in accord with theoretical predictions [13–15], originally made for copper, on the energies of formation of mono-vacancies and interstitial atoms.

A natural extension of this result is the working hypothesis that self-diffusion in these metals is due to a mono-vacancy mechanism. For many years self-diffusion data have indeed been interpreted in terms of mono-vacancies. For such a mechanism the activation energy of self-diffusion, defined in terms of the temperature dependence of the tracer self-diffusion coefficient $D^T$ by

$$Q^{SD} \equiv d(\ln D^T)/d(1/kT) , \qquad (1.1)$$

is related to the energy of formation, $E_{1V}^F$, and the energy of migration, $E_{1V}^M$, of the mono-vacancies according to

$$Q^{SD} = E_{1V}^F + E_{1V}^M . \qquad (1.2)$$

The validity of (1.2), and thus the correctness of the hypothesis that self-diffusion is due to a mono-vacancy mechanism, may be tested by experiment, since $E_{1V}^F$ and $E_{1V}^M$ can in principle be obtained separately.

$E_{1V}^F$ may be obtained either from the quenched-in resistivity as a function of the quenching temperature $T_q$ or from the temperature dependence of the equilibrium concentration of vacant lattice sites, provided that di-vacancies, tri-vacancies, etc.

may be neglected compared with the equilibrium concentration of mono-vacancies[*].

$E_{1V}^M$ may be obtained from annealing experiments on quenched specimens under conditions where mono-vacancies are the only intrinsic point defects present and where the influence of impurities is negligible.

In the literature numerous examples may be found where it was claimed that (1.2) had been verified, sometimes for the same metal with different sets of values for $Q^{SD}$, $E_{1V}^F$, and $E_{1V}^M$. Critical examination of these examples as well as both the discussions in the literature and in this volume indicate that such claims should be considered with a certain degree of reservation.

The difficulty in deciding whether (1.2) is verified or not arises from the difficulty in ascertaining whether the quenching experiments have been carried out under ideal conditions. If the quench was too slow, vacancy losses or excessive association to vacancy clusters may have occurred, leading to too low a value of $E_{1V}^F$. On the other hand, the faster the quench the more likely it is that the specimen has been damaged during the quenching. (The frequently used procedure of extrapolating the quenched-in resistivity to infinite quenching speed, as reasonable as it may seem at first sight, may enhance the undesirable effects of quenching strains.) In the annealing of quenched specimens, the concentration range in which the vacancy concentration is large enough for impurities to be negligible and at the same time small enough for di-vacancy formation to be unimportant, may be quite narrow (if it exists at all) and difficult to realize even in very pure samples (compare, e.g., the article of Chik [19] in this volume).

In view of these difficulties, it appears advisable to start the discussion of vacancy properties not by attempting to verify eq. (1.1) with the help of quenching experiments, but to try to exploit first those experimental data that involve the equilibrium concentrations of the point defects. Such experiments (which we shall call for short "equilibrium experiments", although many of them involve transport properties and are therefore not equilibrium measurements in the true sense of the word) have several advantages over the non-equilibrium experiments such as those involving quenching, irradiation, or cold-working. The accurate characterization of the specimens is less critical in the equilibrium measurements. In particular, the influence of impurities is less important than in some of the quenching and irradiation experiments. The basic theory required for interpretation of the equilibrium experiments is more straightforward and simpler than that for the non-equilibrium experiments, although its actual application may be not without pitfalls and re-

---

[*] In fcc metals simple theoretical arguments show in agreement with experiment that di-vacancies have a lower activation energy of migration and are substantially more mobile than mono-vacancies [16–18]. This means that their fractional contribution to the coefficient of self-diffusion is larger than to the total concentration of vacant sites. If it can be shown that self-diffusion in fcc metals is via mono-vacancies only, then the contribution of di-vacancies (and of larger vacancy clusters, unless their binding energies are extraordinarily high) to the equilibrium concentration of vacant sites may be disregarded. See section 2.3.

quires good physical judgment. Equilibrium measurements have in general to be carried out at quite high temperatures. It is often not easy to achieve the experimental accuracy that is necessary in order to obtain significant results, and the literature is certainly not free from accounts of equilibrium measurements that have eventually proved to be misleading.

Among the experiments involving the equilibrium concentrations of point defects the measurements of self-diffusion coefficients are of particular importance, since under favourable conditions (if suitable radioisotopes are available, and in a suitable – usually not too wide – range of temperatures) tracer self-diffusion coefficients can now be determined with an accuracy of a few percent. Any conclusions that we can draw from such self-diffusion experiments should therefore be particularly reliable and helpful in the interpretation of other experiments that are subject to larger uncertainties. As the next step we shall then consider other high-temperature transport experiments, in particular the transport of matter in a temperature gradient and in an electric field, and the various methods for deducing information on the concentrations of points defects in thermal equilibrium. The accuracy of these techniques does not yet reach the standards set by the self-diffusion experiments. The last-mentioned group includes the simultaneous measurement of the change of the lattice-parameter, $\Delta a/a$, and of the specimen length, $\Delta l/l$, which was mentioned at the beginning and which permits an unequivocal interpretation in terms of the total concentrations of vacant lattice sites, $C_V$, and of occupied interstices, $C_I$, according to (for cubic crystals)

$$3(\Delta l/l - \Delta a/a) = C_V - C_I \,. \tag{1.3}$$

The questions we shall ask when analysing the self-diffusion and other high-temperature experiments are the following:

(i) How can we decide whether the measured activation energy of self-diffusion, $Q^{SD}$, is to be interpreted in terms of (1.2) or not?

(ii) If eq. (1.2) is not valid, i.e., if defects other than mono-vacancies contribute to the self-diffusion coefficient, how can we nevertheless extract reliable information on mono-vacancies from the self-diffusion data?

(iii) How can we deduce from high-temperature experiments reliable information on point defects other than mono-vacancies, e.g., di-vacancies?

The answers to questions (i) and (ii) are important even if the self-diffusion coefficient is found to obey within experimental accuracy the Arrhenius equation

$$D^T(T) = D_o^T \exp(-Q^{SD}/kT) \,, \tag{1.4}$$

with temperature independent pre-exponential factor $D_o^T$ and temperature independent activation energy $Q^{SD}$, since even in this case we have no *a priori* guarantee that $Q^{SD}$ is given by eq. (1.1).

The general discussion just outlined will be contained in section 2. In section 3 we shall then turn to the discussion of individual metals with particular emphasis on those fcc metals for which fairly definite conclusions may already be drawn.

## 2. General discussion

### 2.1. Self-diffusion
#### 2.1.1. Standard theory for mono-vacancies

The *concentration of mono-vacancies* in thermal equilibrium is given by

$$C_{1V}^{eq} = \exp(-G_{1V}^F/kT) = \exp(S_{1V}^F/k)\exp(-E_{1V}^F/kT), \tag{2.1}$$

where $G_{1V}^F$, $S_{1V}^F$ and $E_{1V}^F$ denote the free energy, the entropy and the energy of formation of a mono-vacancy, respectively. Boltzmann's constant and the absolute temperature are denoted, as usual, by $k$ and $T$.

Let $D_{1V}$ be the *diffusion coefficient* of a mono-vacancy. In general, diffusion coefficients in crystals are second-rank tensors. For the time being we shall confine ourselves to cubic crystals, where these tensors reduce to scalar quantities; the extension to, say, hexagonal crystals is fairly simple. If we make the assumption that a vacancy diffuses by jumps to nearest neighbour sites only, we may write

$$D_{1V} = g_{1V}^M\, a^2\, v_{1V}^o\, \exp(S_{1V}^M/k)\exp(-E_{1V}^M/kT). \tag{2.2}$$

In (2.2) $a$ is the edge length of the elementary cube, $E_{1V}^M$ is the activation energy of migration and has the physical meaning of the energy barrier for the jump of an adjacent atom into the vacancy, $S_{1V}^M$ and $v_{1V}^o$ denote the entropy of migration and the attempt frequency associated with such a jump. The quantity $g_{1V}^M$ is a geometrical factor which is determined by the crystal geometry and which has to be worked out by application of the Einstein-Smoluchowski relation between the diffusion coefficient and the mean square displacement per unit time. For nearest-neighbour jumps in the fcc, the bcc, and the simple cubic lattice we have $g_{1V}^M = 1$.

If the mono-vacancy migration energy $E_{1V}^M$ is known, the only unknown on the right-hand side of (2.2) is the product $v_{1V}^o\exp(S_{1V}^M/k)$. For the purpose of comparison of different metals and different diffusion mechanisms it is expedient to subdivide this product by adopting a definite description for the determination of the attempt frequency $v_{1V}^o$. We shall adopt the following description: Consider the potential energy diagram of an atom of mass $m$ moving from its lattice site over the saddle point of height $E_{1V}^M$ into the vacant site, and assume that the potential energy is a sinoidal function of the position of the atom. The frequency factor $v_{1V}^o$ is then defined as the frequency of the small-amplitude oscillations of the atom of mass $m$ in the minima of the potential energy profile. We obtain for fcc crystals

$$v_{1V}^o = \frac{1}{a}\left(\frac{E_{1V}^M}{m}\right)^{\frac{1}{2}} \tag{2.3a}$$

and for bcc crystals

$$v_{1V}^o = \frac{1}{a}\left(\frac{2E_{1V}^M}{3m}\right)^{\frac{1}{2}}. \tag{2.3b}$$

We may now combine (2.1) and (2.2) to define the *macroscopic self-diffusion coefficient* for a mono-vacancy mechanism,

$$D_{1V}^{SD} = D_{1V}\, C_{1V}^{eq} \ . \tag{2.4}$$

$D_{1V}^{SD}$ is the diffusion coefficient pertaining to the transport of matter associated with the diffusion of the equilibrium concentration of mono-vacancies. The macroscopic diffusion coefficient may be deduced from a so-called thermal diffusion experiment (transport of matter in a temperature gradient) or an electrodiffusion experiment (transport of matter in an electric field); for more details the reader is referred to section 2.2 and to the article by Hehenkamp in this volume [20].

We have to make a clear distinction between the macroscopic self-diffusion coefficient $D^{SD}$ and the *tracer self-diffusion coefficient* $D^T$. The latter is defined as the diffusion coefficient of a tracer atom in a crystal in the absence of concentration gradients of defects or tracer atoms, and of temperature gradients or electric fields. As first pointed out by Bardeen and Herring [21], for self-diffusion via a defect mechanism $D^{SD}$ and $D^T$ differ from each other. The physical reason for this is that even if the *defects* carry out a random motion the *tracer atoms* do not. If a tracer atom has just exchanged its site with a vacancy, the probability that its next jump brings it back to its original position (which is now vacant) is larger than the probability that the next jump takes it to any other of the adjacent sites. In a defect mechanism of self-diffusion, successive jumps of tracer atoms are correlated. The measure of the degree of correlation is the correlation factor $f$ defined by the relationship

$$D^T = f \cdot D^{SD} \ . \tag{2.5a}$$

In a general anisotropic crystal the correlation factor is a fourth-rank tensor. For cubic crystals it reduces again to a scalar. A high degree of correlation corresponds to small values of $f$ (e.g., $f = 0$ for the self-diffusion via a defect mechanism in an infinitely long one-dimensional chain), whereas vanishing correlation (e.g., for self-diffusion through direct exchange of neighbouring atoms or ring mechanisms, or an interstitial [but not an interstitialcy] mechanism) corresponds to a value $f = 1$. Different defect mechanisms of self-diffusion have different correlation factors. If the difference in mass (and hence in the attempt frequency as defined above) between the tracer and the host atoms is neglected, the correlation factor for simple mechanisms is simply a number that may be calculated from the crystal geometry. Numerical values for the correlation factor for a mono-vacancy mechanism of self-diffusion in some of the cubic crystal structures defined by

$$f_{1V} = D_{1V}^T / D_{1V}^{SD} \tag{2.5b}$$

are given in table 1 according to Compaan and Haven [22]. An approximate expression is

$$f_{1V} = 1 - 2/z + \dots \ , \tag{2.6}$$

Table 1

Correlation factors for tracer self-diffusion via mono-vacancies, $f_{1V}$, and via di-vacancies, $f_{2V}$.

| | $z$ | $1 - 2/z$ | $f_{1V}$ [22] | $f_{2V}$ [37] |
|---|---|---|---|---|
| Diamond | 4 | 0.5 | 0.5 | − |
| Simple cubic | 6 | 0.6667 | 0.65549 | − |
| Body-centered cubic | 8 | 0.7500 | 0.72149 | − |
| Face-centered cubic | 12 | 0.8333 | 0.78145 | 0.475 |

where $z$ is the coordination number of the crystal structure. The factor 2 in (2.6) arises from the fact that the back-jump of a tracer to the site from which it came un-does two vacancy jumps.

Measurements of the temperature dependence of tracer self-diffusion coefficients are usually represented in terms of Arrhenius' law (1.4). Compilations of $Q^{SD}$ and of $D_0^T$ for metals may be found in a number of text and reference books. Particular-ly recommended for its critical selection of the experimental data is that in the fourth edition of Smithell's Metals Reference Book [23] (compiled by A.D.Le Claire).

By inserting (2.5), (2.4) and (2.1) into (1.4), we obtain for the activation energy of self-diffusion (for short: the self-diffusion energy) by the mono-vacancy mechan-ism the expression

$$Q^{SD} = E_{1V}^F + E_{1V}^M = Q_{1V}^{SD} \tag{2.7}$$

and, confining ourselves again to cubic crystals, for the corresponding pre-exponen-tial factor

$$D_0^T = f_{1V} \, g_{1V}^M \, a^2 \, \nu_{1V}^0 \, \exp[(S_{1V}^F + S_{1V}^M)/k] \ . \tag{2.8}$$

The interpretation of measured (temperature independent) values of $Q^{SD}$ and $D_0^T$ in terms of (2.7) and (2.8) may be called the *standard interpretation of self-dif-fusion*. Eq. (2.7) is identical with (1.2). In section 1 we have already raised the question of how the validity of this equation may be tested. If we do not wish to invoke non-equilibrium measurements to determine $E_{1V}^M$ for the reasons discussed in the introduction, we cannot test (2.7) directly. However, approximate necessary conditions for the validity of the standard interpretation may be derived from (2.8). Provided we have an estimate of $E_{1V}^M$ to be used in (2.3), the only unknown quantity on the right-hand side of (2.8) is the sum $S_{1V}^F + S_{1V}^M$. The entropy of for-mation, $S_{1V}^F$, is related to the change of the vibration spectrum of the crystal upon the introduction of a vacancy. The entropy of migration, $S_{1V}^M$, is determined by the change in the lattice vibration spectrum associated with the transfer of an atom from a lattice site adjacent to a vacancy to the saddle-point configuration. By its very nature, $S_{1V}^F$ has to be positive. There are strong arguments that the sum $S_{1V}^F + S_{1V}^M$ has also to be positive. For the noble metals, calculations for $S_{1V}^F$ are available which indicate that its magnitude should be about $0.5\,k$ to $1.2\,k$ [24]. Calculations of $S_{1V}^M$ are much less reliable than those of $S_{1V}^F$ since little is known about the atomic force constants in the saddle-point configuration. The available estimates indicate that for the close-packed metals $S_{1V}^F + S_{1V}^M$ is unlikely to exceed a few $k$. In table 2 we have calculated numerical values for $D_0^T$ from (2.8) for various fcc metals using a tentative value of $S_{1V}^F + S_{1V}^M = 2.5\,k$ and reasonable assumptions for $E_{1V}^M$. If the measured values of $D_0^T$ differ by more than a factor of two from the calculated value, this should be taken as an indication that the interpretation of the measured data in terms of eqs. (2.7) and (2.8) might not be justified. In this case the possibilities that the activation energies and entropies are not temperature independent and/or that mechanisms other than the mono-vacancy mechanism contribute to the self-diffusion coefficient should be considered.

## 2.1.2. Temperature dependence of energies and entropies

We have carried out the discussion of section 2.1.1 under the assumption that the activation energy of self-diffusion and the pre-exponential factor are independent of temperature, but the equations of section 2.1.1 remain valid if this assumption is not made. At a fixed reference temperature, the energy and the corresponding entropy are independent of each other. It is important to realize, however, that the *temperature variations* of the energy and of the entropy are no longer independent from each other but are related by the thermodynamic relationship [25]

$$\left(\frac{\partial S}{\partial T}\right)_p = \frac{1}{T}\left(\frac{\partial E}{\partial T}\right)_p. \tag{2.9}$$

Eq. (2.9) is easily derived from the thermodynamic formulae

$$G = E - TS \tag{2.10}$$

and

$$\left(\frac{\partial G}{\partial T}\right)_p = -S. \tag{2.11}$$

(It is assumed that we consider conditions of constant pressure throughout, so that the appropriate free energy is the Gibbs free energy $G$. The appropriate energy is not the internal energy $E$ but the enthalpy $H$. However, to remain in accord with the general usage, we shall nevertheless use the symbol $E$ and call it simply "energy".)

From (2.9) we see that an energy can only depend on temperature if the associated entropy does also (see also [26]). All entropies have to be temperature dependent in the temperature range where quantum statistics rather than classical statistics must be used. This means that one has to be careful if one compares activation energies measured well below the Debye temperature with measurements above

Table 2

Calculated values for the attempt frequency $\nu^o_{1V}$ of mono-vacancies and pre-exponential factors $D^T_o$ (assuming $S^F_{1V} + S^M_{1V} = 2.5\,k$) for various metals. $A$ is the atomic weight.

| | $a$ [Å] | $A$ | $E^M_{1V}$ [eV] | $\nu^o_{1V}$ [$10^{12}$ s$^{-1}$] | $\nu^o_{1V} f_{1V} a^2$ [$10^{-3}$ cm$^2$ s$^{-1}$] | $D^T_o$ [cm$^2$ s$^{-1}$] |
|---|---|---|---|---|---|---|
| Au | 4.07 | 197 | 0.89 | 1.61 | 2.8 | 0.034 |
| Ag | 4.08 | 108 | 0.88 | 2.16 | 2.8 | 0.034 |
| Cu | 3.61 | 63 | 1.04 | 3.47 | 3.5 | 0.043 |
| Pt | 3.92 | 195 | 1.38 | 2.10 | 2.5 | 0.031 |
| Ni | 3.52 | 59 | 1.35 | 4.20 | 4.1 | 0.050 |
| Al | 4.04 | 27 | 0.62 | 3.66 | 4.7 | 0.057 |
| Pb | 3.49 | 207 | 0.60 | 1.51 | 1.4 | 0.017 |

the Debye temperature. Above the Debye temperature the entropies are independent of temperature as long as the harmonic approximation may be used, i.e., as long as thermal expansion may be neglected. Considering the equilibrium concentration of mono-vacancies, eq. (2.1), as an example, it is obvious that the anharmonicity of the lattice vibrations and the accompanying thermal expansion give rise to a relaxation of the vacancy configuration which increases with increasing temperature. This means that $(\partial S^F_{1V}/\partial T) > 0$ and, according to (2.9), $(\partial E^F_{1V}/\partial T) > 0$. The Arrhenius plot $\ln C^{eq}_{1V}$ versus $(kT)^{-1}$ shows upward curvature at high temperatures. This is seen from the relationship

$$\frac{d(\ln C^{eq}_{1V})}{d(1/kT)} = -E^F_{1V}(T) , \qquad (2.12)$$

which is easily derived from (2.1), (2.9) and (2.11) and which is valid for any temperature variation of $E^F_{1V}(T)$ [25]. In agreement with physical intuition, the equilibrium concentration of vacancies at high temperatures is higher than if the thermal expansion had been disregarded. This can also be seen from

$$\frac{\partial^2 G}{\partial T^2} = -\frac{\partial S}{\partial T} = -\frac{1}{T}\frac{\partial E}{\partial T} , \qquad (2.13)$$

which shows that the thermal expansion causes the free energy of formation of a vacancy to decrease more rapidly with temperature than it would do otherwise. It should be noted that this additional reduction in the *free* energy is of necessity accompanied by an *increase* in the *energy*!

The preceding arguments are perfectly general and hold not only for energies and entropies of formation but also for energies and entropies of migration. The generality of these arguments has not always been appreciated and has led to confusion in the recent literature on the temperature dependence of migration energies [27]. In order to arrive at eq. (1.1) for the energy of self-diffusion, when both sides of the equation are temperature dependent, one has to make the assumption that the temperature dependence of such factors as $a^2$ and $\nu^0_{1V}$ may be neglected compared with those resulting from the energy and entropy. In cases where this approximation is not justified it may easily be corrected for.

Let us now consider the order of magnitudes of the temperature dependences which one might expect. Since it is much easier to visualize the physical origin of the temperature dependence of the entropies than that of the energies, we shall start with a consideration of $\partial S/\partial T$. In a close-packed metal one does not expect a drastic change of the vacancy configuration, since this is largely determined by the crystal geometry and by the metallic binding forces, which are known to vary rapidly with the interatomic separation. It appears reasonable to assume that the change in $S^F_{1V}$ in going from the Debye temperature to the melting point is less than the value of $S^F_{1V}$ at the Debye temperature, since the formation of a vacancy is a much stronger perturbation of the lattice vibration spectrum than the subsequent change of the vacancy configuration due to anharmonic effects. In view of what has been said in section 2.1.1, this means that the expected variations in $S_{1V}^F$ in close-packed metals between the Debye temperature and the neighbourhood of the melting point is at best of the order of a few tenth of Boltzmann's constant $k$ [28]. The expected variation of $E_{1V}^F$ is thus rather small, and it may suffice to make the simplest possible assumption, namely, that $E_{1V}^F$ varies linearly with temperature. This leads to

$$E_{1V}^F(T) = E_{1V}^F(T_o) + \alpha k(T - T_o) \tag{2.14a}$$

and

$$S_{1V}^F(T) = S_{1V}^F(T_o) + \alpha k \ln(T/T_o) . \tag{2.14b}$$

Here $T_o$ is a reference temperature, which should not be chosen too far below the Debye temperature, since otherwise the effects of quantum statistics, which are not well described by (2.14), would have to be taken into account. Since in the discussions on the identification of the annealing stages the comparison between mono-vacancy migration energies deduced from high-temperature experiments and those obtained from recovery experiments plays an important role, it is expedient to choose $T_o$ in the temperature range in which these recovery experiments are usually performed, i.e., for gold near room temperature. Typically the ratio between the absolute melting temperature $T_m$ and this annealing temperature is of the order 3.5 to 4. This means that $\alpha = 0.2$ leads to an entropy variation between $T_o$ and $T_m$ of about $0.26 \, k$. For the noble metals this would correspond to an increase of the mono-vacancy formation energy between the temperature of typical annealing experiments and the melting point of about 0.02 eV.

The preceding qualitative arguments are in agreement with estimates by Levinson and Nabarro [29] and Girifalco [30]. These authors do not use (2.14a, b), but employ instead a power expansion of $G_{1V}^F(T)$ up to the second power in $(T - T_o)$. Because of (2.13) such an expansion misses out the linear term in the temperature dependence of $E_{1V}^F(T)$ and the logarithmic terms in $S_{1V}^F(T)$ and $G_{1V}^F(T)$, which should be present in the *high-temperature* expansions considered in all the work discussed here. The numerical values of Levinson and Nabarro and of Girifalco can therefore not be compared directly with those of Seeger and Schumacher [28] and of Nowick and Dienes [31] (see below), but it is, nevertheless, clear that they are not in conflict with the conclusion that in the close-packed metals the temperature dependence of the formation energy of mono-vacancies is rather small.

If the environment of the defect is less densely packed, we expect a stronger temperature variation of the entropy and hence a larger α-value. This applies to the formation energies and entropies of mono-vacancies in non-close-packed structures* and possibly also near transformation temperatures (fusion, crystallographic transformation). A larger α is also expected for the *entropy of migration* in the close-

* For a discussion of diamond-structure semiconductors see Seeger and Chik [32].

packed metals, since the saddle-point configuration is presumably more sensitive to anharmonic effects than the ground state configuration of a vacancy. Numerical estimates for the entropies of migration and their temperature dependences are quite difficult, since very little is known of the force constants in saddle-point configurations. In the context of self-diffusion we are particularly interested in the sum $\alpha_F + \alpha_M$, where the subscript F refers to the formation and the subscript M to the migration of mono-vacancies. $\alpha_F + \alpha_M$ has been estimated by Nowick and Dienes [31] as being not larger than unity (in units of $k$). This estimate still leaves room for the possibility that $\alpha_M$ is distinctly larger than $\alpha_F$ and is in full agreement with the intuitive thinking on close-packed metals which we have described above.

Flynn [31a] has recently reconsidered and extended Zener's theory of the entropy of diffusion [25], which relates this quantity to the temperature dependence of the shear modulus. He points out that in such a model a non-linear temperature variation of the elastic constants would result in a temperature dependent activation energy. From the comparison with a simple model for the vacancy formation energy Flynn concludes that in mono-atomic crystals the relative temperature dependence of the vacancy formation energy should be about $\frac{1}{3}$ of that of the vacancy migration energy. This is in agreement with the arguments given above. Estimates of temperature dependences of the formation and migration energies from the few reliable data available on the temperature dependence of elastic constants at high temperatures lead to the same orders of magnitudes as the estimates given above.

The evaluation of measured self-diffusion data taking into account the temperature of the activation energies and entropies will be considered in section 2.1.3.

### 2.1.3. Self-diffusion by more than one mechanism

At the end of section 2.1.1 we mentioned as a second possibility (in addition to the temperature dependences discussed in section 2.1.2) to account for deviations from the mono-vacancy mechanism, the inclusion of diffusion mechanisms other than mono-vacancy diffusion.

In addition to the diffusion through the bulk, self-diffusion may also occur along short-circuiting paths such as dislocations or grain boundaries. This will be considered separately in section 2.1.5.

So far no clear-cut evidence has been found in metals that interstitials contribute to self-diffusion, although for the non-close-packed metals this possibility should be kept in mind for future discussions. In silicon, which does have a very open structure, the evidence that at high temperatures self-diffusion is dominated by an interstitial mechanism is very strong. On the other hand, in Ge, which has the same crystal structure as silicon but is not quite as loosely packed as Si, it appears that interstitials do not contribute substantially to self-diffusion [32].

The most interesting additional mechanism which we have to consider here is that of di-vacancy diffusion. In fcc metals di-vacancies are more mobile than mono-vacancies [16—18], and they may make a noticeable contribution to self-diffusion even if their concentration is much smaller than that of the mono-vacancies (see the remarks in section 1).

In thermal equilibrium, the di-vacancy concentration, $C_{2V}$, is given in terms of the mono-vacancy concentration, $C_{1V}$, by

$$C_{2V} = \frac{z}{2} C_{1V}^2 \exp(G_{2V}^B/kT)$$

$$= \frac{z}{2} C_{1V}^2 \exp(\Delta S_{2V}/k) \exp(E_{2V}^B/kT) \ . \tag{2.15}$$

In (2.15) $z/2$ denotes the number of distinct possible orientations that a di-vacancy may take up. (If the di-vacancies consist of two adjacent vacancies as they presumably do in the fcc metals, $z$ is the coordination number of the crystal structure.) $G_{2V}^B = E_{2V}^B + T\Delta S_{2V}$ denotes the free energy of binding, $E_{2V}^B$ the binding energy, and $\Delta S_{2V}$ the association entropy of di-vacancies. These quantities are related to the formation energies and entropies as follows:

$$E_{2V}^B = 2E_{1V}^F - E_{2V}^F \tag{2.16a}$$

$$\Delta S_{2V} \equiv -S_{2V}^B = S_{2V}^F - 2S_{1V}^F \ . \tag{2.16b}$$

The di-vacancy diffusion coefficient may be written as

$$D_{2V} = g_{2V}^M a^2 \nu_{2V}^0 \exp(S_{2V}^M/k) \exp(-E_{2V}^M/kT) \ . \tag{2.17}$$

Here $E_{2V}^M$ and $S_{2V}^M$ denote the energy and entropy of migration of the di-vacancy. In fcc crystals, where it is usual to consider that the movement of a di-vacancy occurs by jumps of atoms that are nearest neighbours of both vacant sites, the attempt frequency may be calculated from the same model as in the mono-vacancy case and is given by

$$\nu_{2V}^0 = \frac{1}{a} (E_{2V}^M/m)^{\frac{1}{2}} \ . \tag{2.18}$$

The geometrical factor is in this case

$$g_{2V}^M = \tfrac{1}{6} \ . \tag{2.19}$$

The macroscopic self-diffusion coefficient for a di-vacancy mechanism may be written as

$$D_{2V}^{SD} = g_{2V}^{SD} D_{2V} C_{2V} \ . \tag{2.20}$$

The factor $g_{2V}^{SD}$ is determined by the crystal structure and follows from simple geometrical considerations. For fcc crystals we have [3,33]

$$g_{2V}^{SD} = 4 \ . \tag{2.21}$$

(The corresponding geometrical factor for mono-vacancies, $g_{1V}^{SD}$, is unity in all cases considered in this paper, and has therefore not been written explicitly.)

If we insert all the numerical factors into (2.20), we obtain for fcc crystals

$$D_{2V}^{SD} = 4\,a^2\,\nu_{2V}^o\,\exp\left[(S_{2V}^M + S_{1V}^F + \Delta S_{2V})/k\right]\,\exp\left(-\frac{Q_2}{kT}\right), \qquad (2.22)$$

where

$$Q_2 \equiv 2E_{1V}^F - E_{2V}^B + E_{2V}^M . \qquad (2.22a)$$

Similar considerations may be carried out for tri-vacancies, quadri-vacancies, etc. For these larger multiple vacancies, however, the geometries of the low-energy and saddle-point configurations are not *a priori* clear and may vary from metal to metal. Some of these possibilities have been discussed in the literature [34—36]. In the present paper these larger clusters will not be treated in detail.

The macroscopic self-diffusion coefficient due to bulk-diffusion of vacancy type defects is given by

$$D_V^{SD} = D_{1V}^{SD} + D_{2V}^{SD} + D_{3V}^{SD} + \ldots , \qquad (2.23a)$$

and the corresponding tracer self-diffusion coefficient is

$$D_V^T = f_{1V}\,D_{1V}^{SD} + f_{2V}\,D_{2V}^{SD} + f_{3V}\,D_{3V}^{SD} + \ldots . \qquad (2.23b)$$

In (2.23b) $f_{iV}$ denotes the correlation factor for $i$-fold vacancies.

Before (2.23a) or (2.23b) may be compared with experiment, the temperature dependence of the energies and entropies has to be considered. Similar considerations as those in section 2.1.2 apply. In many metals, the dominant terms in (2.23a) and (2.23b) are the mono-vacancy terms. In such cases the temperature dependences of the multiple-vacancy energies and entropies lead to corrections of corrections, and it may suffice to use the same parameters for the multiple vacancies as for mono-vacancies. In such cases, additional free parameters characterizing the temperature dependence of, say, the di-vacancy formation and migration energies could not be determined from the experimental data anyway.

With these simplifications, the explicit expression for the tracer self-diffusion coefficient in fcc crystals due to mono-vacancy and di-vacancy migration reads [28]

$$D^T = D_{10}\,\exp(-Q_1/kT)\,\exp(2\alpha\ln T/T_o)$$

$$\times \exp[-2\alpha(T-T_o)/T]\,[1 + D_{21}\,\exp(-Q_{21}/kT)] . \qquad (2.24)$$

Eq. (2.24) contains five adjustable parameters, namely

$$\alpha = \tfrac{1}{2}\,(\alpha_M + \alpha_F) , \qquad (2.25)$$

characterizing the temperature dependence of the activation energies and entropies of self-diffusion,

$$Q_1 = E_{1V}^F + E_{1V}^M , \qquad (2.26a)$$

$$D_{10} = a^2 \, \nu^o_{1V} \, f_{1V} \, \exp(S^M_{1V}/k) \, \exp(S^F_{1V}/k) \,, \tag{2.26b}$$

characterizing the mono-vacancy contribution, and

$$Q_{21} \equiv Q_2 - Q_1 = E^F_{1V} - E^M_{1V} + E^M_{2V} - E^B_{2V} \,, \tag{2.27}$$

$$D_{21} \equiv D_{20}/D_{10} = 4 \, \frac{f_{2V}}{f_{1V}} \exp\left(\frac{S^F_{1V} + \Delta S_{2V}}{k}\right) \frac{\nu^o_{2V} \, \exp(S^M_{2V}/k)}{\nu^o_{1V} \, \exp(S^M_{1V}/k)} \,, \tag{2.28}$$

characterizing the ratio of the di-vacancy contribution to the mono-vacancy contribution to the tracer self-diffusion coefficient. The corresponding expressions for the macroscopic self-diffusion coefficients are obtained from the preceding equations by putting the correlation factors equal to unity. The application of the equations to the measurements of self-diffusion of various metals will be covered in section 3.

### 2.1.4. Isotope effect and correlation factors

The jump frequency of an atom into an adjacent vacancy depends on the mass of the atom, as shown by (2.3). The masses of the long-lived isotopes that are used for tracer self-diffusion coefficients are different from those of the atoms in the matrix, which may or may not contain different stable isotopes.

It is therefore not quite correct to insert, as we have done, the diffusion coefficients of mono-vacancies, di-vacancies etc. into the expression for the self-diffusion coefficient, since these are quantities pertaining to the interchange of the vacant sites with all atoms of the crystal and not just to the migration of the tracer isotope.

We shall see presently that the correlation factor for tracer diffusion depends on the ratio of the tracer mass to the mass of the abundant isotope. This may be used for the experimental determination of the correlation factor. However, for all but very light materials such as hydrogen, helium, and lithium, these "isotope effects" are so small that they may be disregarded in the analysis of the "usual" diffusion experiments.

Let us illustrate these general remarks by considering self-diffusion via a mono-vacancy mechanism. Fig. 1 shows a vacancy surrounded by isotopes of the abundant mass $m$ and by one tracer atom of mass $m^I$. As indicated in fig. 1, the frequencies $\nu$ and $\nu^I$ with which the vacancy exchanges its site with an atom depends on the mass of that atom. If, for example, $\nu^I > \nu$, the vacancy exchanges its site more frequently with an adjacent atom of mass $m^I$ than with an adjacent atom of mass $m$. Successive jumps of the tracers are more correlated than those of the abundant atoms; the correlation factor for tracer diffusion must hence be smaller than if we had assumed $\nu^I = \nu$. This is indeed borne out by detailed calculations.

Under simple conditions (see below), which hold approximately for mono-vacan-

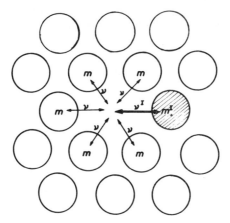

Fig. 1. Jump frequencies $\nu$ and $\nu^I$ of two different isotopes of masses $m$ and $m^I$ in a close-packed lattice.

cy diffusion in the cubic metals, the correlation factor for the isotope I assumes the form [38–40]

$$f^I_{1V} = \frac{u}{\nu^I + u} \;,$$

(2.29)

where $u$ depends on the crystal structure and on $\nu$, but not on $\nu^I$. If we consider now a second isotope II, an analogous equation holds for its correlation factor $f^{II}$. The ratio of the tracer self-diffusion coefficients of the two isotopes is given by

$$\frac{D^I}{D^{II}} = \frac{f^I_{1V}\,\nu^I}{f^{II}_{1V}\,\nu^{II}} \;.$$

(2.30)

Elimination of $u$ and $f^{II}$ from the preceding equations gives the following relationship:

$$\frac{D^I - D^{II}}{D^{II}} = f^I_{1V}\,\frac{\nu^I - \nu^{II}}{\nu^{II}} \;.$$

(2.31)

Unless we deal with very light elements or isotopes with a large mass difference, (2.31) may for practical purposes be simplified to

$$\frac{\delta D^T}{D^T} = f_{1V}\,\frac{\delta \nu}{\nu} \;,$$

(2.32)

where $\delta D^T$ and $\delta \nu$ denote the variation of the tracer self-diffusion coefficient and the vacancy jump frequency with the tracer mass. In $D^T$, $f_{1V}$ and $\nu$ the variations with the tracer mass may be disregarded. Under this simplifying assumption the correlation factors $f_{1V}$ reduce to numbers that depend only on the crystal structure and on the diffusion mechanism (table 1).

Eq. (2.32) may be used in three different ways to interpret measurements of $\delta D^T/D^T$, which may be performed if two or more suitable isotopes are available:

(i) If the mechanism of self-diffusion is firmly established, and hence $f$ is known, (2.32) may be used to calculate $\delta\nu/\nu$. If equations like (2.3) hold and if the entropies entering into the self-diffusion coefficient are independent of the masses, one would expect

$$\frac{\nu^I - \nu^{II}}{\nu^{II}} = \left(\frac{m^{II}}{m^I}\right)^{\frac{1}{2}} - 1 \approx -\frac{1}{2}\frac{\delta m}{m}, \qquad (2.33)$$

where $\delta m$ is the difference of the tracer masses. Significant deviations from this value indicate that the picture of vacancy migration by jumps involving the translational motion of only one atom is too simple.

According to Mullen [41] and LeClaire [42] such deviations are accounted for by the following generalization of (2.33):

$$\frac{\nu^I - \nu^{II}}{\nu^{II}} = \Delta K \left[\left(\frac{m^{II}}{m^I}\right)^{\frac{1}{2}} - 1\right]. \qquad (2.34)$$

Here $\Delta K$ denotes the fraction of the total *translational* kinetic energy in the saddle-point configuration that is possessed by the jumping atom *. If the movement of a vacancy involves the translation of essentially only one atom, $\Delta K = 1$ holds, i.e., (2.33) is valid. For a spread-out vacancy, however, the movement of which involves translational motions of several atoms, we have $0 < \Delta K < 1$. Isotope effect measurements may thus give information on the configuration of vacancies. If the configuration of the vacancy changes with temperature, we expect a temperature variation of $\Delta K$.

(ii) If one has an estimate of $\Delta K$, one may determine the correlation factor $f$ and, by comparison with a table of $f$-values for various diffusion mechanisms, the diffusion mechanism. Since $\Delta K < 1$, in favourable cases certain diffusion mechanisms may be excluded.

(iii) If more than one diffusion mechanism contributes to the tracer self-diffusion coefficient, the isotope effect will be a weighted average of the isotope effects of the individual mechanisms, with the relative contributions of the individual mechanisms as weighting factors. Since these relative contributions are in general temperature dependent, the isotope effect should be temperature dependent even if the $\Delta K$-factors involved may be taken as temperature independent. For example, for the case of mono-vacancy and di-vacancy contributions (section 2.1.3), the isotope effect is given in a self-explanatory notation (all $D$'s refer to tracer self-diffusion) by

---

* LeClaire [42] points out that for $\Delta K < 1$, the quantity $u$ in (2.29) can no longer be independent of the tracer mass. Therefore, (2.31) will no longer be exactly true. As long as $\Delta K$ is not too small compared with unity, the necessary corrections are negligible. For estimates of the correction terms see LeClaire [42].

$$\frac{D^{I}-D^{II}}{D^{II}} = \frac{D^{II}_{1V}}{D^{II}}\left(\frac{f^{I}_{1V}}{f^{II}_{1V}}\frac{\nu^{I}_{1V}}{\nu^{II}_{1V}} - 1\right) + \frac{D^{II}_{2V}}{D^{II}}\left(\frac{f^{I}_{2V}}{f^{II}_{2V}}\frac{\nu^{I}_{2V}}{\nu^{II}_{2V}} - 1\right). \quad (2.35)$$

By making use of (2.30), (2.31) and (2.34) we may write in the mono-vacancy term of (2.35)

$$\frac{f^{I}_{1V}}{f^{II}_{1V}}\frac{\nu^{I}_{1V}}{\nu^{II}_{1V}} - 1 = f^{I}_{1V}\,\Delta K_{1V}\left[\left(\frac{m^{II}}{m^{I}}\right)^{\frac{1}{2}} - 1\right] \approx -\tfrac{1}{2}f_{1V}\,\Delta K_{1V}\,\delta m\,.$$

$$(2.35a)$$

For the di-vacancy term in (2.35) the assumption that in (2.29) $u$ is independent of the tracer jump frequency is not valid. As Bakker [43] shows in detail, within the numerical accuracy required we may nevertheless simplify (2.35) to

$$\frac{\delta D^{T}}{D^{T}} = -\tfrac{1}{2}\left[f_{1V}\,\Delta K_{1V}\frac{f_{1V}D^{SD}_{1V}}{D^{T}} + f_{2V}\,\Delta K_{2V}\frac{f_{2V}D^{SD}_{2V}}{D^{T}}\right]\frac{\delta m}{m}, \quad (2.36)$$

where $\Delta K_{iV}$ denotes the $\Delta K$-factor for the individual mechanism.

From the preceding discussion it is clear that in the most general case too many unknowns affect the magnitude of the isotope effect, so that additional information is needed to draw definite conclusions on the nature of diffusion mechanism.

Table 3 contains the available measurements of the isotope effect on self-diffusion in pure metals. Let us discuss these results from the viewpoint that the dominant mechanism for self-diffusion is the mono-vacancy mechanism. Table 3 gives a column with the values

$$\frac{1}{f_{1V}}\frac{1-D^{II}/D^{I}}{1-(m^{I}/m^{II})^{1/2}}$$

For a mono-vacancy mechanism with $\Delta K_{1V} = 1$, these values should be unity. The inclusion of a $\Delta K$-factor smaller than unity and/or of a di-vacancy contribution could only lower these values.

We conclude from table 3 that in Pd the di-vacancy contribution to self-diffusion is negligible and that the $\Delta K$-factor for mono-vacancies is unity within experimental accuracy, i.e., that the migration of a vacancy occurs by the jump of one atom, without much displacement of the other neighbours of the vacancy. This is an important result, since it suggests that it might be a good approximation to assume $\Delta K = 1$ also for other close-packed metals with high melting points. The deviations from $\Delta K = 1$ that have been observed for Ag and $\gamma$-Fe would then have to be interpreted in terms of multiple vacancy contributions to the self-diffusion coefficient. For Ag, the isotope effect has been measured only for one temperature; as we shall see in section 3.1.4, the di-vacancy contribution calculated from the isotope effect

Table 3a

Isotope effect of self-diffusion in face-centred cubic metals.

| Solvent (melting temp. $T_m$) | Tracers I | II | Temperature of measurement [°C] | $1-(D^{II}/D^I)$ [%] | $\dfrac{1-(D^{II}/D^I)}{1-(m^I/m^{II})^{\frac{1}{2}}}$ | $\dfrac{1}{f_{IV}}\dfrac{1-(D^{II}/D^I)}{1-(m^I/m^{II})^{\frac{1}{2}}}$ | References |
|---|---|---|---|---|---|---|---|
| Pd (1553°C) | 103Pd | 112Pd | 1452.5<br>1502.6 | 3.36 ± 0.2<br>3.32 ± 0.2 | 0.82<br>0.81 | 1.05 ± 0.05<br>1.03 ± 0.05 | [44] |
| Ag (960°C) | 105Ag | 111Ag | 930 | 1.84 ± 0.1 | 0.67 | 0.86 ± 0.05 | [45] |
| Cu (1083°C) | 64Cu | 67Cu | 894 to 1061 | 1.55 ± 0.3 | 0.67 | 0.87 ± 0.04 | [141] |
| γ-Fe (1530°C) | 55Fe | 59Fe | 1171<br>(1188)<br>1236<br>1286<br>1306<br>1349 | 2.28 ± 0.15<br>(1.64 ± 0.15)<br>2.22 ± 0.24<br>2.07 ± 0.2<br>1.97 ± 0.3<br>1.71 ± 0.25 | 0.66<br>(0.47)<br>0.64<br>0.60<br>0.57<br>0.49 | 0.85 ± 0.06<br>(0.61 ± 0.06)<br>0.83 ± 0.09<br>0.77 ± 0.08<br>0.73 ± 0.1<br>0.63 ± 0.05 | [46] |
| | 52Fe | 59Fe | 1368 | 3.24 ± 0.08<br>3.25 ± 0.08 | 0.53<br>0.53 | 0.679 ± 0.017<br>0.676 ± 0.017 | [46a] |
| | 55Fe | 59Fe | 1452 | – | 0.77 | 0.98 ± 0.05 | [47] |

Table 3b

Isotope effect of self-diffusion in body-centred-cubic metals.

| Solvent (melting temp. $T_m$) | Tracers I | II | Temperature of measurement [°C] | $1-(D^{II}/D^I)$ [%] | $\dfrac{1-(D^{II}/D^I)}{1-(m^I/m^{II})^{\frac{1}{2}}}$ | $\dfrac{1}{f_{1V}}\dfrac{1-(D^{II}/D^I)}{1-(m^I/m^{II})^{\frac{1}{2}}}$ | References |
|---|---|---|---|---|---|---|---|
| Na (97.7°C) | $^{22}$Na | $^{24}$Na | 40 to 97.2 | | see fig. 11 | | [48,49] |
| α-Fe (1530°C) | $^{55}$Fe | $^{59}$Fe | 869 | | 0.66 | 0.91 ± 0.07 | [47] |
| | $^{52}$Fe | $^{59}$Fe | 896 | 2.81 ± 0.15 | 0.459 | 0.631 ± 0.034 | [46a] |
| | | | 896 | 2.34 ± 0.13 | 0.382 | 0.525 ± 0.029 | |
| | | | 895 | 3.07 ± 0.30 | 0.502 | 0.691 ± 0.067 | |
| | | | 895 | 2.64 ± 0.09 | 0.431 | 0.593 ± 0.021 | |
| δ-Fe (1530°C) | $^{55}$Fe | $^{59}$Fe | 1452 | | 0.71 | 0.98 ± 0.06 | [47] |
| | $^{52}$Fe | $^{59}$Fe | 1460 | 2.01 ± 0.04 | 0.328 | 0.451 ± 0.009 | [46a] |
| | | | 1460 | 2.06 ± 0.04 | 0.337 | 0.464 ± 0.009 | |
| | | | 1433 | 2.08 ± 0.03 | 0.340 | 0.468 ± 0.007 | |
| | | | 1433 | 2.06 ± 0.03 | 0.337 | 0.464 ± 0.007 | |
| | | | 1412 | 2.03 ± 0.03 | 0.332 | 0.457 ± 0.007 | |
| | | | 1412 | 2.09 ± 0.03 | 0.342 | 0.470 ± 0.007 | |
| | | | 1410 | 2.07 ± 0.03 | 0.338 | 0.465 ± 0.007 | |
| | | | 1410 | 2.08 ± 0.02 | 0.340 | 0.468 ± 0.005 | |

Table 3c

Isotope effect of self-diffusion in hexagonal-close-packed zinc ($T_m = 430°$).

| Tracers | | Temperature of measurement [°C] | $1-(D^{II}/D^I)$ [%] | | $\dfrac{1-(D^{II}/D^I)}{1-(m^I/m^{II})^{\frac{1}{2}}}$ | $\dfrac{1}{f_{IV}}\dfrac{1-(D^{II}/D^I)}{1-(m^I/m^{II})^{\frac{1}{2}}}$ | References |
|---|---|---|---|---|---|---|---|
| I | II | | parallel c-axis | perpendicular c-axis | | | |
| $^{65}$Zn | $^{69}$Zn | 418 | 2.10 ± 0.04 | 2.23 ± 0.04 | | | |
| | | 411 | 2.03 ± 0.04 | 2.12 ± 0.04 | averages over the | | |
| | | 397 | 2.16 ± 0.03 | 2.38 ± 0.04 | temperature ranges investigated | | |
| | | 383 | 2.19 ± 0.08 | 2.31 ± 0.04 | | | |
| | | 349 | 2.11 ± 0.03 | 2.16 ± 0.04 | | | |
| | | 316 | 2.05 ± 0.03 | 2.29 ± 0.03 | ∥c : 0.70 | ∥c : 0.92 ± 0.02 | [50] |
| | | 289 | 2.10 ± 0.03 | 2.28 ± 0.05 | ⊥c : 0.74 | ⊥c : 0.94 ± 0.02 | |
| $^{65}$Zn | $^{69}$Zn | 412 | 2.03 ± 0.07 | 1.96 ± 0.04 | ∥c : 0.67 | ∥c : 0.88 ± 0.03 | [51,52] |
| | | 383 | 1.90 ± 0.08 | 2.08 ± 0.09 | ⊥c : 0.71 | ⊥c : 0.90 ± 0.03 | |

under the assumption $\Delta K_{1V} = \Delta K_{2V} = 1$ agrees very well with that obtained from the temperature dependence of the tracer self-diffusion coefficient.

Very recently isotope effect measurements on copper by Rothman and Peterson [141] have become available. In the temperature region investigated a possible temperature dependence of the isotope effect falls within the limits of error of the measurements. This indicates that in copper the di-vacancy contribution is small and that $\Delta K_{1V} < 1$ (see also section 3.1.6).

According to the measurements of Heumann and Imm [46] the isotope effect in $\gamma$-Fe depends on the temperature; if the data at $1188°C$, which clearly fall outside the trend of all other measurements, are omitted, the isotope effect decreases with increasing temperature. This is in agreement with a significant di-vacancy contribution, which is indeed expected to increase with increasing temperature. For the purpose of discussing the temperature dependence of the isotope effect it is convenient to rewrite (2.36) as follows:

$$-\frac{2}{f_{1V}}\frac{m\,\delta D^T}{D^T\,\delta m} = \Delta K_{1V}\left[1 - \frac{f_{1V}\,\Delta K_{1V} - f_{2V}\,\Delta K_{2V}}{f_{1V}\,\Delta K_{1V}}\,\frac{f_{2V}\,D_{2V}^{SD}}{D^T}\right]. \quad (2.36a)$$

The application of (2.36a) to the isotope effect data on $\gamma$-Fe [46,46a] with the assumption $\Delta K_{1V} = \Delta K_{2V} = 1$ would yield the result that at high temperatures the diffusion current would be almost completely carried by di-vacancies, with virtually no contribution from mono-vacancies. Since this is an unlikely result, we have to conclude that in $\gamma$-Fe the $\Delta K$-factors are smaller than unity. Unfortunately, the available measurements of $D^T(T)$ on $\gamma$-Fe are not accurate enough to permit a further analysis. Sufficiently accurate measurements of the isotope effect and the tracer diffusion coefficient, i.e., the left-hand sides of (2.36a) and (2.23b), as functions of temperature, may be analysed in terms of mono-vacancy and di-vacancy contributions if simple assumptions about the $\Delta K$'s (e.g., $\Delta K_{1V} \approx \Delta K_{2V} \approx$ const.) and the temperature dependences of the activation energies and entropies are made. Detailed measurements of the self-diffusion isotope effects over a wide temperature range would therefore be most welcome.

2.1.5. Paths of high diffusivity

Structural inhomogeneities in crystals may give rise to locally enhanced diffusivities. This has been studied by both experiment and theory in considerable detail for grain-boundaries [38]. Enhanced diffusion should also occur along dislocation lines [53–56]. Diffusion along such paths of high diffusivity are characterized by lower activation energies and smaller pre-exponential factors than those of bulk diffusion. They become, therefore, more and more significant the lower the temperature. Contributions to the over-all diffusion coefficient by high-diffusivity paths tend to increase the low-temperature diffusion coefficient and to decrease the low-temperature activation energy relative to the values that one would obtain from an extrapolation of the bulk-diffusion values. These contributions are sensitive to the degree of perfection of the samples used. The increase of the low-temperature diffusion coefficients is the larger the higher the density of the imperfection involved (grain-boundaries, dislocations).

From the viewpoint of obtaining accurate values of the bulk self-diffusion coefficient, paths of high diffusivity (or, as they are often called, "short-circuiting paths") constitute an undesirable perturbation. The effects of grain-boundaries may be eliminated by employing single crystals or specimens with very large grain sizes. The effects of dislocation short-circuits may be reduced by employing well-annealed specimens with small dislocation densities. Whether paths of high diffusivities have made a large contribution in any given diffusion experiment may be judged from the penetration plots, since the penetration laws for bulk-diffusion and short-circuit diffusion are different. Diffusion along high-diffusivity paths gives rise to "tails" in the penetration plots. Small contributions from short-circuits are difficult to detect, however.

The lower the temperature, the faster is the diffusion along dislocations etc. in comparison with bulk-diffusion. If one wishes to minimize the influence of diffusion short-circuits, one has to avoid large diffusion times, i.e., it is necessary to use small diffusion distances. The work of Ermert, Rupp, and Sizmann [57] on gold constitutes a good example for this approach to low-temperature bulk self-diffusion coefficients. This will be discussed in section 3.1.2.

### 2.1.6. Nuclear magnetic resonance techniques for measuring self-diffusion coefficients *

Measurements of nuclear magnetic resonance provide an alternative approach to the experimental determination of self-diffusion coefficients and supplement, where applicable, the tracer measurements. There are, however, important differences between tracer and nuclear magnetic measurements. By means of *tracer measurements* we determine the mass-flow of a small concentration of atoms (tracers) in a matrix, which in the case of self-diffusion consists of isotopes of the same element but with different masses. The deduction of the macroscopic self-diffusion coefficient from the tracer experiments requires a knowledge of the correlation factor discussed in section 2.1.4. The *nuclear magnetic resonance experiments* measure jumps of atoms of the abudant isotope(s). A necessary requirement is that these isotopes have nuclear spins $\hbar I > 0$.

Up to the present time four principal NMR-techniques for determining diffusion coefficients have been employed:

(i) Spin echos in a magnetic field gradient [58,59]. This technique determines the diffusion of nuclear magnetization associated with the translational motion of

---

* In writing this section the authors had the benefit of illuminating discussions with Drs. F. Noack and G.Siegle. They are particularly indebted to Dr. G.Siegle for making available to them the text of a lecture on the subject of this section.

atoms. It constitutes therefore the most direct technique. However, for the application to solids it has the disadvantage that, as long as static field gradients are employed, it requires a magnitude of the self-diffusion coefficient which in crystals is reached even in favourable cases only close to the melting point. The recently developed method of *pulsed* field gradients [60–62], however, permits us to extend the region of measurable diffusion coefficients down to about $10^{-9}$ cm$^2$/s.

(ii) Frequency and temperature dependence of the spin-lattice relaxation time $T_1$ near the minimum of $T_1$ [58,63–65]. For a given model, the mean time $\tau$ between jumps of the atoms of the abundant isotope may be deduced as a function of temperature. The method is applicable in the temperature range in which $\omega_0 \tau \approx 1$, where $\omega_0$ is the Larmor frequency of the nuclear spins. In practice this places a restriction on the order of magnitude of the self-diffusion coefficient of or larger than $10^{-9}$ cm$^2$/s.

(iii) Motional narrowing of NMR line-width [66]. This is essentially a measurement of the temperature dependence of the spin-spin relaxation time $T_2$. In a rigid lattice the Zeeman energies of the individual spins show a considerable spread, since the magnetic fields due to the other nuclear spins may differ widely from nucleus to nucleus. If the mean time $\tau$ between jumps of the atoms becomes shorter than the spin-spin relaxation time of the rigid lattice, the influence of the local magnetic fields is averaged out. The spin-spin relaxation time increases, since the Zeeman levels become sharper. For a given diffusion mechanism, the relationship between $\tau$ and $T_2$ may be calculated. This method may be used as long as $\tau$ is less than or comparable with the rigid lattice spin-spin relaxation time, which varies from metal to metal but is typically of the order of magnitude of $10^{-4}$ s. This means that diffusion coefficients down to about $10^{-12}$ cm$^2$/s may be obtained in this way. Not many tracer measurements of bulk self-diffusion are available in this range. Therefore the motional narrowing NMR studies are a welcome supplement of the low-temperature tracer self-diffusion measurements.

The method has, however, a number of weaknesses:

(a) Although the relationship between diffusion coefficient and spin-spin relaxation time may be calculated for a given model, the calculation of the line-width is not yet satisfactory. This means that the *absolute* value of $\tau$ may be determined only with considerably more uncertainty than its temperature variation.

(b) The range over which the temperature dependence of $\tau$ may be determined is not more than about one and a half orders of magnitude.

(c) Even in the motionally narrowed region, i.e. at high temperatures, a finite line-width due to field inhomogeneities persists. This finite rest width must be subtracted by curve-fitting, which introduces additional uncertainties, particularly in the high-temperature range of the measurements (compare fig. 5).

(iv) Temperature- and frequency dependence of the spin-lattice relaxation time $T_1$ after adiabatic demagnetization in a rotating coordinate system [67,68].
As indicated in (ii), the mean time between atomic jumps, $\tau$, may be deduced from the spin-lattice relaxation time $T_1$ in the environment of $\omega_0 \tau_0 = 1$. The studies of

small diffusion coefficients, and hence large $\tau$-values, would require small Larmor frequencies $\omega_0$. Associated with a decrease of the Larmor frequency by a reduction of the magnetic field is a reduction of the nuclear magnetization, and hence of the sensitivity of the method. This difficulty may be circumvented by demagnetizing adiabatically. During *adiabatic* demagnetization the short-range order of the spin-system, consisting in a preferential alignment of the spins along the *local* magnetic fields, is preserved. Since local fields are randomly orientated, the net magnetization in zero field is nevertheless zero. The practical difficulty that a magnetic field of the order of magnitude of 20 kOe cannot be reduced to zero adiabatically, i.e., in a time short compared with $T_1$, is circumvented by demagnetizing the sample in a frame rotating with the Larmor frequency. Remagnetization after a time less than the spin-lattice relaxation time in zero field leads again to the previous magnetization. By studying the magnetization as a function of the time spent in the demagnetized state the relaxation of the spin-order may be studied. Jumps of the atoms occurring during the demagnetized period destroy the order of the spins and may be detected in this way. This technique is applicable for mean times between jumps that are smaller than the spin-lattice relaxation time due to the conduction electrons. This means that in metals $\tau$-values up to about 1 s or self-diffusion coefficients as small as about $10^{-15}$ $cm^2/s$ may be studied. (In non-conductors, even slower atomic motions may be investigated.)

We see that the NMR techniques may be divided into two subgroups according to whether they yield self-diffusion coefficients near the high-temperature end of the conventional tracer measurements — i.e., near the melting point (methods (i) and (ii)) — or near the low-temperature end of these measurements (methods (iii) and (iv)). The ways in which the NMR measurements belonging to one of these groups may supplement the tracer measurements are quite different.

The main problem associated with tracer measurements near the melting point is their interpretation. We have seen that a high-temperature curvature of the Arrhenius plot of self-diffusion coefficients may be caused either by the temperature variation of the activation energy and entropy of self-diffusion or by the contribution of a second mechanism, such as di-vacancies in addition to mono-vacancies. The way in which two different diffusion mechanisms combine in either NMR-method (i) or (ii) is different from the way they combine in tracer measurements. Furthermore, the relationship between (i), which measures a macroscopic self-diffusion coefficient and (ii), which yields mean times between atomic jumps, depends on the diffusion mechanism. High-temperature NMR measurements, if carried out with sufficient precision, may therefore be of considerable help in interpreting self-diffusion data at high temperatures.

In section 2.1.5 we have seen that the extension of tracer self-diffusion data to low temperatures encounters the difficulties that undesirable short-circuiting effect may interfere. It was pointed out that, for measurements of very small bulk self-diffusion coefficients in crystals, it is essential to keep the diffusion distances as small as possible. This is achieved in an ideal way by the techniques (iii) and (iv), since these measure the mean times between individual jumps, i.e., the "diffusion distance" involved is just the interatomic distance. Short circuiting effects should therefore be completely negligible.

When we compare the potentialities of (iii) and (iv) for extending the self-diffusion measurements to low temperatures, it is clear that (iv) is superior to (iii). We have already listed the main weaknesses of (iii). All these weaknesses are avoided by the $T_1$-measurement after adiabatic demagnetization in a rotating frame. This method has the additional virtue of being capable of measuring diffusion coefficients down to even lower temperatures than (iii). There can be little doubt that this method will become an important tool for self-diffusion studies at low temperatures. It appears that the theory relating the NMR measurements by this method to the self-diffusion coefficient is capable of further improvement and that in principle more information could be extracted from the measurements than has been done hitherto.

### 2.1.7. Mössbauer effect

The characteristic time scale in Mössbauer spectroscopy is the mean life time, $\tau_L$, of the excited state; it determines the width of the Mössbauer resonance lines. The resonance will be broadened when the mean jump frequency of the resonance atom approaches $\tau_L^{-1}$. In favourable cases it should therefore be possible to study the diffusion of Mössbauer atoms by means of the line-broadening [67]. The mean life time of typical Mössbauer isotopes is of the order of magnitude $10^{-8}$ s to $10^{-9}$ s. The corresponding diffusion coefficients are of the order of magnitude $10^{-8}$ cm$^2$/s, i.e., in the high-temperature region of diffusion coefficients.

Knauer and Mullen [70,71] have recently shown that the Mössbauer isotope $^{57}$Fe shows a line-broadening in Cu and Au that is proportional to the diffusivities of Fe in Cu and in Au and that is presumably caused by the diffusion of Fe in these metals. The possibility of using Mössbauer line-broadening as a tool for studying diffusion in crystals has thus been demonstrated experimentally. However, the agreement between theory and experiment is not yet perfect, and it is clear that further work must be done before Mössbauer spectroscopy may be considered a reliable tool for studying self-diffusion mechanisms (see also the article of Gonser [72] in this volume).

### 2.2. *Migration in electrical fields and thermal gradients*

The subjects of transport of matter in an electrical field (also called electro-migration, electro-diffusion or electro-transport) and in a temperature gradient (also called thermal migration, thermo-diffusion or thermal transport) are treated in a separate contribution to this volume [20]. In addition to this article by Hehenkamp the reader is referred to the review articles by Verhoeven [73] on electro-transport in metals, by Allnatt and Chadwick [74] on thermal diffusion in crystalline solids, by Howard and Lidiard [75] and to the book by Manning [39]. The two last mentioned reviews emphasize particularly the theoretical aspects, the first one from the viewpoint of the thermodynamics of irreversible processes, and the latter from the atomistic viewpoint.

In the present paper we shall not discuss these matters in any detail but confine ourselves to a few remarks on the relationships between self-diffusion measurements and electro- and thermo-diffusion.

a) Electro- and thermo-diffusion involve the transport of matter. The relevant diffusion coefficient is therefore the macroscopic self-diffusion coefficient $D^{SD}$ and not the tracer coefficient $D^T$. For a unique mechanism, the ratio $D^T/D^{SD}$ is the correlation factor $f$. From measurements of $D^T$ and $D^{SD}$ the correlation factor could in principle be determined. This has indeed been done for ionic crystals, for which $D^{SD}$ may be obtained from measurements of the ionic conductivity. In contrast to the situation in simple ionic crystals the coupling parameter of the metal ions to the electrical field, the effective charge, is not *a priori* known, so that only the temperature variation and not the absolute value of $D^{SD}$ may be determined. An analogous situation obtains for thermal transport, in which the "coupling parameter", the heat of transport, is a quantity characteristic of each diffusion mechanism but not simply related to other better-known parameters.

More interesting in metals is the case that two (or more) mechanisms contribute significantly to self-diffusion. Let us consider the case of mono-vacancy and di-vacancy contributions in fcc metals. Since $f_{2V}$ is smaller than $f_{1V}$, the relative contribution of di-vacancies is larger for electro- or thermo-transport than for tracer self-diffusion. Therefore the effective activation energy should be larger for the transport of matter than for self-diffusion. An example for this appears to be platinum, where for both electro-migration [76] and thermo-migration [77,78] effective activation energies exceeding that of tracer self-diffusion have been found and where according to Schumacher, Seeger and Härlin [79] one has a noticeable di-vacancy contribution to the tracer self-diffusion coefficient. Wever [80] has suggested that in Pt the difference between the activation energies measured in the transport experiments and the self-diffusion energy as measured in the tracer-experiments (which itself contains a di-vacancy contribution) might be caused by di-vacancies. An analogous explanation may apply in other cases.

b) Wever, Adam and Frohberg [81] have pointed out another influence of the existence of correlation in tracer measurements on the relationship between self-diffusion and transport activation energies. In one-dimensional diffusion via a vacancy mechanism the correlation factor may be very small. Its order of magnitude is given by the reciprocal number of sites between vacancy sinks or sources. In an infinite one-dimensional chain it is zero. Let us now consider "pipe diffusion" via a vacancy mechanism along a dislocation. If this may be considered as one-dimensional diffusion, for small jog densities, i.e., at low or moderate temperatures, the correlation factor of this high-diffusivity path should be small compared with unity. Diffusion along such a short circuit will contribute to the macroscopic diffusion coefficient already in a temperature range in which it does not yet make a detectable contribution to tracer experiments. In this way one can understand why in number of metals the activation energy of electro- or thermo-transport is far below that of tracer self-diffusion. For further details the reader is referred to the paper by Wever, Adam and Frohberg. It will be seen that the two effects discussed under (a) and (b) have opposite signs. A detailed analysis is therefore required before final conclusions can be reached.

c) In section 2.1.4 we have discussed the isotope effect in tracer experiments. We have seen that for a unique mechanism its magnitude is determined by the product of the correlation factor $f$ and the kinetic energy factor $\Delta K$. The expressions for the macroscopic diffusion coefficients do not contain the correlation factor, whereas the relationship between the isotope masses and the jump frequencies, which involves $\Delta K$ (see eq. (2.34)), is the same in both cases. From a comparison of the isotope effect in tracer diffusion on one hand and in thermo- or electro-transport on the other hand it is therefore in principle possible to separate the factors of the product $f \cdot \Delta K$. For further discussions of this subject the reader is referred to papers by Lodding [82,83] and by Barr [84].

## 2.3. *Equilibrium concentrations of point defects*

In principle any property that is affected by the presence of point defects and that can be measured at high temperatures may be used to study the equilibrium concentration of point defects. However, in practice only very few methods are useful. Almost all conceivable methods suffer from two disadvantages:

(i) The effect of a unit concentration of point defects is not known, so that the factor of proportionality between the physical effect due to the point defects and their concentration is an unknown parameter.

(ii) Since at high temperatures it is not possible to have a crystal without point defects, one cannot directly measure the "background" caused by the "ideal", i.e. defect-free, crystal. The background, which must be subtracted from the measured effect in order to obtain the point defect contribution, must be obtained by extrapolation from low temperatures, and this may introduce substantial uncertainties.

## 2.3.1. Direct determination of the concentration of vacant sites

Both difficulties are avoided by the simultaneous measurement of the X-ray lattice parameter and the specimen length, mentioned in section 1. The method appears to have been first conceived by Berry [85] (whose theoretical argument was not completely correct) and was first applied to a metal (Al) by Feder and Nowick [1]. During the last few years it was extensively used by several groups, in particular detail by Simmons, Balluffi and coworkers. (For the references pertaining to the work on pure metals see section 1).

The basic idea of the method is well known: If a vacancy were created in an otherwise rigid crystal by taking an atom away from an internal site and putting it on the surface, the dimensions of the unit cell as measured by X-rays would remain unchanged, whereas the volume of the crystal would be increased by one atomic volume. Creation of an interstitial atom would have the opposite effect on the crystal volume. It can be shown that the elastic relaxation around point defects distributed statistically in a crystal affects the macroscopic volume and the volume of the unit cell equally. The same is true of thermal expansion. The difference between the macroscopic volume and the X-ray volume of a crystal is hence proportional to the number of vacant sites minus the number of interstitial sites occupied by self-interstitials. (Association of, say, two mono-vacancies to one di-vacancy leaves this expression unaltered.) For cubic crystals this expression takes the form, already given as (1.3),

$$\frac{\Delta l}{l} - \frac{\Delta a}{a} = \tfrac{1}{3} (C_V - C_I) \, , \qquad\qquad (2.37)$$

provided that the interstitials and vacancies are created so as to preserve the cubic symmetry on the average. In (2.37), $C_V$ and $C_I$ denote the total concentrations of vacant sites or interstitials. The quantities $\Delta l/l$ and $\Delta a/a$ are the relative changes of the specimen length and the X-ray lattice parameter from a point-defect-free reference state, for which usually room-temperature is taken. In non-cubic crystals the left-hand side has to be replaced by a more general expression, e.g., in hexagonal metals pertaining to both the $a$- and the $c$-axis.

From the sign of the left-hand side of (2.37) one can immediately say whether the dominant defects in thermal equilibrium are interstitials or vacancies. Since in monoatomic crystals such as metals vacancies and interstitials can be created independently from each other, it is unlikely that the equilibrium concentrations have a fixed relationship to each other. If the free energy of formation of one of them is sufficiently smaller than that of the other, the defect with the higher free energy of formation may be neglected. In all metals so far investigated the sign of (2.37) was found to indicate the dominance of vacancy type defects, and no indication of a noticeable interstitial contribution was observed. In the following we shall therefore disregard $C_I$ and interpret the measurements according to

$$3 \left( \frac{\Delta l}{l} - \frac{\Delta a}{a} \right) = C_V = C_{1V} + 2C_{2V} + 3C_{3V} + \dots \, . \qquad (2.38)$$

In thermal equilibrium the concentrations of di-vacancies, tri-vacancies, etc., are coupled to those of the mono-vacancies by equations of the form (2.15).

If the left-hand side of (2.38) could be measured with high precision over a wide range, one could determine the individual terms on the right-hand side of (2.38) on account of their different temperature dependences. Unfortunately the experimental accuracy is quite limited. The left-hand side of (2.38) may be measured with an accuracy of $1 \times 10^{-5}$ to $2 \times 10^{-5}$. The concentration of vacant sites at the melting point, $C_V(T_m)$, lies between $10^{-4}$ and $10^{-3}$ for most metals. This means that even at the melting point the experimental error is between about 1% and 10%. Since we are dealing with a difference measurement, the absolute error is approximately independent of the temperature, whereas the relative error increases strongly with decreasing concentration and temperature. This must be taken into account in least squares fits.

Further remarks on the evaluation of the experimental data, particularly if considered in conjunction with the self-diffusion data, will be made in section 2.4.

## 2.3.2. Calorimetric measurements

The technique described in section 2.3.1 has the advantage that it neither introduces an unknown constant of proportionality nor requires the empirical elimination of "background" effects. The first feature is shared by calorimetric measurements (determinations of specific heats or of heat contents as functions of temperature), since the "constant of proportionality" in these experiments is the energy of formation of the vacancies. This quantity may be determined from the *temperature dependence* of the excess heat content due to the vacancies. However, the background problem remains.

The calorimetric measurements are discussed in detail in the contributions by Kraftmakher and Strelkov and by Hoch to this volume [86,87]. From the comparison of the calorimetric measurements with those obtained by the $(\Delta l/l - \Delta a/a)$-technique, which is at present confined to metals with melting points below 1100°C, it is apparent that the calorimetric measurements tend to give much higher vacancy concentrations and much higher entropies of vacancy formation. (The only exception to this are the calorimetric measurements on Al by Guarini and Schiavini [88], which will be discussed below.) The discrepancy is clearly outside the experimental error of the $(\Delta l/l - \Delta a/a)$-technique and is presumably due to inadequate corrections for the heat capacities of the "defect-free" crystals associated with the anharmonicities of the lattice vibrations. This conclusion has also been reached by Hoch [87] as a result of a critical evaluation of the experimental data obtained by the various calorimetric techniques. Even if these anharmonicity effects were properly allowed for, the present accuracy of most calorimetric measurements would not permit to determine equilibrium vacancy concentrations of the magnitude found by the $(\Delta l/l - \Delta a/a)$-method. In contrast to the opinion held by Kraftmakher and Strelkov [86] these results suggest strongly that for the high melting point metals, for which a comparison between the two techniques is not possible, the rather larger vacancy formation entropies given by the calorimetric techniques are also unrealistic.

Guarini and Schiavini [88] used an isothermal microcalorimeter [89]. They obtained the heat absorbed by the formation of vacancies following a small temperature change as the difference between the measured temperature change of the specimen and an exponential time dependence of the temperature, which would be observed if no "reactions" were going on in the specimen. With regard to the "background" they must make the assumption that the heat capacity of the specimen in the absence of these "reactions" is constant over the small temperature range over which the heat due to the vacancy formation is absorbed. Up to the present time the data of Guarini and Schiavini are the only calorimetric measurements which yield vacancy concentrations that are not in conflict with direct determinations described in section 2.3.1 (see also section 3.1.4).

2.3.3. Electrical resistivity and thermo-electric power measurements

The methods we are going to discuss now suffer from the two disadvantages mentioned at the beginning of section 2.3. Notwithstanding two of these methods are of considerable practical interest. For further discussions and additional references see the paper by Kraftmakher and Strelkov [86].

At high temperatures the *electrical resistivity* of metals shows a progressive increase above the values expected for "defect free" metals. This extra resistivity is ascribed to the additional scattering of electrons at point defects in thermal equilibrium. Different semi-empirical methods were used in the literature to estimate the ideal lattice resistivity in the absence of defects. The excess resistivity was then attributed to mono-vacancies. This procedure appears to have been applied for the first time by MacDonald [90], who investigated several alkali metals (Li, Na, K). Later on resistivity studies were performed on Au [91–93], Ag [94], Cu [91], Al [95], and Pt [96]. The mono-vacancy formation energies derived from some of these measurements [94,95] are in fairly good agreement with the results of the more direct determinations of vacancy concentrations, whereas others reveal considerable deviations. This indicates that the background problem has not always been solved in a satisfactory manner.

In recent years the influence of point defects on the *thermo-electric power* of metals has been studied by several authors. However, most of these investigations deal with quenched specimens. The authors are aware of only one paper that studies point defects in *thermal equilibrium*. Bourassa, Lazarus and Blackburn [97] determined the effect of high pressure on the high-temperature thermo-electric power of Al and Au. In Al the temperature dependence of the change in thermo-electric power with pressure was found to depart significantly from a mono-vacancy model. This departure is attributed by these authors to di-vacancies and impurity vacancy pairs. In Au the data were consistent with a mono-vacancy model.

2.4. *Combined analysis of high-temperature and self-diffusion data*

In section 2.1.3 an explicit expression for the tracer self-diffusion coefficient due to mono-vacancy and di-vacancy migration, eq.(2.24), has been derived which also takes into account the temperature dependence of the activation energies and entropies. In order to analyse the observed temperature dependence of the tracer self-diffusion coefficient, eq. (2.24) is fitted to the data by a least square procedure. Eq. (2.24) contains five adjustable parameters, namely the quantities $\alpha$, $Q_1$, $D_{10}$, $Q_{21}$, $D_{21}$.

If the Arrhenius plot of the data points were linear within the experimental accuracy, only two parameters $Q_1$ and $D_{10}$ could be determined from such a fit. In most cases the data exhibit only a small curvature. Therefore we cannot expect to determine all three remaining parameters uniquely from a least squares fit. A practical procedure is to choose discrete values of $D_{21}$ and $2\alpha$ within plausible physical ranges, and to adjust $D_{10}$, $Q_1$ and $Q_{21}$ so as to give a minimum in the mean-square deviation. The result of this procedure we may plot as a chart of $Q_1$,

$Q_{21}$, and $D_{10}$ as functions of $D_{21}$ and $2\alpha$ in the physically interesting range. (Within this range the mean square deviation does sometimes not reveal a minimum with respect to $2\alpha$ and $D_{21}$, the absolute minimum lying outside the interesting range. However, in most cases the mean square deviation is essentially constant in the whole field. Small variations are presumably without physical significance.) An example for such a chart will be given in section 3.1.2.

For a number of different metals (Au, Ag, Cu, Al, Pb, Na, Cd) direct determinations of the equilibrium concentrations of vacant sites, $C_V$, as described in section 2.3.1 are available. Confining ourselves to mono- and di-vacancies, the concentration of vacant lattice sites is given by

$$C_V = C_{1V} + 2C_{2V} . \tag{2.39}$$

The concentrations of mono-vacancies,

$$C_{1V} = \exp(S_{1V}^F/k) \exp(-E_{1V}^F/kT) = \exp(-G_{1V}^F/kT) , \tag{2.40}$$

and di-vacancies $C_{2V}$ are coupled by eq. (2.15).

The accuracy of $C_V(T)$-measurements is, as already mentioned in section 2.3.1, rather limited. In most cases only two independent quantities, e.g., the magnitude of $C_V$ at some temperature near the melting point and the slope of the $\ln C_V$ versus $1/kT$-plot can be deduced with sufficient reliability. We shall now discuss how to make full use of these informations:

In thermal equilibrium $C_{1V}$ is given in terms of the total concentration $C_V$ by

$$C_{1V} \leqslant \frac{1}{2z} \exp(-G_{2V}^B/kT) \, [\sqrt{1 + 4z \, C_V \exp(G_{2V}^B/kT)} - 1] . \tag{2.41}$$

The equality in (2.41) holds if only mono- and di-vacancies are taken into account. If larger clusters are present the inequality is valid. From (2.40) and (2.41) we obtain

$$E_{1V}^F \geqslant G_{2V}^B + kT \, \{S_{1V}^F/k + \ln 2z - \ln [\sqrt{1 + 4z \, C_V \exp(G_{2V}^B/kT)} - 1] \}. \tag{2.42}$$

By inserting the total vacancy concentration $C_V$ at a temperature near the melting point into (2.42) an inequality is obtained which must be satisfied by $G_{1V}^F$ and $G_{2V}^B$. For applications to a specific case it is convenient to plot $E_{1V}^F$ versus $G_{2V}^B$ (or $E_{2V}^B$), with $S_{1V}^F$ as a parameter. By making use of the fact that $S_{1V}^F$ must be positive, a lower limit for $E_{1V}^F$ can be deduced.

In order to evaluate the temperature dependence of $C_V$ we use eq. (2.41) to calculate $C_{1V}(T)$ from the experimental data for different values $E_{2V}^B$ and $\Delta S_{2V}$ and determine $E_{1V}^F$ and $S_{1V}^F$ by a least-square fit. (In accordance with the remarks of section 2.3.1 the data points must be weighed according to the relative errors of $C_V$.) The result may be plotted in the $E_{1V}^F - G_{2V}^B$ chart mentioned above. By making use of the fact that $\Delta S_{2V}$ should be positive, an upper limit for $E_{1V}^F$ can be deduced.

Thus we obtain a physically admissible field in the $E^F_{1V} - G^B_{2V}$ plane. Sets of the four quantities $S^F_{1V}$, $E^F_{1V}$, $E^B_{2V}$ and $\Delta S_{2V}$ which are compatible with the measurements of $C_V(T)$, must fall within this field. Examples will be discussed in section 3.

Finally let us consider the equilibrium concentration data in connection with the self-diffusion analysis. From eqs. (2.26a) and (2.27) we obtain

$$E^F_{1V} = G^B_{2V} + Q_{21} + E^M_{1V} - E^M_{2V} - T\Delta S_{2V} \qquad (2.43)$$

and

$$E^F_{1V} = \tfrac{1}{2} G^B_{2V} + \tfrac{1}{2}(Q_2 - E^M_{2V}) - \tfrac{1}{2} T\Delta S_{2V} . \qquad (2.44)$$

In a $E^F_{1V} - G^B_{2V}$ chart (2.43) and (2.44) are to be represented by straight lines of slope 1 and $\tfrac{1}{2}$ respectively. These straight lines have to intersect in the physically admissible field of the chart. The intercepts of these straight lines with the $E^F_{1V}$-axis yield the quantities $Q_{21} + E^M_{1V} - E^M_{2V} - T\Delta S_{2V}$ and $\tfrac{1}{2}(Q_2 - E^M_{2V} - T\Delta S_{2V})$, in which $Q_{21}$ and $Q_2$ are already known from the analysis of the self-diffusion data.

Utilizing the combined analysis of concentration and diffusion data we may determine mono- and di-vacancy properties by a trial and error procedure within narrow limits. How far we may proceed in a specific case depends on the completeness and reliability of the data available.

## 2.5. Relation to quenching experiments

As mentioned in the introduction, the mono-vacancy formation energy $E^F_{1V}$ may be obtained from quenching experiments by studying the quenched-in resistivity as a function of the quenching temperature $T_q$. The mono-vacancy migration energy $E^M_{1V}$ may in principle be determined from the recovery of quenched specimens. The detailed comparison of the results of such experiments with those obtained from equilibrium measurements is, however, beyond the scope of the present paper.

The determination of the vacancy formation energy from quenching experiments is discussed in the paper by Siegel, Balluffi, Lie and Seidman [98] in this volume. The specific problems arising in the attempts to deduce informations on vacancy properties from the annealing of quenched metals are discussed in the contribution by Chik [19]. We confine ourselves to a few additional remarks.

Annealing experiments are carried out at temperatures that are much lower than those employed in equilibrium measurements. This raises three problems:

1) For a given total vacancy concentration, the association to multiple vacancies plays a much larger role in annealing experiments than in high-temperature experiments. The situation is aggravated by the fact that in fcc metals di-vacancies are considerably more mobile than mono-vacancies (see section 1). This means that effective migration energies determined from quenched specimens are heavily weighted towards the contribution from di-vacancies. Even for di-vacancy binding energies as low as 0.1 eV one has to go to vacancy concentrations of the order of $10^{-6}$ or lower in order to observe the mono-vacancy migration energy in the annealing of quenched metals.

2) Since, as outlined, the determination of mono-vacancy migration energies from annealing experiments requires extremely small vacancy concentrations, one will almost inevitably get into a range of concentrations comparable with the impurity concentration. Again, at the annealing temperatures the degree of association of vacancies with impurities is much larger than at high temperatures and impurities with a typical impurity-vacancy binding energy of about 0.1 eV may have a noticeable effect on the annealing characteristics.

It appears that the difficulties just described have recently been overcome for gold by Koehler [99] and his associates [27,100]. The energy of migration which they observe in quenched gold for small vacancy concentration is, when extrapolated to zero impurity content, 0.89 eV; this is in excellent agreement with the result obtained from the analysis of high-temperature measurements (see section 3.1.2).

3) We have seen in section 2.1.3 that in general the energy of migration of mono-vacancies decreases with decreasing temperature. Different values of $E_{1V}^M$ will therefore have to be used for high-temperature and for annealing experiments. In section 2.1.3 we introduced the reference temperature $T_o$. Usually $T_o$ may be chosen in the temperature range in which annealing experiments are carried out, e.g., for the noble metals near room temperature. The quantity $E_{1V}^M(T_o)$, which enters the analysis of the high-temperature data, may then be compared directly with the results of annealing experiments.

## 3. Application to specific metals

### 3.1. *Face-centered cubic metals*
### 3.1.1. General remarks

Most fcc metals show a slight upward curvature in the Arrhenius plots of tracer self-diffusion coefficients at high temperatures, although the details vary from metal to metal. It appears as if individual features of each metal, such as its di-vacancy properties, determine the magnitude of the deviations from linear Arrhenius plots of self-diffusion coefficients. In all fcc metals so far investigated the effect is much weaker than the well-known nonlinearities in the anomalous bcc metals [101] and has therefore often gone unnoticed in the earlier literature. This may be partly due to the fact that until recently no accurate measurements of self-diffusion coefficients over large temperature ranges were available. The experimental situation is changing rapidly, however. In the following subsections, we shall have opportunity to discuss several recent extensive determinations of self-diffusion coefficients.

Most high temperature determinations of the equilibrium concentration of vacant lattice sites reported in the literature concern fcc metals. At present the information available from equilibrium measurements is therefore most complete for these metals. Nevertheless further measurements would be highly desirable; they are expected to contribute substantially to our understanding of vacancies in metals.

### 3.1.2. Gold

The analysis of self-diffusion and equilibrium concentration data has been reported in detail elsewhere [102]. The analysis of self-diffusion was based on one hand on the most reliable high-temperature self-diffusion data [103–105] and on the other hand on two measurements of low-temperature self-diffusion by Gainotti and Zecchina [106] and by Ermert, Rupp and Sizmann [57]. Usually low temperature diffusion coefficients (below about $10^{-12}$ cm$^2$ s$^{-1}$) reflect a considerable contribution of short-circuits according to section 2.1.5. However, the above mentioned papers used very small diffusion distances *, and their data appear to be not affected by short circuits. Recent measurements by Whitton and Kidson [108], which cover a similar temperature range as those of Emert et al. [57], have been left out in our analysis. The values of the diffusion coefficients reported by these authors are almost one order of magnitude higher than those of Ermert et al., whose results are in excellent agreement with the data of Gainotti and Zecchina. Presumably this big difference, which is far outside of the experimental error, is due to a systematic error in the determination of the penetration depth in the work of Whitton and Kidson and/or to an influence of short circuits.

The measurements of tracer self-diffusion coefficients selected by us cover a total range of about $2 \times 10^9$. Within this wide range the curvature of the Arrhenius-plot is small and the Nowick-Dienes curvature parameter [31] $B/R = 0.93$ is rather low compared with the values for other metals. These experimental results indicate that in gold the temperature dependence of the activation energies for diffusion and the contribution of di-vacancies to the tracer self-diffusion coefficient are small. This means that the analysis described in section 2.4 is well applicable **. Fig. 2 contains the results in form of a chart of $Q_1$, $Q_{21}$, and $D_{10}$ as functions of $D_{20}$ and $2\alpha$ in the physically interesting field.

High temperature determinations of the equilibrium concentrations of vacant lattice sites are available from the measurements of Simmons and Balluffi [7]. The informations about vacancy properties contained in these data are illustrated in fig. 3, which gives the $E_{1V}^F - G_{2V}^B$ chart discussed in section 2.4. Using this chart in conjunction with the results of the self-diffusion analysis we are able to derive the consistent set of self-diffusion parameters and vacancy properties given in table 4 ***.

---

* Ermert et al. [57] applied an electrochemical sectioning technique which has been described by Whitton and Davies [107]. They succeeded in removing layers about 20 Å thick from gold single crystals. With this technique diffusion profiles of radioactive $^{198}$Au of only about 1000 Å in depth may be investigated.

** The experimental results indicate clearly that the very strong temperature dependence of the mono-vacancy migration energy in gold assumed by Stoebe and Dawson [103] is unrealistic (see also the comments by Schumacher [110] and fig. 2 of ref. [102]).

*** The comparison with quenching results (see, e.g., fig. 7 of ref. [98]) indicates that the experimental error at the low-temperature end of the measurements of Simmons and Balluffi [7] exceeds that stated in the original paper. In their combined analysis, Seeger and Mehrer [102] found that the best values of $S_{1V}^F$ and $E_{1V}^F$ were indeed a few percent higher than one would expect from the analysis of Simmons' and Balluffi's measurements alone.

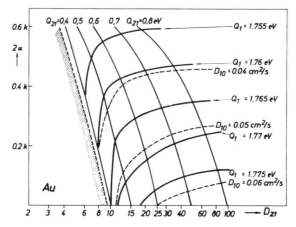

Fig. 2. Analysis of the gold self-diffusion data in terms of a mono-vacancy-di-vacancy model, allowing for a temperature dependence of the activation parameters, according to Seeger and and Mehrer [102].

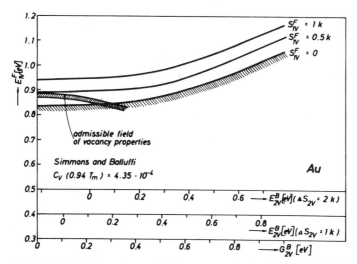

Fig. 3. Analysis of the high-temperature equilibrium concentration data on gold. The bold solid lines are calculated from $C_V (0.94\ T_m) = 4.35 \times 10^{-4}$; the descending hatched band is calculated from the temperature dependence of $C_{1V}$. According to Seeger and Mehrer [102].

The value $Q_1 = 1.76$ eV is by 0.05 eV lower than the value $Q_1 = 1.81$ eV quoted in the literature [103], which up to the present has generally been accepted as the optimum. The earlier value had been derived merely using the standard interpretation of self-diffusion. The value $E_{1V}^M = 0.89$ eV for the mono-vacancy migration energy is well supported by recent quenching results [27,100] as already mentioned

Table 4

Self-diffusion parameters and vacancy properties of gold according to Seeger and Mehrer [102].
(The underlined value has been determined by an independent method; see text.)

| Self-diffusion | Mono-vacancies | Di-vacancies |
|---|---|---|
| $D_{10} = 0.04$ cm$^2$ s$^{-1}$ | $E_{1V}^F = 0.87$ eV | $E_{2V}^B \leqslant 0.16$ eV |
| $Q_1 = 1.76$ eV | $E_{1V}^M = 0.89$ eV | $\nu_{20} \exp \dfrac{S_{2V}^M}{k} = 1.5 \times 10^{13}$ s$^{-1}$ |
| $D_{21} = 14$ | $S_{1V}^F = 0.5\,k$ | $E_{1V}^M - E_{2V}^M + E_{2V}^B = \underline{0.26\ eV}$ |
| $Q_{21} = 0.61$ eV | | |
| $a = 0.2\ (T_0 = 273°K)$ | $\nu_{10} \exp \dfrac{S_{1V}^M}{k} = 1.9 \times 10^{13}$ s$^{-1}$ | $E_{2V}^M \leqslant 0.79$ eV |

in section 2.5. The mono-vacancy formation energy $E_{1V}^F = 0.87$ eV is lower than the original value [7] of 0.94 eV which had not been corrected for the temperature de- pendence of $E_{1V}^F$ and di-vacancy contributions *.

An upper limit of about 0.16 eV can be placed on the di-vacancy binding energy $E_{2V}^B$. This supports strongly the view that in gold $E_{2V}^B$ is low. This low value concurs with the small curvature of the Arrhenius plot of the tracer self-diffusion coefficient mentioned above.

From the "equilibrium" data alone the di-vacancy migration energy $E_{2V}^M$ can be obtained only within limits so wide that they are of little practical value. We consider therefore additional quenching results of Chik [111,112]. From the nucleation of stacking-fault tetrahedra this author obtained $E_{1V}^M - E_{2V}^M + E_{2V}^B = 0.26$ eV (underlined value in table 4). Using this value we may place an upper limit of $E_{2V}^M < 0.79$ eV on the di-vacancy migration energy.

3.1.3. Nickel

The failure of the standard interpretation of self-diffusion for face-centred cubic metals was for the first time recognized in the case of nickel [113]. In recent years a particularly large number of measurements has been done on this metal (see, e.g., table 1 in [113]). The main disadvantage of these older measurements is that

* 0.87 eV is the room-temperature value of $E_{1V}^F$; since $a_F > 0$, the high-temperature value is higher. However, in any case it is lower than 0.94 eV since $a_F < 2a$.

they mostly cover rather narrow temperature ranges. However, when considered together they indicate clearly the tendency for $D_0^T$ and $Q^{SD}$ to increase with increasing temperature. Furthermore, the rather large $D_0^T$-values determined at high temperatures ($D_0^T = (3-5)$ cm$^2$ s$^{-1}$) are not consistent with reasonable mono-vacancy properties (see table 2). Therefore Seeger, Schottky and Schumacher [113] tentatively tried to explain the curvature of the Arrhenius plot in terms of the contribution of multiple vacancies (in particular di-vacancies), neglecting a possible temperature dependence of defect entropies and energies. In a following paper Seeger and Schumacher [28] investigated the influence of a correction due to a temperature dependence of the activation parameters. In both cases the analysis was complicated by the fact that measurements of different authors performed with different experimental techniques and subject to different experimental errors had to be combined.

Recently, Bakker [114] has carried out one single, accurate investigation over a wide temperature range. These measurements clearly confirmed the tendency for the apparent activation energy $Q^{eff}$ and the apparent pre-exponential factor $D_0^{eff}$ to increase with temperature (fig. 4). The quantities $Q^{eff}$ and $D_0^{eff}$ have been determined in the following way: Bakker's data points were fitted by a sum of two exponentials. Then the apparent activation energy was determined from the slope of the tangent to this curve, and the apparent pre-exponential factor was obtained from the intersect of the tangent with the ordinate axis in fig. 4.

Compared with the effects of di-vacancies and temperature dependences of activation parameters, a contribution of tri-vacancies has only a weak influence on the self-diffusion parameters, as already recognized by Seeger et al. [113] and Bakker [114]. In the case of nickel it seems therefore at the present time justified to neglect larger multiple vacancies in thermal equilibrium.

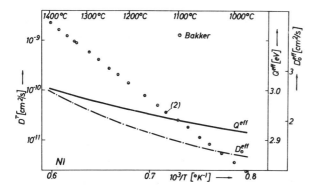

Fig. 4. Self-diffusion data on nickel according to Bakker [114]. Temperature dependence of the apparent activation energy $Q^{eff}$ and of the apparent pre-exponential factor $D_0^{eff}$ (see text).

Table 5

Consistent set of self-diffusion parameters and vacancy properties of nickel. (Underlined values have been determined by independent methods; see text.)

| Self-diffusion | Mono-vacancies | Di-vacancies |
|---|---|---|
| $D_{10} = 0.19$ cm$^2$ s$^{-1}$ | $E_{1V}^F = 1.39$ eV | $E_{2V}^B = \underline{0.3\ \text{eV}}$ |
| $Q_1 = 2.77$ eV | $E_{1V}^M = 1.38$ eV | $\Delta S_{2V} = 1.8\,k$ |
| $Q_{21} = 0.54$ eV | $S_{1V}^F = 1.5\,k$ | $E_{2V}^M = \underline{0.82 \pm 0.03\ \text{eV}}$ |
| $D_{21} = 30$ | $\nu_{1V}^o \exp\dfrac{S_{1V}^F}{k} = 5 \times 10^{13}$ s$^{-1}$ | $\nu_{2V}^o \exp\dfrac{S_{2V}^M}{k} = \underline{2 \times 10^{13}\ \text{s}^{-1}}$ |
| $a = 0.2$ $(T_0 = 273°$K$)$ | | |

We have reanalysed Bakker's data by the method described in section 2.4. An attempt to rationalize the results in terms of vacancy properties leads to table 5. The underlined values have been determined by magnetic methods. Since nickel is ferromagnetic, magnetic aftereffect measurements (for details and further references see the article by Kronmüller in this volume [115]) are possible. Such investigations yield rather directly the di-vacancy frequency factor and the di-vacancy migration energy [116–119]. With somewhat minor accuracy $E_{2V}^B$ and $\Delta S_{2V}$ have also been obtained from these measurements. These values are supported by annealing experiments [120,121]. The remaining vacancy properties follow from the self-diffusion parameters by a trial and error procedure within narrow limits.

In nickel no high-temperature determinations of the equilibrium concentrations of vacant lattice sites are available, mainly because of experimental difficulties. Using the values of table 5, we may determine some interesting quantities which have not yet been determined directly. The concentration of mono-vacancies at the melting point according to eq. (2.39) comes out to be $4 \times 10^{-4}$ if $\alpha_F = 0$, and $5.7 \times 10^{-4}$ if $\alpha_F = 2\alpha = 0.4\,k$. The fraction $2C_{2V}/C_{1V}$ of vacant lattice sites associated in di-vacancies is found to be 23%. According to this analysis, the ratio of the contributions of di-vacancies and mono-vacancies to the diffusion current of tracer atoms, $D_{21} \exp(-Q_{21}/kT)$, turns out to be 66% at the melting point. Such a high di-vacancy contribution should result in a decrease of the isotope-effect with increasing temperature. Measurements of the isotope-effect in nickel would therefore be interesting.

### 3.1.4. Aluminium

Aluminium is well-known to be a difficult material for self-diffusion measurements by means of radioactive isotopes. It is nevertheless of great interest to us, since low-temperature NMR-measurements are available. Taken together with the

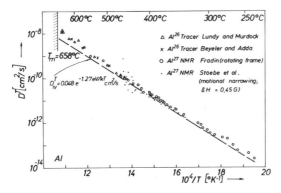

Fig. 5. Arrhenius plot of tracer self-diffusion coefficients on aluminium. The data points of the motional narrowing NMR measurement have to be determined from the difference of the measured line width $\delta H$ and the linewidth $\delta H_x$ in the completely narrowed region. Especially in the high-temperature range (at about 450°C) this procedure introduces large errors.

high-temperature tracer measurements they indicate a stronger curvature of the self-diffusion Arrhenius plot (fig. 5) than for any other fcc metal.

In the high-temperature region two independent measurements of tracer self-diffusion coefficients [122,123], performed with the conventional sectioning technique, are available. Since these data agree well with each other, the criticism occasionally voiced [124] against the measurements of Lundy and Murdock [122] does not seem to be justified.

Aluminium is a standard material for nuclear magnetic resonance measurements. In the intermediate temperature region several NMR determinations of the self-diffusion coefficient have been performed [125–127]. However, only the recent measurements of Fradin and Rowland [126] are fully qualified for the present type of analysis. These authors utilized the method of adiabatic demagnetization in a rotating frame, described in section 2.1.7. The indirect low-temperature determinations of the diffusion coefficient from the shrinkage of voids by Volin and Balluffi [124] have been disregarded in our analysis, since they involve assumptions whose uncertainties exceed the error limits which we require. The data used by us cover a wide range of about 6 orders of magnitude *.

The high-temperature determinations of the equilibrium concentration of vacant lattice sites by Simmons and Balluffi [3] and by Bianchi, Mallejac, Janot, and Champier [4] agree very well with each other as may be seen from fig. 6. In fig. 6 the

---

* Its chemical properties qualify Al for the application of the method of Whitton and Davies [107]. One may therefore hope that in the future tracer determinations of the low temperature diffusion coefficient will become available. This would serve as a most welcome check on the absolute magnitude of the self-diffusion coefficients derived from NMR measurements.

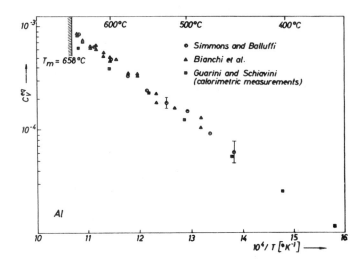

Fig. 6. Comparison between two different direct determinations of equilibrium concentrations of vacant lattice sites [3,4] and the calorimetric measurements of Guarini and Schiavini [88] on aluminium. The bars indicate how an absolute error of 1.5 × 10⁻⁵ of the concentration mea-surement influences the relative errors of the data points.

calorimetric measurements of Guarini and Schiavini [88] already discussed in sec-tion 2.3.2 have also been included. (The points indicated in fig. 6 were obtained in the following way: All the heat absorbed by the formation of vacant lattice sites following a temperature change was attributed to the formation of mono-vacancies, whose formation energy according to table 6 was assumed to be $E_{1V}^{F} = 0.65$ eV.) In the numerical analysis these data have not been used.

At the melting point the fraction of vacant lattice sites is $9 \times 10^{-4}$. This high value suggests, as does also the substantial curvature of the Arrhenius plot of the self-diffusion coefficient, that di-vacancies and possibly also larger vacancy clusters contribute considerably to the high-temperature equilibrium properties. In the present analysis tri-vacancies and larger clusters are neglected, but in view of the high concentration of vacant sites near the melting point it appears likely that this is not justified and that corrections of the reported values will be necessary when tri-vacancies are taken into account. The discussion to be given here should there-fore be considered as preliminary.

In fig. 7 we give the $E_{1V}^{F} - E_{2V}^{B}$ chart according to the above mentioned equili-brium concentration measurements. The vacancy parameters deduced from the analysis of self-diffusion and concentration data are collected in table 6.

The ratio of the contributions of di-vacancies and mono-vacancies to the tracer self-diffusion coefficient, $D_{21} \exp(-Q_{21}/kT)$, at the melting point comes out as high as 85%. The fraction of vacant lattice sites $2C_{2V}/C_{1V}$ associated in di-vacancies

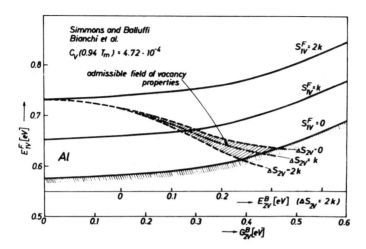

Fig. 7. Analysis of the high-temperature equilibrium concentration data on aluminium [3,4] (see fig. 6). Sets of vacancy parameters which are compatible with the data have to lie within the hatched field.

Table 6

Self-diffusion parameters and vacancy properties in aluminium. (The underlined value has been determined by an independent method; see text.)

| Self-diffusion | Mono-vacancies | Di-vacancies |
|---|---|---|
| $(T_0 = 273\,^\circ\mathrm{K})$ | | |
| $Q_1 = 1.27$ eV | $E^F_{1V} = 0.65$ eV | $E^B_{2V} \approx 0.25$ eV |
| $D_{10} = 0.037$ cm$^2$ s$^{-1}$ | $E^M_{1V} = 0.62$ eV | $\Delta S_{2V} \approx 1.2\,k$ |
| $D_{21} = 15$ | $S^F_{1V} = 0.8\,k$ | $E^M_{1V} - E^M_{2V} + E^B_{2V} = \underline{0.33\ \mathrm{eV}}$ |
| $Q_{21} = 0.23$ eV | | |
| $a = 0.2$ | | |

at the melting point is found to be about 43%. This has the consequence that the activation energy for self-diffusion via mono-vacancies $Q_1$ comes out to be about 0.2 eV lower than the value revealed by the standard interpretation of the tracer self-diffusion measurements [122,123]. For the same reason $E^F_{1V}$ and $S^F_{1V}$ are lower than the values of a simple mean square fit of the equilibrium concentration data to one straight line [3,4]. The value of the migration energy $E^M_{1V}$ seems to be compatible with what is known from quenching experiments [99,128].

The di-vacancy properties are less accurate than the mono-vacancy properties. However, the high binding energy has also direct support from quenching experiments. The underlined value $E_{1V}^M - E_{2V}^M + E_{2V}^B = 0.33$ eV in table 6 has been determined by Chik [19] with an independent method. Together with $E_{2V}^B = 0.25$ eV this leads to $E_{2V}^M - E_{2V}^B = 0.29$ eV. This low value seems to be not unreasonable if we keep in mind that in quenching experiments apparent activation energies in this range have been observed [128].

### 3.1.5. Silver

Recent measurements of the tracer self-diffusion coefficient by Reimers [129] reveal a curvature of the Arrhenius plot in the vicinity of the melting point. This non-linearity had not been observed in former experiments [130,131], presumably since not enough data points were available. The present analysis is based on the self-diffusion data reported by Reimers and the equilibrium concentration measurements of Simmons and Balluffi [6].

According to the $(\Delta l/l - \Delta a/a)$-measurements at the melting point of Ag only $1.7 \times 10^{-4}$ lattice sites are vacant [6]. Because of this low value the relative experimental errors are large. An attempt to evaluate the data points in order to get a $E_{1V}^F - E_{2V}^B$-chart gave no convincing results. We confined the evaluation to the absolute magnitude of $C_V$ near the melting point. Assuming $S_{1V}^F = 0$ we obtain $E_{1V}^F = 0.93$ eV; for $S_{1V}^F = 1\,k$ we obtain $E_{1V}^F = 1.03$ eV.

In view of the above mentioned uncertainties we refrain from giving a list of vacancy properties as in the case of the metals discussed above and restrict ourselves to a consistent set of self-diffusion parameters in table 7.

It is interesting to note that this is in good agreement with a measurement of the isotope effect by Peterson and Barr [45], listed in table 3. These authors report the value

$$f = -2\frac{m\,\delta D^T}{D^T\,\delta m} = 0.67 \pm 0.04 \tag{3.1}$$

at the temperature of 930°C.

Table 7
Self-diffusion parameters for silver.

$Q_1 = 1.90$ eV

$D_{10} = 0.22$ cm$^2$/sec

$Q_{21} = 0.37$ eV

$D_{21} = 16$

$a = 0.1\ (T_0 = 273°\text{K})$

Assuming $\Delta K_{1V} = \Delta K_{2V} = 1$ (compare section 2.1.4), we calculate from (2.36a) with the self-diffusion parameters listed in table 7 $f_{calc} = 0.69$. Within the experimental errors this is consistent with the experimental value. This result appears to indicate that in silver, as in palladium, the assumption $\Delta K = 1$ is permissible.

### 3.1.6. Copper

High-temperature equilibrium concentration data are available from the work of Simmons and Balluffi [5]. Although the concentration of vacant lattice sites is rather low ($2 \times 10^{-4}$ at the melting point), an evaluation of the temperature dependence of the data points led to consistent results. They are illustrated in the $E_{1V}^F - G_{2V}^B$ chart of fig. 8. Various investigations [132–136] (see also Seeger and Schumacher [137]) indicate that in Cu the di-vacancy binding energy is relatively low, of the order 0.12 eV. Reasonable values for the mono-vacancy parameters appear thus to be $E_{1V}^F = 1.05$ eV and $S_{1V}^F = 0.4 \, k$.

Copper is a difficult material for self-diffusion measurements by means of radioactive tracers, since the half-life time of the commonly used tracer isotope $^{64}$Cu is only about 13 hours. In spite of this difficulty the literature contains quite a long list of self-diffusion measurements with $^{64}$Cu. In fig. 9 those three of these data sets [138–140] that appeared best qualified for the attempted analysis are represented. It is seen that the data show considerable scatter, and that it would be difficult to draw definite conclusions from these results.

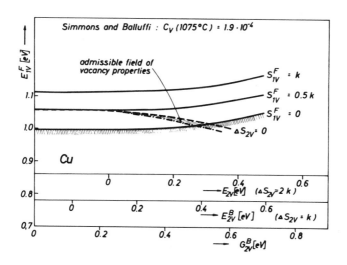

Fig. 8. Analysis of the high-temperature equilibrium concentration data on copper [5].

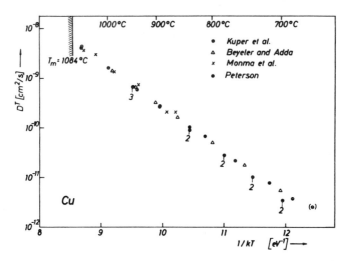

Fig. 9. Arrhenius plot of tracer self-diffusion coefficients of copper [138–141].

Fortunately, very recently detailed measurements with the isotope $^{67}$Cu, which has a 61 h half-life, have become available [141]. They are also shown in fig. 9 (corrected for the isotope effect to make the data comparable with the $^{64}$Cu results). The $^{67}$Cu-data are well suited for an analysis of the temperature dependence of $D^{\mathrm{T}}$. The results will be published elsewhere [142]. We shall only report here the main results: In the physically interesting range of $D_{21}$-values two minima of the least square deviation are obtained. The magnitude of the di-vacancy contribution to the self-diffusion coefficient is very different for the two solutions. Only the solution with the small di-vacancy contribution is compatible with the weak temperature dependence of the measured isotope effect (table 3). This leads to $Q_1 \approx 2.10$ eV and $Q_{21} \approx 0.5$ eV. Together with the $E_{1V}^{\mathrm{F}} = 1.05$ eV (see above) the mono-vacancy migration energy is found to be $E_{1V}^{\mathrm{M}} \approx 1.05$ eV, in full agreement with determinations from cold-work and quenching experiments [134,135]. The $Q_{21}$-value is also in good agreement with the determination of $E_{2V}^{\mathrm{M}} - E_{2V}^{\mathrm{B}}$ from quenching experiments [132,133,135]. The view-point [136] that these determinations of mono-vacancy and di-vacancy properties are fully compatible with the high-temperature data has thus been confirmed by the recent self-diffusion measurements.

## 3.2. Body-centred cubic metals
### 3.2.1. General remarks

With few exceptions (Cr, Mo) it appears that the tracer self-diffusion is faster in body-centred cubic metals than in face-centred metals under comparable circumstances. Whereas the self-diffusion coefficients at the melting points are about

$10^{-8}$ cm$^2$ s$^{-1}$ in most fcc metals, they are about $10^{-7}$ cm$^2$ s$^{-1}$ in most bcc metals.

Curvatures of the Arrhenius plots are well-known for a number of bcc metals. The so-called anomalous metals (Ti, Zr, U, V) exhibit a much stronger nonlinearity than fcc metals [101]. For critical surveys of the attempts to explain the behaviour of these anomalous metals in terms of different models we refer the reader to a paper by Lazarus [143] and a recent note by Nowick [144].

The "normal" bcc metals, which include the alkali metals, Mo and Fe, appeared to show no unusual features in their diffusion behaviour. Therefore in the past these metals were believed to obey the standard interpretation discussed in section 2.1.1. However, there is now strong evidence that this is no more true than for the fcc metals we have discussed. Peart and Askill [145] for the first time tried to consider "normal" and anomalous bcc transition metals from a common point of view. They assume that the individual di-vacancy properties determine the order of magnitude of the deviations from a simple Arrhenius law.

In the present review we restrict ourselves to a brief discussion of two alkali metals (Na, Li), and of V as a representative for the anomalous metals.

## 3.2.2. Sodium

Self-diffusion measurements in sodium cover only about two orders of magnitude [146–148]. Apart from the immediate environment of the melting point sodium behaves within this range as "normal" metal ($D_0^T$ = 0.22 cm$^2$ s$^{-1}$, $Q^{SD}$ = 0.45 eV). In the data points a di-vacancy contribution may be hidden. However, since the temperature range is rather narrow this could not be brought out by an analysis of the temperature dependence of $D^T$. A possible contribution of di-vacancies would be qualitatively in agreement with the isotope effect measurements [147,148] and the high-temperature equilibrium concentration data [10,11]. The isotope effect in fig. 10 shows a gradual decrease with increasing temperature. According to section 2.1.4 this is to be expected for a di-vacancy contribution. Furthermore, since the concentration of vacant lattice sites is high ($C_V(T_m)$ = 7.5 $\times$ $10^{-4}$), a considerable fraction of vacant sites may be expected to be associated in di-vacancies, even if the binding energy is small. In fig. 11 we give the $E_{1V}^F - G_{2V}^B$ chart according to the most reliable high-temperature concentration data [11] (only that part of the chart is represented where $C_{1V} > 2C_{2V}$). Fig. 11 shows that even if di-vacancies are taken into account, $S_{1V}^F$ is considerably higher than for fcc metals. This result supports the existence of a strongly relaxed or extended vacancy originally proposed by Nachtrieb et al. [149]. (Extended vacancies appear to be also present in Ge and Si [32]). Strongly relaxed vacancies should have a rather small $\Delta K$-factor (section 2.1.4), since several atoms will participate in their translational motion. Specifically, the data would be compatible with the idea that up to about 80°C the mono-vacancy configuration in sodium is that of a "split" vacancy, i.e., an interstitial atom inserted between two adjacent vacancies. Such a defect would have a $\Delta K$-value equal to or smaller than one half. Between 80°C and the melting point this vacancy configuration may become more and more relaxed with increasing tem-

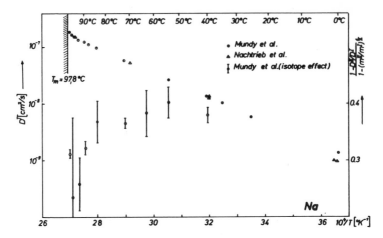

Fig. 10. Arrhenius plot of tracer self-diffusion measurements [146–148] and isotope effect parameter [148] of sodium.

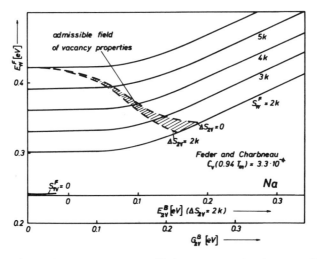

Fig. 11. Analysis of high-temperature equilibrium concentration data on sodium [11].

perature, with an accompanying decrease of $\Delta K$ with increasing temperature. However, as long as the analysis of these effects remains qualitative, we must consider this interpretation of the isotope effect and its temperature dependence as tentative.

In the very vicinity of the melting point the self-diffusion data (see fig. 10) reveal a sharp upward curvature of the Arrhenius plot. This "premelting phenomenon" has also been observed in Li [150]. It cannot be due to di-vacancies since this interpretation would require unreasonably high $D_{20}$-values. A more likely interpretation would be in terms of a strong spreading out of the extended vacancies over a narrow temperature range as indicated above. Such an interpretation would account for the drop of the isotope effect near the melting point in terms of a strong temperature variation of $\Delta K$.

### 3.2.3. Lithium

For several reasons the diffusion and defect properties of Li are particularly interesting. Theoretical interest arises from the relatively simple electronic structure and the extremely high Debye temperature (relative to the melting point). NMR studies may be performed. The easy availability of pure $^7$Li and $^6$Li permits isotope effects to be measured in both a $^7$Li and a $^6$Li matrix.

Direct measurements [150–152] and NMR-determinations [153–155] of the self-diffusion coefficient are available. However, the NMR-studies reported until now mainly give the activation energy $Q^{SD}$. They do not yield very accurate absolute values for $D^T$ and therefore are not qualified for the analysis of section 2.3.

In lithium we have to distinguish between two tracer self-diffusion coefficients, namely that of $^7$Li in $^6$Li, denoted by $D^{7(6)}$, and that of $^6$Li in $^7$Li, denoted by $D^{6(7)}$. Fig. 12 gives the Arrhenius plots of these two tracer diffusion coefficients. $D^{6(7)}$ is larger than $D^{7(6)}$ by about 20%.

We shall discuss this result in terms of the mono-vacancy mechanism. It is necessary to consider the dependence of the correlation factor (2.29) on the jump frequency $\nu^M$ of the matrix atoms. If we assume that there is no mass-dependent interaction with the vacancy, the correlation factor for a mono-vacancy mechanism in a bcc lattice is ($\nu^T$ = jump frequency of the tracer atom)

$$f_{1V}^{T(M)} = \frac{8\nu^M}{3\nu^T + 8\nu^M}. \tag{3.2}$$

The tracer self-diffusion coefficient is given by ($a$ = lattice constant)

$$D^{T(M)} = C_{1V}^{T(M)} f_{1V}^{T(M)} a^2 \nu^T , \tag{3.3}$$

where $C_{1V}^{T(M)}$ is the probability of finding a mono-vacancy on a site adjacent to a tracer atom.

From (3.3) we find

$$\frac{D^{I(II)} - D^{II(I)}}{D^{II(I)}} = \frac{C_{1V}^{I(II)}}{C_{1V}^{II(I)}} \frac{f_{1V}^{I(II)}}{f_{1V}^{II(I)}} \frac{\nu^I}{\nu^{II}} - 1 = \frac{C_{1V}^{I(II)}}{C_{1V}^{II(I)}} \frac{3\nu^{II} + 8\nu^I}{3\nu^I + 8\nu^{II}} - 1 \tag{3.4}$$

and, by introducing (2.3b) into (3.4),

$$\frac{D^{6(7)} - D^{7(6)}}{D^{7(6)}} = 1.036 \frac{C_{1V}^{6(7)}}{C_{1V}^{7(6)}} - 1 . \tag{3.5}$$

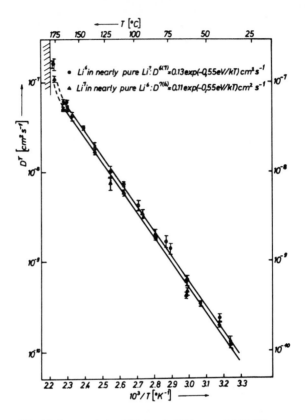

Fig. 12. Isotope inter-diffusion in lithium metal [150].

In order to fit the experimental results, $C_{1V}^{6(7)}$ would have to be considerably larger than $C_{1V}^{7(6)}$. Qualitatively, this is to be expected, since the lattice vibration spectrum will be affected by both the vacancy and by the atom of a mass differing from that of the matrix. In lithium, where on account of its high Debye temperature quantum statistics must be applied over the whole range of the solid phase, an attraction between a vacancy and a light isotope is indeed predicted. Whether this effect is large enough to account for the observations cannot be said without detailed calculations. However, if a substantial interaction of the vacancies with the isotopic impurities exists, the analogous model to fig. 1, which leads to (3.2), is too simple and must be extended. Furthermore, all calculations of jump frequencies, including that of the $\Delta K$-factor (disregarded in the above considerations) must be based on quantum statistics and not on classical statistics. Clearly, the isotope effects in Li present an interesting field for further research.

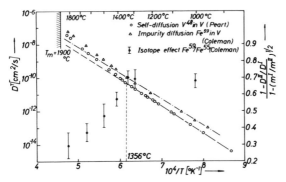

Fig. 13. Tracer self-diffusion [156,157] and impurity diffusion of iron [159,160] in vanadium.
Isotope effect parameter for impurity diffusion of iron in vanadium.

### 3.2.4. Vanadium

Vanadium is a metal which is usually included among the anomalous bcc metals.
The measurements of Peart [156,157] represented in fig. 13 agree at least in the
high temperature region very well with those of Lundy [158]. The Arrhenius plot
is non-linear. At the first glance there seem to be two separate straight lines with a
transition point at about 1356°C rather than a continuous curve. A very similar behaviour shows the impurity diffusion coefficient for $^{59}$Fe as measured by Coleman,
Wert and Peart [159,160] (see fig. 13). These data suggest that two mechanisms of
diffusion operate in vanadium. Further evidence comes from the large change of
the isotope effect parameter for Fe diffusion in V at high temperatures. Coleman
et al. pointed out that the diffusion data over the entire temperature range can be
analysed as a sum of two exponentials (the sum of two exponentials is not two
straight lines on a semi-logarithmic plot, but shows curvature; however in the present
case the curvature may be small except in the region at about 1356°C because of the
large differences between both the pre-exponential factors and the activation energies).

At low temperatures diffusion via mono-vacancies predominates. The isotope
effect parameter below 1356°C constitutes quantitative evidence for mono-
vacancy diffusion. The value of the isotope effect is very close to the correlation
factor $f_{1V} = 0.72$ for the body-centred cubic lattice. This result is to be expected
for diffusion via mono-vacancies, if $\Delta K_{1V}$ is very close to 1.

At high temperatures a second diffusion mechanism seems to operate. Both interstitialcy and di-vacancy diffusion would be compatible with the values of the isotope effect at high temperatures. Coleman et al. tend to prefer the di-vacancy mechanism as the possible high-temperature mechanism. However, the pre-exponential
factor $D_{20}^T = 1400$ appears to be too large to be attributed to di-vacancies. It appears
possible that the high-temperature self-diffusion involves extended defects with
larger entropies of formation. For a decision between vacancy-type and interstitial-

type simultaneous measurements of thermal and X-ray lattice parameters at high temperatures would be valuable.

### 3.3. *Hexagonal metals*

Diffusion in hcp metals is anisotropic. There are separate diffusion coefficients $D_\parallel^T$ and $D_\perp^T$ for tracer diffusion parallel and perpendicular to the $c$-axis of the crystal. However, the differences in diffusivity are small, at least for the well-investigated hexagonal metals Zn [161–163, 50–52], Cd [164–167] and Mg [161,168].

In the case of zinc the isotope effect measurements listed in table 3 indicate that diffusion via mono-vacancies dominates. Within the limits of error the isotope effect parameter is temperature independent. A predominating mono-vacancy mechanism is compatible with the magnitude of the pre-exponential factors $D_{0\parallel}^T = 0.13$ cm$^2$ s$^{-1}$ and $D_{0\perp}^T = 0.18$ cm$^2$ s$^{-1}$ [50].

The situation seems to be similar for cadmium, although no isotope effect measurements are available for this metal. The pre-exponential factor is in the same range of magnitude as in the case of Zn. The high-temperature concentration data of Feder and Nowick [12] give $C_V(T_m) = 6.2 \times 10^{-4}$. This magnitude suggests that some vacant sites are associated into di-vacancies unless the binding energy $E_{2V}^B$ is very low. However, the magnitudes of the pre-exponential factors of the self-diffusion coefficients indicate that di-vacancies do not contribute considerably to the diffusivity.

Magnesium appears to be different. The pre-exponential factors of the self-diffusion coefficients are about one order of magnitude higher than for zinc and cadmium. Therefore a di-vacancy contribution to the diffusion coefficient must be expected for this metal.

### Acknowledgment

The authors gratefully acknowledge correspondence with N.L.Peterson, Argonne National Laboratory, and the communication of results prior to publication.

### References

[1]  R.Feder and A.S.Nowick, Phys. Rev. 109 (1958) 1959.
[2]  S.Nenno and J.W.Kauffman, J. Phys. Soc. Japan 15 (1960) 220.
[3]  R.O.Simmons and R.W.Balluffi, Phys. Rev. 117 (1960) 62.
[4]  G.Bianchi, D.Mallejac, C.Janot and G.Champier, Compt. Rend. Acad. Soc. Paris 263 (1966) 1404.
[5]  R.O.Simmons and R.W.Balluffi, Phys. Rev. 129 (1963) 1533.
[6]  R.O.Simmons and R.W.Balluffi, Phys. Rev. 119 (1960) 600.
[7]  R.O.Simmons and R.W.Balluffi, Phys. Rev. 125 (1962) 862.
[8]  F.M.d'Heurle, R.Feder and A.S.Nowick, J. Phys. Soc. Japan 18 Suppl. II (1963) 184.
[9]  R.Feder and A.S.Nowick, Phil. Mag. 15 (1967) 805.

[10] G.A.Sullivan and J.W.Weymonth, Phys. Letters 9 (1964) 89; Phys. Rev. 136 (1964) A1141.
[11] R.Feder and H.P.Charbnau, Phys. Rev. 149 (1966) 464.
[12] R.Feder and A.S.Nowick, Bull. Am. Phys. Soc. 12 (1967) 388; private communication.
[13] H.B.Huntington and F.Seitz, Phys. Rev. 61 (1942) 315.
[14] A.Seeger, E.Mann and R.v.Jan, J. Phys. Chem. Solids 23 (1962) 639.
[15] R.A.Johnson, J. Phys. Chem. Solids 26 (1965) 75; Phys. Rev. 145 (1966) 423.
[16] J.H.Bartlett and G.J.Dienes, Phys. Rev. 89 (1953) 848.
[17] A.C.Damask, G.J.Dienes and A.C.Weizer, Phys. Rev. 113 (1959) 781.
[18] G.Schottky, Z. Physik 160 (1960) 16.
[19] K.P.Chik, this volume.
[20] Th.Hehenkamp, this volume.
[21] J.Bardeen and C.Herring, Imperfections in nearly perfect crystals, eds. W.Shockley, J.H. Hollomon, R.Maurer and F.Seitz (J.Wiley and Sons, Inc., New York, 1952) p. 261.
[22] K.Compaan and Y.Haven, Trans. Faraday Soc. 52 (1956) 786.
[23] Metals Reference Book, Vol. II, 4th edition, ed. C.J.Smithells (Butterworth, London, 1967) p. 637.
[24] G.Schmid, G.Schottky and A.Seeger, Phys. Stat. Sol. 4 (1964) 439.
[25] C.Zener, Imperfections in nearly perfect crystals, eds. W.Shockley, J.H.Hollomon, R. Maurer and F.Seitz (J. Wiley and Sons, Inc., New York, 1952).
[26] G.B.Gibbs, Acta Met. 13 (1967) 926.
[27] T.Kino and J.S.Koehler, Phys. Rev. 162 (1967) 632.
[28] A.Seeger and D.Schumacher, Mat. Sci. Eng. 2 (1967) 31.
[29] L.M.Levinson and F.R.N.Nabarro, Acta Met. 15 (1967) 785.
[30] L.A.Girifalco, Scripta Met. 1 (1967) 5.
[31] A.S.Nowick and G.J.Dienes, Phys. Stat. Sol. 24 (1967) 461.
[31a] C.P.Flynn, Phys. Rev. 171 (1968) 682.
[32] A.Seeger and K.P.Chik, Phys. Stat. Sol. 29 (1968) 455.
[33] G.Schottky, Phys. Letters 12 (1964) 95.
[34] G.Schottky, Z. Physik 159 (1960) 584.
[35] R.M.J.Cotterill and M.Doyama, Lattice defects in quenched metals, eds. R.M.J.Cotterill, M.Doyama, J.J.Jackson and M.Meshii (Academic Press, New York, 1965) p. 653.
[36] M.De Jong and J.S.Koehler, Phys. Rev. 129 (1963) 49.
[37] R.E.Howard, Phys. Rev. 144 (1966) 650.
[38] P.G.Shewmon, Diffusion in solids (McGraw-Hill Book Company, New York, 1963).
[39] J.R.Manning, Diffusion kinetics for atoms in crystals (Van Norstrand Company, Inc., Princeton, 1968).
[40] A.D.Le Claire, Correlation effects in diffusion in solids, in: Solid State, vol. X, Physical Chemistry — An Advanced Treatise (Academic Press, New York) Chapter 6, to be published.
[41] J.G.Mullen, Phys. Rev. 121 (1961) 1649.
[42] A.D.Le Claire, Phil. Mag. 14 (1966) 1271.
[43] H.Bakker, Phys. Stat. Sol. 31 (1969) 271.
[44] N.L.Peterson, Phys. Rev. 136 (1964) A 568.
[45] N.L.Peterson and L.W.Barr, to be published; quoted in S.J.Rothman and N.L.Peterson, Phys. Rev. 154 (1967) 552.
[46] Th.Heumann and R.Imm, J. Phys. Chem. Solids 29 (1968) 1613.
[46a] C.H.Walter and N.L.Peterson, Phys. Rev. 178 (1969) 922.
[47] D.Graham, Bull. Am. Phys. Soc. 11 (1966) 331.
[48] L.W.Barr and J.N.Mundy, p. 171 in ref. [101].
[49] J.N.Mundy, L.W.Barr and F.A.Smith, Phil. Mag. 14 (1966) 785.

[50] N.L.Peterson and S.J.Rothman, Phys. Rev. 163 (1967) 645.
[51] A.P.Batra and H.B.Huntington, Bull. Am. Phys. Soc. 11 (1966) 183.
[52] A.P.Batra, Phys. Rev. 159 (1967) 487.
[53] R.Smoluchowski, Phys. Rev. 87 (1952) 482.
[54] E.Hart, Acta Met. 5 (1957) 597.
[55] A.A.Hendrickson and F.S.Machlin, Trans. AIME 200 (1954) 1053.
[56] L.C.Luther, J. Chem. Phys. 43 (1965) 2213.
[57] U.Ermert, W.Rupp and R.Sizman, Jül. Conf. 2 (Vol. I) 1968, p. 30.
     See also: W.Rupp, U.Ermert and R.Sizman, Phys. Stat. Sol. 33 (1969) 509.
[58] A.Abragam, The principles of nuclear magnetism (Oxford Clarendon Press, London, 1962).
[59] R.Hausser, G.Maier and F.Noack, Z. Naturforsch. 21a (1966) 1410.
[60] J.E.Tanna, Rev. Sci. Instr. 36 (1965) 1086.
[61] E.Stejskal and J.E.Tanna, J. Chem. Phys. 42 (1965) 288.
[62] J.Murday and M.Cotts, J. Chem. Phys. 48 (1968) 4838.
[63] D.Holcomb and R.Norberg, Phys. Rev. 98 (1955) 1074.
[64] D.Zamir, R.Wayne and R.Cotts, Phys. Rev. 151 (1966) 264.
[65] M.Hanabusa and N.Bloembergen, J. Phys. Chem. Solids 27 (1966) 363.
[66] I.Ebert and G.Seifert, Kernresonanz in Festkörpern (Akad. Verlagsges., Leipzig, 1966).
[67] D.Ailion and C.Slichter, Phys. Rev. 137 (1965) 235.
[68] S.Hartmann and E.Hahn, Phys. Rev. 128 (1962) 2046.
[69] K.S.Singwi and A.Sjölander, Phys. Rev. 120 (1960) 1093.
[70] R.C.Knauer and J.G.Mullen, Phys. Rev. 174 (1968) 711.
[71] R.C.Knauer and J.G.Mullen, Appl. Phys. Letters 13 (1968) 150.
[72] U.Gonser, this volume.
[73] J.Verhoeven, Met. Rev. 8 (1963) 311.
[74] A.R.Allnatt and A.V.Chadwick, Chem. Rev. 62 (1967) 681.
[75] R.E.Howard and A.B.Lidiard, Report on Progress in Physics, Vol. XXVII (1964) p. 161.
[76] H.B.Huntington and S.C.Ho, J. Phys. Soc. Japan 18, Suppl. II (1963) 202.
[77] S.C.Ho, Th.Hehenkamp and H.B.Huntington, J. Phys. Chem. Solids 26 (1965) 251.
[78] S.C.Ho, J. Phys. Chem . Solids 27 (1966) 1331.
[79] D.Schumacher, A.Seeger and O.Härlin, Phys. Stat. Sol. 25 (1968) 359.
[80] H.Wever, private communication.
[81] H.Wever, P.Adam and G.Frohberg, Acta Met. 16 (1968) 1289.
[82] A.Lodding, Z. Naturforsch. 21a (1966) 1348.
[83] A.Lodding, Phys. Stat. Sol. 22 (1967) 157.
[84] L.W.Barr, Phil. Mag. 15 (1967) 1037.
[85] C.P.Berry, J. Appl. Phys. 24 (1954) 658.
[86] Ya.Kraftmakher and P.G.Strelkov, this volume.
[87] M.Hoch, this volume.
[88] G.Guarini and G.M.Schiavini, Phil. Mag. 14 (1966) 47.
[89] A.Z.Fuhrman, G.Guarini and G.M.Schiavini, Nuovo Cimento 34 (1969) 1774.
[90] D.K.C.MacDonald, J. Chem. Phys. 21 (1953) 177; J. Chem. Phys. 21 (1953) 2097.
[91] C.J.Meehan and R.R.Eggleston, Acta Met. 2 (1954) 680.
[92] K.Misek and J.Pollak, J. Phys. Soc. Japan 18, Suppl. II (1963) 179.
[93] S.D.Gertsriken and B.F.Sliusar, Ukr. Fiz. Zh. 2 (1957) 376,
[94] A.Ascoli, E.Germagnoli and G.Guarini, Acta Met. 14 (1966) 1002.
[95] R.O.Simmons and R.W.Balluffi, Phys. Rev. 117 (1960) 62.
[96] Ya.Kraftmakher and E.B.Lanina, Fiz. Tverd. Tela 7 (1967) 123.
[97] R.R.Bourassa, D.Lazarus and D.A.Blackburn, Phys. Rev. 165 (1968) 853.
[98] R.W.Siegel, R.W.Balluffi, K.H.Lie and D.N.Seidman, this volume.

[99]  J.S.Koehler, this volume.
[100]  R.K.Sharma, C.Lee and J.S.Koehler, Phys. Rev. Letters 19 (1967) 1379.
[101]  Diffusion in Body-Centred Cubic Metals, Conference in Gatlinburg, Tennessee (ASM, 1965).
[102]  A.Seeger and H.Mehrer, Phys. Stat. Sol. 29 (1968) 231.
[103]  S.M.Makin, A.H.Rowe and A.D.Le Claire, Proc. Phys. Soc. 70 (1957) 545.
[104]  H.M.Gilder and D.Lazarus, J. Phys. Chem. Solids 26 (1965) 2081.
[105]  D.Duhl, K.I.Hirano and M.Cohen, Acta Met. 11 (1963) 1.
[106]  A.Gainotti and L.Zecchina, Nuovo Cimento 40B (1965) 295.
[107]  J.L.Whitton and J.A.Davies, J. Electrochem. Soc. 111 (1964) 1347.
[108]  J.L.Whitton and G.V.Kidson, Can. J. Phys. 46 (1968) 2589.
[109]  T.G.Stoebe and H.J.Dawson, Phys. Rev. 166 (1968) 621.
[110]  D.Schumacher, Phys. Letters 27A (1968) 99.
[111]  K.P.Chik, Phys. Stat. Sol. 10 (1965) 659.
[112]  K.P.Chik, Phys. Stat. Sol. 10 (1965) 675.
[113]  A.Seeger, G.Schottky and D.Schumacher, Phys. Stat. Sol. 11 (1965) 363.
[114]  H.Bakker, Phys. Stat. Sol. 28 (1968) 569.
[115]  H.Kronmüller, this volume.
[116]  A.Seeger, H.Kronmüller and H.Rieger, Z. Angew. Phys. 18 (1965) 377.
[117]  A.Seeger, in: Magnetismus (Internationale Konferenz Dresden 1966) (Deutscher Verlag
        für Grundstoffindustrie, Leipzig, 1967) p. 160.
[118]  A.Seeger, F.Walz and H.Kronmüller, J. Appl. Phys. 38 (1967) 1312.
[119]  F.Walz, Phys. Stat. Sol. 20 (1968) 245.
[120]  H.Mehrer, H.Kronmüller and A.Seeger, Phys. Stat. Sol. 10 (1965) 725.
[121]  H.Mughrabi and A.Seeger, Phys. Stat. Sol. 19 (1967) 251.
[122]  T.S.Lundy and J.F.Murdock, J. Appl. Phys. 33 (1962) 1671.
[123]  M.Beyeler and Y.Adda, J. Phys. 29 (1968) 345.
[124]  T.Volin and R.W.Balluffi, Phys. Stat. Sol. 25 (1968) 163.
[125]  T.G.Stoebe, R.D.Gulliver, T.O.Ogurtani and R.A.Huggins, Acta Met. 13 (1965) 701.
[126]  F.Y.Fradin and T.J.Rowland, Appl. Phys. Letters 11 (1967) 207.
[127]  J.J.Spokas and C.P.Slichter, Phys. Rev. 113 (1959) 1462.
[128]  T.Federighi, Lattice defects in quenched metals, eds. R.M.J.Cotterill, M.Doyama, J.J.
        Jackson and M.Meshii (Academic Press, New York, 1965) p. 217.
[129]  P.Reimers, Metall 22 (1968) 577.
[130]  C.T.Tomizuka and E.Sonder, Phys. Rev. 103 (1956) 1182.
[131]  R.E.Hoffman and D.Turnbull, J. Appl. Phys. 22 (1951) 634.
[132]  A.Seeger, V.Gerold and M.Rühle, Z. Metallk. 54 (1963) 553.
[133]  A.Seeger, V.Gerold, K.P.Chik and M.Rühle, Phys. Letters 5 (1963) 107.
[134]  F.Ramsteiner, W.Schüle and A.Seeger, Phys. Stat. Sol. 7 (1964) 937.
[135]  F.Ramsteiner, G.Lampert, A.Seeger and W.Schüle, Phys. Stat. Sol. 8 (1965) 863.
[136]  A.Seeger, Phys. Letters 12 (1964) 176.
[137]  A.Seeger and D.Schumacher, Lattice defects in quenched metals, eds. R.M.J.Cotterill,
        M.Doyama, J.J.Jackson and M.Meshii (Academic Press, New York, 1965) p. 15.
[138]  A.Kuper, H.Letaw, L.Slifkin, E.Sonder and C.Tomizuka, Phys. Rev. 96 (1954) 1224.
[139]  M.Beyeler and Y.Adda, J. Phys. 29 (1968) 345.
[140]  K.Monma, H.Suto and H.Oikawa, Nippon Kinzoku Gakkaishi 28 (1964) 192.
[141]  S.J.Rothman, N.L.Peterson, L.C.Robinson and L.J.Nowicki, Bull. Am. Phys. Soc. 14
        (1969) 388;
        S.J.Rothman and N.L.Peterson, submitted to Phys. Stat. Sol.
[142]  H.Mehrer and A.Seeger, submitted to Phys. Stat. Sol.
[143]  D.Lazarus, p. 155 in ref. [101].
[144]  A.S.Nowick, Commun. Solid State Phys. 2 (1969) 30.

[145] R.F.Peart and J.Askill, Phys. Stat. Sol. 23 (1967) 263.
[146] N.H.Nachtrieb, E.Cataleano and J.A.Weil, J. Chem. Phys. 20 (1952) 1185.
[147] L.W.Barr and J.N.Mundy, p. 171 in ref. [101].
[148] J.N.Mundy, L.W.Barr and F.A.Smith, Phil. Mag. 14 (1966) 785.
[149] N.H.Nachtrieb, J.A.Weil, E.Cataleano and A.W.Lawson, J. Chem. Phys. 20 (1952) 1189.
[150] A.Ott and A.Lodding, Jül. Conf. II (Vol. I) 1968, p. 48.
[151] A.Ott, J.N.Mundy, L.Löwenberg and A.Lodding, Z. Naturforsch. 23a (1968) 771.
[152] A.N.Naumov and G.Ya.Ryskin, Zh. Techn. Fiz. 29 (1959) 189.
[153] D.F.Holcomb and R.E.Norberg, Phys. Rev. 98 (1955) 1074.
[154] R.A.Hultsch and R.G.Barnes, Phys. Rev. 125 (1962) 1832.
[155] D.C.Ailion and C.P.Slichter, Phys. Rev. 137 (1965) A235.
[156] R.F.Peart, p. 235 in ref. [101].
[157] R.F.Peart, J. Phys. Chem. Solids 26 (1965) 1855.
[158] T.S.Lundy and C.M.Mettargue, Trans. AIME 233 (1965) 243.
[159] M.G.Coleman, Bull. Am. Phys. Soc. 13 (1968) 487.
[160] M.G.Coleman, A.C.Wert and R.F.Peart, Phys. Rev. 175 (1968) 788.
[161] H.B.Huntington, G.A.Shirn and E.S.Wajda, Acta Met. 1 (1953) 512.
[162] F.E.Jaumot and R.L.Smith, J. Metals 8 (1956) 137.
[163] E.S.Wajda, G.A.Shirn and H.B.Huntington, Acta Met. 3 (1955) 39.
[164] W.Hirschwald and W.Schrödter, Z. Phys. Chem. 53 (1967) 1.
[165] K.A.Mahmoud and R.Kamel, Acta Met. 5 (1957) 476.
[166] K.Apel, S.Häntzsch and K.–E.Prescher, Z. Metallk. 58 (1967) 401.
[167] Y.Masuda, J. Phys. Soc. Jap. 13 (1958) 592.
[168] P.G.Shewmon, J. Metals 8 (1956) 918.

## Note added in proof

(i) Dr. N.L.Peterson, Argonne National Laboratory, has called our attention to the following:

The statement (section 2.1.5) that in order to suppress short-circuit diffusion, long diffusion times must be avoided, is not true as a general statement. Temperature, diffusion time, and diffusion distance have to be chosen such that volume diffusion rather than short-circuit diffusion dominates, and this *may* require long diffusion times. Detailed discussions of the necessary requirements have been given by L.G.Harrison, Trans. Faraday Soc. 57 (1961) 1191, T.S.Lundy and R.E.Pawel, Trans. Met. Soc. AIME 245 (1969) 283, and W.Rupp, U.Ermert and R.Sizmann, Phys. Stat. Sol. 33 (1969) 509, to which the reader is referred to for details.

(ii) The reader's attention is drawn to a recent review by N.L.Peterson on "Diffusion in metals" (Solid State Phys. 22 (1968) 409), which unfortunately appeared too late to be taken into account in the present paper. In particular, Peterson's review should be consulted in connection with the topic treated in section 2.2.c.

## Discussion

*R. W. Siegel:* With regard to your use of the temperature dependence of $C_V$ as measured by Simmons and Balluffi in order to obtain an upper limit to the divacancy binding energy in gold, I believe that their low temperature data, from which your upper limit essentially derives, is not sufficiently accurate for your limit to have any firm meaning. Having seen these calculations in your paper with Mehrer, Balluffi has conveyed to me his feelings that their low temperature measurements were not of sufficient accuracy for the conclusions which you draw from them. I also understand that Simmons had cautioned you regarding the overinterpretation of this data previously.

*A. Seeger:* It is, of course, difficult to judge the accuracy of experimental data entirely on the basis of the information published in the original paper. In the particular case of the Simmons-Balluffi gold experiments (Phys. Rev. 125 (1962) 862) I agree that the experimental errors of the measurements must be larger than stated in the Simmons-Balluffi paper. This is based on the experience in the Seeger-Mehrer analysis (Phys. Stat. Sol. 29 (1968) 231) that no reasonable solution to both the Simmons-Balluffi and the self-diffusion data can be found if the errors given by Simmons-Balluffi in their gold paper are taken literally. In our analysis we have therefore already admitted a larger error than originally stated. It may be that we have still been too conservative. An even larger error would allow the formation energy of monovacancies in gold to become larger by a few hundredths of an eV. The conclusions regarding the smallness of the divacancy binding energy would not be altered substantially, since a large divacancy binding energy is incompatible with the self-diffusion data unless very extreme and unsupported assumptions are made. (As pointed out by Balluffi in a private communication, the apparent fit in the Wang-Seidman-Balluffi paper (Phys. Rev. 169 (1968) 553) of the high-divacancy-binding energy formula to the self-diffusion data is misleading, since an error in plotting was made.) Even if the serious difficulties with the self-diffusion data are disregarded, the Simmons-Balluffi gold measurements would be compatible with the Wang-Seidman-Balluffi analysis only if their error were so large that it would become doubtful whether they should be used at all.

May I suggest that the Simmons-Balluffi measurements on gold be repeated as soon as possible? That a less ambiguous job can be done is apparent from the facts that in aluminium measurements by two different groups give excellent agreement between themselves and also with calorimetric data (see our paper), and that in copper, where the melting point concentration of vacancies is considerably lower than in gold, none of the difficulties encountered in gold are experienced (see our paper and a forthcoming communication to Phys. Stat. Sol. by Mehrer and myself).

*H. I. Dawson:* Professor Seeger has used a high single vacancy migration energy in gold as obtained by Kino and Koehler. In this work, the $E_{1V}^M$ value of about 0.9 eV implies a low divacancy binding energy of about 0.15 eV. Since Professor Koehler had just told us that he now accepts the high $E_{2V}^B$ value of about 0.4 eV, I would like to know how this affects the value of 0.9 eV for $E_{1V}^M$.

*A.Seeger:* A divacancy binding energy in gold as high as 0.4 eV would be incompatible with the interpretation of the Kino-Koehler migration energy of about 0.9 eV in terms of monovacancy migration. If the divacancy binding energy were as high as 0.3 eV or 0.4 eV (which, I am confident, it is not), I could not see any possibility for a consistent interpretation of the Kino-Koehler or the self-diffusion data. I am therefore unable to say what the monovacancy migration energy would be if the divacancy binding energy were substantially larger than the upper limit deduced in our paper.

*H.I.Dawson:* If the divacancy binding energy in gold is about 0.2 eV, then the contribution of divacancies to the self-diffusion at low temperatures should be negligible. Since the low temperature self-diffusion energy is about 1.75 eV [T.G. Stoebe and H.I.Dawson, Phys. Rev. 166 (1968) 621; U.Ermert, W.Rupp and R.Sirmon, Jül-Conf.-2 (Vol. I) 1968, p. 30] this means that for diffusion via single vacancies the activation energy $Q$ is about 1.75 eV. Using this information, one can determine the motion energy $E_{1V}^M$ for a single vacancy in gold from 1.75 eV = $E_{1V}^F + E_{1V}^M$. $E_{1V}^F$ is well known. The mean value of at least ten independent determinations is 0.97 eV with a standard deviation of only 0.010 eV (Stoebe and Dawson, op. cit.). Using these values, one obtains $E_{1V}^M$ = 0.78 eV which is significantly less than the value of 0.89 eV proposed by Seeger.

*A.Seeger:* The low-temperature value of $E_{1V}^F + E_{1V}^M$ in gold (i.e., the value which one would obtain around room temperature, and which is lower than the high-temperature value on account of the temperature dependences of $E_{1V}^F$ and $E_{1V}^M$) may be as low as Dawson suggests. From a least-square analysis of all the self-diffusion data considered reliable, which is thought to give better results than those obtainable from the low-temperature self-diffusion measurements alone, Seeger and Mehrer (Phys. Stat. Sol. 29 (1968) 231) deduce the low-temperature value $E_{1V}^F + E_{1V}^M$ = 1.76 eV. In so far there is agreement between Dawson's viewpoint and ours. Where we take exception is to Dawson's statement that $E_{1V}^F$ is well known to be (0.97 ± 0.01) eV.

Consider fig. 7 of the review paper by Balluffi, Siegel, Lie and Seidman in this volume, in which all the quenching data on gold are plotted that could be extrapolated to infinite quenching speed (in order to correct for vacancy losses during quenching). One notes that although the data fall on a continuous curve, they do not give an exponential in $(kT)^{-1}$ with a constant energy of formation. If a tangent is drawn to the low-temperature part of the curve one finds an effective formation energy of 0.92 eV. This value pertains to a temperature of about 500°C. The room temperature value may be as low as $E_{1V}^F$ = 0.91 eV. Combined with the above value $E_{1V}^F + E_{1V}^M$ = 1.76 eV, one finds as the room-temperature value of the monovacancy migration energy $E_{1V}^M$ = 0.85 eV or 0.84 eV. If the resistivity values obtained from both low-temperature and high-temperature quenches are to be employed for the determination of $E_{1V}^F$, the latter have to be corrected for the divacancy contribution. If a small divacancy binding energy of about 0.1 eV, corresponding to a high-temperature free energy of divacancy binding of about 0.3 eV, is assumed and a small temperature dependence of $E_{1V}^F$ is allowed for ($\alpha_F = 0.1$–$0.2$ in the notation of our paper), the curvature of the Arrhenius plot in fig. 7 of Balluffi, Siegel, Lie, and Seidman is eliminated and about the same result is obtained as before. If a large binding energy $E_{2V}^B = 0.4$ eV is assumed, the divacancy correction is larger and the monovacancy formation energy obtainable from the quenched-in resistivity is even smaller. However, in my opinion such a large divacancy binding energy is incompatible with the self-diffusion data.

As said in our paper, the analysis of the Simmons-Balluffi data leads to $E_{1V}^F = 0.87$ eV. If the Simmons-Balluffi data are considered in conjunction with the quenched-in resistivity, an intermediate value for $E_{1V}^F$ is obtained, which depends somewhat on the resistivity per vacancy assumed.

Throughout the preceding discussion we have made the assumption that the quenched-in resistivities contain no contribution from quenching strains. Since such contributions are more likely in high-temperature quenches than in low-temperature quenches, corrections for quenching strains would tend to lower the $E_{1V}^F$ values obtainable from quenching experiments. Taking into account all available data other than the direct measurements of migration energies, one may thus say that the low-temperature migration energy of monovacancies in gold is most likely to lie between 0.84 eV and 0.90 eV. In my opinion, it must be larger than the value of 0.78 eV suggested by Dawson.

*J.S.Koehler:* From quenching data from 700°C we obtain $E_V^M = (0.87 \pm 0.04)$ eV on experiments done on fast quenched gold ($dT/dt > 4 \times 10^4$ °C/sec). We also obtain $E = (0.71 \pm 0.04)$ eV on slow quenched gold ($dT/dt < 2 \times 10^4$ °C/sec). We believe that the difference arises because in fast quenched gold one has a large sink density. The observed annealing follows second order kinetics and the annealing is determined by $V_1 + V_1 \to V_2$. After the slow quench from 700°C we observe 1st order annealing. The sink density is about $2 \times 10^{-8}$ and the rate determining process is $V_2 \to$ sink.

*A.Seeger:* The migration energy $E_{1V}^M = (0.87 \pm 0.04)$ eV obtained after fast quenches of gold from relatively low temperatures agrees very well with the monovacancy migration energy deduced by us from self-diffusion and other high-temperature data, and is, as explained in my reply to one of Dawson's remarks, also compatible with the attempts to determine the monovacancy formation energy from quenching experiments. If, as Professor Koehler says, second order kinetics are observed, the most natural explanation is indeed that the rate-determining process is the migration of monovacancies to form divacancies, which subsequently move very rapidly to sinks.

With regard to the interpretation of the annealing kinetics after slow quenches, the migration energy $E = (0.71 \pm 0.04)$ eV lies within the range of values for the divacancy migration energy $E_{2V}^M$ obtained from the analysis in the Seeger-Mehrer paper on gold. I have nevertheless doubts whether all the effective activation energies observed in a broad band around 0.7 eV should be interpreted as pertaining to $E_{2V}^M$; I rather feel that $E_{2V}^M$ lies near the upper edge of this band, and that the values in the band should be interpreted as effective activation energies involving reactions between monovacancies, divacancies and possibly also larger vacancy clusters.

*J. Friedel:* Dobrzynski in Lille has shown from Green's functions methods that the Einstein model is a good approximation for computing the entropy of defects above the Debye temperature. In the Einstein model, there is no binding entropy between light isotopes and vacancies. As a result I would guess that, if it exists, the binding entropy is small at least at high temperatures.

*J.Takamura:* We have recently made the computer calculations on the binding entropy change when free vacancies are associated with isotopic impurities, by using the model crystal, with the expectation that the entropy change may be affected by the mass of impurity atoms, since we have some experimental indications that the binding entropy is influenced by the mass of impurity atoms.

However, contrary to our expectation, the results show that, as far as the harmonic oscillation model is concerned and the high temperature approximation is used, the entropy change was not affected by the mass.

The reason for this is not clear, but might be sought in other contributions such as unharmonic ones, for which, however, we do not have any idea to make suitable calculations.

*A.Seeger:* It can be shown quite generally that in the range of validity of Boltzmann statistics a system of coupled harmonic oscillators does not show an isotope effect in any of its thermodynamic properties. The results of the calculations reported by Professor Friedel and Professor Takamura appear thus as special cases of this general theorem. However, the important point about lithium, in which according to the views expressed in our paper a finite isotope effect in the binding entropy between vacancies exists, is that in the entire solid phase Boltzmann statistics cannot be applied, since the Debye temperature is close to the melting point. Quantum statistics must be used, and these permit indeed a mass dependence of the thermodynamic quantities including the binding entropy between vacancies.

# EQUILIBRIUM CONCENTRATION OF VACANCIES IN METALS *

Ya. A. KRAFTMAKHER and P. G. STRELKOV **

*Institute of Inorganic Chemistry, Academy of Science, Nowosibirsk, USSR*

## 1. Introduction

The existence of point defects in solids has already been predicted by Frenkel [1] some 40 years ago. He showed that the thermal mobility in crystal lattices should be associated with the presence of vacancies and interstitials. The lattice defects increase the entropy of the crystal. Therefore the free energy has a minimum value for a certain defect concentration, which increases with increasing temperature. In close-packed *metals* the formation of interstitials requires more energy than that of vacancies. The predominance of vacancy formation has been demonstrated in ref. [2]. An anomalous increase of the thermal expansion of several metals [3] and silver halides [4] near the melting point has been observed already some time ago (fig. 1). Similar anomalies were found for the specific heat of alkali metals [5].

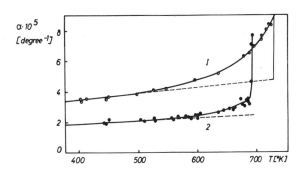

Fig. 1. Thermal expansion of AgCl (1) and zinc (2) at high temperatures [3,4].

* The original paper in Russian was translated (on magnetic tape) into German by B.Ensslen and then translated into English by D.Schumacher.
** Deceased on 2 November 1968 at the age of seventy.

These phenomena were later interpreted in terms of the formation of point defects in the lattice. The formation energies of defects in silver halides [6] and alkali metals [7] were calculated. Subsequently one observed an increase of the electrical resistivity of metals which were quenched rapidly from high temperatures. Formation and migration energies of vacancies were deduced from quenching and annealing experiments. This technique was later on widely applied. Vacancy formation in metals is also studied by means of stored energy and volume change measurements during the annealing of quenched specimens, and by electrical resistivity and thermal expansion studies at high temperatures. At the present time we know for a number of metals the energies of formation and migration of vacancies. The sum of these two quantities is usually close to the activation energy of self-diffusion. Further progress in recent years includes the interaction of vacancies with dislocations and foreign atoms, the formation of vacancy agglomerates, and other phenomena.

A serious problem is still the actual value of the equilibrium concentration of vacancies, since the various techniques give different results. From quenching experiments and Simmons-and-Balluffi-type high temperature studies it was generally concluded that the equilibrium defect concentration in metals at the melting point is of the order of 0.1%. Contrary to these data one has observed in many metals a pronounced increase of the specific heat at elevated temperatures. This has been observed in potassium and sodium [5,7], in lead and aluminium [8], in thorium [9], molybdenum, tantalum, and graphite [10]. In refs. [7] and [8] the increase of specific heat was interpreted in terms of vacancy formation. A series of specific heat measurements was performed on a number of refractory metals by means of the modulation technique. These experiments permitted a determination of the formation energies and concentrations of vacancies in these metals. This procedure yielded vacancy concentrations of the order of 1% at the melting point.

For a critical discussion of this discrepancy we have to compare all methods of determination of equilibrium concentration and consider all experimental evidence. We shall try to demonstrate that specific heat measurements are the most reliable technique for the determination of equilibrium concentrations, provided that these concentrations are not too small. It will consequently be shown that high vacancy concentrations as obtained by this technique are *not* in contradiction with other experimental data and theoretical assumptions.

If we consider the entropy change during vacancy formation to be due to configurational entropy alone, the equilibrium concentration of vacancies is given by

$$C_V \sim \exp(-E^F/kT) , \qquad\qquad (1)$$

where $E^F$ is the formation energy. An additional entropy contribution arises, however, from changes of vibrational frequencies (Einstein's model), so that a pre-exponential factor $> 1$ should be inserted in (1) [2]. Furthermore we have to consider the temperature dependence of the formation energy which gives rise to a further pre-exponential factor. If we take the vacancy formation energy in a first approximation as a linear function of temperature ($E^F = E_o^F - AT$), we have

$$C_V = \exp(-F/kT) = \exp(S/k) \exp(-E_o^F/kT) .\qquad(2)$$

Here $E_o^F$ is the formation energy at $T=0$, while $F = E_o^F - TS$ is the free energy of vacancy formation, taking into account additional entropy changes and the temperature dependence of the formation energy. The pre-exponential factor in (2) cannot be predicted yet theoretically. The determination of the vacancy concentration has consequently to be done by evaluation of experimental data. In recent years a large number of theoretical and experimental studies of defect formation in solids has been published and compiled in a series of monographies and reviews [12–20].

A change in temperature alters the vacancy concentration in a crystal. It has been established that internal imperfections like dislocations and grain boundaries act as vacancy sources and sinks. The time required for the establishment of equilibrium at high temperatures is small because of the high density of these imperfections.

A rise in temperature increases the energy of a crystal by an amount which is proportional to the formation energy and the vacancy concentration. Similarly the specific heat increases by

$$\Delta c_p = ((E_o^F)^2/kT^2) \exp(S/k) \exp(-E_o^F/kT) .\qquad(3)$$

The formation energy and concentration of vacancies can be determined from the specific heat increment. To this end one has to plot $\log T^2 \Delta c_p$ over $1/T$, which gives $E_o^F$, and can then calculate $S/k$ for the observed value of $E_o^F$.

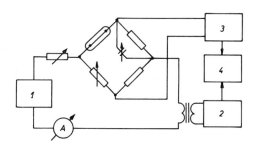

Fig. 2. Bridge circuit for the measurement of the specific heat. 1 – rectifier, 2 – low-frequency generator, 3 – selective amplifier, 4 – electron beam oscillograph.

## 2. Experimental techniques

A detailed description of the techniques of specific heat measurements has been published elsewhere [21–25]. The increase in heat capacity associated with vacancy formation has been confirmed by all experimental techniques, and the data obtained are in agreement with each other. We therefore give only a brief survey of techniques employed, but describe in some detail the modulation technique used in the present study.

The widely used *drop method* consists of a determination of the enthalpy of the hot specimen. The enthalpy is measured by means of an increase in temperature of a calorimeter into which the hot specimen is placed. The specific heat is calculated by differentiation of the temperature dependence of the enthalpy. The additional enthalpy due to vacancy formation is rather small. This technique has been employed in recent years only.

The specific heat of a solid in a temperature interval between low and room temperatures can best be measured by means of an *adiabatic calorimeter* (see [26]). This technique has the highest precision; the experimental errors range from 0.1 to 0.2% [27]. For increasing temperatures it is difficult to maintain adiabatic conditions, and consequently the experimental errors become larger. Adiabatic calorimeters have been described and results have been published up to temperatures of about 1000°C. At these temperatures the error is 1% or even more.

In the *pulse heating* technique the power put into the specimen can outweigh the changes of heat release during the experiment. The increase in temperature is determined by means of the electrical resistivity, by pyrometric techniques or by means of a thermocouple. At high temperatures the experimental error amounts to several percent.

In the *modulation technique* the specimen is heated by alternating current. This procedure leads to thermal oscillations about a mean value, the amplitude of which is related to the heat capacity of the specimen. This method of measuring the heat capacity was already pointed out by Corbino [28]. The application of periodic temperature oscillations offers certain advantages over the heating by individual power pulses. In earlier studies, the amplitudes of temperature oscillations were determined by means of the current fluctuations of the thermo-electronic emission of the specimen [29–31]. In recent years, however, one has used the temperature dependence of the electrical resistivity, as well as photoelectric and thermoelectric signals. We used in our experiments compensation circuits which were independent of the amplitude of the temperature oscillations (see refs. [32–34]). This technique facilitates the measurements and increases the precision.

Consider a wire specimen which is heated by a current $I = i_0 + i \sin \omega t (i \ll i_0)$. The specimen temperature and its resistance perform periodic oscillations with the frequency $\omega$: $T = T_0 + \theta$, $\Delta R = (dR/dT)\theta$. The power balance leads to the differential equation

$$d\theta/dt + (K/mc)\theta = (2i_0 iR/mc) \sin \omega t , \qquad (4)$$

where $m$ and $c$ are the mass and specific heat, respectively, of the specimen, and $K$ is the derivative of the heat release of the specimen with respect to temperature.

The solution of this equation has the form

$$\theta = \theta_0 \sin(\omega t - \varphi), \qquad \theta_0 = (2i_0\, iR/mc\,\omega)\sin\varphi,$$

$$\mathrm{tg}\,\varphi = mc\,\omega/K . \tag{5}$$

Considering the temperature oscillations and the phase shift with respect to the alternating component of the current, the electrical impedance of the specimen is similar to the impedance of a real resistance $R$ which is by-passed by a capacitor $C$, while $R$ and $C$ are related to the heat capacity of the specimen by the relation

$$mc = (2i_0^2/\omega^2 RC)\,dR/dT \qquad (\sin\varphi \approx 1) . \tag{6}$$

On the basis of (6) the specific heat of a specimen can be determined by a bridge connection, in which the specimen is mounted in one bridge arm (see fig. 2). The bridge balance is controlled by means of a high resistivity selective amplifier which is tuned on the modulation frequency of temperature.

All measured quantities (the direct current, the frequency of the AC, the bridge parameters corresponding to equilibrium) can be determined with high precision. The principal experimental error in the specific heat measurement depends therefore mainly on the precision of the temperature dependence data for the electrical resistivity. (The specimen temperature is determined from the electrical resistivity, and it occurs in eq. (6) as $dR/dT$.) This derivative depends fortunately only weakly on the temperature. For tungsten and molybdenum, for example, this temperature dependence amounts to 1% per 100° at elevated temperatures. The modulation technique offers therefore a high reliability of the experimental data, although the exact determination of the experimental error may sometimes be difficult.

A modulation technique has also been proposed for measuring thermal expansion [35,36] and electrical conductivity [37], the latter giving directly the differential characteristics (coefficient of thermal expansion and temperature coefficient of the resistivity). These techniques are convenient for the study of vacancies in metals.

## 3. Results

In this chapter we are going to compile studies of vacancy formation in metals by means of specific heat measurements which came to our knowledge. Values of formation energies ($E_0^F$) and equilibrium vacancy concentrations ($C_V$) are given only in cases where the original authors interpreted their data in such terms. The metals are grouped according to increasing melting temperatures $T_M$. $Q$ is the activation energy of self diffusion.

*Caesium.* Specific heat measurements by adiabatic calorimetry yield

$$C_V = \exp(4.9)\exp(-0.28\ \mathrm{eV}/kT), \qquad C_V(T_M) = 0.26\% \ [38].$$

*Rubidium.* According to specific heat measurements, $E_0^F = 0.27$ eV [39]. Specific heat increment was also observed in [38]. $Q = 0.41$ eV [40].

*Potassium.* Specific heat measurements [39] suggest $E_0^F = 0.39$ eV. Other measurements by adiabatic calorimetry [5,7] give

$$C_V = \exp(2.55) \exp(-0.23 \text{ eV}/kT) \quad \text{and} \quad C_V(T_M) = 0.48\%.$$

$Q = 0.42$ eV [41].

*Sodium.* According to specific heat data [5,7]

$$C_V = \exp(3.1) \exp(-0.255 \text{ eV}/kT) \quad \text{and} \quad C_V(T_M) = 0.76\%.$$

Specific heat measurements were also performed by Martin [42]. For two different techniques of separating the specific heat associated with vacancies he obtained

1. $C_V = \exp(3.9) \exp(-0.305 \text{ eV}/kT)$, i.e., $C_V(T_M) = 0.38\%$ and
2. $C_V = \exp(6.5) \exp(-0.405 \text{ eV}/kT)$, i.e., $C_V(T_M) = 0.22\%$.

$Q = 0.44 - 0.45$ eV [43,44]. Therefore, the first technique should be preferred. Thermal expansion studies [45,46] suggest $C_V(T_M) < 0.1\%$.

*Lead.* Specific heat measurements (pulse technique) [8] give $E_0^F = 0.48$ eV and $C_V(T_M) \approx 0.2\%$. The vacancy formation energy has been confirmed by other techniques. Thermal expansion measurements yielded rather low vacancy concentrations $(C_V(T_M) \approx 0.02\%)$ [47–49].

*Aluminium.* Specific heat measurements using the pulse technique give [8]:

$$E_0^F = 1.17 \text{ eV}, \quad C_V(T_M) \approx 0.2\%.$$

The vacancy formation energy seems to be too high. Thermal expansion studies yielded 0.1% for $C_V(T_M)$ [50–53]. In enthalpy measurements a value of $C_V(T_M) = 0.06\%$ was obtained [54]. $Q = 1.3 - 1.5$ eV [55,56].

*Gold.* The majority of vacancy formation studies was performed on gold, and all classical experimental techniques were employed. High temperature thermal equilibrium studies yielded vacancy-induced electrical resistivity increments which are one order of magnitude larger than those obtained in quenching experiments. The vacancy formation energy is close to 1 eV. According to Simmons and Balluffi [57]

$$C_V(T_M) = 0.07\%.$$

For stored energy measurements on quenched specimens, values of $C_V(T_M) = 0.045\%$ [58] and 0.21% [59] were obtained. Our own measurements of the specific heat [60] suggest (fig. 3)

$$C_V = \exp(3.15) \exp(-1.0 \text{ eV}/kT), \quad C_V(T_M) = 0.4\%.$$

Taking the vacancy-induced electrical resistivity increment from ref. [61], one obtains $\Delta\rho/C_V = 1.5 \ \mu\Omega$ cm/at % vacancies. On the other hand, the ratio of stored energy over resistivity increment $\Delta E/\Delta\rho$ suggests 0.8 cal/g $\mu\Omega$ cm, which is close to the value reported by De Sorbo [58], namely 0.63 cal/g $\mu\Omega$ cm. The activation energy for self-diffusion amounts to roughly 1.9 eV [62,63].

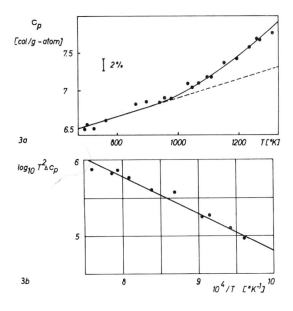

Fig. 3. a) Specific heat of gold at elevated temperatures. b) Determination of the formation energy of vacancies in gold.

*Copper.* The specific heat was measured on bulk specimens at a modulation period of several seconds by determining the amplitude of temperature oscillations by means of a thermocouple [64]. These measurements yield

$$C_V = \exp(3.7)\exp(-1.05\ \text{eV}/kT), \quad C_V(T_M) = 0.5\%\ [65].$$

This vacancy concentration is appreciably higher than that given by Simmons and Balluffi, namely 0.02% [66].

*Platinum.* High temperature specific heat and electrical resistivity measurements [67] yield

$$C_V = \exp(4.5)\exp(-1.6\ \text{eV}/kT), \quad C_V(T_M) = 1\%$$

and

$$\Delta\rho_V = 0.021\ \Omega\text{cm}\exp(-1.6\ \text{eV}/kT), \quad \Delta\rho_V(T_M) = 2.4\ \mu\Omega\text{cm}$$

and consequently

$$\Delta\rho_V/C_V = 2.4\ \mu\Omega\text{cm/at\% vacancies}.$$

The formation energies are in agreement for the two techniques. This agreement is not merely due to the fact that the specific heat was measured by the modulation technique using the temperature dependence of the electrical resistivity, since the

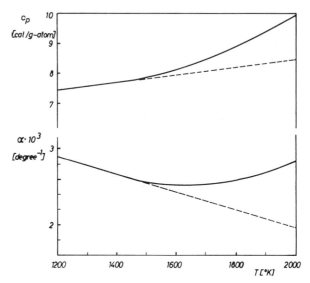

Fig. 4. Specific heat and temperature coefficient of the electrical resistivity of platinum at high temperatures.

increase of the temperature coefficient of the resistivity is appreciably larger than the increase of the specific heat (fig. 4). The resistivity increment was appreciably larger than that observed in the earlier quenching experiments. There is, however, agreement with the quenching experiments reported by Jackson [68] (fig. 5). This is apparently the only case where agreement has been obtained between quenching and thermal equilibrium experiments.

The thermal expansion of platinum at elevated temperatures was measured in ref. [69]. The measurements were performed by the modulation technique using a compensation circuit [36]. The results are shown in fig. 6, together with the data obtained by the X-ray technique [70]. The vacancy formation energy was determined from a plot of $\log T^2 \, \Delta\alpha$ versus $1/T$ and amounted to 1.7 eV. Assuming that the volume of a vacancy is one half atomic volume, the vacancy concentration at the melting point is found to be 0.8%. This value is close to that obtained in the specific heat experiments.

The vacancy formation energy as determined from the temperature dependence of the specific heat and electrical resistivity, is close to that reported by Jackson [68] and is roughly $\frac{1}{2}$ of the activation energy of self-diffusion, for which 2.96 eV [71] and 2.89 eV [72] were reported.

*Titanium.* Specific heat measurements using the modulation technique [73] yield

$$C_V = \exp(5.15) \exp(-1.55 \text{ eV}/kT) , \quad C_V(T_M) = 1.7\% .$$

$$Q = 2.6 \text{ eV} \ [74].$$

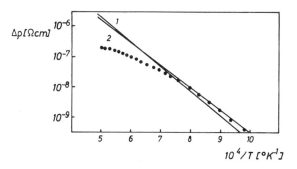

Fig. 5. Electrical resistivity increment in platinum. 1 — present results. 2 — data of Jackson [68].

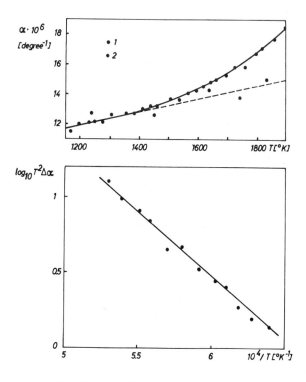

Fig. 6. Thermal expansion of platinum as a function of temperature (above) and in semilogarithmic plot (below). 1 — present results. 2 — see ref. [70].

*Zirconium.* Specific heat measurements using the modulation technique [75] yield

$$C_V = \exp(4.6) \exp(-1.75 \text{ eV}/kT), \quad C_V(T_M) = 0.7\% .$$

Self-diffusion data [76] were later reinterpreted, and the calculated activation energy turned out to be 2.83 eV [77].

*Chromium.* Specific heat measurements by the drop method [78] yield

$$C_V = \exp(3.65) \exp(-1.2 \text{ eV}/kT), \quad C_V(T_M) = 6\%.$$

Apparently the vacancy formation energy is too low, since the activation energy for self diffusion amounts to 3.2 eV [79,80]. Correspondingly, the vacancy concentration $C_V(T_M)$ is too high.

*Niobium.* Specific heat measurements using the modulation technique [81] yield

$$C_V = \exp(4.15) \exp(-2.04) \text{ eV}/kT), \quad C_V(T_M) = 1.2\%.$$

The drop technique [82] gives

$$C_V = \exp(3.55) \exp(-1.68 \text{ eV}/kT), \quad C_V(T_M) = 2.7\%.$$

$$Q = 4.15 \text{ eV} [83].$$

*Molybdenum.* The high temperature increase of the specific heat was observed in papers [10] and [84]. Our own modulation technique experiments [85] yielded

$$C_V = \exp(5.7) \exp(-2.24 \text{ eV}/kT), \quad C_V(T_M) = 4.3\%.$$

$$Q = 4-5 \text{ eV} [86-89].$$

*Tantalum.* The specific heat increase has been observed in [10] and [84]. According to our modulation technique experiments [90],

$$C_V = \exp(5.45) \exp(-2.9 \text{ eV}/kT), \quad C_V(T_M) = 0.8\%.$$

$$Q = 4.8 \text{ eV} [91].$$

*Tungsten.* The modulation technique yields [92]

$$C_V = \exp(6.5) \exp(-3.15 \text{ eV}/kT), \quad C_V(T_M) = 3.4\%.$$

From quenching [93] and annealing [94,95] experiments, values of

$$E_o^F = 3.3 \text{ eV and}$$

$$E_{1V}^M = 3.3 \text{ eV},$$

respectively, were reported. $Q = 6.6$ eV (recent ref. [96,97]). These data are in good agreement.

In fig. 7 we have plotted our specific heat data for tungsten [92] together with the data of Löwenthal [98], which were obtained by means of the modulation technique and employing the radiation oscillations of the specimen, and the data of ref. [99] where the drop technique was employed. At 3100°K the extra enthalpy due to vacancies is still of the order of magnitude of the experimental error in the

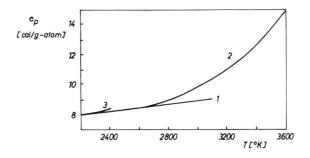

Fig. 7. Specific heat of tungsten at high temperatures: 1 – ref. [99]. 2 – present results. 3 – ref. [98].

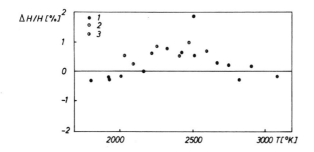

Fig. 8. Relative change of enthalpy of tungsten at high temperatures. 1 – ref. [99]. 2 – ref. [100]. 3 – ref. [101].

enthalpy determination. Therefore, the drop technique did not exhibit an increase in specific heat. The data obtained by the drop technique are, however, not in contradiction to the direct specific heat measurements. In fig. 8 we compare the experimental enthalpy data [99–101] with the results of enthalpy calculations on the basis of specific heat measurements [92]. Since the specific heat measurements [92] were performed above 1500°K only, the fitting has to be done at a certain reference temperature. As reference temperature we took 2000°K, i.e. a temperature, at which a specific heat increase associated with vacancies is still absent. Fig. 8 shows that in the high temperature range the experimental enthalpy data are in excellent agreement with the enthalpy calculations, in which vacancy contributions were accounted for.

## 4. Discussion

The formation energies of vacancies in metals were determined from specific heat measurements according to eq. (3). The experimental data can well be represented

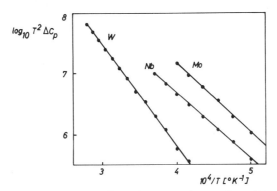

Fig. 9. Determination of vacancy formation energy in Mo, Nb, and W.

by this relation which accounts for vacancy formation (fig. 9). This is particularly evident in the case of tungsten. Between 2400 and 3600°K the quantity $T^2 \Delta C_p$ varies by a factor of more than 100, but all data are on a straight line.

The vacancy formation energies for metals usually amount to one half of the activation energy of self-diffusion and are roughly proportional to the melting point ($E_0^F \approx 9\ kT_M$).These relations hold for both fcc and bcc structures and in a large range of melting temperatures (fig. 10). This fact and the values of the vacancy concentration demonstrate that in the refractory bcc metals self-diffusion occurs via a vacancy mechanism and not via a ring mechanism. The approximate equality of vacancy formation and migration energies favour the vacancy formation mechanism proposed by Schottky.

Hence the vacancy formation energies as obtained from specific heat data are not in contradiction to the conventional concepts. The vacancy concentrations found by this technique are, however, by one order of magnitude larger than previously  assumed. The available data must therefore be examined with respect to their reliability for the determination of equilibrium concentrations [102,103].

Most of the studies of vacancy formation in metals were performed by measuring the *electrical resistivity* increase in quenched specimens. Theoretical estimates and experimental data show that the quench efficiency decreases when the melting point is approached. In direct thermal equilibrium measurements the resistivity increment is usually several times larger than the quench-induced increment. But also the thermal equilibrium technique is not unambiguous since the relative change in resistivity due to vacancy formation is small and the temperature dependence of the resistivity of a defect-free crystal is not known precisely. An incorrect extrapolation of the temperature dependence of the electrical resistivity in intermediate temperature ranges leads to appreciable errors.

*Thermal expansion* data are also frequently used for the determination of vacancy concentrations in metals. This technique leads, however, apparently to low values for vacancy concentrations. Internal imperfections are the predominant

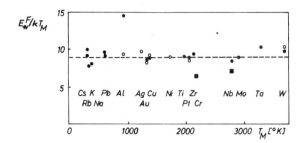

Fig. 10. The vacancy formation energies are proportional to the absolute melting temperature. Methods of determination:

        • specific heat measurements

        ■ enthalpy measurements

        ○ other techniques (most probable values).

sources and sinks of vacancies. To some extent vacancy formation may occur *without* an overall volume change. On the other hand, the lattice relaxation around a vacancy, which in many studies is not accounted for, leads also to underestimates of the vacancy concentration.

*Stored energy* measurements on quenched specimens have the disadvantage that for *high* quenching temperatures the quenching is associated with vacancy losses, whereas for *low* quenching temperatures it is difficult to measure precisely the stored energy. This technique has been employed to determine the vacancy concentration in gold. The data reported in refs. [58] and [59] differ by a factor of five.

Neither leads measurement of *volume changes* during annealing of quenched specimens to unambiguous data, since the results depend to a large extent on the quench efficiency and the nature of the processes occurring the annealing [104].

The *specific heat* measurements involve the extrapolation of data for intermediate temperatures to determine the vacancy contribution. For most metals the melting point is appreciably higher than the Debye temperature. Therefore the temperature dependence of the specific heat of a vacancy-free (ideal) crystal is determined by the difference of the specific heats $c_p$ and $c_v$, the electronic specific heat and a possible modification of $c_v$ due to anharmonicity. All these factors lead to a linear and rather weak temperature dependence of the specific heat. For constant pressure and at elevated temperatures, it is of the order of $10^{-3}$ cal/g at degree$^2$. On the other hand, the increase in specific heat due to vacancy formation is rather high: For a concentration of 0.5%, for example, it amounts to 1 cal/g at degree. The weak temperature dependence of the specific heat of the ideal crystal and the large effect due to vacancy-induced changes mean that the extrapolation of the intermediate temperature data has little influence on the vacancy concentrations and formation energies deduced, provided the concentrations are not too small. The specific heat measurements have in all cases led to vacancy formation energies which are consistent with the available activation energies of self-diffusion and the results of other studies of vacancy formation, except for aluminium, for which the obtained vacancy formation energy is too high [8]. However, since the specific heat increase in aluminium is rather small, the experimental uncertainties lead to a relatively high experimental error. Therefore the aluminium results should not be taken to discard the specific heat technique in general.

The specific heat increase due to vacancy formation can easily be separated from premelting effects associated with impurity atoms. The latter effect exhibits a stronger temperature dependence than the vacancy effect, i.e., it is observed in a more narrow temperature interval close to the melting point [105]. Among the metals investigated by us, platinum, copper and gold had the highest purity (impurity content of the order of 0.01%). At 100 degrees below the melting point, the vacancy-induced specific heat increase is in these metals at least one order of magnitude larger than the possible premelting effect.

It appears therefore justified to conclude that specific heat measurements are well suited for the study of vacancy formation and particularly for the determination of the equilibrium concentration, provided that the vacancy concentration is sufficiently large. It is recommended to determine the specific heat directly, since the additional, vacancy-induced enthalpy is rather small.

There is apparently a correlation between the vacancy equilibrium concentration and the vapour pressures above metal surfaces [106]. This is seen from the fact that the largest vacancy concentrations are observed in chromium, tungsten and molybdenum. For metals with a low vapour pressure like lithium, mercury and tin the specific heat increases and correspondingly the vacancy concentrations are small. This is corroborated also by thermal expansion data [3]: The increase of the expansion coefficient due to vacancy formation is large in zinc and cadmium and practically negligible in bismuth.

It must be checked whether or not the high vacancy concentrations in metals as obtained from specific heat data are in agreement with other reliable experimental data or theoretical estimates. A natural check of the data is the comparison with self-diffusion in metals. The self-diffusion coefficient reads for a vacancy mechanism

$$D = D_0 \exp(-Q/kT) , \tag{7}$$

where

$$D_0 = \gamma \frac{a^2}{6} \nu \exp(S_{1V}^F + S_{1V}^M)/k .$$

Here $S_{1V}^F$ and $S_{1V}^M$ are the single vacancy formation and migration entropies, respectively, $\gamma$ is a factor of the order of magnitude 1, $a$ is the lattice parameter, and $\nu$ is the Debye frequency. It is well known that $S_{1V}^M$ is considerably smaller than $S_{1V}^F$ [11]. Results of $S_{1V}^M$-determinations from the measured $D_0$-values, taking $S_{1V}^F$ from

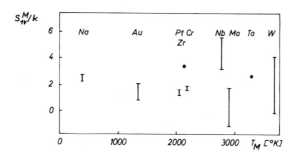

Fig. 11. Comparison of specific heat derived vacancy formation data with self-diffusion data (see text).

the specific heat data, are plotted in fig. 11. The straight lines correspond to the experimental scatter of the $D_o$-data. The diagram shows that the high values for the vacancy concentrations are not in disagreement with the self-diffusion data ($S_{1V}^M > 0$). Taking, however, a vacancy concentration of 0.1% at the melting point, then the agreement with self-diffusion measurements requires $S_{1V}^M > S_{1V}^F$.

The high values of the pre-exponential factor in the expression for the vacancy equilibrium concentration are due to the entropy change of the crystal as the result of a decrease of the vibrational frequency of atoms in the vicinity of the vacancy and to the temperature dependence of the vacancy formation energy associated with thermal expansion (in a first approximation linear). The experimentally determined vacancy formation energies (similarly the activation energies for self-diffusion) are practically the result of an extrapolation to $T = 0°K$ of the temperature dependence of the free energies of vacancy formation which occurs at elevated temperatures. The limited experimental precision does not permit yet to detect a possible difference between the real temperature dependence of the free vacancy formation energies and a linear temperature dependence. The $S_{1V}^F$-values obtained from the specific heat measurements can be understood by assuming that the atomic vibration frequencies in the neighbourhood of a vacancy decrease by 20–30% and that a similar decrease of the vacancy formation energy occurs between $T = 0°K$ and the melting point. These assumptions appear entirely justified. It is, for example, well known that a change by 30–40% of the elastic constants between $T = 0°K$ and the melting point is typical for metals. Furthermore it must be considered that vacancy formation in metals is studied at elevated temperatures, where the thermal expansion coefficient increases, so that the temperature dependence of the vacancy formation energies is larger here than in the middle of the entire temperature interval.

Vacancy formation energies in metals amount to roughly $\frac{1}{3}$ of the heat of evaporation. These two quantities should have similar temperature dependences. A comparison with the available data on the evaporation of metals [107] shows that the relative changes (with respect to temperature) of the free energies for vacancy formation and for evaporation have the same order of magnitude (fig. 12).

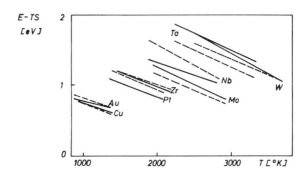

Fig. 12. Temperature dependences of the free energies for vacancy formation and evaporation,
respectively, in metals.
———— vacancy formation. — — — — — evaporation (one third).

These remarks demonstrate that the high equilibrium concentrations of vacancies in metals, as obtained from the specific heat measurements, are not at all in
conflict with other available experimental evidence or theoretical estimates. The concept of lower levels for the vacancy concentrations results from experimental techniques which have a tendency to give low concentration data. Furthermore, we have
available only recently vacancy data for high melting point metals in which the
vacancy concentrations are particularly large.

There are two problems that should be solved:

1. Why is in bcc refractory metals the contribution of vacancies to the electrical
resistivity so small?

2. Why do different experimental techniques give different vacancy concentrations, but essentially similar values for the formation energies?

When the specific heat is measured at a sufficiently high rate of temperature
change, the vacancy concentration does not attain the equilibrium values. The specific heat of the specimen should then correspond to that of the vacancy-free lattice.
Such measurements would best demonstrate that the specific heat increase is
actually associated with vacancy formation. This kind of experiment has been proposed some time ago already [108,109]. In the case of lead and aluminium this
predicted effect has been demonstrated [110]. According to these data it is justified to extrapolate linearly from intermediate temperatures to elevated temperatures
in order to determine the vacancy contribution to the specific heat. In refractory
metals this effect has not been observed, although the initial heating rates amounted
to 60000°C/sec [84]. To retain vacancies in tungsten by quenching, one needs
quenching rates of the order of $10^6$ °C/sec. In specific heat measurements one expects the same effect for similar rates of temperature change. A possible technique
is the quenching by means of the helium-II-technique [93], since for the determination of the specific heat one has to measure only the heat release and the cooling
rate of the specimen after the current turn-off.

## 5. Some questions for the opponents

The conclusion of high vacancy concentrations in metals (of the order of 1% at the melting point) is not unanimously agreed upon by all workers active in the field. We should like to ask the opponents a few questions, the answer of which might be helpful for an understanding.

1. The appreciable specific heat increase in metals at elevated temperatures is usually interpreted in terms of vacancy formation. Is there an alternative interpretation of this effect?

2. Are there any objections against eq. (3) for the determination of the vacancy concentration from the specific heat increase?

3. Are there any theoretical arguments which discard vacancy concentrations of the order of 1% in metals?

4. Is it possible to understand the high values of the pre-exponential factor in the self-diffusion coefficient when the vacancy concentration near the melting point is of the order of 0.1%?

5. Are the assumptions of a decrease of atomic vibration frequencies in the neighbourhood of a vacancy and a temperature dependence of the vacancy activation parameters exaggerated?

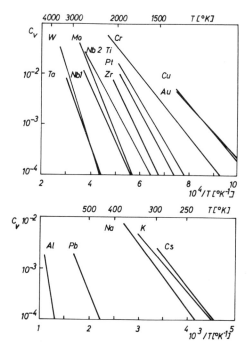

Fig. 13. Temperature dependence of the equilibrium concentration of vacancies in metals.

In conclusion it is felt that there is nowadays considerable evidence which suggests for metals equilibrium vacancy concentrations at the melting point of up to 1% (fig. 13), while the pre-exponential factor in the expression for the vacancy concentration is presumably of the order of $10^2$.

## References

[1] J.I.Frenkel, Z. Physik 35 (1926) 652.
[2] C.Wagner and M.Schottky, Z. Physik. Chem. B11 (1930) 163.
[3] W.Haschkowsky and P.G.Strelkov, J. Phys. USSR 12 (1937) 45.
[4] P.G.Strelkov, J. Phys. USSR 12 (1937) 73.
[5] L.G.Carpenter, T.F.Harle and C.J.Steward, Nature 141 (1938) 1015.
[6] A.W.Lawson, Phys. Rev. 78 (1950) 185.
[7] L.G.Carpenter, J. Chem. Phys. 21 (1953) 2244.
[8] T.E.Pochapsky, Acta Met. 1 (1953) 747.
[9] D.C.Wallace, Phys. Rev. 120 (1960) 84.
[10] N.S.Rasor and J.D.McClelland, J. Phys. Chem. Solids 15 (1960) 17.
[11] N.F.Mott and R.W.Gurney, Electronic processes in ionic crystals (Oxford, 1948).
[12] G.J.Dienes and G.H.Vineyard, Radiation effects in solids (Interscience Publ., New York, 1957).
[13] Vacancies and other point defects in metals and alloys (London, 1958).
[14] W.M.Lomer, in: Progress in metal physics (Pergamon Press, London, 1959) Vol. 8.
[15] H.G.van Bueren, Imperfections in crystals (Amsterdam, 1960).
[16] J. Phys. Soc. Japan 18, Suppl. 1–3 (1963).
[17] J. Phys. Radium 24, No. 7 (1963).
[18] A.Damask and G.J.Dienes, Point defects in metals (Gordon and Breach, New York, London, 1963).
[19] Lattice defects in quenched metals (Academic Press, New York, London, 1965).
[20] Theory of crystal defects (Prague, 1966).
[21] Physicochemical measurements at high temperatures (Butterworths Scient. Publ., London, 1959).
[22] Progress in international research on thermodynamic and transport properties (Academic Press, New York, 1962).
[23] V.A.Kirillin and A.E.Sejndlin, Study of thermodynamic properties of solids (GAI, Moskow, Leningrad, 1963).
[24] Advances in thermophysical properties at extreme temperatures and pressures (ASME, New York, 1965).
[25] L.P.Filippov, Measurements of thermal properties of solid and liquid metals at high temperatures (Izd. MGU, Moscow, 1967).
[26] P.G.Strelkov, E.S.Ickevich, V.N.Kostrjukov, G.G.Mirskaja and B.N.Samojlov, Zh. Fiz. Khim. 28 (1954) 459.
[27] A.A.Skljankin and P.G.Strelkov, Zh. Prikl. Mekhan. i Techn. Fiz. No. 2 (1960) 100; Zh. Prikl. Mekhan. i Techn. Fiz. No. 2 (1963) 161.
[28] O.M.Corbino, Phys. Z. 11 (1910) 413.
[29] K.K.Smith and P.W.Bigler, Phys. Rev. 19 (1922) 268.
[30] L.I.Bockstahler, Phys. Rev. 25 (1925) 677.
[31] C.Zwicker, Z. Physik 52 (1928) 668.
[32] Ya.A.Kraftmakher, Zh. Prikl. Mekhan. i Techn. Fiz. No. 5 (1962) 176.

[33] Ya.A.Kraftmakher, Zh. Prikl. Mekhan. i Techn. Fiz. No. 2 (1966) 144.
[34] Ya.A.Kraftmakher, in: High temperature studies (Nauka, Nowosibirsk, 1966) p. 5.
[35] Ya.A.Kraftmakher and J.M.Ceremisina, Zh. Prikl. Mekhan. i Techn. Fiz. No. 2 (1965) 114.
[36] Ya.A.Kraftmakher, Zh. Prikl. Mekhan. i Techn. Fiz. No. 4 (1967) 143.
[37] Ya.A.Kraftmakher, in: Studies in solid state physics, 2nd series (Nauka, Nowosibirsk, 1967) p. 223.
[38] J.D.Filby and D.L.Martin, Proc. Roy. Soc. A284 (1965) 83.
[39] D.K.C.McDonald, in: Defects in crystalline solids (London, 1955).
[40] D.F.Holcomb and R.E.Norberg, Phys. Rev. 98 (1955) 1074.
[41] J.N.Mundy, L.W.Barr and F.A.Smith, Phil. Mag. 15 (1967) 411.
[42] D.L.Martin, Phys. Rev. 154 (1967) 571.
[43] N.H.Nachtrieb, E.Catalano and J.A.Weil, J. Chem. Phys. 20 (1952) 1185.
[44] J.N.Mundy, L.W.Barr and F.A.Smith, Phil. Mag. 14 (1966) 785.
[45] G.A.Sullivan and J.W.Weymouth, Phys. Rev. 136A (1964) 1141.
[46] R.Feder and H.P.Charbnau, Phys. Rev. 149 (1966) 464.
[47] R.Feder and A.S.Nowick, Phys. Rev. 109 (1958) 1959.
[48] F.M.d'Heurle, R.Feder and A.S.Nowick, in: ref. [16].
[49] R.Feder and A.S.Nowick, Phil. Mag. 15 (1967) 805.
[50] S.Nenno and J.W.Kauffman, Phil. Mag. 4 (1959) 1382.
[51] R.O.Simmons and R.W.Balluffi, Phys. Rev. 117 (1960) 52.
[52] D.King, A.J.Cornish and J.Burke, J. Appl. Phys. 37 (1966) 4717.
[53] G.Bianchi, D.Mallejac, C.Janot and G.Champier, Compt. Rend. Acad. Sci. Paris 263B (1966) 1404.
[54] G.Guarini and G.M.Schiavini, Phil. Mag. 14 (1966) 47.
[55] T.S.Lundy and J.F.Murdock, J. Appl. Phys. 33 (1962) 1671.
[56] T.E.Volin and R.W.Balluffi, Phys. Stat. Sol. 25 (1968) 163.
[57] R.O.Simmons and R.W.Balluffi, Phys. Rev. 125 (1962) 862.
[58] W.DeSorbo, Phys. Rev. 117 (1960) 444.
[59] V.A.Pervakov and V.I.Chotkevič, Dokl. Akad. Nauk. SSSR 134 (1960) 1328.
[60] Ya.A.Kraftmakher and P.G.Strelkov, Fiz. Tverd. Tela 8 (1966) 580.
[61] C.J.Meechan and R.R.Eggleston, Acta Met. 2 (1954) 680.
[62] H.C.Gatos and A.D.Kurtz, Trans. AIME 200 (1954) 616.
[63] H.M.Gilder and D.Lazarus, J. Phys. Chem. Solids 26 (1965) 2081.
[64] Ya.A.Kraftmakher, in: Studies in solid state physics, 2nd series (Nauka, Nowosibirsk, 1967) p. 219.
[65] Ya.A.Kraftmakher, Fiz. Tverd. Tela 9 (1967) 1850.
[66] R.O.Simmons and R.W.Balluffi, Phys. Rev. 129 (1963) 1533.
[67] Ya.A.Kraftmakher and E.B.Lanina, Fiz. Tverd. Tela 7 (1965) 123.
[68] J.J.Jackson, in: ref. [19].
[69] Ya.A.Kraftmakher, Fiz. Tverd. Tela 9 (1967) 1528.
[70] J.W.Edwards, R.Speiser and H.L.Johnston, J. Appl. Phys. 22 (1951) 424.
[71] G.V.Kidson and R.Ross, Intern. Conf. Radioisotopes Sci. Res. (Paris, 1957).
[72] F.Cattaneo, E.Germagnoli and F.Grasso, Phil. Mag. 7 (1962) 1373.
[73] V.O.Sestopal, Fiz. Tverd. Tela 7 (1965) 3461.
[74] J.F.Murdock, T.S.Lundy and E.E.Stansbury, Acta Met. 12 (1964) 1033.
[75] O.M.Kanel and Ya.A.Kraftmakher, Fiz. Tverd. Tela 8 (1966) 291.
[76] G.Kidson and J.McGurn, Can. J. Phys. 39 (1961) 1146.
[77] G.V.Kidson, Can. J. Phys. 41 (1963) 1563.
[78] V.A.Kirillin, A.E.Sejndlin, V.Ja.Čechovskoj and I.A.Žukova, TVT 5 (1967) 1124.
[79] W.C.Hagel, Trans. AIME 224 (1962) 430.
[80] J.Askill and D.H.Tomlin, Phil. Mag. 11 (1965) 467.

[81] Ya.A.Kraftmakher, Fiz. Tverd. Tela 5 (1963) 950.
[82] V.A.Kirillin, A.E.Šejndlin, V.Ja.Čechovskoj and I.A.Žukova, TVT 3 (1965) 395.
[83] T.S.Lundy, F.R.Winslow, R.E.Pawel and C.J.McHargue, Trans. AIME 233 (1965) 1533.
[84] R.E.Taylor and R.A.Finch, J. Less Common Metals 6 (1964) 283.
[85] Ya.A.Kraftmakher, Fiz. Tverd. Tela 6 (1964) 503.
[86] E.V.Borisov, P.L.Gruzin, L.V.Pavlinov and G.B.Fedorov, in: Metallurgy and metallo-
     graphy of pure metals (MIFI, 1959).
[87] W.Danneberg and E.Krautz, Z. Naturforsch. 16a (1961) 854.
[88] J.Askill and D.H.Tomlin, Phil. Mag. 8 (1963) 997.
[89] L.V.Pavlinov and V.N.Bykov, Fiz. Metal. i Metalloved. 18 (1964) 459.
[90] Ya.A.Kraftmakher, Zh. Prikl. Mekhan. i Techn. Fiz. No. 2 (1963) 158.
[91] R.L.Eager and D.B.Langmuir, Phys. Rev. 89 (1953) 911.
[92] Ya.A.Kraftmakher and P.G.Strelkov, Fiz. Tverd. Tela 4 (1962) 2271.
[93] H.Schultz, Acta Met. 12 (1964) 761.
[94] H.Schultz, Acta Met. 12 (1964) 649.
[95] D.Jeannotte and J.M.Galligan, Phys. Rev. Letters 19 (1967) 232.
[96] R.L.Andelin, J.D.Knight and M.Kahn, Trans. AIME 233 (1965) 19.
[97] L.N.Larikov, L.F.Černaja and T.K.Jacenko, in: Properties and applications of heat resis-
     tant alloys (Nauka, Moskow, 1966) p. 28.
[98] G.C.Lowenthal, Australian J. Phys. 16 (1963) 47.
[99] V.A.Kirillin, A.E.Šejndlin, V.Ja.Čechovskoj and V.A.Petrov, Dokl. Akad. Nauk. SSSR
     144 (1962) 390.
[100] V.A.Kirillin, A.E.Šejndlin and V.Ja.Čechovskoj, Dokl. Akad. Nauk. SSSR 142 (1962) 1323.
[101] V.Ja.Čechovskoj, B.Ja.Šumjackij and K.A.Jakimovič, IFZh 5, No. 10 (1962) 13.
[102] Ya.A.Kraftmakher and P.G.Strelkov, Fiz. Tverd. Tela 8 (1966) 1049.
[103] Ya.A.Kraftmakher, in: Studies in solid state physics, 1st series (Nauka, Nowosibirsk,
     1967).
[104] V.S.Kopan, Fiz. Metal. i Metalloved. 19 (1965) 569.
[105] V.N.Kostrjukov and P.G.Strelkov, Zh. Fiz. Khim. 28 (1954) 1825.
[106] B.F.Ormont, Dokl. Akad. Nauk SSSR 153 (1963) 1115.
[107] S.Dushman, Scientific foundations of vacuum technique (New York, London, 1962).
[108] E.Korostoff, J. Appl. Phys. 33 (1962) 2078.
[109] S.Z.Bokštejn, B.S.Bokštejn, A.A.Žuchovickij, S.T.Kiškin and Ju.S.Nečaev, in: Mobility
     of atoms in crystal lattices (Naukova dumka, Kiew, 1965).
[110] Ju.S.Nečaev, Thesis, Moscow Institute for Steels and Alloys (1967).

## Editors' note

To the editors' great regret, Ya.A.Kraftmakher's and P.G.Strelkov's contribution
could not be presented orally at the conference. In section 5 of their written contribution, the authors address five questions to the opponents to their viewpoint.
Most of these questions were discussed in connection with M.Hoch's presentation
at the conference. The outcome of these discussions is to a considerable extent reflected in Hoch's written contribution. It appeared nevertheless desirable to attempt
a reply to Kraftmakher's and Strelkov's questions. The responsibility for the following comments on section 5 of Kraftmakher's and Strelkov's paper is A.Seeger's.

1. An alternative interpretation of the specific heat increase in metals at elevated
temperatures is possible in terms of the anharmonicity of the lattice vibrations. This

is the interpretation adopted in Hoch's written contribution to the conference. In the metals so far investigated in detail, the contribution to the specific heat by the vacancies appears to be small compared with these anharmonicity effects.

2. No objections in principle, provided that $E_0^F$ is interpreted as the vacancy formation energy at the temperature of the measurement. However, due to anharmonic contributions it may be difficult to determine in practice what the excess specific heat $\Delta C_p$ due to vacancies is.

3. We are not aware of any *direct* theoretical argument that would forbid vacancy concentrations of the order of 1% in metals near the melting point. However, if we take the experimental values for the energies of formation of vacancies, such melting point concentrations would require entropies of vacancy formation that could only be understood theoretically if the vacancies were strongly relaxed, at least at high temperatures. For metals with dense structures such as the fcc and bcc lattices, and high melting points, i.e., strong bonding, this appears to be unlikely and in disagreement with existing calculations.

4. Yes. As shown in the contribution of Seeger and Mehrer to this volume, the measured pre-exponential factors of the self-diffusion coefficient of the fcc metals are compatible with melting point vacancy concentrations between $10^{-3}$ and $10^{-4}$ if divacancy contributions to the self-diffusion coefficient and possible temperature dependences of the activation energies and entropies are taken into account. A similarly detailed analysis has not yet been performed for the high-melting point bcc metals, but it appears likely that it will lead to essentially the same conclusion, with the possibility that in some cases rather strong divacancy contributions are required (R.F.Peart and J.Askill, Phys. Stat. Sol. 23 (1967) 263). We cannot see a general reason why $S_{1V}^F$ should be larger than $S_{1V}^M$.

5. The published calculations on entropies of formations of moderately or weakly relaxed vacancies in metals indicate that one cannot expect formation entropies much in excess of 1 k or a strong temperature dependence of the formation energy. Kraftmakher's and Strelkov's assumptions would require very strongly relaxed vacancies, which, as said in the reply to question 3, appear unlikely for the high-melting point metals under discussion. Furthermore, a comparison with the discussion by Seeger and Mehrer (this volume) shows that, apart from questions concerning the orders of magnitudes, the treatment of the temperature dependence of the formation energy by Kraftmakher and Strelkov is not quite correct.

# EQUILIBRIUM MEASUREMENTS IN
# HIGH MELTING MATERIALS

M.HOCH

*Department of Materials Science and Metallurgical Engineering,*
*University of Cincinnati, Cincinnati, Ohio, USA*

## 1. Introduction

The creation of defects, such as vacancies, in a metal or a crystal is detectable by characterizing any physical property which is influenced by the vacancy. The evaluation of the influence of the defects can be done by investigating the property at temperature, called equilibrium measurements, or by investigating the property in quenched samples, that is at room temperature or below on samples which have been heated to high temperatures. If the interpretations of the experiments are correct, then all methods should give the same energy and entropy of formation for the defects and identical concentrations at the melting point.

In close packed and body centered cubic metals the defects which are formed at elevated temperatures are vacancies. The formation of vacancies is a thermally activated process, their concentration increases exponentially with temperature and thus is the maximum in a solid at its melting point. As the effect of vacancies is proportional to their concentration, it is obvious that measurements to characterize the vacancies should be carried out as close to the melting point as possible.

The most direct method to evaluate the influence of vacancies is the simultaneous measurement of the bulk expansion and X-ray lattice parameter. This method has been developed by Simmons and Balluffi [1] and applied to metals, melting up to 1300°K. The temperature limit for these types of measurements is caused by experimental difficulties in keeping constant temperature on extremely large samples.

To determine the concentration of vacancies in metals which melt at temperatures above 1300°K, one can measure the resistivity and its variation with temperature [2], or specific heat and its variation with temperature [3]. In the case of high temperature measurements of the resistivity and also of the specific heat, the effect of vacancies is obtained by extrapolating low temperature data to obtain the resistance or specific heat of a hypothetical vacancy-free solid. The difference between the experimental data and the hypothetical, vacancy free solid is then ascribed to the formation of vacancies. Similar processes or interpretations can be carried out

81

on bulk thermal expansion measurements [4] where again the low temperature thermal expansion is extrapolated to high temperatures and subtracted from the experimental data. The most common quench technique to study vacancies is to measure the resistivity at low temperatures on samples quenched from different temperatures [5].

In an earlier paper [3] the vacancy formation energies of the refractory metals chromium, niobium, and molybdenum have been evaluated from high temperature specific heat measurements. Kraftmakher and Strelkov [6] reviewed the vacancy formation energies and concentrations of vacancies in metals. As pointed out [3,6] the interpretation of high temperature specific heat data yield vacancy concentrations 10 to 100 times larger than those obtained from simultaneous bulk and X-ray expansion measurements.

In the present paper the various methods used to determine the specific heat of metals at elevated temperature are reviewed, and results obtained by the different methods compared.

The methods used to evaluate the experimental data and extract the properties of vacancies from them are discussed, and it is shown that all the experimental data can be explained on the basis of anharmonic contributions to lattice vibrations, and not to vacancy formation.

Resistivity and quenching experiments will not be discussed.

## 2. Experimental techniques

The high temperature specific heat measurements can be grouped into four general techniques: 1) drop calorimetry, also called the technique of mixtures; 2) adiabatic calorimetry; 3) micro-cooling calorimetry and 4) transient technique. Each of the methods used in the past few years will be reviewed briefly. Finally it is shown, that the various techniques give results which agree with each other. Only a few examples are given which connect the various methods.

### 2.1. Drop calorimetry
Drop calorimetry has been used extensively to obtain specific heat data in the temperature range above room temperature to 3500°K and is the only direct calorimetric method applicable above 1500°K. The method consists of heating a specimen in a furnace to the required temperature $T$ and then transferring it very rapidly (by dropping or pulling up) to a calorimeter, the heat being released by the sample while it cools from its temperature $T$ to the temperature of the calorimeter (either 273°K or 298°K). The first drop calorimeter operating up to 3000°K was that of Hoch and Johnston [7] where the furnace was an induction heated vacuum furnace and the calorimeter was a Bunsen ice calorimeter. The calorimeter designed by Conway and Hein [8] heats the sample in a tungsten ribbon furnace in an argon, helium or hydrogen atmosphere and the calorimeter used is a modified

Parr calorimeter. The calorimeter designed by Kirillin, Scheindlin and Chekhovskoy [9] uses a resistively heated graphite or tungsten tube furnace, heated either in argon or in vacuum, and the calorimeter is of the copper block type. In all three types of design it has to be ascertained that the sample transfer from the furnace to the calorimeter is done rapidly so that the calorimeter does not pick up heat from the furnace and that the heat loss from the sample during the drop is negligible. The drop calorimeter gives the heat content, from which the specific heat is obtained by differentiation.

### 2.2. *Adiabatic calorimetry*

In an adiabatic calorimeter [10] the sample is suspended in a container which serves as an adiabatic shield. A certain amount of energy is added to the specimen and the specimen temperature rise is determined. From the mass of the specimen, the energy input and the temperature rise the average specific heat is determined. The adiabatic method gives directly the specific heat as the temperature rise is limited to a few degrees. Corrections for non-adiabatic conditions and the presence of the heater on the mean specific heat have to be carried out. The adiabatic method is capable of yielding specific heat data up to $1500°K$.

### 2.3. *Cooling-microcalorimetry*

In the just recently developed cooling-microcalorimeter [11] the sample, heated to temperature $T_1$, is lowered into the isothermal microcalorimeter which is thermostated at a temperature $T_2$ $(T_1 - T_2 \leqslant 70°K)$. The cooling of the sample, as measured by the thermopile voltage, $s$, is given by

$$s = K e^{-t/\tau} + E(t) , \tag{1}$$

where $K$ and $\tau$ are calorimeter constants, and $E(t)$ is a function of time, related to the extra power $Q(t)$ released or absorbed during the cooling due to a structural reaction (e.g., order-disorder, vacancy formation etc.). In the absence of a structural reaction, the cooling is exponential.

### 2.4. *Transient technique*

Transient techniques used to determine the specific heat of a specimen use a thin wire which is kept at a certain temperature by passing a current through the sample. Using an additional short pulse (duration 0.005 to 0.4 sec) the temperature of the sample is suddenly raised. From the current and voltage pulse the power and the resistance are obtained. The temperature of the wire is obtained from the temperature-resistance relationship of the specimen. This method has been used by Pochapsky [12] and Taylor and Finch [13]. Its disadvantage is that one has to know accurately the variation of the resistance with temperature.

A modification of this rapid transient technique was developed by Rasor and McClelland [14], who enclosed a heavy wire, $\frac{1}{4}''$ in diameter, in a large furnace. The furnace was heated to a certain temperature $T$. The wire in the center of the fur-

nace is under thermal equilibrium. A current is passed through the wire, causing
the wire temperature to rise slowly. From the rise in the wire temperature (determined by optical pyrometry) and the voltage and current the specific heat is determined. This method approximates adiabatic conditions.

The modulation method of Kraftmakher [15] is a steady state method which
consists in heating a wire by direct current, and superimposing on this a sinusoidal-
ly varying alternating current. The wire is in one branch of a bridge circuit. From
the frequency of the alternating current, the magnitude of the direct current, the
variation of the resistance of the wire with temperature, and from the resistance
and capacitance of the other components of the bridge circuit, the specific heat of
the sample is obtained. This method has the advantage that it is a steady state
method; its disadvantage is that it requires the knowledge of the variation of the resistance with temperature of the sample.

## 3. Comparison of experimental results

Table 1 compares the specific heat of copper obtained by Kraftmakher [16]
using the modulation technique and by Brooks et al. [10], using an adiabatic calorimeter. Brooks and Bingham [17] showed that their data on aluminum using adiabatic calorimetry agree with Pochapsky's [12] transient technique. Table 2 contains the specific heat data obtained on molybdenum by Conway [18] (as evaluated by Hoch [22]), Kraftmakher [10], Kirillin et al. [20], Rasor and McClelland
[14] and by Taylor and Finch [13]. The agreement is extremely good, especially
if one takes into account that Conway's [18] data extend only to 2600°K and
that the numbers for Rasor and McClelland [14] and Taylor and Finch [13] had
to be read off a relatively small graph.

These few examples show that the specific heat data obtained by various
methods agree quite well. It is thus obvious that the experimental technique is not
responsible for the extremely large vacancy concentrations calculated from specific
heat data [3,6]. It, therefore, must be due to the interpretation of the high temperature specific heat for the various metals.

Table 1
Specific heat of copper.

| Author | $c_p$ (cal/mole °K) | | |
|---|---|---|---|
| | 800°K | 1000°K | 1200°K |
| Kraftmakher [16] | 6.62 | 6.90 | 7.43 |
| Brooks et al. [10] | 6.69 | 7.02 | 7.56 |

Table 2
Specific heat of molybdenum.

| Author | $C_p$ (cal/mole °K) | | |
|---|---|---|---|
|  | 1000°K | 2000°K | 2800°K |
| Hoch [22] (Conway) | 6.70 | 8.66 | 11.91 |
| Kraftmakher [19] | 6.82 | 8.61 | 14.25 |
| Rasor, McClelland [14] | 6.64 | 8.88 | 12.40 |
| Taylor, Finch [13] | 6.60 | 8.50 | 12.40 |
| Kirillin et al. [20] | 6.81 | 8.56 | 12.21 |

## 4. Theory and discussion

The interpretation of the high temperature specific heat for metals which yields a large concentration of vacancies at the melting point is based on the Grüneisen-Mie equation of state [21]. This model gives for the specific heat at constant pressure

$$c_p = c_V(1 + 3\alpha_L \gamma T) + \gamma_{el} T . \qquad (2)$$

In this equation, $c_p$ is the specific heat at constant pressure, $c_V$ is the specific heat at constant volume, $\alpha_L$ is the linear thermal expansion coefficient, $\gamma$ is the Grüneisen constant, and $\gamma_{el}$ is the electronic specific heat. It has been assumed in the calculations carried out up to date that $\alpha_L$, $\gamma$ and $\gamma_{el}$ are constant, (or do not vary greatly with temperature) and thus the specific heat at constant pressure (lattice and electronic contributions only) is a linear function of $T$:

$$c_p = a + bT . \qquad (3)$$

Any deviation from this relationship at high temperatures is ascribed to the formation of vacancies, adding to eq. (3) the excess specific heat in the form of

$$c_{ex} = (E^F/RT^2) \exp(S^F/R) \exp(-E^F/RT) , \qquad (4)$$

where $E^F$ and $S^F$ are the heat and entropy of formation of the vacancy. The high temperature specific heat of various metals was interpreted using a combination of eq. (3) and (4), namely

$$c_p = a + bT + (E^F/RT^2) \exp(S^F/R) \exp(-E^F/RT) \qquad (5)$$

by Hoch [3], Kirillin et al. [20] and Kraftmakher [6,16]. The justification of this analysis lies in the theoretical considerations of Foreman [23], Stedman, Almqvist and Nilsson [24], Keller and Wallace [25], and Lloyd [26]. These authors discuss the anharmonic contributions to the specific heat at high temperatures. They all stop at terms proportional to $T$, neglecting higher order terms. In these theoretical calculations not even the sign of the anharmonic contribution is fixed: Stedman, Almqvist and Nilsson [24], and Keller and Wallace [25] calculate a negative, Lloyd [26] and Foreman [23] a positive anharmonic contribution.

Leibfried [27] pointed out that the Grüneisen-Mie equation of state will not satisfactorily represent anharmonic contributions to the specific heat. Hoch [22], based on Leibfried's [27] calculations, investigated the contribution of higher order anharmonic terms to the specific heat of refractory metals. Hoch [22] showed that the specific heat of Cr, Mo, W, Nb, and Re can be expressed as

$$c_p = 3RF(\theta_D/T) + cT + dT^3 , \tag{6}$$

where $F(\theta_D/T)$ is the Debye function from $T = \theta_D$ to the melting point. This equation has fewer coefficients than eq. (5) used previously. For Cr, Mo and W, where $\gamma_{el}$ is independent of temperature, $c \approx \gamma_{el}$, $\gamma_{el}$ being determined from low temperature measurements [29]. The total contribution of the higher order anharmonic terms to the heat content of the solid at the melting point, $T_M^4 d/4$, is the same in the 5 metals, being equal to 3700 cal/mole. To show that eq. (6) is also valid for fcc metals, that terms proportional to $T^2$ are not needed, and that an equation having a $T^2$ instead of a $T^3$ term is not satisfactory, the data of Brooks et al. on aluminum [17] and copper [10] were analyzed, taking $314°K$ as $\theta_D$ for Cu, and $405°K$ for Al. If eq. (6) is correct, plotting $[c_p - 3RF(\theta_D/T)]/T$ versus $T^2$ should yield a straight line, if an equation of the type

$$c_p = 3RF(\theta_D/T) + eT + fT^2 \tag{7}$$

is valid, a plot of $[c_p - 3RF(\theta_D/T)]/T$ versus $T$ should be a straight line. Fig. 1 represents the data of Brooks and Bingham [17] and shows that eq. (6) is the correct representation. Fig. 2 shows the data of Brooks et al. [10] on copper; again, eq.(6) represents the data; even the small rise at high temperature is within experimental error, which can be estimated from all the data obtained by Brooks et al. at 500°C, and plotted in fig. 2. The data of Kraftmakher [16] are not shown, because in this type of representation they scatter too much. In Al, $[c_p - 3RF(\theta_D/T)]/T$ $= 0.8 \times 10^{-3} + 2.0 \times 10^{-9} T^2$ in cal/mole $°K^2$ and in Cu $[c_p - 3RF(\theta_D/T)]/T$ $= 0.81 \times 10^{-3} + 0.35 \times 10^{-9} T^2$ in cal/mole $°K^2$. In both cases, the first term is much larger than $\gamma_{el}$ ($0.17 \times 10^{-3}$ cal/mole $°K^2$ in Cu, $0.36 \times 10^{-3}$ cal/mole $°K^2$ in Al) showing that anharmonic terms contribute significantly to the first term. The contribution of higher order anharmonic terms to the total heat content at the melting point, $T_M^4 d/4$, is 300 cal/mole in Cu, and 380 cal/mole in Al; they are equal within experimental error.

It is apparent from the work of Hoch [22] on chromium, molybdenum, tungsten, niobium and rhenium and the present analysis of the data of Brooks et al. [10,17] on copper and aluminum that the high temperature specific heat of metals can be represented by eq. (6) which, it must be pointed out again, contains one

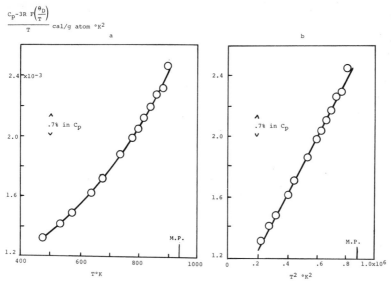

Fig. 1. Specific heat of aluminum as a function of temperature, data of Brooks and Bingham [17], (table 2)

a) $[c_p - 3RF(\theta_D/T)]/T$ versus $T$

b) $[c_p - 3RF(\theta_D/T)]/T$ verus $T^2$

to show that eq. (6) is correct representation. $\lozenge$ represents 0.7% error in $C_p$, accuracy of data according to authors.

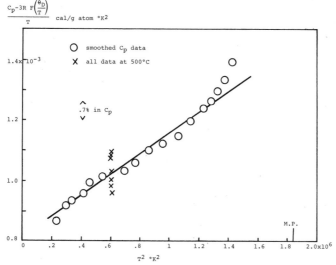

Fig. 2. Specific heat of copper as a function of temperature, data of Brooks et al. [10] (table 3). $\lozenge$ represent 0.7% error in $c_p$, accuracy of data according to authors. Crosses indicate all data at 500°C.

coefficient less than eq. (5) used previously. Thus the major part of the high temperature rise in specific heat can be ascribed to anharmonic contributions to the vibrational spectrum, rather than to the formation of vacancies. The following arguments support strongly this conclusion.

The method of Guarini and Schiavini [11] gives the concentration of vacancies in aluminum at the melting point as 0.06% in excellent agreement with 0.07% obtained by Simmons and Balluffi [28] using bulk expansion and X-ray lattice parameter measurements. Thus calorimetric measurements can give data on vacancy concentrations which agree with other measurements, if the specific heat of a vacancy-free ideal crystal is estimated correctly, or is not required.

Guarini and Schiavini [11] noted how slowly the vacancies which are formed at high temperature diffuse to sinks during cooling in the microcalorimeter. Pochapsky [12], using a transient technique, noted that even with very short pulses of 0.001 to 0.100 seconds duration, the heating should be so fast that the diffusion of vacancies into the solid from sinks and grain boundaries would lag, and this should be noticeable on the heating curve. No such lag was observed. Taylor and Finch [13] used pulses of the same duration as Pochapsky [12] and varied their heating rates from 1000 to 60000°K per second. They did not notice any change in specific heat with heating rate. Rasor and McClelland [14] on the other hand heated their samples at a rate of 50°K per second and their specific heat data agree with those of Taylor and Finch [13]. The observations of Pochapsky [12], and the 1000-fold variation in heating rate used by Rasor and McClelland [14] and Taylor and Finch [13], where no difference in specific heat could be observed, indicates that the rise in specific heat cannot be due to the formation of vacancies.

Obviously, close to the melting point vacancies will contribute to the specific heat. Assuming that the heat and entropy of formation of vacancies obtained by expansion and X-ray lattice parameter measurements are correct, this contribution is within the experimental accuracy of 1%, which can be obtained presently for specific heat measurements. Specific heat data with an accuracy of 0.1% or better from the Debye temperature to the melting point are required to be able to obtain concentration and energies of formation of vacancies from specific heat data.

## References

[1] R.O.Simmons and R.W.Balluffi, J. Appl. Phys. 31 (1960) 2284.
[2] Ya.A.Kraftmakher and E.B.Lanina, Fiz. Tverd. Tela 7 (1965) 123.
[3] M.Hoch, The energy and entropy of vacancy formation in body-centered cubic refractory metals, GE-TM 65–12-2 (1965).
[4] P.Jongenburger, Phys. Rev. 106 (1957) 66.
[5] H.Schultz, Lattice Defects in Quenched Metals, eds. R.M.J.Cotterill, M.Doyama, J.J.Jackson and M.Meshii (Academic Press, New York, 1965) p. 761.
[6] Ya.A.Kraftmakher and P.G.Strelkov, Fiz. Tverd. Tela 8 (1966) 1049; see also this volume p. 55.

[7] M.Hoch and H.L.Johnston, J. Phys. Chem. 65 (1961) 855.
[8] J.B.Conway and R.A.Hein, in: Advances in Thermophysical Properties at Extreme Tem-
    peratures and Pressures (ASME, 1965), p. 131.
[9] V.A.Kirillin, A.E.Scheindlin and V.Ya.Chekhovskoy, in: High Temperature Technology
    (Butterworths, 1964) p. 471.
[10] C.R.Brooks, W.E.Norem, D.E.Hendrix, J.W.Wright and W.G.Northcutt, J. Phys. Chem.
    Solids 29 (1968) 565.
[11] G.Guarini and G.M.Schiavini, Phil. Mag. 14 (1966) 47.
[12] F.F.Pochapsky, Acta Met. 1 (1953) 747.
[13] R.E.Taylor and R.A.Finch, J. Less-Common Metals 6 (1964) 283.
[14] N.S.Rasor and J.D.McClelland, J. Phys. Chem. Solids 15 (1960) 17.
[15] Ya.A.Kraftmakher, Zh. Prikl. Mechan. Tekhn. Fiz. 1962 (1962) 176; see also this volume,
    p. 55.
[16] Ya.A.Kraftmakher, Fiz. Tverd. Tela 9 (1967) 1850.
[17] C.R.Brooks and R.E.Bingham, J. Phys. Chem. Solids 29 (1968) 2641.
[18] J.B.Conway, R.A.Hein, R.M.Fincel Jr. and A.C.Losekamp, General Electric Co., NSP,
    TM 64-2-8.
[19] Ya.A.Kraftmakher, Fiz. Tverd. Tela 6 (1964) 503.
[20] V.A.Kirillin, A.E.Scheindlin, V.Ya.Chekovskoy and V.A.Petrov, in: Proc. of the 4th Symp.
    on Thermophys. Properties (ASME, April 1–4, 1968) p. 54.
[21] N.F.Mott and H.Jones, The theory of the properties of metals and alloys (Dover Publica-
    tions, New York, 1958).
[22] M.Hoch, The high temperature specific heat of body centered-cubic refractory metals,
    GE-TM.
[23] A.J.Foreman, Proc. Phys. Soc. 79 (1962) 1124.
[24] R.Stedman, L.Almqvist and G.Nilsson, Phys. Rev. 162 (1967) 549.
[25] J.M.Keller and D.C.Wallace, Phys. Rev. 126 (1962) 1275.
[26] P.Lloyd, Australian J. Phys. 17 (1964) 269.
[27] G.Leibfried, Gittertheorie der mechanischen und thermischen Eigenschaften der Kristalle,
    Handbuch der Physik, Vol. VII, part 1 (Springer-Verlag, Berlin, 1955) p. 104.
[28] R.O.Simmons and R.W.Balluffi, Phys. Rev. 125 (1962) 862.
[29] C.Kittel, Introduction to solid state physics (John Wiley and Sons, Inc., New York, 1954).

## Discussion

*J.Bass:* Quenching studies, both measuring resistivity and using electron microscope, seem to give vacancy concentrations in agreement with Simmons and Balluffi.
Would you comment on this?

*M.Hoch:* I have shown in the paper that calorimetric measurements, where the
specific heat of the vacancy-free ideal crystal is not required, give the correct
vacancy concentration. The disagreement in other calorimetric measurements is due
to an incorrect estimation of the specific heat of the vacancy-free ideal crystal.

*H.Wenzl:* In platinum it takes about 100 msec at about 1000°K to establish the
vacancy equilibrium concentration after a fast temperature change (R.Sizmann and
H.Wenzl, Z. Naturforsch. 18a (1963) 637). If the heating frequency used in the
modulation technique is larger than 0.1/sec this effect must be accounted for in the
analysis of the experimental data.

*M.Hoch:* In transient techniques, pulses as short as 0.001 sec and heating rates of 60000°K/sec gave the same specific heat as slow equilibrium measurements. Actually this is part of our argument that the rise in specific heat at elevated temperature is mainly due to anharmonic contributions and not to vacancies.

*J.Friedel:* Extrapolating the electron contribution to $C_V$ from low temperature measurements is dangerous. As for the Pauli susceptibility, it is well known that large deviations should occur, i.e.,

$$C_V = \gamma T + A T^2 + B T^3 + \dots .$$

In a metal such as niobium where the Fermi level is probably within a peak of density of states, the leading term in $C_V$ after the linear one is probably strongly negative. These terms in $T^n$ ($n > 1$) should be taken into account in your analysis.

*M.Hoch:* Although we cannot separate anharmonic contributions from higher order electronic terms, the coefficients in $c_p$ with $T^n$ ($n > 1$) in the analysis contain both. Thus your comments were taken into account.

# STUDY OF POINT DEFECTS IN METALS BY ELECTRO- AND THERMOTRANSPORT

Th.HEHENKAMP

*Institut für Metallforschung, Universität Münster, Germany*

## 1. Introduction

It is generally accepted that transport phenomena in pure solid metals are rate controlled by vacancies, at least in fcc lattices. The vacancy, therefore, is the first type of point defect to be considered here. Vacancies exist in thermal equilibrium at elevated temperatures, where self-diffusion and other types of forced transport take place. However, not only self-transport is possible and interesting to study but also transport of impurity atoms in dilute concentrations as interstitial defects or as substitutional atoms. Therefore, these two types of defects have to be included in this review. The information about these point defects to be gained from transport measurements is concerned with the energetic interaction of impurities with the jump-rate-controlling vacancies i.e. information on correlation effects. The most interesting aspect, however, is the study of the activated state (the jumping atom in the saddle point configuration) in more detail than is possible with any other method. Electrotransport measurements give details of the scattering cross sections for collisions of the charge carriers with the atoms in this state, whereas study of thermotransport may provide information concerning the energy distribution between the jumping atom, the neighboring atoms and the lattice.

To what extent the theoretical and experimental aspects have been clarified so far, will be discussed in detail in the next sections separately for the different types of mass transport based on the most frequently used theoretical models. This approach is hoped to give a basis for understanding of present as well as future developments in these fields.

## 2. Electrotransport

This transport effect results from passage of a d.c. current of high density through a metal or alloy and was discovered qualitatively as early as 1861 by Gerardin [1] in liquid solder. In solid metals the first successful experiments were carried out by Coehn and Specht [2], Seith [3] and Jost [4].

These authors investigated the transport of highly mobile interstitial impurities. At that time electrotransport was thought to be some kind of electrolysis. It was therefore quite surprising to observe a transport of metallic ions, supposed to be positively charged, toward the anode as was found for very dilute gold atoms in a lead matrix [5]. Seith and Wever [6] introduced a marker motion technique for their transport measurements in intermetallic phases of the β- and γ-Hume-Rothery type, first in the copper-aluminium system. They discovered that in the electron conducting β-phase the flow was directed toward the anode whereas in the hole-conducting γ-phase it was going in the opposite direction, each constituent of the alloy having an individual transport velocity. These experiments yielded the important result, that electrotransport cannot be described simply by an electrolysis of charged ions but is mainly due to some friction force between the atoms and the charge carriers as had already been suggested earlier by Skaupy [7]. Seith and Wever [8] assumed that the momentum transfer from electrons to mobile atoms gives rise to the transport directed to the anode whereas holes move these atoms in the direction toward the cathode. In addition to this friction force there was still the idea of an interaction of some kind of ionic charge with the electric field. For electron conductors these two forces are opposite in sign. For hole conductors they are both directed toward the cathode. There have been no detailed experimental investigations as to magnitude or nature of this ionic charge so far.

In 1956 Wever [9] discovered for the first time electrotransport in a pure metal (copper), using also a marker technique. This investigation gave rise to many theoretical considerations of electrotransport problems. A detailed review has been given by Verhoeven [10]. Here we shall deal only with the three most frequently used models.

First, quoted by Wever [9], Huntington gave an approximate solution of the forces controlling electrotransport in a pure metal and refined the model in later work [11,12]. The total force $F$ acting on the transported atoms in this model is given by

$$F = F_i - F_{ei} = ZeE \left(1 - \frac{1}{2} \frac{\Delta\rho_d}{\rho} \frac{N}{N_d} \frac{m^*}{|m^*|}\right) = z^* eE \qquad (1)$$

where $e$ is the elementary charge, $Z$ the valence of the metal, and $\Delta\rho_d$ the extra resistivity introduced by the scattering potential of the jumping atom in the activated state. $N_d$ is the density of such activated atoms, $N$ the density of atoms. The ratio $m^*/|m^*|$ gives the sign of the friction force, $\rho$ is the specific resistivity of the sample. Besides the two terms $F_i$ and $F_{ei}$ taking care of the ionic charge of the jumping atom (first term) and the friction force (second term), this formula contains the results of the hypothesis of Seith and Wever [8] concerning the change in sign of the friction force when turning from electron to hole conduction. It has become usual to combine these terms as an effective charge $z^*$ introduced by eq. (1), which is the primarily measurable quantity. This will be shown below.

The formula given by Huntington is based on the following assumptions. The density of electrons is equal to $Z$ times the number of metallic ions per $cm^3$, $Z$ being the valence of the metal. The atom jumping into a vacancy can be described approximately as an interstitial in the activated state. Its ionic charge is introduced on an essentially intuitive basis and assumed to be equal to the valence. The friction force is described by a temperature independent scattering resistivity $\Delta\rho_d$ and is supposed to act primarily on atoms in or near the saddle point. It decreases toward the original or final stable lattice positions. The force law between these positions is approximated by a sinusoidal function. Taking the average over the total jump one obtains the factor of $\frac{1}{2}$. A different approximation for the force law modifies this numerical factor.

Fiks [13] approaches the problem from a somewhat different point of view. He also calculates the friction force $F_{ei}$ exerted by the electrons on the ions and finds in his first paper

$$F_{ei} = eEnl\sigma_i ;$$

where $E$ is the electric field, $n$ the concentration of electrons, $e$ the charge of the ion as well as that of the electron, $l$ the mean free path of the electrons and $\sigma_i$ the scattering cross section of the ion for electrons. The total force is then assumed to be the sum of this friction force and again a static force of the electric field on the ion, which is $e \cdot E$. Hence

$$F = F_i - F_{ei} = eE\,(1 - nl\sigma_i) . \tag{2}$$

For natural ions of the matrix in stable lattice positions $\sigma_i$ equals $1/ln$. Therefore the resulting force on these is zero, in contrast to the force on matrix atoms in the activated state or on impurity atoms for which $nl\sigma_i \neq 1$. In that case Fiks replaces $\sigma_i$ by $\sigma_i^*$ ($\sigma_i^* > \sigma_i$), since an activated ion should cause more scattering than a normal ion. Up to here Fiks has assumed that the concentration of free electrons in the metal $n_e$ equals the concentration of atoms $n_a$.

This restricts his considerations to monovalent matrices or impurities and also to cases, where the density of electrons equals the density of ions. In general, however, the concentration of electrons may deviate from this assumption. Furthermore, the charge of impurities may differ from the charge of matrix ions in stable lattice positions as well as in the activated state. Fiks attributes then to a normal ion an effective charge $q_i$, whereas the activated ions have a charge of $q_i^*$. Electroneutrality then requires the introduction of a mean effective charge $\bar{q}$, which is given by $\bar{q} = n_e/n_a$. One must also replace $l$ by $\bar{l}$, where $\bar{l} = l/n_a\bar{\sigma}$.

The resulting force on the activated complex is then given by

$$F_i = eE\left(q_i^* - \bar{q}\frac{\sigma_i^*}{\bar{\sigma}}\right) = eE\left(q_i^* - \frac{n_e}{n_a}\frac{\sigma_i^*}{\bar{\sigma}}\right) . \tag{3}$$

In the simple case $n_e = n_a$ considered in eq. (2) one can express $\sigma_i$ as a function of a scattering resistivity $\Delta\rho_d$ per unit concentration of defects and $nl$ as a function of the specific resistivity of the matrix $\rho$ using Mott's [14] relations

$$F = eE \left(1 - \frac{\Delta\rho_d}{\rho} \frac{N}{N_d}\right).$$ (4)

It has not been generally realized in literature that this formula is derived for $n_e = n_a$ only and that it excludes multivalent impurities. This is the reason for some different interpretations of the theory of Fiks [15,16]. In the general case a detailed calculation of $\sigma_i^*$ as well as $\bar{\sigma}$ is necessary. Also a determination of the charge of the activated impurity ion is needed.

Glinchuk [17] has amended the model of Fiks for the case of additional hole contributions to the friction force. He obtains in analogy to Fiks's derivation for electrons

$$F_{ei} = (n_h l_h \sigma_h - n_e l_e \sigma_e) eE.$$ (5)

His analysis shows that in the case of mixed conduction not only the respective scattering cross sections but also the mean free path and the density of electrons $n_e$ and holes $n_h$ play an important role.

This view is corroborated by Fiks [18–23] who in his later work investigated theoretically the cross sections and the densities $n_e$ and $n_h$ in considerable detail. Here he gives a deep insight into the quantum mechanical processes involved in the scattering process. Fiks finally describes the driving force for electrotransport in terms of a dynamic effective charge. This dynamic charge is determined from the condition of mechanical equilibrium between the field force acting upon the atoms of the metal and the force that results from momentum transfer to the lattice by the conduction electrons (or holes). In deriving eq. (2) this type of reasoning has been applied for a simple case. For metals with a closed Fermi surface the dynamic effective charge may be calculated in a more rigorous fashion without taking into account Umklapp-processes. In the general case, where the Fermi surface is not open, the dynamic charge depends not only on the geometry of the Fermi surface but also on the scattering mechanism. Fiks further replaces the scattering cross sections $\sigma_i^*$ also by average values $\bar{\sigma}_i^*$ and obtains therefore essentially the same result as Huntington. The average is again dependent on the particular force law used. Therefore the numerical factor of $\frac{1}{2}$ in the friction force should be taken as a reasonable first approximation. In general it has to be treated as a variable unknown and plays the same role as the permeation factor in electrochemistry.

The third model has been developed by Bosvieux and Friedel [24]. These authors distinguish three cases.

a) *Impurities in interstitial positions*

In this model the interstitial is not submitted to any direct field force since its charge is shown to be completely screened. The only force is the friction force, which, as in Huntington's model, has the same sign as that of the charge carriers (negative for electrons, positive for holes) and is proportional to the valence $Z$ of the matrix:

$$F = \mp Z \frac{\Delta \rho_d}{\rho} \frac{N}{N_d} eE. \qquad (6)$$

Adda and Philibert [25] have pointed out in their review of electrotransport that in contrast to most of the other theories (see also Mangelsdorf [26], Klemm [27] and Baranowski [28]) the force acting upon the interstitial does not depend explicitly on the charge of that interstitial.

b) *Vacancies in a pure metal*

Here the force is again a function of the position of the metallic ion, whether it is close to its equilibrium position or close to a vacancy. It is submitted to two forces, one is due to its interaction with the vacancy, the other to the electric field force. If the ion is in the activated state, Bosvieux and Friedel assume in the same way as Huntington that it behaves approximately like an interstitial. In this position the authors obtain a force on this interstitial-like ion

$$F_A = -ZeE \frac{\Delta \rho_d^{(z)}}{\rho} \frac{N}{N_d^{(z)}} \qquad (7)$$

where $\Delta \rho_d^{(z)}$ and $N_d^{(z)}$ are the extra resistivity and the concentration, respectively, of the activated ions. In order to estimate the magnitude of $\Delta \rho_d^{(z)} N / N_d^{(z)}$ the authors propose to use the following relation which is valid in Born's approximation:

$$\frac{\Delta \rho_d^{(z)} N}{N_d^{(z)}} = \lambda Z^2 . \qquad (8)$$

$Z$ stands for the valence of the interstitial considered, $\lambda$ is a constant depending on the nature of the metal. The variation of the force $F_A$ during the jump is supposed to be a sinusoidal function. This is the same argument as proposed by Huntington in his model.

The resulting force on a metallic ion in a pure metal migrating by means of a vacancy mechanism is then

$$F = \tfrac{1}{2} ZeE \left[ 1 + C \mp \frac{\Delta \rho_d^{(z)}}{\rho} \frac{N}{N_d^{(z)}} \right] , \qquad (9)$$

where $C$ is given by

$$C = \frac{4 \tau m Z e^4}{3 \pi \hbar^3} [J_0(b) - 2 J_2(b)]$$

and depends in a complicated way on the interatomic distance $b$, the relaxation time $\tau$ and the valence $Z$. $C$ usually is negative.

c) *Substitutional impurity at dilute concentrations*

The solute of valence $z + Z$ is distributed in a matrix of valence $Z$. Here $z$ is the excess valence. The resulting force is obtained in a similar fashion as in case b) and reads for a very dilute solution

$$F = \tfrac{1}{2} ZeE \left[ 1 + C \mp \frac{N}{\rho} \left( \frac{\Delta\rho_d^{(z)}}{N_d^{(z)}} + \frac{\Delta\rho_d^{(z+Z)}}{N_d^{(z+Z)}} \right) \right] . \tag{10}$$

### 2.1. Formal comparison of these models

All models proposed agree in that they contain two terms, the first accounting for the ionic field force, the second for the friction force. So in general they all can be represented in the form

$$F = \left[ a(Z + C) \mp b \, \frac{\Delta\rho_d N}{\rho N_d} Z \right] eE \tag{11}$$

where

$a = 1;\quad C = 0;\quad b = 0.5$ — Model of *Huntington* for vacancy migration in pure metals

$a = 0.5;\ C < 0;\quad b = 0.5$ — Model of *Bosvieux and Friedel for vacancy* migration in a pure metal

$a = 0;\quad C = 0;\quad b = 0.5$ — For interstitial impurities

$a = 0.5;\ C < 0;\quad b = 0.5$ — For substitutional impurities migrating via a vacancy mechanism ($\Delta\rho_d$ as sum eq. (10))

$a = \dfrac{q_i^*}{Z};\quad C = 0;\quad b = \dfrac{n_e}{n_a} \dfrac{1}{\beta Z} .$ — Model of *Fiks* for all types of defects ($\beta$ = numerical factor)

The differences between these models have become smaller in the past as far as the friction force is concerned. It must, however, be pointed out, that these models have been applied to experiments during different stages of their development in different forms. This must be kept in mind when we discuss the experimental results below. Differences exist still in the field force. The only model that provides also some means for a rough calculation of the scattering resistivities is that of Bosvieux and Friedel.

Before one can try to compare these models with experiments, it is necessary to check further relations between these forces and the measurable quantities. For what is observable in experiments is not the force itself but the flux of matter, which is produced by the force.

Mass transport can be understood as the result of a random diffusion biased by an external field in a certain direction. The driving energies in metals are always small compared to $kT$. As a result the Nernst-Einstein equation is applicable and relates the observable transport velocity $v$ with the driving forces $F$ by means of the mobility $M$.

$$v = MF, \text{ where } M = D/kT \equiv D^*/kTf \tag{12}$$

and

$$D = D_0 \exp(-Q/RT) \,.$$

$D$ is the true statistical diffusion coefficient, $D^*$ is the self-diffusion coefficient as obtained from tracer measurements, $f$ is the correlation factor.

The mobility is controlled essentially by the diffusion coefficient which, in this derivation, is supposed to be the true statistical diffusion coefficient $D$. The work of Bardeen and Herring [29] has shown that one does not always measure this quantity directly in experiments but one observes different values, depending on the experimental technique used. These values are related to the true statistical $D$ by the correlation factors $f$.

For this reason one encounters here many additional problems. It is not too surprising that the question of the choice of the proper diffusion coefficient in eq. (12) has been treated differently in the literature. Wever [9], in his first investigation of transport in a pure metal, already pointed out that the correlation factor $f$ has to be accounted for in transport experiments if one takes the self-diffusion coefficient $D^*$ from radioactive tracer measurements. Most of the later work in pure metals has followed this line. Particularly the early experiments, however, have been evaluated *without* taking $f$ into account. For transport of impurities one has usually argued in analogy to the case of a pure metal, supposing implicitly that the fluxes of the components are independent of each other. Archipova et al. [30] on the other hand claim that $f$ has to be *excluded* if one measures mobility and mass transport simultaneously by means of tracers. In view of the considerable error introduced by taking a wrong mobility the question of the correlation factor has to be investigated in more detail.

## 2.2. Mobility to be used in transport measurements

Values of $f$ are easily obtainable for self-diffusion measurements employing radioactive tracers of the same metal and are named $f_0$ in this simple case. $f_0$ can be determined from the coordination number (number of next nearest neighbors of a vacancy) and is therefore essentially given by the type of lattice. As computed by Compaan and Haven [31], $f_0$ equals 0.781 in fcc and 0.72 in bcc structures. In the case of diffusion of impurity atoms in the matrix the correlation factor is not determined by the geometry of the lattice alone but depends also on energetic interactions of the impurities with matrix atoms as well as the jump-rate-controlling vacancies. The impurity tracer is not chemically equivalent with the matrix atoms. The geometrical as well as the energetic interactions of the different atoms and the vacancies give rise to so called cross terms in a thermodynamical treatment of diffusion. This mutual interaction can only be expected if the motion of at least two distinguishable atomic species is controlled by a third one, the vacancy. An interstitial therefore is not subjected to any correlation at all ($f = 1$). The correlation factor for impurities depends on the particular couple of atoms under unvestigation. At present there exists no comprehensive theory to predict $f$ from first principles.

All efforts to obtain values for $f$ are based to some extent on experimental data so far.

Lidiard [32] evaluates the change in self-diffusivity in a given matrix upon addition of impurities. Le Claire [33] has based his considerations on the changes in activation energy of impurity diffusion compared to matrix self-diffusion and the change in the preexponential factor $D_0$ in both cases. Manning [34] has found by a computer fit of many diffusion data available, interconnected by certain theoretical considerations, that values of $f$ are restricted to certain ranges. The results obtained from different models, details of which are reviewed by Adda and Philibert [25], do not agree very well, leaving still a remarkable margin of error. Values for $f$ may also be obtained experimentally by measurements of the isotope effect from

$$f = \frac{(D_1/D_2) - 1}{\sqrt{m_1/m_2} - 1} \tag{13}$$

where $m$ is the isotope mass, and $D$ the diffusion coefficient for the two isotopes 1 and 2, respectively. This relation is valid as long as $\sqrt{m_1/m_2} = D_1/D_2$ for $f = 1$. Since for interstitials, where $f = 1$, this relation can be checked and is satisfied in some [35] but not all cases [36,37] one must generally introduce an additional factor $\Delta K$, which takes care of the deviations from the square root of the masses ratio not caused by the correlation effects. Unfortunately this $\Delta K$ is unknown in most cases. $f \cdot \Delta K$ represents actually the product of the correlation factor and the fraction of kinetic translation energy of the atom at the saddle point. $\Delta K = 1$ is equivalent to the case where the jumping atoms keeps all its translational energy during the entire jump. Furthermore the isotope effect is very small and precision is obtainable only for light elements with a high ratio in isotopic masses.

These results for the correlation factor are obtained by taking into consideration diffusion only. In the case of transport under the influence of external forces the interaction of the matrix atoms A, the impurity atoms B and the vacancies with each other as well as with the electrons have to be considered, too.

This mutual interaction of the different species has been studied from a thermodynamical point of view by several authors [38–42], most recently by Van Doan and Brebec [16] for electrotransport and by Mock and Lazarus [43] for thermotransport. Both cases are very similar. In these approaches, the flux $J$ of components A and B as well as that of the vacancies and electrons is given by a set of equations, namely – following the nomenclature used by Adda and Philibert [25] –

$$J_A = -\frac{L_{AA}}{T}\frac{d}{dx}(\hat{\mu}_A - \mu_V) - \frac{L_{AB}}{T}\frac{d}{dx}(\hat{\mu}_B - \mu_V) - \frac{L_{Ae}}{T}\hat{\mu}_e$$

$$J_B = -\frac{L_{BA}}{T}\frac{d}{dx}(\hat{\mu}_A - \mu_V) - \frac{L_{BB}}{T}\frac{d}{dx}(\hat{\mu}_B - \mu_V) - \frac{L_{Be}}{T}\hat{\mu}_e \tag{14}$$

where $L_{ik}$ are the phenomenological coefficients relating the thermodynamical forces to the respective fluxes $J$.

These equations have already been simplified which is possible if the fluxes are measured with respect to a reference system fixed to the average atomic velocity $\bar{v}$. In this reference system

$$J_A + J_B = -J_V .$$

The vacancies are supposed to be in thermal equilibrium everywhere. According to Blackburn [44], rather large electric fields or temperature gradients are required to establish a considerable deviation of the vacancy concentration from equilibrium. Hence $d\mu_v/dx = 0$. It should be noted that this is valid only for very dilute solutions. In larger concentration gradients $\mu_v$ may generally be dependent on $x$. The thermodynamical forces are the derivatives of the potentials

$$\hat{\mu}_i = \mu_i + z_i^* \, e\Phi \qquad (i = A, B, V \text{ and } e) \quad \text{with } E = d\Phi/dx .$$

For $i = e$

$$\mu_e = E_f \qquad \text{and} \qquad \frac{d\mu_e}{dx} = \frac{dE_f}{dx} = 0$$

where $E_f$ is the Fermi energy. Equations (14) then reduce to

$$J_A = -D_A \frac{\partial n_A}{\partial x} - \frac{L_{AA}}{T} \left[ z_A^* + \frac{L_{AB}}{L_{AA}} z_B^* \right] eE$$

$$J_B = -D_B \frac{\partial n_B}{\partial x} - \frac{L_{BB}}{T} \left[ z_B^* + \frac{L_{BA}}{L_{BB}} z_A^* \right] eE .$$

(15)

Here $D_A$ and $D_B$ are the intrinsic diffusion coefficients, $n_A$ and $n_B$ the number of atoms A and B per unit volume.

If B is the solute, $D_B$ approaches $D_{B*}^A$, the impurity diffusion coefficient of B* in A, when $n_B$ becomes small (very dilute solution); $L_{BB}$ then becomes $n_B D_{B*}^A/k$. Therefore, for very small values of $n_B/n_A$

$$J_B = -D_{B*}^A \frac{\partial n_B}{\partial x} - \frac{n_B D_{B*}^A}{kT} \left[ z_B^* + \frac{L_{BA}}{L_{BB}} z_A^* \right] eE .$$

(16)

It is obvious that the "cross-terms" $L_{BA} = L_{AB}$ lead to a coupling between the forces acting upon A atoms and those influencing B. Both fluxes are not independent of each other any more.

In the simplest case B is a tracer of A. In that event one has to replace B* by A* and $z_B^*$ by $z_A^*$, which are equal to a first approximation. Then

$$J_{A}^* = -D_{A*}^A \frac{\partial n_{A*}}{dx} - \frac{n_{A*} D_{A*}^A}{kT} z_{A*} \left( 1 + \frac{L_{A*A}}{L_{A*A*}} \right) .$$

(17)

The ratio $L_{A*A}/L_{A*A*}$ is related [25] to the correlation factor $f_0$ by

$$\frac{1}{f_0} = 1 + \frac{L_{A*A}}{L_{A*A*}} .$$

(18)

Therefore eq. (17) can be written as

$$J_{A*} = -D_{A*}^A \frac{\partial n_{A*}}{dx} - \frac{n_A^* D_{A*}^A}{kTf_o} z_A^* \, eE .$$

(19)

The first term is the diffusion term, the second one the transport term. The mobility apparently is $D^*/kTf_o = D/kT$. If one measures therefore diffusion (first term) and transport (second term) at the same time with a radioactive tracer, it is necessary to take into account $f_o$, since the transport essentially is uncorrelated. This is in disagreement with [30]. It has been pointed out already that $f_o$ is essentially determined by the structure of the lattice.

If B, however, is an impurity tracer or atom, one has to use the complete eq.(15). Here the correlation is, as has been shown, contained in the cross term $L_{BA}$ and has no longer a purely geometrical nature. To see an analogy to the simple case considered previously one can rewrite eq. (16) by

$$J_B = -D_{B*}^A \frac{\partial n_B}{\partial x} - \frac{n_B D_{B*}^A}{kT} z_B^* \left(1 + \frac{L_{BA}}{L_{BB}} \frac{z_A^*}{z_B^*}\right) eE .$$

(20)

The influence of the cross term $L_{BA}$ comes in, but not fully, as for the tracer of the matrix, but multiplied by $z_A^*/z_B^*$. If one introduces formally a correlation factor $f_B$ for impurity transport in analogy to that for self-transport $f_o$, eq. (20) may be written as

$$J_B = -D_{B*}^A \frac{\partial n_B}{\partial x} - \frac{n_B D_{B*}^A}{kT} z_B^* \left[1 + \frac{z_A^*}{z_B^*} \left(\frac{1}{f_B} - 1\right)\right] ,$$

(21)

as pointed out by Hehenkamp, Herzig and Heumann [45].

According to Howard and Lidiard [45a] the formally introduced $1/f_B$ can be related to measurable values, the tracer diffusivities $D_{A*}^A$ and $D_{B*}^A$ of solvent and solute respectively as well as the intrinsic diffusion coefficients $D_A$ and $D_B$ by

$$\frac{1}{f_B} = 1 + \frac{11}{9} \frac{D_{A*}^A}{D_{B*}^A} - \frac{D_A}{D_B}$$

which may be simplified to

$$\frac{1}{f_B} = 1 + \frac{D_{A*}^A}{D_{B*}^A} \left(\frac{1}{f_o} - 1\right)$$

(21a)

for a very dilute solution ($D_A = D_{A*}^A$) taking $\frac{11}{9}$ equal to $1/f_o$ for a fcc structure.

This detailed discussion clarifies the situation concerning the use of the proper correlation factor and takes account of Lodding's remarks at this conference as to whether $f$ has to be included or not. In pure metals the correlation factor $1/f_o$ enters fully, whereas for impurity transport only the fraction $(1/f_B - 1) z_A^*/z_B^*$ enters. This has not always been realized. In these cases the assumption of independent fluxes is not longer justified. $f_B$ should vary with temperature. This is obvious from eq. (21a) and is also the result of many experiments as evaluated from the isotope effect [36]. Le Claire has for this reason objected to the extrapolation of $z$ versus $1/\rho$ curves (see also discussion p. 118) since this variation had not been taken into account. Since in the case in question (Sb in Au) $z_A^*/z_B^*$ is only of the order of 0.2, the modification of the correlated diffusion coefficient $D_{B*}^A$ by the terms in brackets amounts to less than 10%. A 20% variation of $f_B$ gives rise to an error of 2% only which is far below the present experimental accuracy. It should be noted, that correlation effects can also become very pronounced if $z_A^*/z_B^*$ becomes large, which is possible, for example, in multivalent matrices such as aluminum.

The two factors *mobility* and *force*, which determine the experimentally measurable velocity $v$, have been discussed in detail now. We shall now give a brief review of the experimental techniques used in order to get an idea of the confidence to be given to individual experimental results.

## 2.3. *Experimental techniques*

The current experimental techniques to measure electro- and thermotransport have been reviewed and discussed in an earlier paper by Hehenkamp [46]. Therefore our account can be brief on this topic.

Most of the transport measurements in pure metals are still performed by means of marker motion techniques. Here the important problem is the determination of the temperature, the accuracy of which has been considerably improved by the use of optical pyrometers employing light sensitive resistors or phototransistors [47]. The direct attachment of thermocouples has turned out to be dangerous since after a certain time the emf. of this couple is influenced by impurities diffusing in from the specimen.

In recent years isothermal techniques are also more frequently used. Here it is possible to determine the diffusivity $D$ and transport velocity $v$ simultaneously in one experiment. Usually a transport-modified Fick's second law is applied in the simplified form

$$\frac{\delta c}{\delta t} = D \frac{\delta^2 c}{\delta x^2} \pm v \frac{\delta c}{\delta x} \tag{22}$$

where $D$ and $v$ are constant. It has been shown previously [48,15] that well-known solutions of the diffusion equation without transport term are also solution of this linear differential equation (22), provided that the coordinate $x$ is shifted by $vt$ in the direction of the transport. For the most frequently used boundary condition, a thin layer placed between two halves of a specimen, forming a sandwich, the solution $c(x,t)$ is given by

$$c(x,t) = \frac{S}{2\sqrt{\pi D t}} \exp\left[-\frac{(x \mp vt)^2}{4Dt}\right] . \tag{23}$$

For thick layers the proper solution can be expressed as

$$c(x,t) = \tfrac{1}{2}\, c_a \left[ 1 - \text{erf}\ \frac{x \mp vt}{2\sqrt{Dt}} \right], \tag{24}$$

where $c_a$ is the initial concentration of the alloy placed between the two other parts of a pure metal sandwich.

By plotting $\ln c(x,t)$ versus $\xi^2 = (x \mp vt)^2$, one obtains for the first case a straight line with slope $1/4Dt$. In the second case, $c/c_a$ is plotted versus $x$ on probability paper. Here, $D$ can also be determined from the slope of that plot. From $D$ the temperature can be determined very precisely.

From eqs. (1), (12) and $E = \rho j$, the final expression for $v$ is found to be

$$v = MF = \frac{D}{kT}\ \rho j z^* e, \tag{25}$$

where $j$ is the current density. The question of $D$ to be used has already been discussed. $D$-values obtained from the above plots can be used immediately, but have to be divided by $f_0$ for self-transport in a pure metal or have to be multiplied by

$$\left[ 1 + \frac{z_A^*}{z_B^*}\left( \frac{1}{f_B} - 1 \right) \right] \tag{26}$$

for impurity transport, where $f_B$ is the correlation factor for that impurity as defined in eq. (21).

In many papers the ratio $v/j$ is logarithmically plotted versus $1/T$. Such a plot should exhibit a slope close to the activation energy of diffusion $Q$, since $\rho$ is approximately proportional to $T$ (which cancels against $T$ in the denominator) and since often $z^*/f$ experimentally appears to be independent of temperature. However, some experimental results deviate strongly from this. Usually a $Q$ much lower (about 0.5) than $Q$ for diffusion is observed. Many different models have been proposed to take account for these phenomena. Wever [49] has suggested that for dislocation pipe diffusion the correlation may be different from that for bulk diffusion. He attributes therefore the deviations to the factor mobility. Klotsman et al. [30] argue that the scattering cross section may vary strongly with temperature which is in contrast to the usual assumption of a fairly temperature-independent extra resistivity. It must be pointed out also that correlation for dislocation pipe diffusion enters according to eq. (21) not fully for impurity transport but multiplied by $z_A^*/z_B^*$. Therefore it may be detectable to a larger degree where $z_A^* > z_B^*$ whereas the opposite holds for $z_B^* > z_A^*$. Most recent experiments have, however, shown that the activation energies are very close for transport and diffusion in many cases.

## 2.4. Experimental results

### 2.4.1. Electrotransport of interstitial impurities

An excellent and critical review of the results for interstitial impurities has recently been published by Oriani and Gonzalez [50]. They listed results in cases where several different interstitial impurities were studied in the same matrix. The different interstitial solutes as H, D, N and O migrate in a given solvent such as $\alpha$- and $\gamma$-Fe, Ni, Y, Th and $\beta$-Ti always to the same electrode, the direction depending on the matrix metal. This can be interpreted easily in terms of the model given by Bosvieux and Friedel [24] assuming that there is no direct field force. In this case only momentum transfer from the holes and electrons should be controlling the direction of interstitial migration. This holds as long as addition of a certain amount of impurity does not change the electronic behavior of the matrix (dilute solution). There are two exceptions: N in $\gamma$-Fe [51] and O in $\beta$-Ti [52]. In the first case the sign could be an error, since $z^*$ was rather small $(-0.1)$, in the second case one weight percent of oxygen has been added, which might have changed the electronic structure of titanium.

Generally, very little temperature dependence of $z^*$ has been found within experimental accuracy which ranges between 10 and 30%. There have also been measurements of H in Pd [53] where hydrogen moves to the cathode as carbon does in cobalt. In the latter case Hehenkamp [54] found a decrease in $z^*$ from about +9 at 800°C to +6 at 1400°C. Such a decrease is to be expected from the model of Bosvieux and Friedel. The crucial question, however, whether there is a direct field force on the interstitial or not cannot be answered yet with any confidence. In cobalt the hole drag apparently is more effective than the electron drag, but the ratio of both might change in the temperature interval as investigated in [55]. Also the experimental accuracy is still not high enough to extract the field force from the data.

Bibby [56] has tried to tackle the problem of the direct field force on the interstitial with a different type of experiment, the electromigration in a Hall field. He supposes that perpendicular to the direction of the current and the magnetic field a static Hall field only acts upon the interstitials. This static character, however, of the Hall field must be doubted in a matrix with mixed conduction where interband transitions may give rise to compensation currents also in the direction of the Hall field. The situation is still not clear.

It is very interesting to note that Oriani and Gonzalez [50] observed an isotope effect for migration of H and D in $\alpha$-Fe and Ni. $z^*$ for D was about 55 to 25% higher than $z^*$ for H.

### 2.4.2. Electrotransport in pure metals

A detailed review of many of the experimental results is given by Adda and Philibert [25]. Generally, in metals with almost exclusive electron conduction as the alkali metals, Ag, Au and Al the momentum transfer is clearly the predominant force. These elements therefore show a transport to the anode. In the case of copper, which also belongs to this group, the purity of the sample plays apparently an important role [57]. It is also generally accepted that the density of electrons enters into the momentum transfer term as stated in eq. (11). Nevertheless there is still a remarkable scattering in the data obtained for a given metal from different authors

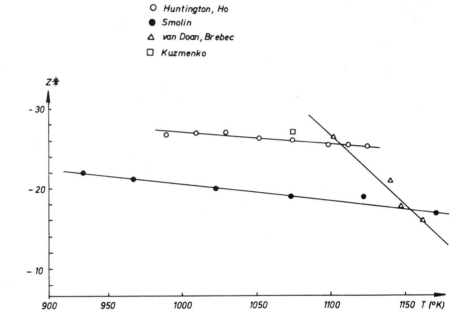

Fig. 1. Effective charge $z^*$ as function of temperature for electrotransport in pure silver. Data referring to [16, 63, 66, 101].

as is shown for Ag, Al and Au in figs. 1, 2 and 3. There are apparently systematic errors involved since the deviations are sometimes much larger than the stated mean error. Evidently experimental accuracy has become much better in recent years but in many cases still does not permit to check more of the theory than only the sign of the transport direction. Here the two important problems are to check whether the momentum transfer term in eq. (11) is proportional to $1/\rho$, and to obtain a reasonable figure for the direct field force by plotting $z^*$ versus $1/\rho$.

Unfortunately in many recent papers employing marker techniques $z^*/f$ has been found almost independent of temperature within experimental accuracy. D'Amico and Huntington [58] observed for $\gamma$-uranium a constant value of $z^*/f = -1.6$. The quantity $Dz^*/f$ showed therefore the same temperature dependence as $D$ and hence the same activation energy. Campbell and Huntington [59] measured also electrotransport in Zr. The result was a small value of $z^*/f = +0.3$, which again was almost constant. Also the complex conduction mechanism of these metals may play a role.

In this context the results of Thernqvist and Lodding [60] in lithium are very interesting since the theory should apply primarily to the alkali metals. The effective

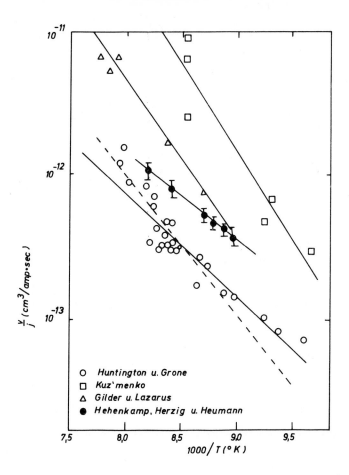

Fig. 2. log $v/j$ versus $1/T$ for electrotransport in pure gold. Data referring to [11,15,102,103].

charge $-z^*$ in fig. 5 shows indeed a slight decrease with temperature attributed to the $1/\rho$-dependence of the friction term postulated by theory and is therefore plotted as a function of $1/\rho$. The scattering resistivity $\Delta\rho_d$ was found to be fairly independent of temperature (fig. 5) and to amount to $0.62 \pm 0.03$ $\mu\Omega$ cm/at % defects. This is consistent with the theoretical assumptions of a temperature *in*dependent scattering resistivity. It offers the possibility to evaluate the direct field force on the jumping atom by extrapolation of $\rho^{-1} \to 0$. Results of such extrapolations are not presented by the authors [60] but are easily seen to lie in the order of $+1$. The scattering resistivity of $0.62$ $\mu\Omega$ cm/at % defects is considerably lower than the estimate for vacancies in Li of $1.2$ $\mu\Omega$ cm/at %. The latter value, however, is comparable to that obtained by Sullivan for sodium, namely $0.44$ $\mu\Omega$ cm/at % [61]. The reason

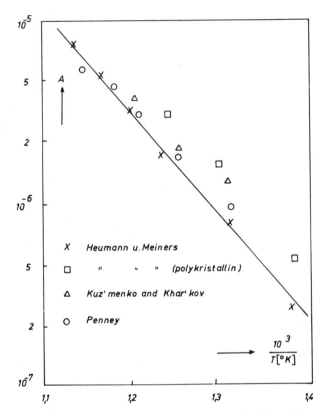

Fig. 3. log $A = \tau\, V_m T/\rho$ versus $1/T$ for electrotransport in pure aluminium: Data referring to [104,105,106].

for these low values is not clear, but is expected to arise from a considerable relaxation of the atoms around a vacancy in the alkali metals [62].

In polycrystalline zinc and cadmium and also lead, i.e. in metals with a small positive Hall coefficient at room temperature, a mass transport was found toward the anode by Kuzmenko [63] and Lodding [64]. This was often quoted as being in contrast to the prediction of the hypothesis of Wever and Seith [8], which was substantiated by all theories later, that excess hole conduction should lead to cathode directed mass flow. It is evident that the Hall effect is not a suitable measure of the quantities determining the force. Secondly, the Hall effect is measured usually at much lower temperatures than those where electrotransport takes place. It is therefore quite interesting to study this question in more detail. This was done for the first time by Routbort and Huntington [65] in zinc single crystals which are anisotropic not only in their diffusivities in and perpendicular to the hexagonal planes but also in their Hall constants. These authors did not find a simple correla-

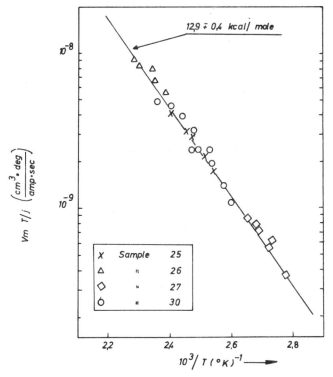

Fig. 4. log $v_m$ $T/j$ versus $1/T$ for electrotransport of Li [60].

tion between the Hall constants and the respective effective charges. It was, however, reported that Hall constants in zinc have the tendency to become negative at higher temperatures. $z^*$ was found to be also anisotropic, namely $z_\perp^*/f = -5.6$ and $z_\parallel^*/f = -2.55$.

The values mentioned so far have been obtained by surface marker techniques. There are also a few well founded isothermal measurements of transport in a pure metal carried out by means of radioactive tracers employing a thin layer technique. Gilder and Lazarus [15] marked the original interface by a radioactive $HfO_2$-marker insoluble in the matrix. These authors observed for [195]Au electromigration in gold an effective charge of about −8, independent of temperature. Van Doan and Brebec [16] used the same technique to transport [110]Ag in silver and observed values for $z^*$ decreasing with temperature stronger than $1/\rho$. These data are presented also in fig. 1. Similar techniques but without special markers at the original interface have also been used by Kuzmenko [63]. In his technique, later adopted by Archipova et al. [30] and Smolin [66], it is necessary to break the two parts of the "sandwich" apart after the transport in order to establish from here the anodic as well as the cathodic penetration profiles. This method has been critizized by Gilder

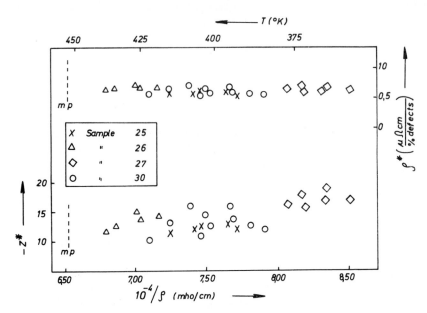

Fig. 5. Effective charge $z^*$ versus $1/\rho$ for electrotransport in Li, $\rho^* = \Delta\rho_d$ plotted versus $T$.
(Thernqvist and Lodding [60]).

and Lazarus [15] as either impossible, if the sandwich has a sound weld, or as introducing an uncontrolled impedance to the flow of matter if this is not the case. Data
obtained in this way have shown differences, when compared to those supplied by
other sources. The data given by Smolin [66] in fig. 1 seem to lie in the proper
range but it should be noted that the mobilities given by this author are higher by
two orders of magnitude with respect to self-diffusion data.

### 2.4.3. Electrotransport of substitutional impurities

Many data for electrotransport of substitutional impurities, a considerable fraction of which is also reported in [10] and [25], were obtained with various modifications of the "sandwich" technique mentioned already. The concentration profile
is usually measured by means of radioactive tracers. The methods, however, differ
much in their efficiency to obey properly the boundary conditions for eqs. (23) or
(24). Hence some of them have a rather limited accuracy.

Impurity transport has been studied by Frantsevich [67] and Smolin [68]. Archipova et al. [30] used the Kuzmenko technique mentioned above for electrotransport of noble metal impurities in a noble metal matrix. Van Doan and Brebec
[16] measured migration of Sb in Ag employing the technique developed by
Gilder and Lazarus [15], who themselves also performed two preliminary experiments of Sb-transport in Au. Most of these experiments yielded again the result that

either $z^*$ is constant within experimental error or varies much more rapidly as function of temperature than does $1/\rho$. The data usually show a considerably larger scattering than the estimated mean error.

Hehenkamp [46,69,70] therefore has tried to improve the accuracy of isothermal measurements by employing electron microprobe analysis for the determination of the concentration profile and its transport which is given by the shift relative to the lattice fixed reference system. First electrotransport of Sb in Cu was investigated [71]. Previous measurements by Kuzmenko [72] and Stepper and Wever [73] yielded rather different values for $z^*$ of about 45 and between 300 and 500, respectively. The method employed by [73] was different from the former and based upon resistometry. Microprobe analysis has improved the reproducibility of the measurements remarkably. A detailed report will be given in a forthcoming paper [74] for very dilute solutions as well as for concentrations up to about 3 at % Sb. It was possible to show that the friction term, which here by far is the most pronounced term, must be of the form of a constant scattering resistivity divided by the total resistivity of the sample, in agreement with theory. This total specific resistivity can be written as

$$\rho = \rho_0 + \zeta = \rho_0 + \alpha c ,$$

where the matrix contributes the temperature dependent $\rho_0$, whereas the impurities cause an additional temperature independent $\zeta$. This, to a first approximation, is proportional to the concentration $c$. $\alpha$ is the residual resistivity introduced by 1 at % of impurity atoms.

According to eq. (11)

$$z^* = a(Z + C) \mp bZ \frac{\Delta\rho_d N}{\rho N_d} .$$

In the limit of

$$a(Z + C) \ll bZ \frac{\Delta\rho_d N}{\rho N_d} ,$$

the transport velocity is given by

$$v = \frac{D}{kT} \, bZej \, \frac{\Delta\rho_d N}{(\rho_0 + \alpha c)N_d} (\rho_0 + \alpha c) = \frac{D}{kT} \, ej \, \frac{\Delta\rho_d N}{N_d} \, bZ .$$

It follows immediately that $v$ is independent of $c$, although the electric field has increased considerably. Therefore, the simplified transport equation is still applicable with constant $v$. If the dependence of the friction force were different from our assumption, a remarkable change in transport velocity would occur. This argument holds as long as the first term in eq. (11) is negligibly small and consequently the field force. Furthermore it is supposed that the mobility does not change with concentration. In fact, experiments show that the simplified transport equation is still applicable as a good approximation at impurity contents of a few tenth of a per-

cent, where, at the temperature of the experiments, the increase of the electric field
for Sb in Cu is already in the order of 20–50%. This behavior can be expected only
if $z^*$ is not a constant but depends on $1/\rho$ where $\rho = \rho_0 + \alpha c$. If on the other hand $v$
is found to depend on the concentration, the field term may be extracted as func-
tion of the concentration, taking proper account of possible changes of the mobility
associated with $c$.

This investigation for larger concentration ranges requires, however, the solution
of a nonlinear transport equation, which is presently performed by use of a digital
computer.

It should be noted that this experimental proof of the existence of a $1/\rho$ dependence of the friction force is obtained in a single and isothermal experiment. Therefore, the temperature dependence of the correlation factor $f_B$, which for most elements is unknown at present, does not enter into consideration. $z^*$ for Sb in Cu was
found in a range between $-55$ to $-100$ depending on temperature. There are good
reasons to believe, that the data reported by [73] come much closer to these values,
if one takes the change in mobility properly into account. The mobility increases in
Cu-Sb alloys rapidly with increasing antimony content. This can be expected from
the phase diagram because of the sharp drop in solidus temperature upon addition
of antimony. Also, the increase of the electron/atom ratio has to be accounted for
following Fiks' model.

In order to keep possible deviations from the simplified eq. (22) to a minimum
and to have them eventually calculable, the method with a thick layer eq. (24) has
been employed with a dilute alloy of well known initial concentration, which does
not vary during an experiment. This has also the advantage of providing two independent results of a single run at each welding interface.

The thin layer technique mostly used with radioactive tracers may be dangerous
to apply in cases where an impurity is deposited with high scattering resistivity and
high mobility. High current densities and particularly thick deposits tend to keep the
peak concentration $S/2\sqrt{\pi Dt}$ high for a longer period of time. Under these conditions, eq. (22) eventually becomes unapplicable because of local changes in $D$ and $v$
and has to be replaced by a nonlinear equation. Unfortunately most authors give no
data concerning the thickness of the initial deposit. Values of about 1 $\mu$m reported
by Kuzmenko [72] certainly are too high for avoiding these difficulties.

Therefore Hehenkamp, Herzig and Heumann [75] studied electrotransport of
Sb in Au with a *thick* layer technique and evaluated the profiles by means of electron microprobe analysis again. An example is given in fig. 6. A plot of $v/j$ versus
$1/T$ yields (fig. 7) a pseudoactivation energy of 1.23 eV which is very close to the
activation energy of diffusion of 1.34 eV (fig. 8). Taking $f_B = 0.65$ as a rough estimate for the correlation factor, they obtained $\Delta\rho_d = 8.9$ $\mu\Omega$ cm/at % Sb for the
activated ion.

$z^*$, plotted against $1/\rho$, showed in the range of experiments a linear dependence
within experimental error. An extrapolation to $1/\rho = 0$ seems justified because of
the relatively unimportant contribution from the correlation factor as has been al-

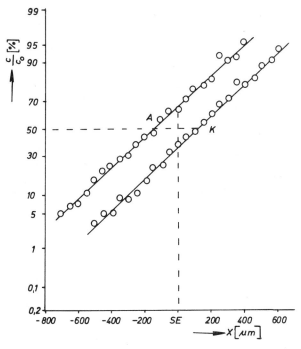

Fig. 6. Penetration profile for electrotransport of Sb in Au [75]. A refers to the anodic, K to the cathodic welding interfaces, located both at SE. Plot on probability paper.

ready pointed out in discussing Le Claire's remarks in the section 2.2.4. A value of $a(Z + C) = + 4.3$ is observed. This extrapolated value naturally has a relatively high margin of error. The scattering resistivity of 8.9 $\mu\Omega$ cm/at % Sb at the saddle point is to be compared to the extra resistivity of 1 at % Sb distributed homogeneously in the matrix, namely 6.67 $\mu\Omega$ cm/at %. Such a comparison has been made also by Van Doan and Brebec [16] for Sb in Ag. Evaluating their experimental data in the same way, a $\Delta\rho_d$ of about 14 $\mu\Omega$ cm/at % Sb is obtained for the activated state as an average, compared to 7.26 $\mu\Omega$ cm/at % Sb in the homogeneous alloy matrix. Using Born's approximation as outlined by Bosvieux and Friedel [24], one should expect 19.75 $\mu\Omega$ cm/at %. Friedel pointed out at this conference that this should be taken as a very rough guess. A more detailed theoretical calculation performed by Huntington, Van Doan and Feit [76] and based on a method developed by Harrison [77] yielded a value of 16.4 $\mu\Omega$ cm/at % for Sb in Ag for the activated ion. The agreement between the value obtained experimentally for Sb in Au and Born's approximation is not as good as that for silver. A comparison to Sb in Cu [74] seems to indicate a decrease of the ratio in going from Cu to Au as a matrix metal. It must, however, be checked, whether the solution of Sb in Au, which shows the largest deviation from Born's approximation, is actually of the substitutional type and not of an

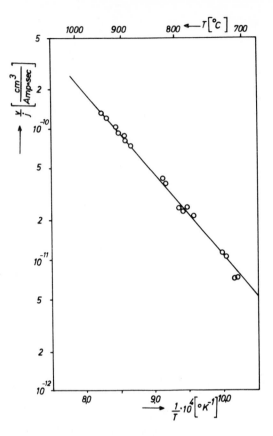

Fig. 7. log $v/j$ versus $1/T$ for electrotransport of Sb in Au [75].

interstitial nature. In that case the scattering resistivity at the saddle point should almost agree with the residual resistivity of Sb in Au to a first approximation. Diffusion of Sb in Au has also been measured and can best be represented by

$$D_{Sb}^{Au} = 1.14 \times 10^{-2} \exp\left(-\frac{1.34 \text{ eV}}{kT}\right) \text{ [cm}^2/\text{sec] .}$$

These data give some hints also in this direction, since the activation energy is
lowered more than would be expected from the model of Lazarus [78] and Le
Claire [33]. The preexponential factor has decreased also. In addition the solubility
of antimony is much smaller in gold than in copper or silver, where the range of
solubility still seems to be controlled by the electron/atom ratio following Hume-
Rothery's rules.

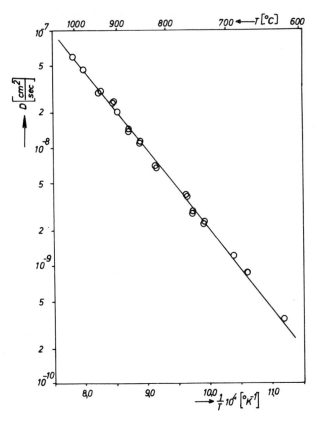

Fig. 8. log $v/j$ versus $1/T$ for impurity diffusion of Sb in Au [75].

## 2.5. Summary electrotransport

At present the three most frequently used theoretical models to describe electro-transport in solid metals agree as far as the friction force is concerned. Experimental evidence for the form of this term is provided in the case of rather careful measurements in pure metals, e.g. the measurements in lithium by Thernqvist and Lodding [60] giving $\Delta\rho_d$ of 0.62 $\mu\Omega$ cm/at % defect. For impurity transport, the $1/\rho$-dependence can be checked by changing concentrations [74]. The fact that the simplified transport equation (22) still is applicable, although the field increases with growing impurity content considerably, is explainable only in terms of such a $1/\rho$-dependence. The detailed study of the mobility to be used in transport measurements shows that the impurity correlation does not enter fully but multiplied by a factor depending on the ratio of the effective charges of matrix and impurity $z_A^*/z_B^*$. This simplifies the situation where this ratio is very small since no detailed knowledge of $f_B$ is needed. On the other hand it is impossible then to determine $f_B$ from transport measurements. Comparison of the scattering resistivities in the activated states with expected data was possible so far only by using Born's approximation which generally should give too high values [79]. Better theoretical calculations are therefore of much interest. The agreement of such a first calculation [76] and observed values for Sb in Ag is fair in consideration of the experimental accuracy of that work [16]. In all cases mentioned the scattering resistivity of impurity atoms at the saddle point was found to be larger than the residual resistivity of the same impurity distributed homogeneously in the matrix.

The least known quantity in eq. (11) is the parameter describing the field force. Unfortunately the experimental accuracy is still not high enough at present to argue here in favor of or against one of the proposed models. It seems possible to study the dependence of $z^*$ upon concentration with higher accuracy in order to get a better answer to this open question.


## 3. Thermotransport

Although this effect was discovered at almost the same time as electrotransport by Ludwig [80] and later independently by Soret [81] in liquids (it is therefore sometimes called Ludwig-Soret effect) it has drawn attention much later than electrotransport for solid metals and alloys. In 1954 Darken and Oriani [82] observed an unmixing in dilute alloys experimentally. Stimulated by the proposal of Shockley [83] and the following discussion by Brinkman [84] and Le Claire [85] the interest in thermotransport has steadily grown.

Huntington [86], in a recent paper, has given a review of the driving forces of thermotransport. The flux resulting from it can generally be written again as a product of the force times the mobility (see also eqs. (12) and (25)), i.e.

$$J_i = \frac{N_i D_i}{kT} \frac{1}{T} \frac{dT}{dx} Q^* ,$$

where $N_i$ is the concentration of the transported species i and $D_i$ the corresponding diffusion constant. The problem of the proper $D_i$ to be used has been discussed already in detail for electrotransport. In order to apply these ideas to thermotransport one must only replace $eE$ by $(1/T)(dT/dx)$ and $z_i^*$ by $Q_i^*$. Therefore, for thermotransport in pure metals, $D_i$ is given by $D_i^*/f_o$, if $D_i^*$ is measured with radioactive tracers. For thermotransport of impurity atoms B in dilute concentrations, the impurity diffusion coefficient $D_{B^*}^A$ has to be multiplied by

$$1 + \frac{Q_A^*}{Q_B^*} \left( \frac{1}{f_B} - 1 \right)$$

in analogy to eqs. (21) and (26).

The quantity $Q_i^*$ is called the apparent heat of transport. Huntington [86] distinguishes several mechanisms, which may contribute to $Q^*$. First the intrinsic thermotransport is discussed following detailed considerations by Shewmon [87] and

Jost [88] involving the kinetic treatment of this problem by Wirtz [98]. For the
motion of vacancies these models predict that the intrinsic heat of transport is given
by

$$Q_{\text{int}} = \beta E^{\text{M}} - E^{\text{F}} \tag{27}$$

where $E^{\text{M}}$ is the activation energy for vacancy motion and $E^{\text{F}}$ the enthalpy of
vacancy formation. The quantity $\beta$ depends on the distribution of the energy at the
beginning of the jump and should therefore be closely related to $\Delta K$, which has
been discussed in connection with the correlation and isotope effects. Lodding [89]
has explained that if the same mechanisms are operative in self-diffusion, electro-
and thermotransport, the factor $\Delta K$ may be measured directly by transport experiments using different isotopes. So far there is no system known for this to happen.
There have been no detailed calculations for $\beta$. Huntington gives as a preliminary result in fcc lattices a $\beta$-value of approximately 0.8. Other contributions to $Q^*$ may
come from the direct scattering of phonons by lattice defects and impurity atoms
as was pointed out first by Fiks [90]. Probably this direct transfer of momentum
is unimportant, whereas phonons may influence the jumping atom indirectly as has
been shown by Schottky [91] and emphasized by Haven [92]. This indirect interaction is caused by the perturbation of the phonon distribution due to the existence
of a vacancy or defect, which tends to enhance the flow of atoms. This factor is particularly interesting for non-metals where only phonons can carry heat, but an
estimate has shown, that the contributions to $Q^*$ from here are very small. The
larger effects predicted by [91] are attributable to the fact that the calculation is
limited to a one-dimensional chain, where a vacancy is a total interruption. Its influence therefore is largely overestimated. Nevertheless eq. (27) can be modified by
an enhancement factor $\alpha$, i.e.

$$Q^*_{\text{int}} = \alpha \beta E^{\text{M}} - E^{\text{F}} .$$

Electrostatic fields may also influence the heat of transport. Although usually no external electric field is applied in thermotransport experiments, there is always the
Thomson effect. Its contribution may be appreciable and is given by [86]

$$Q^*_{\text{i Th}} = e Z_{\text{st}} \eta_{\text{Th}} T$$

where $\eta_{\text{Th}}$ is the Thomson coefficient and $Z_{\text{st}}$ the effective charge of the moving
atom seen by the static field. This would be equivalent to a $(Z + C)$ in eq. (11). Here
again the question of the direct field force is involved. Huntington [86] has given
some arguments to support the idea that the screening by the electrons does not
change the charge of the ion to a large degree. Here some interconnection of thermo-
and electrotransport as outlined by Oriani [93] can be visualized, which is to be expected, if both transport phenomena are dealing with the same saddle point configuration.

In a metallic specimen the charge carriers also influence the moving species
directly as pointed out by Fiks [94] and Gerl [95]. Their arguments have been
limited to single-band metals. Huntington has extended the model for the multiband

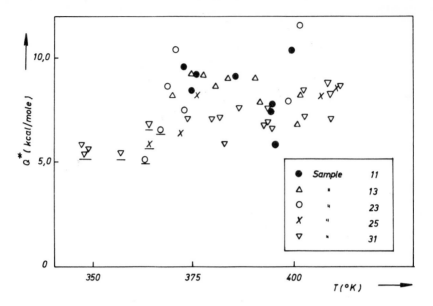

Fig. 9. $Q^*$ versus $T$ for thermotransport in lithium (Thernqvist and Lodding [60]).

case. This contribution should be equivalent to the friction term in electromigration (eq. (2)). Summing up all contributions one obtains finally an expression for the apparent heat of transport for the species i which reads

$$Q_i^* = \alpha\beta\, E^M - E^F - eZ_{st}\, \eta_{Th}\, T + \frac{(\pi\, kT)^2}{6\mu}\, nl\, \sigma_i \, ,$$

where $\mu$ is the Fermi level. This equation has been applied to measurements of Ho, Hehenkamp and Huntington [96] in Pt. The experimental value of $Q^*$ is in fair agreement with this model.

Oriani [97], in a detailed treatment of thermotransport from a thermodynamical point of view, has pointed out that the experimentally determined heat of transport does not contain contributions from equilibrium thermodynamic quantities. Therefore, the theory of Wirtz [98] and the kinetic models based upon this theory are found to be incompatible with the thermodynamics of irreversible processes. Gonzalez and Oriani [93] first pointed out the close connection between the sign of $z^*$ in electrotransport and $Q^*$ for thermotransport. A general correlation, however, is not to be expected. Another detailed and critical review of thermotransport has been compiled by Allnatt and Chadwick [107].

Some of the experimental methods are mentioned in [46] and [25]. Recently Mock and Lazarus [43] introduced a technique similar to that for isothermal electrotransport [15] in addition to the usual techniques employing marker motion or steady state measurements [99,100]. The evaluation is much more difficult since

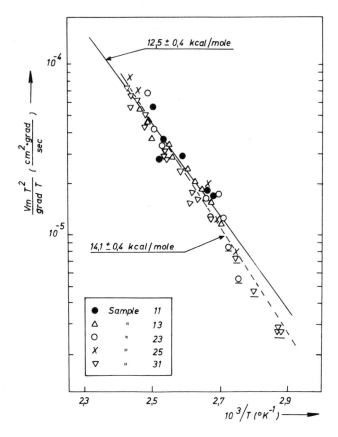

Fig. 10. $T^2 v$/grad $T$ versus $1/T$ for thermotransport in lithium (Thernqvist and Lodding [60]).

the penetration curves become unsymmetrical due to the presence of the temperature gradient. The solution is therefore based on the isothermal case. The variations of $T$ in the vicinity of the thin layer are taken into account using a higher order polynomial as approximation. The formula therefore is similar to eq. (23).

## 3.1. Experimental results

The most complete review of the data known at present has been given recently by Oriani [97] separately for self-transport in pure metals, interstitials and substitutional impurities. As was already mentioned for electrotransport, the sign of $Q^*$ for different interstitial solutes in a given matrix is the same again. Values for $Q^*$ range from −45 to +20 kcal/mole and are particularly high for transition metals.
The same is observed for thermotransport in pure transition metals. This can be interpreted by the model of Huntington [86] for the multiband case as was done for Pt [96].

Thernqvist and Lodding [60] investigated also thermotransport in lithium metal. They discovered here an isotope effect for $^6$Li and $^7$Li, which was found in a solid metal for the first time. Their data for $Q^*$ are presented in fig. 9. The activation energy for transport appears again to be close to that for self-diffusion, as shown in fig. 10. Average values for $Q^*$ of $8.2 \pm 1.3$ kcal/mole are obtained. This value is discussed in the light of the Wirtz-Brinkman [98,84] model.

There are certain arguments that mass transport in lithium may be governed by competitive mechanisms where vacancies and interstitialcies may play a role since the magnitude of $Q^*$ is relatively high as compared to the activation energy for self-diffusion.

### 3.2. Summary thermotransport

This phenomenon appears to be more complex to investigate than electrotransport. The experimentally observable heat of transport has been subdivided into several contributions in order to understand better the sign and the magnitude in the various cases from kinetic models. In metals the contribution of the charge carriers appears to be distinct. This contribution also is held responsible for the large values observed in transition metals. Experimental evidence for most of the theory is, however, still lacking. Certain correlations between thermo- and electrotransport can be expected, entering directly as the field force into the contribution from the Thomson field and into the friction force for interaction with the charge carriers. Also a connection to the factor $\Delta K$ describing the fraction of translational kinetic energy kept by the jumping atom may exist.

### Acknowledgements

The author is very much indebted to Prof. Dr. Th.Heumann for stimulating discussions. This work was supported by the Deutsche Forschungsgemeinschaft.

### References

[1] M.Gerardin, Compt. Rend. 53 (1861) 727.
[2] A.Coehn and W.Specht, Z. Phys. 62 (1930) 1.
[3] W.Seith and O.Kubaschewski, Z. Elektrochem. 41 (1935) 551.
[4] W.Jost and R.Linke, Z. Physik. Chem. B29 (1935) 127.
[5] W.Seith and H.Etzold, Z. Elektrochem. 40 (1934) 829.
[6] W.Seith and H.Wever, Z. Elektrochem. 57 (1953) 891.
[7] F.Skaupy, Z. Physik 3 (1920) 178.
[8] W.Seith and H.Wever, Naturwissenschaften 19 (1954) 447.

[9] H.Wever, Z. Elektrochem. 60 (1956) 1170.
[10] J.Verhoeven, Met. Rev. 8 (1963) 311.
[11] H.B.Huntington and A.R.Grone, J. Phys. Chem. Solids 20 (1961) 76.
[12] H.B.Huntington and P.S.Ho, J. Phys. Soc. Japan Suppl. II, 18 (1963) 202.
[13] V.B.Fiks, Fizika Tverdogo Tela 1 (1959) 16; Sov. Phys. Sol. State 1 (1959) 14.
[14] N.F.Mott and H.Jones, The Theory of the Properties of Metals and Alloys (Oxford, 1936).
[15] H.M.Gilder and D.Lazarus, Phys. Rev. 145 (1966) 508.
[16] M.N.Van Doan and G.Brebec, Rapport CEA-R-3480, Paris, April 1968.
[17] M.D.Glinchuk, Ukrain. Fiz. Zhur. 4 (1959) 684.
[18] V.B.Fiks, Fizika Tverdogo Tela 6 (1964) 2723.
[19] V.B.Fiks, Fizika Tverdogo Tela 1 (1959) 1321; Soviet Phys. Sol. State 1 (1960) 1212.
[20] V.B.Fiks, Fizika Tverdogo Tela 5 (1963) 2213; Soviet Phys. Sol. State 5 (1963) 1611.
[21] V.B.Fiks, Fizika Tverdogo Tela 4 (1962) 1863; Soviet Phys. Sol. State 4 (1962) 1366.
[22] V.B.Fiks, Fizika Tverdogo Tela 6 (1964) 1589; Soviet Phys. Sol. State 6 (1964) 1251.
[23] V.B.Fiks, Fizika Tverdogo Tela 6 (1964) 2307; Soviet Phys. Sol. State 6 (1965) 1828.
[24] C.Bosvieux and J.Friedel, J. Phys. Chem Solids 23 (1962) 123.
[25] Y.Adda and J.Philibert, La Diffusion dans les Solides (Presses Universitaires de France, Paris, 1966).
[26] P.C.Mangelsdorf, J. Chem. Phys. 33 (1960) 1151.
[27] A.Klemm, Z. Naturforsch. 8a (1953) 397; 9a (1954) 1031.
[28] B.Baranowski, Roczniki Chem. 29 (1955) 129;
A.S.Cukrowski, Bull. Acad. Polon. Sci. Ser. Sci. Chim. 10 (1962) 135.
[29] J.Bardeen and C.Herring, Atom Movements (American Soc. Metals, Cleveland/Ohio, 1950) p. 87.
[30] N.K.Archipova, S.M.Klotsman, A.N.Timofeev and I.Sh.Trakhtenberg, Phys. Stat. Sol. 16 (1966) 729; 18 (1966) 847.
[31] K.Compaan and Y.Haven, Trans. Faraday Soc. 52 (1956) 786.
[32] A.B.Lidiard, Phil. Mag. 5 (1960) 1171.
[33] A.D.Le Claire, Phil. Mag. 7 (1962) 141.
[34] R.E.Howard and J.R.Manning, Phys. Rev. 154 (1967) 561.
[35] A.J.Bosman, Thesis Amsterdam (1960).
[36] J.G.Mullen, Phys. Rev. 121 (1961) 1649.
[37] Th.Heumann and R.Imm, J. Phys. Chem. Sol. 29 (1968) 1613.
[38] D.Heitkamp, Phys. Stat. Sol. 24 (1967) 341.
[39] R.E.Howard and A.B.Lidiard, Rep. Progr. Phys. 27 (1964) 161.
[40] A.B.Lidiard, Thermodynamics, Vol. 2 (Proceedings Series IAEC, Vienna, 1966) p. 3.
[41] Y.Adda, G.Brebec, M.N.Van Doan, M.Gerl and J.Philibert, Thermodynamics, Vol. 2 (Proceedings Series IAEC, Vienna, 1966) p. 255.
[42] K.P.Gurov and M.G.Cudinov, Fiz. Metallov i Metallovedenie 22 (1966) 321.
[43] W.Mock and D.Lazarus, Thesis, Dept. Phys. and Mat. Research Lab., Univ. of Illinois (1968).
[44] D.A.Blackburn, Phys. Stat. Sol. 23 (1967) 177; see also Jül.-Conf. 2 (Vol. I) 1968, p. 82.
[45] Th.Hehenkamp, Ch. Herzig and Th.Heumann, to be published.
[45a] R.E.Howard and A.B.Lidiard, Acta Met. 13 (1965) 443.
[46] Th.Hehenkamp, Z. Metallkunde 58 (1967) 545.
[47] Th.Hehenkamp, Rev. Sci. Instr. 33 (1962) 229.
[48] Th.Hehenkamp, Thesis Münster 1959, Acta Met. 14 (1966) 788.
[49] H.Wever, Acta Met. 15 (1967) 443; 16 (1968) 1289.
[50] R.A.Oriani and O.D.Gonzalez, Trans. AIME 239 (1967) 1041.
[51] W.Seith and Th.Daur, Z. Elektrochem. 44 (1938) 256.
[52] F.Claisse and H.P.Koenig, Acta Met. 4 (1956) 650.

[53] C.Wagner and G.Heller, Z. Phys. Chem. 46 (1940) 242.
[54] Th.Hehenkamp, Acta Met. 14 (1966) 788.
[55] I.M.Frantsevich and I.I.Kovenskii, Dopovidi Akad. Nauk Ukrain SSR No. 5 (1961) 636; No. 7 (1961) 908; No. 9 (1961) 1169; No. 11 (1961) 1471.
[56] M.J.Bibby, Can J. Phys. 44 (1966) 2375.
[57] G.A.Sullivan, J. Phys. Chem. Sol. 28 (1967) 347.
[58] J.F.D'Amico and H.B.Huntington, to be published.
[59] D.R.Campbell and H.B.Huntington, Phys. Rev., to be published.
[60] P.Thernqvist and A.Lodding, Jül.-Conf. 2 (Vol. I) 1968, p. 55.
[61] G.A.Sullivan, Phys. Rev. 154 (1967) 605.
[62] J.N.Mundy, L.W.Barr and F.A.Smith, Phil. Mag. 14 (1966) 785.
[63] P.P.Kuzmenko, Ukrain. Fiz. Zhurn. 7 (1962) 117.
[64] P.Thernqvist and A.Lodding, Z. Naturforsch. 21a (1966) 1311.
[65] J.L.Routbort and H.B.Huntington, to be published.
[66] M.D.Smolin, Fiz. Tverd. Tela 9 (1967) 1807; Soviet Phys. Solid State 9 (1967) 1415.
[67] I.M.Frantsevich, D.F.Kalinovich, I.I.Kovensky and V.V.Penkowski, Int. Conf. Radioisotopes Scient. Research UNESCO/NS/RIC/29 (Pergamon Press, 1957) p. 194; Doklady Akad. Nauk SSSR 121 (1958) 277; Soviet Phys. Doklady 3 (1958) 842; Ukrain. Fiz. Zhur. 3 (1958) 124; 552.
[68] M.D.Smolin, Fiz. Tverd. Tela 7 (1965) 2186; Soviet Phys. Sol. State 7 (1966) 1758; Fiz. Metallov Metalloved. 21 (1966) 935; Phys. Metals Metallogr. 21 (1966) 121.
[69] Th.Hehenkamp, Microchim. Acta (Wien) Suppl. III (1968) 79.
[70] Th.Hehenkamp, J. Appl. Phys. 39 (1968) 3928.
[71] Th.Hehenkamp, Habilitationsschrift Münster (1966).
[72] P.P.Kuzmenko, L.F.Ostrovski and V.S.Kovalchuk, Fiz. Metallov Metalloved. 13 (1962) 406; Phys. Metals Metallogr. 13 (1962) 83; Fiz. Tverd. Tela 4 (1962) 490; Sov. Phys. Sol. State 4 (1962) 356.
[73] H.J.Stepper and H.Wever, J. Phys. Chem. Sol. 28 (1967) 1103.
[74] Th.Hehenkamp, to be published.
[75] Th.Hehenkamp, Ch.Herzig and Th.Heumann, Jül.-Conf. 2 (Vol. I) 1968, p. 69.
[76] H.B.Huntington, M.N.Van Doan and M.Feit, to be published.
[77] W.A.Harrison, Pseudo Potentials in the Theory of Metals (Benjamin, New York, 1966).
[78] D.Lazarus, Diffusion in Metals, in: Solid State Physics 10 (Academic Press, New York, 1960) p. 71.
[79] F.J.Blatt, Phys. Rev. 108 (1957) 285.
[80] C.Ludwig, Akad. Wiss. Wien. Math. Naturw. Kl. 20 (1856) 539.
[81] Ch.Soret, Arch. de Genève 3 (1879) 48.
[82] L.S.Darken and R.A.Oriani, Acta Met. 2 (1954) 841.
[83] W.Shockley, Phys. Rev. 91 (1953) 1563.
[84] J.A.Brinkman, Phys. Rev. 93 (1954) 345.
[85] A.D.Le Claire, Phys. Rev. 93 (1954) 344.
[86] H.B.Huntington, J. Phys. Chem. Sol. 29 (1968) 1641.
[87] P.G.Shewmon, Diffusion in Solids (McGraw-Hill, New York, 1963).
[88] W.Jost, Diffusion in Solids (Academic Press, New York, 1960).
[89] A.Lodding, Phys. Stat. Sol. 22 (1967) 157.
[90] V.B.Fiks, Fizika Tverdogo Tela 3 (1961) 3994; Soviet Phys. Solid State 3 (1961) 724.
[91] G.Schottky, Phys. Stat. Sol. 8 (1965) 357.
[92] Y.Haven, Bull. Am. Phys. Soc. II 12 (1967) 389.
[93] O.D.Gonzalez and R.A.Oriani, Trans. AIME 233 (1965) 1878.
[94] V.B.Fiks, Fizika Tverdogo Tela 5 (1963) 3473; Soviet Phys. Sol. State 5 (1964) 2549.
[95] M.Gerl, J. Phys. Chem. Sol. 27 (1966) 1331.

[96] P.S.Ho, Th.Hehenkamp and H.B.Huntington, J. Phys. Chem. Solids 26 (1965) 251.

[97] R.A.Oriani, J. Chem. Phys., to be published.

[98] K.Wirtz, Z. Physik 44 (1943) 221.

[99] D.Jaffee and P.G.Shewmon, Acta Met. 12 (1964) 515.

[100] W.Biermann, D.Heitkamp and T.S.Lundy, Acta Met. 13 (1965) 71.

[101] P.S.Ho and H.B.Huntington, J. Phys. Chem. Solids 27 (1966) 1319.

[102] P.P.Kuzmenko and E.I.Kharkov, Ukrain. Fiz. Zhur. 3 (1958) 528; 5 (1960) 428.

[103] Th.Hehenkamp, Ch.Herzig and Th.Heumann, Symp. Electro- and Thermotransport, Münster (1965).

[104] R.V.Penney, J. Phys. Chem. Solids 25 (1964) 335.

[105] Th.Heumann and H.Meiners, Z. Metallkunde 57 (1966) 571.

[106] P.P.Kuzmenko and E.I.Kharkov, Ukrain. Fiz. Zhur. 4 (1959) 401; 537.

[107] A.R.Allnatt and A.V.Chadwick, Chem. Rev. 67 (1967) 681.

## Discussion

*A.D.Le Claire:* By way of excusing my model for not having produced an explanation of impurity diffusion in lithium, I must point out that the equation Dr. Lodding uses in his calculations (eq. (5) in ref. [60]) is valid only as a considerable approximation for very fast diffusers. It was derived for discussing diffusion of Na in K and the approximations were made in the light of estimates of activation energy derived from the impurity potential in K. It might not then be valid in Li, even for fast diffusers, so it may not be surprising that it does not lead to agreement with Dr. Lodding's experiments. This does not mean of course that a more correct expression *would* give agreement. There are some unusual experimental results for diffusion of impurities in alkali metals and the theory would seem to need modifications to accomodate them. I think we should take account of the relaxation about defects (large in the alkalis) and of size differences between solute and solvent, which can be quite appreciable. Perhaps the most striking difficulty is that K is a fast diffuser in Na, which can be understood in terms of monovalent theory (1964), but Na is also a fast diffuser in K, for which at the same time the theory is quite incapable of accounting.

*A.R.E.Lodding:* In your paper you are plotting $z_{eff}$ versus $\rho^{-1}$, and by extrapolation to infinite resistivity you obtain $z'$ in Huntington's or Fiks' formula. Your result is $z'/f = 5.0$. What are your margins of error?

In lithium self-transport we are also getting a reasonable straight line in the corresponding diagram, and the intercept on the $z_{eff}$-axis yields $z' = 1.0$. The standard error margin, however, becomes about unity. Our old self-transport results on In and Zn also suggest straight lines, with $z_{eff}$ increasing with rising $\rho^{-1}$, but the scatter is too great to allow any useful conclusions concerning $z'$. It would certainly be valuable, if the extrapolation turned out to yield the "true" charge of the solute, i.e. for antimony presumably not far from 5, and for lithium self-transport nearly unity.

*Th.Hehenkamp:* The error depends here mainly on the accuracy of the data for $v/j$ and $D$ since $D$ is measured simultaneously. For other techniques also the error in

$T$ may be important. In our measurements $D$ was accurate to about 5% and $v/j$ to roughly 10%. The data for $Z_{eff}$ therefore may have a total margin of error of 15–20%. Plotting these data versus $1/T$ the scatter seems to be somewhat smaller in our case as compared to yours. Nevertheless we agree that the extrapolated value still may have a remarkable margin of error, the magnitude of which is not easy to estimate due to possible systematic errors involved.

*A.D.Le Claire:* You have assumed that the correlation factor for Sb diffusion in gold is 0.64 and independent of temperature, but I should be very surprised if it were independent of temperature. The only direct measurement of such a tempera-ture dependence are those for Zn in Cu, but they show a considerable variation of $f$ with $T$ (20–30%) over the experimental temperature range. Such a variation is ex-pected theoretically, and the same theoretical considerations suggest that there may be an even larger variation for Sb in Au, the volume difference being larger in this case.

*Th. Hehenkamp:* Since not much about $f$ for the case in question was known, a temperature independent value was a first rough guess. A closer investigation of this problem has revealed the fact, that for impurity transport the correlation fac-tor does not enter fully but multiplied by several factors which for antimony in gold reduce its influence to an entirely negligible fraction. This can be seen from eq. (21) and (21a) for a very dilute alloy, where

$$1/f = 1 + \frac{D_{A*}^A}{D_{B*}^A} \left( \frac{1}{f_0} - 1 \right) \frac{z_A^*}{z_B^*}$$

using the same nomenclature as in ref. [75].

*J.Friedel:* I believe that for diffusion of substitutional impurities the effective charge $Z'$ is somewhat like a mystery: Huntington's formula I feel is wrong, and my formula with Bosvieux is at best a very rough guess indeed.

# PART 2

# VACANCIES IN QUENCHED FCC METALS

# DETERMINATION OF CONCENTRATIONS
# AND FORMATION ENERGIES AND ENTROPIES
# OF VACANCY DEFECTS FROM QUENCHING EXPERIMENTS *

R. W. BALLUFFI, K. H. LIE and D. N. SEIDMAN

*Department of Materials Science and Engineering, Cornell University, Ithaca, New York, USA*

R. W. SIEGEL

*Department of Materials Science, State University of New York at Stony Brook,
Stony Brook, L.I., New York, USA*

## 1. Introduction

The population of vacancy defects present in thermal equilibrium may be expressed generally in the form

$$C_V = C_{1V} + 2C_{2V} + \ldots + nC_{nV}$$

$$= \alpha_1 \, \exp(S_{1V}^F/k) \, \exp(-E_{1V}^F/kT)$$

$$+ 2\alpha_2 \, \exp(S_{2V}^F/k) \, \exp(-E_{2V}^F/kT)$$

$$+ \ldots + n\alpha_n \, \exp(S_{nV}^F/k) \, \exp(-E_{nV}^F/kT) , \tag{1}$$

where $n$ indicates the size of the vacancy cluster, $\alpha_n$ is a constant related to the lattice geometry of the cluster, and $S_{nV}^F$ and $E_{nV}^F$ are the entropy and energy of formation, respectively, of a cluster of size $n$ which may be functions of temperature. The goal of a quenching experiment aimed at obtaining the equilibrium concentrations and properties of the vacancy defects is to quench the specimen from an elevated temperature, $T_q$, to a relatively low temperature, rapidly enough to freeze-in the defects present at $T_q$. Ideally, it is desired to freeze-in the entire equilibrium vacancy defect population in an unperturbed state and, after quenching from

* This work was supported by the U.S. Atomic Energy Commission and the National Science Foundation. Additional support was received from the Advanced Research Projects Agency through the use of the technical facilities of the Materials Science Center at Cornell University.

various $T_q$, to measure the $C_{n\mathrm{V}}$ individually allowing the absolute determination of the various $S_{n\mathrm{V}}^{\mathrm{F}}(T)$ and $E_{n\mathrm{V}}^{\mathrm{F}}(T)$.

Unfortunately, this goal cannot be realized in practice, and the purpose of the present work is to examine in some detail the various problems which arise when one attempts to extract quantitative information about vacancy defects from quenching experiments. The problems are taken up in the same order as they occur in quenching experiments. Firstly, it is emphasized in section 2 that real quenches are quite non-ideal, and that the original equilibrium population present just before quenching is generally significantly altered during the quench. The various perturbing effects are then analyzed and discussed. Secondly, the problems which are encountered in measuring vacancy defect concentrations in specimens after quenching are discussed in section 3. Finally, in section 4, the problems involved in deducing defect energies and entropies of formation from various types of defect concentration data are discussed.

The emphasis in the present work is on the general principles involved, and no attempt is made to present an encyclopedic review of existing experimental results. However, selected data are used wherever possible to illustrate various phenomena. It is unfortunate that in most cases suitable data are available for only one metal, i.e., gold.

In order to simplify the presentation, a list of conclusions is given at the end of each section.

## 2. Real versus ideal quenches

Inherent perturbing effects which are present in real quenches include:
(1) Clustering of the vacancy defect population during the quench.
(2) Loss of vacancy defects to sinks such as dislocations during the quench.
(3) Generation of additional defects by plastic deformation occurring during the quench.
Let us consider these perturbing effects in detail.

### 2.1. *Clustering of the defect population during quenching*

As the crystal is rapidly cooled during the quench, the defects become supersaturated and tend to cluster to at least some degree in cases where positive binding energies exist. This effect is impossible to avoid in reasonably dense systems, since the number of jumps required for a given defect to meet another defect during the quench is generally much smaller than the total number of jumps which the defect could make before being frozen-in during even fast quenches. This effect has been considered by a number of authors, and in order to illustrate the principles involved let us examine the frequently investigated case of the formation of di-vacancies from mono-vacancies during the quenching of an fcc metal. Ignoring any defect losses and considering only the redistribution of mono-vacancies and di-vacancies, the appropriate approximate equations [1] are

$$\frac{dC_{1V}}{dt} = -168\,\nu C_{1V}^2 \exp(-E_{1V}^M/kT)$$
$$+ 28\,\nu C_{2V} \exp(-[E_{1V}^M + E_{2V}^B]/kT)\,, \tag{2}$$

$$C_{1V} + 2C_{2V} = C = \text{constant}\,, \tag{3}$$

$$T = T(t)\,, \tag{4}$$

where $\nu$ is the atomic vibrational frequency, $E_{2V}^B$ is the di-vacancy binding energy, and $T(t)$ is the temperature during the quench. Fujiwara [2] was the first to solve the non-linear eq. (2) using computer techniques. He found the following behavior under typical quenching conditions:

(1) At high temperatures where the defects associate and dissociate rapidly, the mono-vacancy and di-vacancy populations are able to maintain quasi-equilibrium with each other even in the face of the rapid cooling: i.e., the respective populations follow the relation

$$C_{2V} = 6C_{1V}^2 \exp(E_{2V}^B/kT)\,. \tag{5}$$

(2) Upon further cooling, a point is reached where the association and dissociation rates become sufficiently sluggish so that the maintenance of quasi-equilibrium is no longer possible. Very soon after that the defects become "frozen-in", and no further changes in their concentrations occur. The freezing-in of the defect distributions occurs rather suddenly near a critical temperature designated as $T^*$.

We have used a computer to calculate $C_{1V}$ and $C_{2V}$ during quenching using eqs. (2) through (4) for a range of conditions and defect parameters which might be typical of an fcc metal, and some results are given in fig. 1 and table 1. As expected (fig. 1), the ratio $C_{2V}/C_{1V}$ is maintained in quasi-equilibrium during the early part of the quench at elevated temperatures but eventually becomes frozen-in at a constant value at lower temperatures. As seen in table 1, the final value of $C_{2V}/C_{1V}$ is very sensitive to the values of $E_{2V}^B$ and $T_q$, and variations of two (or more) orders of magnitude are possible depending upon the choice of these parameters.

Clustering effects are of little importance for cases where the di-vacancy binding energy is $\lesssim 0.1$ eV. Since in many cases the binding energy may be larger than this, we conclude that significant clustering may often occur. Unfortunately, there is a serious lack of any reliable experimental information regarding the properties or the degree of clustering of small vacancy clusters. Of considerable importance is the fact that the degree of clustering is relatively insensitive to the quenching rate. The results show that when the di-vacancy binding energy is significant it is generally

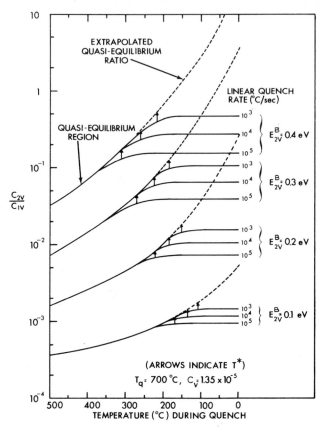

Fig. 1. The ratio of di-vacancies to mono-vacancies, $C_{2V}/C_{1V}$, versus temperature during a quench from 700°C for various values of $E_{2V}^B$ and linear quench rate. The curves were calculated using eqs. (2) through (4) for a closed mono-vacancy-di-vacancy system with $E_{1V}^F = 0.94$ eV, $E_{1V}^M = 0.90$ eV, $S_{1V}^F = 0$, $S_{2V}^B = 0$ and $\nu = 10^{13}$ sec$^{-1}$. The arrows indicate values of $T^*$ calculated using eq. (7).

impossible to avoid appreciable clustering even with the use of extremely fast quenches.

As first pointed out by Koehler et al. [3], an estimate of $T^*$ may be obtained by a simple analytical method. The rate at which $C_{1V}$ must decrease with time in order to maintain quasi-equilibrium during cooling at the rate $dT/dt$ is easily obtained from eqs. (3) and (5) and is given by

$$\left(\frac{dC_{1V}}{dt}\right)^{\circ} = \frac{12C_{1V}^2 \cdot E_{2V}^B \exp(E_{2V}^B/kT)}{kT^2 \left[1 + 24C_{1V} \exp(E_{2V}^B/kT)\right]} \left(\frac{dT}{dt}\right). \tag{6}$$

On the other hand, the actual rate at which $C_{1V}$ decreases as a result of mono-vacancies meeting to form di-vacancies is just the first term on the right hand side of eq.

Table 1

The ratio of di-vacancies to mono-vacancies $(C_{2V}/C_{1V})$ frozen-in at low temperatures after linear quenches from $T_q$ for a closed mono-vacancy-di-vacancy system with $E_{1V}^F = 0.94$ eV, $E_{1V}^M = 0.90$ eV, $S_{1V}^F = 0, S_{2V}^B = 0$ (i.e., the di-vacancy binding entropy) and $\nu = 10^{13}$ sec$^{-1}$.

$T_q = 500°C;$    $C_V = 0.075 \times 10^{-5}$

| $E_{2V}^B$(eV) | $C_{2V}/C_{1V}$ quenching rate (°C sec$^{-1}$) | | |
|---|---|---|---|
| | $10^3$ | $10^4$ | $10^5$ |
| 0.10 | $0.807 \times 10^{-4}$ | $0.658 \times 10^{-4}$ | $0.537 \times 10^{-4}$ |
| 0.20 | $0.879 \times 10^{-3}$ | $0.595 \times 10^{-3}$ | $0.400 \times 10^{-3}$ |
| 0.30 | $0.656 \times 10^{-2}$ | $0.388 \times 10^{-2}$ | $0.227 \times 10^{-2}$ |
| 0.40 | $0.359 \times 10^{-1}$ | $0.188 \times 10^{-1}$ | $0.098 \times 10^{-1}$ |

$T_q = 700°C;$    $C_V = 1.35 \times 10^{-5}$

| $E_{2V}^B$(eV) | $C_{2V}/C_{1V}$ quenching rate (°C sec$^{-1}$) | | |
|---|---|---|---|
| | $10^3$ | $10^4$ | $10^5$ |
| 0.10 | $0.146 \times 10^{-2}$ | $0.118 \times 10^{-2}$ | $0.950 \times 10^{-3}$ |
| 0.20 | $0.157 \times 10^{-1}$ | $0.107 \times 10^{-1}$ | $0.726 \times 10^{-2}$ |
| 0.30 | $0.107$ | $0.654 \times 10^{-1}$ | $0.394 \times 10^{-1}$ |
| 0.40 | $0.469$ | $0.276$ | $0.157$ |

$T_q = 900°C;$    $C_V = 9.18 \times 10^{-5}$

| $E_{2V}^B$(eV) | $C_{2V}/C_{1V}$ quenching rate (°C sec$^{-1}$) | | |
|---|---|---|---|
| | $10^3$ | $10^4$ | $10^5$ |
| 0.10 | $0.974 \times 10^{-2}$ | $0.788 \times 10^{-2}$ | $0.638 \times 10^{-2}$ |
| 0.20 | $0.961 \times 10^{-1}$ | $0.673 \times 10^{-1}$ | $0.468 \times 10^{-1}$ |
| 0.30 | $0.520$ | $0.345$ | $0.224$ |
| 0.40 | $1.844$ | $1.184$ | $0.744$ |

(2). In the quasi-equilibrium regime this association term must be large compared with $(dC_{1V}/dt)^0$. As the temperature drops, however, the association term decreases, and we might expect to obtain an estimate of the freezing-in temperature by setting $T^*$ equal to the temperature at which the association term becomes small enough to equal $(dC_{1V}/dt)^0$. The result is

$$T^* = \frac{E_{2V}^B \exp[(E_{2V}^B + E_{1V}^M)/kT^*]}{14\nu \, kT^* \sqrt{1+48C_{1V} \exp(E_{2V}^B/kT^*)}} \left(\frac{-dT}{dt}\right)_{T=T^*}. \tag{7}$$

Values of $T^*$ calculated from eq. (7) are shown by the arrows in fig. 1, and are seen to fall in the middle of the temperature ranges where freezing-in occurs. It is also noted that the quasi-equilibrium ratio at $T^*$ is only slightly higher (10–20%) than the actual final frozen-in ratio, and that, therefore, the final ratio may be calculated with fair accuracy from eqs. (7) and (5) without the bother of using the computer.

So far we have considered only the simplest case of mono-vacancies clustering into di-vacancies. In general, it is necessary, of course, to consider the possible formation of clusters of all sizes. Cotterill [4] has carried out approximate clustering calculations for a more complicated defect system in which clusters as large as quadri-vacancies were allowed to form. As might be expected, such a system behaves in a manner which is qualitatively similar to the simple mono-vacancy-di-vacancy system already described. The various reactions capable of forming the different clusters freeze-in at slightly different temperatures during the quench and eventually all cluster concentrations become completely frozen-in. More details are available in ref. [4].

It is well established that large defect clusters, visible by transmission electron microscopy, are formed in many cases when a quenched metal containing a high vacancy supersaturation is annealed at a low temperature. The following question therefore arises. Is it possible to quench at a sufficient rate to restrict the clustering during the quench to the formation of small mobile clusters, or are larger more immobile clusters formed which are capable of growing into large visible clusters during low temperature annealing? Meshii et al. [5] have shown that the formation of larger visible clusters in quenched gold and aluminium requires nucleation, and they have demonstrated that the nucleation occurs only below a critical temperature ($\sim 160°C$ in gold). Furthermore, by quenching at reasonably rapid rates they were able to avoid completely the formation of any nuclei for the large visible clusters. These results indicate that the formation of relatively large immobile clusters may be generally avoided in quenching experiments.

As shown above, it is impossible to avoid clustering in systems where the clusters possess significant binding energies even when extremely fast quenches are used. If we assume that the $C_{nV}$ can be measured individually after quenching to $T_0$ it is obvious that the $C_{nV}$ which are measured experimentally will be those in quasi-equilibrium at $T^*$ rather than the desired concentrations in true thermal equilibrium at $T_q$. It might be thought that in this situation the $C_{nV}$ could be measured as functions of quenching rate after quenching from a fixed $T_q$, and that the desired values of $C_{nV}$ corresponding to thermal equilibrium at $T_q$ could then be obtained by extrapolating the results to an infinite quenching rate. However, inspection of the results in fig. 1 shows that such an extrapolation would be very long and uncertain and would therefore be quite unreliable. This is more clearly shown in fig. 2

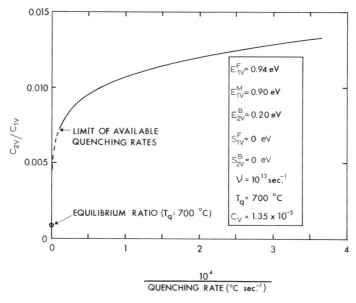

Fig. 2. The calculated ratio of di-vacancies to mono-vacancies, $C_{2V}/C_{1V}$, frozen-in after a quench from 700°C as a function of the linear quenching rate for the specific vacancy parameters given. This example shows the large uncertainty in attempting to extrapolate measured $C_{nV}$ data after quenching to obtain the equilibrium $C_{nV}$ values at the quench temperature, $T_q$ (i.e., at infinite quenching rate).

where the nature of the extrapolation may be seen for a specific case. Since $10^5$ °C sec$^{-1}$ is about the upper limit of present available quenching rates, it appears that there is no quenching method currently available which will allow the reliable determination of the true thermal equilibrium values of the $C_{nV}$.

Conclusions:

(1) At least some degree of clustering in the form of small mobile clusters occurs during usual quenching in systems where the clusters possess significant binding energies. The results are relatively insensitive to the quenching rate. The extent of such clustering naturally depends directly upon the properties of the small clusters. Unfortunately, there is a serious lack of any reliable information regarding either the properties or the degree of clustering of these defects.

(2) Cluster concentrations become frozen-in rather abruptly at some critical temperature during quenching.

(3) The formation of relatively large immobile clusters may be generally avoided during quenching.

(4) Even if the concentrations of the individual clusters could be measured individually after quenching as a function of quenching rate, attempts to extrapolate the results to an infinite quenching rate in order to obtain the individual cluster concentrations originally present in thermal equilibrium at $T_q$ would most likely fail.

## 2.2. *Vacancy losses during quenching*

In specimens quenched at finite rates a certain fraction of the supersaturated vacancies is inevitably lost at sinks which are present in the specimen during the quench. Possible sinks include the free surface, grain boundaries, subgrain boundaries (dense planar arrays of dislocations), and the random 3-dimensional dislocation network. As pointed out below in section 2.3, dislocations may be generated in plastic deformation during quenching, and, therefore, the possible sinks include those present in the specimen just before the quench as well as those generated during the quench. It is also possible under special circumstances (i.e., slow quenches, or cases where sinks are absent [†]) for the supersaturated defects to build up larger clusters during the quench so that large immobile vacancy precipitates (i.e., dislocation loops, voids, stacking-fault tetrahedra, etc.) form which in turn act as vacancy sinks during their growth. We regard this possibility as a special case, however, and shall not consider it further. The relative importance of the sinks mentioned above depends, of course, upon their relative densities and the efficiency with which they absorb vacancy defects.

In recent years there has been an increasing awareness that vacancy losses during quenching play an important role in quenching experiments, and a number of workers have quenched at different rates in order to evaluate the losses as a function of quenching rates. Flynn et al. [7], in one of the most complete studies, obtained the results shown in fig. 3 for the case of gold. The data show a total defect resistivity (concentration) loss which increases as the quenching rate is decreased or the quenching temperature is increased. At sufficiently low quenching temperatures essentially all losses were avoided by quenching at moderately fast rates. For any given quenching temperature the data may presumably be corrected for quenching losses (and the thermal equilibrium defect resistivity [concentration] may be deduced) by extrapolating the quenched-in resistivity increment to infinite quenching rate as shown in fig. 4. Comparison of figs. 4 and 2 shows that the technique of extrapolating to infinite quenching rate as a means of correcting for losses due to finite quenching rates is considerably more reliable for correcting for losses than for clustering. Loss data showing the same general features have been obtained in other investigations with gold [8–10], platinum [11] and aluminium [12], and also in work in progress on bcc metals by Bass and coworkers [13].

The general features of this behavior are readily understood in terms of the relative numbers of the supersaturated defects which are able to reach the sinks by diffusion during the quench. However, the attainment of a detailed quantitative understanding of the results is considerably more difficult. The simplest model which can be visualized is one in which only one vacancy type defect is present, and where the specimen contains a constant density of fixed sinks during the quench which operate with a sufficiently high efficiency to maintain the point defect concentra-

[†] For example (see ref. [6]), large vacancy precipitates have been formed by clustering in single crystals of almost dislocation-free copper during furnace cooling (quenching?).

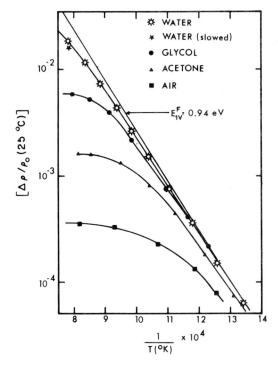

Fig. 3. The fractional resistivity quenched into 0.041 cm dia gold wires as a function of quench temperature for various quenching media and, therefore, quenching rates from the work of Flynn et al. [7]. Quenching times for the various media were in the range $0.025$ sec (water) $\leqslant \tau_q \leqslant 4.3$ sec (air).

tion in their direct vicinity at the instantaneous equilibrium concentration called for by the specimen temperature. Under these conditions the defect loss is controlled by the amount of defect diffusion which can take place to the sinks during the quench in the presence of the continuously varying equilibrium boundary condition at the surface of the sinks. Flynn et al. [7] showed that a reasonably accurate approximate solution to this problem could be obtained in the form of an eigenfunction expansion, and, furthermore, showed that for linear quenches the fractional loss of the total vacancy concentration to fixed sinks is a function which depends only on the combined parameter $D_q T_q \tau_q$ where $D_q$ is the defect diffusivity at $T_q$ and $\tau_q$ is the time required for the quench. However, in order to calculate actual losses for given types of sinks it is necessary to carry out detailed calculations utilizing the appropriate eigenfunctions. In the present work we have avoided these complications and have calculated defect losses in a typical quenched system by direct numerical integration of the defect diffusion equation in the presence of an appropriate temperature (time) dependent diffusivity and equilibrium temperature (time) dependent boundary conditions at the sinks.

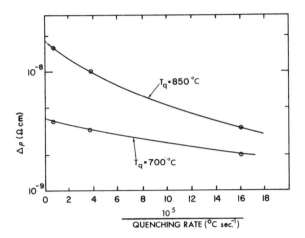

Fig. 4. The quenched-in resistivity increment in gold from two different quench temperatures, $T_q = 700°C$ and $850°C$, as a function of quenching rate from the work of Flynn et al. [7]. This example shows the reliability of the technique of extrapolating to infinite quenching rate to correct for vacancy losses during quenching.

The dominant sinks are expected to be dislocations, and to a lesser degree, subgrain boundaries. It has been shown elsewhere [14] that typical planar sub-boundaries consisting of dislocations which act as high efficiency sinks should act as perfect planar sinks. Since the subgrain size is generally smaller than the grain size (or specimen size), we may regard the subgrains as the most important planar type sinks and therefore we need only consider the sub-boundaries and dislocations in our calculations. Unfortunately, it has not been practicable to calculate the losses due to the simultaneous presence of both dislocations and sub-grain boundaries. We have therefore calculated losses to each of these sink types separately on the assumption that it alone is operative. This procedure, of course, tends to overestimate the loss which would occur at each sink type in the actual combined case. Idealized models for calculating the diffusion to each type of sink were employed. The dislocation structure was represented by an array of straight parallel dislocations each surrounded by a cylindrical diffusion cell of radius $(\pi N_d)^{-\frac{1}{2}}$ where $N_d$ is the dislocation density, while the subgrains were represented by spheres of radius $R$. Extensive discussions of these idealized models have been given elsewhere [7,10,14–16]. Dislocation densities and subgrain radii in quenched gold have been measured [16,17] and are of order $\sim 5 \times 10^7$ cm$^{-2}$ and $60$–$200\mu$ respectively. Some results for a simple assumed mono-vacancy system containing sinks at the above densities are given in figs. 5 and 6 [†]. It is seen in fig. 6 that the dislocations are the dominant sinks under these conditions.

[†] We have verified that fractional losses in fig. 5 are a unique function of $(D_q T_q \tau_q)$ as predicted by Flynn et al. [7].

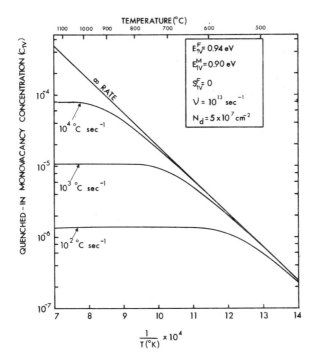

Fig. 5. The quenched-in mono-vacancy concentration $C_{1V}$, as a function of quench temperature for various linear quenching rates. The curves were calculated for a simple mono-vacancy system with the vacancy parameters shown and with a dislocation sink density of $5 \times 10^7$ cm$^{-2}$.

The calculated results (figs. 5 and 6) show behavior which is at least qualitatively similar to the experimental results (figs. 4 and 5). Such idealized calculations therefore are capable of offering at least a good semi-quantitative explanation of defect losses during quenching. However, the following simplifying assumptions have been made which require further discussion:

(1) the dislocations act as perfect line sinks during the entire quench,
(2) the dislocation density is constant during the quench,
(3) only one defect type is present, and clusters (and clustering) are neglected,
(4) an idealized fixed sink structure is an acceptable approximation.

The situation with respect to the efficiency of the dislocation network as line sinks for supersaturated vacancies has been extensively reviewed by Balluffi and Seidman in several papers [10,15,16,18]. The general conclusion is that the network climbs with a relatively high efficiency (i.e., a rate which is within a factor of 1/10 to 1 of the maximum possible diffusion limited rate) under conditions of moderate to strong defect supersaturation. There is some evidence, summarized in a recent paper by Wang et al. [10], that the sink efficiency, in gold at least, is

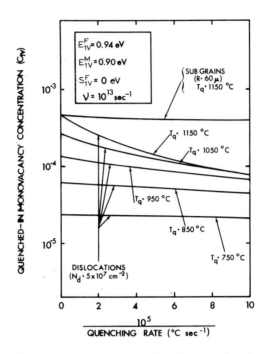

Fig. 6. The quenched-in mono-vacancy concentration, $C_{1V}$, as a function of quenching rate
for various quench temperatures, $T_q$. The curves were calculated for a simple mono-vacancy
system with the vacancy parameters shown. Separate curves are shown for losses to subgrain
boundaries and dislocations.

somewhat reduced when the vacancy supersaturation (i.e., the driving force for climb)
is in the range corresponding to a vacancy chemical potential $\gtrsim 0.1$ eV. This would
suggest that the defect losses during the early part of the quench during the period
of relatively low supersaturation might be lower than calculated above on the assumption of perfect sinks. We note that Kino and Koehler [9] have suggested that
line tension may play a significant role in controlling the dislocation sink action
during quenching when dislocation segments must bow out in order to climb. They
argue that the network is then inoperative during the initial period of the quench until enough vacancy supersaturation ($\cong 1\%$) is built up to provide the driving force
required to bow out the segments. However, if the network is initially annealed it is
unlikely that significant amounts of bowing are necessary for climb during the early
stages of the quench during which the supersaturation is building up to only $\sim 1\%$.
Furthermore, even if the dislocations were inoperative during this period the overall

effect on the losses would be exceedingly small [†]. We conclude that dislocation line tension effects may be ignored in a consideration of the loss problem.

The assumption that the dislocation density is constant is undoubtedly a poor approximation in many cases since, as discussed in section 2.3, there is considerable evidence that significant dislocation generation and movement occur under many quenching conditions. Losses could be enhanced considerably in such cases due to the sweeping up effect of the moving dislocations.

In systems with significantly high cluster binding energies the cluster diffusion to sinks could be important, and would have to be considered in calculating the losses. Flynn [19], for example, has indicated some analytical techniques which might be useful in coping with this problem. So far, no extensive calculations of losses in the presence of clustering have been made.

The effects of non-uniformly distributed dislocations on annealing kinetics have been investigated by Ham [20], and the effects of non-uniformly shaped subgrain boundaries have been discussed by Flynn et al. [7]. The general conclusion is that the idealized models described above should be reasonably good approximations under usual conditions.

In view of the difficulties mentioned above we have not attempted to obtain a close quantitative fit of the idealized loss model to existing data. In the case of gold, for example, there is the added difficulty of current uncertainty with respect to the properties of mono-vacancies and di-vacancies [10,21]. It should also be emphasized that there is only *one case* [17] (i.e., the case of gold) in which dislocation densities have been measured directly in quenched metals. Values in the range of $\sim 5 \times 10^7$ cm$^{-2}$ were found. Further measurements of this quantity would be of great interest.

As a final topic we would like to discuss the accuracy with which quenching data can be corrected for losses by quenching at different rates and then extrapolating the results to an infinite quenching rate as in fig. 4. This technique, which has been criticized recently by Seeger and Mehrer [22], is of great importance, since it is potentially the only way in which the effect of losses may be eliminated by a direct method. The technique has been criticized on the basis that the results are perturbed by specimen deformation which increases with the quenching rate. However, as Jackson [23] has shown (see section 2.3), the effects of deformation are generally to reduce quenched-in point defect concentrations rather than enhance them, since the sink effect of strain induced dislocations is more important than the produc-

---

[†] Kino and Koehler [9] also suggest that significant nucleation of vacancy precipitates could occur during the short initial period during which the dislocations are assumed to be inoperative. However, since any vacancy concentration decrease during this period would be relatively small such processes would proceed independently of the rapidity of the sink action at the dislocations. It should also be pointed out that much larger supersaturations are required to nucleate vacancy precipitates than bow out dislocations, and that the critical temperature for vacancy precipitate nucleation in quenched gold is about 160°C.

tion of new point defects by the deformation. If experiments show increments which increase with increased quenching rate and approach a finite limit at the limit of an infinite quenching rate, then it is reasonable to suppose that the decreased time available for the diffusional loss to sinks more than compensates for the effects of any increase in the dislocation sink density. Since this is found to be generally the case [7–12], we conclude that the true equilibrium increment with no losses is obtained at the limit of infinite quenching rate. In this respect it is of interest to examine the results of a number of experiments of this type which have been performed on gold (fig. 7). The high temperature points of Simmons and Bal-

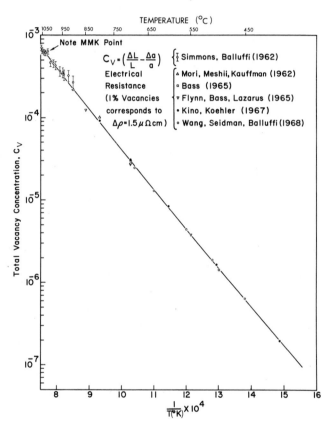

Fig. 7. The total concentration of vacant lattice sites in gold as a function of temperature as determined by equilibrium measurements [24] and quenched-in electrical resistivity [7–10,12], where the quenched-in increments were obtained by extrapolations to infinite quenching rate. The resistivity data were fitted together using a common temperature scale [26] and the value of $\rho_0(25^\circ C) = 2.25 \times 10^{-6}$ $\Omega$ cm (ref. [25]), and were converted to concentrations using $1.5 \times 10^{-6}$ $\Omega$ cm as the resistivity of 1 at % of vacant sites.

luffi [24] were obtained from measurements of specimen length and X-ray lattice parameter changes under equilibrium conditions and represent values of the total absolute concentration of vacant lattice sites. The remaining data, with the exception of the low temperature data point of Bass [25], were obtained from electrical resistivity quenching experiments where the quenched-in increments were obtained by extrapolations to infinite quenching rates. The corresponding concentrations were calculated from these data using $1.5 \times 10^{-6}$ $\Omega$ cm as the resistivity of 1 at % of vacant sites. This value is seen to produce a smooth grafting together of the high temperature absolute measurements of Simmons and Balluffi and the remaining resistivity based data. Wherever necessary the data were converted to a common temperature scale corresponding to the resistance versus temperature data of Meechan and Eggleston [26]. All data were also normalized to agree with the value of $2.25 \times 10^{-6}$ $\Omega$ cm for the resistivity of gold at $25°C$ from ref. [25]. The data are all seen to fall remarkably well on a single curve. The mean absolute percentage deviation of the 18 data points, all obtained by the extrapolation technique, was 4.4%. The relatively good agreement of the data obtained in these different investigations support the conclusion that this extrapolation technique is a reliable method for obtaining equilibrium concentrations from quenching experiments.
Conclusions:

(1) Appreciable vacancy defect losses, primarily to dislocations and to a lesser extent to subgrain boundaries, generally occur in specimens quenched from elevated temperatures.

(2) A relatively simple model based upon defect diffusion limited losses to existing dislocations (and subgrain boundaries) is capable of explaining the main features of existing loss data.

(3) Exact and reliable calculations of losses are complicated by:
(a) a lack of precise knowledge regarding the sink efficiency of dislocations; (b) possible increases in the dislocation sink density during the quench; and (c) a lack of knowledge of the degree of defect clustering during the quench and the effect of such clustering on the losses.

(4) The method of correcting for defect losses during quenching by quenching at different rates and extrapolating the quenched-in increment to infinite rate in order to obtain equilibrium concentrations is a legitimate technique.

## 2.3. Effects of quenching strains

A rapidly quenched specimen is always at least slightly strained during rapid quenching because of: (1) the internal stress, due to differential thermal contraction, which is present when the outside of the specimen is cooled relative to the interior; (2) the applied stress due to the hydrodynamic drag which is exerted on the specimen if it is plunged into a liquid quenching medium [†]. Plastic straining by these

---

[†] This latter effect is, of course, absent in specimens which are gas-quenched in still gases.

Table 2
Calculated [a] maximum plastic shear strain in gold wires due to internal thermal stresses after linear quenching into water.

| Wire dia (cm) | Max. heat flux removed in quench (cal cm$^{-2}$ sec$^{-1}$) | Max. cooling rate (°C sec$^{-1}$) | Shear strain ($\times 10^5$) |
|---|---|---|---|
| 0.041 | 240 | $40 \times 10^3$ | 1.5 |
| 0.152 | 225 | $10 \times 10^3$ | 8.5 |
| 0.317 | 210 | $4.6 \times 10^3$ | 25.0 |

[a] All data from ref. [23].

means may affect quenching results in two ways: (a) the straining produces unwanted extra point defects and dislocations; and (2) the extra dislocations act as sinks for both the original equilibrium vacancy population and any point defects generated during the quench. The *a priori* effect of plastic straining may, therefore, be to either increase or decrease the defect concentration obtained after quenching relative to the equilibrium concentration depending upon the relative magnitudes of the two effects described above.

The various possibilities have been investigated extensively by Jackson [23] both theoretically and experimentally. Jackson calculated the maximum plastic shear strains in gold wires due to internal thermal stresses after linear quenching into water, and the results are shown in table 2. He also calculated the hydrodynamic stretching strains in initially straight gold wires after fast quenching into water (see table 3). The results show that the thermally generated strains increase with increased wire diameter, whereas the hydrodynamically induced strains behave in the opposite manner. Furthermore, the thermally generated strains are very small (of the order of $10^{-5}$) for specimens with diameters similar to those usually employed in quenching experiments (i.e., $< 0.041$ cm). On the other hand, the hydrodynamic strains may become as large as $3 \times 10^{-3}$ for wires of diameter near 0.005 cm. Jackson [23] presents extensive experimental evidence which indicates that the calculated quenching strains in tables 2 and 3 are of the correct order of magnitude.

We must now consider the point defect and dislocation effects which may be expected from the quenching strains indicated above. If it is assumed for purposes of making preliminary order-of-magnitude estimates that the point defect production and dislocation generation in plastic deformation are *independent* of temperature, then we may estimate from experiments at, or below, room temperature that $\sim 10^{-7}$ atom fraction point defects are generated in gold by a strain of $10^{-3}$ (see refs. [27,28]). This concentration is equal to the concentration of vacancies in thermal equilibrium at about 375°C (i.e., $T(°K)/T_m(°K) = 0.48$, where $T_m$ is the melting temperature). Since 375°C is an unusually low quenching temperature for gold, we may conclude that the point defect concentration induced by quenching

Table 3

Calculated [a] hydrodynamic stretching strain in initially straight 10.2 cm long gold wire after fast quenching [b] in water.

| Wire dia (cm) | Stretching strain ($\times 10^4$) |
|---|---|
| 0.0051 | 33.5 |
| 0.0102 | 21.1 |
| 0.0203 | 13.2 |
| 0.0406 | 8.3 |
| 0.0813 | 5.5 |
| 0.163 | 3.3 |
| 0.325 | 1.4 |

[a] All data from ref. [23].

[b] Fast quenching refers to the use of a characteristic optimum velocity of the specimen relative to the water (see ref. [23] for complete discussion).

strains would be of minor importance under all conditions except in thin specimens liquid-quenched from very low quenching temperatures.

An upper limit of the dislocation density generated in gold by a quenching strain of $10^{-3}$ may also be estimated from low temperature data giving resistance increases due to deformation [27,28] and the specific resistivity of dislocations [29]. The result is about $4 \times 10^7$ dislocations $cm^{-2}$. (This is an upper limit, of course, since dislocation annealing would undoubtedly occur at elevated quenching temperatures.) In the case of resistivity quenching experiments the resistance of the above dislocations would be about the same as that of the strain generated point defects and would therefore again be of little importance except in thin specimens liquid-quenched from very low quenching temperatures.

The effect of strain generated dislocations as sinks for vacancy defects during quenching is much more difficult to estimate. If we assume that the strain generated dislocations are present during the entire quench and act as stationary perfect line sinks for supersaturated vacancies during the quench, then it is readily shown, using the methods employed in section 2.2, that a dislocation density of $4 \times 10^7$ $cm^{-2}$ could absorb a significant fraction of the vacancies which were present just before the quench. It must be emphasized, however, that these assumptions are highly oversimplified. The continuous production and thermal annealing of the strain induced dislocations at the elevated temperatures would tend to decrease the average density below that estimated above. However, the newly generated dislocations would sweep through the sea of supersaturated vacancies, and would, therefore, absorb more vacancies than a stationary array of dislocations. Without attempting any detailed calculations of this complex problem we may conclude that for sufficiently high quenching temperatures it seems highly likely that a significant fraction of vacancies may be absorbed at dislocations generated by strains during quenching.

Jackson [23] has carried out a series of decisive experiments which are consistent with the previous discussion. He quenched 0.041 cm dia platinum wires at a rate of $5.5 \times 10^4$ °C $\sec^{-1}$ under conditions where the specimen could be strained a predetermined amount by an externally applied force during the quench. The point defect resistance increment after quenching when strain was applied, $\Delta R(\epsilon)$, was then compared to the increment obtained after a similar quench in the absence of strain, $\Delta R(0)$. The results are shown in table 4. It is seen that significant fractions of the vacancy concentrations were absorbed at dislocations generated by strains greater than $10^{-3}$ during quenches from the highest temperature. The sink action of the dislocations generated by the straining during the quenching more than compensated for the number of excess point defects generated by the straining. Jackson also concluded that the concentration of vacancies produced by unit strain in platinum is much the same at all temperatures between 78°K and elevated quenching temperatures. We note that these conclusions are consistent with the demonstration by Ruoff and Balluffi [30] that the large so-called strain enhanced bulk diffusion effects reported by many authors in the past must have been due to experimental errors, or in some cases, to short circulating along dislocations.

Effects of quenching strains generally consistent with the above discussion are apparent in a large number of quenching experiments. For example, Ascoli et al. [31] found evidence for strain induced defects in water quenched 0.0041 cm dia platinum wires. More recently Kino and Koehler [9] quenched 0.016 cm thick gold ribbons into water and found a small excess resistivity increment after quenching from very low temperatures which was most likely due to strain-induced defects. The only work in disagreement with the present point of view is that of Takamura [32] who claimed evidence for the production of huge numbers of vacancies by quenching strains in water quenched gold rods with diameters in the range of 0.10 to 0.30 cm. This investigator claimed that the number of vacancies produced by quench strains was of the same order of magnitude as the equilibrium number of va-

Table 4

The quantity $\Delta R(\epsilon)/\Delta R(0)$ determined experimentally after quenching strained and unstrained 0.041 cm dia platinum wires from various temperatures [a].

| Plastic shear strain ($\times 10^4$) | $\Delta R(\epsilon)/\Delta R(0)$ | | |
|:---:|:---:|:---:|:---:|
| | $T_q = 1500$°C | $T_q = 1200$°C | $T_q = 900$°C |
| 1 | 0.995 | 1.00 | 1.00 |
| 3 | 0.99 | 1.00 | 1.00 |
| 10 | 0.96 | 1.00 | 1.00 |
| 30 | 0.85 | 0.98 | 0.995 |
| 70 | 0.73 | 0.85 | 0.96 |
| 150 | 0.68 | 0.74 | 0.93 |
| 250 | 0.60 | 0.69 | 0.94 |

[a] All data from ref. [23].

cancies after quenches from temperatures as high as 850°C. These results are seen to be in direct contradiction to the conclusions of Jackson [23]. Moreover, more recent quenching experiments by Fraikor and Hirth [33] using specimens similar to those of Takamura have failed to reproduce the Takamura results, and instead are consistent with Jackson's work and the present point of view. We may therefore argue that the Takamura results should not be taken as evidence against the present conclusions.

Conclusions:

(1) Thermally induced quenching strains during the water quenching of normal specimens (dia $< 0.041$ cm) are small, i.e., $< 10^{-5}$.

(2) Hydrodynamic stretching strains during the water quenching of normal specimens are larger, i.e., $\sim 8 \times 10^{-4}$ for dia $= 0.041$ cm and $\sim 34 \times 10^{-4}$ for dia $= 0.005$ cm.

(3) The number of vacancies generated by quenching strains is expected to be small relative to the number quenched-in except for the case of thin specimens liquid quenched from very low quenching temperatures.

(4) Quenching strains of the order of $10^{-3}$ may be expected to generate enough dislocations to absorb a significant fraction of the vacancies initially present at elevated quenching temperatures.

(5) At elevated temperatures quenching strains cause a net loss of vacancies, since the sink effect of the dislocations which are generated more than compensates for the extra point defects produced by the deformation.

## 3. Measurements of vacancy defect concentrations

Having considered the inherent perturbations to the high temperature equilibrium vacancy population caused by quenching, we now consider the problem of measuring the concentrations of the vacancy defects which have been quenched into a pure metal. Ideally one would like to be able to measure directly the individual concentrations of the various vacancy clusters, $C_{nV}$, which are present after quenching. However, as pointed out below, only approximate values of the total quenched-in concentration of vacant lattice sites, $C_V$, have been made to date.

### 3.1. Direct determination of the individual concentrations of vacancy clusters, $C_{nV}$

The only presently available technique for a direct determination of the various $C_{nV}$ is field ion microscopy (FIM) *. This technique could, in principle, give a measure of the partition between mono-vacancies, di-vacancies and higher order clusters present after a quench. An absolute measurement of the $C_{nV}$ by FIM would in addi-

---

* Because of the great potential importance of this technique in solving some of the long-standing difficulties emphasized in the present paper we give a fairly extensive discussion of some important problems associated with FIM experiments. (See also papers of E.W.Müller and of J.M.Galligan at this conference.)

tion yield the binding energy of the various clusters. As an example, consider a system consisting of only mono-vacancies and di-vacancies as in fig. 1. If this system were quenched from $900°C$ the observed ratio $C_{2V}/C_{1V}$ would be determined by the di-vacancy binding energy (see table 1). Hence, it should be possible to distinguish between a low binding energy (0.1 eV) where di-vacancies would be essentially non-existent ($\sim$ 1 out of every 156 defects would be a di-vacancy) and a high binding energy (0.4 eV) where $\sim$ 2 out of every 3 defects would be a di-vacancy [†]. We now proceed to examine some of the complications associated with the use of FIM for the direct determination of $C_{nV}$.

The most significant problems involved in the determination of $C_{nV}$ by FIM are: (1) the presence of artifact defects; (2) stress induced defect migration caused by the electric field on the specimen which would tend to reduce the concentration of defects; and (3) the sampling problems associated with observing a statistically significant defect concentration.

Possible sources [34] of artifact defects are:

(i) defects formed as the result of field evaporation performed in a helium-neon gas mixture [35];

(ii) field induced chemical etching in the presence of water vapor in the case of tungsten and platinum [36];

(iii) preferential field evaporation of solute atoms in dilute alloys;

(iv) a lowering of the free energy of formation of a mono-vacancy due to the tensile stress produced by the large electric field at the surface of a specimen. The first two sources of artifact defects listed here do not present a serious problem since they may be controlled by the experimentalist. The third item is also not a serious handicap if the investigations are restricted to high purity ($\gtrsim$ 99.9999 wt %) specimens. The most serious possible cause of artifact defects is (iv) which we shall consider in some detail. We first consider the possibility that the electric field on the tip provides a high enough tensile stress to induce significant bulk defect concentrations. Then we consider the possibility that significant numbers of defects can be generated on the stressed crystal surface planes.

The problem of stressed induced mono-vacancies in the bulk is a two-fold question involving the formation of a mono-vacancy at a source and the subsequent migration of the mono-vacancy from its source. Both the formation and migration processes are affected by the large electric field on the specimen. In the present discussion we shall first consider the effect of the electric field on the thermodynamic equilibrium concentration (without regard to the kinetics of achieving equilibrium) at the imaging temperature ($T$). We then proceed to discuss the possibility of vacancies migrating from sources in order to establish equilibrium. The bulk equilibrium mono-vacancy concentration as a function of pressure, $p$, and temperature is, of course, given by

---

[†] We have assumed a quenching rate of $10^5$ °C sec$^{-1}$ for this illustrative example.

$$C_{1V}(p,T) = \exp(-G^F_{1V}/kT) , \qquad (8)$$

where $G^F_{1V}$ is the Gibbs free energy of formation. Eq. (8) may also be expressed in the form

$$C_{1V}(p,T) = C_{1V}(p_o,T) \exp\left[\frac{V^F_{1V}\,|p-p_o|}{kT}\right] , \qquad (9)$$

where $V^F_{1V}$ is the volume of formation of a mono-vacancy, $p_o$ is the gas pressure in the FIM, and $p$ is the pressure on the surface of the tip due to the electric field. It has often been assumed [37] that a semi-reasonable model for the specimen tip is a sphere of radius $r$, so that the tension, $|(p - p_o)|$, acting on the surface is given by $\epsilon\epsilon_o E^2/2$ (in mks units) [38] where $E$ is the electric field (volts m$^{-1}$) at the surface of the tip. Hence, the effect of the field is to increase the *bulk* mono-vacancy concentration relative to its equilibrium value at $p_o$ and $T$. The quantity of concern then is the value of $C_{1V}(p,T)$ at the imaging temperature. It is not sufficient to compare only roughly the size of $G^F_{1V}$ relative to $V^F_{1V}|(p-p_o)|$, since at the typical imaging temperatures used in field ion microscopy the value of $kT$ is quite small. For example, even if the quantity $[G^F_{1V} - V^F_{1V}|(p-p_o)|]$, i.e., the effective formation energy, were as small as 0.1 eV the induced mono-vacancy concentration at 20°K would only be $\sim 6 \times 10^{-25}$. Hence, a more suitable criterion for the lack of field induced vacancies, within the context of the above model, would more realistically be the condition that $C_{1V}(p,T) < 10^{-6}$. Even if the bulk thermodynamic

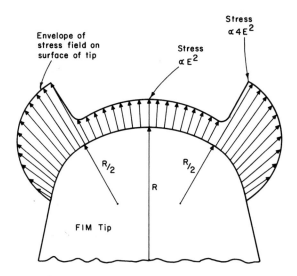

Fig. 8. A schematic representation of the stress distribution on a typical field ion microscope specimen tip end form caused by the imaging field, **E**. The end form is described by two radii of curvature $R$ and $R/2$.

equilibrium concentration of mono-vacancies at low temperatures in the presence of $E$ could be $\geqslant 10^{-6}$, there would still exist the question of the kinetics of the process at 20°K. In order for mono-vacancies to diffuse from their sources * into the specimen the effective mono-vacancy motion energy $\{[G_{1V}^{M} - V_{1V}^{M}|(p-p_{o})|]\}$ would have to be very small at 20°K. We shall very shortly show that this situation is not achieved (at least for the case of platinum) at temperatures below $\sim 78°K$. Our general conclusion for the above case is that bulk stress-induced vacancies are highly improbable unless the following two conditions are met:

(1) $G_{1V}^{F} \leqslant V_{1V}^{F}|(p-p_{o})|$; (2) $G_{1V}^{M} \leqslant V_{1V}^{M}|(p-p_{o})|$.

We now consider the case of mono-vacancy generation on stressed crystal surface planes. The above simple spherical model for the tip is, however, not physically realistic, since one should actually solve for the three dimensional stress distribution in a non-spherical tip subjected to a set of surface tractions which varies something like that illustrated schematically in fig. 8. This is a rather difficult analytic problem because of the variable boundary condition on the tip surface, and, hence, the exact stress distribution within the tip is presently unknown. However, one can obtain an estimate of how the surface tension falls off with distance from the surface by analogy to the problem of a cone subjected to a point load [39]. For the latter problem, neglecting the angular dependence, all of the stresses fall off as $1/r^2$. Hence, one would expect that the state of stress at and near the surface would be very important with respect to the lowering of the free energy of formation of a vacancy.

Schwoebel [40] has recently used a nearest neighbor binding model to calculate the energy of formation of a mono-vacancy, $[(G_{1V}^{F})_{hkl}]$, on various crystallographic surface planes of fcc crystals †. The general result he finds is that, as the coordination number of an atom on a given plane decreases, the mono-vacancy concentration increases. The calculations which Schwoebel made were for unstressed crystal surface planes, while we are interested in the vacancy concentration on a crystal surface plane $(hkl)$ in the stressed state. The effective formation energy for a mono-vacancy on an $(hkl)$ surface plane in the stressed state is

$$[(G_{1V}^{F})_{hkl} - (\Delta V_{1V}^{F})_{hkl}|(p-p_{o})|_{hkl}] , \qquad (10)$$

where $(V_{1V}^{F})_{hkl}$ is the volume of formation of a vacancy on the $(hkl)$ plane, and $|(p-p_{o})|_{hkl}$ is the tensile stress acting on $(hkl)$. Unfortunately this quantity is rather difficult to evaluate at present, but it is conceivable that it *could* be a good deal smaller than $[G_{1V}^{F} - V_{1V}^{F}|(p-p_{o})|]$, so that $C_{1V}[p,T,(hkl)]$ might become significant at even the rather low FIM imaging temperatures. It is also necessary that the effective migration energy be small on the $(hkl)$ plane so that the kinetics

---

* For a tip with a radius of 500 Å the main source of mono-vacancies would be the free surface since the probability of having a grain boundary or a dislocation in a volume of $\sim 10^{-15}$ cm$^3$ is relatively small.

† Further calculations by Beeler, presented in this conference, for a bcc crystal show the same general characteristics.

of the process are fast enough to allow the plane to achieve the equilibrium value $C_{1V}[p,T,(hkl)]$. We conclude that the case of mono-vacancy generation on stressed surface crystal planes is probably a more realistic situation than bulk-stress-induced vacancies.

We now consider the effect of the electric field on the diffusivity of already present mono-vacancies.

The effect of the stress produced by the evaporation or imaging electric field is to increase the diffusivity of vacancies and therefore to cause a stress induced migration which could lower the observed value of $C_{nV}$. For mono-vacancies the diffusion coefficient is given by

$$D_{1V} = a^2 \nu \exp[-G_{1V}^M/kT] \ , \tag{11}$$

where $a$ is the lattice parameter, and $G_{1V}^M$ is the Gibbs free energy of migration. Following procedures similar to those employed in obtaining eq. (9) from eq. (8) it can be shown that

$$D_{1V}(p,T) = D_{1V}(p_o,T) \exp[(\tfrac{2}{3} - \gamma) \chi \, |(p - p_o)|]$$

$$\times \exp[\frac{V_{1V}^M}{kT} \, |(p - p_o)|] \ , \tag{12}$$

where $\gamma$ is the Grüneisen constant, $\chi$ is the expandability, and $V_{1V}^M$ is the volume of migration of a mono-vacancy [†] . Since $V_{1V}^M |(p - p_o)|$ is positive, the field will cause a mono-vacancy to anneal at an apparently lower temperature than it would in the absence of the field. Let us now consider the magnitude of this effect. In table 5 we present the results of a calculation of the mono-vacancy diffusion coefficient in platinum in the stressed and unstressed state, where a value of $V_{1V}^M = 0.2$ atomic volume was assumed [††]. It is seen (for this value of $V_{1V}^M$) that the diffusion coefficient in the stressed state is not large enough to produce an *observable* effect as long as the specimen is maintained at or below 78°K. Physically what is required is that the value of the diffusion coefficient in the stressed state be small enough so that the root mean square diffusion distance ($\sqrt{\overline{x^2}} = \sqrt{2D_{1V}t}$) is less than one lattice spacing, so that even sub-surface vacancies are not caused to diffuse out of the specimen by the electric field. This is seen to be the case for the illustrative calcula-

[†] The quantities $a$, $\nu$ and $G_{1V}^M$ were all considered to be pressure dependent in the derivation of eq. (12). We have assumed that the lattice frequency obeys the Grüneisen relationship, that $\gamma$ and $\chi$ are temperature independent, and that the lattice expandability is the negative of the lattice compressibility.

[††] The only measurement of $V_{1V}^M$ has been made by Emrick [41] by measuring the pressure dependence of the annealing rate of defects (mono-vacancies or di-vacancies?) in quenched gold. He obtained a value of 0.15 atomic volume for $V_{1V}^M$.

Table 5

Effect of the evaporation field on the mono-vacancy diffusivity [a] in a platinum field ion microscope specimen.

| $T(°K)$ | $D_{1V}(p_o,T)$ $(cm^2 \ sec^{-1})$ | $\exp[V^M_{1V}\|(p-p_o)\|/kT]$ | $D_{1V}(p,T)$ $(cm^2 \ sec^{-1})$ |
|---|---|---|---|
| 4 | $2.03 \times 10^{-1766}$ | $1.33 \times 10^{237}$ | $2.71 \times 10^{-1529}$ |
| 78 | $1.08 \times 10^{-92}$ | $1.45 \times 10^{12}$ | $1.57 \times 10^{-80}$ |
| 273 | $4.46 \times 10^{-28}$ | $2.98 \times 10^3$ | $1.33 \times 10^{-24}$ |

a) The mono-vacancy diffusivity was calculated from eq. (12) taking $\nu = 2 \times 10^{13} \ sec^{-1}$ and $G^M_{1V} = 1.40$ eV (ref. [41]). The evaporation field was taken to be $500 \times 10^8$ volts m$^{-1}$. We neglected the $[(\frac{2}{3}-\gamma)\chi\|(p-p_o)\|]$ term since it is negligible with respect to $\dfrac{V^M_{1V}}{kT}\|(p-p_o)\|$. To evaluate the former term we took $\gamma = 3.3$ and $\chi = 3.6 \times 10^{-13} \ cm^2$ dyne$^{-1}$.

tion of mono-vacancies in platinum at temperatures less than $\sim 78°K$[†].

The sampling problem in FIM is a result of the fact that the vacancy defect concentrations in quenched metals are quite small. A reasonable quenched-in vacancy defect concentration for a rapid quench from near the melting point of platinum is $\sim 2 \times 10^{-4}$. Hence, one would have to examine at least 5,000 atom sites in order to find only 1 defect. Thus the experimentalist must be prepared to field evaporate through many atomic net planes in his search for vacancy defects. A statistically significant number of defects would be $\sim 100$ for a $C_{nV}$ determination, which implies examining $5 \times 10^5$ atom sites on high index net planes where each atom is fully resolved. A main difficulty with examining these $5 \times 10^5$ atom sites is that the atomic resolution is a function of the size of the plane. An excellent example of this phenomenon has been given by Brenner [42] who dissected the (332) plane of tungsten one atom at a time and resolved a mono-vacancy only when the number of lattice sites on this plane had been reduced to 15. Therefore an accurate determination of $C_{nV}$ would require on the order of $5 \times 10^5$ frames of film because of the

† D.G.Brandon (in Field Ion Microscopy, eds. J.J.Hren and S.Ranganathan (Plenum Press, New York, 1968) p. 66) has recently suggested a different model to explain the effect of the electric field on the motion energies of point defects. His model involves comparing the stored elastic energy per atom to the motion energy of the point defect. We do not believe that this comparison has any physical relevance to the problem of stress induced defect motion.

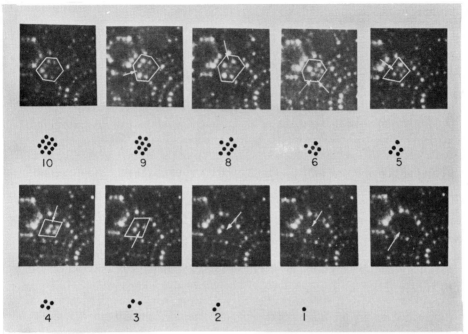

Fig. 9. The atom by atom dissection of a (334) plane of tungsten initially containing 10 atoms. The configuration and number of atoms remaining are presented schematically below each frame for clarification. The arrows indicate the sites from which the atoms were removed between successive frames. Field ion micrographs are from work by R.M.Scanlan, D.L.Styris and D.N.Seidman [43].

necessity for careful incremental field evaporation of atomic net planes. This problem obviously requires some automation of the pulse field evaporation amplifier and camera recording system †. An example of the atom by atom dissection of the (334) plane of tungsten, using the data recording system in our laboratory at Cornell, is shown in fig. 9. A quantity as large as $5 \times 10^5$ frames of film is by no means prohibitive †† by modern technological standards, and in addition, many of the techniques of scanning film have already been solved by high energy nuclear physicists [44].

The experimental applications of the FIM to the problem of absolute determinations of $C_{n\text{V}}$ have been rather sparse. The first application of the FIM to this problem was made by Müller [45]. He quenched a platinum specimen from near the

---

† At Cornell University [43] we have constructed an external image intensification, data recording and analysis system for a field ion microscope with exactly the above problem in mind.

†† The quantity $5 \times 10^5$ frames of film represents approximately 30 rolls of 1000-foot film spools.

melting point, then prepared an FIM tip of this specimen and subsequently field evaporated through 71 successive (201) planes to find 5 vacant lattice sites among the 8,500 atoms inspected. This small number of observations is clearly not statistically significant, but the experiment illustrates the feasibility of this type of investigation. A more recent experiment on the same problem has been conducted by Speicher et al. [46]. They focussed their attention on *unquenched* well-annealed platinum specimens and found mono-vacancy concentrations as high as $7.5 \times 10^{-3}$ on the (012) plane at 21°K. They attributed this to bulk stress induced mono-vacancies associated with the field evaporation process. These concentrations are considerably too high to be induced by bulk stresses. It is relatively easy to show † that an evaporation field of $\sim 21$ volts Å$^{-1}$ would be required to induce a bulk concentration of $7.5 \times 10^{-3}$ at 21°K. We therefore tentatively suggest that the anomalously high vacancy concentrations on the (012) plane may have been the result of an exceedingly low value of $[(G_{1V}^{F})_{hkl} - (V_{1V}^{F})_{hkl}|(p-p_0)|_{hkl}]$ in combination with a small value of $[(G_{1V}^{M})_{hkl} - (V_{1V}^{M})_{hkl}|(p-p_0)|_{hkl}]$.

As part of a general program on vacancy defects in gold we are employing the FIM as a research instrument and have succeeded in obtaining well developed, stable end forms of gold [47]. An example of a gold specimen imaged with a 25% Ne-He gas mixture at $\sim 16$°K is shown in fig. 10. At present, detailed experiments are in progress on the imaging characteristics of gold specimens and a number of controversial questions concerning vacancy defects in gold.

In conclusion, it is emphasized that the field ion microscope has a very strong potential for solving a number of outstanding problems concerning vacancy defects, but that there are associated problems with respect to artifact vacancies, data recording, and data reduction that must also be simultaneously solved if this potential is to be realized.

### 3.2. Direct determination of the total concentration of vacant sites, $C_V$

Although field ion microscopy offers the only presently available method for determining the individual $C_{nV}$ values, two other techniques can be used to find the total concentration of quenched-in vacant sites, $C_V$, directly: i.e., transmission electron microscopy and simultaneous measurements of length and lattice parameter changes. The use of electron microscopy to determine $C_V$ requires that all of the quenched-in vacancy defects precipitate into observable and recognizable defect clusters. Under this condition, and if the relationship between the precipitate size and the number of vacant sites stored in the precipitate is known, the total quenched-in vacant site concentration can be directly determined. Cotterill [48] was the first to use this technique for concentration determinations over a range of

---

† The expression for the equilibrium concentration of mono-vacancies was taken to be $\exp(1.5)\exp(-1.5 \text{ eV}/kT)$ from the work of Jackson [11], and a value of 0.5 atomic volume was used for $V_{1V}^{F}$. The value of $|(p-p_0)|$ necessary to satisfy eq. (9) for a concentration of $7.5 \times 10^{-3}$ at 21°K is $2 \times 10^{12}$ dyne cm$^{-2}$.

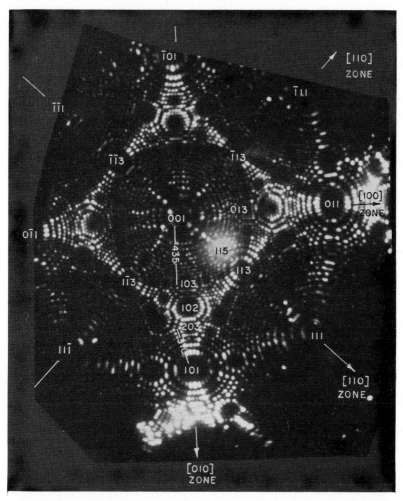

Fig. 10. A field ion micrograph of a well developed, stable end form of gold, imaged with a 25% Ne-He gas mixture at ~ 16°K. Micrograph from research of D.G.Ast and D.N.Seidman [47].

quenching temperatures. His results were in poor agreement with the measured equilibrium concentrations for gold [24], but this was probably a result of sampling difficulties. Considerable care in statistical sampling must be taken if this technique is to be used successfully. Regions (e.g. near grain boundaries) in which significant defect losses have occurred during either quenching or subsequent low temperature annealing must be avoided. In addition, perturbations of the defect structure caused by the thin film techniques (e.g. dislocation loop loss from thin foils) must be avoided or taken into account [49]. The problem of having a detailed knowledge of the relationship between the size of the vacancy precipitates and the number of vacant sites stored may be considerable. In cases where the precipitate structure is incompletely understood, as in the case of "black-spot defects" [50], evaluation of the total site concentration by this technique may prove inaccurate.

Another direct technique for the determination of the total quenched-in concentration, which somewhat surprisingly has never been performed on quenched metals, is the simultaneous measurement of length and lattice parameter changes. These measurements, which have provided our most unambiguous knowledge of the total vacant site concentrations in metals under thermal equilibrium conditions, are well suited to concentration determinations in quenched metals. If $f$ is the fractional atomic volume relaxation around a vacancy, then the fractional length change upon the addition of a concentration $C_V$ of vacant sites (assuming isotropic dilation) is given by

$$\frac{\Delta L}{L} = \tfrac{1}{3} C_V (1 - f) , \tag{13}$$

and the fractional lattice parameter change is given by

$$\frac{\Delta a}{a} = -\tfrac{1}{3} C_V f . \tag{14}$$

Subtracting (14) from (13), we obtain the well known relation

$$C_V = 3(\Delta L/L - \Delta a/a) . \tag{15}$$

If a specimen is quenched and then annealed at temperatures at which the vacancy defects anneal only at pre-existing sinks such as dislocations, grain boundaries and surfaces, with measurements of $\Delta L$ and $\Delta a$ being made in the as-quenched condition, at intermediate points, and in the fully annealed state, then the total vacant site concentration present in the material may be directly determined by eq. (15). A graphic representation of this type of measurement is shown in fig. 11 where a value of $f = \tfrac{1}{4}$ is assumed, and the curves for $3\Delta L/L$ and $3\Delta a/a$ have been plotted together so that their asymptotes in the fully annealed state superimpose. The difference between the two curves is always equal to the absolute value of $C$ in the metal.

### 3.3. Indirect determination of the total concentration of vacant sites, $C_V$

Most of the experimental investigations of defect concentrations in quenched metals have utilized indirect techniques in which a measurement of the total change in some macroscopic property, $\Delta p$, caused by quenching is made, and this change is then related to the concentration of vacancy defects through a knowledge of the property change per defect. In general

$$\Delta p = \sum_n p_n C_{nV} , \tag{16}$$

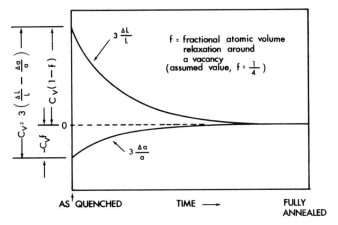

Fig. 11. A graphic representation of the measurement of the total vacant site concentration, $C_V$, by the simultaneous measurement of length and lattice parameter changes after quenching. The curves for $(3\Delta L/L)$ and $(3\Delta a/a)$ have been plotted together so that their asymptotes in the fully annealed state superimpose. The difference between these curves is then equal to $C_V$.

where $p_n$ is the change in $p$ due to unit concentration of vacancy clusters of size $n$. If we define an average value, $A$, for the change in $p$ due to unit concentration of individual vacant lattice sites (i.e., averaged over all cluster sizes) then

$$\Delta p = \left[ \frac{\displaystyle\sum_n p_n C_{nV}}{\displaystyle\sum_n n C_{nV}} \right] C_V = A\, C_V . \qquad (17)$$

If the $p_n$ vary linearly with $n$ (i.e., $p_n = n p_1$) then $A = p_1$. Eqs. (16) and (17) show that $C_V$ is only strictly proportional to $\Delta p$ when either no clustering is present or the $p_n$ vary linearly with $n$. Possible effects due to non-linearity have been customarily ignored in quenching experiments and eq. (17) has, therefore, been employed, with the tacit assumption that $A$ is independent of $C_V$, as an approximation to obtain $C_V$. The quantitative nature of this approximation may be illustrated by using the simple mono-vacancy-di-vacancy model which was used previously to calculate the clustering results given in table 1, section 2.1. Defect losses during quenching are neglected, and various amounts of clustering which depend upon the quenching temperature, the di-vacancy binding energy, and the quenching rate are present in the final quenched specimen. Values of the measured total property increment $\Delta p$ after quenching were calculated under the following two assumptions:

$$\Delta p = p_1 C_{1V} + 2.0\, p_1 C_{2V} , \qquad (18)$$

and

$$\Delta p = p_1 C_{1V} + 1.8 \, p_1 C_{2V} \, . \tag{19}$$

In eq. (19) it is assumed that $p_2 = 1.8 \, p_1$ (i.e., the value of $p$ for an isolated vacant site decreases by 10% when it joins a di-vacancy). Some results are shown in fig. 12 where the dependence of the Arrhenius plot on the assumptions expressed in eqs. (18) and (19) is shown. The effect of the assumed non-linearity only becomes noticeable at high binding energies where large amounts of clustering are present after quenching. As may be seen maximum differences of about 10% occur in the values of $\Delta p$ obtained. These results indicate that errors of this magnitude could conceivably be present in the determination of $C_V$ from $\Delta p$ data if it is simply assumed that $p_n$ varies linearly with $n$. Fortunately, the 10% figure calculated above is an extreme value, since it corresponds to both a large amount of clustering and a large assumed non-linearity. The actual importance of this effect in most cases is undoubtedly considerably smaller. For example, in the case of electrical resistivity the resistivity per di-vacancy is thought to be only $\sim 5\%$ lower than the resistivity due to two well spaced mono-vacancies [51]. It appears likely, therefore, that eq. (17), with the assumption of constant $A$, may be used as a reasonably good approximation under most conditions. A possible exception to this is in the measurement of stored energy release in defect systems where large binding energies exist. A major problem in the indirect techniques is the determination of the proportionality factor $A$ in eq. (17). To date, the only direct ways in which this has been accomplished is by comparing quenched-in property changes with either absolute vacancy defect concentrations measured under thermal equilibrium conditions (see, for example, ref. [24]) or total vacancy concentrations measured by transmission electron microscopy (see, for example, ref. [52]). In addition, approximate values have been obtained from the results of theoretical calculations. We shall not give a detailed discussion of these results here. Instead, we shall focus attention on a number of other complications which exist in the various indirect methods for determining $C_V$.

Bulk properties for which such measurements have been made include electrical resistivity, volume or length, and stored energy. A bibliography of much of this work may be found elsewhere [53].

### 3.3.1. Resistivity measurements

Measurements of electrical resistivity changes caused by quenching have been used to a great extent since the pioneering experiments of Koehler and coworkers [54]. In terms of measuring quenched-in defect concentrations, measurements of the low temperature electrical resistivity (normally either at $4.2°K$ or $78°K$) are performed on specimens in the well annealed state prior to quenching and then in the as-quenched condition. The difference in these resistivities is then taken to be directly proportional to the total concentration of quenched-in vacant lattice sites. It is normally assumed that Matthiessen's rule, in which the total resistivity can be

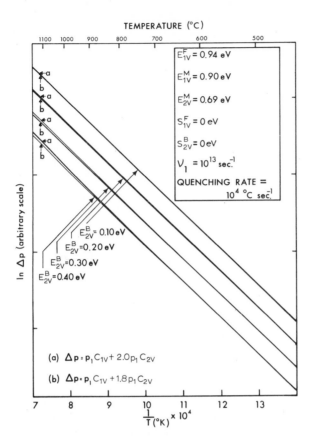

Fig. 12. The effect of non-linearity of the $p_n$ on the observed ln $\Delta p$ versus $1/T$ plot. The curves were calculated for a closed mono-vacancy-di-vacancy system using the parameters given. Two cases were considered: (a) the linear case, where $p_2 = 2p_1$, and (b) a non-linear case, where $p_2 = 1.8 p_1$. The curves are presented using an arbitrary vertical scale for clarity.

represented as the sum of a temperature dependent lattice resistivity and a temperature independent point defect contribution [55], is valid i.e.,

$$\rho = \rho_o(T) + \rho_V C_V ,$$

where $\rho_V$ is the resistivity per unit concentration of vacant lattice sites. Although some deviation from Matthiessen's rule may in general be expected, the deviations should be negligible for vacancy defects at $4.2°K$. At $78°K$, however, deviations of up to 10% may occur [56,57]. Under most conditions, changes in residual resistivity may therefore be related closely to the total quenched-in vacant site concentrations if the resistivity per unit concentration of vacant sites is known. The advantages of resistivity measurements are the precision with which they can be made, and the fact that the as-quenched state is compared directly with that existing prior to the quench. As such, resistivity measurements provide probably the most accurate method for the comparison of quenched-in total vacancy concentrations from the same quench temperature [50,52].

### 3.3.2. Volume or length change measurements

Dilatometric measurements have also been used extensively in the study of quenched-in vacant site concentrations in metals (see, for example, refs. [32] and [33]). These investigations, which have been performed on fcc metals, have measured the difference between the specimen length (length changes being related to the isotropic volume changes by $3(\Delta L/L) = \Delta V/V$) just after quenching to the length after the quenched-in defects have been fully annealed at relatively low temperatures. The observed length change may then, in principle, be related to the quenched-in concentrations if the volume change per vacant site is known. Since in these measurements, in contrast to those utilizing quenched-in resistivity increments, the as-quenched specimen is not related directly to the defect-free specimen prior to quenching, significant additional problems may arise. Here the quantity measured is $\delta(\Delta p)$ which may be written in the form

$$\delta(\Delta p) = [\Delta p(t = 0) - \Delta p(t = \infty)] ,$$

where $t$ is the time of low temperature annealing after quenching. In general, $\Delta p (t = \infty) \neq 0$, and, therefore, the desired quantity $\Delta p (t = 0)$ cannot be determined directly. The nature of the vacancy defect annealing, e.g. to dislocations or precipitates, may play an important role in determining the value of $\Delta p (t = \infty)$. If, as an example of an extreme case, a system of quenched-in vacancy defects having zero lattice relaxation subsequently precipitate in the form of large three-dimensional voids, the normal $\Delta L$ technique would lead to an apparent conclusion of no quenched-in defects! Another related problem in length change measurements can result from the assumption that an isotropic metal contracts isotropically as the vacancy defects are annihilated at sinks. In the work of Fraikor and Hirth [33] this assumption led to observed apparent vacancy defect concentrations which were considerably smaller than should have been caused by the quenching treatment performed. This anomalous behavior was explained on the basis that their cylindrical single crystal specimens contained a grown-in sub-boundary network consisting primarily of edge dislocations parallel to the axis of the wire. Defect decay to these dislocations then produced an anisotropy in the volume contraction such that very little contraction of the wire length occurred. Clearly, similar effects could also be a problem in the $(\Delta L/L - \Delta a/a)$ technique discussed in section 3.2.

### 3.3.3. Other bulk property measurements

Measurements of changes in properties such as thermoelectric power, and coercive field strength and differential susceptibility in ferromagnetic metals, which are sensitive to the presence of point defects may also be used in the same sense as electrical resistivity measurements for the measurement of the total quenched-in defect concentration. As they offer no essential departure from the discussion already presented they will not be discussed here further. Calorimetric measurements [58] of the energy stored in specimens quenched from various temperatures, in contrast to other bulk property measurements, enable one to measure the contribution to the property per vacancy, i.e., the formation energy, in the same experiment by determining the stored energy release as a function of quenching temperature. Thus, this technique, in principle, provides a self-contained set of measurements of the total quenched-in vacancy defect concentration if the quenched-in vacancy population consists only of mono-vacancies. However, it should be emphasized that this measurement is not absolute as are the measurements described in section 3.2. The possibility of significant non-linear $p_n$ behavior (i.e., non-zero cluster binding energies) reduces its value somewhat.

## 3.4. Measurements sensitive to anisotropic vacancy defect clusters

In addition to the methods discussed above, which are in general applicable to the determination of the concentration of any quenched-in defects, other techniques exist for the measurement of the concentrations of specific defect types which do not have the same symmetry as the lattice in which they exist. These are the measurements of anelastic relaxation and the magnetic after-effect.

### 3.4.1. Anelastic relaxation measurements

The existence of vacancy clusters in a lattice may give rise to an anelastic relaxation (a reversible time-dependent response in one of the compliance coefficients). This relaxation is due to the repopulation of vacancy clusters among sites which are initially equivalent, but which become nonequivalent under an applied stress. The only defects which give rise to this relaxation are ones which have a group symmetry which is lower than the crystal group symmetry of the host lattice [59]. The strength of the relaxation has been shown by Zener [60] and Nowick and Heller [59] to be proportional to the cluster concentration. Hence, anelastic relaxation measurements are ideally suited for revealing the presence of defects such as di-vacancies (as originally suggested by R.R.Hasiguti [61]).

The number of reported measurements of this type are surprisingly few, in view of the obvious selectivity of this technique with respect to defect species. The first reported experiments, performed on quenched gold, were by Neuman [62] who failed to find a relaxation which could be clearly attributed to di-vacancies. Neuman's failure to observe the di-vacancy peak was largely due to experimental difficulties. He measured a background damping in well annealed gold wire specimens of $6 \times 10^{-4}$ to $9 \times 10^{-4}$, which is quite high when one considers the fact that the strength of the di-vacancy relaxation was expected to have a value [62] of only $\sim 3C_{2V}$. Okuda and Hasiguti [63] have reported a relaxation in gold at $-50°C$ which was quenched from $1000°C$. They attributed this relaxation to the presence of di-vacancies, but unfortunately they did not measure either the frequency dependence or the concentration dependence of the strength of the relaxation. Hence, the existence of this peak is not firmly established. Very recently Franklin and Birnbaum [64] have found a relaxation in gold which was quenched, *in situ*, from 800°C. The strength of the relaxation was found to anneal in the same temperature range as the defect in gold which according to resistivity measurements migrates with an energy of about 0.70 eV and which has been tentatively identified as the di-vacancy [10].

In conclusion, we wish to emphasize the need for carefully planned anelastic relaxation measurements for confirming the presence of higher order vacancy clusters. These measurements must be performed *in situ* to avoid deforming the specimens, great care should be taken to avoid thermal strains during quenching, and a careful check of the frequency, concentration and orientation dependence of the relaxation must be made to confirm the physical significance of the relaxation.

### 3.4.2. Magnetic after-effect measurements

Magnetic after-effects, such as the disaccommodation of the initial susceptibility, which are due to the reorientation of defect clusters may also be used to identify different defect species [65]. We note that these measurements are restricted to ferromagnetic metals (e.g. Fe, Ni) and hence represent a rather specialized set of measurements. For a discussion of these experiments the reader is referred to the paper by Kronmüller [66] presented at this conference.

Conclusions:

(1) The only presently available technique for the direct determination of the various $C_{nV}$ is field ion microscopy. This technique has a strong potential for solving a number of outstanding problems concerning vacancy defects. However, several experimental difficulties must be solved if this potential is to be fully realized.

(2) There is a need for precise direct measurements of the total quenched-in concentration of vacant lattice sites using such techniques as transmission electron microscopy and the simultaneous measurement of length and lattice parameter changes after quenching.

(3) The only data of high accuracy which are available are from measurements of property changes, $\Delta p$, due to the quenched-in defects. Of these measurements, those which compare the as-quenched state directly with that existing prior to the quench (e.g. electrical resistivity changes) have the least inherent problems. However, the change in the property per unit concentration of vacant lattice sites, $A$, must be known, and further careful measurements of these quantities are needed.

(4) Selective indirect measurements which are sensitive to the symmetry difference between a defect cluster and its host lattice (e.g. anelastic relaxation measurements) can provide important information regarding the concentrations, and nature, of the specific quenched-in defects.

## 4. Determination of formation energies and entropies

In principle, if measurements of the equilibrium concentrations of the $C_{n\mathrm{V}}$ are available as a function of $T$, the $E_{n\mathrm{V}}^{\mathrm{F}}(T)$ and $S_{n\mathrm{V}}^{\mathrm{F}}(T)$ may be determined in a straightforward manner. Since we have in equilibrium that

$$C_{n\mathrm{V}}(T) = \alpha_n \exp(S_{n\mathrm{V}}^{\mathrm{F}}/k) \exp(-E_{n\mathrm{V}}^{\mathrm{F}}/kT) , \tag{20}$$

and the basic thermodynamic relationship

$$\frac{\partial E_{n\mathrm{V}}^{\mathrm{F}}(T)}{\partial T} = T \frac{\partial S_{n\mathrm{V}}^{\mathrm{F}}(T)}{\partial T} , \tag{21}$$

it is readily shown that

$$E_{n\mathrm{V}}^{\mathrm{F}}(T) = -k \frac{\partial \ln C_{n\mathrm{V}}}{\partial (1/T)} . \tag{22}$$

The usual plot of $\ln C_{n\mathrm{V}}$ versus $1/T$ will then display curvature if $E_{n\mathrm{V}}^{\mathrm{F}}(T)$ is significantly temperature dependent, but, in any case, $E_{n\mathrm{V}}^{\mathrm{F}}(T)$ may be determined from the local slope of this plot using eq. (22). As noted previously, however, there have been no direct measurements of the $C_{n\mathrm{V}}$, and only the field-ion microscope technique seems to offer hope in this direction. If it could be demonstrated using such a technique that clustering after quenching is insignificant, then the mono-vacancy properties could be readily determined using the above procedure. However, if significant clustering is present the situation becomes ambiguous since, as shown in section 2.1, clustering during the quench makes the determination of the original cluster distributions at $T_q$ impossible by any direct technique [†].

At the present time the only data of any high accuracy which are available are measurements of total property change increments, $\Delta p$, as a function of temperature. As discussed in section 3.3, non-linear effects due to clustering should be relatively small under usual conditions, and therefore, $C_{\mathrm{V}}$ may be taken to be closely proportioned to $\Delta p$. The problem is then reduced to obtaining information about the vacancy defects from $\Delta p$ data where it is assumed that $\Delta p = A\,C_{\mathrm{V}}$ and $A$ is assumed independent of $C_{\mathrm{V}}$. If an Arrhenius plot of $\ln \Delta p$ versus $1/T$ is constructed, it might be hoped that information could be obtained from its shape. Curvature of such a plot could be expected if:

(1) Appreciable concentrations of clusters were present in thermal equilibrium at $T_q$;

---

[†] We emphasize that we are concerned in this paper with the information which can be obtained from quenching experiments *per se*. It may, of course, be possible to deduce original cluster distributions using certain models and assumptions regarding the clustering kinetics during the quench. However, a considerable amount of additional information is then required, e.g., the diffusivities of the defects.

(2) only mono-vacancies were present, but $E_{1V}^F$ (and $S_{1V}^F$) were appreciably temperature dependent.

These possibilities could lead to confusion in the interpretation of the plot, and it is therefore important to estimate the magnitudes of the curvature which could arise from these effects separately.

### 4.1. Arrhenius plot curvature due to thermal equilibrium cluster populations

We consider here only the relatively simple case where di-vacancies constitute the only significant clusters present. Under these conditions

$$C_V = C_{1V} + 2C_{2V} = C_{1V} + 12C_{1V}^2 \exp(-S_{2V}^B/k) \exp(E_{2V}^B/kT) , \quad (23)$$

or

$$C_V = C_{1V} \{1 + 12 \exp[(S_{1V}^F - S_{2V}^B)/k] \exp[(E_{2V}^B - E_{1V}^F)/kT]\} . \quad (24)$$

Values of $\Delta p = A\,C_V$ as a function of $1/T$ were calculated for a range of possible parameters, and the results are shown in fig. 13. As expected, the second term in eq. (24), representing the di-vacancy contribution to the total concentration, makes a contribution at the higher temperatures which increases with an increase in either the quantity $(S_{1V}^F - S_{2V}^B)$ or $(E_{2V}^B - E_{1V}^F)$. The di-vacancy contributions are appreciable at the higher temperatures for the higher di-vacancy binding energies and are seen to produce noticeable curvature in these cases. We note that the curves shown in fig. 13 (and in the following fig. 14) are arranged arbitrarily on the vertical scale and are presented mainly to demonstrate how the curves change *shape* and *slope* as the assumed defect parameters are varied. (It is instructive in the present context to sight along these curves or to lay a straight edge along them in order to better observe any curvature.) We estimate that the curvature in Group 3 ($S_{1V}^F = 0$) would be too small to detect experimentally. In Group 2 ($S_{1V}^F = 1k$) curvature might be detectable for $E_{2V}^B > 0.3$ eV, while for Group 3 ($S_{1V}^F = 2k$) curvature might be detectable for $E_{2V}^B > 0.2$ eV. However, extremely high precision data would be required over a wide temperature range. These values are physically possible, and therefore, we may conclude that barely detectable curvatures in the Arrhenius plot could conceivably arise due to the presence of equilibrium di-vacancies under certain conditions. It is noted that the plot of the experimental data for gold in fig. 7 shows slight positive curvature which may possibly lie outside experimental uncertainty. It is interesting to speculate that this may provide support for the relatively high di-vacancy binding energy model of Wang et al. [10] for gold. Similar phenomena might be expected due to the presence of higher order clusters if the binding entropies and energies are of the necessary magnitudes.

### 4.2. Arrhenius plot curvature due to temperature dependent energies and entropies of formation

We consider the simple case where only mono-vacancies are present and where $S_{1V}^F$ and $E_{1V}^F$ are temperature dependent. Following the recent treatment by

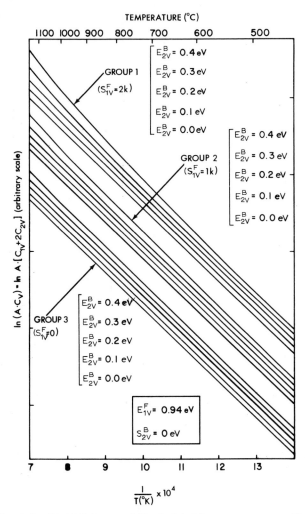

Fig. 13. Arrhenius plots of $\ln(A\,C_V)$ versus $1/T$ calculated for a mono-vacancy-di-vacancy system in thermal equilibrium using eq. (24) with the various vacancy parameters given, showing the variation of curvature and slope as the defect parameters are changed. The curves are presented using an arbitrary vertical scale for clarity.

Nowick and Dienes [67] we assume that $E_{1V}^F$ is not strongly dependent upon temperature and use a first order expansion of $E_{1V}^F$ in the form

$$E_{1V}^F(T) = E_{1V}^F(T_o) + B(T - T_o),\qquad(25)$$

where $T_o$ is a reference temperature, and $B$ is a constant. Since it is thermodynamically necessary that $S_{1V}^F = -(\partial G_{1V}^F/\partial T)_p$, it follows that

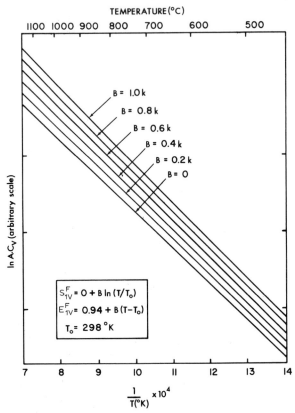

Fig. 14. Arrhenius plots of $\ln(A\,C_{1V})$ versus $1/T$ calculated for a mono-vacancy system with a temperature dependent energy and entropy of formation using eq. (27) with various values of the parameter $B$ consistent with eq. (28). The curves are presented using an arbitrary vertical scale for clarity.

$$S_{1V}^{F}(T) = S_{1V}^{F}(T_{o}) + B\ln(T/T_{o}) .\tag{26}$$

Using eqs. (25) and (26), we therefore have

$$C_{1V} = \exp\left\{\frac{S_{1V}^{F}(T_{o}) + B\ln(T/T_{o})}{k}\right\}\ \exp\left\{\frac{-[E_{1V}^{F}(T_{o}) + B(T - T_{o})]}{kT}\right\} .\tag{27}$$

Nowick and Dienes have shown, using quite reasonable thermodynamic estimates, that almost certainly

$$|B| \leqslant 1.0\,k .\tag{28}$$

Flynn [68] has given an approximate expression recently for the temperature dependence of the free energy of formation of a vacancy which involves mainly the temperature dependence of the elastic shear modulus. We have used the elastic data of Chang and Himmel [69] for the noble metals to evaluate typical temperature dependences of $E_{1V}^F$ from Flynn's work, and we find temperature dependences which are in the same range as those predicted by Nowick and Dienes [67], i.e., $|B| < k$. Values of $\Delta p = A\,C_{1V}$ as a function of $1/T$ were therefore calculated using eq. (27) for different values of $B$ consistent with eq. (28) taking $T_0 = 298°K$, $E_{1V}^F(T_0)$ = 0.94 eV and $S_{1V}^F(T_0) = 0$. The results are shown in fig. 14. Some positive curvature which increases with $B$ is evident. However, the curvature is relatively small, and is undoubtedly below the level of detection by present methods.

### 4.3. Discussion

The above results show that there are definite limits to the information which can be obtained from Arrhenius plots of $\ln \Delta p$ versus $1/T$. If detectable curvature is found, the presence of relatively high concentrations of equilibrium clusters is indicated. On the other hand, if no detectable curvature is observed it cannot be concluded that the formation energy is temperature independent or that the effects of clusters are insignificant and that the results should be interpreted solely on the basis of mono-vacancies. For example, if apparent mono-vacancy formation energies are derived from the average slopes of the various curves in fig. 13, which do not exhibit detectable curvature, results which differ by as much as 5% are obtained. Similarly, results differing by as much as 7% are obtained from the curves in fig. 14. It may be concluded that errors of this magnitude (or less) could result if the *a priori* assumption is made that the slope is proportional to a temperature independent mono-vacancy formation energy.

It need hardly be added that entropies of formation can only be derived when concentration data are available, i.e., the value of $A$ in the relation $\Delta p = A\,C$ must be known.

It is clear that detailed and unambiguous information about the vacancy defects present in quenched systems cannot be obtained from quenching experiments which consist of measurements of $C_V$ only. Measurements of the concentrations, $C_{nV}$, of the different types of vacancy defect clusters which may be present are urgently required. In certain cases additional information from other types of experiments (e.g. annealing experiments) may be used in attempts to interpret quenching experiments. Further discussion of these possibilities is given elsewhere in this conference.

Conclusions:

(1) If the $C_{nV}$ are known as a function of $T$, $E_{nV}^F(T)$ (and $S_{nV}^F(T)$) may be obtained in a simple manner from the local slope of the Arrhenius plot.

(2) Unfortunately, it has not been possible to obtain appropriate absolute $C_{nV}$ data, and generally the only data of any high accuracy which are available are measurements of total defect property changes, $\Delta p$, due to the quenched-in defects.

It is usually a good approximation to assume that $\Delta p$ is proportional to the total concentration of vacant sites, $C_V$.

(3) Large defect cluster populations present in equilibrium at high temperatures may cause observable curvature of a ln $\Delta p$ versus $1/T$ plot. However, the absence of observable curvature does not necessarily mean that cluster concentrations were negligible, and that the data can be interpreted solely in terms of mono-vacancies. The determination of an apparent value of $E_{1V}^F$ from the slope of such a curve, differing significantly from the actual value, could result.

(4) It is unlikely that detectable curvature in a plot of ln $\Delta p$ versus $1/T$ can result from the temperature dependence of $E_{1V}^F(T)$. However, the average slope of such a curve (and hence the average apparent value of $E_{1V}^F$) may depend significantly upon the temperature dependence of $E_{1V}^F(T)$.

(5) Entropies of formation can only be derived from concentration data (i.e., the value of $A$ in the relation $\Delta p = A\,C_V$ must be known). There is, in general, an urgent need for absolute measurements of the $C_{nV}$ as a function of temperature.

## References

[1] M.Doyama, Lattice defects in quenched metals, eds. R.M.J.Cotterill et al. (Academic Press, New York, 1965) p. 163.

[2] H.Fujiwara, Technical report, Contract Nonr 1834 (12) 46–22–55–363, Department of Physics, University of Illinois, Urbana, Illinois.

[3] J.S.Koehler, M.de Jong and F.Seitz, J. Phys. Soc. Japan 18, Supplement 111 (1963) 1.

[4] R.M.J.Cotterill, Lattice defects in quenched metals, eds. R.M.J.Cotterill et al. (Academic Press, New York, 1965) p. 97.

[5] M.Meshii, J.A.McComb, K.Y.Chen and T.H.Mori, The nature of small defects, ed. M.J. Makin (H.M. Stationary Office, 1966) p. 84.

[6] F.W.Young Jr., T.O.Baldwin and F.A.Sherill, Lattice defects and their interactions, ed; R.R.Hasiguti (Gordon and Breach, New York, 1967) p. 543.

[7] C.P.Flynn, J.Bass and D.Lazarus, Phil. Mag. 11 (1965) 521.

[8] T.Mori, M.Meshii and J.W.Kauffman, J. Appl. Phys. 33 (1962) 2776.

[9] T.Kino and J.S.Koehler, Phys. Rev. 162 (1967) 632.

[10] C.G.Wang, D.N.Seidman and R.W.Balluffi, Phys. Rev. 169 (1968) 553.

[11] J.J.Jackson, Lattice defects in quenched metals, eds. R.M.J.Cotterill et al. (Academic Press, New York, 1965) p. 467.

[12] J.Bass, Phil. Mag. 15 (1967) 717.

[13] R.Gripshover, J.Zetts and J.Bass, Report Jül. Conf. 2 (Vol. I) 1967, p. 228.

[14] K.H.Lie and R.W.Balluffi, to be published.

[15] D.N.Seidman and R.W.Balluffi, Lattice defects and their interactions, ed. R.R.Hasiguti (Gordon and Breach, New York, 1967) p. 911.

[16] D.N.Seidman and R.W.Balluffi, Phys. Stat. Sol. 17 (1966) 531.

[17] D.N.Seidman and R.W.Balluffi, Phys. Rev. 139 (1965) A1824.

[18] R.W.Balluffi, Interactions between dislocations and point defects, ed. B.L.Eyre (H.M. Stationary Office, to be published).

[19] C.P.Flynn, Phys. Rev. 134 (1964) A241.

[20] F.S.Ham, J. Appl. Phys. 30 (1959) 915.

[21] K.P.Chik, D.Schumacher and A.Seeger, Phase stability in metals and alloys, eds. P.S.Rudman et al. (McGraw-Hill, New York, 1967) p. 449.
[22] A.Seeger and H.Mehrer, Phys. Stat. Sol. 29 (1968) 231.
[23] J.J.Jackson, Lattice defects in quenched metals, eds. R.M.J.Cotterill et al. (Academic Press, New York, 1965) p. 479.
[24] R.O.Simmons and R.W.Balluffi, Phys. Rev. 125 (1962) 862.
[25] J.Bass, Phys. Rev. 137 (1965) A765.
[26] C.J.Meechan and R.R.Eggleston, Acta Met. 2 (1954) 680.
[27] D.N.Seidman and R.W.Balluffi, Phil. Mag. 10 (1964) 1067.
[28] W.H.Aarts and R.K.Jarvis, Acta Met. 2 (1954) 87.
[29] Z.S.Basinski, J.S.Dugdale and A.Howie, Phil. Mag. 8 (1963) 1989.
[30] A.L.Ruoff and R.W.Balluffi, J. Appl. Phys. 34 (1963) 2862.
[31] A.Ascoli, M.Asdente, E.Germagnoli and A.Manara, J. Phys. Chem. Solids 6 (1958) 59.
[32] J.Takamura, Lattice defects in quenched metals, eds. R.M.J.Cotterill et al. (Academic Press, New York, 1965) p. 521.
[33] F.J.Fraikor and J.P.Hirth, J. Appl. Phys. 38 (1967) 2312.
[34] E.W.Müller, in: Field Ion Microscopy, eds. J.J.Hren and S.Ranganathan (Plenum Press, New York, 1968) p. 92.
[35] O.Nishikawa and E.W.Müller, J. Appl. Phys. 35 (1964) 2806.
[36] J.F.Mulson and E.W.Müller, J. Chem. Phys. 38 (1963) 2615.
[37] E.W.Müller, Advances in electronics and electron physics, ed. L.Marton (Academic Press, New York, 1960) Vol. 13, p. 83.
[38] B.I.Bleany and B.Bleany, Electricity and magnetism (Oxford University Press, London, 1957) p. 28.
[39] A.I.Lur'e, Three dimensional problems of the theory of elasticity (Interscience, New York, 1964) p. 137.
[40] R.L.Schwoebel, J. Appl. Phys. 38 (1967) 3154.
[41] R.M.Emrick, Phys. Rev. 122 (1961) 1720.
[42] S.S.Brenner, United States Steel Corporation Report PR300 (1965);
S.S.Brenner, High temperature, high resolution microscopy (Gordon and Breach, New York, 1968).
[43] R.M.Scanlan, D.L.Styris, D.N.Seidman and D.G.Ast, Cornell University Materials Science Center Report No. 1159 (1969).
[44] Bubble and Spark chambers, ed. R.P.Shutt (Academic Press, New York, 1967) Vol. 2.
[45] E.W.Müller, Z. Physik 156 (1959) 399.
[46] C.A.Speicher, W.T.Pimbley, M.J.Attardo, J.M.Galligan and S.S.Brenner, Phys. Letters 23 (1966) 194.
[47] D.G.Ast and D.N.Seidman, Appl. Phys. Letters 13 (1968) 348.
[48] R.M.J.Cotterill, Phil. Mag. 6 (1961) 1351.
[49] M.Meshii, Lattice defects in quenched metals, eds. R.M.J.Cotterill et al. (Academic Press, New York, 1965) p. 387.
[50] R.W.Siegel, Phil. Mag. 13 (1966) 337.
[51] C.P.Flynn, J. Phys. Radium 23 (1962) 654.
[52] R.W.Siegel, Phil. Mag. 13 (1966) 359.
[53] Lattice defects in quenched metals, eds. R.M.J.Cotterill et al. (Academic Press, New York, 1965).
[54] J.E.Bauerle and J.S.Koehler, Phys. Rev. 107 (1957) 1493;
J.W.Kauffman and J.S.Koehler, Phys. Rev. 88 (1952) 149.
[55] J.M.Ziman, Electrons and phonons (Oxford University Press, London, 1960) p. 337.
[56] H.Bross, Z. Naturforsch. 14a (1959) 560.

[57] R.R.Conte, J.Dural and Y.Quéré, Jül. Conf. 2 (Vol. I) 1968, p. 235.
[58] W.DeSorbo, Phys. Rev. 117 (1960) 444.
[59] A.S.Nowick and W.R.Heller, Advanc. Phys. 12 (1963) 251.
[60] C.A.Zener, Elasticity and anelasticity of metals (University of Chicago Press, Chicago, 1948).
[61] R.R.Hasiguti, J. Phys. Soc. Japan 8 (1953) 798.
[62] C.H.Neuman, Ph. D. Thesis (Physics), University of Illinois (1963);
     C.H.Neuman, J. Phys. Chem. Solids 27 (1966) 427.
[63] S.Okuda and R.R.Hasiguti, J. Phys. Soc. Japan 19 (1964) 242.
[64] D.Franklin and H.K.Birnbaum, University of Illinois, private communication (1968).
[65] H.Rieger, Z. Metallk. 54 (1963) 229;
     H.Jäger, ibid 55 (1964) 17;
     A.Seeger, H.Kronmüller and H.Rieger, Z. angew. Physik. 18 (1965) 377.
[66] H.Kronmüller, this volume.
[67] A.S.Nowick and G.J.Dienes, Phys. Stat. Sol. 24 (1967) 461.
[68] C.P.Flynn, Phys. Rev. 171 (1968) 682.
[69] Y.A.Chang and L.Himmel, J. Appl. Phys. 37 (1966) 3567.

## Discussion

*K.P.Chik:* I would like to comment on the computation of the critical temperature $T^*$. The calculations are done for a linear quench rate. If the quench rate near the final temperature decays exponentially, the quasi-equilibrium between single and di-vacancies is probably maintained (see Doyama's calculation in the Argonne conference 1964).

*R.W.Siegel:* We have concerned ourselves in this paper with relatively rapid quenches such that non-equilibrium cluster concentrations are frozen-in. It is clear that if one lets the cooling rate become small enough, quasi-equilibrium and even equilibrium conditions may be maintained. However, as shown by the results presented in table 1 of our paper, the degree of clustering, for a given set of vacancy parameters, is relatively insensitive to the quenching rate.

*J.Takamura:* 1. I agree with the comment of Dr. Chik. We have calculated the change in the defect population during the quench, by taking into account that only the excess vacancies at the temperature during the quench are annihilated or are associated with each other. The results are a little different from those obtained by the method Dr. Siegel has mentioned.

2. In principle, the method of extrapolating the quenching rate is good as Dr. Siegel mentioned. However, the most difficult problem is the determination of the average quenching rate, because the whole cooling curve depends on what quenching medium is used. For example, the cooling curve for water is almost linear, but that for brine is exponential. So I would like to suggest to use *our* method of extrapolating the specimen thickness, which can eliminate both effects of quenching rate and quenching strain.

*R.W.Siegel:* In the method for correcting for defect losses by extrapolation to infinite quenching rate, ideally, one would like to be able to vary the quenching rate while using the same quenching medium (e.g. by varying the gas pressure in a gas quench) so that the cooling curves all have the same shape. However, as shown by the good fit of the extrapolated quenching data for gold presented in fig. 7 of our paper, the problem of using a variety of quenching media does not appear serious.

With respect to the method of extrapolation to zero specimen thickness, it would appear from Jackson's calculations of the size dependence of the hydrodynamic stretching strains that serious problems may be encountered in this technique if liquid quenches are used.

*P.Wilkes:* The experiment measuring length change and X-ray lattice parameter change after quenching is currently starting at Manchester.

The main difficulty in the early stages of the work is the requirement for thick specimens to support the dilatometer. Dilatometry offers a powerful tool for this type of study. Professor Jones at Aberdeen has produced an electrical dilatometer capable of detecting length changes down to $10^{-10}$ cm. This offers the possibility of studying very small vacancy supersaturations with obvious advantages.

*R.W.Siegel:* It is good to hear that this experiment is being performed. Thick specimens are not necessarily required for the dilation measurements, as shown, for example, in the work of Bauerle and Koehler.

*H.I.Dawson:* It appears that the conclusions drawn from your calculations are rather insensitive to the precise choice of the vacancy parameters. In other words, your conclusions leave room for the various values for vacancy parameters proposed in the literature. One can therefore draw the general conclusion that such calculations will not further improve our knowledge on vacancy properties at the present time, until more reliable results emerge from laboratory experiments.

*R.W.Siegel:* The intent of the calculations presented in our paper was to examine a number of problems concerning quenched-in defects in metals and not to draw conclusions at this time about specific vacancy parameters. As such, various values of controversial parameters (e.g. $E_{2V}^{B}$) were used. Some of the calculations are strongly dependent upon the precise choice of vacancy parameter. For example, the results of the clustering calculations presented in fig. 1 of our paper show a difference of almost three orders of magnitude in the frozen-in $C_{2V}/C_{1V}$ ratio between systems with di-vacancy binding energies of 0.1 eV and 0.4 eV. It is just this type of calculation which will be required to determine the di-vacancy binding energy when this ratio can be measured directly using field ion microscopy.

# ELECTRICAL RESISTIVITY MEASUREMENTS
## OF VACANCY ANNEALING *

### J.S.KOEHLER

*Department of Physics, University of Illinois, USA*

## 1. Introduction

Electrical resistance measurements have been used for more than twenty years to study the generation and the annealing of defects in solids. In this paper we shall attempt to describe what has been learned from electrical resistance measurements on metals.

Resistance measurements are ideal in some ways. The measurement can be made quickly (within about 30 seconds) and accurately. In some recent measurements on gold wires and strips made by Lee [1] a change in resistivity of 0.01 percent was detectable. The total increase in resistance studied after 3 MeV electron irradiation at about $100°K$ was $\Delta\rho_0 = 5 \times 10^{-9}$ ohm cm. This enables one to follow resistivity versus time in considerable detail. Therefore resistivity measurements are well suited for the determination of the kind of defect annealing kinetics and for the determination of the effective migration energies associated with annealing. Several groups are now engaged in making continuous measurements of resistivity versus time.

A major disadvantage of a resistivity measurement is that it is completely nonselective, i.e., the increase in resistivity above that of the annealed metal is proportional to *all* the many defects present. Dislocations, interstitial atoms, lattice vacancies, impurities, defect clusters, stacking faults, etc. all contribute to the measured resistivity. It is therefore very difficult to do experiments in which a unique atomic process can be demonstrated.

The equations which describe the microscopic behavior of the sample are complicated. Let us attempt to write them out in order to describe some of the complications which may arise:

$$\Delta\rho = a_1C_1 + a_2C_2 + a_3C_3 + a_4C_4 + \ldots + a_nC_n + \ldots . \tag{1}$$

* Research supported by U.S. Army Research Office, Durham, under contract DA-31-124-ARO(D)-65.

Here the $C_i(r, t)$ represent the fractional concentrations of the various defects present. The $a_i$ measure the contributions of the various defects to the resistivity. Changes in defect concentrations with space and time are described by a series of coupled differential equations (usually non-linear) which might look as follows [2]:

$$\dot{C}_{1V} = -2A(T)\,C_{1V}^2 + 2B(T)\,C_{2V} - A(T)\,C_{1V}\,C_i + D_{1V}\nabla^2 C_{1V} - C(T)\,C_{2V}C_{1V}$$

$$\dot{C}_{2V} = +A(T)\,C_{1V}^2 - B(T)\,C_{2V} \qquad\qquad\qquad + D_{2V}\,\nabla^2 C_{2V} - C(T)\,C_{2V}C_{1V}$$

$$\dot{C}_{3V} = \qquad\qquad\qquad\qquad\qquad\qquad\qquad + C(T)\,C_{2V}C_{1V} \qquad (2)$$

$$\dot{C}_c = \qquad\qquad\qquad\qquad + A(T)\,C_{1V}C_i + D_c\nabla^2 C_c \quad - E(T)\,C_c$$

$$\dot{C}_i = \qquad\qquad\qquad\qquad - A(T)\,C_{1V}C_i$$

where $C_{1V}, C_{2V}, C_{3V}$ are the vacancy, divacancy and trivacancy concentrations; $C_i$ and $C_c$ are the impurity and the vacancy-impurity complex concentrations. The coefficients are

$$A(T) = 84v_1\ \exp[-E_{1V}^M/kT]$$

$$B(T) = 14v_2\ \exp[-(E_{1V}^M + E_{2V}^B)/kT]$$

$$C(T) = A(T)$$

$$D_{1V} = a^2 v_1\ \exp[-E_{1V}^M/kT]$$

$$D_{2V} = \tfrac{1}{8}\,a^2 v_2\ \exp[-E_{2V}^M/kT]$$

$$D_c = \tfrac{1}{16}a^2 v_c\ \exp[-E_c^M/kT]$$

$$E(T) = 14v_c\ \exp[-(E_{1V}^M + E_{iV}^B)/kT]\ .$$

The above equations are idealized in several respects: First we have assumed no long-range interaction between the defects. Second, if long range interactions between defects and sinks exist, then the $\nabla^2$ terms must be modified. The defect concentrations in eqs. (2) can be functions of position (near a sink) and of time. In addition the migration energies which appear in $A, B, C, D_{1V}$ and $D_{2V}$ may be dependent on the local strain and may therefore be a function of position. *These equations are useful both for describing equilibrium and nonequilibrium situations.*

## 2. Annealing in gold

Consider the annealing of very pure gold ($C_i \cong 10^{-6}$). We discuss gold because it is the best known metal. We shall use it as an example of the simplest situations thus far studied. Later we shall compare the information available for other metals with that known for gold.

### 2.1. Quenching

Simmons and Balluffi [3] showed by lattice parameter and length measurements that at temperatures near the melting point gold contains lattice vacancies, and possibly multiple vacancies in thermal equilibrium. Bauerle and Koehler [4] and many others have attempted to quench in the defects present at high temperature. Only recently has a clear-cut demonstration of a successful quench in which the quenched-in resistivity is independent of quench rate, been given [5]. From the Simmons-Balluffi [3] experiments, the self-diffusion measurements [6], and from the resistivity quenched in versus the quenching temperature one obtains $E_{1V}^F$, $S_{1V}^F$, and $\Delta\rho_{1V}$. The values for gold are:

$$E_{1V}^F = 0.94 \pm 0.02 \text{ eV}$$

$$S_{1V}^F = (1.0 \pm 0.5)\, k$$

$$\Delta\rho_{1V} = (1.5 \pm 0.3) \times 10^{-4} \text{ ohm cm}.$$

In addition one can set an upper limit on the divacancy binding energy from the fact that the self-diffusion constant plotted versus the reciprocal of the absolute temperature is a straight line near the melting point [7]. Thus one finds that $E_{2V}^B < 0.55$ eV.

Consider next the annealing of a quenched specimen. Kino and Koehler [5] and Lee and Koehler [1] found that after a fast quench of very pure gold from 700°C one observes second-order annealing kinetics associated with a high migration energy, i.e. $E^M = 0.90 \pm 0.04$ eV. On the other hand Ytterhus and Balluffi [8] and Siegel [9] found $E^M = 0.71 \pm 0.03$ eV for pure gold quenched from 700°C. They attributed this migration energy to tightly bound divacancies. Both investigators used the slope change method to determine the effective migration energy. In addition both sets of observers used very pure gold having a measured ratio $\rho(25°C)/\rho(4.2°K)$ greater than 2500.

Recently Sharma and Koehler [7] have been able to obtain either result by altering the rate of quench. After a fast quench from 700°C ($dT/dt > 5 \times 10^4$°C/sec) one observes second-order annealing kinetics and the high migration energy which is believed to be the single vacancy migration energy. After a slow quench from 700°C ($dT/dt < 2 \times 10^4$°C/sec) one observes first-order annealing kinetics and $E_{2V}^M = 0.71 \pm 0.04$ eV. After a slow quench the sink density is very low ($C_s \cong 2 \times 10^{-8}$). This sink density agrees with the tetrahedra density seen by Siegel [9] by electron microscopy in pure gold quenched from 700°C.

The results can be understood as follows: In all of the above experiments the important reactions are: Vacancies migrate encountering other vacancies forming tightly bound divacancies. The divacancies then migrate to fixed sinks. In the case of the slow quenches the sink density is so low that the rate-limiting process is divacancy migration to the sinks. In the fast quenched specimens we believe that a higher sink density is present so that the rate-limiting process is divacancy formation by vacancy migration. One can show [7] that the two limiting cases occur when a parameter $\alpha$ is much larger or much smaller than unity. The parameter $\alpha$ is

$$\alpha = \frac{7\nu_1}{\nu_2} \frac{C_V}{C_s} \exp - \frac{(E_{1V}^M - E_{2V}^M)}{kT} \tag{3}$$

where $\nu_1$ and $\nu_2$ are the vibration frequencies of atoms next to a single vacancy and a divacancy, respectively. $C_V$ is the total vacancy concentration. When $\alpha \gg 1$ one observes first-order annealing governed by divacancy migration. In principle the transition from divacancy-limited to vacancy-limited migration should be observable simply by following the behaviour of a slow quenched sample as the vacancy concentration drops. For slow quenched specimens the sink density is so low that this would be difficult. At $100°C$ if the sink density is $2 \times 10^{-8}$ and $E_{1V}^M - E_{2V}^M = 0.20$ eV. $\alpha$ is unity when $C_V = 4.8 \times 10^{-7}$ (with $\nu_1/\nu_2 = 3$).

We believe that the sink density is large in fast quenched samples, but at present we have no reliable measurements. Equation (3) could be used to obtain measurements of the sink density. The vacancy concentration quenched into gold by a fast quench from $700°C$ is about $2 \times 10^{-5}$. For $\alpha$ to be less than unity at $100°C$ the sink density must be greater than $0.8 \times 10^{-6}$. Seidman and Balluffi [10] and Jackson [11] have shown by electron microscopy that a small amount of plastic deformation introduces additional vacancy sinks into gold. Ytterhus and Balluffi [8] found that 1% tensile deformation after quenching from $700°C$ increased the rate of annealing by about a factor of ten but the measured migration energy was still $0.72 \pm 0.02$ eV. It is conceivable that deformation at high temperature is more effective. Further experiments will be needed to clarify this matter.

There is another experimental observation on gold which is of interest. In fast quenched, deformed, and electron-irradiated gold one sees the same migration energy [12]. We believe that for very pure gold this represents the vacancy migration energy. This belief stems from the fact that the observed migration and formation energies add to give the activation energy for self diffusion (i.e. $0.90 \pm 0.04 + 0.94 \pm 0.02 = 1.84 \pm 0.06$ eV whereas Gilder and Lazarus [13] give $Q = 1.83 \pm 0.02$ eV). The migration energy 0.90 eV pertains to 6N gold and one finds that as the purity decreases the observed migration energy decreases dropping from $0.90 \pm 0.04$ eV for $\rho_c(4.2°K) = 0.07 \times 10^{-9}$ ohm cm to $0.80 \pm 0.05$ eV for $\rho_c(4.2°K) = 0.40 \times 10^{-9}$ ohm cm. The purity is indicated by the size-corrected resistivity of the sample at $4.2°K$. The size correction was made by using equations given by Sondheimer [14], Fermi surface area given by Chambers [15] and assuming diffuse scattering of conduction electrons at the specimen surface.

Two possibilities which might be responsible for such behaviour are: It is possible that as proposed by Lazarus [11] multivalent impurities lead to impurity vacancy complexes which diffuse more rapidly than lattice vacancies. This would lower the migration energy as the total impurity concentration increased. Such an explanation would only fit the data if the migration energy of the complex decreased as the valence difference between the impurity atom and the gold atom increased. The binding energy of the complex must not decrease as the valence difference increases. Since the resistivity increase is proportional to the square of the valence difference one would then observe a systematic decrease of the effective migration energy with an increase in $\rho_c$ (4.2°K). Consider orders of magnitude. Linde [17] found that for gold

$$\rho_c(4.2°K) = 6.4 \times 10^{-5} \, z^2 C_i = \text{ohm cm} ,$$

where $z$ is the valence difference and $C_i$ is the fractional impurity concentration. If the average $z$ is two then $C_i = 1.56 \times 10^{-6}$ when $\rho_c(4.2°K) = 0.4 \times 10^{-9}$ ohm cm. The vacancy concentration quenched in from 700°C is about $2 \times 10^{-5}$. Thus a vacancy is ten times more likely to encounter another vacancy than it is to encounter an impurity. Hence a very low migration energy would be required for the complexes. In addition the sink concentration in a fast quenched sample is, we believe, about $10^{-6}$. Thus for several reasons this model does not seem promising.

It is also possible that changing the purity of the sample changes the sink density resulting from a fast quench. Suppose the sink density is lower in impure samples; $C_s$ could depend on the yield stress at some critical temperature and the yield stress would increase as the impurity concentration increased. If $\alpha$ of eq. (3) is not too far from unity a decrease in $C_s$ might increase the divacancy migration time to sinks by an amount sufficient to alter the effective migration energy. At present we have no data concerning this possibility.

In summary it must be admitted that we do not have a well established reason for the dependence of the effective migration energy on purity in fast quenched gold specimens.

## 2.2. Irradiation

If 99.999% or 99.9999% pure gold is electron-irradiated at 100°K Shinomura [18] has shown that interstitial platelets are produced. These platelets lie on the (111) planes and are nucleated at impurities or at impurity clusters. Lee and Koehler [1] have shown that the amount of stage II annealing found in 3 MeV electron-irradiated gold is a decreasing function of purity as measured by $\rho_c(4.2°K)$. Fig. 1 shows an example of this behaviour; the impure wire shows much more annealing below stage III. Note also how continuous the stage II annealing is. Another effect of purity is also evident in fig. 1. The fraction of the initial damage remaining after completion of stage III decreases as purity increases. For the sample of highest purity less than 3% of the initial damage is left after completion of stage III.

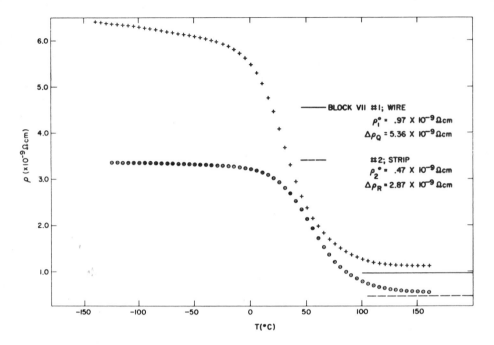

Fig. 1. Impurity dependence of the annealing in stages II and III of gold after 3 MeV electron irradiation.

In gold we believe that the stage II annealing and the annealing which occurs above stage III result from the effects of the strain fields from the interstitial clusters which alter the vacancy migration energy. A calculation has been made [19] which shows that the vacancy migration energy is very sensitive to local strain. Changes of $E_V^M$ of ± 0.1 eV occur relative to the strain-free value when a vacancy is 25 Å from a dislocation or an interstitial cluster containing a hundred interstitials. The continuous distribution of activation energies results from the variation of strain with distance from the cluster or from the dislocation.

## 3. Other metals

Vacancy annealing has also been carefully studied in aluminium, silver, and platinum. Some measurements have also been made on nickel, copper, and tungsten. In general the accuracy and completeness of the data decreases as the difficulty of quenching increases. In most cases quenching is difficult because the metal oxidizes and may in some cases also dissolve oxygen.

*Aluminium:* Simmons and Balluffi [20] measured the equilibrium vacancy concentration in aluminium near its melting point. They find $E_{1V}^F = 0.75 \pm 0.07$ eV and $S_{1V}^F = 2.2k$ and $\Delta\rho_{1V} = 3.0 \times 10^{-6}$ ohm cm/at %. Wintenberger [21] from the annealing of quenched aluminium found $E_{1V}^M = 0.58 \pm 0.05$ eV. Doyama and Koehler [22] found $E_{1V}^M = 0.60 \pm 0.05$ eV, $E_{2V}^M = 0.50 \pm 0.04$ eV and $E_{2V}^B = 0.17 \pm 0.05$ eV. Zamboni and Federighi [23] observed $E_{1V}^M = 0.62 \pm 0.03$ eV and $E_{2V}^M = 0.42 \pm 0.04$ eV. The formation energy, determined by Bradshaw and Pearson [24], Panseri and Federighi [25], Detert and Stander [26], and Locati and Federighi [27] is $E_{1V}^M = 0.76 \pm 0.02$ eV. Bass [28] obtains $E_{1V}^F = 0.73 \pm 0.03$ eV. There is an interesting discrepancy between the resistivities quenched into aluminium and the equilibrium vacancy resistivities observed at high temperatures by Simmons and Balluffi [20]. The equilibrium resistivity at a given high temperature is about a factor of two larger than the resistivity quenched in from that temperature. There are two possible explanations: First, probably not all of the vacancies are quenched in. This would enable one to understand why the quenchers observe less resistivity. If this is so than it is difficult to understand why the formation energy agrees with the Simmons-Balluffi value. There is a second possibility. Simmons and Balluffi obtained their vacancy resistivity by subtracting an extrapolation of the lattice resistivity versus temperature from the observed resistivity near the melting temperature. A small error in their extrapolation of the lattice resistivity to higher temperature could alter their value for the resistivity associated with lattice vacancies.

One other point should be made. Fradin and Rowland [29], Lundy and Murdock [30] and Balluffi and Volin [31] have measured self-diffusion in aluminium over temperatures ranging from 116°C to 636°C. If the logarithm of the diffusion coefficient is plotted against the reciprocal of the absolute temperature some curvature is apparent. This suggests that $Q$, the activation energy for self-diffusion is not a constant over the temperature range mentioned. Various reasons for this behaviour have been suggested, but the matter is not yet well understood.

*Silver:* Simmons and Balluffi [32] from equilibrium measurements near the melting point found that $E_{1V}^F = 1.09 \pm 0.10$ eV. Since the activation energy for self-diffusion in silver is $1.91 \pm 0.01$ eV one estimates the vacancy migration energy to be $0.82 \pm 0.11$ eV. Doyama and Koehler [33] did quenching of silver in a glass bulb which was carefully evacuated to $10^{-9}$ mm of mercury, baked out and then filled with spectroscopic helium. They found $E_{1V}^F = 1.10 \pm 0.04$ eV, $E_{1V}^M = 0.83 \pm 0.05$ eV, $E_{2V}^M = 0.57 \pm 0.03$ eV, and using pulsing to break up divacancies $E_{2V}^B = 0.38 \pm 0.05$ eV. Cuddy and Machlin [34], using similar techniques, found $E_{1V}^F = 1.10 \pm 0.01$ eV and $E_{2V}^M = 0.57 \pm 0.06$ eV. Note that in both gold and silver the divacancy binding energy is large and is about 45% of the vacancy migration energy. Since divacancies are highly mobile in both gold and silver they will play a role in many phenomena.

*Platinum:* Jackson [35] finds from quenching measurements that $E_{1V}^F = 1.51 \pm 0.04$ eV, $E_{1V}^M = 1.38 \pm 0.05$ eV and $E_{2V}^M = 1.10 \pm 0.03$ eV. The divacancy binding energy is $E_{2V}^B = 0.40 \pm 0.10$ eV. Self-diffusion was measured by Catteneo, Germagnoli and Grasso [36]. They find $Q = 2.89 \pm 0.04$ eV; thus self-diffusion is by lattice vacancies in platinum.

The experiments described thus far although difficult enough are easy in comparison with annealing studies on, say, quenched copper. Copper forms a non-protective oxide and also dissolves oxygen. The bcc metals dissolve appreciable amounts of interstitial impurities such as nitrogen and carbon.

*Copper:* Simmons and Balluffi [37] measured the equilibrium vacancy concentration near the melting point. Assuming an entropy of formation $S_{1V}^F = 1.5k$ they find $E_{1V}^F = 1.17 \pm 0.10$ eV. Budin, Denayron, Lucasson and Lucasson [38] quenched in hydrogen and found $E_{1V}^F = 1.17 \pm 0.06$ eV. Wright and Evans [39] quenched into distilled outgassed water from a mixture of dry nitrogen and carbon monoxide. They found $E_{1V}^F = 1.14 \pm 0.06$ eV, $E_{1V}^M = 0.85 \pm 0.15$ eV, $E_{2V}^M = 0.71 \pm 0.04$ eV. Since the activation energy for self-diffusion in copper is $Q = 2.05 \pm 0.02$ eV [40] the Wright and Evans formation energy would give a vacancy migration energy $E_{1V}^M = Q - E_{1V}^F = 0.91 \pm 0.08$ eV.

*Lead.* Feder and Nowick [41] measured the equilibrium vacancy concentration by lattice parameter and length measurements. They find $E_{1V}^F = 0.49 \pm 0.10$ eV and $S_{1V}^F = (0.7 \pm 2.0)k$. Hoffman, Pickus and Ward [42] measured the activation energy for self-diffusion. They find $Q = 1.05 \pm 0.03$ eV. Thus $E_{1V}^M$ is $0.56 \pm 0.13$ eV.

*Nickel:* Nachtrieb and Handler [43] found that the activation energy for self-diffusion is $Q = 2.90 \pm 0.03$ eV. Scherrer, Lozes and Deviot [44] in a paper presented at this conference find $E_{1V}^M = 1.40 \pm 0.02$ eV, $E_{2V}^M = 0.85 \pm 0.05$ eV. These researchers used helium gas quenching in an initially baked out and evacuated system. From $Q$ this gives $E_{1V}^F = 1.50 \pm 0.05$ eV.

In a few cases the *entropy of vacancy formation* has been measured. In gold Simmons and Balluffi gave $S_{1V}^F = (1.0 \pm 0.5)k$. Kino and Koehler quenched gold from 600°C at various rates between $2 \times 10^4$°C/sec and $10^5$°C/sec and found that the amount quenched in was independent of rate. This indicates that they quenched in all the vacancies present in equilibrium at 600°C. The quenched-in resistivity was $1.36 \times 10^{-9}$ ohm cm. This together with the Simmons-Balluffi formation energy and formation entropy enables one to calculate $\Delta \rho_{1V} = (1.5 \pm 0.3) \times 10^{-6}$ ohm cm/at. % for the resistivity increment associated with lattice vacancies in gold.

In aluminium Simmons and Balluffi give $S_{1V}^F = (2.4 \pm 0.5)k$ and Detert and Stander give $S_{1V}^F = (2.3 \pm 0.5)k$. Bass has given a recent summary of the quenching data for aluminium. His data gives $\Delta \rho_Q = 1.9 \times 10^{-10}$ ohm cm at $T_Q = 555.6$°K (282.4°C). Using $E_{1V}^F = 0.76$ eV and $S_{1V}^F = 2.35k$ one finds that $\Delta \rho_Q = 1.23 \times 10^{-6}$ ohm cm/at. %. This result seems too low.

## 4. Summary

What has been accomplished and what remains to be done if we consider problems involving lattice vacancies in metals? In the case of pure fcc metals we are well on our way towards a reasonable understanding of the field. In many cases we know the properties of single vacancies and of divacancies with some accuracy.

When we consider vacancy clusters we know a little about large clusters, but our knowledge about trivacancies, quadravacancies and other small clusters is almost non-existent. The same is true about vacancy-impurity complexes. In dilute copper and silver alloys we know the diffusion coefficients of the solvent and of the impurity as a function of the impurity concentration but we do not have measured impurity-vacancy binding energies. In aluminium containing small amounts of either magnesium or silver Beaman, Balluffi and Simmons [45] find very small binding energies (i.e. less than 0.08 eV).

In the case of bcc metals we know very little. One of the major problems has been the difficulty in keeping the metal pure enough so that one can be confident that impurities do not play a role in the annealing.

Thus we know something, but certainly not everything.

# References

[1] C.Lee and J.S.Koehler, Phys. Rev. 176 (1968) 813.
[2] M.de Jong and J.S.Koehler, Phys. Rev. 129 (1963) 40;
    A.D.Le Claire and A.B.Lidiard, Phil. Mag. 1 (1956) 518.
[3] R.O.Simmons and R.W.Balluffi, Phys. Rev. 125 (1962) 862.
[4] J.E.Bauerle and J.S.Koehler, Phys. Rev. 107 (1957) 1493.
[5] T.Kino and J.S.Koehler, Phys. Rev. 162 (1967) 632.
[6] S.M.Makin, A.H.Rowe and A.D.Le Claire, Proc. Phys. Soc. (London) 70B (1957) 545;
    M.Gilder and D.Lazarus, J. Phys. Chem. Solids 26 (1965) 2081.
[7] R.K.Sharma and J.S.Koehler, Phys. Rev., to be published.
[8] A.Ytterhus and R.W.Balluffi, Phil. Mag. 11 (1965) 707.
[9] R.W.Siegel, Phil. Mag. 13 (1966) 337.
[10] D.N.Seidman and R.W.Balluffi, Phil. Mag. 10 (1964) 1067.
[11] J.J.Jackson, Acta Met. 11 (1963) 1245.
[12] R.K.Sharma, C.Lee and J.S.Koehler, Phys. Rev. Letters 19 (1967) 1379.
[13] H.M.Gilder and D.Lazarus, J. Phys. Chem. Solids 26 (1965) 2081.
[14] E.H.Sondheimer, Advan. Phys. 1 (1952) 1.
[15] R.G.Chambers, Proc. Roy. Soc. A215 (1952) 481.
[16] D.Lazarus, Solid state physics, Vol. 10, eds. F.Seitz and D.Turnbull (Academic Press, New York, 1960) p. 71.
[17] See N.Mott and H.Jones, *Theory of the properties of metals and alloys* (Oxford Press, 1936) p. 295.
[18] Y.Shimomura, Phil. Mag. 19 (1969) 773.
[19] J.S.Koehler, Phys. Rev., to be published.
[20] R.O.Simmons and R.W.Balluffi, Phys. Rev. 117 (1960) 52.
[21] M.Wintenberger, Compt. Rend. Acad. Sci. Paris 242 (1956) 128.
[22] M.Doyama and J.S.Koehler, Phys. Rev. 134 (1964) A522.
[23] L.Zamboni and T.Federighi, see article by T.Federighi in Lattice Defects in Quenched Metals, eds. Cotterill, Doyama, Jackson and Meshii (Academic Press, New York, 1965) p. 217.
[24] F.J.Bradshaw and S.Pearson, Phil. Mag. 2 (1957) 570.
[25] C.Panseri and T.Federighi, Phil. Mag. 3 (1958) 1223.
[26] K.Detert and I.Stander, Z. Metallk. 52 (1961) 677.

[27] D.Locati and T.Federighi, see reference [23].

[28] J.Bass, Phil. Mag. 15 (1967) 717.

[29] F.Y.Fradin and T.J.Rowland, Appl. Phys. Letters 11 (1967) 207.

[30] T.S.Lundy and J.F.Murdock, J. Appl. Phys. 33 (1962) 1671.

[31] T.E.Volin and R.W.Balluffi, Phys. Stat. Sol. 25 (1968) 163.

[32] R.O.Simmons and R.W.Balluffi, Phys. Rev. 119 (1960) 600.

[33] M.Doyama and J.S.Koehler, Phys. Rev.127 (1962) 21.

[34] L.J.Cuddy and E.S.Machlin, Phil. Mag. 7 (1962) 745.

[35] J.J.Jackson, in: Lattice Defects in Quenched Metals, eds. Cotterill, Doyama, Jackson and
     Meshii (Academic Press, New York, 1965) p. 467.

[36] F.Cattaneo, E.Germagnoli and F.Grasso, Phil. Mag. 7 (1962) 1373.

[37] R.O.Simmons and R.W.Balluffi, Phys. Rev. 129 (1963) 1533.

[38] C.Budin, F.Denayrow, A.Lucasson and P.Lucasson, Compt. Rend. Acad. Sci. Paris 256
     (1963) 1518.

[39] P.Wright and J.H.Evans, Phil. Mag. 13 (1966) 521.

[40] A.Kuper, H.Letaw, L.Slifken, E.Sonder and C.T.Tomizuka, Phys. Rev. 96 (1954) 1224;
     Phys. Rev. 98 (1955) 1870.

[41] R.Feder and A.S.Nowick, Phil. Mag. 15 (1967) 805.

[42] R.E.Hoffman, F.W.Pickens and R.A.Ward, Trans. AIME 206 (1956) 483.

[43] N.H.Nachtrieb and G.S.Handler, J. Chem. Phys. 23 (1955) 1569.

[44] S.Scherrer, G.Lozes and B.Deviot, Report Jül. Conf. 2 (Vol. I) (1968) p. 167.

[45] D.R.Beaman, R.W.Balluffi and R.O.Simmons, Phys. Rev. 137 (1965) A917.

## Discussion

*W.Bauer:* I would like to comment on the two recovery peaks found in the resistivity recovery near room temperature of prequenched and electron-irradiated aluminium. Our experiments conducted at $10°K$ and those of Dr. Lucasson conducted near $80°K$ show essentially the same temperature spread ($\sim 60°K$). In our case there is a large simultaneous concentration of mobile interstitials, whereas in Dr. Lucasson's case there is a negligible concentration of mobile interstitials. According to your model (interstitial clusters as sinks for vacancies) one would expect differences in the peaks separation between the two cases. This is not observed.

*J.S.Koehler:* Should a difference in the stage III annealing behaviour be observed depending on whether the irradiation temperature of the aluminium is $10°K$ or $100°K$? My opinion is that the result will depend on the purity of the aluminium. For sufficiently high purity the $10°K$ irradiation will give more interstitial clusters than the $100°K$ irradiation and the two will anneal differently. In impure specimens the impurity nucleation will dominate interstitial cluster formation and no difference will be observed. Just how high a purity is required is difficult to predict. Good electron microscopy on aluminium below stage III would be helpful.

*M.Wuttig:* This is a comment concerning the annealing kinetics of the peak which you interpreted as due to the migration of defects (vac.) to clusters. If this is true the $t^{\frac{3}{5}}$ time dependence as derived by Bullough (J. Metals Sci., May 1968) should be observed. Do you see any evidence of this?

*J.S.Koehler:* The derivation by Bullough and Stanley assumes that the drift in the potential field is much more important than the random walking. Also it neglects changes in the migration energy of the vacancy caused by the strain field of the interstitial cluster.

An attempt was made to fit the annealing to a $t^{\frac{3}{5}}$ law for electron-irradiated six nines gold during a long isothermal anneal at 30°C. The fit was not very good. It was off by more than 12%. Second order annealing gave a better fit.

*K.Misek:* I would like to make two remarks concerning the residual resistance measurements:

(1) In most experiments the residual resistance $R$ is measured, and then the residual resistivity $\rho$ is calculated. The resistance ratio, which allows for this calculation, is usually measured before the experiments start. No objections can be raised, if the dimensions of the specimen do not change. If the dimensions change, it is possible to determine $\Delta\rho$ using the formula

$$\Delta\rho = \rho_0 \left( \frac{1}{k'} - \frac{1}{k} \right),$$

where $\rho_0$ is the resistivity at 0°C, $k = R_{0°C}/R_{4.2°K}$ is the resistance ratio of the annealed specimen, $k'$ is the resistance ratio of the worked specimen [K. Misek, Canad. J. Phys. 65 (1967) 355].

(2) Experimentally determined residual resistivity is significant only under the condition, that defects are uniformly distributed on the cross section of the specimen. If it is not so, i.e., if the distribution of defects is macroscopically inhomogeneous, the residual resistance is not proportional to the defect concentration. It is obvious that torsional plastic deformation of a wave or high-speed quenching from below the melting point, and probably the irradiation of a wire, having circular cross section, might create experimental conditions causing systematic errors in defect concentrations as derived from the residual resistance.

*J.S.Koehler:* Mainly we use the resistivity ratio to give us a measure of the total impurity content of our samples before any experiments are done on them. In this condition the electron mean free path is often of the same order as the sample thickness. In such a case the size correction is large; in some cases it drops the resistivity at 4.2°K by a factor of four. Diffuse scattering is assumed at the specimen surface.

After defects have been introduced the size correction is negligible. We have checked to see whether the size correction can alter the activation energies determined by slope-change but the correction does not alter the values obtained.

*K.Misek:* The size-effect may influence $\Delta\rho$ only when the mean free path of electrons is (range of order) equal to the size of the specimen and may be as high as 10% of $\Delta\rho$. (See the above mentioned reference.)

*M.J.Druyvesteyn:* Is it not very dangerous to obtain the kinetics of the annealing (reaction) from isotherms when it is known that an activation-spectrum exists (not *one* activation energy)?

*J.S.Koehler:* Yes, it is very dangerous to obtain the reaction kinetics when a spectrum of activation energies exists. However, in six nines gold and in five nines aluminium the annealing spectrum consists of a single peak with a half width which is about 10% of the activation energy at the peak (i.e. $\pm 0.075$ eV/0.85 eV). We believe that with such a simple spectrum a single long isothermal will give the correct kinetics, particularly if it is taken at a temperature in the middle of the stage III annealing. It must be admitted, however, that further studies should be made of the details of the annealing kinetics. Our initial crude studies on electron-irradiated gold give second-order annealing kinetics at the temperature associated with most rapid annealing.

*M.Feller-Kniepmeier:* Are there any equilibrium measurements showing a dependence of the migration energy from impurity concentrations?

Do the migration energies as derived from quenching experiments have a general meaning? If so, the self-diffusion coefficient of metals should be dependent on the impurity content.

*J.S.Koehler:* The diffusion coefficients of metals do depend on the impurity content. In a dilute alloy the substitutional impurities diffuse with a different activation energy than the solvent atoms. In addition, the solvent tracer atoms also have their diffusion altered. For a survey see the article by D.Lazarus in volume 9 of Advances in Solid State Physics, eds. Seitz, Turnbull. Beaman, Simmons and Balluffi have made equilibrium lattice parameter and length measurements on aluminium containing a few percent of magnesium or silver. They found the magnesium vacancy binding energy is zero; the silver vacancy binding energy is 0.08 eV $\pm 0.05$ eV (Phys. Rev. 134 (1964) A532).

*J.R.Beeler:* Computer experiments in our laboratory based on the migration and binding energies cited by Prof. Koehler show clearly that large changes in the effective migration energy measured can indeed be caused by an impurity concentration of 0.1 the vacancy concentration. Only for impurity concentrations less than about 0.01 the vacancy concentration did the impurity content exert only a micron influence.

*E.W.Mueller:* The original material used for the experiments, particularly Ag and Cu, may have been fairly pure. However, what is the actual oxygen content of these materials *after* the annealing and quenching experiment? It is known from electron emission research that it is impossible to remove a microlayer of absorbed oxygen from the metals discussed, even when the common UHV techniques are employed. Such a microlayer is a source of considerable contamination of the bulk due to diffusion during annealing. I suggest determination of oxygen content *after* the quenching and resistivity measurements, for instance by activation analysis.

*J.M.Galligan:* I would like to draw attention to the quenching experiments of Davidson (Phys. Stat. Sol. vol. 28 (1968)) where different values for activation energies in quenched copper, such as those mentioned by Professor Koehler were found.

*J.W.Corbett:* I find much of this data gratifying, as does Prof. Seeger (but for different reasons!), and have some comments I will reserve for the panel discussion. Let me, however, ask a question about your point on vacancies in stage III. Do you have any comments on platinum?

*J.S.Koehler:* Dr. Schilling will discuss platinum.

*J.A.Venables:* Have you been able to satisfy yourself that the temperature shift between the stages after quenching and irradiation can be accounted for solely by the different number of jumps to sinks in the two cases?

*J.S.Koehler:* We are satisfied that the number of jumps to the sinks differs in the two cases by amounts large enough to explain the difference in peak temperature. It is possible that a slightly lower activation energy is observed in the irradiation case, but in gold and in aluminum any difference which exists lies within the present limits of error of the determination of $E_V^M$. For example, Lee finds $E_{\mathrm{eff}}^{\mathrm{irrad}} = 0.85 \pm 0.03$ eV for six nines gold and $E_{\mathrm{eff}}^{\mathrm{quench}} = 0.86 \pm 0.02$ eV. For five nines aluminum, Lwin and Doyama find $E_{\mathrm{eff}}^{\mathrm{irrad}} = 0.61 \pm 0.04$ eV for low vacancy concentration.

*R.W.Siegel:* Your results on the dependence of the measured effective migration energy in quenched gold on the specimen purity and quench rate are quite interesting. However, further experiments seem to be required in order to understand these effects. In contradiction to the results shown, I have found no dependence of

$$E_{\mathrm{eff}}^M = 0.70 \pm 0.04 \text{ eV}$$

on specimen purity over the range

$$1380 \leqslant \frac{\rho(25^\circ\mathrm{C})}{\rho(4.2^\circ\mathrm{K})} \leqslant 22500$$

or on sink density up to a directly measured density of $4.3 \times 10^{15}$ cm$^{-3}$ in rapidly quenched gold (quench rate $\geqslant 5 \times 10^4 {}^\circ$C/sec) annealed over the temperature range $40^\circ\mathrm{C} \leqslant T_A \leqslant 100^\circ\mathrm{C}$. Some of these results, in the highest purity range, are compared in fig. 2.

*J.S.Koehler:* The data you give in fig. 2 is associated with sink densities of $8.6 \times 10^{-8}$ or less. Calculations indicate that sink densities of the order of $2 \times 10^{-6}$ are required to give the high activation energy and second order annealing. Kino and Koehler (Phys. Rev. 162 (1967) 632), Lee and Koehler (Phys. Rev. 176 (1968) 813), and Sharma (unpublished) have all observed the high activation energy and second order annealing in 6 nines gold fast quenched from 700$^\circ$C.

*H.I.Dawson:* In regard to Professor Koehler's presentation I would like to com-

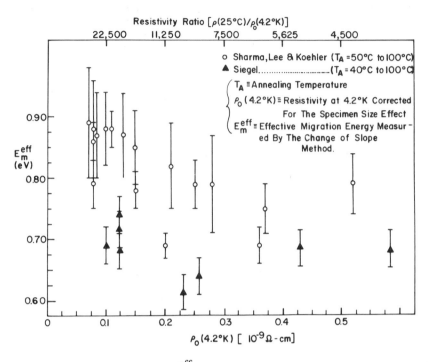

Fig. 2. The effective migration energy ($E_m^{eff}$) in quenched gold as a function of the base resistivity [$\rho_0(4.2°K)$] for specimens annealed in the temperature range 40 to 100°C. The work of Sharma et al. exhibits a purity-dependent migration energy, while the data of Siegel are seen to display a constant migration energy of 0.70 eV in the same range of specimen purity. The base resistivities for both sets of data, reported on the abscissa, were corrected for the specimen size effect employing identical correction factors in the standard equations.

ment that we have to carefully assess the problems we are facing in recovery studies or we may never arrive at the right conclusions. In this regard we may learn from the history of quenching studies: About ten years ago, it seemed that the work by Bauerle and Koehler (J.E.Bauerle and J.S. Koehler, Phys. Rev. 107 (1957) 1493) had solved the problem of the recovery of quenched-in vacancies in gold to a great extent. In 1963, de Jong and Koehler (M.de Jong and J.S.Koehler, Phys. Rev. 129 (1963) 40) pointed out that this was not the case and developed a model, which again seemed to explain most of the vacancy behaviour in gold, even in much detail. In 1967 things have changed again (T.Kino and J.S.Koehler, Phys. Rev. 162 (1967) 632), and once more in the present presentation by Professor Koehler. If we do not learn from history, things will change again.

# ANNEALING AND CLUSTERING OF QUENCHED-IN VACANCIES IN F.C.C. METALS

K.P.CHIK

*Institut für Physik am Max-Planck-Institut für Metallforschung, Stuttgart*

## 1. Introduction

Of the three well-known ways of introducing point defects into metals, namely, quenching, cold-working, and irradiation with energetic particles, quenching is the simplest in the sense that in f.c.c. metals only vacancy type defects are created. Thus, if we have available means of detecting the presence of vacancies, we may hope by carrying out annealing experiments to obtain direct information about vacancy parameters, such as migration energies of vacancies and binding energies of small vacancy clusters, e.g. divacancies. Experimentally the measurement of residual electrical resistivity is almost exclusively used to detect the presence of vacancies. The reason for that is that high precision measurements may be made with relatively simple equipment. The annealing process is studied either isothermally or isochronally, and resulting annealing curves can be analysed to give information on characteristic rate constants and activation energies.

Early quenching experiments seemed to give encouraging results especially for gold. Bauerle and Koehler [1] gave the monovacancy migration energy $E_{1V}^M$ for gold as $(0.82 \pm 0.05)$ eV and the formation energy of a monovacancy $E_{1V}^F$ as $(0.98 \pm 0.03)$ eV. The sum of these two energies agreed with the self-diffusion activation energy in gold ($Q^{SD} = 1.81$ eV [2]), and this good agreement was taken as evidence of the success of quenching experiments.

Numerous reports of quenching different f.c.c. metals followed these early gold measurements. A comprehensive survey of the quenching results up to 1964 is given in the Proceedings of the Conference on Lattice Defects in Quenched Metals held in that year at the Argonne National Laboratory [3]. As a result of the information gained from quenching, it is now known that the annealing processes of quenched-in vacancies can be very complicated. It is sometimes difficult to find unambiguous interpretations of experimental results and the complications which arise in quenching experiments may be attributed to several factors.

At low quenched-in vacancy concentrations, where one would expect simple annihilation of monovacancies at inexhaustible sinks, small amounts of highly mo-

bile defect clusters (e.g., divacancies) can have considerable effect upon the annealing kinetics. Similarly, small amounts of impurities may have significant effects on annealing even in metals such as gold, which can be obtained in a high state of purity.
These problems will be discussed in section 2.

At high vacancy concentrations, the clustering of vacancies becomes important.
However, our knowledge of small vacancy clusters is insufficient to enable us to interpret satisfactorily the experimental results. Vacancy cluster nucleation after high
temperature quenches can be studied using transmission electron microscopy techniques. It is found that impurities influence the vacancy cluster nucleation process,
and we are then confronted with the question as to whether a homogeneous or a
heterogeneous nucleation process takes place. These questions will be discussed in
detail in section 3.2.

It has been customary to deduce effective migration energies from measured annealing kinetics. However, the interpretation of these energies becomes difficult when
more than one type of vacancy defect is participating in the diffusion process. The effective migration energies are then not directly related to a simple physical quantity.
Their values may depend on the experimental conditions and on the method of
analysis. Recent measurements on quenched gold have led to a quite different spectrum of effective migration energies than that obtained previously. The interpretation of these results is still a controversial topic. This problem will be discussed in
section 3.3.

In this paper, the main emphasis is placed on attempting to correlate realistic
mathematical models with experimental results. In this way, it is hoped to give a
better appreciation of the difficulties involved and to facilitate careful planning of
future experimental work. The experimental techniques of studying annealing will
be omitted. Readers interested in this aspect may refer to [3] and [4]. Neither is
it attempted to give a list of vacancy parameters; these may be found in [3] and
in [5].

## 2. Annealing at low vacancy concentrations

### 2.1. *Mono-vacancy annealing*

Let us consider a simple system in which mono-vacancies are the only point defects present. The vacancies anneal out at inexhaustible sinks, e.g., dislocations,
grain-boundaries etc.

The simplest way of treating this problem theoretically is to apply the chemical
rate theory, which disregards any fluctuation of the vacancy distribution. The
chemical rate equation reads in the present case

$$\mathrm{d}C_{1V}/\mathrm{d}t = -\alpha\, D_{1V}\, C_{1V} \,, \tag{1}$$

where $C_{1V}$ and $D_{1V}$ are the concentration and the diffusion coefficient of monovacancies, and $\alpha$ is a geometrical factor that depends on the nature of the sinks and on the sink density. $\alpha$ may be obtained from a comparison of eq. (1) with diffusion theory or random walk theory [4,6].

The solution of eq. (1) gives a simple exponential vacancy decay, namely,

$$C_{1V}(t) = C_{1V}(0) \exp(-\alpha D_{1V} t) . \tag{2}$$

A more rigorous way of treating the above problem makes use of diffusion theory. Diffusion theory treats the whole crystal as a continuum but takes into account a concentration gradient near the sinks. We then have

$$\partial C_{1V}(x,t)/\partial t = D_{1V} \nabla^2 C_{1V}(x,t) . \tag{3}$$

Analytical solutions to eq. (3) have been given for specific types of sinks. In general, the solutions can be represented as a sum of exponentials with different time constants $\tau_n$. At large times, a single time constant $\tau_0$ is sufficient since higher order terms decay more rapidly and the vacancy decay becomes again first order.

Ham [7] considered a simple cubic lattice of spherical particles of radius $r_0$, which act as sinks. Each particle is surrounded by an equivalent sphere of radius $r_s$. If $r_0 \ll r_s$, $C(x,t)$ is independent of $x$ except very near the particles. The time constant $\tau_0$ is given by

$$\tau_0 = 1/\lambda_0^2 D_{1V} \tag{4}$$

and

$$\lambda_0^2 \approx \frac{3r_0}{r_s^3} \left[ 1 + \frac{9r_0}{5r_s} \right] . \tag{5}$$

Thus, comparing eq. (5) with eq. (2), we have

$$\alpha = 1/\lambda_0^2 . \tag{6}$$

More complicated cases considering dislocations, stacking fault tetrahedra, and dislocation loops as sinks were considered by Flynn [8].

The most realistic treatment of vacancy annealing is the simulation method (Monte-Carlo Method) [6,9,10]. This method takes account of the discrete nature of atomic jumps and any fluctuation in vacancy concentration. Its disadvantage is that no analytical solution can be given. Each individual case has to be treated separately. Mehrer [6] has shown that in the monovacancy annealing case, transients, as predicted by diffusion theory, do not exist. Thus the whole annealing obeys first-order kinetics. We thus see that in this case the chemical rate theory gives a reasonable description of the annealing behaviour, except for perhaps a small numerical factor [6].

The monovacancy annealing model described above shows that the monovacancy migration energy is the single activation energy governing the rate of the annealing process. If we can produce this monovacancy annealing condition experimentally, the monovacancy migration energy may be determined. This is in fact what we attempt to achieve by quenching from low temperatures and thereby keeping the vacancy concentration low.

## 2.2. *Experimental results on low-temperature quenches*

Many reports indicate that the annealing kinetics are not first order even for a vacancy concentration of $10^{-5}$ or lower. The annealing rate appears to depend on the purity of the quenched samples.

In quenched gold, Emrick [11] found that after extensive prequench heat treatment at high temperature in air for a 700°C quench the annealing half-time, $\tau_{1/2}$, increased and the annealing kinetics became faster than first order. Similarly, Ytterhus [12] found that first-order kinetics could only be observed under certain conditions, e.g., in his case for $\tau_{1/2} \approx 140$ h at 40°C. For $\tau_{1/2}$ larger than this value the annealing was again faster than first order. The $\tau_{1/2}$ were found to increase with increasing resistivity ratio (RR) of the specimen, measured between room temperature and 4.2°K before quenching. Since the RR is related to the concentration of scattering centres for conduction electrons, a high RR indicates indirectly a high specimen purity. Thus it seems that the occurrence of annealing rates of higher than first order at low vacancy concentration is connected with specimen purity.

Little attention has been paid to the study of isothermal anannealing at low vacancy concentrations in very pure specimens. However, let us examine the few available results as summarized in table 1. Aluminium, gold and platinum are the three f.c.c. metals that may be obtained in high purity. From table 1, we see that for samples with RR > 3000, second order kinetics have been observed with possible deviations at large annealing times. Kino and Koehler [13] found that in their measurements on quenched gold first-order kinetics were observed only at an annealing temperature of 150°C after quenching from 489°C.

We may summarize the general features of annealing in the low vacancy concentration range for the three f.c.c. metals Au, Al, and Pt as follows: In general, second order kinetics at the beginning of annealing are obeyed with deviations at large annealing times. The extent to which second order kinetics are observed depends on the annealing temperature. Further high precision measurements would be most useful to test this general conclusion.

## 2.3. *Mono- and divacancy annealing model*

In order to explain the occurrence of annealing kinetics faster than first order described in the last section, we are led intuitively to take divacancies into account. Let us consider that both mono- and divacancies migrate to sinks. We may then set up the differential equations

$$dC_{1V}/dt = 2K_2\,C_{2V} - 2K_1\,C_{1V}^2 - K_3\,C_{1V} \tag{7a}$$

Table 1

Summary of isothermal annealing results in quenched f.c.c. metals for low vacancy concentrations.

| Metal | $C_{1V}$ | $\Delta\rho(\Omega$ cm$)$ | $T_A(°C)$ | Description | References |
|---|---|---|---|---|---|
| Au | $7 \times 10^{-7}$ | | 150 | 1st order kinetics | |
| RR $>4000$ | $2 \times 10^{-6}$ to $10^{-5}$ | | 150 | 2nd order kinetics | [13] |
| Al | $1.5 \times 10^{-6}$ | $2.5 \times 10^{-10}$ | 0 | 2nd order kinetics | |
| RR $= 4200$ | $1.6 \times 10^{-6}$ | $2.66 \times 10^{-10}$ | 22 | | [14] |
| | $4.4 \times 10^{-6}$ | $7.36 \times 10^{-10}$ | 0 | 2nd order up to 60% annealing | |
| zone-refined | $1.6 \times 10^{-6}$ | $2.71 \times 10^{-10}$ | 25 | 2nd order kinetics | |
| Al | $9 \times 10^{-6}$ | $15.43 \times 10^{-10}$ | | | [15] |
| | $3.8 \times 10^{-5}$ | $62.64 \times 10^{-10}$ | | | |
| Pt | | $36 \times 10^{-10}$ | 300 | 2nd order up to 60% annealing | [16] |
| RR $>3000$ | | | | | |
| Pt | | $60 \times 10^{-10}$ | 420 | 1st order kinetics | [17] |
| RR $= 1600$ | | | 440 | | |
| Pt | | | 360 to 460 | 2nd order with deviation at long annealing times | [18] |
| RR $= 600$ | | $50 \times 10^{-10}$ | | | |

$$dC_{2V}/dt = K_1 C_{1V}^2 - K_2 C_{2V} - K_4 C_{2V} , \tag{7b}$$

where $K_n$ are reaction constants. These equations (7) have been solved numerically by Damask and Dienes [2] for specific sets of vacancy parameters.

The most interesting special case is the steady state approximation. This means that the formation, dissociation, and annihilation of divacancies is in dynamical equilibrium, i.e., we set $dC_{2V}/dt = 0$. We have then from eq. (7b)

$$C_{2V} = \frac{K_1 C_{1V}^2}{K_2 + K_4} . \tag{8}$$

Under these conditions, the solution of eq. (7a) is

$$\frac{1}{C_{1V}} = \left(\beta + \frac{1}{C_{1V}^o}\right) \exp(K_3 t) - \beta , \tag{9}$$

where

$$\beta = \frac{2K_1 K_4}{K_3(K_2 + K_4)} \tag{10}$$

and $C_{1V}^o$ is the initial vacancy concentration.

This solution enables us to explain the experimental results discussed in section 2.2 *.

For $K_3 t \ll 1$, we obtain second-order kinetics by expanding the exponential term, namely

$$\frac{1}{C_{1V}} - \frac{1}{C_{1V}^o} = \left(\beta + \frac{1}{C_{1V}^o}\right) K_3 t . \tag{11}$$

For $K_3 t \gg 1$, eq. (9) reduces to first-order kinetics, i.e.

$$\frac{C_{1V}}{C_{1V}^o} = (1 + \beta\, C_{1V}^o) \exp(-K_3 t) . \tag{12}$$

We thus see that the extent of second-order kinetics observable is determined solely by the magnitude of $K_3 t$. If only interactions between nearest neighbours are considered, the $K$'s in eq. (7) are written as

$$K_1 = 84\, \nu_{1V}^M \exp(-E_{1V}^M/kT) \tag{13a}$$

$$K_2 = 14\, \nu_{2V}' \exp[-(E_{2V}^M + E_{2V}^B)/kT] \tag{13b}$$

$$K_3 = \alpha_1 D_{1V} \tag{13c}$$

$$K_4 = \alpha_2 D_{2V} \tag{13d}$$

$K_1$ determines the formation rate of $V_2$ and $K_2$ the dissociation rate of $V_2$; the $\alpha_n$ are functions of the sink density, and the $\nu$'s are frequency factors.

Experimentally, an effective migration energy $E_{\text{eff}}^M$ of the annealing process is very often determined by the slope-change method where $E_{\text{eff}}^M$ in such case is de-

---

* In electrical resistivity measurements, one measures (to a good approximation) the total vacancy concentration, i.e. the sum of the mono- and divacancy concentrations. However, under the condition of eq. (8), the contribution of divacancies to the total concentration is small, so that it is permissible to compare eq. (9) with the resistivity measurements.

fined as $-d[\ln(dC_V/dt)]/d(1/kT)$. Due to the temperature dependence of the pre-exponential factor in eq. (9), $E^M_{eff}$ determined by the slope-change method for the mono- and divacancy annealing model is *not* equal to the migration energy of a single defect.

For $K_2 \gg K_4$, $\beta$ in eq. (9) may be written as

$$\beta = 2\frac{\nu^M_{2V}}{\nu^M_{1V}} \exp(\Delta S_{2V}/k) \exp[(E^M_{1V} + E^B_{2V} - E^M_{2V})/kT] . \tag{14}$$

$\Delta S_{2V}$ is the increase in vibrational entropy when two monovacancies form a divacancy. Eq. (11) may then be rewritten as

$$1/C_{1V} - 1/C^o_{1V} = \{A \exp[-(E^M_{2V} - E^B_{2V})/kT]$$
$$+ (1/C^o_{1V}) \exp(-E^M_{1V}/kT)\}Bt , \tag{11a}$$

where $A$ and $B$ are constants.

It may be seen from eq. (11a) that if $(1/C^o_{1V}) \exp(-E^M_{1V}/kT) \gg \exp[-(E^M_{2V} - E^B_{2V})/kT]$, the effective migration energy $E^M_{eff}$ approaches the value for monovacancy migration, $E^M_{1V}$.

Mono- and divacancy annealing has also been considered by Mehrer [6] using computer simulation methods. Under the condition that $V_2$ diffuses much faster than $V_1$, a second-order annealing kinetic is obtained in agreement with chemical rate theory. If the slopes of the plot $C^o_{1V}/C_{1V}$ versus annealing time calculated from rate theory and from the simulation method are compared, the rate theory predicts a slope larger by a factor of about 2.

### 2.4. Comparison of experimental results with the mono- and divacancy annealing model

Equation (9) can be used to fit the experimental isothermal annealing curves. If the initial quenched-in vacancy concentration is known and the sink density (e.g. in well annealed samples) is low so that $K_2 \gg K_4$, $\beta$ is the only unknown parameter. The constant $(1 + \beta C^o_{1V})K_3$ can be determined from the slope of the linear part of the plot $C^o_{1V}/C_{1V}$ versus time. It remains to choose a suitable value for $\beta$ so that the whole annealing curve may be fitted. According to eq. (14), the temperature dependence of $\beta$ gives directly the quantity $(E^M_{1V} + E^B_{2V} - E^M_{2V})$. Furthermore, it should be noted that this method does not require the use of specimens of identical sink density and identical initial vacancy concentration, whereas these conditions must generally be satisfied in the conventional methods of activation energy determination such as the Meechan-Brinkman or the cross-cut methods [4]. The accuracy of evaluating $(E^M_{1V} + E^B_{2V} - E^M_{1V})$ with the help of eq. (9) depends, however, on the precision of measuring the tail of the annealing curve. To check the steady-state approximation, the results obtained may be substituted into eq. (7) which may then be solved by a computer numerically without approximation. The solutions are then compared with the experimental results.

As an illustration, some of the results listed in table 1 are analysed in this way.

For aluminium, the only available isothermal annealing curve that falls in the right annealing temperature range is due to DeSorbo and Turnbull [14]. Here the deviations from second-order kinetics are appreciable after large times. Fig. 1 shows the theoretical fit to the experimental results with $\beta = 8.5$. Assuming the pre-exponential factor of $\beta$ to be 2, one obtains for Al a value of
$E_{1V}^M + E_{2V}^B - E_{2V}^M = 0.33$ eV.

Fig. 2 shows the theoretical fit to the results of Jackson [16] on platinum. Combining the results of Polak [18] with those of Jackson [16], we have for Pt $E_{1V}^M + E_{2V}^B - E_{2V}^M = 0.37$ eV, (fig. 3). This appears to agree with the results of Schumacher et al. [17].

For gold, one may make use of the quenching results of Emrick [11] and obtain $E_{1V}^M + E_{2V}^B - E_{2V}^M \approx 0.3$ eV (fig. 4). In the case of Au, the value of $(E_{1V}^M + E_{2V}^B - E_{2V}^M)$ has been determined independently from electron microscope observations [19] to be 0.26 eV, thus in satisfactory agreement with the above result.

It must be emphasized that all the results obtained in this section are deduced from experiments which were not designed for such an analysis and it would be most interesting to have available more precise measurements undertaken specifically for such purposes.

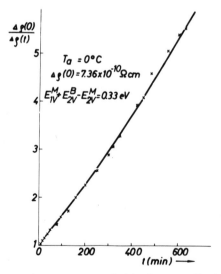

Fig. 1. Isothermal recovery of quenched-in resistivity in zone-refined Al after low-temperature quench, taken from data of DeSorbo and Turnbull [14]. The solid line represents the fitting of eq. (9) with $\beta \, C_{1V}^0 = 8.5$ to experimental results. $\Delta\rho(0)$ denotes the initial quenched-in resistivity.

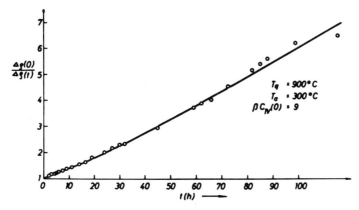

Fig. 2. Isothermal recovery of quenched-in resistivity in Pt after low-temperature quench, taken from data of Jackson [16]. The solid line represents the fitting of eq. (9) to experimental results.

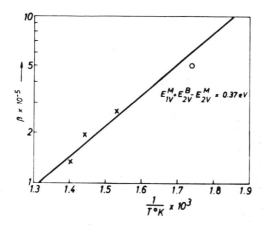

Fig. 3. Determination of $E_{1V}^M + E_{2V}^B - E_{2V}^M$ in Pt from the temperature dependence of $\beta$. The circle o corresponds to the value obtained from Jackson's data [16] and the crosses x from Polák's results [18].

### 2.5. Influence of impurities on annealing kinetics

So far only vacancy annealing in ideally pure specimens has been considered. What would we expect if impurities were present that could react with the vacancy defects and how does the impurity-vacancy interaction influence the evaluation of activation energies?

Let us first consider the simplest case, where only monovacancies and single impurity atoms are present and react according to the following scheme:

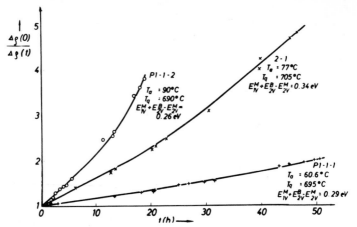

Fig. 4. Isothermal recovery of quenched-in resistivity in Au after low-temperature quench, taken from data of Emrick [11]. The solid lines represent the fitting of eq. (9) to experimental results.

$$V_1 + i \overset{K_7}{\underset{K_8}{\rightleftharpoons}} X,$$

$$V_1 \overset{K_3}{\rightarrow} \text{sink},$$  (15)

$$X \overset{K_9}{\rightarrow} \text{sink}.$$

The $K_n$ are the corresponding reaction constants. The complex X is formed by the combination of a vacancy with an impurity atom i, and can be mobile or immobile ($K_9 = 0$).

If X is *immobile*, the kinetic equations may be written as

$$dC_X/dt = K_7 C_i^o C_{1V} - K_7 C_X C_{1V} - K_8 C_X,$$

$$dC_{1V}/dt = -K_7 C_i^o C_{1V} + K_7 C_X C_{1V} + K_8 C_X - K_3 C_{1V}.$$  (16)

Equations (16) have been solved numerically by Damask and Dienes [4] and also by Sosin [20]. In general, it is found that there is an initial transient with rapid increase of the complex X followed by a steady decay of X and $V_1$.

In order to illustrate the complexities involved, three special cases are discussed here all of which lead to an exponential decay:

a) The steady state condition holds for the formation of X and $C_X \ll C_i^o$. Experimentally, this may correspond to a high temperature anneal. The decay of the total defect concentration $C$ is given by

$$C = C_{1V}^o \left[1 + \frac{K_7}{K_8} C_i^o\right] \exp\left[-\frac{K_3 t}{1 + (K_7/K_8)C_i^o}\right].$$  (17)

The effective migration energy as determined by the slope-change method is

$$E_{\text{eff}}^{M} = E_{1V}^{M} + \frac{12\, C_i^o E_X^B\, \exp(E_X^B/kT)\, \exp(\Delta S_X/k)}{1 + 12\, C_i^o\, \exp(E_X^B/kT)\, \exp(\Delta S_X/k)}\,, \tag{18}$$

where $E_X^B$ and $\Delta S_X$ are the binding energy and binding entropy of the vacancy-impurity complex. Thus the presence of an immobile impurity-vacancy complex raises the effective migration energy.

   b) For short annealing times $C_X \approx 0$. Here the monovacancy migration controls the rate process of annealing [20] and we have

$$C_{1V} = C_{1V}^o \exp[-(K_3 + K_7 C_i^o)t]\,. \tag{19}$$

The effective migration energy is then the monovacancy migration energy. Experimentally, this condition may correspond to low-temperature annealing.

   c) Once more we have the steady-state conditions as in a) but the complex X is now *mobile* and has a migration energy $E_X^M$. The solution is [4]

$$C = C_{1V}^o \left[ 1 + \frac{K_7}{K_8}\, C_i^o \right] \exp(-Kt)\,, \tag{20}$$

where

$$K = \frac{K_3 K_8 + K_7 K_9\, C_i^o}{K_8 + K_7\, C_i^o}\,. \tag{21}$$

We may write

$$\begin{aligned}
E_{\text{eff}}^{M} = E_{1V}^{M} &+ \frac{12 C_i^o\, E_X^B\, \exp(E_X^B/kT)\, \exp(\Delta S_X/k)}{1 + 12 C_i^o\, \exp(E_X^B/kT)\, \exp(\Delta S_X/k)} \\[2mm]
&- \frac{g(E_{1V}^M + E_X^B - E_X^M)\, \exp[(E_{1V}^M + E_X^B - E_X^M)/kT]}{1 + g\, \exp[(E_{1V}^M + E_X^B - E_X^M)/kT]}
\end{aligned} \tag{22}$$

where $g$ is an appropriate numerical factor. In this case, $E_{\text{eff}}^M$ can be *lower* than $E_{1V}^M$ if $E_X^M < E_{1V}^M$.

   The above consideration may be extended to include divacancies. The resulting annealing kinetics are even more complicated. Again for steady-state conditions and weak binding of X, the kinetics are the same as in the pure case, namely

$$\frac{1}{C_{1V}} = \left[ \frac{1}{C_{1V}^o} + \beta \right] \exp\left[ \frac{K_3 t}{1 + (K_7/K_8)C_i^o} \right]\,, \tag{23}$$

where X is assumed to be immobile and the formation of divacancy-impurity complexes is neglected. The effective migration energy is again raised by the presence of the immobile complex X:

$$E_{\text{eff}}^{\text{M}}(\text{impure}) = E_{\text{eff}}^{\text{M}}(\text{pure}) + \frac{g' E_X^B C_i^o \exp(E_X^B/kT)}{1 + g' C_i^o \exp(E_X^B/kT)} \ . \tag{24}$$

Here $g'$ is an appropriate numerical factor.

Another special case has been considered by Sosin and Bauer [21], who assumed the impurity concentration independent of time. The differential equations thus become linear and can be solved exactly.

A detailed list of the kinetic equations for vacancy-impurity interactions has been given by Doyama [22], where different configurations of the impurity-vacancy complex are discussed.

As may be seen from the above analysis, impurity-vacancy interactions lead to a deviation from first- or second-order kinetics. The magnitude of the deviation depends on the strength of the interaction. Moreover, more than *one* kind of impurity complex can be present. The electrical resistivity measurements are further complicated by the fact that the resistivity of an impurity-vacancy complex may be quite different  from that of a vacancy, and we know little about the resistivity of such complexes. Great care should therefore be taken when interpreting the experimental results. For more complicated cases, a computer fitting of experimental results with appropriate models may be useful. Certainly one does not expect to be able to deduce all defect parameters solely from electrical resistivity measurements.

A lowering of the effective migration energy obtained by slope-change method due to impurities has been reported by Sharma, Lee and Koehler [23]. These workers measured the effective migration energy in gold quenched from 700°C for specimens with RR between 4000 and 30 000. $E_{\text{eff}}^{\text{M}}$ was found to increase with increasing RR, thus indicating a lower $E_{\text{eff}}^{\text{M}}$ in impure specimens. Camanzi et al. [24] found that in Au-1at %Pt $E_{\text{eff}}^{\text{M}}$ is about 0.1 eV lower than in pure gold quenched under similar conditions. Gegel, Speiser, and Beeler [25] suggested that the Cu-$V_1$ complex in gold has a migration energy of 0.56 eV, which is even lower than the migration energy of a divacancy. These results may indicate that some vacancy-impurity complexes in gold can be mobile having a migration energy lower than that of monovacancies.

Deviot, Octor and Scherrer [26] quenched Ni with Cu concentration of the order of $10^{-3}$. They observed two main annealing stages, one lying between 500°K and 600°K and a second stage beyond 750°K. In the first stage, first-order kinetics were observed with a migration energy of $(1.53 \pm 0.05)$ eV. This value is close to $E_{1V}^{\text{M}}$ in Ni. It was proposed that this is the migration of impurity-vacancy complexes. This may, however, be merely an effective migration energy as discussed in case a).

Quéré found complicated annealing kinetics in quenched silver containing $2 \times 10^{-5}$ oxygen. A whole range of energies was found between 1.0 eV and 1.3 eV. Thus the special cases discussed above are not appropriate to describe the vacancy-oxygen interaction in Ag. Quéré explained his results as being due to the trapping of vacancies by oxygen during the quench. Subsequent annealing leads to the decomposition of the oxygen-vacancy complexes.

A large number of quenching experiments on dilute Al alloys have been reported and are mostly concerned with the determination of the impurity-vacancy binding energy [28] or with studying the isochronal annealing behaviour [29]. A lowering of the migration energy in Al $- 0.8 \times 10^{-4}$ Mg alloys to $0.47 \pm 0.02$ eV compared to the value 0.55 eV in zone-refined Al has been reported by Kino et al. [30]. They further found that $E_{\mathrm{eff}}^{\mathrm{M}}$ is unaltered by introducing a concentration of $1 \times 10^{-4}$ of Si into Al.

The present state of knowledge of V-i interactions is still insufficient to permit the effects of impurities on annealing experiments to be determined in detail.

## 3. Vacancy annealing at high vacancy concentrations

### 3.1. General discussion

At high vacancy concentrations, the contribution of divacancies to the annealing process of quenched-in vacancies becomes of greater importance. There is also a tendency to form larger vacancy clusters which may eventually grow to stacking-fault tetrahedra, dislocation loops, or voids. The annealing process at high vacancy concentration includes then the simultaneous diffusion of different mobile defect types and the nucleation and growth of vacancy clusters.

The concept of effective diffusion coefficients [31,32] has proved to be very useful in attempting to describe the diffusion process with several types of mobile defects. By considering the diffusion as a random walk problem, Schottky [31] arrives at the general formula

$$D_{\mathrm{eff}} = \frac{C_{1V}D_{1V} + 2C_{2V}D_{2V} + 3C_{3V}D_{3V} + \ldots}{C_{1V} + 2C_{2V} + 3C_{3V} + \ldots} \qquad (25)$$

where the $D_{nV}$'s are the diffusion coefficients for the $n$-multiple vacancies. Usually in the literature only terms up to divacancies are considered. However, as will be shown in the next section, the contribution of trivacancies can be significant at high vacancy concentrations. A useful approximation is to assume a local thermal equilibrium among different types of defects. Then the divacancy and the trivacancy concentrations are related to $C_{1V}$ by

$$C_{2V} = p\, C_{1V}^2 \,, \qquad p = 6 \exp(\Delta S_{2V}/k) \exp(E_{2V}^{\mathrm{B}}/kT) \,, \qquad (26)$$

and

$$C_{3V} = q\, C_{1V}^3 \,, \qquad q = 8\,\exp(\Delta S_{3V}/k)\,\exp(E_{3V}^B/kT)\,. \tag{27}$$

If the diffusion takes place in a concentration gradient [32,4], then eq. (25) is replaced by

$$D_{\text{eff}} = \frac{C_{1V}D_{1V} + 4C_{2V}D_{2V} + 9C_{3V}D_{3V} + \dots}{C_{1V} + 4C_{2V} + 9C_{3V}}\,. \tag{28}$$

Flynn [33] pointed out that eq. (28) is not exactly correct for describing the defect diffusion to sinks, since eq. (28) is only applicable when the concentration in the lattice can produce the necessary gradient to drive the diffusion. He found that the correct expression for $D_{\text{eff}}$ is given by eq. (25) if the defect concentrations at large distances from the sink are used for the corresponding $C_{nV}$.

The advantage of using $D_{\text{eff}}$ is that the whole annealing process can be described by the single differential equation

$$dC/dt = -\lambda^2 D_{\text{eff}}\, C \,, \tag{29}$$

where $C$ is the total concentration of mobile defects and $\lambda^2$ is a parameter which depends on the sink distribution. The effective migration energy is then given by $E_{\text{eff}}^M = -d(\ln D_{\text{eff}})/d(1/kT)$ (see section 3.3).

A special case of eq. (29) is that in which $\lambda^2$ is time independent (fixed sink concentration) and $2D_{2V} C_{2V} \gg D_{1V} C_{1V}$. If the trivacancies and larger clusters are neglected, then eq. (29) becomes

$$\frac{dC}{dt} = -\lambda^2 \frac{2a^2 \nu_{2V}^M \exp(\Delta S_{2V}/k)\,\exp[-(E_{2V}^M - E_{2V}^B)/kT]}{1 + 24\,\exp(\Delta S_{2V}/k)\,\exp(E_{2V}^B/kT)\,C}\, C^2 \,, \tag{30}$$

where $a$ is the lattice constant. If $24\,\exp(\Delta S_{2V}/k)\,\exp(E_{2V}^B/kT) \cdot C \ll 1$ the kinetics are second order, and

$$E_{\text{eff}}^M = E_{2V}^M - E_{2V}^B \,. \tag{31}$$

Quenching results on copper have been explained very well with such a model [34,35].

If cluster formation takes place during the annealing process, $\lambda^2$ is a function of time or of vacancy concentration. In order to describe the whole annealing process, it is necessary to find a suitable expression for $\lambda^2$, or a rate equation for cluster formation. By combining this with the diffusion equation, the whole problem can in principle be solved. Since the clustering process must involve small vacancy clusters such as trivacancies, comparison of experimental results with the nucleation model may give further information on properties of clusters.

## 3.2. Vacancy cluster nucleation models

The most straight forward way of studying the nucleation problem theoretically is to set up equations for the formation and dissociation of clusters containing $n$ vacancies ($n = 1, 2, 3, \ldots$) and to solve the equations by means of a computer. The difficulty with such calculations is the large number of unknown parameters that have to be assumed. Some simplifying assumptions have to be applied in order to reduce the computer calculation in time. Damask and Dienes [4] have in this way treated the problem up to octavacancies. The decomposition of clusters larger than $V_2$ was not permitted and only $V_1$ and $V_2$ were allowed to migrate to sinks. The cluster concentration decreases with increasing cluster size after long annealing. Kiritani [36] considers that the size of a cluster is controlled by the reaction of absorbing vacancies balanced by the reaction of vacancy escape from the cluster. He calculated the size distribution after twenty such reactions. The maximum of the size distribution is shifted to larger clusters if the probability of the escape of vacancies from the clusters is small.

However, all such computer calculations give only a qualitative idea of the nucleation process.

Another method of approach was adopted by Davis and Hirth [37],who extended the nucleation theory of condensation to describe the nucleation of dislocation loops in quenched Al. The nucleation rate of loops was then controlled by the free energy of dislocation loops at the critical size. By estimating the free energy of the loop from continuum theory, they obtained an astonishingly low nucleation rate as compared with experimental results. Davis [38] improved the calculation by using the free energy of a vacancy disc. He claimed that the model explained well the experimental nucleation results on quenched Al which were reported by Kiritani [36]. However, it is doubtful whether a macroscopic theory is able to describe the nucleation process, since the latter is certainly atomistic in nature. Futhermore, the model only takes account of the migration of monovacancies, whereas, as pointed out in section 3.1, the diffusion at high vacancy concentration involves divacancies and possibly trivacancies.

The most interesting approach is via the chemical rate theory. In order to simplify the problem some plausible assumptions must be made. This was first done by deJong and Koehler [39] on the nucleation of stacking fault tetrahedra in quenched gold. These workers assumed that the nuclei for tetrahedron formation were tetravacancies formed by the migration of a monovacancy to an *immobile* trivacancy. The diffusion of mobile defects was described by eq. (28) involving terms up to divacancies. A closed solution was obtained for the vacancy decay which described well the S-shaped resistivity annealing curve obtained after quenching from high temperatures [1].

The main drawback of this model is that the kinetics of nucleation which are predicted are in disagreement with experimental results obtained from electron microscope observations [19]. According to this model, the nucleation process extends over half of the total time required for complete vacancy annealing, whereas experiments have shown that the nucleation is a very fast process [40, 41, 19]. For example, for an initial vacancy concentration of $1.2 \times 10^{-4}$, about 50% of the total number of nuclei are formed at the first 10 min of annealing at $22^{\circ}$C, whereas the total time required for complete annealing out of quenched-in vacancies requires at least 50 h.

A model which overcomes this difficulty was developed by Chik [42]. The important features of this model are:

1) The stable nuclei are hexavacancies. They are formed either by collisions between mono-, di- and trivacancies or between two trivacancies.

2) Mono-, di- and trivacancies are in local thermal equilibrium with each other, but the trivacancies are also *mobile*, and have migration energies lying between $E_{1V}^M$ and $E_{2V}^M$.

The nucleation rate is then given by

$$dC_K/dt = 6g_{K1} \frac{D_{2V}}{a^2} C_{1V}C_{2V}C_{3V} + 8g_{K2}\frac{D_{3V}}{a^2}C_{3V}^2 \qquad (32)$$

$g_{K1}$ and $g_{K2}$ are the combination numbers for the formation of the nuclei.

The mono-, di- and trivacancies are assumed to be in local thermal equilibrium with each other. The annealing rate of the mobile vacancies is then given by

$$\frac{dC}{dt} = -g_S \frac{D_{\text{eff}}}{a^2} CC_K , \qquad (33)$$

where $g_S$ is the geometrical factor for annealing at sinks.

Three different diffusion models have been considered. Model $\alpha$) assumes a constant capture radius for the vacancy sinks, i.e., $g_S$ is a constant. Model $\beta$) assumes that $g_S$ is proportional to the size of the sink, i.e., $g_S = g_S' \sqrt{(C_{1V}(0)-C_{1V})/C_K}$, where $g_S'$ is now a constant. Model $\gamma$) assumes that the divacancy concentration controls the rate of annealing-out of the vacancy defects. Eq. (33) is then replaced by

$$\frac{dC_{2V}}{dt} = -g_S \frac{D_{2V}}{a^2} C_{2V} C_K . \qquad (33a)$$

Here only the results for model $\alpha$) are reproduced. For details, the reader is referred to the original paper [42]. In [42] the formation of nuclei by a collision of two trivacancies was not taken into account. This can be done by substituting in [42] $g_K$ by

$$g_K^{\text{eff}} = g_{K1} + \tfrac{4}{3} g_{K2} \frac{D_{3V}}{D_{2V}} \frac{q}{p} , \qquad (34)$$

In contrast to $g_K$, $g_K^{\text{eff}}$ is temperature dependent. By solving eq. (32) and eq. (33), we immediately obtain the final nuclei density. For model $\alpha$), we have

$$C_K = \left[\frac{6}{5}\frac{g_K^{\text{eff}}}{g_S} \cdot q \Lambda(0)\right]^{\frac{1}{2}} \cdot \left[C_{1V}(0)^{\frac{5}{2}} -(C_{1V}^{\min})^{\frac{5}{2}}\right] , \qquad (35)$$

where $C_{1V}(0)$ is the initial monovacancy concentration and $\Lambda(0)$ is a function of $p$, $q$ and $C_{1V}(0)$ [42]. $C_{1V}^{\min}$ is the minimum vacancy concentration below which the trivacancy formation becomes unlikely; it is found experimentally to be

$$C_{1V}^{min} = 0.4 \exp[-(0.26 \pm 0.06)eV/kT] . \tag{36}$$

The nucleation kinetics are obtained by resubstituting eq. (35) into eq. (32) followed by integration, which gives

$$\frac{1-x}{1+x} = \exp(-t/\tau) \tag{36a}$$

with

$$1/\tau = 12 g_K^{eff} \frac{D_{2V}}{a^2} pq \frac{C_{1V}(0)^6}{C_K(\infty)} \tag{36b}$$

and

$$x = C_K(t)/C_K(\infty) .$$

From eq. (35) we see that the functional dependence of $C_K$ on vacancy concentration is determined by the two parameters $p$ and $q$ defined in eqs. (26) and (27). If $C_K$ can be measured experimentally as a function of vacancy concentrations and annealing temperatures, information on di- and trivacancy binding energies may be obtained by comparing the experimental results with theory.

The electron microscope observations on quenched gold showed that the nucleation process of stacking-fault tetrahedra can be stopped by heating above a critical temperature [40]. Thus above the critical nucleation temperature only the nuclei formed at low temperatures can grow. In this way, the nucleation kinetics of stacking-fault tetrahedra have been studied [19,45]. The results may be well fitted with eq. (36) (fig. 5).

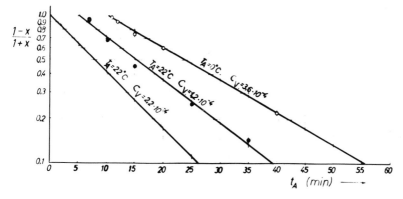

Fig. 5. Nucleation kinetics of stacking-fault tetrahedra in quenched gold plotted according to eq. (36a) [42]. $x$ is the fraction of nuclei formed during time $t_A$.

The dependence of the final stacking-fault tetrahedra density on vacancy concentration after full annealing in quenched gold has been measured [19] at three annealing temperatures. These results were compared with the nucleation models described above by assuming that each nucleus grows to a stacking-fault tetrahedron resolvable in the electron microscope, i.e., the stacking-fault tetrahedra density is taken as identical with the nuclei density $C_K(\infty)$. To fit the experimental results with eq. (35), we should take ideally $p$ and $q$ as adjustable parameters and attempt to obtain the minimum least square error of good fit. It was found, however, that the value of $q$ was rather insensitive to the choice of $p$, but an upper limit for the divacancy binding energy could nevertheless be set at about 0.2 eV. In [42], the results were fitted to the nucleation theory by assuming a divacancy binding energy of 0.09 eV and a binding entropy $\Delta S_{2V}$ of 2.2 k. The results of $q$ were not much affected by a slight variation on the value of $p$. For trivacancies, the following values were deduced

$$E_{3V}^B = 0.3 \text{ eV} \quad \text{and} \quad \Delta S_{3V} = 2.5 \text{ k to 3k} . \quad (37)$$

At present no corresponding nucleation model has been developed for the formation of dislocation loops in quenched Al. The nucleation of dislocation loops in quenched Al differs in one respect from that of stacking-fault tetrahedra in quenched gold. The rate of nucleation becomes *faster* as the annealing temperature is lowered and seems to have a maximum around $-20°C$ [36,43], in contrast to the nucleation behaviour of quenched gold. However, it is interesting to note that the nucleation kinetics of loops can be approximately described by eq. (36a), if $x$ now has the meaning of the fraction of dislocation loops nucleated at time $t$ (fig. 6) [44]. The decrease of nucleation rate with increasing annealing temperatures in quenched Al may indicate that small dislocation loops formed at the early stage of nucleation are less stable than small stacking-fault tetrahedra so that the loops tend to dissolve back into the lattice during the annealing above room temperature. More quantitative investigations may provide better understanding of the nucleation mechanisms of dislocation loops in quenched aluminium.

### 3.3. Heterogeneous nucleation of vacancy clusters

The nucleation models discussed in the last section are based on the assumption of homogeneous nucleation, i.e., it is assumed that the nuclei are not formed at preferred sites such as impurity atoms. There is experimental evidence which suggests that — depending on circumstances — a heterogeneous or a homogeneous type of nucleation occurs. We shall summarize these results and consider subsequently the question of heterogeneous nucleation in terms of a simplified model.

Let us first consider the experimental evidence pertaining to the question whether the nucleation of vacancy clusters is a homogeneous or a heterogeneous process.

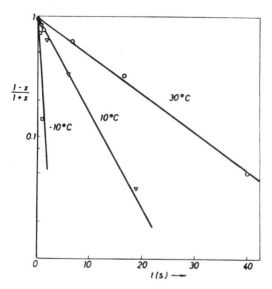

Fig. 6. Nucleation kinetics of dislocation loops in quenched Al [43]. Equation (36a) can be fitted to the experimental results.

In gold Segall and Clarebrough [46] found that the prequench heat treatment of
the samples had a pronounced influence on the stacking-fault tetrahedra density observed. Samples heated in reducing atmospheres (CO) showed a much higher cluster
density than those heated in oxidizing atmospheres. The authors suggested that the
impurities in the samples are reduced to metallic form by CO, and then act as
nucleating sites. This suggests that heterogeneous nucleation is in fact possible.

Ytterhus and Balluffi [12] further found that long annealing of gold wires in air
increases the resistivity ratio. After the long annealing treatment in air, the surface
of the wire was etched, and the subsequent chemical analysis of the bulk showed a
smaller impurity content than that without such heat treatment. This suggested
that some of the impurities might have diffused to the surface of the wire and were
lost by evaporation during the heat treatment or were removed from the surface by
the etching process after the heat treatment. Similar refining effects are also reported for platinum [47].

Siegel [48] measured the stacking-fault tetrahedra density in gold quenched
from $900°C$ as a function of the RR. He found that the stacking-fault tetrahedra
density decreased monotonically with increasing RR in the range examined. It was
concluded that the nucleation of stacking fault tetrahedra in quenched gold must
be a heterogeneous process.

Meshii et al. [44] investigated the effect of prequench heat treatment in oxidizing atmosphere on the nucleation of stacking-fault tetrahedra in quenched gold.
These workers found that the density of stacking-fault tetrahedra decreases with

increasing prequench heating time at 1000°C in an oxidizing atmosphere, and after 10 min of such heat treatment the tetrahedra density becomes constant. They further found that the nature of nuclei for stacking-fault tetrahedra formed in specimens after the 10 min heat treatment was different from that in specimens without the heat treatment; in the former case, the critical temperature below which nuclei can be formed was 120°C, whereas in the latter case the critical temperature was 160°C. A higher critical temperature may mean higher stability of the nuclei. These results indicated that two types of nucleation mechanisms were present. The authors suggested that the nucleation mechanism after the saturation of the oxidizing effect might be homogeneous. Meshii et al. did not simultaneously measure the residual resistivity of the sample as a function of oxidizing time. Ytterhus and Balluffi [12] found, however, that the residual resistivity decreased to a minimum after 60 min annealing at 1000°C in an oxidizing atmosphere. Comparing these results with the work of Meshii et al. [44], the tetrahedra density then becomes constant before the minimum resistivity is reached, i.e. there is a saturation effect of tetrahedra density as a function of increasing specimen purity, in contrast to the results of Siegel [48]. Further experiments are necessary to clarify the discrepancies between these results.

The important question in studying heterogeneous nucleation processes is to find out what kind of impurities have strong enough interactions with vacancies to cause a heterogeneous nucleation and what concentration of such impurities is needed to produce heterogeneous nucleation. Experimentally, we are confronted with the difficulty of obtaining high-purity samples which contain only one type of impurities with known concentration, so that the interference from other types of impurities is eliminated.

Let us now attempt a rough estimate of the effects of impurities on heterogeneous nucleation. The model for homogeneous nucleation which is discussed in section 3.2 may easily be extended to heterogeneous nucleation at impurity atoms. If the formation of di- and trivacancies is not suppressed altogether by the presence of impurity atoms, vacancy clusters may be nucleated by the collision of mono- and divacancies with a vacancy-impurity complex X or by collision of a trivacancy with the complex X, i.e. we suppose that the nucleus for stacking-fault tetrahedra formation at impurities is made up of 4 vacancies with an impurity atom relaxed into the vacancy cluster. The rate of nuclei formation at impurities is then

$$\frac{dC_K}{dt}(\text{hetero}) = g_K^i \, D_{2V} C_{1V} C_{2V} C_X \,, \tag{38}$$

where $C_K(\text{hetero})$ and $g_K^i$ respectively denote the nuclei concentration and the geometrical factor due to heterogeneous nucleation, and $C_X$ is the concentration of a vacancy-impurity complex.

According to section 3.3, the rate of homogeneous nucleation is

$$\frac{dC_K}{dt}(\text{homo}) = g_K \, D_{2V} C_{1V} C_{2V} C_{3V} \,. \tag{39}$$

The ratio of nuclei density due to heterogeneous and homogeneous nucleation is then given approximately as

$$\frac{C_K^2(\text{hetero})}{C_K^2(\text{homo})} \approx \frac{5}{3} \frac{rC_i^o \left[1 + 3pC_{1V} + \left(\frac{27}{5}\right) qC_{1V}^2\right]}{q\left[1 + \left(\frac{10}{3}\right)pC_{1V} + \left(\frac{45}{7}\right)qC_{1V}^2\right]} \frac{1}{C_{1V}^2}, \tag{40}$$

where

$$r = 12 \exp(\Delta S_X/k) \exp(E_X^B/kT). \tag{41}$$

$E_X^B$ and $\Delta S_X$ denote the binding energy and the association entropy of the vacancy-impurity complex. If the impurity-vacancy interaction is strong, all the impurities are bound to vacancies. Then

$$C_X = C_i^o \tag{42}$$

$C_i^o$ is the total impurity concentration. Substituting eq. (42) into eq. (38) one obtains an upper limit for the nucleation rate of $C_K^i$. The minimum impurity concentration that would make heterogeneous nucleation equally probable as homogeneous nucleation is obtained by equating eq. (39) with eq. (38). We then have

$$C_i^o \geqslant \frac{g_K}{g_K^i} C_{3V}. \tag{43}$$

Using the trivacancy parameters given in section 3.3, $C_{3V}$ is of the order of $10^{-5}$ for a total vacancy concentration of about $10^{-4}$ in the region of room temperature. Equation (43) applies to impurities of very strong vacancy-impurity interaction; for a smaller binding energy of the impurity-vacancy complex $E_X^B$, $C_i^o$ should be even higher. Thus homogeneous nucleation should be dominant for samples with total impurity concentration less than $10^{-5}$ atomic fraction. The heterogeneous nucleation mechanism becomes more competitive at higher annealing temperatures, since $C_{3V}$ decreases with increasing temperature for a given total vacancy concentration.

An interesting way of studying impurity effects on vacancy clustering is to use dilute alloys with solute concentrations of the order of $10^{-3}$. If high-purity metals are used in alloying, the concentration of impurities other than the solute can be kept around $10^{-5}$ so that the solute is the main type of impurity present.

At present some data are available for dilute gold alloys and the results are summarized in table 2. It is interesting to note that the impurities can be broadly divided into two groups, the strongly interacting and the weakly interacting types. The divalent impurities belong to the former group and have pronounced effects on the cluster density; the monovalent and the transitional impurities belong to the weakly interacting group. However, the results listed in table 2 are still incomplete. A more systematic study of heterogeneous nucleation may yield informations on vacancy-impurity interactions.

Quader and Dodd [50] have studied the nucleation kinetics in pure gold and in dilute gold alloys (Au-Cd, Au-Zn) in some detail. They found that the kinetics

Table 2
Effect of impurities on the observable density of stacking-fault tetrahedra in quenched gold.

| Impurity | Conc. of impurity | Effect | References |
|---|---|---|---|
| Ag | $10^{-3}, 5 \times 10^{-3}$ | SFT | [45] |
| Cu | $1.5 \times 10^{-3}$ | density | [49], [45] |
| Pt | $10^{-2}$ | not affected | [24] |
| Fe | ? | | [45] |
| Zn | $1.5 \times 10^{-3}$ | SFT | [50] |
| Cd | $8.7 \times 10^{-4}, 1.7 \times 10^{-3},$ $3.5 \times 10^{-3}$ | density much increased | [50] |
| Mg | $2 \times 10^{-4}, 5 \times 10^{-4}$ | | [49] |

of nucleation were characterized by activation energies of 0.28 eV, 0.34 eV and 0.42 eV for zone-refined, Cd-doped, and Zn-doped gold respectively. Furthermore Zn atoms may nucleate dislocation loops in the early stages of preaging with an activation energy of 0.7 eV. In order to compare the experimental results with a quantitative nucleation model, one needs to know the total quenched-in vacancy concentration and the final cluster density after complete annealing. Unfortunately, these values are not given in the paper of Quader and Dodd [50].

In electron microscope observations the density of observable vacancy clusters fluctuates by ± 50%. If one compares the cluster density observed in a dilute alloy with that in the pure metal, one can say that the impurity effect on nucleation is small when the observed densities in the two cases agree within ± 50%. This corresponds to those impurities in table 2 classified as weakly interacting. To give a rough estimate of the binding energy of such weakly interacting impurities we may make use of eq. (40) and set $C_K$(hetero) $\leqslant C_K$(homo), corresponding to the experimental accuracy obtainable in determining $C_K$ from electron microscope observations discussed above. As an example, we take $T = 0°C, C_{1V} = 10^{-4}$, $p = 4200, q = 3 \times 10^7$, and $C_i^o = 10^{-3}$. Substituting these values into eq. (40) and putting eq. (40) equal to unity, we obtain $r = 200$, or as an upper limit $E_X^B = 0.07$ eV $(\Delta S_X = 0)$. The binding energy deduced here is indeed small, indicating a weak interaction between vacancy and impurity atom.

So far only results on dilute gold-alloys have been discussed. In aluminium alloys most of the reported electron microscope observations of vacancy cluster formation used specimens with impurity concentrations greater than $10^{-2}$. The cluster formation in Al-alloys is complicated by the formation of helices or dislocation loops of other than Frank type [51].

Aluminium doped with In (concentration of $10^{-4}$ to $10^{-3}$) is found to increase the dislocation loop density [52]; a similar effect is also observed for aluminium doped with about $10^{-2}$ Si or Mg [53]. A general scheme for differentiating between strongly and weakly interacting impurities as in table 2 does not seem to be possible from loop formation in quenched aluminium. A great deal of effort has been expended in determining the binding energy between vacancy and impurity atoms in aluminium. The experimental results have been summarized by Takamura [28] and various theoretical treatments are given by Hastiguti [54] and by Sprusil and Valvoda [55].

### 3.3. Effective migration energy

The activation energy deduced from a high temperature quench is usually lower than that deduced from a low temperature quench. The lower activation energy was formerly interpreted as the divacancy migration energy. We know now that such an interpretation is not always justified. As indicated in section 3.1, if the mono- and divacancies are in local thermal equilibrium and the divacancies are more mobile than the monovacancies, the effective migration energy can reach a minimum value equal to $E_{2V}^M - E_{2V}^B$. Examples of this kind have been found in Cu [34,35] and Pt [17]. In more complicated cases, the effective migration energy depends on vacancy concentration and annealing conditions.

The concentration dependence of the effective migration energy has been studied in greatest detail in quenched gold. However, the interpretation of these results remains controversial. DeJong and Koehler [57] first reported the variation of effective migration energy with vacancy concentration. They explained the results in terms of the effective diffusion coefficient for mono- and divacancies assuming a local thermal equilibrium among the migrating defects. By fitting the results with effective migration energies calculated from the effective diffusion coefficients they found $E_{1V}^M + E_{2V}^B - E_{2V}^M = 0.26$ eV and $E_{2V}^B = 0.1$ eV.

Ytterhus and Balluffi [12] have since measured the concentration dependence of the effective migration energies in quenched gold and found results different from those of deJong and Koehler [57]. $E_{\text{eff}}^M$ was found to have a constant value of about 0.7 eV over a very large vacancy concentration range between $10^{-5}$ and about $7 \times 10^{-5}$. Later Balluffi's group found that the 0.7 eV value also was observed in different annealing temperature ranges. It should be noted, however, that the experimentally determined effective migration energies were scattered over at least 0.1 eV. Thus, such measurements are unable to give fine details. Balluffi and coworkers [58] explain the 0.7 eV activation energy as being the migration energy of divacancies. In order that divacancies can exist in appreciable concentration even at as low a concentration as $10^{-5}$, the binding energy of a divacancy must be as large as 0.4 eV. It has been shown later by Chick et al. [56] that an apparently constant $E_{\text{eff}}^M$ can be obtained in the high concentration range around $10^{-4}$ if the trivacancies are taken as mobile with a migration energy lying between $E_{1V}^M$ and $E_{2V}^M$.

The most recent measurements on the concentration dependence of effective migration energies in quenched gold were reported by Kino and Koehler [13]. At low concentrations, around $4 \times 10^{-6}$ to $2 \times 10^{-5}$, the effective migration energies measured between 140°C and 150°C gave an average value of 0.9 eV which fell to 0.78 eV at vacancy concentrations around $6 \times 10^{-5}$. Again the values obtained for $E_{\mathrm{eff}}^{\mathrm{M}}$ varied over a wide range.

A detailed analysis of self-diffusion data and high temperature equilibrium measurements in gold [5,59] gives the best value for $E_{1\mathrm{V}}^{\mathrm{M}}$ as 0.89 eV. Fig. 7 shows the theoretical $E_{\mathrm{eff}}^{\mathrm{M}}$ calculated from eq. (25) for different annealing temperatures taking terms up to trivacancies. The parameters used in the calculations are consistent with the most recent results obtained from self-diffusion analysis, and from electron-microscope observations. An interesting result is that at low temperatures for a vacancy concentration between $10^{-5}$ and $10^{-4}$ the calculated $E_{\mathrm{eff}}^{\mathrm{M}}$ has a large plateau around 0.7 eV. This plateau is obtained only if $E_{3\mathrm{V}}^{\mathrm{M}}$ lies between $E_{2\mathrm{V}}^{\mathrm{M}}$ and $E_{1\mathrm{V}}^{\mathrm{M}}$. If $E_{3\mathrm{V}}^{\mathrm{M}}$ is smaller than $E_{2\mathrm{V}}^{\mathrm{M}}$, $E_{\mathrm{eff}}^{\mathrm{M}}$ falls monotonically with increasing vacancy concentration.

The plateau around 0.7 eV in fig. 7 falls into the range of effective migration energies reported by Ytterhus and Balluffi [12] for annealing temperatures between 30°C and 40°C and may provide an explanation for the observation of an apparently constants $E_{\mathrm{eff}}^{\mathrm{M}}$ around 0.7 eV over a wide range of vacancy concentration. The shaded areas in fig. 7 show the scatter of the experimentally determined $E_{\mathrm{eff}}^{\mathrm{M}}$ The calculated $E_{\mathrm{eff}}^{\mathrm{M}}$ for an annealing temperature of 150°C are in fair agreement with the results of Kino and Koehler [13], who have made the measurements between 140°C and 150°C. Since the experimental error for the determination of $E_{\mathrm{eff}}^{\mathrm{M}}$

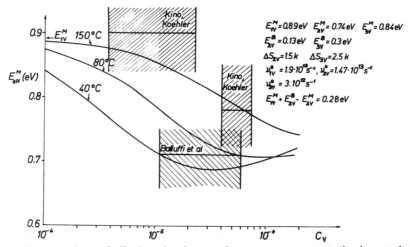

Fig. 7. The dependence of effective migration energies on vacancy concentration in quenched gold. The parameters used in the calculation are listed in the figure. The experimental results of effective migration energies are represented by the shaded areas, which show the scatter of the measured energies. The results of Kino and Koehler [13] were measured at 140°C and 150°C, and the results of Balluffi et al. [12] at 30°C and 40°C.

is large, one should not place too much emphasis on extracting exact informations from effective migration energy determinations.

Trivacancies have not been taken into account seriously for the interpretation of quenching results in metals other than gold. Aluminium is a metal into which a large vacancy concentration ($> 10^{-4}$) can be quenched. It is to be expected that trivacancies play an important role in aluminium.

Two quenching experiments which have been reported on gold have been performed in a less conventional way. Gegel, Speiser and Beeler [25] measured the thermo-electric power of quenched gold wires as a function of temperature, whilst the specimen temperature was raised at a constant rate from $77°K$ to $360°K$ ($0.416°K/s$). A spectrum of activation energies was calculated from the annealing curve. The results were interpreted by comparison with model computer calculations using rate equations. Gegel et al. deduced $E_{2V}^B$ as 0.07 eV. In the computer calculation the trivacancies are assumed to be immobile.

Wang, Seidman, and Balluffi [58] measured the vacancy loss at high annealing temperature around $500°C$ by electrical resistivity measurements. By means of a rapid-data-acquisition system, the annealing time for periods between 100 msec and 10 min could be controlled and registered. The vacancy loss was compared with a diffusion model involving mono- and divacancies in thermal equilibrium. By means of a computer programme, the results were fitted by varying eight parameters until the optimum fit was obtained. The eight free parameters were $S_{1V}^F$, $E_{1V}^F$, $E_{1V}^M$, $D_{1V}^o$, $E_{2V}^B$, $\Delta S_{2V}^B$, $E_{2V}^M$, and $D_{2V}^o$. $S_{1V}^F$ and $E_{1V}^F$ denote the formation entropy and formation energy of a monovacancy. The resultant values were as follows: $E_{1V}^M =$ 0.90 eV, $E_{2V}^M = 0.69$ eV, $E_{1V}^F = 0.94$ eV, and $E_{2V}^B = 0.40$ eV. Seeger and Mehrer [59] have shown, however, that the parameters deduced by Wang et al. are not consistent with the self-diffusion data. According to Seeger and Mehrer the self-diffusion data favour a lower binding energy for divacancies.

## 4. Conclusions

In the preceding sections, we have tried to relate experimental results on vacancy annealing and clustering with realistic theoretical models. It is seen that even in simple cases such as annealing of vacancies at low vacancy concentration in ideally pure samples, the effective migration energy determined by the conventional slope-change method is not related to a single physical quantity. Impurities present in samples can influence appreciably the annealing behaviour of the quenched-in vacancies and make the interpretation of quenching results more difficult. Even in ideally pure specimens, complications arise when larger vacancy clusters other than divacancies are formed. One has then to decide what type of defect clusters have to be taken into account. It has been shown in section 3 that in gold mobile trivacancies play probably an important role in vacancy annealing at higher concentrations. In metals other than gold, not much attention has been placed on the role of trivacancies or other larger vacancy clusters in the annealing process. It is true that we know little about trivacancies, but this should not prevent us recognizing the importance of including these defects in our interpretation of vacancy annealing behaviour.

Most quenching experiments have been done with the conventional method of measuring the quenched-in residual electrical resistivity. The annealing processes were usually analysed by deducing the effective migration energies from the comparison of isothermal annealing curves at different temperatures. The drawbacks of the conventional experimental technique become evident when we try to interpret the experimental results critically. Firstly, the electrical resistivity measurements cannot differentiate between different types of defects present simultaneously in the samples, but give us only information on the total effect caused by all types of defects present. This means that the measurement of electrical resistivity alone does not give sufficient information about vacancy interactions or vacancy-impurity interactions. Secondly, the effective migration energies deduced from isothermal annealing curves are not related to a simple physical quantity except in several special cases. Finally, the evaluation of effective migration energies from experimental curves involves appreciable errors. Thus the determination of effective migration energies from quenching experiments does not give precise information on vacancy properties.

As shown in section 2, the conventional resistivity measurements may provide valuable information in case of *very pure* and well annealed specimens at low vacancy concentrations. Under these conditions the steady-state approximation of the mono- and divacancy annealing model is applicable. By fitting the theoretical equations derived from this model to experimental results, it is possible to deduce directly the physical quantity $E_{1V}^M + E_{2V}^B - E_{2V}^M$, which is not an effective migrating energy. It is hoped that experiments will be done specifically for the purpose of determining $E_{1V}^M + E_{2V}^B - E_{2V}^M$.

In view of the above discussion, it may be rewarding in future quenching experiment to develop new techniques of investigations. Especially interesting will be those which can distinguish between different types of defects, e.g. field-ion microscopy.

Our knowledge about vacancy-impurity interactions is incomplete. It would certainly be interesting to have a better understanding of vacancy-impurity interactions, so that we may achieve better control of the impurity influence on annealing behaviour. As shown in section 3, a systematic study of heterogeneous nucleation of vacancy clusters in dilute gold alloys may provide valuable information.

The author wishes to thank Professor A.Seeger and Dr.H.Mehrer for helpful discussions and Dr. H.J.Blythe for carefully reading the manuscript.

# References

[1] J.E.Bauerle and J.S.Koehler, Phys. Rev. 107 (1957) 1493.

[2] S.M.Makin, A.H.Rowe and A.D.LeClaire, Proc. Phys. Soc. B70 (1957) 545.

[3] Lattice Defects in Quenched Metals, ed. by R.M.J.Cotterill, M.Doyama, J.J.Jackson and M.Meshii (Academic Press, New York and London, 1965).

[4] A.C.Damask and G.J.Dienes, Point Defects in Metals (Gordon and Breach, New York, London, 1963).

[5] A.Seeger and H.Mehrer, this volume.

[6] H.Mehrer, Jül. Conf. 2 (Vol. 1) 1968 p. 643; Z. Naturforsch., in press.

[7] F.S.Ham, J. Chem. Phys. Solids 6 (1958) 335.

[8] C.P.Flynn, Phys. Rev. 133 (1964) A587.

[9] O.Krisement, Phys. Kondens. Materie 1 (1963) 326.

[10] A.Scholz, Phys. Stat. Sol. 14 (1966) 169.

[11] R.M.Emrick, Phys. Rev. 122 (1961) 1720.

[12] J.A.Ytterhus and R.W.Balluffi, Phil. Mag. 11 (1965) 707.

[13] T.Kino and J.S.Koehler, Phys. Rev. 162 (1967) 632.

[14] W.DeSorbo and D.Turnbull, Phys. Rev. 115 (1959) 560.

[15] M.Doyama and J.S.Koehler, Phys. Rev. 134 (1964) A522.

[16] J.J.Jackson, Lattice Defects in Quenched Metals, ed. by R.M.J.Cotterill, M.Doyama, J.J. Jackson and M.Meshii (Academic Press, New York and London, 1965) p. 479.

[17] D.Schumacher, A.Seeger and O.Härlin, Phys. Stat. Sol. 25 (1968) 359.

[18] J.Polák, Phys. Stat. Sol. 21 (1967) 581.

[19] K.P.Chik, Phys. Stat. Sol. 10 (1965) 659.

[20] A.Sosin, Phys. Rev. 122 (1961) 1112.

[21] A.Sosin and W.Bauer, Phys. Rev. 147 (1966) 478.

[22] M.Doyama, Phys. Rev. 148 (1966) 681.

[23] R.K.Sharma, C.Lee and J.S.Koehler, Phys. Rev. Lett. 19 (1967) 1379.

[24] A.Camanzi, N.A.Mancini, E.Rimini and G.Schianchi, Jül. Conf. 2 (Vol. 1) 1968, p. 154.

[25] H.Gegel, R.Speiser and J.R.Beeler Jr., Lattice Defects and their Interactions (Honolulu Conference, 1965), ed. by R.R.Hasiguti (Gordon and Breach, Science Publishers, New York etc., 1967) p. 181.

[26] B.Deviot, H.Octor and S.Scherrer, Jül. Conf. 2 (Vol. 1) 1968, p. 176.

[27] Y.Quéré, J. Phys. Soc. Japan 18, Suppl. III, 91 (1963).

[28] J.Takamura, Lattice Defects in Quenched Metals, ed. by R.M.J.Cotterill, M.Doyama, J.J. Jackson and M.Meshii (Academic Press, New York and London, 1965) p. 521.

[29] T.Federighi, Lattice Defects in Quenched Metals, ed. by R.M.J.Cotterill, M.Doyama, J.J. Jackson and M.Meshii (Academic Press, New York and London, 1965) p. 217.

[30] T.Kino, S.Kabemoto and S.Yoshida, J. Phys. Soc. Japan 18, Suppl. III (1963) 85.

[31] G.Schottky, Z. Physik 160 (1960) 16.

[32] J.S.Koehler, F.Seitz and J.E.Bauerle, Phys. Rev. 107 (1957) 1499.

[33] C.P.Flynn, Phys. Rev. 134 (1964) A241.

[34] A.Seeger, V.Gerold, K.P.Chik and M.Rühle, Phys. Letters 5 (1963) 107.

[35] F.Ramsteiner, G.Lampert, A.Seeger and W.Schüle, Phys. Stat. Sol. 8 (1965) 863.

[36] M.Kiritani, J. Phys. Soc. Japan 20 (1965) 1834.

[37] T.L.Davis and J.P.Hirth, J. Appl. Phys. 37 (1966) 2112.

[38] T.L.Davis, J. Appl. Phys. 38 (1967) 3756.

[39] M.deJong and J.S.Koehler, Phys. Rev. 129 (1963) 49.

[40] T.Mori and M.Meshii, Acta Met. 12 (1964) 104.

[41] T.Mori and M.Meshii, Electron Microscopy 1964, ed. by M.Titlbach, Vol. A (Publishing House of the Czechoslovak Academy of Sciences, Prague, 1964) p. 237.

[42] K.P.Chik, Phys. Stat. Sol. 10 (1965) 675.
[43] A.Sato, Y.Shimomura, M.Kiritani and S.Yoshida, J. Phys. Soc. Japan 22 (1967) 1198.
[44] M.Meshii, J.A.McComb, K.Y.Chen and T.H.Mori, The Nature of Small Defect Clusters.
    (United Kingdom Atomic Energy Authority Report R5269) ed. by M.J.Makin, Vol. 1,
    (H.M.Stationary Office London, 1966) p. 84.
[45] M.Meshii, Lattice Defects in Quenched Metals, ed. by R.M.J.Cotterill, M.Doyama, J.J.
    Jackson and M.Meshii (Academic Press, New York and London, 1965) p. 387.
[46] R.L.Segall and L.M.Clarebrough, Phil. Mag. 9 (1964) 865.
[47] K.Misek, Czech. J. Phys. B17 (1967) 647.
[48] R.W.Siegel, Phil. Mag. 13 (1966) 337.
[49] I.A.Johnston, P.S.Dobson and R.E.Smallmann, Jül. Conf. 2 (Vol. 1) 1968, p. 140.
[50] M.A.Quader and R.A.Dodd, Phil. Mag. 17 (1968) 575.
[51] R.E.Smallman and A.Eikum, Lattice Defects in Quenched Metals, ed. by R.M.J.Cotterill,
    M.Doyama, J.J.Jackson and M.Meshii (Academic Press, New York and London, 1965)
    p. 591.
[52] F.C.Duckworth, T.R.Ramachandran and J.Burke, Jül. Conf. 2 (Vol. 1) 1968, p. 185.
[53] K.H.Westmacott, R.S.Barnes, D.Hull and R.E.Smallman, Phil. Mag. 6 (1961) 929.
[54] R.R.Hasiguti, J. Phys. Soc. Japan 20 (1965) 625; 21 (1966) 1223.
[55] B.Sprusil and V.Valvoda, Acta Met. 15 (1967) 1269.
[56] K.P.Chik, D.Schumacher and A.Seeger, Phase Stability in Metals and Alloys, ed. by P.S.
    Rudman et al. (McGraw-Hill Book Co., New York, 1967) p. 449.
[57] M.deJong and J.S.Koehler, Phys. Rev. 129 (1963) 40.
[58] C.G.Wang, D.N.Seidman and R.W.Balluffi, Phys. Rev. 169 (1968) 553.
[59] A.Seeger and H.Mehrer, Phys. Stat. Sol. 29 (1968) 231.

## Discussions

*J.Bass:* Does Dr. Chik think that the existence of first-order and second-order kinetics (as opposed to *nearly* first-order or *nearly* second-order) has been well established experimentally? Small deviations from these "orders" can cause substantial changes in the "effective migration energies" estimated from experimental data.

*K.P.Chik:* I would not say that the first-order and second-order kinetics are *well* established experimentally. In fact, even the mono- and divacancy annealing model does not predict pure second-order or first-order kinetics during the whole range of annealing time. The presence of impurities may further cause larger deviations from first- or second-order kinetics, leading to other values for the effective migration energies. That is why I emphasize that one should be cautious in the interpretation of effective migration energies. In the method I have described (section 2.3), we can determine directly the physical quantity $E_{1V}^{B} + E_{2V}^{B} - E_{2V}^{M}$, which is not an effective migration energy.

*R.W.Siegel:* I would like to disagree with the basic assumption of your model for a low divacancy binding energy in gold. Your model is based upon the assumption that vacancy precipitates are formed by homogeneous nucleation in your experiments after quenching. However, a number of investigators, including Clarbrough, Segall and coworkers, and myself have looked at this problem and no direct evidence has been found for homogeneous nucleation, and to the contrary, these investigations have given strong direct experimental evidence that the observed vacancy precipitates form by heterogeneous nucleation at impurity sites. These experiments have been performed on material which apparently covers the range of specimen purity which is presently available. It would seem necessary, in light of this considerable evidence, that if your model for the low divacancy binding energy is to have a reasonable basis that some direct experimental evidence for homogeneous nucleation of stacking fault tetrahedra be found. In this respect, I would like to mention that identification of the vacancy-type defect, which moves with a migration energy of 0.70 eV as the divacancy with a binding energy of approximately 0.4 eV is in one way based upon the way in which the vacancy precipitates nucleate in gold after quenching.

*K.P.Chik:* I would like to make clear that my nucleation model for stacking fault tetrahedron formation does not *a priori* assume a low divacancy binding energy in gold. Rather, the comparison of experimental results with this nucleation model gives us a set of vacancy parameters which are consistent among themselves and with other results such as self-diffusion data. This consistency serves as a justification for the assumptions of the nucleation model. A strong evidence for a low divacancy binding energy is given by Seeger and Mehrer (phys. stat. sol. 29 (1968) 231) who analysed the self-diffusion data for gold in the temperature range from 300°C to 1050°C together with the high temperature equilibrium data of Simmons and Balluffi (Phys. Rev. 125 (1962) 862) by a least square procedure. They found that the best fit to the experimental data results in sets of parameters which lead to a low binding energy of divacancies of $\approx 0.1$ eV without any serious assumptions on the magnitude of the binding entropy of divacancy, $\Delta S_{2V}$, whereas a larger binding energy of 0.4 eV for the divacancy is not compatible with the parameters deduced from the least square analysis. We are also of the opinion that the activation energy of 0.70 eV found experimentally "over a wide range of conditions" should not be identified as the divacancy migration energy, but rather as an effective migration energy. The apparently constant activation energy of 0.7 eV is actually a band of experimental values more than 0.1 eV wide. The recent results of Kino and Koehler (Phys. Rev. 162 (1967) 632) indicate strongly that the defect governing the recovery in pure gold at low vacancy concentrations is not the "0.70 eV – defect" but the monovacancy with a migration energy of about 0.90 eV.

The question of heterogeneous nucleation is discussed in the text of my paper.

*J.Friedel:* It is interesting to study heterogeneous nucleation as a mean of looking at impurity-vacancy interaction. From that aspect, the table you gave was quite suggestive with the exception of Cu pointed out by Siegel. The impurities which do not seem to have an effect are known from diffusion measurements to repell vacancies and vice versa. This also agrees with Deplanté's theoretical analysis of the electronic effect of transitional and polyvalent impurities (J. Phys. 23 (1962) 609; J. Phys. Chem. Solids 26 (1965) 38).

   *K.P.Chik:* As to the effect of Cu on the nucleation of stacking fault tetrahedra in quenched gold, both Meshii (Lattice Defects in Quenched Metals, ed. by R.H.J. Cotterill et al. (Academic Press, 1965) p. 387, and Johnson, Dobson and Smallman (this conference; Jül. Conf. 2 (Vol. 1) 1968, p. 140) found that the density of stacking-fault tetrahedra in quenched dilute gold alloy containing 1000 ppm to 5000 ppm Cu does not differ from that in pure gold. This is in agreement with the conclusion that monovalent impurities have a weak interaction with vacancies in gold. The results of Siegel (Phil. Mag. 13 (1966) 337) who reported an increase of tetrahedra density by the addition of much smaller Cu concentration ($\approx 20$ ppm) disagree with the above conclusions. It is not sure whether this discrepancy is due to the difference in Cu concentration used in the different experiments. This question may be settled by performing experiments on gold alloys with Cu content at about hundred ppm level.

PART 3


RADIATION DAMAGE IN FCC METALS

# PRODUCTION RATES OF FRENKEL DEFECTS
# DURING LOW-TEMPERATURE IRRADIATIONS

H. J. WOLLENBERGER

*Van de Graaff-Labor, Aachen, der Kernforschungsanlage Jülich GmbH, Germany*

## 1. Introduction

The irradiation of a crystal with energetic particles produces Frenkel defects in the lattice. The production rate is defined as the increment of the atomic concentration of Frenkel defects produced per unit of integrated particle flux density (unit of dose). Production rate measurements at temperatures low enough to prevent thermally activated migration of the defects have been used to study the process of atomic displacement. The main fields of activity may be characterized by the terms threshold energy for atomic displacement and saturation behaviour of the defect production. Measurements at elevated temperatures at which the interstitials migrate by thermal activation have been used to study the interaction between these interstitials and the vacancies, impurity atoms and dislocations present in the sample. With the present article it is not intended to give a complete review of all investigations performed in the three fields. Instead, the more general results are discussed in view of conclusive interpretations and open questions.

## 2. Threshold energy for atomic displacement

### 2.1. *General remarks*

The minimum energy which must be transferred to a lattice atom in order to produce a stable Frenkel defect is called the threshold energy for atomic displacement $T_d$. It is related to the interatomic potential. Hence, an experimental determination of the threshold energy provides in principle the possibility of determining the interatomic potential in the energy range of the threshold (about 25 eV). However, the quantitative relation between the threshold energy and the interatomic potential have been calculated analytically only by approaching many-body collisions by two-body collisions and neglecting the thermal vibration of the lattice atoms. The most detailed information has been obtained numerically by computer experiments [1] in which the actual many-body collisions were simulated in a model of body-centred iron.

Because of the lattice structure the threshold energy $T_d$ depends on the direction of the recoil momentum (knock-on direction) with respect to the crystal axes. There will be a minimum threshold $T_o$ valid for a certain knock-on direction. This minimum threshold has been determined by measuring production rates as a function of the energy transferred to the lattice atoms in polycrystalline samples. Below the minimum threshold the production rate is zero and above it is positive and changes somehow with the transferred energy. This energy dependence of the production rate is given by the energy dependence of the total cross section defined by eq. (2) and by the angular dependence of the threshold energy. At a certain transferred energy $T$ atomic displacements are possible only for such knock-on directions for which $T$ exceeds $T_d$. This restriction of the defect production to limited solid angles is described by the displacement probability which can be determined by production rate measurements in polycrystals. The angular dependence of the threshold energy, however, cannot be derived in a unique manner from measurements in polycrystals. It can be derived from single crystal measurements if certain favourable conditions are fulfilled.

The knocked-on atoms are capable of producing additional defects if the recoil energies are considerably larger than the threshold $T_d$. In heavy particle irradiations (neutrons, deuterons, $\alpha$-particles) most of the defects are produced by such energetic atoms. This multiple defect production has been studied by production rate measurements as a function of large transferred energies.

Experimentally, the required variation of transferred energies is achieved by irradiating with electrons of various energies in the order of magnitude of 1 MeV. The radiation-induced Frenkel defect concentrations were determined almost always by means of electrical resistivity measurements, making the assumption that the resistivity increase is proportional to the atomic defect concentration $C$. For the production rate in terms of the electrical resistivity (resistivity damage rate) we obtain then

$$\frac{d\Delta\rho}{d\phi} = \rho_F \frac{dC}{d\phi} = \rho_F \, \sigma_d \,, \tag{1}$$

where $\rho_F$ is the resistivity increase per unit concentration of Frenkel pairs, $dC/d\phi$ the production rate, and $\sigma_d$ the total cross section of the lattice atoms to become displaced from their regular lattice sites into stable interstitial positions by the collisions between the radiation particles and the lattice atoms. The proportionality of $C$ and $\Delta\rho$ is not self-evident. Indeed deviations are known to occur due to the scattering of the conduction electrons at the sample surface or due to deviations from Matthiessen's rule. Both effects will be discussed below (sections 2.2.1 and 3.3).

## 2.2. Displacement probability for polycrystals

### 2.2.1. Single defect production

The behaviour of the damage rate as a function of the electron energy is demonstrated in fig. 1 which contains all data published for polycrystalline aluminium *. The deviation of the data from different laboratories indicate the difficulties in electron dose measurements. The error of the resistivity measurements can in general be kept negligibly small compared with the observed systematic deviations. The

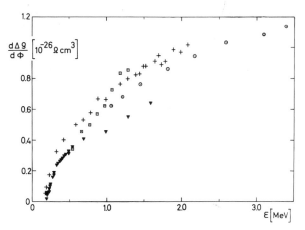

Fig. 1. Resistivity damage rates for polycrystalline aluminium as a function of electron energy. (□ ref. [16], + ref. [11], ▽ data of ref. [7] corrected recently for the electrical size effect, ⊙ ref. [8]).

damage rate decreases with decreasing electron energy and at a certain electron energy it drops below the limit given by the sensitivity of the measurement. From the papers of the last three years one deduces the minimum damage rate being measurable with an uncertainty of 10% to be about $3 \times 10^{-29}$ $\Omega \mathrm{cm}^3$ **. With a $\rho_F$ of $3 \times 10^{-4}$ $\Omega \mathrm{cm}$ this production rate limit corresponds to a displacement cross section $\sigma_d$ of 0.1 barn.

The evaluation of data such as shown in fig. 1 is based upon a comparison with calculated cross sections. The electron-atom collisions leading to atomic displacements are governed by the Coulomb interaction between the high energetic electrons and the atom nuclei. According to Mott's theoretical treatment [4] of this scattering problem we can calculate *** the cross section of the atoms for obtaining recoil

---

* Reviews of energy dependent production rates are given in refs. [2,3].
** The number is based upon a smallest resistivity increase being detectable of $3 \times 10^{-13}$ $\Omega \mathrm{cm}$, an electron beam current density of 5 $\mu \mathrm{A/cm}^2$ and an irradiation time of 10 hours.
*** Approximate expressions, for practical purpose, are given in ref. [5].

energies between a given lower limit and the maximum transferred energy in the
form

$$\sigma = \int_{T_0'}^{T_{\max}(\epsilon)} K_M(\epsilon, T)\, dT, \tag{2}$$

where $K_M(\epsilon, T)\, dT$ is the differential cross section of the atoms for obtaining recoil
energies between $T$ and $T + dT$ by collisions with electrons of energy $\epsilon$ according to
Mott. With the minimum threshold energy $T_0$ as the lower bound of the integral $\sigma$
would equal the displacement cross section if the threshold energy were an isotropic property. Because of the lattice structure, however, it depends on the knock-
on direction with respect to the crystal axes [1]. In a polycrystalline sample, therefore, a collision with a recoil energy larger than the minimum threshold $T_0$ will or
will not lead to a stable interstitial depending upon the displacement direction. Only
part of the collisions which are considered in eq. (2) produce stable Frenkel defects.
This partial effectiveness is described by the displacement probability $p(T)$. With
this function the displacement cross section $\sigma_d$ is given by

$$\sigma_d = \int_{T_0}^{T_{\max}(\epsilon)} p(T)\, K_M(\epsilon, T)\, dT \tag{3}$$

with $0 \leqslant p(T) \leqslant 1$. Thus $p(T)$ describes phenomenologically the energy dependence
of production rates to be expected in polycrystals with respect to the energy dependence of $\sigma$ (eq. (2)).

The evaluation of $p(T)$ from experimental data is usually performed in the following way. Experimental displacement cross sections are derived from the resistivity
damage rates using eq. (1) *. Then displacement cross sections calculated according
to eq. (3) with an assumed one or more parametric $p(T)$ function are fitted to the
experimental data by varying the characteristic parameters of $p(T)$. An exact fitting
would mean that the equation

$$\frac{d\Delta\rho}{d\phi}(\epsilon) = \rho_F \int_{T_0}^{T_{\max}(\epsilon)} p(T)\, K_M(\epsilon, T)\, dT \tag{4}$$

is satisfied for all used electron energies $\epsilon$.

Before discussing results we shall look briefly at an example for violation of the
proportionality given by eq. (1) which is especially relevant in threshold energy determinations.

---

* In section 3.2.1 it is shown that $\sigma_d$ can be obtained from damage rates only by extrapolating
  to vanishing radiation induced defect concentration. However, saturation effects can be neglected for the small defect concentrations usually produced in order to measure damage rates
  as a function of electron energy.

If the sample is very thin and of high purity, the scattering of the conduction electrons at the sample surface contribute to the electrical resistivity. As a consequence the resistivity damage rate in such a sample is larger than that of the bulk material although the production rate $dC/d\phi$ is equal to that in the bulk material as has been shown by simultaneous irradiation of a thin and a thick aluminium foil [6]. With increasing defect concentration the enhanced damage rate in the thin sample decreases and approaches that of the bulk material. Fortunately, most of the damage rate measurements in polycrystals have been performed with samples thick enough to represent the bulk material. But in those cases in which thin samples have been used surface scattering has often been neglected. In the case of the Al damage rates in fig. 1 the original data reported for foils of 20 $\mu$ thickness [7] have been corrected later [8]. The corrected data in fig. 1 are about 25% smaller than the original data.

Now we proceed in discussing the determination of the $p(T)$ function. The simplest type of function assumed for the fitting according to eq. (4) is the step function defined by

$$p(T) = \begin{matrix} 0 & \text{for} & T < T_d \\ 1 & \text{for} & T \geqslant T_d . \end{matrix} \qquad (5)$$

It represents an isotropic threshold energy $T_d$. The fitting result for gold using a step

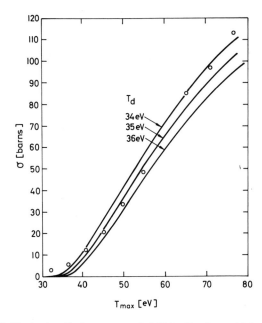

Fig. 2. Single step displacement probabilities fitted to gold data [9].

function [9] is shown in fig. 2. The data indicate that the actual $p(T)$ is not zero below 34 eV as the respective step function does. At higher energies the actual $p(T)$
obviously increases with $T$ whereas the step function is constant above 34 eV. Moreover this fitting yields an $\rho_F$ (eq. (4)) of about $0.9 \times 10^{-4}$ $\Omega$cm, a value which is
smaller than the resistivity increase per unit concentration of vacancies ($1.6 \times 10^{-4}$
$\Omega$cm [10]). At present there is no evidence from other experiments or theory that
the resistivity contribution of a Frenkel defect could be smaller than that of one of
its components. Similar unsatisfactory results have been obtained for other metals.

Much better fits are obtained when using a stair case function for $p(T)$ as has
been shown for aluminium and copper [11]. This kind of function seems to represent the anisotropy of the threshold energy in good approximation even in the case
of only a few steps [1]. The first step of the staircase function rises at the minimum
threshold $T_0$. This onset of the defect production must be identified with the onset
of the observable damage rate in the experiment. The real onset of the defect production cannot be observed due to the limited sensitivity. With increasing sensitivity,
therefore, the minimum threshold will be found at lower energies. The limit of
0.1 barn given above corresponds to an uncertainty of at least 3 eV for $T_0 = 19$ eV
in copper [12], for instance. This uncertainty is of remarkable influence on determinations of the interatomic potential. Moreover, there are indications that the
defect production in the energy range close to the minimum threshold can be due
to impurity atoms [13]. Systematic investigations of this effect have not yet been
performed.

Another difficulty arises because of the increased number of parameters. In the
case of the single step function the values of $T_0$ as well as of $\rho_F$ were obtained from
the fitting process. With the staircase function this is no longer the case. For reasons
of simplicity we approximate the staircase function by a linear increasing $p(T) =$
$\alpha(T - T_0)$ for $T \geqslant T_0$. Exact fitting corresponds to the equation

$$\frac{d\Delta\rho}{d\phi}(\epsilon) = \rho_F \, \alpha \int_{T_0}^{T_{max}(\epsilon)} (T - T_0) \, K_M(\epsilon, T) \, dT \qquad (6)$$

satisfied for all electron energies used. Now, the fitting yields only the product $\rho_F \alpha$
besides the value of $T_0$. A good fitting primarily indicates that the shape of the
probability function has been chosen properly. Information about the numerical
value of $\alpha$ or generally of $p(T)$ at a given value of $T$ can only be obtained if $\rho_F$ is
known. Since this quantity has not been determined experimentally with a sufficient
accuracy for any metal, at present the displacement probability $p(T)$ cannot yet be
derived quantitatively. The energy dependence of $\rho_F p(T)$, however, gives us qualitative information about the anisotropy of the threshold energy. A quantitative knowledge of $p(T)$ would give us additionally the energy range covered by the angular
dependent threshold energies. But it would not enable us to derive the angular dependence of the threshold energy for the following reason: if the angular dependence

is described only by the threshold energy values valid for the three main cubic crystal axes and the smoothest function is assumed between these axes (expansion into cubic harmonics) [14], which is certainly a very simple model, one gets already a three-parametric description of the angular dependence. The simultaneous determination of three parameters from the displacement probability function, however, is ambiguous.

Damage rates have been measured as a function of electron energy for a large number of metals. However, it has been shown that the fitting according to eq. (4) was generally not very sensitive to the shape of $p(T)$ [11,15]. Hence, our knowledge about the anisotropy of the threshold energy in the metals is still rather restricted. Much more reliable results might be obtained by a drastic reduction of the uncertainty of the damage rate measurements to about 0.1%.

### 2.2.2. Multiple defect production

A much better situation with respect to the information obtainable from measurements exists at higher energies at which multiple production contributes appreciably to the defect production. In the case of aluminium the measurements have been extended up to 3.3 MeV electron energy [8] as shown in fig. 1. This energy corresponds to a maximum transferred energy of about 1100 eV which is about 70 times the minimum threshold. Primary knocked-on atoms (knocked-on by the electrons) with such high recoil energies are capable to displace further atoms from their regular lattice size by atom-atom collisions. If the number of Frenkel defects produced in the average by a primary atom with the recoil energy $T$ is $n(T)$, the total displacement cross section will be

$$\sigma_d = \int_{T_o}^{T_{max}(\epsilon)} p(T) \, n(T) \, K_M(\epsilon, T) \, dT .  \tag{7}$$

In fig. 3 the $p(T)n(T)$ function which fits best to the data points in fig. 1 is plotted versus the recoil energy $T$ [8]. Here $\rho_F$ has been assumed to be $4.4 \times 10^{-4}$ $\Omega$cm. The experimental uncertainty of the damage rates in fig. 1 leads to an uncertainty of the slope of the solid line above 200 eV (fig. 3) of $\pm$ 2%. Above 600 eV the uncertainty of $p(T)n(T)$ increases rapidly because the contribution of displacements with such high recoil energies to the total defect production is very small [8].

It is reasonable to assume that the increase of $p(T)n(T)$ above 200 eV is due to the increase of $n(T)$ alone. The linearity indicates that the energy dissipation in the collision cascade initiated by the primary atom with energy $T$ proceeds via two-body collisions as has been assumed in ref. [17]. These authors obtained

$$n(T) = T/2T_d^s \quad \text{with} \quad T \geqslant 2T_d^s  \tag{8}$$

for a step function at $T_d^s$ as displacement probability acting in the secondary collisions

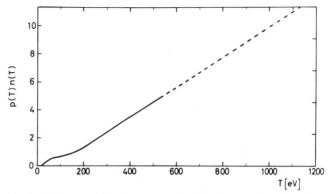

Fig. 3. Displacement function versus transferred energy for aluminium
with $\rho_F = 4.4 \times 10^{-4}$ $\Omega$cm [8].

(atom-atom collisions). From the slope of the curve in fig. 3 one derives

$$n(T) = T/93\,\text{eV} . \tag{8a}$$

Eqs. (8) and (8a) yield $T_d^s = 46.5$ eV. In table 1 this value is given together with the average transferred energy $T$ and corresponding values for deuteron and neutron irradiation [18]. For the heavy particle irradiations most of the defects are produced within large cascades in which a considerable number of defects recombine spontaneously due to the high defect density (see section 3.3). This loss of defect concentration leads to an enhanced $T_d^s$ in eq. (8). In the case of deuterons the average transferred energy is in fact comparatively low (see table 1) but the number of defects which are produced within a few but very large cascades is appreciable.

Table 1
Effective threshold energies according to Kinchin and Pease [17] for aluminium.

| Irradiation particles | Average transferred energy $\bar{T}$ (eV) | Effective threshold energy * $T_d^s$ (eV) |
|---|---|---|
| Electrons | 56 | 46.5 |
| Deuterons | 375 | 56 |
| Neutrons | $10^4$ | 65 |

* Obtained for $\rho_F = 4.4 \times 10^{-4}$ $\Omega$cm.

As has been shown in section 2.2.1 the step function is not a good approximation for the displacement probability. Therefore, it is suitable to assume another type of function also for the secondary displacements. The function $n(T)$ has been

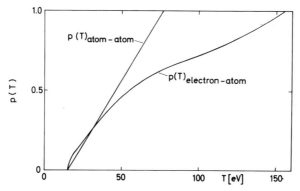

Fig. 4. Displacement probability for atom-atom and electron-atom collisions
in aluminium with $\rho_F = 4.4 \times 10^{-4}$ $\Omega$cm [8].

calculated for a linear increasing displacement probability and hard core interaction
between the colliding atoms [19]. Comparing the theoretical results with the experimental value (eq. (8)) yields the slope of the linear displacement probability if the
minimum threshold is taken to be equal to that found in the single displacement
range (electron-atom collision) [8]. In fig. 4 the obtained displacement probability
for the atom-atom collisions is shown together with the displacement probability
function obtained in the low energy range. Obviously, the displacement probability
increases faster with the energy in atom-atom collisions than in the primary electron-
atom collisions. This different behaviour is found for all possible values of $\rho_F$ and is
unaffected by the uncertainty of the displacement probability in the low-energy
range (see section 2.2.1). With a forward scattering law for the atom-atom collisions
[20] the difference between both displacement probabilities becomes even larger
[8]. At present, aluminium is the only metal which has been investigated in such a
detailed manner in the range of multiple defect production.

### 2.3. Single crystal experiments

As we have seen in the preceding sections the angular dependence of the threshold energy cannot be obtained in a unique manner from measurements in polycrystals. Hence, the question arises whether such information can be obtained from
single crystal measuremnents. The answer cannot be given off-hand. The main difficulty arises from the Coulomb scattering law with its strong preference of small
angle scattering. The forward-scattering of the electrons is equivalent to large recoil
angles of the knocked-on atoms with respect to the incident electron direction [5].
The transferred energy is

$$T = T_{max} \cos^2\theta , \qquad (9)$$

where $\theta$ is the angle between the incident electron direction and the knock-on direction. The differential cross section of the atoms for obtaining recoil energies between $T$ and $T + dT$ is approximately proportional to $T^{-2}$, i.e., proportional to $\cos^{-4}\theta$ according to eq. (9). Even in the case of an incident electron direction being exactly aligned to a crystal axis the displacement directions are distributed within a solid angle around the chosen crystal axis. The solid angle is limited by that angle $\theta_L$ at which the transferred energy $T$ drops below the threshold $T_d$. This distribution of knock-on directions induced by unidirectional electrons restricts the possibility for observing details of the angular dependence of the threshold energy. Significantly different values of the threshold energy valid within not to small solid angles, however, should be detectable. The basic question which anisotropy is still detectable by production rate measurements in single crystals has not yet been treated quantitatively in the literature.

An additional problem for single crystal irradiations comes from the multiple scattering of the electrons passing through a crystal which leads to a distribution of electron flight directions around the direction of the incident beam. As a consequence the knock-on directions will be spread out even more. If the overwhelming majority of the electrons shall not deviate from incident direction by more than 10 degrees, for example, the sample crystals must have a thickness in the order of $1\,\mu$ for almost all metals [21]. The preparation of such thin single crystals involves a number of problems. Mainly high impurity contents complicate the interpretation of damage rates. The impurity content should be in the order of 1 ppm or less to avoid subthreshold defect production [13]. This kind of production would mask the onset of the normal atom displacement, i.e., the normal minimum threshold energy. Samples of high purity and a thickness in the order of $1\,\mu$, however, exhibit a remarkable influence of the electrical size effect [6]. In addition, the magnitude of the size effect may depend on the crystal orientation with respect to the direction of the measuring current. But nothing is known about this effect from measurements at present. Therefore, the influence of the size effect must be measured for each investigated orientation by comparing the resistivity damage rates in two crystals of different thicknesses, similar to the procedure for polycrystals [6].

Production rate measurements in single crystals have been reported for copper [22], gold [3], and iron [23]. The copper samples were of non-uniform thickness ranging from 6 to $18\,\mu$. The residual resistivities were so high that the influence of the size effect on the production rate was negligible. In three different orientated samples ($\langle 100 \rangle$, $\langle 110 \rangle$, $\langle 111 \rangle$) the onset of defect production occurred at maximum transferred energies between 15 and 20 eV. The authors conclude from this result that the threshold energies for $\langle 100 \rangle$ as well as $\langle 110 \rangle$ displacements is about 19 eV whereas the onset of the defect production in the $\langle 111 \rangle$ sample reflects mainly the defect production in the $\langle 100 \rangle$ and $\langle 110 \rangle$ directions. A quantitative evaluation of the production rate curves for the energy range above the minimum threshold has not been presented. Such an evaluation would certainly be troublesome because of the large influence of the multiple electron scattering. The identical energies found for the onset of the defect production in the $\langle 100 \rangle$ and the $\langle 110 \rangle$ samples might also be caused by this effect if the threshold for these both directions deviate by no more than 10 eV [24].

In gold [3] the information is even poorer. The sample thicknesses were $5.4\,\mu$ and $9\,\mu$. Residual resistivities are not given. Absolute values of the production rate could not be obtained in the sample geometry. The authors observed approximately equal energy dependence of the production rates between 1.5 and 2.2 MeV electron energy for a polycrystal, a ⟨110⟩, and a ⟨111⟩ oriented crystal. Only in the near onset region below 1.5 MeV and the ⟨110⟩ sample exhibits a considerably larger production rate than the other ones. The authors conclude from the data that the threshold valid for ⟨110⟩ as well as for ⟨111⟩ should be approximately 35 eV. Here the same objection as in the case of copper can be raised. Moreover, studies of the production rate as a function of the radiation induced-defect concentration show a peculiar behaviour of the damage rate even at such low defect concentrations as have been used in the threshold energy determinations (see section 3.3).

In the case of iron [23], ⟨111⟩ and ⟨100⟩ samples with thicknesses between 15 and $25\,\mu$ have been irradiated. The residual resistivities were about $8 \times 10^{-7}\ \Omega$cm. With this value the influence of the size effect on the resistivity damage rate is negligible [6]. The onset of defect production has been observed in the ⟨111⟩ and the ⟨100⟩ samples at a maximum transferred energy of about 20 eV. Production rates have been calculated for an anisotropic threshold energy similar to that found by computer experiments [1] and fitted to the data which had to be normalized due to difficulties with the sample geometry. The authors could fit the calculated curve also to a small peak observed in the damage rate versus electron energy curve below 0.6 MeV and, therefore, explained it by the anisotropy of the threshold energy. It should be noticed, however, that in these experiments the incident electron beam was considerably divergent *. Under these circumstances it can hardly be understood how the anisotropy of the threshold energy can be seen so clearly in the damage rate curve as it is the case for the above mentioned peak. This difficulty does not arise if the peak is explained by damage production due to impurity atoms [13].

Normalized damage rate data were often used for the fitting procedure as it has been done also in the present case [23]. It must be emphasized that this method is not appropriate to give quantitative information about threshold energies above the minimum value $T_0$. The normalization procedure consists simply in a division of all damage rates by that valid at a certain electron energy, namely the normalization energy. This method has often been applied in the early days when the single step function (eq. (5)) was used for fitting to polycrystal data [25]. As it can be seen from eq. (4), a division of the left and right hand side of the equation by the respective production rates valid for the normalization energy eliminates the constant

---

* The electrons had to pass through two 125 $\mu$ Al windows before impinging on the sample. The multiple scattering in the windows leads to a considerable divergence of the beam. At 0.6 MeV, for instance, the characteristic scattering angle $\theta_{1/e}$ is about 30 degrees if only the second window is considered [3].

$\rho_F$. Hence, no information could be obtained about the value of $\rho_F$ whereas a fit to *absolute* damage rates gives $\rho_F$ as well as $T_d$, as shown in section 2.2.1. If a linearly increasing displacement probability, as a first approximation of an anisotropic threshold energy, is taken for the fit, one sees immediately from eq. (6) that the normalization eliminates $\rho_F$ as well as $\alpha$. With the elimination of the slope $\alpha$ of the linear increasing displacement probability, however, the absolute scale of $p(T)$ has been lost. Hence, it cannot be learned even from an exact fit whether the threshold energy ranges from the minimum $T_0$ to $2T_0$ or $5T_0$, for instance. The same is naturally true for even more complicated displacement probability functions.

A fit to monocrystal data requires a displacement probability function which represents the anisotropy of the threshold energy in the vicinity of that crystal axis being aligned to the electron beam. Obviously, a single step function representing an isotropic threshold energy cannot be used for the fit. Hence, the absolute scale of the threshold energies above $T_0$ cannot be obtained just as in the case of polycrystals. The good fit obtained for the iron data [23], therefore, does not verify the threshold energy values adopted for the calculations. It only indicates that the shape of the displacement probability has been chosen properly.

## 2.4. Conclusions

Resistivity damage rates have been measured as a function of electron energy for a large number of metals. The minimum threshold energies derived from these data depend on the sensitivity of the measurements. With an enhanced sensitivity the minimum threshold might be observed at lower energies. This uncertainty is of remarkable influence on the determination of interatomic potentials. There are indications that a sensitivity enhancement of the usual resistivity measurements will not necessarily lead to more exact threshold energies. Impurity effects might mask the real thresholds. Presumably, a new method for threshold energy determination using high-voltage electron microscopy [26] will become interesting here.

Furthermore, from resistivity damage rates measured in a polycrystal, the displacement probability $p(T)$ times $\rho_F$, the resistivity increment per unit of defect concentration, can be obtained. As long as the values of $\rho_F$ are not known from other experiments, absolute displacement probabilities cannot be evaluated. As a consequence, the maximum threshold energies are still unknown for all metals. The shape of the $p(T)$ functions could be derived only with large uncertainties. A considerable improvement of the measuring accuracy combined with the use of higher electron energies would yield much better results.

Irradiations with electrons of sufficiently high energies can give valuable information on multiple defect production as has been shown for aluminium. For other metals, much higher electron energies than 3 MeV, the usual maximum value available, are required.

From monocrystal irradiations, only the minimum threshold energies have been obtained up to now. More information can be obtained by a considerable improvement of the specimen preparation. It is not yet quite clear how much quantitative information about the angular dependence of the threshold energy can be obtained in principle from monocrystal irradiations.


## 3. Spontaneous and sub-threshold recombination

### 3.1. *General remarks*

It is evident that a vacancy and an interstitial must be separated by a certain minimum distance in order to form a mechanically stable Frenkel defect. If the separation does not exceed this limit, vacancy and interstitial will recombine spontaneously, i.e., without thermal activation. The spontaneous recombination volume is defined by that volume around a given type of defect (interstitial, for instance) which is occupied by those lattice sites at which the other type of defect (the vacancy) is unstable. Its influence on the production of stable Frenkel defects can be seen easily. Let the Frenkel defect $I_2 - V_2$ be produced in the neighbourhood of the already existing Frenkel defect $I_1 - V_1$ (fig. 5). If the later produced vacancy $V_2$

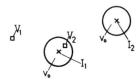

Fig. 5. Effect of spontaneous recombination.

lies within the spontaneous recombination volume of the previously produced interstitial $I_1$, the pair $I_1 - V_2$ will recombine spontaneously. Consequently, the production process of $I_2 - V_2$ has not increased the Frenkel defect concentration. With increasing Frenkel defect concentration the probability of such events will increase and hence the Frenkel defect production per incident particle will decrease. Indeed, a large number of irradiations with different particles and different metals have shown such a saturation behaviour of the production rate.

The concept of spontaneous recombination is based upon the static stability of Frenkel defects. It does not consider the way by which defects are introduced into the lattice. There is another effect, a dynamic one, which may cause a decrease of the production rate with increasing defect concentration and which would be closely connected with the way by which the defects are introduced. The irradiation of a crystal causes not only above-threshold energy transfers to the lattice atoms but also sub-threshold energy transfers. It seems likely that sub-threshold energy transfers to the neighbouring atoms of a stable close Frenkel pair will induce its recombination. This sub-threshold recombination is not included in the concept of spontaneous recombination because there a second defect must be produced within the recombination volume of the first requiring an above-threshold energy transfer.

## 3.2. *Theory*

### 3.2.1. Spontaneous recombination

The influence of the spontaneous recombination on the defect production has been studied extensively by simulating production and spontaneous recombination in a computer model [27]. In an analytical treatment of the problem, spontaneous as well as sub-threshold recombinations have been considered [28]. The quantitative influence of the spontaneous recombination on the production rate can be shown in a simplified manner. To a first approximation, only the interaction between vacancies and interstitials is considered; that between equivalent defects, i.e., overlapping of spontaneous recombination volumes, is neglected. Let a displacement collision produce a new Frenkel defect $I_n - V_n$ in the neighbourhood of $I_C - V_C$ which is one of the already existing Frenkel defects of concentration $C$. Then there are four different local correlations between $I_n - V_n$ and $I_C - V_C$ with respect to the interstitial vacancy interaction. In table 2 these correlations are given together with their probabilities of occurrence $p_i$ and the resultant defect balance $b_i$. In the

Table 2
Spontaneous recombination effect on the defect production (for denotation see text).

| Local correlation | Probability of occurrence | Balance of the number of stable Frenkel defects $b_i$ |
|---|---|---|
| Both $I_n$ and $V_n$ in stable positions | $p_1 = (1 - v_0 C)(1 - v_0 C)$ * | $b_1 = +1$ |
| $I_n$ in a stable position, $V_n$ within the spont. recomb. vol. of $I_C$ | $p_2 = (1 - v_0 C)$ | $b_2 = 0$ |
| $V_n$ in a stable position (the spont. recomb. vol. of $I_n$ includes $V_C$) | $p_3 = (1 - v_0 C)$ | $b_3 = 0$ |
| $V_n$ within the spont. recomb. vol. of $I_C$ and $V_C$ within the spont. recomb. vol. of $I_n$ | $p_4 = (v_0 C)^2$ | $b_4 = -1$ |

* The quantity $v_0$ is the spontaneous recombination volume measured in atomic volumes.

average the production of one Frenkel defect will enhance the number of stable Frenkel defects by unity with the probability

$$\sum_i p_i b_i = 1 - 2v_0 C \tag{10}$$

according to table 2. Hence the production rate in a lattice containing Frenkel defects of concentration $C$ will be

$$dc/d\phi = \sigma_d (1 - 2v_0 C) . \tag{11}$$

The second approximation considers the overlapping of recombination volumes which reduces $v_0$ to an average effective value $v(C)$. The production rate becomes then

$$dc/d\phi = \sigma_d(1 - 2vC) .$$ (12)

If we consider only single overlapping, i.e., the overlapping volume is formed only by two recombination volumes, one obtains

$$v(C) = v_0 - \tfrac{1}{2}\delta v(C) ,$$ (13)

where $\delta v$ is the average overlapping volume (fig. 6). The quantity $\delta v$ can be easily calculated according to a suggestion of Dettmann [29]. We describe the recombination volume $v_0$ by

$$v_0 = \frac{1}{v_A} \int_V D(\mathbf{r}) \, d\mathbf{r} ,$$ (14)

where $v_A$ and $V$ are the atomic and the crystal volume, respectively, and

$$D(\mathbf{r}) = \begin{array}{ll} 1 & \text{for} \quad \mathbf{r} \text{ within } v_0 \\ 0 & \text{for} \quad \mathbf{r} \text{ beyond } v_0 \end{array} .$$ (15)

Then, the average overlapping volume will be

$$\delta v = \frac{1}{v_A^2} \int C \, d\mathbf{R} \int D(\mathbf{r}) \, D(\mathbf{r} - \mathbf{R}) \, d\mathbf{r} ,$$ (16)

where the second integral gives the overlapping volume for a given distance $R$ be-

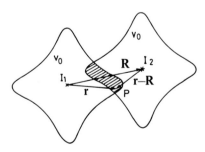

Fig. 6. Sketch for the calculation of the average overlapping volume.

tween two interstitials. The first integral containing the atomic concentration of
Frenkel defects considers the probability for finding two interstitials with the distance $R$. With the substitution $\mathbf{r} - \mathbf{R} = \mathbf{r}'$ one obtains

$$\delta v = \frac{C}{v_A^2} \int D(\mathbf{r}') \, d\mathbf{r}' \int D(\mathbf{r}) \, d\mathbf{r} . \tag{17}$$

Now, each of the integrals gives one recombination volume leading to

$$\delta v = C v_o^2 \tag{18}$$

and with eq. (12)

$$v(C) = v_o(1 - \tfrac{1}{2}v_o C) . \tag{19}$$

Eqs. (12) and (19) yield

$$dC/d\phi = \sigma_d(1 - v_o C)^2 . \tag{20}$$

This simple relation agrees very well with the numerical data obtained in the computer simulations [27] up to high defect concentrations [30]. Obviously, the effect
of multiple overlapping on the production of stable defects can be neglected as we
have done in deriving eq. (12). Indeed the general solution of the problem yields a
third order term in $C$ in the form of $v_o^3 C^3/100$ [28].

### 3.2.2. Sub-threshold recombination

The occurrence of sub-threshold recombination depends upon the stability of
close Frenkel pairs against sub-threshold energy transfer to the interstitials or their
neighbouring atoms as well as on the interaction between the irradiating particles
and the lattice atoms. Consequently, a sub-threshold annihilation rate can be written in the form

$$dC/d\phi = -g C \sigma_s , \tag{21}$$

where $\sigma_s$ is the cross section of the atoms for obtaining sub-threshold recoil energies
being larger than a threshold $T_s$. The latter is the minimum energy which must be
transferred in order to induce a recombination. The factor $g$ takes into account that
not all defects given by the concentration $C$ might be annihilated by sub-threshold
collisions (more separated vacancies and interstitials) and that certainly not all impact directions with respect to the close pair axes will be favourable for inducing
the recombination. Both effects would cause $g$ to be smaller than unity. On the
other hand, if a number of atoms in the close-pair region is sensitive to sub-threshold

energy transfers with regard to defect annihilation, the above effects could be compensated more or less. At present, we have not enough theoretical information for a prediction of the value of $g$. In addition, eq. (21) gives only an integral description of the sub-threshold recombination. In reality, $g$ as well as $\sigma_s$ will certainly be different for Frenkel pairs of different extension (see section 3.3).

The cross section for sub-threshold energy transfers, however, has been calculated for electron irradiation [31,32]. It is of particular interest, since the effects of spontaneous and sub-threshold recombination could be separated experimentally for this kind of irradiation (section 3.3). It is reasonable to distinguish two different cross sections, that of the atoms for obtaining a recoil energy larger than $T_s$ directly by electron-atom collisions and that of the atoms for obtaining this recoil energy via atom-atom collisions induced by a primary atom. We call the first cross section $\sigma_s^p$ indicating that only primary knocked-on atoms are considered and the second one $\sigma_s^s$ because the respective atoms are secondary atoms in a collision cascade. The cross section $\sigma_s^p$ is given by

$$\sigma_s^p = \int_{T_s}^{T_o} K_M(\epsilon, T)\, dT . \tag{22}$$

The upper bound $T_0$ is the minimum threshold for atomic displacements, in accordance with our definition of sub-threshold energy transfers. The cross section $\sigma_s^s$ can be written to a first approximation [31], according to Kinchin and Pease [17], as

$$\sigma_s^s = \frac{1}{2T_s} \int_{T_s}^{T_o} T\, K_M(\epsilon, T)\, dT . \tag{23}$$

Since sub-threshold energies can be transferred to atoms also by primaries with energies larger than $T_0$ the upper bound of the integral in eq. (23) should properly be $T_{max}$. However, the value of the integral does not change much if $T_0$ is replaced by $T_{max}$, at least not for those values of $T_s$ which are discussed below.

A lower limit of $T_s$ should be the activation energy for thermal activated annihilation of close pairs. The activation energies determined during the stage I (close pair) annealing are less than 0.1 eV for copper and gold, for instance. In fig. 7 the cross sections $\sigma_s^p$ and $\sigma_s^s$ calculated according to the Mott series are shown for gold and different values of $T_s$ as a function of the electron energy $\epsilon$. For comparison the term $2v_0\sigma_d$ is shown which governs the reduction of the production rate due to spontaneous recombination (eq. (11)) as $g\sigma_s$ might do it due to sub-threshold recombination. The value of $v_0$ has been taken from the experimental result described in section 3.3 and $\sigma_d(\epsilon)$ from ref. [33]. It is clear from fig. 7 that the sub-threshold recombination will contribute significantly to the saturation behaviour if the threshold lies really below 1.0 eV and the factor $g$ is not smaller than 0.1.

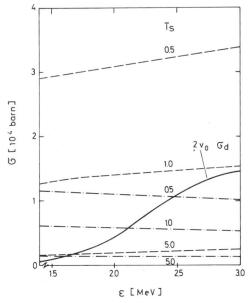

Fig. 7. Cross sections for sub-threshold recombination and spontaneous recombination versus electron energy in gold ($-\cdot-\cdot-\ \sigma_s^P; -----\ \sigma_s^S$).

The different energy dependences of $2v_0\sigma_d$ and $\sigma_s$ offers an experimental possibility for separating both effects. If a gold sample containing radiation-induced Frenkel pairs of concentration $C$ is irradiated with electrons of an energy less than 1.4 MeV no additional defects will be produced, i.e., no spontaneous recombination will take place. But the sub-threshold recombination effect is approximately equal to that acting during the preceding above-threshold irradiation because $\sigma_s^P$ as well as $\sigma_s^S$ are approximately independent of the electron energy $\epsilon$. Thus, an annihilation rate according to eq. (21) should be observable.

Another experimental separation should be possible by annealing a defect-containing sample at such an elevated temperature that all close pairs are eliminated. After this annealing the factor $g$ in eq. (21) and hence the sub-threshold recombination effect will be zero whereas the spontaneous recombination should — to a first approximation — occur as before. Both methods are treated in the next section.

## 3.3. Experiments

We discuss only those of the large number of experiments in literature which allow a separation of the spontaneous recombination effect from that of the sub-threshold recombination. In fig. 8 the drastic influence of the kind of irradiating particle on the saturation behaviour of copper is shown by plotting the relative production rates $(1/\sigma_d)dC/d\phi$ versus the radiation-induced resistivity increment $\Delta\rho$. An evaluation with respect to spontaneous recombination only (eq. (12)) would yield

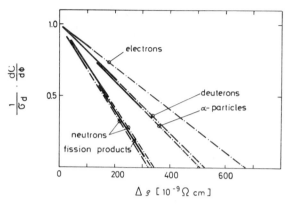

Fig. 8. Relative production rates versus radiation-induced resistivity increment for copper (solid lines — measured range, dashed lines — extrapolations, electrons [31], deuterons [34], α-particles [35], neutrons [36], fission products [37].

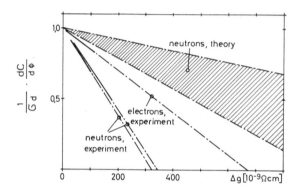

Fig. 9. Relative production rates versus radiation-induced defect concentration for copper [31].

the largest spontaneous recombination volume for neutrons and the smallest one for electrons. The analytical calculations [28] as well as the computer simulations [27] indeed predict different average recombination volumes $v$ for neutron and electron irradiation, but in the opposite sense. The segregation of vacancies and interstitials and the high defect densities in the cascades produced by neutron irradiation lead to an overlapping of recombination volumes already in the first cascade. As a consequence, the average recombination volume is smaller from the very beginning of a neutron irradiation than $v_0$ occurring at the beginning of an electron irradiation. In fig. 9 the discrepancy between the theoretical and the experimental curve obtained for copper is demonstrated. The initial recombination volume $v_0$ required for the theoretical calculation has been obtained by fitting eq. (11) to the electron irradiation data neglecting sub-threshold recombination effects. The degree of overlapping

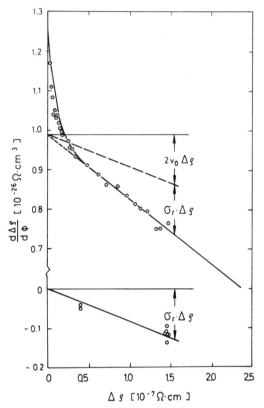

Fig. 10. Resistivity damage rates during above and sub-threshold irradiation versus radiation induced resistivity for gold [32].

within the defect cascades has been assumed within certain limits leading to the dashed region instead of the definite curve [38]. From fig. 9 one must conclude that the saturation behaviour of the experimental production rate during neutron irradiation is mainly due to dynamically induced recombination.

A direct experimental separation of both recombination effects requires an irradiation during which only one of the two effects is operative. The sub-threshold recombination alone should be observable during an irradiation of a sample containing Frenkel defects with particles of such a low energy that the maximum transferred energy is smaller than the threshold for atomic displacements. This is most easily done by electron irradiation, as it has been described in the preceding section. Such experiments have been reported up to now for gold [32] and platinum [39]. In figs. 10 and 11 the production rate curves of both metals for 3.0 MeV and 1.4 MeV are plotted. For both metals the electron energy of 1.4 MeV corresponds to a maximum transferred energy approximately equal to the minimum

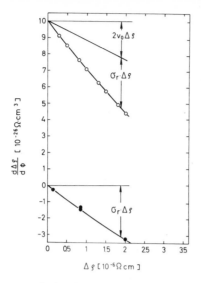

Fig. 11. Resistivity damage rates during above and sub-threshold irradiation versus radiation induced resistivity for platinum [39].

threshold of atomic displacement. The 1.4 MeV irradiation indeed diminishes the defect concentration obtained by the 3 MeV irradiation, i.e., a radiation-induced annihilation rate is observed. The slope of this annihilation rate curve corresponds to the product $g\sigma_s$ (eq. (21)) which we call somewhat inconsistently for the sake of briefness the cross section for sub-threshold recombination $\sigma_r$. If $\sigma_r$ does not depend on the electron energy as it has been found in section 3.2.2 for $\sigma_s$ the sub-threshold recombination contributes to the reduction of the production rate at 3 MeV as it is shown in figs. 10 and 11 *. The evaluation of the curves according to eqs. (11) and (21) yields the spontaneous recombination volume and the recombination cross sections given in table 3. It could be shown for platinum that the sub-threshold recombination influences preferentially those Frenkel defects which are annihilated at the low temperature side of the thermal annealing spectrum (close pairs) as it has been assumed in section 3.3.2 (fig. 12).

For copper and aluminium the sub-threshold recombination effect has been determined by the second method mentioned in section 3.2.2 since sub-threshold electron energies were not available [39]. In figs. 13 and 14 the production rate measures during 2.7 MeV electron irradiation are plotted versus the irradiation induced resistivity increment. The temperatures indicated at the data points are the temperatures of the annealing treatments prior to the measurement of the data points at 4.2°K. These data has been interpreted [39] as follows. The curve meas-

---

* In gold only the linear part of the curve at defect resistivities above $50 \times 10^{-9}$ $\Omega$cm is taken as representative for the normal saturation behaviour. The "tail" at the beginning of the curve will be discussed below.

Table 3
Spontaneous recombination values and cross sections for sub-threshold recombination.

|  | Al | Cu | Pt | Au |
|---|---|---|---|---|
| $\rho_F$ ($10^{-4}$ $\Omega$cm) * | 4.4 | 2.5 | 7.5 | 3.3 |
| $v_0$ (atomic vol) | ? ** | 125 | 48 | 135 |
| $\sigma_r$ (kbarn) | 7.1 | 3.9 | 15 | 8.0 |

\* The values of $\rho_F$ have been chosen as an average of those given in literature.
\*\* The evaluation of the aluminium data is questionable since the production rate curve corrected for the sub-threshold recombination does not follow exactly a second order polynom according to eq. (20).

ured primarily, i.e., without pre-annealing, are due to both effects, the spontaneous recombination and the sub-threshold recombination. The points measured after a pre-annealing at a given temperature represent the influence of the spontaneous recombination as well as that of the sub-threshold recombination acting still on those defects which have not been annealed at the given annealing temperature. The decrease of the production rate given by the data points obtained after annealing at the highest temperatures represent the influence of spontaneous recombination only. By this way the spontaneous recombination volumes $v_0$ and the total cross sections $\sigma_r$ given in table 3 have been obtained.

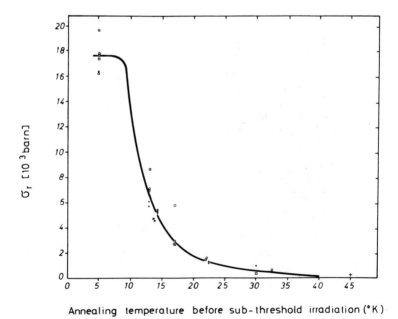

Fig. 12. Influence of pre-annealing on the cross section for sub-threshold recombination [39].

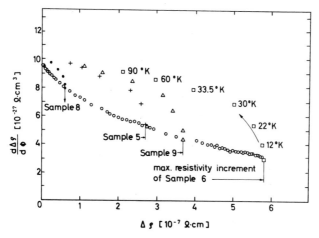

Fig. 13. Influence of pre-annealing on the resistivity damage rates in aluminium [39].
(Temperatures indicated are those of pre-annealing.)

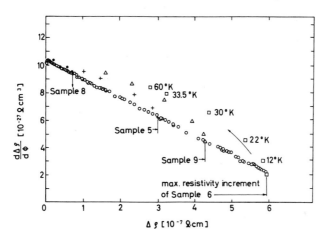

Fig. 14. Influence of pre-annealing on the resistivity damage rates in copper [39].
(Temperatures indicated are those of pre-annealing.)

The same method has been applied also to platinum [39]. Thus the cross section $\sigma_r$ could be obtained at 3.0 MeV in addition to the determination at 1.4 MeV. The values are $1.6 \times 10^4$ and $1.4 \times 10^4$ barn for 1.4 and 3.0 MeV, respectively, indicating a weak energy dependence as it has been found for $\sigma_s$ in section 3.2.2 for gold (fig. 7).

An interesting difference between copper and aluminium has been observed by measuring the fractional annealing at different temperatures as a function of the defect concentration as shown in figs. 15 and 16 [39]. A decrease of the fraction of

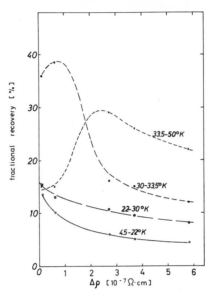

Fig. 15. Fractional recovery observed in the indicated temperature ranges versus radiation induced defect concentration for aluminium [39].

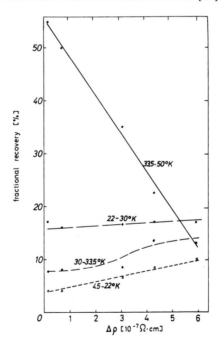

Fig. 16. Fractional recovery observed in the indicated temperature ranges versus radiation induced defect concentration for copper [39].

Frenkel defects annealing below 33°K is expected for aluminium due to the preferential influence of the sub-threshold recombination on these defects. An increase as it is seen for copper below 30°K, however, leads to the conclusion that there is still another mechanism which enhances the production of the close pairs with increasing defect concentration. The authors interpret this effect by sub-threshold transformation of more distant Frenkel defects to closer ones. The cross section for such a transformation from defects annealing in stage $I_B$ to those annealing in stage $I_A$ was estimated from the measurements to be about $10^4$ barns [40].

The tail of the production rate curve of gold at low defect concentrations (fig. 10) brings in an additional complication. Similar tails were observed previously during heavy particle irradiations and were interpreted by dynamical close pair recombination via focused collision sequences [36]. A similar evaluation of the present gold data yields an average range of the focused collision chains in the order of $10^4$ atomic distances. Since the average transferred energy is about 55 eV in a 3 MeV electron irradiation, this long range is consistent only with an energy loss in the focused collision chain smaller than $5.5 \times 10^{-3}$ eV per atomic distance which is about two orders of magnitude smaller than the values calculated for copper [41,42]. It is hard to see why the energy loss should be so much smaller in gold than in copper.

On the other hand, the tail can as well be explained by interstitial-vacancy-recombination due to long range interstitial migration. A suitable check for freely migrating interstitials is the comparison of the defect production rates in a vacancy doped and an undoped sample [43]. The result of such an experiment [44] is shown in fig. 17. The doping consisted in a 10°K irradiation with subsequent annealing at 80°K. This procedure is believed to introduce single vacancies and trapped or clustered interstitials. Indeed, the production rate is smaller in the doped sample as it is expected if the added vacancies increase the probability for interstitial-vacancy annihilation. The quantitative result, however, suggests a vacancy influence on the spontaneous recombination rather than on mobile interstitials. In the latter case the initial damage rate of the doped sample should be equal or even smaller than $0.8 \times 10^{-26}$ $\Omega$cm$^3$, the damage rate of the undoped sample at $\Delta\rho = 1.2 \times 10^{-7}$ $\Omega$cm (doping resistivity) (see section 4.2). The observed effect is much smaller and can be explained quantitatively by the influence of the added vacancies on the spontaneous recombination in the same way as it has been done for quenched platinum [39,45]. Our result, therefore, does not give an evidence for a long-range interstitial migration. On the other hand, if there exists a strong interstitial-interstitial attraction the influence of doping-induced vacancies could be reduced significantly.

An entirely different explanation of the tails considers a possible non-additivity of different resistivity contributions *. Such a non-additivity of the resistivity contributions of point defects and dislocations has been treated theoretically [46]. These calculations show that the tails of the production rate curves in neutron-

---

* We refer only to observations in thick samples. Thus, an influence of the electrical size effect (section 2.2.1) can be disregarded.

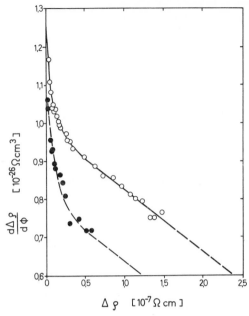

Fig. 17. Resistivity damage rates versus radiation-induced resistivity for gold [44] (○ well-annealed sample, residual resistivity $\rho_0 = 4.5 \times 10^{-9}$ $\Omega$cm, ● pre-irradiated and annealed at 80°K, $\Delta\rho_{dop} = 120 \times 10^{-9}$ $\Omega$cm).

irradiated deformed samples [47] can be explained quantitatively by the above mentioned non-additivity. There are indications that non-additivity occurs for the resistivity contributions of quenched-in defects and Frenkel pairs in platinum [39,45]. In the case of gold the same tails have been observed in well-annealed samples as well as in heavily doped samples (see fig. 17). Thus, the deviation from the additivity of certain resistivity contributions would have to be the same at very different values of the total resistivity (at $\rho_0$ and $\Delta\rho_{dop}$). Such a behavior seems to be inconsistent with all we know about the non-additivity of resistivity contributions [46]. Obviously, further investigations are required to find a satisfactory interpretation of the damage production in gold.

### 3.4. Conclusions

The saturation behaviour of the defect production has been studied in a large number of metals for both heavy particle and electron irradiation. In the case of electron irradiation two effects could be separated which contribute to about equal parts to the saturation behaviour; the spontaneous and the sub-threshold recombination. The dependence of the spontaneous recombination on the defect concentration has been observed in accordance with theoretical predictions for copper, gold, and platinum. The numerical evaluation yields the recombination volumes multiplied by

$\rho_F$, the resistivity increments per unit of defect concentration. With $\rho_F$ values between $5 \times 10^{-4}$ and $10 \times 10^{-4}$ $\Omega$cm, one obtains recombination volumes between 50 and 100 atomic volumes, in agreement with the results of computer calculations. From the sub-threshold recombination effect a cross section of the radiation-induced defects to become annihilated by sub-threshold energy transfers can be derived. For the above mentioned values of $\rho_F$ the sub-threshold recombination cross section lies in the order of $10^3$ barn (platinum $10^4$ barn). This order of magnitude can be explained only if the threshold energy for dynamically induced close pair recombination is less than 1 eV.

A comparison of the production rate curves measured during heavy particle irradiations with that for electron irradiation shows a considerably larger sub-threshold recombination effect for heavy particle irradiations. In addition to the sub-threshold collisions between irradiating particles and atoms we have here the sub-threshold collisions initiated by the energetic collision cascades. Quantitative information about the sub-threshold recombination effect in heavy particle irradiations is not available up to now.

## 4. Interaction of freely migrating interstitials with other lattice defects

### 4.1. *General remarks*

In this chapter defect production rates are discussed which have been measured at elevated temperatures where interstitials migrate freely. This occurs in most of the metals below the boiling point of liquid nitrogen [2]. Therefore, production rates of this kind have generally been measured during 80°K irradiation. Although a number of measurements have been reported for heavy particle irradiations we prefer to discuss only those performed with electron irradiations. In this case the experimental results can be explained more easily, while the general conclusions are the same as for heavy particle irradiations.

In the early days of research in radiation damage, production rate measurements at 80°K have mainly been analysed in view of the question whether or not the interstitials migrate freely at this temperature [48,49]. Already at that time the utility of such measurements has been outlined for studying the interaction of the interstitials with other lattice defects [50]. However, it has been just in the last two years that this interaction has been studied in more detail. The influence of quenched-in vacancies on the defect production has been studied in platinum at 90°K [43] and in gold at 80°K [51]. In both cases the free migration of the interstitial at the irradiation temperature has been derived from the results. For copper the question of di-interstitial formation in stage I as well as that of vacancy migration in stage III has been studied by production rate measurements at 80°K [52].

The analytical calculation of the defect production at elevated temperatures consists in a straightforward treatment of the diffusion problem [52]. It leads to analytical expressions for the production rate of defects being in stable positions at the irradiation temperature as a function of the radiation-induced defect concentration. The influence of other point defects introduced by any doping procedure on the production rate can be calculated as well [52]. It is not intended to represent these calculations here. Instead, a qualitative description of the phenomena is preferred, since it illustrates more clearly the underlying physical processes.

## 4.2. *Experiments*

### 4.2.1. Production rates in well-annealed samples

The first significant observation during 80°K irradiations is a strong non-linear increase of the radiation induced resistivity with the particle dose at least in high-purity specimens as shown in fig. 18 for zone-refined copper [50]. From this curve the resistivity damage rate $d\Delta\rho/d\phi$ can be derived as a function of radiation-induced resistivity increment $\Delta\rho$. As can be seen also in fig. 18 the damage rate decreases non-linearly with increasing resistivity. At the beginning of the curve the decay of the damage rate per unit of resistivity increment is much larger than in the case of spontaneous and sub-threshold recombination below 10°K (section 3.3).

The remarkable influence of the defect concentration on the damage rate can be explained by the following model [50]: At 80°K the freely migrating interstitials responsible for stage-$I_E$ annealing (in Cu at about 50°K) move very rapidly. Hence, the instantaneous concentration of free interstitials in the lattice is very small and clustering of them is unlikely. Instead, the interstitials encounter impurities and dislocations and become trapped or they recombine with earlier produced vacancies.

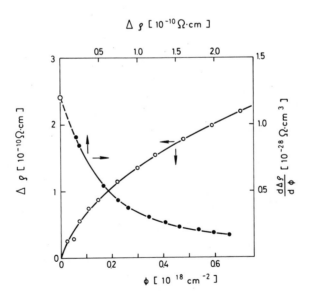

Fig. 18. Damage production at 80°K in zone-refined copper [50].

For each trapped interstitial an immobile single vacancy is left in the lattice. Now, the production rate is the concentration increment of Frenkel defects consisting of trapped interstitials and vacancies produced per unit of particle dose. Correspondingly, the radiation-induced resistivity increment is composed of the contributions caused by the vacancies and the trapped interstitials which certainly yield another value of $\rho_F$ than that of free vacancies and interstitials.

Three kinds of traps are conceivable: unsaturable, saturable, and nucleation traps. The different attributes characterize the different behaviour of the capture radius of the traps. For unsaturable traps the capture radius is independent of the number of interstitials captured per trap whereas for saturable traps the capture radius decreases with increasing number of trapped interstitials. At nucleation traps the capture radius increases with increasing number of trapped interstitials. Unsaturable traps have been observed in copper over an extended range of radiation induced-defect concentration [52]. With unsaturable traps the concentration of trapping sites (concentration of traps times capture volume) remains constant whereas that of recombination sites (vacancy concentration times capture volume of vacancies) increases with increasing defect concentration. Hence, the migrating interstitials have an increasing recombination probability and the number of trapped interstitials per produced migrating interstitial or per irradiating particle decreases with increasing defect concentration. The mathematical solution of this problem yields a hyperbolic decay of the production rate with increasing defect concentration. Therefore, a convenient test of the experimental data is a plot of the reciprocal production rate versus the defect concentration. A straight line in this plot as it has been found for copper [52] indicates unsaturable traps. (The intersection of the production rate curves in figs. 18, 19, 20, 22 and 23 with the ordinate has been obtained by an extrapolation of the above mentioned straight line to vanishing defect concentratioin.)

The influence of the trap concentration on the production rate curve is demonstrated in fig. 19 for aluminium of different purity [53]. The initial production rates are the same in both samples. For a given resistivity increment, however, the decay is different indicating that a certain vacancy concentration reduces the production rate more effectively in the purer sample. This is exactly what is expected according to our model since the ratio of the concentration of recombination sites to that of trapping sites is larger in the purer sample for a given vacancy concentration, i.e., resistivity increment. The same behaviour has been found for copper [52].

The influence of irradiation temperature is shown in fig. 20 for copper [54]. The stage II annealing was small during the irradiations at 223°K and at the lower temperatures. The curves have been corrected for this effect. Obviously the initial production rate is independent of the temperature at least up to 223°K. At 283°K the stage III annealing was remarkable already from the very beginning of the irradiation. For that reason the initial production rate is significantly smaller than those at the lower temperatures. For a given resistivity increase (defect concentration) the decay of the production rate is the larger the higher the irradiation temperature. Within

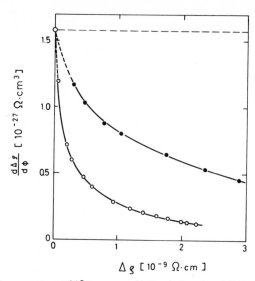

Fig. 19. Resistivity damage rates at 80°K versus radiation induced resistivity for aluminium of different purity [53] (● 4–9's, ○ 6–9's).

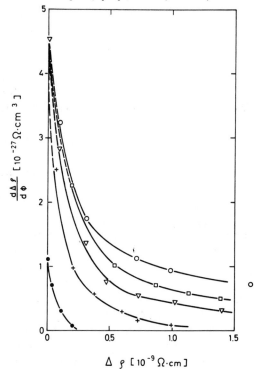

Fig. 20. Influence of temperature on the resistivity damage rate curve for copper [54] (○ 83°K, □ 123°K, △ 173°K, + 223°K, ● 283°K).

our model this leads to the conclusion that the effective concentration of trapping sites (concentration times capture radius) decreases with increasing temperature. The behaviour of the initial production rates implies an evidence against a thermal conversion of the interstitial [55] between 83 and 223°K. If a thermally activated conversion of the interstitial configuration from that migrating freely in stage $I_E$ with an activation energy of 0.1 eV into that migrating freely in stage III with 0.7 eV would occur, then the second configuration should be immobile within the temperature range between the conversion temperature and that of the beginning of stage III (about 230°K in the present case [54]). An immobile interstitial, however, would have only a very small chance to recombine with vacancies due to spontaneous recombination. Consequently, no marked decrease of the production rate with increasing $\Delta\rho$ should be observable in fig. 20. Since this is not the case, no immobile interstitial is produced instead of the mobile one at least up to 223°K [57].

### 4.2.2. Production rates in doped samples

The application of production rate measurements at elevated temperatures for studying doping effects consists simply in a comparison of the production rate curves of a well-annealed and the doped samples. More precisely, the decay of the production rate caused by the doping-induced resistivity increase $\Delta\rho_{dop}$ is compared with that caused by an equal radiation-induced resistivity $\Delta\rho$ in the well-annealed sample. This method is demonstrated now for three different doping treatments: (i) quenching, (ii) irradiation at 5°K and annealing in stage I, and (iii) irradiation at 80°K and annealing in stage III.

(i) The effect of quenching is shown in fig. 21 for platinum [43]. The initial production rate is much smaller in the quenched sample than in the well-annealed sample. Obviously, the quenched-in vacancies reduce the production rate with high efficiency. Since such a high efficiency cannot be explained for the case of an immobile interstitial the result represents evidence for the free migration of the interstitial. The same conclusion could be drawn from the results obtained for gold [51].

(ii) The effect of irradiation at 5°K and subsequent stage-I annealing on the 80°K production rate curve can be seen in fig. 22 for copper [52]. The initial production rate is smaller in the doped sample than in the well-annealed one, as it is expected, because the vacancies remaining immobile during stage I annealing and those surviving the stage I annealing behave like the vacancies introduced during the subsequent 80°K production rate measurement. A given resistivity increment $\Delta\rho$ reduces the production rate in the doped sample by a much smaller amount than that in the well-annealed sample (fig. 22). Since the vacancies left after the doping procedure behave like those introduced during the irradiation, this different reduction must be due to a different concentration of trapping sites. In fig. 19 we have seen that the decay of the production rate per unit of radiation-induced defect concentration is smaller in a less pure sample. Hence the pre-irradiation and stage I annealing has enhanced the concentration of trapping sites. The only cancidates for such newly produced traps are di-interstitials or even larger interstitial clusters.

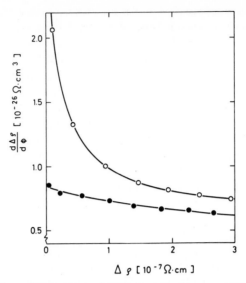

Fig. 21. Influence of quenching on the resistivity damage rate curve at 90°K for platinum [43].
(○ well-annealed sample, ● quenched sample).

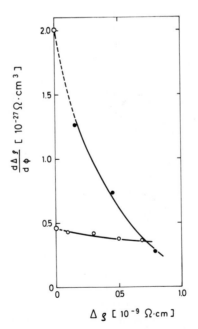

Fig. 22. Influence of stage I annealing on the resistivity damage rate curve at 80°K for copper [52]
(● well-annealed sample, ○ pre-irradiated at 5°K and pre-annealed at 80°K).

The formation of di-interstitials during stage I annealing has been excluded in ref. [56]. These authors have found experimentally that the annealing curves of a sample irradiated at 10°K and one irradiated at 80°K are approximately identical between 80°K and the end of stage III if both samples had the same resistivity increment at 80°K. Since approximately equal amounts of resistivity, i.e., of defect concentration, annealed out at corresponding temperatures the same species of defect must have migrated in both samples. The further conclusions are based on different presumptions. In ref. [56] the vacancies have been taken as immobile up to the end of stage III which is still an open question [2,57]. The conclusions drawn above from the production rate measurements at 80°K, however, are based only on the presumption that the vacancies are immobile up to 80°K. This has been accepted in all published annealing models [57]. It seems reasonable, therefore, to accept the formation of di-interstitials during stage I annealing and to explain the result of ref. [56] by vacancy migration in stage III.

(iii) The question of vacancy mobility within stage III can be studied successfully by means of 80°K production rate measurements. Fig. 23 shows the curves of a well-annealed sample and of a doped one, where the doping procedure consisted in an irradiation at 80°K and a subsequent annealing at a temperature slightly below the end of stage III [52]. Again the initial production rate of the doped specimen is smaller than that of the well-annealed sample due to those vacancies which have

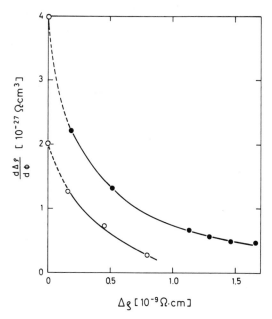

Fig. 23. Influence of stage III annealing on the resistivity damage rate curve at 80°K for copper (ref. [52]) (● well-annealed sample, ○ pre-irradiated at 80°K and pre-annealed at 293°K).

survived stage III annealing. If we compare, however, the effectiveness of the doping-induced resistivity $\Delta\rho_{dop}$ and that of $\Delta\rho$ (radiation-induced at $80°K$) in reducing the production rate with respect to the initial value of $4 \times 10^{-27}$ $\Omega cm^3$, we find a significant difference. The resistivity increment $\Delta\rho_{dop} = 1.6 \times 10^{-9}$ $\Omega cm$ has reduced the production rate to $2 \times 10^{-27}$ $\Omega cm^3$, whereas an equal value of $\Delta\rho$ has reduced it to about $0.5 \times 10^{-27}$ $\Omega cm^3$. Thus the resistivity increment left after stage III annealing reduces the production rate less effectively than an equal resistivity increment introduced at $80°K$. Obviously the resistivity contributions of vacancies and interstitials to $\Delta\rho$ must have been altered during the stage III annealing in such a way that in $\Delta\rho_{dop}$ the fractional resistivity increment of the vacancies is smaller than in $\Delta\rho$ *. This can be due either to a decrease of the fractional vacancy resistivity increment or to an increase of the fractional interstitial resistivity increment. The first case is possible only by vacancy clustering with a decrease of the resistivity contribution per vacancy, or by a partial vacancy annealing at fixed sinks in which case the vacancy concentration is diminished relative to that of the interstitials. Clustering or annealing at fixed sinks, however, requires mobile vacancies.

An increase of the fractional resistivity increment of the interstitials is possible only by such a configuration change which enhances the resistivity increment per interstitial. It has been pointed out that the latter case is to be expected if a thermal interstitial conversion would occur between $80°K$ and the end of stage III [58]. As has been derived from the production rate curves in fig. 20, a thermal interstitial conversion does not occur below $223°K$, i.e., the beginning of stage III annealing. Therefore, the thermal conversion would have to occur within the temperature range of stage III and would have to enhance the resistivity contribution per interstitial contrary to the result obtained in ref. [59]. Thus, the curves in fig. 23 can be explained either by vacancy migration in stage III or within the frame of the conversion-two-interstitial model with the above restriction for the thermal conversion.

Finally, it must be repeated that the interpretation of the $80°K$ production rate curves given here is only qualitative and in certain cases oversimplified. For each example treated, however, a detailed and quantitative description can be found in the respective references.

### 4.3. Conclusions

At $80°K$ the interstitial migrates freely in most of the investigated metals. During an irradiation at this temperature the production of stable defects is governed by the interaction between the migrating interstitials and other defects being present in a sample. This fact can be used fruitfully to study defect arrangements created by certain doping treatments. By this way the defect re-arrangement caused by stage I

---

* In ref. [52] the change of the respective capture volumes has been determined separately. The result still reinforces the above requirements for the fractional resistivity increments.

and stage III annealing has been investigated in copper. It has been concluded from the results that di-interstitials are formed during stage I annealing and that vacancies migrate during stage III annealing. This method is considerably advantageous compared with the conventional annealing studies. It gives information on how the ratio $p_v/p_i$ of the vacancy and the interstitial contribution to a certain property has been altered by the annealing procedure whereas the conventional annealing study shows only the change of the sum $p_v + p_i$.

If the doping-induced defect configuration is known, the mobility of the interstitial can be examined. By this way the interstitial migration has been demonstrated by comparison of quenched and unquenched samples of platinum and gold at 90°K and 80°K, respectively.

Future work should be directed to detailed studies of the interaction between the migrating interstitials and impurities in order to reduce the number of unknown parameters in the production rate equations.

## Acknowledgements

The author is gratefully indebted to Dr. F.Dworschak, Dr. H.Schuster, Dr. P.Winterhager, and Dr. J.Wurm for helpful discussions and critically reading the manuscript. Special thanks are due to Professor Dr. A.Seeger for critical comments he made during the editorial work.

## References

[1] C.Erginsoy, G.H.Vineyard and A.Englert, Phys. Rev. 133 (1964) A 595.
[2] J.W.Corbett, in: Solid State Physics, Supplement 7 (Academic Press, New York, 1966).
[3] A.Sosin and W.Bauer, in: Studies in Radiation Effects, vol. III, ed. G.J.Dines (Gordon and Breach, New York).
[4] N.F.Mott and H.S.Massey, The Theory of Atomic Collisions (Oxford, 1965) p. 226.
[5] See ref. [2], chapter II.
[6] F.Dworschak, H.Schuster, H.Wollenberger and J.Wurm, Phys. Stat. Sol. 21 (1967) 741.
[7] H.H.Neely and W.Bauer, Phys. Rev. 149 (1966) 535.
[8] J.Wurm, Thesis, Technische Hochschule Aachen (1969).
[9] W.Bauer and A.Sosin, Phys. Rev. 135 (1964) A 521.
[10] R.O.Simmons and R.W.Balluffi, Phys. Rev. 129 (1963) 1533.
[11] G.W.Iseler, H.I.Dawson, A.S.Mehner and J.W.Kaufman, Phys. Rev. 146 (1966) 468.
[12] W.Bauer and A.Sosin, J. Appl. Phys. 37 (1966) 1780.
[13] W.Bauer and A.Sosin, J. Appl. Phys. 35 (1964) 703.
[14] R.v.Jan and A.Seeger, Phys. Stat. Sol. 3 (1963) 465.
[15] C.H.Sherman, L.F.Lowe and E.A.Burke, Phys. Rev. 145 (1966) 145.
[16] P.G.Lucasson and R.M.Walker, Phys. Rev. 127 (1962) 485.
[17] G.H.Kinchin and R.S.Pease, Rept. Progr. Phys. 18 (1955) 1.
[18] W.Köhler and W.Schilling, Nukleonik 7 (1965) 389.
[19] Ch.Lehmann, Nukleonik 3 (1961) 1.

[20] J.Lindhard, V.Nielsen and M.Scharff, Mat. Fys. Medd. Dan. Vid. Selsk. 36, No. 10 (1968).
[21] See ref. [3], chapter II.
[22] A.Sosin and K.Garr, Phys. Stat. Sol. 8 (1965) 481.
[23] J.Lomer and M.Pepper, Phil. Mag. 16 (1967) 1119; see also: M.Pepper, Thesis, University of Reading, Great Britain.
[24] J.Wurm, private communication.
[25] P.G.Lucasson and R.M.Walker, Phys. Rev. 127 (1962) 485.
[26] M.J.Makin, Phil. Mag. 18 (1968) 637.
[27] G.Lück and R.Sizmann, Phys. Stat. Sol. 14 (1966) 507.
[28] K.Dettmann, G.Leibfried and K.Schroeder, Phys. Stat. Sol. 22 (1967) 423.
[29] K.Dettmann, private communication.
[30] M.Balarin and O.Hauser, Phys. Stat. Sol. 10 (1965) 475.
[31] H.Schuster, Thesis, Technische Hochschule Aachen (1968); see also Report: Jül-451-FN (1968).
[32] F.Dworschak, Ch.Lehmann, H.Schuster, H.Wollenberger and J.Wurm, in: Proc. of the Intern. Conf. on Solid State Physics Research with Accelerators, 1967, BNL 50083 (C-52), p. 327.
[33] H.E.Schepp, Diplomarbeit, Technische Hochschule Aachen (1967).
[34] H.G.Cooper, J.S.Koehler and J.W.Marx, Phys. Rev. 97 (1955) 599.
[35] E.Klement, Thesis, Technische Hochschule München (1966).
[36] G.Burger, H.Meissner and W.Schilling, Phys. Stat. Sol. 4 (1964) 281.
[37] T.H.Blewitt, Solid State Division Annual Progress Report, ORNL-3017, UC 34; see also Physics and Mathematics TJB-4500, 15th ed. (1960).
[38] K.Dettmann, G.Leibfried and K.Schröder, Phys. Stat. Sol. 22 (1967) 433.
[39] G.Duesing, H.Hemmerich, W.Sassin and W.Schilling, Jül-Conf-2 (Vol. I) 1968, p. 246.
[40] W.Sassin, private communication.
[41] J.B.Gibson, A.N.Goland, M.Milgram and G.H.Vineyard, Phys. Rev. 120 (1960) 1229.
[42] G.Duesing and G.Leibfried, Phys. Stat. Sol. 9 (1965) 463.
[43] G.Duesing, H.Hemmerich, D.Meissner and W.Schilling, Phys. Stat. Sol. 23 (1967) 481.
[44] H.E.Schepp, F.Dworschak, H.Schuster, H.Wollenberger and J.Wurm, to be published.
[45] G.Duesing, see discussion to this paper.
[46] K.Fischer, Phys. Kondens. Materie 6 (1967) 171.
[47] M.L.Swanson and G.R.Piercy, Can. J. Phys. 42 (1964) 1605.
[48] C.J.Meechan and J.A.Brinkman, Phys. Rev. 103 (1956) 1193.
[49] J.W.Corbett, R.B.Smith and R.M.Walker, Phys. Rev. 114 (1959) 1452, 1460.
[50] R.M.Walker, Proc. Intern. School of Physics "E. Fermi", ed. D.S.Billington (Academic Press, New York, 1962).
[51] J.S.Koehler, this volume.
[52] F.Dworschak, H.Schuster, H.Wollenberger and J.Wurm, Phys. Stat. Sol. 29 (1968) 75, 81.
[53] H.H.Neely and A.Sosin, Phys. Rev. 152 (1966) 623.
[54] D.Becker, F.Dworschak, H.Schuster and H.Wollenberger, to be published.
[55] W.Bauer, A.Seeger and A.Sosin, Phys. Letters 24A (1967) 195.
[56] W.Bauer and A.Sosin, Phys. Letters 24A (1967) 193.
[57] W.Schilling et al., this volume.
[58] P.G.Lucasson, see discussion to this paper.
[59] W.Frank, A.Seeger and G.Schottky, Phys. Stat. Sol. 8 (1965) 345.

## Discussion

*P.Lucasson:* I should like to remark that in the field of stage III, the simple experiments of quenches or of irradiations which we are speaking about do not seem to give us sufficient evidence to support one interstitial model or the other. I think that we should rather look for "characteristic" or "specific" experiments. From this point of view, I am wondering whether the doping experiments of Dr. Wollenberger (which he explained by a third kind of interstitial) might not be explainable by the thermal conversion of interstitial atoms and thus give a specific proof for the latter model.

In Dr. Wollenberger's experiment, a copper specimen is electron irradiated at 80°K and the production rate (P.R.) is plotted versus defect concentration (in terms of resistivity increase $\Delta\rho = \rho_F C_F$). At $\Delta\rho_1$ (see fig. 24) the irradiation is stopped and the specimen is annealed in the stage-III temperature range down to the remaining resistivity increment $\Delta\rho_2$. Then the specimen is irradiated again at 80°K. Dr. Wollenberger finds that at this time the production curve is no longer the same as before, but that the production rate versus concentration (in terms of resistivity increment) is now higher (curve N'M' instead of NM).

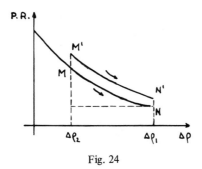

Fig. 24

Let us first remark that the "classical" features of stage III (second order kinetics and mutual vacancy-interstitial annihilation reactions) are of no use to explain this behaviour, because under these conditions vacancies and interstitials play quite symmetrical roles, and there would be no reasons why the production rate should not follow the curve MN in the second irradiation. Instead we have to look for something else, for some property which should not be "symmetrical" or reversible with temperature. Now, if we admit that a thermal conversion of interstitials occurs somewhere below or in the stage-III temperature range, the explanation is straightforward: After annealing down to the resistivity increment $\Delta\rho_2$, the internal state of the specimen is no longer represented by point M, because what is left in the sample should be a different kind of Frenkel pairs, with a different spontaneous recombination volume and a different Frenkel pair resistivity. In other words, both units in the production rate versus resistivity increment diagram are now different from those in the first experiment. So the results Dr. Wollenberger obtained would seem to support the two-interstitial model.

*H.Wollenberger:* During my talk I was not able to present production rate measurements at temperatures between 83°K and 283°K because of the limited time. These data (see fig. 20 and the respective discussion in the author's paper) rule out a thermal conversion at temperatures below the beginning of stage III annealing. Thus, our results you have referred to can be explained within the frame of the conversion-two-interstitial model only if the conversion occurs within the temperature range of stage III annealing and if it enhances the resistivity contribution of the interstitial. The latter condition contradicts the result obtained in ref. [59] of the author's paper. On the other hand our results can well be explained by vacancy migration in stage III.

*H.Wenzl:* What limits can be given for the resistivity per Frenkel pair from the available experimental data? If no upper limit can be given as yet, a) why and b) how does this influence the displacement probability in aluminium, if $\rho_{F_{max}} = 600 \, \mu\Omega cm/$ unit conc?

*H.Wollenberger:* The evaluation of experimental production rates consists in a fitting of calculated displacement cross sections to the data, using a displacement probability function with one or more parameters. The lowest values of $\rho_F$ are obtained if a single step function is used. These minimum values are generally smaller than the resistivity increments per unit atomic vacancy concentration.

In the case of aluminium the displacement probability reaches unity at 150 eV for $\rho_F = 4.4 \times 10^{-4} \, \Omega cm$ (see fig. 4 of the preceding paper). For $\rho_F = 6 \times 10^{-4} \, \Omega cm$ it would reach unity at about 200 eV.

We have no theoretical prediction or experimental information, at which transferred energy the displacement probability reaches unity.

*W.Bauer:* I have three remarks:

1. The quantity $T_d$ ($\approx 45$ eV) in the aluminium discussion is only a parameter in the multiple displacement regime, as you presented it. Is there a relation between $T_d$ and $\bar{T}_d$ from your work?

2. You have correctly pointed out the problems surrounding accurate damage rate measurements in single crystals (size effect, geometrical factor, etc.). I think it is fair to point out that if the data are normalized at a given energy, approximate (3–4 eV) threshold energies may be deduced in single crystal work. This is important for the determination of interatomic potentials.

3. Finally, I remark on the analysis of your 80°K irradiations. Since you have demonstrated that $(d\Delta\rho/d\phi)|_{80°K}$ is extremely sensitive to the defects in the lattice, I would think it is important to include vacancy and interstitial clusters (as seen in the electron microscope) in your analysis.

*H.J.Wollenberger:* 1. We are not able to derive the angular dependent $T_d$ from $\bar{T}_d$.

A more detailed information than $\overline{T}_d$, however, is given by the comparison of the linearly increasing displacement probabilities in fig. 4 of the preceding paper.

2. I agree with you as far as the minimum threshold energies are concerned. For a determination of the higher threshold values, however, normalized data cannot be used.

3. In a recent paper (Phys. Stat. Sol. 29 (1968) 75) we have discussed the influence of defect clustering on the production rate equations.

## Discussion

*G. Duesing:* I should like to mention further experimental results we have given in our contributed paper. These results concern the influence of previously quenched-in vacancies on radiation annealing. The figure shows the damage rate of platinum,

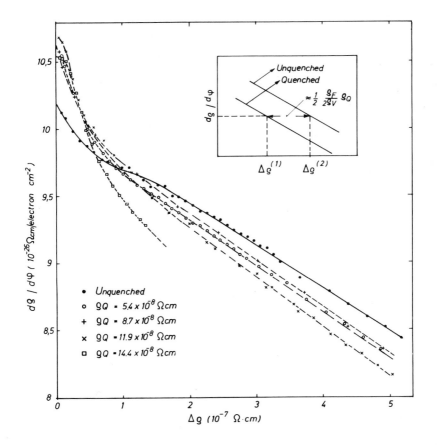

electron irradiated at $4°K$. The solid curve is due to an unquenched sample, the dashed lines are due to differently quenched samples. One sees that for high levels of irradiation damage the damage rate is reduced by excess vacancies. The amount of reduction found in our experiments corresponds very well to the reduction expected from theory due to spontaneous recombinations and recombinations by sub-threshold processes. For low levels of irradiation produced damage, however, the reduction of the damage rate in quenched samples is masked by an increase in the damage rate. This result for low damage levels, which we give here for electron irradiation, has been observed by Hirschbach and Jackson after deuteron irradiation. The interpretation given by these authors is an enhanced damage by focusons which are defocused at divacancies and, instead of being annihilated by them, cause additional displacements. We believe that this collision chain mechanism cannot contribute appreciably to the damage rate enhancement in our electron irradiations. During 3 MeV electron irradiation, only a very few collision chains are formed which have energy enough to produce displacements upon interaction with a distant vacancy. Consequently the probability for such a defocusing process should be very much smaller than in the heavy particle irradiations. We favour the explanation that the increase of the defect production rate is only apparent and is a result of the non-proportionality of resistivity and defect concentration. This non-proportionality originates from a deviation from Matthiessen's rule.

VACANCIES AND INTERSTITIALS IN METALS, NORTH-HOLLAND, AMSTERDAM (1969)

# ANNEALING STAGES IN THE ELECTRICAL RESISTIVITY OF IRRADIATED FCC METALS

## W. SCHILLING

*Kernforschungsanlage Jülich GmbH, Jülich, Germany*

## G. BURGER

*Gesellschaft für Strahlenforschung mbH, München, Germany*

## K. ISEBECK

*Atomic Energy Board, Pretoria, Republic of South Africa*

## H. WENZL

*Physik-Department, Technische Hochschule München, Germany*

## Contents

## Introduction

It is now well established that irradiation with fast particles at low temperatures produces Frenkel defects, i.e., interstitials and vacancies in equal numbers. The primary difference in the damage introduced by different types of irradiation particles, e.g., fast electrons, deuterons, or neutrons, is in the local arrangements of vacancies and interstitials.

Upon warming, thermal vibrations lead to mobility of defects in the damaged samples and enables them to undergo reaction with each other. Some of the more important of these reactions are: annihilation of vacancies and interstitials by recombination, aggregation of defects and trapping of defects at impurities. In an isochronal time-temperature program these reactions lead to so-called annealing stages of the different physical properties of the samples. The details of these annealing stages depend on the activation energy of the mobile defect, the particular type of reaction, the initial distribution of mobile defects and sinks and their interaction potentials.

The majority of the annealing experiments performed so far have employed electrical resistivity as a measure for changes in the defect concentration. These measurements have revealed that in the first annealing stage (stage I) recombination of interstitials and vacancies takes place simultaneously with reactions that conserve part of the interstitials in an immobile form. The detailed nature of these immobile interstitials and, as a consequence, also the interpretation of the higher annealing stages is still a matter of discussion. This situation has now prevailed for more than ten years even though extensive effort has been devoted to the resolution of this problem.

In this situation the question may be raised about the value of recovery studies using electrical resistivity measurements. On the one hand, electrical resistivity measurements have the advantage of high sensitivity and accuracy and are easy to perform. On the other hand, electrical resistivity is very unspecific for the different kinds of defects present in the sample and rather insensitive to aggregation and trapping reactions. Thus it only reflects to a crude approximation the total number of interstitials and vacancies present, irrespective of their detailed arrangement. Consequently all conclusions based on the detailed form of the kinetics (i.e., the time dependence of the electrical resistivity recovery) must be taken with extreme caution and will be avoided as far as possible in this review. More reliable information can be gained from measurements of the dependence of the recovery of electrical resistivity on the initial defect density (dose dependence), on impurities or doping defects and on the type of irradiating particles.

In Part I the recovery in stage I of electron, neutron and heavy charged particle irradiated samples will be reviewed. Since the findings for Cu, Ag, Al, Pt and Ni are rather similar, the data for these fcc metals will be discussed together. For these metals the general features of the annealing in stage I are understood rather well, so therefore the defect configuration present at the end of stage I can be predicted quite safely. Gold, however, shows a quite different annealing structure in the low temperature range. No satisfactory interpretation seems to exist for this anomaly.

In Part II the features of annealing stage II will be discussed. In this stage intrinsic processes, especially for samples containing high initial defect densities, as well as impurity effects are important. The reactions which occur in stage II are not yet understood very well. Nevertheless, in favourable cases a reasonable guess of the defect configuration present at the end of this stage can be made.

Part III deals with annealing stage III. This stage is defined here as that larger recovery stage above stage I in which annihilation of Frenkel pairs by a freely migrating defect is observed. We will try to present experimental evidence which demonstrates that this stage can be ascribed to a unique, freely migrating defect.

Essentially two recovery models have been advanced which predict the nature of this freely migrating defect in stage III: The vacancy model and the conversion-two-interstitial model. These models will be outlined briefly and the restrictions imposed on them by the resistivity data will be discussed. For aluminium, and probably also for platinum and gold, stage III may be interpreted by single vacancy migration. For copper and nickel, the assignment of single vacancy migration to stage III seems to be in contradiction with some of the quenching and equilibrium data. The conversion-two-interstitial model offers an alternative in this dilemma.

# Part I. Stage I

The discovery of a large annealing stage at temperatures below 60°K in the fcc metals Cu and Ag was made by Cooper, Koehler and Marx [1] in 1955. Since then, an extensive amount of literature has accumulated on this subject. However, the pioneering experiments which clarified the nature of the recovery processes in the low temperature range of electron irradiated copper were performed by Corbett, Smith and Walker in 1959 [2,3]. After extensive experimentation on stage I and debate on possible alternate recovery models in the years since this work was first reported, the principle features of their recovery model (CSW-model) for stage I has become generally accepted not only for copper, but also for other fcc metals which show similar annealing behaviour (Ag, Al, Pt, and Ni). In view of this similarity we will discuss the annealing of these metals together.

## I.1. Stage I recovery of electron irradiated Cu, Ag, Al, Pt, Ni

During irradiation with fast electrons the majority of the displacements occur with energies just above the displacement threshold. Therefore, after low temperature irradiation, the damage will be principally in the form of randomly distributed vacancy-interstitial pairs. At low doses the characteristic feature of this distribution is that the mean distance between interstitials is very large compared to the mean distance between vacancies and interstitials. The annealing behaviour of Frenkel defects with this initial damage pattern will be discussed in section I.1.

### I.1.1. *Survey of annealing spectra and recovery model*
The principal features of the recovery in stage I of electron irradiated Cu, Ag, Al, Pt, and Ni are shown by the differential isochronal recovery curves in figs. 1 to 5.

The physical significance of these curves is the following: Each peak in the recovery spectrum indicates that in this temperature range a given defect becomes thermally activated so that it can react with other defects, thereby giving rise to the observed decrease in the electrical resistivity. The initial increase in the reaction rate with temperature is due to the strong increase in the Boltzmann factor which governs the mobility of the reacting defect. At the temperature of the peak this increase is just balanced by the decrease in the reaction rate due to the reduction in the defect concentration accompaning the reaction. Finally when all reaction partners have been removed, the reaction rate is zero again.

For all the metals shown in figs. 1 to 5, stage I consists of a number of sub-peaks which were first detected by Corbett, Smith and Walker [2,3,4] for copper. These authors labelled the peaks in order of increasing temperature $I_A$, $I_B$, $I_C$, $I_D$ and $I_E$. For the other metals the peaks have been labelled in analogy to copper so that stage $I_D$ with its shoulder $I_E$ is always the last prominent substage of stage I.

In Al, Ag and Ni, unlike Cu and Pt, the first close pair peak $I_A$ is missing. The

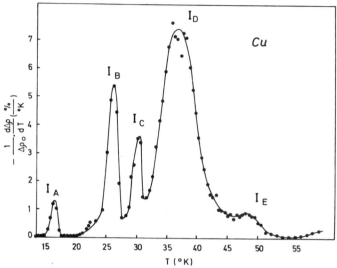

Fig. 1. Stage I recovery spectrum of Cu after low temperature irradiation with 2 MeV electrons to $\Delta\rho_0 = 0.134$ n$\Omega\cdot$cm (1 n$\Omega\cdot$cm $= 10^{-9}$ $\Omega\cdot$cm). The data are taken from ref. [13]. A smooth curve which neglects possible fine structure has been drawn through the published data points.

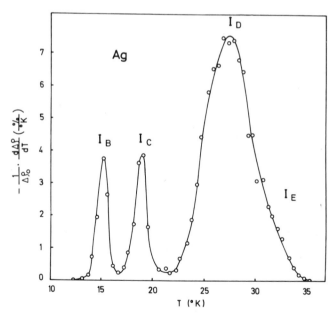

Fig. 2. Stage I recovery spectrum of Ag after low temperature irradiation with 2 MeV electrons to $\Delta\rho_0 = 4.37$ n$\Omega\cdot$cm. The data are taken from ref. [15]. A smooth curve, neglecting possible fine structure has been drawn through the published data points. Probably due to the higher initial defect density stage $I_E$ is not separated clearly from stage $I_D$.

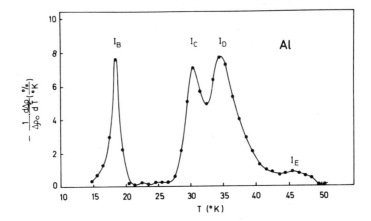

Fig. 3. Stage I recovery spectrum of Al after low temperature irradiation with 0.4 MeV electrons to $\Delta\rho_0 = 0.384$ n$\Omega$·cm. Data are taken from ref. [21].

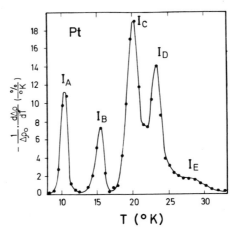

Fig. 4. Stage I recovery spectrum of Pt after low temperature irradiation with 2 MeV electrons to $\Delta\rho_0 = 1.7$ n$\Omega$·cm. Data are taken from ref. [16].

corresponding close pair configuration seems to be unstable in these metals at the temperatures where the irradiations have been performed.

In a number of recent experiments by Kauffman and coworkers [5–9], a variable number of small subpeaks (up to 16 for Cu and 22 for Al) have been reported to be superimposed on the annealing spectra shown in figs. 1 to 3. However, several reasons suggest that this fine structure is due to the experimental procedure rather than to a physical effect. First, the details of the observed fine structure have never been reproduced from one annealing run to another one or by different laboratories. In addition, in some cases, irregularities in the experimental heating program can be

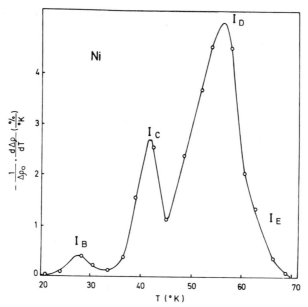

Fig. 5. Stage I recovery spectrum of pure Ni irradiated with 3 MeV electrons to $\Delta\rho_0 = 54$ nΩ·cm. The data are taken from ref. [17]. Due to the high initial defect density stage $I_E$ is not separated clearly from stage $I_D$.

correlated with the occurrence of subpeaks. These irregularities correspond to variations in the effective heating rate and would give rise to substructure in the differential isochronal annealing curve similar in effect to that of a serrated distribution of activation energies. Finally, in a recent experiment it has been shown by Simpson et al. [10] that no fine structure can be observed in aluminium if the isochronal program is performed very carefully with constant holding times and constant temperature steps. In view of these considerations, we believe that it is reasonable at present to disregard this fine structure.

For electron irradiated copper the structure of stage I has been investigated by Corbett et al. [2–4], Meechan et al. [11] and Kauffman and coworkers [5,7,12,13]. Neglecting the fine structure mentioned above the results of the different groups are in good agreement.

For electron-irradiated Ag the structure of stage I has been studied by Kauffman and coworkers [14,15], for Pt by Bauer and Goeppinger [16] and for Ni by Oddou [17] and Peretto et al. [18] and by Dawson et al. [6]. The stage I structure of electron-irradiated Al has been studied by Snead and Shearin [19], Sosin and Garr [20], Dawson et al. [6] and by Chaplin and coworkers [10,21]. Apart from the fine structure there is again good overall agreement between the results of the different groups.

The physical interpretation of the peaks shown in fig. 1 as given by Corbett, Smith and Walker [2,3] is the following: Stages $I_A$, $I_B$ and $I_C$ are due to the recombination of close Frenkel pairs; that is recombination of Frenkel pairs where the interstitial and vacancy are so close together that the energy barrier for recombination is lowered appreciably by their mutual interaction. In stages $I_D$ and $I_E$ interstitials are thought to undergo free migration. Stage $I_D$ is associated with recombination in a small number of steps of interstitials with their own vacancies (correlated recombination), and stage $I_E$ is associated with recombination involving other vacancies and requires a large number of steps (uncorrelated recombination). In addition to recombination in stage $I_E$, the freely migrating single interstitial can also react with other interstitials or impurities, thereby being trapped in the form of immobile agglomerates. These later reactions lead to the retention of vacancies and interstitials in the lattice so that at the end of stage I recovery is not complete.

### I.1.2. *The close pair recovery stages*

The interpretation of the recovery in the stages $I_A$, $I_B$ and $I_C$ by the collapse of close interstitial-vacancy pairs is based on the observation that the reaction kinetics of these stages obeys a pure first order reaction law as given in eq. (1).

$$-\frac{dc}{dt} = c\, \nu_0 \exp(-U/kT) = \frac{c}{\tau},\qquad(1)$$

where $c$ is the concentration of close Frenkel pairs of a given configuration, $U$ the activation energy for their recombination, and $\nu_0$ the attempt frequency. The characteristic of the above reaction law is that the mean lifetime $\tau$ of a close pair of a given type is not dependent on the total number of defects produced by the irradiation or on the addition of doping agents which could act as additional sinks for freely migrating interstitials.

The independence of $\tau$ on the total number of interstitials and vacancies produced by the irradiation has been shown in detail by Corbett et al. [2], Kauffman and coworkers [5,13] for Cu, by Snead et al. for Ag [15], by Sosin and Garr [20] and by Dawson et al. [6] for Al and by Oddou for Ni [17]. In these experiments it has been verified that the positions and form of the close pair peaks in the differential isochronal curves are independent of irradiation dose (see fig. 7 for an example).

The effect of doping agents (impurities, vacancies, dislocations) on the close pair recovery has been studied in a number of experiments: The influence of quenched-in vacancies has been investigated by Bauer and Goeppinger [16] for Pt (see also fig. 8). The effect of defects introduced by prior cold work has been studied by Meechan et al. [11] for Cu and Kauffman and coworkers for Cu [5] and Al [6]. The influence of radiation doping, i.e., of defects introduced by prior high temperature irradiation or low temperature irradiation plus annealing treatment has been investigated by Kauffman and coworkers for Cu [5], Al [6] and Ag [15] and by Corbett et al. for Cu [3].

The effect of small amounts of impurities (Ag and Au) on the close pair recovery has been studied by Sosin and Neely for Cu [22]. Similar experiments have been performed by Snead and Shearin [19] for Al and Oddou et al. [17,23] for Ni. However, the impurity concentrations of 0.3 and 0.5 at% used in the latter experiments are so high that alteration in the close pair recovery spectrum due to direct interactions between impurities and the interstitials of the close pairs can no longer be neglected (see section I.6).

In all the other doping experiments listed above, no influence of the doping agents on the close pair recovery has been observed. This demonstrates again that the interstitials which recombine in the close pair recovery stages do not sample a large number of lattice sites before their annihilation at vacancies.

Also, for deuteron irradiation Jackson and Herschbach have observed that vacancy-, radiation-, impurity- and dislocation-doping has little influence on the close pair recovery of Al [24,25] and Pt [25–28].

The exponential time law for the recovery of close pairs which can be derived from eq. (1) has been checked by Corbett et al. for the substages $I_B$ and $I_C$ in Cu [2], by Oddou for the substages $I_B$ and $I_C$ in Ni [17]. The activation energies and attempt frequencies deduced from these measurements are listed in table 1.

Table 1
Activation energies and attempt frequencies for close pair recovery stages in Cu and Ni. Data are taken from refs. [2,17].

| Substage | Copper | | Nickel | |
|---|---|---|---|---|
| | Activation energy (eV) | $\nu_0$ (sec$^{-1}$) | Activation energy (eV) | $\nu_0$ (sec$^{-1}$) |
| $I_B$ | $0.085 \pm 0.01$ | $0.8 \times 10^{12\pm0.7}$ | 0.085 | $3 \times 10^{12\pm1}$ |
| $I_C$ | $0.095 \pm 0.01$ | $0.8 \times 10^{12\pm0.7}$ | $0.135 \pm 0.03$ (32%) * $0.142 \pm 0.03$ (68%) | |

* Stage $I_C$ consists of a superposition of two first order processes.

It is interesting to note that the observed values of the attempt frequency, $\nu_0$, are about one to two orders of magnitude smaller than the frequency factors typical for diffusion of point defects (e.g., interstitial impurity atoms at high temperatures). This low value may be due to a quantum effect. Since the temperature of stage I is very small compared to the Debye temperatures, the lattice is nearly in its ground state. Consequently, the high frequency vibrations of the lattice atoms or the short wavelength fluctuation of the local amplitudes are strongly suppressed. If, however, the statistical occurrence of such fluctuations around a defect is responsible for its jump rate, we would not expect it to be governed by a Boltzmann factor as indicated in eq. (1). However, it has been speculated by Flynn [29] that the exponential temperature dependence in eq. (1) may still be valid if the migrating defect vibrates mainly in low frequency modes. This would require that the interstitial gives rise to very low lying resonance modes in the frequency spectrum whose occupation number at low temperatures is still determined by a Boltzmann factor. Mössbauer experiments in irradiated Pt [30] indeed indicate the existence of reso-

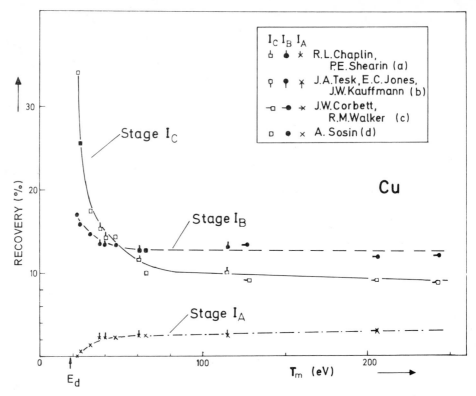

Fig. 6. Energy dependence of the total recoveries in the close pair stages $I_A$, $I_B$ and $I_C$ in Cu. $T_m$ denotes the maximum energy transferred by the incident electrons. $E_d$ denotes the displacement threshold. The data are taken from: a) ref. [31], b) ref. [12], c) ref. [32], d) ref. [33].

nance modes for the stage I defects. Apart from this limited evidence and theoretical speculation, the theory of thermal activation at very low temperatures is in a rather unsatisfactory state.

The population of the different close pair configuration depends sensitively on the energy of the incident electrons. This is demonstrated in fig. 6 where for Cu the relative sizes of the different substages are plotted versus the maximum transferred energy. As can be seen, stage $I_B$, and especially stage $I_C$, decrease appreciably with increasing recoil energy [12,31–33]. The same behaviour has also been observed for stages $I_B$ and $I_C$ in Al [21].

The strong increase in the close pair population when the maximum recoil energy approaches the displacement threshold is just what one would expect if the formation of close pairs is associated with low energy recoil events just above threshold which cannot separate the vacancy and interstitial sufficiently thus leading to interaction of the two defects.

On the other hand, fig. 6 also indicates that stage $I_A$ is different in that its population initially increases with increasing electron energy. A possible explanation of this anomalous behaviour is that the production of the close pair configuration $I_A$ requires a larger energy threshold to be surmounted than that required for the other Frenkel pair configurations (e.g. displacement in an unfavourable lattice direction).

### I.1.3. *Evidence for free migration of interstitials in stage* $I_E$

In the CSW model, interstitials recombine with vacancies by free migration in stages $I_D$ and $I_E$. The experimental evidence for free interstitial migration in stage $I_E$ comes mainly from measurements of the dose dependence of stage $I_E$, from doping experiments and from a study of the defect production during irradiation at temperatures above stage I. We will discuss these three kinds of experiments in turn.

### I.1.3.1. Dose dependence of stage $I_E$

The dose dependence of the recovery in electron irradiated Cu has been studied by Corbett et al. [3] and later by Kauffman and coworkers [5,13]. For electron

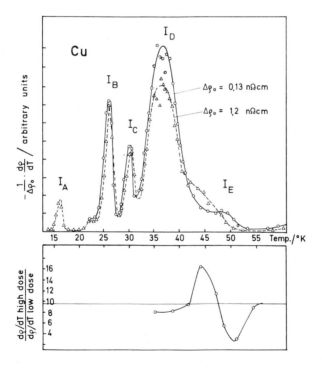

Fig. 7. Comparison of isochronals for two different initial defect densities $\Delta\rho_0$ produced by 2 MeV electron irradiation of Cu. The different heights of the substages $I_D$ are due to slight differences in the normalizations of the two curves. Data are taken from ref. [13]. Smooth curves neglecting possible fine structure have been drawn through the data point. Lower plot: ratio of the recovery slopes for the two isochronals versus annealing temperature.

irradiated Al the dose dependence has been investigated by Sosin and Garr [20] and by Dawson et al. [6] and for Ni by Oddou [17].

In all of these experiments it was observed that stage $I_E$ shifts to lower temperatures with increasing initial defect density. An example for this behaviour is shown in fig. 7 where for almost identical isochronal programs stage $I_E$ shifts from 46.5 to 44.5°K upon increasing the initial defect density by about a factor of ten. The shift in the recovery stage $I_E$ is demonstrated more clearly in the lower part of fig. 7, where the ratio of the recovery rates of the two isochronals are plotted versus the annealing temperature. Each systematic shift of a recovery stage or substage shows up as a typical oscillation in this plot.

As discussed in detail in section I.2.1 the shift of stage $I_E$ with dose indicates directly that the mean number of jumps for a defect to annihilate in stage $I_E$ decreases with increasing defect density. This requires that the mobile defect migrates freely in stage $I_E$, that mobile defects and sinks initially are distributed at random and that the number of possible sinks per mobile effect in the high dose sample is higher than in the low dose sample.

I.1.3.2. Influence of doping agents on stage $I_E$

The introduction of doping agents has two effects on the recovery in stage I: First, due to the excess number of possible sinks, at equal values of fractional recovery, the reaction rate in stage $I_E$ is enhanced in the doped sample over the recovery rate in the undoped sample. Secondly the presence of the doping agents changes the probability that a freely migrating interstitial will survive in stage $I_E$ and so influences the defect retention above stage I.

An example for the first effect is shown in fig. 8 which gives a comparison of recovery curves observed in prequenched and unquenched platinum electron irradiated to about equal doses. Due to the excess number of vacancies in the prequenched sample the mean number of jumps for the free migrating interstitial until annihilation is strongly reduced over that in the unquenched sample. Therefore, stage $I_E$ is shifted to lower temperatures and the ratio plot shows again the typical oscillation. Enhancements of the recovery rate at equal values of fractional recovery in stage $I_E$ similar to that in prequenched Pt have also been reported for radiation doped Al [6] and Cu [5].

For the second effect, the defect retention above stage I, it is essential that the freely migrating interstitials can undergo trapping reactions in stage $I_E$ by which they become immobile and are then conserved for the higher annealing stages.

Possible partners for interstitial trapping are:
a) Another free interstitial. In this reaction the two free interstitials form a di-interstitial.
b) An impurity atom. In this reaction an interstitial-impurity pair is formed.
c) Trapped interstitials. In this reaction a free interstitial is trapped at a di-interstitial or an interstitial impurity pair or at an agglomerate of trapped interstitials. By these reactions larger agglomerates of trapped interstitials can grow around di-interstitials or interstitial impurity pairs.

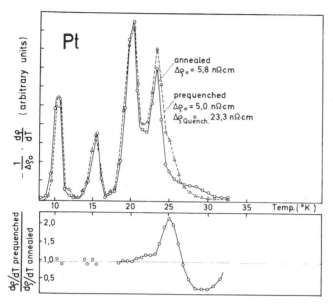

Fig. 8. Comparison of the differential isochronal annealing curves of an annealed and a pre-quenched platinum sample irradiated with 2 MeV electrons to the indicated resistivity changes $\Delta\rho_0$. The resistivity increase by quenching is denoted by $\Delta\rho_{quench}$. Lower plot: ratio of the recovery slopes of prequenched and unquenched sample as a function of annealing temperature. Data are taken from ref. [16].

d) Dislocations. In this reaction a free interstitial is trapped at a dislocation. These trapped interstitials can impede the bowing out of the dislocation under an applied stress. This dislocation pinning effect has been used to demonstrate the arrival of freely migrating interstitials at dislocations in irradiated Cu [34] at the end of stage I.

Experimental evidence for these trapping reactions comes mainly from studies where the samples have been doped with the above mentioned defects prior to an irradiation. Such experiments will be discussed below.

In *undoped samples* the freely migrating interstitials can only react with vacancies or other interstitials forming di-interstitials in the beginning. In the later part of stage $I_E$ these di-interstitials can then grow into larger interstitial aggregates by additional interstitial absorption. Since the ratios of the reaction radii for the different interstitial reactions in stage $I_E$ are independent of the initial defect density, the number of vacancies surviving stage $I_E$ will be a constant fraction of the initial defect numbers (see sections I.2.1 and I.2.2). This number is, of course, equal to the number of interstitials trapped as di-interstitials or larger agglomerates. We, therefore, expect the percentage of defects (measured by the residual electrical resistivity) which remains above stage I to be independent of the initial defect den-

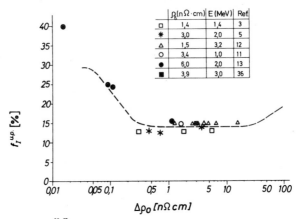

Fig. 9. Defect retention $f_I^{u,p}$ above stage I of undoped pure Cu samples electron irradiated at low temperatures to the initial defect density $\Delta\rho_0$. $\rho_0$ = residual resistivity of the samples before irradiation. $E$ = energy of irradiating electrons.

sity. As shown in fig. 9 this is just the case for damage levels between 0.25 and 25 $n\Omega \cdot cm$ for electron irradiated pure Cu.

The values found in the plateau region of the defect retention in fig. 9 depend slightly on the electron energy. Smaller electron energies tend to yield smaller defect retentions. For Cu [5] and Al [21] this effect has been found to become rather pronounced when the electron energy approaches the displacement threshold. Apparently the decrease in the recoil energies gives rise to smaller separations between interstitials and vacancies which lead to the observed reduction in the probability for an interstitial to escape recombination with its own vacancy (see section I.2.2 and table 3 for further discussion).

Fig. 9 also demonstrates that for very low damage levels the percentage damage remaining after stage I increases strongly. In this region the defect concentrations are so small that recombinations at vacancies and bimolecular reactions between interstitials are suppressed in favour of *trapping* at impurities. Apparently at low enough damage levels, even in the purest samples available, practically all the free interstitials which escape correlated recombination will be trapped by the residual impurities. [The defect retention of 40% observed for the lowest damage level in fig. 9 is inconsistent with the fraction $f_{I_D} \approx 27$ to 30% of defects observed to be present in the beginning of stage $I_E$ [3,13]. Since experiments pertaining to such extremely low damage levels are felt to give less reliable results the observed value of 40% probably does not reflect correctly the total fraction of interstitials which escape correlated recombination.]

A similar suppression of stage $I_E$ by the residual impurities has also been observed

Table 2

Fractional resistivity retention above stage I after a low dose test irradiation at 4°K with fast electrons in doped and undoped fcc metals.

| Material | Electron energy (MeV) | Undoped pure (index u.p.) $f_I^{u.p.} \left(\dfrac{\rho_0}{\Delta\rho_{test}}\right)$ (%) | Alloyed or impure $\dfrac{f_I^{imp}}{f_I^{u.p.}} \left(\dfrac{\rho_{imp}}{\Delta\rho_{test}}\right)$ | Prequenched $\dfrac{f_I^Q}{f_I^{u.p.}} \left(\dfrac{\Delta\rho_{quench}}{\Delta\rho_{test}}\right)$ | Radiation doped (index r.d.) $\dfrac{f_I^{r.d.}}{f_I^{u.p.}} \left(\dfrac{\Delta\rho_{r.d.}}{\Delta\rho_{test}}\right)$ | References |
|---|---|---|---|---|---|---|
| Cu | 1.4 | 13 (~1) | 3.0 (20) * | | 0.35 (2.2) † | [13,22,3] |
| Al | 0.7 | 14 (0.25) | 2.4 (10) ** | | 0.25 (2.0) †† | [6,20] |
| Pt | 2 | 8 (~3) | | 0.25 (13) | 0.31 (20) † | [16,39] |
| Ag | 2 | 26 (~1) | 1.5 (27) | | 0.50 (5.0) †† | [15] |
| Ni | 3 | 16 (~1) | 1.2 (30) *** | | | [17,23] |

* CuAu (0.03%)
** AlZn (0.1%)
*** NiCu (0.5%)
† Doping irradiation at temperatures below stage I plus annealing at 80°K
†† Doping irradiation at 80°K

$\rho_0$ = residual resistivity of nominally pure samples
$\Delta\rho_{test}$ = resistivity increment introduced by test irradiation at low temperatures

for very low damage levels in Ag [15]. Additional evidence for impurity trapping comes from experiments in slightly alloyed samples. Here, the suppression of stage $I_E$ persists to higher damage levels. Table 2 line 4 gives some typical examples *.

In addition to the dislocation pinning experiments mentioned earlier, the trapping of interstitials at dislocations has been detected in Cu by the partial suppression of stage $I_E$ in samples which have been cold worked prior to irradiation [5,11].

Contrary to impurity and dislocation doping, an excess number of vacancies suppresses bimolecular reactions among interstitials in stage $I_E$ and increases their probability for annihilation. This effect has been demonstrated by Bauer and Goeppinger [16] with the observation that the percentage damage remaining above stage I decreases from 8 to 3% in Pt if the samples have been doped with quenched-in vacancies prior to the irradiation (see table 2, column 5). The almost complete recovery in the quenched samples in stage I demonstrates directly that the defects remaining above stage I in the undoped crystals have really been trapped during their free migration and have not been produced by displacement events in a configuration such that they would be immobile throughout stage I.

Another way in which an excess number of vacancies can be introduced into a sample is by the so-called radiation doping treatment: prior to a test irradiation at low temperatures the sample is irradiated at low temperatures and subsequently annealed at temperatures above stage I. These radiation doped samples therefore contain vacancies left from the doping irradiation and interstitials in trapped configurations. This radiation doping treatment reduces the fraction of defects which remain above stage I, again demonstrating the free migration of interstitials in stage $I_E$ for Cu, Al, Pt and Ag. Typical results are summarized in table 2, column 6.

If the defect concentration $\Delta\rho$ remaining after the doping treatment is larger by a factor of 2 than the number of defects $\Delta\rho_{test}$ produced by the test irradiation in pure samples, the percentage damage remaining above stage I is found to be almost independent of the amount of defects introduced by the doping treatment [3]. In this case bimolecular reactions between interstitials in stage $I_E$ are almost completely suppressed and practically all the interstitials which have been introduced by the test irradiation and which migrate freely in stage $I_E$ either recombine with the doping vacancies or join trapped interstitials left from the doping treatment. Therefore, the observed enhancement of the recombination processes in stage $I_E$ in the radiation doped samples leads to the conclusion that the interstitials present in the doped sample in trapped form are less effective in the removal of freely migrating interstitials than the bimolecular trapping reactions between single interstitials in the undoped sample (see also section I.2.2).

Corbett et al. [3] have further demonstrated that the limiting value of the defect

---

* Care has been taken to select data for alloys where the impurity concentrations were low enough that they did not appreciably influence the population of the close pair stages and the recovery in stage $I_D$.

retention in strongly radiation doped samples is smaller if the doping defects are introduced by irradiation at 80°K and not by 4°K irradiation plus subsequent anneal- ing at 80°K. Since the vacancy distribution will be similar after both treatments the reduced trapping ability gives direct evidence that during the high temperature irra- diation larger interstitial aggregates grow around the residual impurities. During the recovery after a test irradiation these aggregates are less effective in trapping free interstitials than the di-interstitials left from a doping irradiation at low tempera- tures plus subsequent annealing treatment.

### I.1.3.3. Defect production at 80°K

Rather direct evidence for free interstitial migration in stage I comes from obser- vations of the defect production at temperatures above stage I. This experimental technique is discussed in detail by Wollenberger in these proceedings [37]. There- fore, only the principal features will be outlined here.

If, for example, the irradiations are performed at 80°K the free interstitials are very mobile and will have a rather short lifetime before reacting with an impurity or vacancy or another interstitial already trapped by an impurity. Therefore during the irradiation the steady state concentration of free interstitials will be so low that bimolecular reactions between them can be neglected. Since the damage rate direct- ly reflects the probability for survival of interstials at 90°K it will decrease with in- creasing accumulation of vacancies during the irradiation. The probability for this

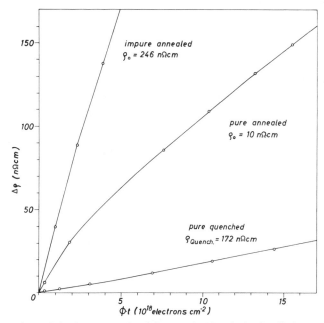

Fig. 10. Comparison of the dose curves for defect production during irradiation at 90°K with 3 MeV electrons in pure, impure and prequenched platinum samples ($\rho_0$ = residual resistivity before irradiation.

survival can also be influenced greatly by the addition of impurities or quenched-in vacancies. An example of this effect is shown in fig. 10, containing dose curves for Pt irradiated at 80°K. The data indicate clearly that impurities enhance the interstitial retention during irradiation, whereas quenched-in vacancies reduce the damage production. A more detailed analysis [38] shows that the reduction in the damage rate of the quenched sample amounts to almost a factor of 20 in the initial part of the dose curves. This strong suppression of defect production again rules out the possibility that displacement events directly produce interstitials in configurations that are immobile throughout stage I.

Damage rate measurements at 80°K in pure and doped Cu and Al [37] yield the same principal findings as those discussed for Pt. Measurements of the defect retention during high temperature irradiation have turned out to be a very sensitive method for the analysis of defect structures in terms of possible sinks or traps for freely migrating interstitials.

### I.1.4. *Correlated recombination in stage $I_D$*

In the preceding chapter evidence has been presented which shows that in stage $I_E$ interstitials migrate freely and either recombine with vacancies or are trapped by reactions with other interstitials, impurities or dislocations. From the dose dependence observed in stage $I_E$ it has been argued that the reaction of the interstitials with the vacancies occurs in a manner that indicates that both kinds of defects are initially distributed more or less at random.

Contrary to this we expect that a recoil event slightly above the threshold energy (which occurs much more frequently than higher energy recoils in electron damage) deposits the interstitial somewhere in the neighbourhood of the vacancy with which it was born. If the concentration of these Frenkel pairs is very low, the mean distance between an interstitial and its own vacancy will be very small compared to the mean distance between the individual Frenkel pairs. We, therefore, expect that when an interstitial becomes mobile and begins to sample the neighbourhood of its birth place there will be a rather high probability that it will find its own vacancy in a variable but small number of jumps. This "correlated recombination" should show up as a separate annealing stage just below stage $I_E$ and should be independent of irradiation dose and doping agents. With increasing dose, the annealing stage for the uncorrelated recovery stage $I_E$ should merge into this stage (see section I.2.1).

All the above mentioned features have been observed experimentally for the annealing stage $I_D$ (see fig. 7 as an example). Therefore, it is very reasonable to identify this stage with the correlated recombination of non-interacting interstitials and vacancies. If this interpretation is correct, one would expect that the reaction in stage $I_D$ is governed by the same activation energy as stage $I_E$, namely the activation energy for free interstitial migration. This crucial point has been investigated by Corbett et al. for copper [3]. Within experimental errors, stages $I_D$ and $I_E$ had the same activation energy. This is one of the cornerstones in the CSW-model.

In the past, the assignment of stage $I_D$ to the correlated recombination of freely migrating interstitials has been criticized by several groups. This criticism was based firstly on the fine-structure reported in some experiments to be superimposed on stage $I_D$ [5,6,35] and secondly on the fact that in nickel, Peretto et al. [18] find that stage $I_E$ is associated with a large magnetic aftereffect whereas stage $I_D$ is not.

The fine structure was taken as an indication of the existence of several closely spaced close pair recovery peaks. However, as discussed in section I.1.1 this fine structure is probably due to experimental factors rather than indicative of a real physical effect.

The magnetic aftereffect observed for the defects which anneal in stage $I_E$ in Ni has been associated by Peretto [18] with the reorientation of the dumb-bell interstitial. If this is correct the CSW-model would require that a measurable magnetic aftereffect should also be associated with stage $I_D$. This has not been observed experimentally. However, the reorientation model is based only on the analysis of the shape of the observed magnetic relaxation peaks and has been criticized by Kronmüller [40]. He pointed out that a model based on the long range diffusion of interstitials to Bloch walls may fit the experimental data equally well and would explain the absence of a magnetic aftereffect for stage $I_D$ in the CSW-model.

For our further discussion we therefore prefer the interpretation that stage $I_D$ is largely due to the correlated recombination of free interstitials with their own vacancy without explicitly excluding the possibility of some admixture of close pair recovery, especially in the early part of stage $I_D$.

## I.2. Annealing theories

In this section we will try to compare the more qualitative findings reported in the previous sections for stages $I_D$ and $I_E$ with theoretical expressions for the time and temperature dependence of the recovery. If the change in the defect concentrations is accomplished by the thermal diffusion of single interstitials to sinks, the dependence of the normalized concentration of Frenkel pairs, $Z$, on time $t$ and on temperature $T$ has the general form

$$Z = \frac{C}{C(0)} = Z(\nu t, \{0\}) , \tag{2}$$

$$\nu = \nu_0 \exp(-U/kT) , \tag{2a}$$

where $C(0)$ is the initial Frenkel pair concentration and $\nu$ the mean number of jumps per second of the migrating interstitial. In addition to the product $\nu t$, the normalized Frenkel pair density also depends on the initial conditions of the defect arrangement, symbolized by $\{0\}$, e.g., initial concentrations of interstitials and their distribution with respect to the vacancies. $U$ is the activation energy for migration of the interstitials and $v_0$ is the attempt frequency for an interstitial to jump to one of its neighbouring equilibrium sites *.

In eq. (2), and in the following equations, the Frenkel pair concentration is thought to denote always the concentration of interstitials or vacancies present in the sample irrespective of their detailed configuration, e.g., as single defects, dimers, larger clusters or entities trapped at impurities. This means that all clustering and trapping processes of interstitials are assumed not to change the Frenkel pair density, $Z$.

Kinetic equations which contain only the total Frenkel pair concentration are especially suited for comparison with resistivity recovery data. If the contribution of an interstitial to the residual resistivity increment is not changed greatly by trapping at other interstitials or impurities, the measured resistivity decrease reflects only the number of interstitials annihilated during the recovery and therefore is roughly proportional to the concentration of Frenkel pairs (see section I.2.2).

Two methods have been developed for the evaluation of $Z$ for different initial defect arrangements: The first method uses Monte-Carlo techniques for a direct computer simulation of the random walk and reactions of the mobile defects [41, 42]. The second method uses correlation functions to characterize the local defect arrangements and sets up a system of differential equations to describe the rate of change of the defect densities and defect correlations under the influence of thermal diffusion and defect reactions [43,44,45].

Frequently, instead of eq. (2), a differential equation of the form

$$-\frac{dZ}{dt} = 4\pi D\, R_0\, Z\, F(Z, \{0\})$$   (3)

is used to characterize the time and temperature dependence of the Frenkel pair concentration. Here, $R_0$ is the reaction radius of vacancies for annihilation by interstitials, and $F(Z, \{0\})$ is a function which depends on the defect concentration, $Z$, and the initial conditions of the defect arrangement, again symbolized by $\{0\}$. The diffusion constant $D$ of the interstitial is given by

$$D = D_0 \exp(-U/kT)$$   (4)

with

$$D_0 = \tfrac{1}{6} v_0 a^2$$   (4a)

and $a$ = jump distance of the interstitial **.

---

* The attempt frequency introduced here is related to the more commonly used attempt frequency $v_0$ for a jump into a particular lattice direction by $v_0 = v_0^* n$, where $n$ = number of saddle points over which the interstitial can jump to an equivalent neighbouring position with activation energy $U$ and $v_0^* \approx 10^{13}$ sec$^{-1}$.
** The factor $\tfrac{1}{6}$ in eq. (4) has to be replaced by $\tfrac{1}{2}$ if the interstitials have the configuration of a crowdion being restricted to uniaxial migration along a $\langle 110 \rangle$ lattice row.

If $F(Z, \{0\})$ has the form of a power law

$$F(Z, \{0\}) = \text{const} \cdot Z^{\gamma-1} , \tag{5}$$

the reaction is said to be of order $\gamma$ in analogy to the notation used in chemical rate theory for gaseous reactions.

In the following sections, the form of the kinetic eq. (3) will be discussed for correlated and uncorrelated initial distributions of vacancies and interstitials.

### I.2.1.1. Uncorrelated recombination

For the recombination of equal numbers of interstitials and vacancies, present in random initial distribution (except for the region $R < R_0$ around the vacancies which is free of interstitials), a second order reaction is known to prevail at larger times. In this case the function $F$ has the limiting form

$$F \equiv F_1 \Rightarrow Z C(0) , \tag{6}$$

where $C(0)$ is the initial concentration of vacancies and interstitials.

The limiting value $Z C(0)$ of eq. (6) is a good approximation only as long as

$$\sqrt{1 - Z} \gg \sqrt{\alpha_0} \tag{7}$$

with

$$\alpha_0 = C(0) \, 4\pi R_0^3 . \tag{7a}$$

For low initial defect densities and small values of the recombination radius $R_0$ this inequality is satisfied for most of the recovery except for a transient initial part where $Z \Rightarrow 1$. The initial departure of the reaction rate from relation (6) depends on the detailed form of the initial distribution of interstitials around the vacancies. For a distribution which is a step function at distance $R = R_0$, Waite [43] finds that the factor $F$ is infinite in the beginning and approaches (6) only when (7) is fulfilled. This behaviour is outlined in fig. 11. In the initial part of the transient (for $1 - Z \ll \alpha_0$) the normalized defect density $Z$ decreases approximately with $\sqrt{Dt}/R_0$. If the step function is replaced by a physically more realistic initial distribution which increases more gradually for $R > R_0$, the initial reaction rate stays finite for $Z \Rightarrow 1$ and the transient in the recovery no longer exhibits the initial $\sqrt{t}$ – time dependence. In many practical cases the initial defect concentrations are low enough, so that the initial transient can be neglected and eq. (6) is a good approximation for most of the recovery.

### I.2.1.2. Uncorrelated recombination plus trapping reactions

If, in addition to annihilation, clustering of free interstitials can also occur, the

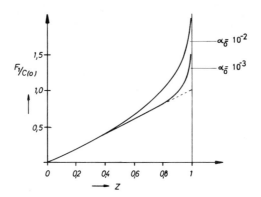

Fig. 11. Typical form of the factor $F \equiv F_1$ in rate eq. (3) for uncorrelated recombination of interstitials and vacancies. The ratio $F_1/C(0)$ is plotted versus $Z = C/C(0)$. A linear relationship characterizes a pure second order reaction. The initial transient has been calculated for an initial distribution of the interstitials around the vacancies which is a step function at $R = R_0$. The parameter $\alpha_0$ is defined by eq. (7a).

following system of reaction equations must be envisaged:

$$i_1 + V \to 0$$
$$i_1 + i_1 \to i_2$$
$$i_1 + i_2 \to i_3$$
$$\cdots\cdots\cdots$$
$$i_1 + i_n \to i_{n+1}$$

where $i_n$ denotes a cluster of $n$-trapped interstitials.

As was shown by Schroeder [45], the diffusion equations of this hierarchy of reaction equations can be transformed into a set of rate equations for the densities of the vacancies, single and multiple interstitials. This set of equations can be solved analytically if the trapping radius $R_n$ of a cluster of $n$ interstitials for $n > 2$ is taken to be constant or if it is assumed that $R_n$ increases linearly with $n$. The choice of recombination radius $R_0$ and the reaction radius $R_1$ for di-interstitial formation is not restricted. If the concentrations of single and multiple interstitials are expressed by the normalized Frenkel pair concentration $Z$, this treatment leads to a rate equation of the form of eq. (3). For equal initial numbers of interstitials and vacancies, Schroeder has shown that the factor $F(Z, \{0\})$ has the general form

$$F \equiv F_2 = C(0)\, f_2(Z) , \tag{8}$$

where $f_2$ depends only on the normalized Frenkel defect concentration $Z$ and not

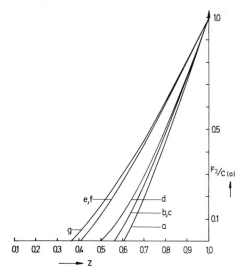

Fig. 12. Typical form of the factor $F \equiv F_2$ in the rate eq. (3) for recombination and clustering of freely migrating interstitials present in uncorrelated initial distribution with an equal number of vacancies. The ratio $f_2 = F_2/C(0)$ is plotted versus $Z = C/C(0)$. The different curves belong to different combinations of trapping and recombination radii. $R_0$ = recombination radius; $R_1$ = reaction radius for di-interstitial formation; $R_n$ = reaction radius for interstitial trapping by a cluster of $n \geqslant 2$ interstitials (taken either proportional to $n$, or constant).

| curve | a | b | c | d | e | f | g |
|---|---|---|---|---|---|---|---|
| $R_1/R_0$ | 1 | 1 | 1 | 1 | $\frac{1}{2}$ | $\frac{1}{2}$ | $\frac{1}{2}$ |
| $R_n/R_0$ | $n$ | $\frac{1}{2}n$ | 1 | 0 | $\frac{1}{4}n$ | $\frac{1}{2}$ | 0 |

The curves calculated for the parameter combinations b and c respectively e and f have equal ratios $R_2/R_0$ and coincide within the accuracy of the drawing.

on the initial Frenkel defect density $C(0)$ (except for a transient behaviour in the very beginning similar to $F_1$). Some typical examples for $f_2$ are outlined in fig. 12. As may be recognized $f_2$, and therefore also the reaction rate, becomes zero at $Z = Z_{uncorr}(\infty)$. At this point only trapped interstitials and vacancies are present with both in relative concentration $Z_{uncorr}(\infty)$.

In fig. 13, the increase of the final fraction of trapped interstitials, $Z_{uncorr}(\infty)$, is shown as a function of the ratio $R_1/R_0$. As can be seen this fraction also depends slightly on the magnitude of $R_2$. The detailed theory shows further that the magnitudes of the trapping radii $R_n$ for $n \geqslant 3$ have very little influence on $Z_{uncorr}(\infty)$, as long as these trapping radii are not unphysically large in comparison with $R_1$ and $R_2$. For this reason the curves b and c and e and f in fig. 12 coincide within the

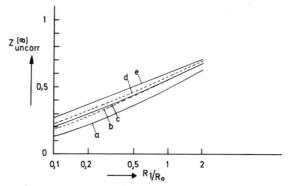

Fig. 13. Calculated total trapping probability $Z_{uncorr}(\infty)$ of interstitials during uncorrelated recombination and clustering processes versus the ratio $R_1/R_0$. The different curves belong to different combinations of the trapping radii $R_n$ of the higher interstitial clusters with $n \geqslant 2$.

| curve | a | b | c | d | e |
|-------|---|---|---|---|---|
| $R_n/R_0$ | 0 | 1 | $\frac{1}{2}n$ | 2 | $n$ |

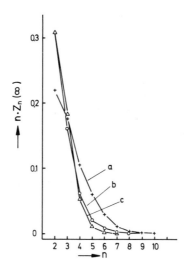

Fig. 14. Calculated cluster-size-distributions of the interstitials trapped in stage $I_E$. $n z_n(\infty)$ is the fraction of interstitials (normalized to the initial defect density) which survives in clusters of $n$ trapped interstitials. The curves a, b and c belong to the different combinations of trapping and recombination radii outlined in the caption of fig. 12.

accuracy of the drawing. Thus we conclude that at the point where di-interstitials and tri-interstitials have been formed in sufficient numbers, that they decisively influence the trapping probability of the single interstitials remaining, the total concentration of free interstitials has already been reduced so much that the build-up of higher interstitial clusters can no longer affect the total number of interstitials retained in trapped configurations. For this reason also the size distribution decreases rapidly for the larger cluster sizes, as shown in fig. 14.

I.2.1.3. Correlated recombination

As discussion in section I.1.4 at low initial defect densities, correlated recombination shows up as a separate annealing stage $I_D$. For this recovery process it is essential that the interstitials are initially situated close to their own vacancy. For the mathematical treatment of this process, the initial defect arrangement is described by a distribution function $\varphi(R)$ where $\varphi(R) \cdot 4\pi R^2 \cdot dR$ is the probability of finding an interstitial in the region between $R$ and $R + dR$ around a vacancy. $\varphi(R)$ is strongly concentrated near the vacancy and several analytical forms have been considered in the literature [13,43–47]: For $R > R_o$

$$\varphi(R) = N\delta(R - (\lambda + 1)R_o) \tag{9a}$$

or

$$\varphi(R) = \frac{N}{R} \exp(-R/\lambda R_o) \tag{9b}$$

or

$$\varphi(R) = N \exp[-(R/\lambda R_o)^2] . \tag{9c}$$

For $R < R_o$, $\varphi(R) = 0$ in all cases. $N$ is a normalization constant and $\lambda$ is a parameter which determines the average separation of the interstitials from the surface of the recombination volume.

If the initial defect density is so low that the mean separation of the Frenkel defects is very large compared to the initial distance between a vacancy and an interstitial in a Frenkel pair, the recovery is made up of two separate contributions. The first is due to the correlated recombination of an interstitial with its own vacancy in a random diffusion process, and the second is due to the uncorrelated recombination of interstitials with other vacancies in the manner described in section I.2.1.1. As may be seen in fig. 15, the mean number of jumps ($\propto 4Dt/R_o^2$) for these two processes differ greatly in the limit of low initial defect densities.

In order to have uncorrelated recombination, an interstitial must have been separated far from its native vacancy and the fraction of interstitials eligible for this process is approximately given by the probability $Z_{corr}(\infty)$ that the interstitial of an isolated Frenkel pair survives correlated recombination at large times. This probability is equal to

$$Z_{corr}(\infty) = 1 - \langle R_o/R \rangle_{\varphi(R)} = \frac{\bar{R} - R_o}{\bar{R}}, \tag{10}$$

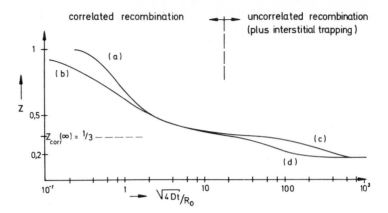

Fig. 15. Typical theoretical recovery curves for stages $I_D$ and $I_E$. The normalized vacancy concentration $Z$ is plotted versus the quantity $\sqrt{4Dt/R_0}$ for different initial distribution functions and defect densities. In the correlated recovery range curves a and b pertain to an initial distribution function of the type given by eqs. (9a) and (9b) respectively, both with $\lambda = \frac{1}{2}$. In the uncorrelated recovery range curves c and d have been calculated for the parameters $\alpha_0 = 4\pi R_0^3 Z_{corr}(\infty)C(0) = 4 \times 10^{-7}$ and $4 \times 10^{-6}$, respectively. The parameters $R_1/R_0$ and $R_{n\geqslant2}$ are taken as 1 and 0, respectively.

where $\langle \ \rangle_{\varphi(R)}$ denotes an average * over the initial distribution function $\varphi(R)$ and $\bar{R}$, as defined by eq. (10), characterizes the average initial separation of the interstitials from their vacancies. According to eq. (10) the total fraction of defects surviving correlated recovery in stage $I_D$ is determined mainly by the relative separation of the mean initial interstitial position $\bar{R}$ from the edge of the recombination volume at $R_0$.

A clear separation of correlated and uncorrelated recovery holds approximately as long as

$$C(0) \, 4R_0^3(Z_{corr}(\infty))^3 \lesssim 10^{-4} \text{ to } 10^{-5} . \tag{11}$$

For initial defect densities up to values determined by eq. (11), less than a few percent of the interstitials which would recombine with their own vacancies in the limit $C(0) \Rightarrow 0$ are annihilated at foreign vacancies. Eq. (11) shows that the separation between correlated and uncorrelated recovery persists to higher initial defect densities for smaller recombination volumes and smaller initial separations of correlated interstitials and vacancies.

In the limit of very low initial defect densities the solution of the diffusion equa-

$$* \ \langle A(R) \rangle_{\varphi(R)} \equiv \int_{R_0}^{\infty} A(R) \, \varphi(R) \, 4\pi R^2 \, dR$$

tion yields a time dependence of the recovery in the form

$$Z - Z_{corr}(\infty) = \langle \frac{R_0}{R} \, \text{erf} \, (\frac{R - R_0}{\sqrt{4Dt}}) \rangle_{\varphi(R)} \, , \tag{12}$$

where

$$\text{erf} \, x \equiv \frac{2}{\sqrt{\pi}} \int_0^x \exp(-\eta^2) \, d\eta \, . \tag{13}$$

Typical recovery curves for the distribution functions of the types (9a) and (9b) are shown in fig. 15.

If the parameters in the distribution functions are chosen such that they yield equal values of $Z_{corr}(\infty)$ (see eq. (10)) one recognizes from fig. 15 that primarily the initial part of the recovery curves obtained from eq. (12) is sensitive to the detailed shape of $\varphi(R)$.

In its final part, the recovery curve (12) can be approximated by

$$Z - Z_{corr}(\infty) = Z_{corr}(\infty) \, R_0/\sqrt{\pi Dt} \tag{14}$$

and is independent of the detailed form of the distribution function $\varphi(R)$. The approximation of eq. (14) is valid when $R - R_0/\sqrt{4Dt} \lesssim 1$, i.e., for the final 30% of the correlated recovery curves shown in fig. 15.

If $Z - Z_{corr}(\infty)$ is taken as a measure for the resistivity recovery in stage $I_D$, eq. (14) would correspond to a pure third order chemical rate equation *.

### I.2.2. Comparison of annealing theories with experiments in stage I

In order to compare the annealing data reported in section I.1.3 and I.1.4 with the recovery models described above, a relation between the measured resistivity change $\Delta\rho$ and the concentration of Frenkel pairs, $C$, must be established. The simplest assumption would be

$$\Delta\rho = \rho_F C \, , \tag{15}$$

where the resistivity per Frenkel pair, $\rho_F$, is constant. This assumption is probably not so bad for stages $I_A$ through $I_D$ where only interstitial-vacancy recombination occurs.

If, however, interstitial clustering or trapping at impurities takes place simultaneously with recombination, relation (15) holds only if the contribution of an interstitial to the scattering cross section for conduction electrons is not changed during

---

* Oddou [17] has observed a time dependence of the form of eq. (14) for an isothermal taken at 60°K in heavily electron irradiated nickel (third order reaction). Since stage $I_E$ could not be separated from stage $I_D$ in this experiment it is possible that his data do not, as assumed by the authors, pertain to recovery in stage $I_E$ but to the end of stage $I_D$ where eq. (14) can be applied.

these trapping processes. However, due to interference effects, e.g., the absolute value of the scattering cross section as well as its anisotropy may be affected, thus leading to a change in the contribution of an interstitial to the resistivity and to deviations from the additivity of the residual resistivities of vacancies and interstitials (Matthiessen's rule). A comparison of the annealing behaviour of the electrical resistivity, stored energy, elastic modulus, and lattice parameter [48] indicates that at the end of stage I the relation (15) seems to break down. Already for this reason detailed conclusions drawn from the observed time dependence of the resistivity recovery in the final part of stage $I_E$ must be viewed with great caution.

But there is still another reason why arguments using apparent reaction orders, $\gamma$, determined from the time dependence of the recovery in stage $I_E$ must be taken with great care. Even in the case that the relation (15) is strictly fulfilled, it is not possible to describe the kinetics of the interstitial-vacancy recombination by a power law of the form of eq. (5) if interstitial clustering occurs simultaneously with recombination at vacancies. This can be recognized immediately if the forms of the functions $F_2$ outlined in fig. 12 are inspected. It is not possible to represent these functions by a power law with a constant reaction order $\gamma-1$. The formal description of the rate eq. (3) by an apparent reaction order $\gamma(C)$ depending on $C$ or by a reaction order $\gamma'$ relating the reaction rate $dC/dt$ to $(\Delta\rho - \Delta\rho(\infty))^{\gamma'}$ has no physical significance. Therefore, all arguments which use apparent reaction orders for stage $I_E$ on the basis of simple chemical rate theory (see eq. (5)) must be regarded as based on incorrect premises and as such are of little physical significance.

There is one feature in common for uncorrelated recombinations with and without simultaneous interstitial clustering and that is the linear dependence of the normalized reaction rate on the initial defect density $C(0)$ as shown by eqs. (6) and (8). Therefore the dose dependence of the isochronal recovery observed for uncorrelated recombination of interstitials and vacancies is retained also in the case of simultaneous interstitial clustering. Measurements of the dose dependence, therefore, contribute an important method for the discrimination between uncorrelated and other recovery processes. From eqs. (6) or (8) one would expect that two isochronal curves taken with the same time-temperature schedule but with different initial defect densities would give slopes at equal values of fractional recovery which would satisfy the following equation:

$$\ln\left(\frac{d\Delta\rho}{dT}\right)_1 - \ln\left(\frac{d\Delta\rho}{dT}\right)_2 = \frac{U}{k}\frac{T_2-T_1}{T_2 T_1} + 2\ln\frac{(\Delta\rho_0)_1}{(\Delta\rho_0)_2}, \tag{16}$$

where the indices 1 and 2 denote the two different irradiation doses. Unfortunately the accuracy of the experimental data reported so far for stage $I_E$ (see section I.1.2.1) is not sufficient to check relation (16) unambigously. However, there seems to be a general tendency towards values smaller than 2 for the factor before the log term. This may indicate that impurity trapping, which generally reduces the dependence of the reaction rate on $C(0)$ could have exerted some influence at the low defect densities investigated.

Using the crude approximation of eq. (15) and the theories outlined in the previous section I.2.1.1 the following quantitative results can be deduced from the experimental data available.

a) According to eq. (10) the ratio $\bar{R}/R_0$ can directly be evaluated from $Z_{corr}(\infty)$, which in turn can be obtained from the defect retention above stage $I_D$, $f_{I_D}$, after normalization to the total defect density present in the beginning of stage $I_D$. If $f_{I_D}$ is taken from recovery curves, where stages $I_D$ and $I_E$ are well separated, the values $\bar{R}/R_0$ listed in table 3 are obtained. In all metals the observed mean separation of the interstitials from their vacancy is rather small and decreases when the mean recoil energy of the displaced atoms approaches the displacement threshold.

Table 3

Evaluation of recovery data in stages $I_D$ and $I_E$

| Element | Electron energy (MeV) | $\bar{R}/R_0$ | $R_1/R_0$ | $R_2/R_0$ | Ref. |
|---------|------------------------|---------------|-----------|-----------|------|
| Cu | 1.4 | 1.6 | 0.9 | 0.6 | [3] |
| Al | 0.22 | 1.3 | 2.3 | 0.6 | [46,21] |
|    | 0.4 | 1.5 | | | |
| Pt | 2.0 | 1.7 | 0.7 | 0.4 | [16,39] |

$\bar{R}$ = mean distance between vacancy and interstitial in a Frenkel pair in the beginning of stage $I_D$ as defined by: $1/\bar{R} = \langle 1/R \rangle_{\varphi(R)}$.
$R_1$ = reaction radius for di-interstitial formation in stage $I_E$;
$R_2$ = reaction radius for interstitial trapping at di-interstitials (with some possible contribution of larger interstitial clusters).
All numbers are given in units of $R_0$ = reaction radius for interstitial-vacancy recombination in stage $I_E$.

b) According to the curve shown in fig. 13 the ratio $R_1/R_0$ can be estimated from the observed defect retention above stage $I_E$ (normalized to the defect density present in the beginning of stage $I_E$). $R_1$ is the reaction radius of single interstitials for agglomeration into di-interstitials. Approximate values of $R_1/R_0$ (taking into account the small influence of trapping by di-interstitials) are given in table 3. The magnitude of the ratios $R_1/R_0$ between 0.7 and 2.3 confirms our earlier conclusion that there exists a strong attractive interaction between interstitials which is comparable with their interaction with vacancies. The physical nature of this strong interaction is not yet understood. The high elastic polarizability of the interstitial (see paper of Wenzl [48] in this proceedings for a more detailed discussion of this subject) or electronic effects may play an important role.

c) An estimate of the reaction radii of di-interstitials for additional single interstitial trapping may be obtained from the radiation doping experiments discussed in section I.1.3.2. If the samples are doped with a large excess of vacancies and di-interstitials remaining from a preceding low temperature irradiation plus annealing treatment, the interstitials produced by a subsequent test irradiation can survive only by joining one of these di-interstitials. Therefore, the defect retention, $f_I^{r.d.}$, above stage I in the radiation doped samples is given by

$$f_I^{r.d.} = f_{I_D}^{u.p.} \frac{R_2}{R_2 + 2R_o}, \qquad (17)$$

where $f_{I_D}^{u.p.}$ is the defect retention in undoped pure samples upon completion of the correlated recovery in stage $I_D$. Approximate values of $R_2/R_o$ deduced from the experimental data of table 2 are summarized in table 3. The smallness of these values justifies the assumption that in undoped samples interstitials primarily survive in form of di-interstitials.

d) According to eq. (12) the form of the initial distribution function $\varphi(R)$ could in principle be obtained from the shape of the isochronal recovery observed in stage $I_D$. However, as discussed in section I.2.1.3 only the initial part of stage $I_D$ is sensitive to the form of $\varphi(R)$, if the parameter $\lambda$ is fixed by the conditions of eq. (10). For most fcc metals this part of stage $I_D$ overlaps with stage $I_C$, so that no definitive conclusions can be drawn. The analysis performed by Corbett et al. [3] for Cu and by Simpson et al. [46] for Al merely indicate, that the $\delta$-function distribution of eq. (9a) is too narrow and that more wide-spread distributions such as given by eqs. (9b) and (9c) are better approximations.

According to eq. (14) the time and temperature dependence of the recovery in the final part of stage $I_D$ is determined only by the parameter $D/R_o^2$. If the activation energy $U$ is known, one can obtain values of $D_o/R_o^2$ from the experimental data. For Cu and Al $D_o/R_o^2 = 0.8 \times 10^{12}$ and $2.5 \times 10^{12}$ sec$^{-1}$ have been observed respectively [3,46]. Although these numbers are uncertain by a factor of 2, an order of magnitude estimate of $R_o/a$ can be obtained by application of eq. (4a). Taking $\nu_o \approx 10^{14}$ sec$^{-1}$ approximate values of $R_o/a$ around 5 and 2.5 are obtained for Cu and Al, respectively. Although a value of $\nu_o$ has been used which is characteristic for high temperature diffusion processes, the estimated values of $R_o/a$ seem to be of the right order of magnitude if compared with the spontaneous recombination volume $V_a^o$. Values of $V_a^o$ can be deduced for Cu and Al from radiation annealing experiments [72] and range between 150 and 80 atomic volumes. The reaction volume $4\pi R_o^3/3$ should be larger than these volumes at least by the number of unstable close pair sites around a vacancy. A value of the attempt frequency $\nu_o$ around $10^{12}$ sec$^{-1}$ as observed for the close pair recovery processes would yield unreasonable small estimates of $R_o/a$. The reason why the high temperature approximation for the jump frequency gives the better description for the low temperature diffusion of interstitials than a description taking into account possible quantum effects (see section I.1.2) is not understood.

I.2.3. *Three dimensional versus crowdion migration in stage I*

The conversion-two-interstitial model as outlined by Seeger in these proceedings [50] attributes stages $I_D$ and $I_E$ to the correlated and uncorrelated recombination of crowdions with vacancies. The basic assumption required by this model is that metastable crowdions are formed during the irradiation at low temperatures. In addition to recombination in stage I these crowdions are able to undergo conversion into a different immobile interstitial configuration which then becomes mobile in stage III. The conversion from the metastable into the stable configuration can be accomplished either by thermal decay of the isolated crowdion (thermal conversion), by interactions of two crowdions encountering each other during thermal migration (double conversion), or by interactions of a crowdion with an impurity atom or converted interstitial or interstitial cluster. Except for thermal conversion, all the other conversion processes are completely analogous to the kind of trapping reactions described in section I.1.3.2.

There is, however, one fundamental difference in the behaviour of crowdions and normal interstitials: A migrating crowdion is constrained to move along the lattice direction which coincides with its axis. Therefore, a crowdion can undergo only one-dimensional migration. As a consequence thereof an isolated crowdion in an infinite lattice without other defects has no chance for final escape from correlated recombination if it cannot bypass its own vacancy.

On the other hand, an interstitial capable of free migration in three dimensions according to eq. (10) always has a finite chance to escape from its own vacancy. The assumption of one-dimensional migration of the stage I interstitial leads to the following contradictions with experimental observations.

1) In an annealing experiment after low temperature irradiation of pure metals, one would expect the fraction of crowdions surviving correlated recombination in stage $I_D$ and consequently the defect retention above stage I to depend strongly on the irradiation dose. In the limit $\Delta\rho_0 \Rightarrow 0$ all the crowdions have to recombine with their own vacancy if thermal conversion and conversion at impurities are excluded. Therefore complete recovery in stage $I_D$ is to be expected. With increasing initial defect densities the probability for crowdions to undergo double conversion with other crowdions increases and therefore also the fractional defect retention above stage I should increase *. Although this idealized behaviour may in practice be altered somewhat by conversion processes at ever present residual impurities, it is difficult to see how the crowdion model could account for the observed independence of the fractional defect retention above stage I on the initial defect density in Cu be-

---

* Contrary to this statement in their theoretical analysis of correlated and uncorrelated crowdion recombination, Frank, Seeger and Schottky [49] obtain a constant value of $z_{corr}(\infty) = 0.5$ for the probability for escape of crowdions from correlated recombination independent of dose, even for the limit $\Delta\rho_0 \Rightarrow 0$ (see eq. (21) of ref. [49]). As outlined above, this result is difficult to understand and is probably caused by illicit simplifications used during their evaluation of the pair distribution function.

tween $\approx 10^{-6}$ to $10^{-4}$ Frenkel defects/atom (see fig. 9). In this concentration range the chance for survival of interstitials above stage I is dominated by interstitial-interstitial reactions and reactions at the residual impurities play a minor role.

2) The crowdion model is unable to account for the observed dose curves for defect production at higher temperatures. As discussed by Wollenberger in his contribution to these proceedings [37], the initial damage rate observed during irradiation at higher temperatures is given by

$$\lim_{\Delta\rho\to 0} \left(\frac{d\Delta\rho}{d\phi t}\right)_{80°K} = \left(\frac{d\Delta\rho}{d\phi t}\right)_{4°K} \cdot f. \tag{18}$$

The observed values of the factor $f$ around $f = 0.3$ for Pt, Cu, and Al are in good agreement with the values $f_{ID}^{u.p.}$ of the fractional defect retention above stage $I_D$ found in annealing experiments after low temperature irradiations. However, the crowdion model would predict, if thermal conversion is excluded, $f = 0$ for pure samples at higher temperatures: At 80°K and at all dose rates employed in actual electron irradiations, the possibility that within the lifetime of a crowdion another crowdion is produced by a subsequent displacement event close enough so that the second crowdion could encounter the first one can be entirely ignored. Therefore, if other conversion processes are impossible, the crowdion has no chance for survival from correlated recombination with its own vacancy and the initial damage rate must be zero.

Also the possibility of conversion of crowdions during 80°K irradiations at residual impurities cannot account for the observed finite values of the initial damage rates: It has been observed in experiments on Cu, Al and Pt [37,51,38] that the initial damage rates were, within experimental error, independent of the residual impurity content which was varied over more than a factor of 20. In contrast to this, the crowdion model would predict a strong dependence of the probability for survival from correlated recombination on the impurity content.

Only if thermal conversion of crowdions is possible, a finite chance for interstitial survival exists at higher temperatures in pure samples. In this case according to a calculation of Schroeder [45], the probability for survival of a crowdion by thermal conversion into an immobile configuration is given by

$$f = f_{c.p.} \left(1 - \exp\left[-(R_p - R_o)\sqrt{\nu_c/D}\right]\right), \tag{19}$$

where $f_{c.p.}$ is the fractional crowdion retention upon completion of the close pair recovery stages and $R_p$ is the distance from the vacancy where the crowdion is stopped after the displacement process, $\nu_c$ is the frequency of thermal conversion and given by $\nu_c = \nu_o \exp(-U_c/kT)$, $U_c$ is the activation energy for thermal conversion and $D$ is the diffusion constant of the crowdion along its axis. Contrary to the case of three dimensional migration (see eq. (10)), the chance of crowdions surviving correlated recombination now would be strongly temperature dependent. For small values of $f$ the temperature dependence is exponential and given by $\exp(U_m - U_c/2kT)$, where $U_m$ is the activation energy for crowdion migration.

The observed values of $f \approx 0.3$ for Cu, Al and Pt at 80°K would imply values of $U_c - U_m$ around 0.05 to 0.08 eV (for $R_p/a = 10$ to 100). In this case the damage rate should increase strongly with irradiation temperatures above 80°K and decrease at lower irradiation temperatures. Experiments performed on Cu to check this effect have shown, however, that the factor $f$ (as defined by eq. (18)) is independent on temperature from 85 to 220°K [37].

Another important consequence of the thermal conversion model would be that at higher temperatures the crowdions are converted rather close to their own vacancy. A simple calculation shows that for $R > R_p$ the converted interstitials are distributed exponentially with

$$W(R) = N \exp\left[-R(v_c/D)^{1/2}\right] \tag{20}$$

where $W(R)$ is the probability to find a converted crowdion at a distance between $R$ and $R + dR$ from the surface of the recombination volume of its vacancy ($N$ = normalization constant).

The relaxation length $(D/v_c)^{1/2}$ of this distribution decreases exponentially with temperature and has the same exponent as $f$ in the limit $f \Rightarrow 1$ (see eq. (19)). As a consequence thereof crowdions having an appreciable chance $f$ for thermal conversion are deposited in converted form rather close to their own vacancy. Therefore, as long as the vacancy concentration $C$ accumulated during the irradiation at high temperatures is small, no influence of the vacancies present on the chance for survival of newly produced crowdion by thermal conversion is expected. As long as

$$C \pi R_o^2 (D/v_c)^{1/2} \lesssim 1 \tag{21}$$

($R_o$ = reaction radius for crowdion-vacancy annihilation) the probability of a crowdion to recombine with a foreign vacancy before thermal conversion is small. The observed damage rate should therefore be unchanged with increasing defect density and a linear increase of $\Delta\rho$ with dose is expected. If reasonable values for $R_o$ ($\sim 3a$) are inserted into eq. (21) one recognizes that the observed damage rate at 80°K should be hardly affected for defect densities up to $C \approx 10^{-4}$ to $10^{-5}$ (for $R_p/a = 10$ to 100). Contrary to this prediction, the typical $\sqrt{\phi t}$ dose dependence of the defect production at 80°K is observed in pure metals even at defect densities of only $10^{-7}$ to $10^{-6}$ [37,38,51,52].

The main possibility of making the crowdion model consistent with the experimental results seems to require the assumption that a fixed fraction of crowdions cannot undergo recombination with their own vacancies, as could be the case if a crowdion's migration line bypassed its own vacancy. These crowdions can then diffuse through the lattice until they find another reaction partner, where trapping, conversion or recombination may occur. However, in this modification of the conversion-two-interstitial model, one might expect that the fraction of crowdions not able to recombine with their own vacancy is connected intimately with the probability for the occurrence of initially defocused collision chains, which initiate focused replacement collision chains in directions perpendicular to the initial recoil direction at distances larger than $R_0$. Since for Cu it has been observed [37] that the factor $f$ in relation (18) decreases only from 0.3 to 0.2 when the electron energy is lowered from 3 to 0.45 MeV, the threshold energy for such defocusing-focusing events cannot be considerably larger than the threshold for normal displacements in contrast to what one would expect intuitively.

### I.3. Stage I recovery of neutron irradiated Cu, Ag, Al, Pt and Ni

In contrast to the isolated Frenkel pairs produced by electron damage, fast neutron irradiation produces highly energetic recoil atoms which initiate large displacement cascades. The spatial structure of these cascades depends on the mean distances the recoiling atoms can travel between two displacement collisions. Theoretical calculations [53] indicate that for metals with low atomic masses such as Al, the displacement cascade defect distribution is rather spread out. In this case the high energy recoils produce a more or less loose assembly of subcascades, each containing only a few Frenkel defects.

However, for the metals with higher atomic mass, such as Cu, Ag, Au and Pt, the local defect density produced by the displacement cascades is so high that spontaneous recombination processes occur frequently. The limiting overall concentration of Frenkel defects remaining in the cascade regions after the self-annealing processes can be estimated from the saturation behaviour of the damage rate observed during neutron irradiation [54]. This concentration is of order of $10^{-1}$ at % for a metal like Cu.

The local distribution of the vacancies and interstitials in the cascade region is influenced by two effects. Both of these effects tend to separate interstitials and vacancies in the cascade zone. First, during the evolution of the cascades the interstitials on the average are deposited at larger distances from the center of the cascade than the vacancies, especially if focusing effects are important. Secondly, the spontaneous recombination processes tend to favour the preferential survival of clusters of interstitials or vacancies. This clustering effect is a consequence of the overlap of the recombination volumes of the interstitials in an interstitial cluster. Due to this overlap, the probability of being involved in a spontaneous recombination process is smaller for each of the interstitials in the cluster than that for isolated interstitials and their chance for survival is accordingly larger. A similar effect also enhances the survival of vacancies in the form of clusters. Model calculations performed by Beeler [55], and by Lück and Sizmann [56] confirm this segregation of interstitials and vacancies under the influence of spontaneous recombination processes.

The recovery spectra observed after low dose neutron damage in the region of

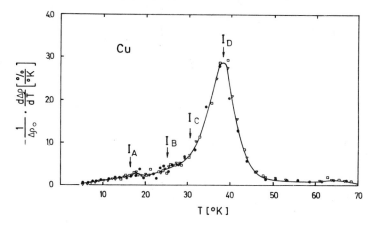

Fig. 16. Differential isochronal recovery in stage I of Cu neutron irradiated at 4.5°K. The different data points pertain to different independent irradiation and annealing runs. All samples contained about equal initial defect densities, $\Delta\rho_0 \approx 2.0$ n$\Omega \cdot$cm. A smooth curve averaging the results of the different runs has been drawn through the data points. The peak temperatures of the substages observed after electron damage are outlined by arrows for comparison. Data are taken from ref. [57].

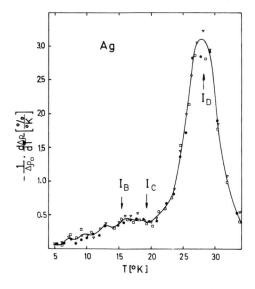

Fig. 17. Differential isochronal recovery in stage I of Ag neutron irradiated at 4.5°K. The different data points pertain to different independent irradiation and annealing runs. All samples contained about equal initial defect densities $\Delta\rho_0 \approx 2.0$ n$\Omega \cdot$cm. A smooth curve averaging the results of the different runs has been drawn through the data points. The peak temperatures of the substages observed after electron damage are outlined by arrows for comparison. Data are taken from ref. [57].

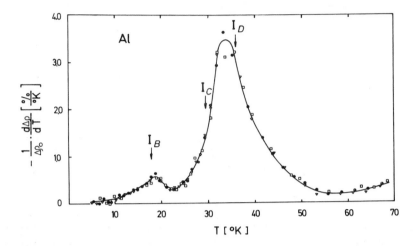

Fig. 18. Differential isochronal recovery in stage I of Al neutron irradiated at 4.5°K. The different data points pertain to different independent irradiation and annealing runs. All samples contained about equal initial defect densities $\Delta\rho_0 = 6.0$ n$\Omega \cdot$cm. A smooth curve averaging the results of the different runs has been drawn through the data points. The peak temperatures of the substages observed after electron damage are outlined by arrows for comparison. Data are taken from ref. [57].

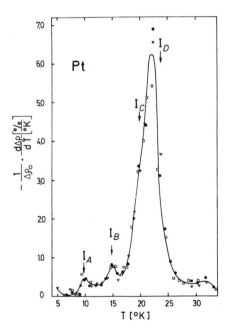

Fig. 19. Differential isochronal recovery in stage I of Pt neutron irradiated at 4.5°K. The different data points pertain to different independent irradiation and annealing runs. All samples contained about equal initial defect densities $\Delta\rho_0 =$ 4.5 n$\Omega \cdot$cm. A smooth curve averaging the results of the different runs has been drawn through the data points. The peak temperatures of the substages observed after electron damage are outlined by arrows for comparison. Data are taken from ref. [57].

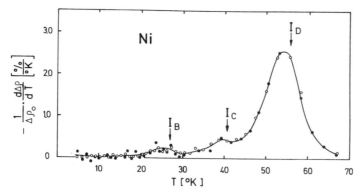

Fig. 20. Differential isochronal recovery in stage I of Ni neutron irradiated at 4.5°K. The different data points pertain to different independent irradiation and annealing runs. All samples contained about equal initial defect densities $\Delta\rho_0 \approx 6.0$ n$\Omega\cdot$cm. A smooth curve averaging the results of the different runs has been drawn through the data points. The peak temperatures of the substages observed after electron damage are outlined by arrows for comparison. Data are taken from ref. [58].

stage I are shown in figs. 16—20 for the metals Cu, Ag, Al, Pt and Ni [57—59]. These data are in good agreement with the recovery spectra reported by Coltman et al. [60] for fast neutron damage of Cu, Ag, Al and Pt. For Ni the same structures as those shown in fig. 20 also have been observed by Peretto [61].

If the structures of figs. 16—20 are compared with the structures observed after low dose electron damage in figs. 1—5, the following differences can be recognized:

1) In the close pair region a more or less continuous background recovery is observed in the neutron irradiated samples which increases with increasing annealing temperature. Only in Pt and Al and perhaps also in Ni are there small peaks in the regions of stages $I_A$, $I_B$ and $I_C$, respectively. Judging from the areas under the differential isochronals also the total amount of recovery in the close pair region is much less after neutron than after electron irradiation. The interpretation of these differences may be as follows: Due to the high local defect density within the cascade region a vacancy-interstitial pair present in one of the close pair configurations will interact strongly with its neighbouring defects. The sharp activation energies for the recombination of the isolated close pairs will therefore be smeared out. In addition, within the cascade zones interstitials and vacancies may accidentally form close pairs in configurations which cannot be populated by electron irradiation. The recovery of these additional close pair types may help to smoothen the distribution of activation energies below stage $I_D$. The small amount of total recovery in the close pair range in neutron irradiated metals compared with electron irradiation is also a consequence of the defect pattern outlined above: Due to the segregation of interstitials and vacancies within the cascade region the probability of finding close pairs is greatly reduced.

2) Although stage $I_D$ is the most prominent recovery stage after neutron damage,

there seems to be no well defined substage $I_E$. Only for Al and Pt there is a small indication of a shoulder on the high temperature side of stage $I_D$. In the other metals stage $I_D$ seems to extend smoothly into the region where stage $I_E$ would be observed in electron irradiated samples containing similar overall defect densities. The absence of a well defined stage $I_E$ even for very low neutron doses can be interpreted as follows: Only interstitial atoms located at the surface of the displacement zone have the possibility of escaping reaction with a partner from its own zone. However, the probability for this escape is rather small. Due to the large extension of the cascade region, an interstitial, when it starts to sample the neighbourhood of its birth place, will have a high probability to return and to react with defects of its own displacement zone *. On the other hand the correlated recombination of interstitials which start near the surface of the displacement zone may involve a much larger mean number of jumps than the correlated recombination of isolated Frenkel pairs. As can be recognized from fig. 15 the time dependence at the end of the correlated recovery scales mainly as $Dt/R_o^2$. This means that a given fractional recovery of interstitials which start outside the cascade region is obtained at times which are by a factor of $(R_{cas}/R_o)^2$ larger than the equivalent times in stage $I_D$ of electron irradiated samples. This explains why after low dose neutron irradiation the correlated recovery stage may extend to higher temperatures where a clearly separated stage $I_E$ is already observed in electron irradiated samples.

3) The third marked difference in the stage I annealing observed after neutron and electron damage is the much higher defect retention $f_I^{u.p.}$ above stage I in neutron irradiated samples. This can be seen by a comparison of the corresponding lines in tables 4 and 2. In part the larger fractional retention of defects in neutron irradiated metals is simply due to the smaller fractional recovery in the close pair range. The main contribution, however, comes from the increased survival of interstitials in stage $I_D$. Whereas after electron damage interstitials can be trapped only in stage $I_E$, after they have escaped correlated recombination with their own vacancy, the interstitials present within a displacement zone are already able to react with other interstitials in stage $I_D$. This is a consequence of the preferred interstitial-interstitial correlation characteristic for the damage pattern in the displacement zones which makes mutual trapping reactions possible even for a small number of jumps of the migrating interstitial.

In addition, the interstitials which have escaped from the displacement zones may have a much higher chance to be involved in a trapping reaction compared to interstitials in stage $I_E$ of electron irradiated samples. These escaped interstitials will mainly face other interstitials as reaction partners. For annihilation, the interstitials would have to find one of the vacancies which are mainly concentrated in the interior of the displacement zones and partially shielded by the interstitials already trapped near the surface of the displacement zone.

---

* An estimate for this probability can be obtained from eq. (10) by replacing $R_o$ by the radius of the cascade zone and $\bar{R} - R_o$ by the initial separation of the interstitial from the "surface" of the cascade zone.

Table 4

Resistivity retention $f_I$ above stage I after a low dose test irradiation with fast neutrons of doped and undoped samples

| Material | undoped, pure $f_I^{u.p.} \left(\dfrac{\rho_0}{\Delta\rho_{test}}\right)$ | prequenched $\dfrac{f_I^Q}{f_I^{u.p.}} \left(\dfrac{\Delta\rho_{quench}}{\Delta\rho_{test}}\right)$ | radiation doped * $\dfrac{f_I^{r.d.}}{f_I^{u.p.}} \left(\dfrac{\Delta\rho_{r.d.}}{\Delta\rho_{test}}\right)$ | cold worked $\dfrac{f_I^{c.w.}}{f_I^{u.p.}} \left(\dfrac{\Delta\rho_{c.w.}}{\Delta\rho_{test}}\right)$ | References |
|---|---|---|---|---|---|
| Cu | 67 (~2) | | 0.85 (5.5) | 1.0 (~5) | [57,65] |
| Al | 55 (0.4) | 0.83 (120) | 0.82 (2.9) | 0.95 (120) | [57,62] |
| Pt | 63 (~2) | 0.65 (3500) | 0.87 (27) | 0.65 (3000) | [57,64] |
| Ag | 73 (~1) | | 0.90 (6.5) | | [57] |
| Ni | 66 (~5) | | 0.85 (5) | | [57] |

* 4.5°K doping irradiation + 120°K annealing

If, however, additional vacancies are introduced by a doping treatment, the interstitials which escape from the interior of the displacement zones have an increased chance for annihilation. Therefore, the recovery at the end of stage I will be enhanced. Experiments of this kind have been performed by Swanson and Piercy [62–64] who observed that the introduction of quenched in vacancies enhances the recovery in stage I of neutron irradiated Al and Pt (see table 4).

A similar enhancement of the recovery in stage $I_D$ has been observed for neutron irradiated Cu, Ag, Al, Pt and Ni in many radiation doping experiments, performed by the Munich group [57]. Typical results are outlined in fig. 21 and table 4.

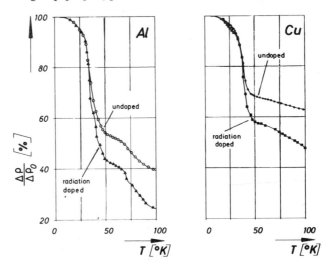

Fig. 21. Comparison of the isochronal recovery after irradiation of undoped and radiation doped Al and Cu with fast neutrons at 4.5°K to the resistivity increments $\Delta\rho_0$ = 6 and 2 nΩ·cm respectively. The doping treatment (irradiation at 4.5°K and subsequent annealing at 120°K) resulted in a resistivity increase of $\Delta\rho_{r.d.}$ = 23 and 12 nΩ·cm in Al and Cu respectively. Data are taken from ref. [57].

The larger recovery of prequenched and radiation doped samples confirms that at the end of stage I, interstitials do escape from their original displacement regions and can annihilate at doping vacancies. If these doping vacancies are present in sufficient numbers and if the trapping effect of the interstitials remaining from the radiation doping treatment can be neglected, all the interstitials evaporating from the displacement zones would be annihilated. Therefore, from the observed differences in the defect retention in undoped and vacancy-doped samples, a lower limit of the fraction of the interstitials evaporating from their displacement zones can be estimated. From the values listed in table 3 we estimate that in Al at least 20% and in Cu at least 15% and in Pt at least 40% of the interstitials are able to annihilate with doping vacancies outside their displacement zones. The observed magnitude of these fractions gives some support to the theoretical prediction that the interstitials tend to be concentrated at the surface and vacancies tend to be concentrated in the interior of the displacement cascades. The larger effect observed for Pt compared to copper is in accordance with the much smaller mean size of the displacement zones produced by fact neutrons in this heavy atom metal.

The influence of dislocations on the defect retention above stage I has been studied in neutron irradiated Cu [65] and Al and Pt [62,63] (see table 3). For Cu, no influence could be recognized, whereas a significant decrease in the defect retention has been observed for Pt. A very small reduction was observed for Al. The increase in the recovery in stage I of Pt has also been confirmed for deuteron damage [28] and is just opposite to the expected enhancement of trapping reactions by dislocations. Apparently the deformed Pt-samples contained so many vacancies produced during cold working at room temperature that their influence as doping agent was dominant.

### I.4. Stage I recovery after heavy charged particle and thermal neutron damage

Heavy charged particles (protons, deuterons or $\alpha$-particles) in the MeV-range produce recoils with maximum transferred energies of the same order of magnitude as fast neutrons. However, due to the high preference of low energy transfers ($1/T$ = spectrum, $T$ = transferred energy) the main recoil energy is much smaller than for neutron damage. Therefore, the defect pattern contains many events in which only a few Frenkel defects have been deposited in local regions, and the gross features of the recovery behaviour are expected to range somewhere between those of electron and neutron irradiated samples.

This prediction characterizes the main appearance of the annealing structures observed in stage I after heavy charged particles irradiation rather well indeed. Typical data are shown in figs. 22 and 23 for $\alpha$-particle irradiated Cu and deuteron irradiated Pt. In these figures it can be recognized that the close pair structures $I_A$, $I_B$ and $I_C$ are more pronounced than in neutron irradiated metals and that a rather well defined stage $I_E$ is observed at low defect densities. In addition, the fractional defect retention above stage I falls inbetween the values observed after electron and neutron damage (see table 5). These general findings have been confirmed for deuteron irradiation of Cu and Ag [67] and of Al [24,68]. Irradiations with $\alpha$-particles of Cu [79] and of Al [69] gave similar results.

Doping experiments (see table 5) performed in heavy charged particle irradiation of Pt [25–28], Al [24,25,69] and Cu [66] have yielded the same general results as discussed for electron damage. The reductions in the defect retention above stage I observed in radiation doped and prequenched samples range between the values listed for electron and neutron damage in tables 2 and 4.

Another type of irradiation which produces a rather unique recoil spectrum is thermal neutron irradiation. Upon capture of thermal neutrons these nuclei emit highly energetic $\gamma$-quanta. The mean recoil energy transferred to the activated atom during

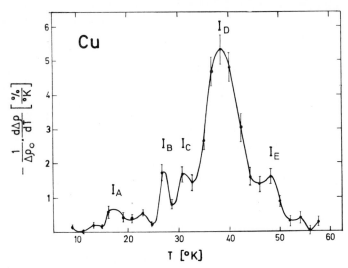

Fig. 22. Recovery spectrum of Cu irradiated with 5 MeV $\alpha$-particles below 10°K to
$\Delta\rho_0 = 1.8$ n$\Omega \cdot$cm. Data are taken from ref. [66].

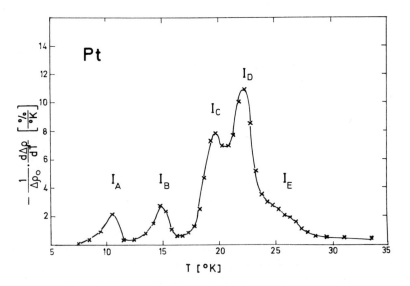

Fig. 23. Recovery spectrum of Pt irradiated with 22 MeV deuteron below 10°K
to $\Delta\rho_0 = 3.8$ n$\Omega \cdot$cm. Data are taken from ref. [26].

Table 5
Resistivity retention $f_I$ above stage I after a low dose test irradiation with heavy charged particles and thermal neutrons

| Material | Irradiation particle | undoped, pure $f_I^{u.p.}$ $(\dfrac{\rho_0}{\Delta\rho_{test}})$ (%) | | prequenched $\dfrac{f_I^Q}{f_I^{u.p.}}$ $(\dfrac{\Delta\rho_{quench}}{\Delta\rho_{test}})$ | | radiation doped $\dfrac{f_I^{r.d.}}{f_I^{u.p.}}$ $(\dfrac{\Delta\rho_{r.d.}}{\Delta\rho_{test}})$ | | Ref. |
|---|---|---|---|---|---|---|---|---|
| Cu | $\alpha$-particles thermal | 33 | ($\sim$1) | | | 0.40 | (12.2) * | [66] |
|    | neutrons | 33 | (4) | | | 0.85 | (1.1) * | [71] |
| Al | $\alpha$ particles | 34 | (2) | | | 0.60 | (7.0) * | [69] |
|    | deuterons | 33 | | | | 0.85 | (0.8) * | [24] |
| Pt | deuterons thermal | 38 | (1) | 0.65 | (5.5) | 0.80 | (3.0) *** | [27] |
|    | neutrons | 25 | (24) | | | | | [70] |

   * 10°K doping irradiation + 100°K annealing
  ** 10°K doping irradiation + 180°K annealing
\*** 10°K doping irradiation + 300°K annealing

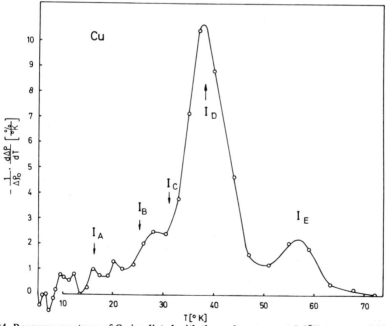

Fig. 24. Recovery spectrum of Cu irradiated with thermal neutrons at 3.5°K to $\Delta\rho_0$ = 0.072 n$\Omega$·cm. Data are taken from ref. [70]. The arrows indicate the peak temperatures observed for the different substages in electron irradiated Cu.

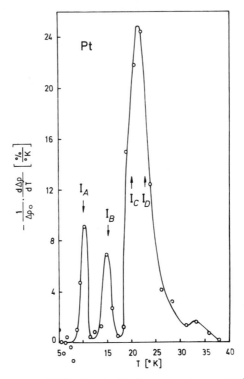

Fig. 25. Recovery spectrum of Pt irradiated with thermal neutrons at 3.5°K to $\Delta\rho_0$ = 0.2 nΩ·cm.
Data are taken from ref. [70]. The arrows indicate the peak temperatures observed for the different substages in electron irradiated Pt.

this emission is of the order of 100 to 500 eV and is sufficient to initiate displacement events producing up to several Frenkel pairs. The recovery after thermal neutron damage has been investigated rather carefully by Coltman et al. [70] for Cu,
Ag, Pt and Ni. Typical examples for Cu and Pt are shown in figs. 24 and 25. The
general features of the observed annealing structures are rather similar to heavy
charged particle damage: The close pair stages can be recognized, at least in Pt,
stage $I_E$ is rather well defined, especially in Cu, and the fractional defect retention
above stage I is also similar to that observed after heavy charged particle damage
(see table 5). Coltman et al. [71] have also investigated the influence of irradiation
dose and radiation doping on the recovery in stage $I_E$ of Cu confirming essentially
the results reported for electron damage.

## I.5. Stage I recovery after high dose irradiation close to saturation

In the preceding chapter the recovery of samples after low dose irradiations with different particles has been discussed. In all these samples the mean distance between the primary knock on events was large compared to the mean diameter of the regions where the damage resulting from one event was concentrated.

However, if the irradiations are carried out until the defect arrays resulting from different primary events are close together and overlap (defect saturation), the following characteristic changes in the recovery spectra occur.

1) In the close pair recovery region the substructure observed after electron and to some extent also after $\alpha$-particle damage is no longer well defined. This effect can be recognized in figs. 26 and 27 for Cu irradiated with electrons and $\alpha$-particles close to saturation. In both the electron and $\alpha$-particle irradiated samples, the gaps between the close pair peaks are filled up and the peaks $I_B$ and $I_C$ are greatly reduced

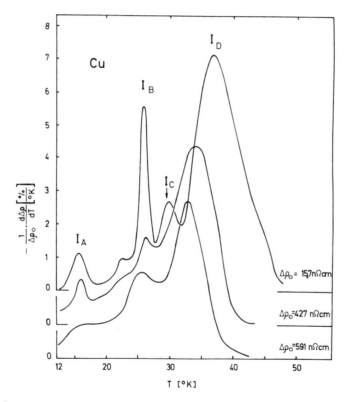

Fig. 26. Influence of defect saturation on the stage I recovery of Cu irradiated with 3 MeV electrons at 4.5°K to the indicated resistivity changes $\Delta\rho_0$. The differential isochronals have been obtained by graphical derivation of smooth curves drawn through the original isochronal data points. Data are taken from ref. [36].

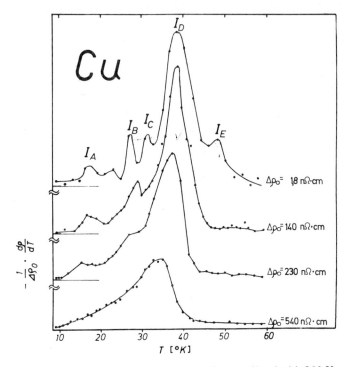

Fig. 27. Influence of defect saturation on the recovery of Cu irradiated with 5 MeV $\alpha$-particles below 8°K to the indicated resistivity changes $\Delta\rho_0$.

when the defect density approaches saturation. In particular, stage $I_C$ seems to be eliminated already at relatively low doses whereas $I_B$ can still be recognized, even after the highest doses achieved in the electron irradiated samples ($1.1 \times 10^{20}$ el/cm$^2$). Rather similar effects have been observed also for high dose electron and $\alpha$-particle irradiated Al (see figs. 28 and 29).

The interpretation of this disappearance of the close pair structure at defect densities close to saturation is the same as that outlined for neutron irradiated metals: The interaction of the close Frenkel pairs with other defects nearby, the preferential destruction of close Frenkel pairs by radiation annealing processes [72] and the population of secondary close vacancy-interstitial pair configurations by the overlaps of individual Frenkel pairs, all cooperate to give an annealing spectrum very similar to that observed for the interior of the cascade regions produced by fast neutrons.

For neutron irradiated samples, as shown in figs. 30 and 31, the annealing behaviour below stage $I_D$ is practically unaltered when the overall defect densities approach saturation. This is not surprising since the defect pattern in the interior of the saturated zones (where most of the close pair recovery occurs) will hardly change

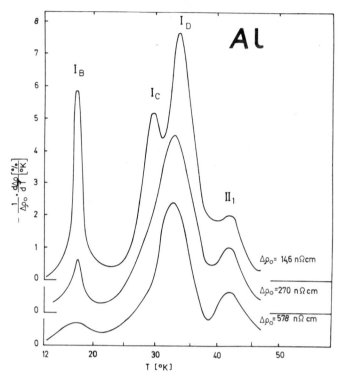

Fig. 28. Influence of defect saturation on the stage I recovery of Al irradiated with 3 MeV electrons at 4.5°K to the indicated resistivity changes $\Delta\rho_0$. The differential isochronals have been obtained by graphical derivation of smooth curves drawn through the original isochronal data points. Data are taken from ref. [36].

when such zones touch or overlap each other at very high irradiation doses.

2) In the regions of stages $I_D$ and $I_E$ the mean number of jumps necessary for a freely migrating interstitial to find a vacancy is reduced very much when the defect density approaches saturation. Therefore, the distinction between correlated and uncorrelated recovery breaks down and only one recovery peak is to be expected. In addition, this peak should shift to lower temperatures when the overall defect density is so high that the mean number of jumps for an interstitial to find a vacancy is decreased, even in the correlated recombination process. Especially, the high temperature side of stage $I_D$, which is associated with the correlated recovery processes involving larger numbers of diffusion steps, should be shifted to lower temperatures. This is indeed the general experimental finding as can be recognized from figs. 26–31. In all cases, stage $I_D$ narrows and its center shifts to lower temperatures when the defect density approaches saturation.

For aluminium at very high doses a small peak, $II_1$, at around 42°K is observed

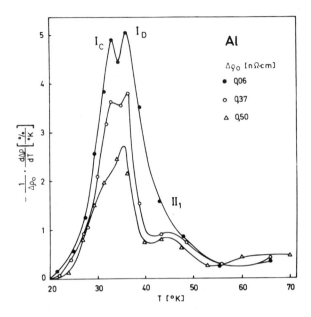

Fig. 29. Influence of defect saturation on the stage I recovery of Al irradiated with 5 MeV
α-particles at 20°K to the indicated resistivity changes. Data are taken from ref. [69].

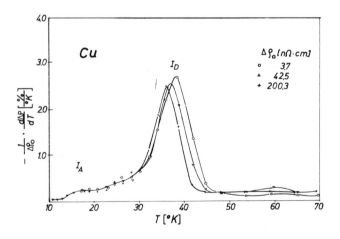

Fig. 30. Influence of defect saturation (cascade overlap) on the stage I recovery of Cu irradiated
with fast neutrons at 4.5°K to the indicated resistivity changes $\Delta\rho_0$. Data are taken from
ref. [57].

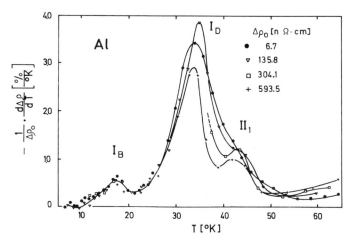

Fig. 31. Influence of defect saturation (cascade overlap) on the stage I recovery of Al irradiated with fast neutrons at 4.5°K to the indicated resistivity changes $\Delta\rho_0$. Data are taken from ref. [57].

after neutron (fig. 31) as well as electron (fig. 28) and α-particle (fig. 29) irradiation. In the high dose range the position of this peak seems to be unaltered for different initial defect densities. Since this peak occurs at temperatures where, for the high defect densities studied, the recovery of the free interstitials is expected to be already completed, this peak cannot be attributed to the annihilation of free single interstitials. For this reason, we incorporate this peak into stage II which will be discussed in chapter II. The situation is puzzling in that for small neutron doses this peak, $II_1$, is buried under the high temperature flank of stage $I_D$ and for small electron doses peak $II_1$ coincides with stage $I_E$. It appears as if electron irradiation populates stage $II_1$, similar to the rest of stage II, only at higher irradiation doses.

3) The probability for an interstitial to be involved in a trapping reaction and therefore the defect retention above stage I is increased. This effect is especially strong for electron irradiated metals as shown in figs. 32 and 33. For aluminium irradiated with 3 MeV electrons the damage remaining above stage I increases from 14% to 50% at an overall defect density of about 0.15 at % Frenkel defects. The interpretation of this effect is again based on the difference in the damage pattern resulting from low and very high dose irradiations. At high doses, the mean distance between the Frenkel pairs resulting from different recoil events becomes comparable to the correlation distance between the vacancy and interstitial in an isolated Frenkel pair. Therefore, the interstitial which starts to sample its neighbourhood in stage $I_D$ has also a finite chance to be trapped by another nearby interstitial as well as the chance of annihilating at its own vacancy. This is quite different from the situation at low doses where in stage $I_D$ an interstitial can react only with its own vacancy. The preferential survival of interstitials segregated during the radiation

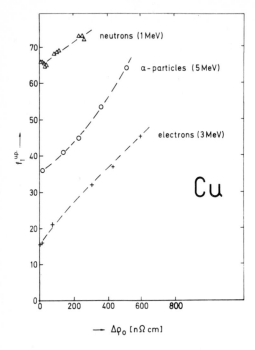

Fig. 32. Fractional defect retention $f_I^{u.p.}$ above stage I (at 60°K) versus defect density $\Delta\rho_0$ introduced by irradiation with different particles in undoped, pure Cu at temperatures below 10°K. Data for neutron, α-particle and electron irradiation were taken from refs. [74,73,36], respectively.

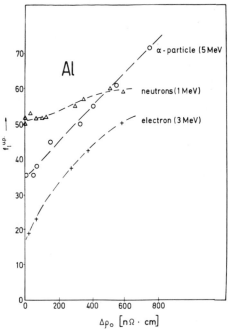

Fig. 33. Fractional defect retention $f_I^{u.p.}$ above stage I (at 60°K) in undoped, pure Al versus defect density $\Delta\rho_0$ introduced by irradiation at 4.5°K (electrons, neutrons) and 20°K (α-particles). Data for neutron, α-particle and electron irradiation are taken from refs. [74,69,36], respectively.

annealing processes results in an additional enhancement of interstitial trapping in stage $I_D$. Similar effects may also be responsible for the increase of the defect retention in $\alpha$-particle and in neutron irradiated samples shown in figs. 32 and 33.

In summary we can say that the recovery is qualitatively the same for samples which contain only local zones saturated with Frenkel defects (neutron irradiation) and for samples which have been saturated homogeneously with Frenkel defects by prolonged electron or $\alpha$-particle irradiation. This general finding has been confirmed recently also for electron and neutron irradiated platinum [39].

### I.6. Stage I recovery in dilute alloys of fcc metals

In chapter I.1.3.2 the influence of impurities on the annealing of stage $I_E$ has been discussed. In order to trap only those interstitials which have escaped correlated recombination, the impurity concentrations are limited to rather small values (10 to 100 ppm). For larger impurity concentrations, the interstitials already in stage $I_D$ have an appreciable chance to escape correlated recombination with their own vacancy by trapping reactions at these impurities. Therefore, the defect retention above stage I increases with increasing impurity concentration at the expense of stage $I_D$ as shown in fig. 34 for $\underline{Cu}Au$ *. This effect is very similar to the influence of defect saturation (see subsection I.5) where, instead of impurities, interstitials compete as trapping partners with the correlated recombination process in stage $I_D$.

The influence of impurities on the defect retention in stage $I_D$ has been calculated recently by Schroeder [45]. According to this calculation, the probability of an interstitial to undergo correlated recombination is reduced by foreign atoms to the fraction:

$$\frac{f_{c.p.}^{f.a.} - f_{I_D}^{f.a.}}{f_{c.p.}^{u.p.} - f_{I_D}^{u.p.}} = \exp(-C_F V_{f.a.}) \langle \frac{R_o}{R} \exp\left[-(3C_{f.a.}V_{f.a.})^{1/2} \frac{R - R_o}{R_{f.a.}}\right] \rangle_{\varphi(R)}, \quad (22)$$

where $f_{c.p.}^{u.p.}$, $f_{c.p.}^{f.a.}$, $f_{I_D}^{u.p.}$ and $f_{I_D}^{f.a.}$ are the fractional defect retention of low temperature irradiated undoped pure (subscript u.p.) and alloyed (subscript f.a. = foreign atom) samples above the close pair stages (subscript c.p.) and above stage $I_D$ (subscript $I_D$) respectively. $C_{f.a.}$ = concentration of foreign atoms, $V_{f.a.}$ and $R_{f.a.}$ are the reaction volume and the reaction radius of a foreign atom for interstitial trapping and $\langle \ \rangle_{\varphi(R)}$ denotes again an average over the initial interstitial distribution $\varphi(R)$. The first exponential factor takes into account the probability of an interstitial not to be displaced directly into the trapping volume of an impurity. The exponential

* The notation $\underline{M}X$ is used to denote an alloy in which the primary metal M has been alloyed with element X. In general X will be present in concentrations of 1 at % or less.

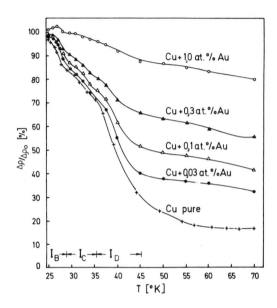

Fig. 34. Influence of slight alloying with Au on the stage I recovery of Cu irradiated with 1 MeV electron at about 5°K to $\Delta\rho_0$ = 1.8 n$\Omega$·cm. Data are taken from ref. [22].

factor in $\langle\ \rangle_{\varphi(R)}$ takes into account the escape from impurity trapping of such freely migrating interstitials which, in a pure sample, would annihilate at their own vacancy. From the data in fig. 34 an estimate of the magnitude of $V_{f.a.}$ and $R_0$ can be obtained. The data yield values for $V_{f.a.}$ of about 100 atomic volumes and $R_0/R_{f.a.} \approx 2$ for a distribution function $\varphi(R)$ of the type given by eq. (9b) *.

From fig. 34 one recognizes that the presence of the Au impurities also reduces the close pair recovery in stages $I_B$ and $I_C$. Since the defect production is practically unchanged in the alloyed samples, one has to conclude that nearby impurities increase the stability of Frenkel defects which ordinarily would contribute to the close pair recovery. The large influence of relatively small impurity concentrations demonstrates that the stabilizing interaction between the impurities and interstitials operates over at least 2 to 3 atomic distances.

Similar suppressions of the recovery in stage I as discussed for CuAu have been observed also for other diluted alloy systems after electron [19,20,23], deuteron [28,67] and neutron irradiation [75].

* The use of a δ-function distribution (see eq. (9a)) would yield values $V_{f.a.}$ = 50 and $R_0/R_{f.a.} \sim 1$ which seem too small compared with the spontaneous recombination volume for Cu determined recently to be about 125 atomic volumes [72].

## I.7. **Recovery of gold between 10 and 35°K**

The recovery behaviour of irradiated gold in the low temperature range between 10 and 35°K seems to be fundamentally different from the behaviour of the other fcc metals. The physical reason for this difference is not yet understood. Therefore, in this chapter the experimental situation will be outlined mainly. Some speculations about the interpretation of the data will be added at the end.

The recovery behaviour of gold has been studied after electron irradiation by Ward and Kauffman [76], Bauer et al. [77,78] and by Snead et al. [15]. Unfortunately, these experiments were not able to establish a reproducible annealing spectrum. In fig. 35 the spectrum of the most recent study is outlined. Subpeaks of similar shape as shown in fig. 35 have also been reported in all the other experiments at 19°K and 15°K. In the earlier experiments [76,78] additional peaks at around 22.5 and 30°K have been observed which are not particularly apparent in fig. 35.

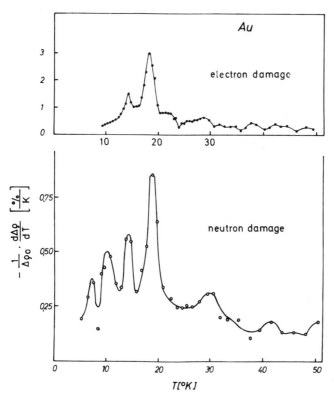

Fig. 35. Recovery spectrum of Au. Upper curve: irradiation with 2 MeV electrons near 10°K to $\Delta\rho_0 = 0.306$ n$\Omega$·cm. Data are taken from ref. [15]. Lower curve: irradiation with fast neutrons at 4.5°K to $\Delta\rho_0 = 2.1$ n$\Omega$·cm. All peaks outlined for neutrons have been reproduced in 3 independent irradiation and annealing runs. Data are taken from ref. [57].

A similar situation holds for deuteron irradiated samples. Also for this type of irradiation, the annealing structures reported by Herschbach [68] and later by Herschbach and Jackson [25] are not in agreement. The later experiment, however, confirms at least the existence of the most prominent peak at 19°K.

After low dose irradiation with fast neutrons the recovery spectrum shown in fig. 35 together with the electron data, has been reproduced in 3 independent runs [57]. This spectrum confirms the peaks at 19 and 15°K, indicates the existence of a peak at 30°K and is in good qualitative agreement with the neutron data reported by Blewitt et al. [79]. Because the neutron irradiations have been performed at lower temperatures than the electron irradiations, additional peaks at 10°K and at 7°K may be present.

The recovery spectrum observed after thermal neutron damage [70] also shows up well defined peaks at 19 and 30°K. The recovery below 15°K shows up broad maxima around 12 and 5.5°K.

After all types of irradiation, a sizable background annealing has been observed to be present at the temperatures considered here ($< 50$°K). This background in the recovery rate does not vanish even at temperatures as low as 5°K.

The total amount of recovery observed between 10 and 35°K differs widely for the different experiments reported. After low dose electron irradiation Ward and Kauffman [76] find about 27%, Bauer et al. [77] report 16% and Snead et al. [15] 20%. This great discrepancy probably indicates serious deficiencies in the exact control of the irradiation temperatures in the different experimental set-ups. For instance, small sparks in the tube of the accelerator can raise the beam intensity and therefore also the heat input into the sample in a sudden manner for a few micro-seconds. Because the heat capacity of the sample is very low at 10°K the sample temperature will show up a very sharp peak which most thermometers are unable to monitor. Nevertheless this sudden temperature peak gives rise to partial annealing of the sample. This effect can be detected if the damage rate is carefully followed during the irradiation. The tube sparks then show up as discontinuities in the dose curve as have been reported by Bauer et al. [77] for one of their gold runs.

After deuteron irradiation [25,68] about 13% recovery is observed between 10 and 35°K, after thermal neutron damage [70] about 22% and after fast neutron damage 13% [54,58,79].

### I.7.2. Dose dependence
The dose dependence of the recovery observed after electron damage has been investigated by Bauer et al. [77] and Snead et al. [15]. No shift of any of the recovery peaks in gold, similar to the shift of stage $I_E$ in copper or aluminium has been detected. The only influence of the initial defect density reported in both experiments is a decrease in the height of the recovery stage around 19°K. The same effect has also been observed after neutron irradiation. For defect densities above 40 n$\Omega \cdot$cm, e.g., the prominent recovery stage at 19°K is practically absent and a continuous background annealing is observed principally between 10 and 35°K [57].

I.7.3. *Doping experiments*

Different investigations of the influence of doping agents on the low temperature irradiation of gold gave rather conflicting results.

Bauer and Sosin [78] reported that quenched-in vacancies had no influence on the recovery of electron irradiated gold whereas Swanson and Piercy [62,63] observed that in fast neutron irradiated samples, the total recovery up to $35°K$ was enhanced from about 10 to 32% by quenched-in vacancies. However, this enhancement is not concentrated on one of the substages, e.g. the peak at $19°K$. It seems to be distributed more or less uniformly over the whole recovery range.

The influence of radiation doping was investigated by Snead et al. [15] after electron and by Burger [57] after fast neutron irradiation. In electron irradiated samples $(\Delta\rho_{rad.dop.}/\Delta\rho_{test} \approx 12)$ an increase of the recovery up to $35°K$ from about 10 to 42% was observed. Again this large enhancement of the recovery was not concentrated on a single substage. For neutron irradiated samples, in several independent runs, radiation doping $(\Delta\rho_{rad.dop.}/\Delta\rho_{test} \approx 25)$ has been found to reduce the recovery up to $35°K$ from 13 to 10%.

The influence of dislocations has been studied by Jackson and Herschbach [28] in deuteron irradiated gold. In several runs a slight decrease of the recovery was observed in the cold worked samples.

In view of the conflicting experimental situation it is not possible to make a safe conclusion as to the influence of doping agents in gold. The best guess, however, seems to be that single vacancies introduced by quenching or by radiation doping with fast electrons increase the recovery at low temperature in a more or less continuous manner. The experiment of Bauer and Sosin [78] which is the only one that disagrees with this statement may be criticized for the fact that the irradiation temperature used was rather high and may well have been different for the quenched (lower thermal conductivity!) and for the annealed sample.

I.7.4. *High temperature irradiation*

In two recent experiments by Koehler [80] and Wollenberger [81], the influence of quenched-in vacancies on the defect production at $80°K$ has been studied. A strong reduction of the defect production was observed for the quenched samples which amounted up to a factor of 7 to 9 in the initial damage rates for samples with a high ratio of quenched-in vacancies to residual impurities $(\Delta\rho_{quench}/\Delta\rho_{test} \approx 15)$. These experiments give direct evidence that practically all interstitials which survive in the unquenched sample during the irradiation at $80°K$ have undergone free migration and trapping reactions. Since the initial damage rates measured at $80°K$ are in reasonable agreement with the values extrapolated from damage production at $10°K$ plus annealing at $80°K$, one has to conclude further that the defects remaining at $80°K$ from a low temperature irradiation have also undergone free migration and trapping reactions. In this respect gold behaves quite similarly to the other fcc metals.

I.7.5. *Annealing models for gold*

According to the conclusions obtained in the preceding section, possible annealing models for gold have to be based on the fact that in this metal interstitials also
migrate over long distances at low temperatures and that practically all defects surviving at 80°K have been trapped during free migration. This rules out any model
[82,50] which attributes the recovery in gold up to stage III as principally due to
close pair annihilation. Although no direct experimental proof has yet been given,
it seems most plausible to speculate that the most prominent low temperature stage
in gold, around 19°K, is the equivalent to stage $I_D$ in the other fcc metals.

If this speculation is correct, the main puzzle which has to be solved is to account
for the small total recovery in this stage or — in other words — for the exceedingly
high chance of interstitials to survive recombination with vacancies. In order to understand this, one can assume that the reaction radius for interstitial-interstitial
trapping is very large compared with the reaction radius for recombination at vacancies and that there exists some mechanism which can extensively suppress correlated recombination. This suppression could be due to large initial separations of
the interstitial and vacancy which could be produced by focussing collisions chains.
According to formula (10) this would yield $\bar{R} \gg R_0$ and therefore large probabilities
for escape from correlated recombination. An alternative to large separations would
be to assume the existence of a potential barrier for the interstitial-vacancy recombination which is a little bit higher than the migration energy of an interstitial.
Model calculations [83] indeed indicate the principal possibility of such a repulsive
interaction between dumb-bell interstitials and vacancies in certain crystallographic
positions.

The continuation of the annealing above the postulated stage $I_D$ after low dose
electron irradiation seems to represent a second difference in the recovery of gold
and the other fcc metals. However, this difference is only apparent. If normalized
to the total recovery observed in stage III, the recovery of gold behaves quite
normally, i.e. the recovery between 35°K and 250°K is comparable in size and in its
structure to the stage II recovery observed in the other fcc metals for similar irradiation conditions. As discussed in chapter II, rearrangement and break up of agglomerates of more than 2 trapped interstitials are perhaps responsible for this "garbage"
annealing.

## I.8. Summary of the defect patterns expected at the end of stage I

For a discussion of the recovery at higher temperatures it is essential to know in
what configuration and distribution vacancies and interstitials survive above stage I.
This defect pattern depends sensitively on the specific experimental situation. However, the rather detailed understanding of the trapping processes for free interstitials,
outlined in the previous sections, allows us to predict rather safely the principal
features of the defect arrangement above stage I. For a discussion of this defect

arrangement it will be useful to distinguish 5 typical experimental situations which will be described in turn.

a) *Pure samples, low dose electron irradiation at 4°K*

At the end of the irradiation at 4°K mainly isolated Frenkel pairs are present. Most of these pairs will annihilate in stage I. However, as described in chapter I.1.3.2 some of the interstitials will be involved in mutual trapping reactions in stage $I_E$ and will therefore be retained at the end of stage I. We, therefore, expect the defects which remain to consist essentially of isolated single vacancies with the interstitials trapped in agglomerates; both types in a random distribution. Since the formation of the di-interstitial is the necessary nucleating step for the formation of larger agglomerates and since the reaction radius per interstitial decreases with increasing cluster size (see table 3) most of the interstitials will be present as di-interstitials and larger agglomerates will be relatively infrequent (see section I.2.1.2). A schematic drawing of the defect pattern is given in fig. 36a.

b) *Slightly alloyed samples, low dose electron irradiation at 4°K*

In this case the primary damage pattern at 4°K will be identical with that of case a). However, the interstitials which survive in stage $I_E$ will now be trapped at foreign atoms. If the number of these foreign atoms is well in excess of the number of the free interstitials only interstitial-impurity pairs will be formed. A schematic picture of this defect arrangement is given in fig. 36b.

c) *Pure samples (with some residual impurities), electron irradiated at 80°K*

In this case, as described in section I.1.3.3, binary reactions of free interstitials are completely suppressed. The first interstitials produced at 80°K will survive mainly by being trapped at the few residual impurities. At a later stage these impurity-interstitial pairs will trap additional interstitials. In this way agglomerates of trapped interstitials will grow around the impurities at higher doses. A schematic view of the expected defect arrangement is given in fig. 36c.

d) *Pure samples, from elements of medium to heavy atomic masses, neutron irradiated at 4°K to low doses*

In this case the primary damage state consists of zones of high local defect density. During stage I these zones will first be depleted by the annihilation of the close interstitial-vacancy pairs. In stage $I_D$ the interstitials inside the zones will either recombine with vacancies or coagulate into clusters of variable size. Those interstitials which have evaporated from the zone surface can also form di-interstitials outside the original defect zones.

The arrangement of the vacancies in the defect zones will show a strong tendency towards clustering. As outlined in section I.3 this is due to two effects. First, the correlated formation of vacancies during the displacement processes by the highly energetic recoil events (depleted zones). Secondly, there will be a preferential survival

312 W.SCHILLING et al.]

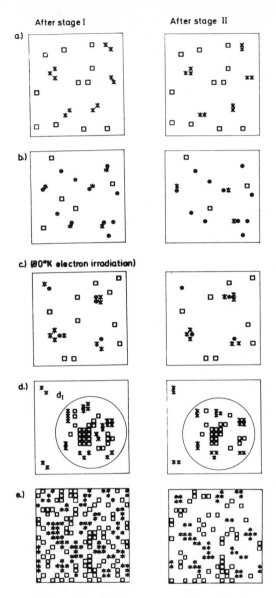

Fig. 36. Schematic view of the defect arrangement expected after stage I and after stage II in 5 typical experimental situations. □ = vacancy, * = interstitial.

Case a. Pure sample electron irradiated at 4°K to low dose.

Case b. Slightly alloyed samples electron irradiated at 4°K to a low dose.

Case c. Pure sample (with some residual impurities) electron irradiated at 80°K.

Case d. Pure sample neutron irradiated at 4°K to a low dose. The situation outlined is probably more typical for metals with heavier atoms like Cu, Ag and not so much for Al.

Case e. Pure sample electron irradiated at 4°K to a defect density close to saturation.

of vacancies in clusters from spontaneous recombination and from thermal annealing in stage I. During spontaneous and thermal annealing an isolated vacancy has a higher chance to be annihilated by an interstitial than a vacancy inside a cluster, which is shielded by the surrounding vacancies. A schematic view of the expected defect arrangement is given in fig. 36d.

e) *Pure samples, electron irradiated at 4°K close to saturation*

In this case we have in principle a situation very similar to the interior of a defect zone produced by a large displacement cascade. Again the interstitials will survive in clusters of variable size. These clusters have been nucleated in part by local accumulations of interstitials which preferentially survive from the extensive radiation annealing processes at high irradiation doses. Also the vacancies will show up a tendency for clustering because single vacancies are annihilated preferentially during radiation and thermal annealing. The vacancy clusters will, however, be smaller than those formed within the displacement zones of case d. The principal features of this defect pattern are outlined in fig. 36e.

# Part II. Stage II

Annealing stage II in the usual notation comprises the recovery in the temperature range between the termination of free interstitial migration in stage I and the beginning of recovery of the second type of free migrating defect in irradiated samples in stage III.

The recovery in stage II depends sensitively on the purity of the sample, the irradiation dose and the type of irradiation particles. The relatively few systematic investigations performed on stage II to date reflect a rather complex behaviour in which impurity effects as well as intrinsic effects are important. The details of the recovery processes responsible for stage II are not yet well understood.

In the following discussion we will try to separate intrinsic recovery processes and impurity effects. Intrinsic processes are dominant in pure samples containing defect densities close to saturation whereas impurity effects show up most clearly in slightly alloyed samples which have been electron irradiated to low doses.

## II.1. Impurity effects in stage II

The influence of impurities on the recovery of low dose electron irradiated aluminium has been studied by Shearin and coworkers [19,87] and by Sosin and coworkers [85,86]. Stage II recovery of slightly alloyed copper has been studied by Martin [88], and by Sosin [89]. The influence of several kinds of foreign atoms on the recovery of electron irradiated nickel has been investigated by Oddou et al. [23,17].

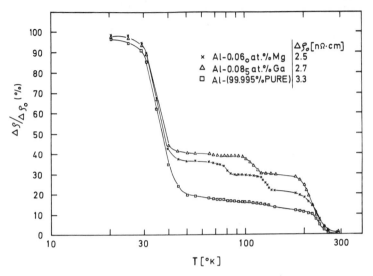

Fig. 37. Recovery of pure and alloyed Al after irradiation with 1 MeV electrons at 20°K to the indicated resistivity changes $\Delta\rho_0$. Data are taken from ref. [86].

The general results of all these experiments is that the addition of impurities gives rise to rather well defined substages in the temperature range of stage II. An example for such substages is given in fig. 37.

Table 6 gives a review of the impurity induced substages for different doping elements and different base materials. As can be recognized, one kind of impurity is able to produce up to three different substages in Cu and up to two well separated substages in Al. However, only a single substage has been observed in NiSi and AlGa, and no appreciable recovery has been found in AlCu or AlAg. The system CuBe shows an abnormal behaviour with a negative recovery peak, i.e., resistivity increase around 150°K.

Some studies of the annealing kinetics have been made for the substages in AlGa and AlMg by Garr and Sosin [86] and for the substages at 60 and 120°K in CuAu by Sosin [89]. These experiments indicate a rather complex recovery behaviour extending over a wider temperature region than one would expect for a singly activated first or second order process. The dose dependence of the substage around 130°K in AlZn has been studied by Peters and Shearin [87]. Similar investigations have been performed for an impurity substage in Cu at 60°K by Snead et al. [13]. In both cases the position of the recovery peak was found to be the same for samples differing by a factor of 5 to 7 in the total resistivity recovery in that particular temperature range.

An interpretation of these impurity stages should take as a starting point the initial defect configuration as outlined in section I.8, i.e., the presence of trapped

Table 6
Impurity induced substages in electron irradiated fcc metals
(dopant concentrations 0.1 to 1 at %)

| Base material | Dopant | Approximate peak temperatures of substages (°K) | References |
|---|---|---|---|
| Cu | Be | ? + 150 (neg.) + 220 | [88] (100°K irr. temp.) |
|  | Au | 60 + 120 + 180 | [91,89] |
|  | Ag | 65 + 120 + 190 | [91,88] |
| Al | Cu, Ag | no substages | [19,86,87] |
|  | Ga | 110 | [86] |
|  | Zn | (100 small) + 130 | [19,85,86,87] |
|  | Mg | 80 + 135 | [86] |
|  | Ge | 95 + 125 | [19,87] |
| Ni | Fe | (75 + 85) | [17,23] |
|  | Sb | (80 + 85) | [17,23] |
|  | Cu | 85 | [17,23] |
|  | Co | 70 | [17,23] |
|  | Si | 240 | [17,23] |

Values in parentheses characterize overlapping substages.

interstitial-impurity pairs together with single vacancies in statistical distribution. For systems like AlCu or AlAg which show no recovery in stage II this situation persists without significant change until the beginning of stage III. For the other systems the following processes are conceivable:

a) *Dissociation of impurity interstitial complexes*

In this model the impurity-interstitial pairs dissociate in stage II. Upon release from their impurities, interstitials then migrate until they recombine with a vacancy giving rise to the observed substage or until they encounter another interstitial. Since the diffusion of the interstitials is strongly delayed by their interaction with the impurities, two interstitials will meet primarily at an impurity. When this occurs, a more stable complex of a di-interstitial trapped at an impurity should be formed. These di-interstitials can then trap additional free interstitials forming tri- and higher order interstitial complexes. The formation of di-interstitials will occur most frequently early in the recovery stage with growth of the higher order complexes becoming more important later on.

This model can account for the existence of more than one substage in alloy systems, such as AlMg, if the assumption is made that also some of the higher complexes can dissociate at temperatures below stage III. The interstitials released by this dissociation then have another chance to recombine with a vacancy or to join one of the other complexes thereby stabilizing it until the next dissociation stage.

The main argument which can be raised against this model is that it predicts relatively large recoveries within these substages. Based on the reaction radii for interstitial-interstitial and interstitial-vacancy reaction deduced for stage $I_E$ in chapter I.2.2 one expects at least 50% of the defects present at the end of stage I to anneal in the first substage, whereas for AlMg only 20% anneal.

Another possibility to account for the existence of several substages for one kind of impurity atom would be to assume that interstitials are released not only from single impurity atoms but also from trapping centers made up of two or more solute atoms in neighbouring positions. However, such a model [88] can be ruled out by the observed independence of the relative population of the different substages $II_A$ and $II_B$, in CuAu on the concentration of solute atoms between 0.03 and 1.0 at % [89]. Similar results have been obtained also for AlMg and AlSi [99,94] after neutron irradiation.

### b) *Rearrangement of interstitial impurity complexes*

In this model it is assumed that the interstitials are not trapped in the energetically most stable position during stage $I_E$ and that it is possible for them to fall into deeper traps upon thermal activation. Several substages at higher temperatures can occur if the transition into the deepest trap occurs through more than one intermediate trapping position. These rearrangements in the configurations of the interstitial-impurity pairs are thought to be accompanied by a reduction of the scattering cross section for conduction electrons and therefore to give rise to the observed recovery in the electrical resistivity. The main argument against this model is that the expected changes in the electrical resistivity are rather small. However, this model has the advantage that it can also account for an increase in the electrical resistivity during a given substage as has been observed for CuBe.

### c) *Rearrangement of interstitial-impurity pairs with partial detrapping*

This model, which has been proposed by Sosin [91], is a combination of models a) and b). The principal feature of this model is that an interstitial during transition from one trapping site into another one should also have a given probability to decay from its thermally activated state into a detrapping position. The resistivity change then comes about by annihilation of interstitials that escaped from their traps. The existence of several substages is accounted for by the postulation of several intermediate trap positions separated by potential wells of increasing heights.

For a real judgment of the feasibility of this model, a much better understanding would be required about the interaction of interstitials with solute atoms. At the present state of understanding, no safe conclusion can be drawn about the mechanism(s) responsible for the different substages observed in alloyed samples.

Slight alloying also influences the recovery observed in stage II after fast neutron irradiation. For the dilute alloys CuAg and CuBe the same peaks have been observed as after electron irradiation [92,75]. Also, the negative recovery rate (resistivity increase) around 150°K has been confirmed in CuBe. For the system CuCd two recovery peaks around 140 and 220°K have been reported, the position of which has been found to be independent of irradiation dose [92].

The recovery after 80°K neutron irradiation of several aluminium based alloys has been investigated by Ceresara et al. [93–95], whereas Dimitrov-Frois and Dimitrov [96–99] have studied the system AlMg in great detail. Their findings suggest the existence of a small additional subpeak at about 155°K which may have been missed in the experiments of Garr and Sosin [86]. The rest of the neutron data in general confirms the subpeaks observed after electron damage.

## II.2. Intrinsic recovery processes in stage II

Intrinsic recovery in stage II is observed primarily in samples containing very high overall or local defect densities. Nevertheless, the behaviour of pure samples electron irradiated to low doses is of fundamental interest, since these samples exhibit a simple well-known defect arrangement above stage I. Both cases will be discussed in turn.

### II.2.1. Intrinsic stage II recovery after low dose electron irradiation

The recovery behaviour after low dose electron irradiation below stage I, of the purest fcc metals studied to date, is still not free from the influence of unavoidable residual impurities. The behaviour of ideally pure samples can therefore only be extrapolated from the observed features of samples with variable residual impurity concentration. The influence of residual impurities on stage II recovery has been investigated to some extent in high purity aluminium [86] and gold [100]. For copper, some conclusions can be drawn from a comparison of the stage II recovery curves reported by the General Electric group [3,52] with the data reported by the Atomic International group [11,90]. The zone refined copper used by the G.E. group probably contained less residual impurities than the material used by the A.I. group. For copper, as well as for aluminium and gold with increasing purity of the samples, the following general trend is observed.

1) The total amount of recovery within stage II becomes rather small (10 to 20% of the damage remaining above stage I).
2) The recovery in stage II is more or less continuous, although some small substages may be present.

From these observations, at least for Al and Cu, the following important conclusion may be derived: Di-interstitials cannot dissociate thermally in stage II. If this were to occur, the free interstitials would face a situation very similar to that in stage $I_E$ of heavily radiation doped samples, i.e., single vacancies and trapped interstitials would be present as the principal reaction partners. However, from the results of the radiation doping experiments discussed in chapter I.1.3.2, we know that in this situation the single interstitials have only a 10 to 20% chance for survival. Since di-interstitials are the dominant form in which interstitials survive above stage I in

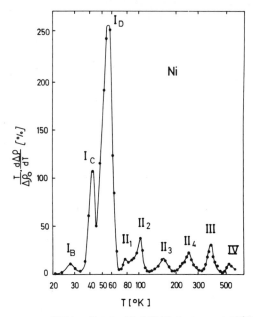

Fig. 38. Recovery spectrum of Ni irradiated with 3 MeV electrons at 20°K to $\Delta\rho_0$ = 54 nΩ·cm. Four intrinsic substages are observed within stage II. Data are taken from ref. [17].

pure metals after low dose electron damage, we would expect – if dissociation of di-interstitials occurs in stage II – a single recovery stage in which a large fraction (~ 80%) of the defects which survived stage I would anneal. Such a recovery stage has not been observed in any of the fcc metals studied to date. Therefore we conclude that di-interstitials cannot dissociate thermally in the temperature range of stage II.

For copper this conclusion may even be extended to temperatures well above stage III. Thermal pulsing experiments performed by Dworschak and Koehler [101] indicate that the two interstitials have a binding energy which must be larger than 1 eV *. The physical reason for this strong interstitial-binding is not understood. It may be possible that the di-interstitial is in an atomic configuration which is quite different from two adjacent single interstitials and is energetically much more stable.

If di-interstitials cannot break up, the small intrinsic recovery observed in stage II must be associated with processes involving other configurations, possibly larger agglomerates of trapped interstitials. This conclusion is supported by the findings

---

* The assumption that there is a strong binding interaction in the di-interstitials is not necessary in the conversion-two-interstitial model (see section III.7.2). This model expects two interstitials to be converted upon encounter with each other in stage $I_E$ from a metastable into another configuration which is immobile up to stage III.

reported in the next section for samples containing high initial defect densities.

In some fcc metals small substages of intrinsic character seem to be superimposed on the continuous background annealing in stage II after low dose electron damage: In aluminium a recovery stage around 75°K has been observed which seems to be independent of the residual impurity concentration [86,87]. Similar impurity independent substages have also been found in Pt around 110°K [16,39] and especially in nickel, where stage II seems to break up into four rather well defined subpeaks (see fig. 38). Since substages at the same temperatures have been observed also after neutron or heavy charged particle irradiation (see table 7) it is suggestive to associate them with rearrangement or dissociation processes of particular smaller interstitial complexes as discussed in the next section.

## II.2.2. Stage II recovery in samples containing high initial defect densities

The discussion in section I.5 showed that samples electron irradiated close to saturation show up a recovery behaviour in stage I which is quite analogous to neutron damage. A similar situation holds also for stage II. This is demonstrated in figs. 39–41 which show the influence of very high initial electron doses on the recovery of Cu, Al, and Pt. Recovery curves observed after low dose neutron damage are included for comparison. As can be seen in these figures, with increasing defect saturation the recovery curves of the electron irradiated samples show an increasing fractional recovery in stage II and tend to become more and more "neutron-like".

An increase of the recovery within stage II similar to that shown in figs. 39–41 has also been observed in Al [69] and Cu [66,73] for low temperature α-particle irradiations close to saturation.

From these findings we have to conclude first, that the recovery observed in these samples in stage II is intrinsic and secondly, that it is intimately connected with high initial defect densities regardless of whether these high defect densities are present in local zones (neutron damage) or distributed more homogeneously all over the lattice (electron irradiation close to saturation).

At the end of stage I, as outlined in section I.8, the common feature, of the defect pattern of all such samples is the presence of larger agglomerates of trapped interstitials along with single and multiple vacancies. Apparently, such a defect pattern is the essential prerequisite for the occurrence of stage II and it seems plausible to assume that changes in this pattern lead to the observed resistivity decrease in stage II. Some possible mechanisms are:

1) Rearrangement within complexes of trapped interstitials giving rise to a decrease in the resistivity increment per interstitial.
2) Detrapping of single interstitials from larger complexes and subsequent annihilation at vacancies.
3) Elimination of configurations of vacancies and trapped interstitials which are thermally unstable due to mutual interaction, e.g., thermally assisted break away of a trapped interstitial from a complex under the attractive stress field of a nearby vacancy or vacancy cluster.

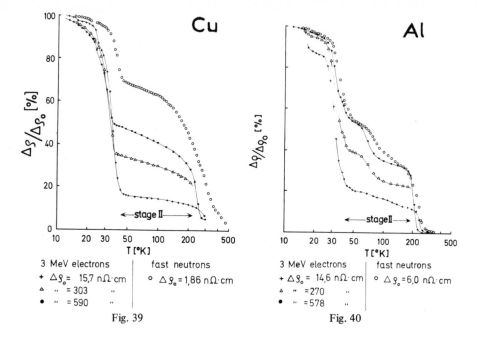

**Cu**

3 MeV electrons
+ $\Delta \vartheta_o$ = 15,7 nΩ·cm
Δ  "  = 303    "
● "  = 590    "

fast neutrons
○ $\Delta \vartheta_o$ = 1,86 nΩ·cm

Fig. 39

**Al**

3 MeV electrons
+ $\Delta \vartheta_o$ = 14,6 nΩ·cm
Δ  "  = 270    "
● "  = 578    "

fast neutrons
○ $\Delta \vartheta_o$ = 6,0 nΩ·cm

Fig. 40

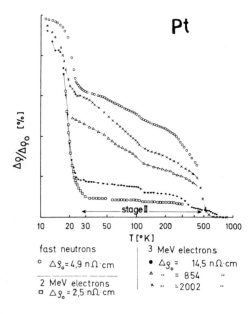

**Pt**

fast neutrons
○ $\Delta \vartheta_o$ = 4,9 nΩ·cm

2 MeV electrons
□ $\Delta \vartheta_o$ = 2,5 nΩ·cm

3 MeV electrons
● $\Delta \vartheta_o$ =  14,5 nΩ·cm
Δ  "  =  854    "
× "  ≐ 2002    "

Fig. 41

Fig. 39. Dose dependence of the iso-chronal recovery of Cu irradiated with 3 MeV electrons at 4.5°K to the indicated resistivity changes $\Delta \rho_o$. An isochronal curve observed after low dose irradiation with fast neutrons is included for comparison. Data are taken from refs. [36, 57].

Fig. 40. Idem for Al.

Fig. 41. Idem for Pt.
Data taken from refs. [39,57] and from ref. [16] for the 2 MeV electron irradiation.

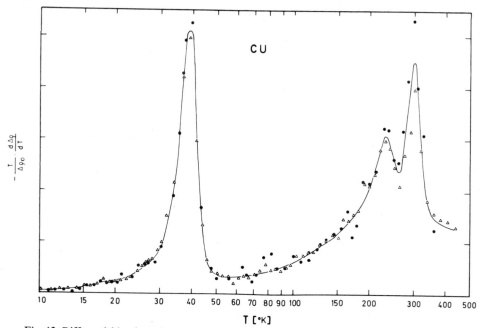

Fig. 42. Differential isochronal recovery spectrum of Cu irradiated with fast neutrons at 4.5°K to $\Delta\rho_0 \approx 2$ n$\Omega$·cm. A smooth curve which averages the results of two independent irradiation and annealing runs has been drawn through the data points. Data are taken from ref. [58].

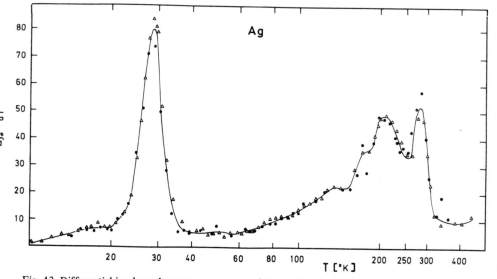

Fig. 43. Differential isochronal recovery spectrum of Ag irradiated with fast neutrons at 4.5°K to $\Delta\rho_0 \approx 2$ n$\Omega$·cm. A smooth curve which averages the results of two independent irradiation and annealing runs has been drawn through the data points. Data are taken from ref. [58].

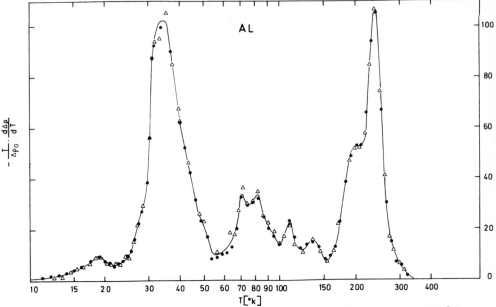

Fig. 44. Differential isochronal recovery spectrum of Al irradiated with fast neutrons at 4.5°K to $\Delta\rho_0 \approx 6 \ n\Omega \cdot cm$. A smooth curve which averages the results of two independent irradiation and annealing runs has been drawn through the data points. Data are taken from ref. [58].

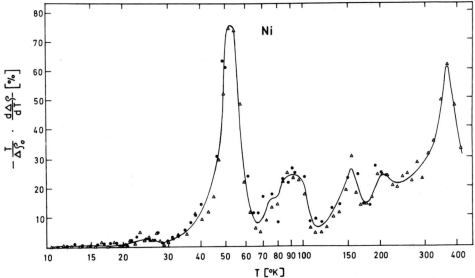

Fig. 45. Differential isochronal recovery spectrum of Ni irradiated with fast neutrons at 4.5°K to $\Delta\rho_0 \approx 5 \ n\Omega \cdot cm$. A smooth curve which averages the results of two independent irradiation and annealing runs has been drawn through the data points. Data are taken from ref. [57].

Some information about the recovery mechanism in stage II can also be inferred from a comparison of the recovery of different physical properties. A detailed discussion of this topic is given by Wenzl in these proceedings [48]. He finds, for example, that for Cu in the temperature range of stage II, the recovery of length change, stored energy, and modulus change (measured at $4°K$) behave differently from the electrical resistivity change. This suggests that not only interstitial-vacancy annihilation occurs, but also that rearrangement processes take place in stage II which have different effects on the various physical properties.

If the annealing structure of stage II is analyzed for neutron irradiated samples, one finds for Cu, Ag and in part also for Au that the recovery is more or less continuous and merges gradually into stage III (see figs. 42 and 43).

On the other hand, for Al, the recovery levels off at the end of stage II before onset of stage III so that there is a clear separation between these stages (see fig. 44). In addition stage II splits up into at least three rather well defined subpeaks *. The first subpeak overlaps the end of stage I at low doses and therefore is missing in fig. 44. However, as discussed in section I.5, at high defect densities substage $I_D$ shrinks and substage $II_1$ can be resolved (see fig. 31).

A split up of stage II in a number of well defined subpeaks is also observed for neutron irradiated Ni, as shown in fig. 45. Pt shows only one well defined intrinsic substage at $110°K$. Table 7 gives a summary of the substages observed in stage II which at the present time can be identified with reasonable confidence as being intrinsic substages.

Table 7
Intrinsic substages observed in stage II after irradiations with different particles

| Metal | Irradiation particle | Peak temperatures | References |
|---|---|---|---|
| Al | fast neutrons | 43 (70 + 83) | [57,102] |
|    | electrons | 45 (74 + 82) | [36,86,87] |
|    | α-particles | 43 (70 + 85) | [69] |
| Ni | fast neutrons | (75 + 90)  160, 210 | [57,79,61] |
|    | electrons (low dose) | (80 + 100) 160, 260 | [17] |
| Pt | fast neutrons | 110 | [57] |
|    | electrons (low dose) | 110 | [39,16] |
|    | deuterons | 110 | [26] |

Values in parentheses characterize overlapping substages.

The dose dependence of the subpeaks observed after neutron irradiation in Al is outlined in fig. 46. Although the isochronal program was not exactly the same for

* The subpeak around $110°K$ to be seen in fig. 44 decreases in height with increasing defect density and seems to vary with the residual impurity content of the sample. Therefore, it may be non-intrinsic and has not been included in table 7.

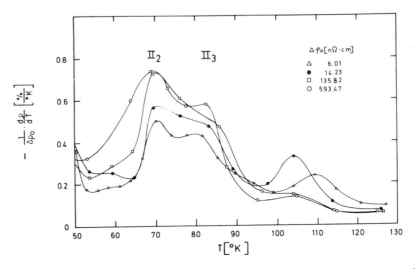

Fig. 46. Dose dependence of the recovery in stage II of Al irradiated with fast neutrons at 4.5°K to the indicated resistivity changes. Data are taken from ref. [102].

the different curves, no systematic shift of the individual peaks can be observed when the defect density varies over two orders of magnitude *. As outlined in table 7 the subpeaks shown in fig. 46 coincide with the subpeaks observed after electron damage.

Also for Ni, an investigation of the dose dependence of the substructure in stage II showed that the positions of the subpeaks are almost independent of the initial defect density [57].

To date, no recovery model has been proposed which accounts fully for the different features of the intrinsic stage II recovery in the different fcc metals. Therefore, only some speculations can be listed.

It seems possible that the more or less continuous nature of the recovery in stage II of Cu could be associated with the complexities inherent in any of the first three mechanisms mentioned earlier in this section and the even more likely possibility that several of these mechanisms could be active simultaneously. The strong increase in the recovery rate near stage III in Cu, e.g., seems to indicate that interactions between the closer vacancy and interstitial configurations can lower the activation energy for the recombination process occurring in stage III. The clear separation of stage II and stage III in Al would then indicate that in this metal the defect density has been reduced to such an extent in stage I and the initial part of

---

* An overall shift of the recovery stage comprising subpeaks $II_2$ and $II_3$ in Al has been reported earlier [84]. This seems to be caused by a different dose dependence of the population of the low temperature and high temperature subpeak.

stage II that stress-induced annihilation is unimportant in the beginning part of stage III.

The occurrence of first order stage II subpeaks in Ni and Al may be associated with the rearrangement or detrapping from some favored specific configurations of trapped interstitials. The occurrence of these subpeaks in electron irradiated samples indicates further that these configurations probably involve only a few trapped interstitials.

## II.3. Summary of the defect pattern expected at the end of stage II

If the assumption is made that mainly rearrangement processes of the larger agglomerates of trapped interstitials and elimination of thermally unstable configurations of interstitials and vacancies occur during stage II, then the gross features of the defect patterns present at the end of stage II can be predicted. As in section I.8 we distinguish between 5 different experimental situations.

a) For pure metals electron irradiated to low doses below stage I (see fig. 36a) we expect little change during stage II. Di-interstitials will still be present together with single vacancies in statistical distribution.

b) For slightly alloyed metals electron irradiated to low doses, no pronounced change of the defect pattern in stage II is expected. As discussed in section II.1, interstitial-impurity complexes involving more than one interstitial or single interstitials in deep traps will be present together with isolated vacancies. The latter situation is outlined in fig. 36b.

c) In the case of pure metals electron irradiated at 80°K, we also expect that no pronounced change in the defect pattern occurs. As shown in fig. 36c, larger interstitial agglomerates are present around the impurities together with isolated vacancies.

d) After neutron damage at low temperatures, we also expect that the main features of the defect pattern will be unaltered through stage II. The majority of the interstitials and vacancies will still be contained within the region of the original displacement zone, only the mean density of the defects will be reduced by elimination of thermally unstable vacancy-interstitial structures. As shown in fig. 36d, larger interstitial agglomerates in stable form will be present together with partially clustered vacancies.

e) In samples saturated with Frenkel defects by electron irradiation at low temperatures no pronounced change of the defect pattern is expected during stage II. Similar to case d) above, only thermally unstable configurations will be eliminated. As shown in fig. 36e, larger clusters of interstitials together with vacancies in a more dispersed form than in d) will still be present. Only the overall defect density will be smaller than at the end of stage I.

# Part III. Stage III

Stage III is defined here as that larger recovery stage observed in irradiated fcc metals above stage I which exhibits the features characteristic of the recombination of a freely migrating defect. For Au, which has no well defined stage I recovery, the large recovery stage observed around room temperature is called stage III.

In accordance with this nomenclature stage III has been identified clearly for Cu, Al, Ag, Au and Ni. For Pt, recent experiments discussed in section III.1 indicate that the recovery stage around 600°K, usually called stage IV, exhibits just the characteristics demanded for stage III above. In order to be consistent with the other metals, we therefore suggest that this stage should be relabelled stage III and will use this notation throughout this paper. The relabelling of stage IV into stage III for Pt has been proposed independently also by Van den Beukel [103] based on a comparison of the recovery stages observed after cold work. He showed that a consistent description of the recovery of deformed fcc metals including Pt requires the above change in the notation.

In the following sections we will first introduce the experimental data available at present and then discuss different recovery models in section III.7. Since the interpretation of stage III is still unsettled and since the different recovery models require quite different kinds of freely migrating defects we will leave the nature of this freely migrating defect open during the discussion of the experimental data and simply call it the "stage III defect".

## III.1. Dose dependence

As discussed in section I.2, any systematic shift of an annealing stage to lower temperatures with increasing dose indicates that the mean number of jumps during the lifetime of the reacting defects in this stage is reduced by an increasing number of irradiation produced defects. This is only possible if the reacting defects annihilate by free migration at sinks which have been produced by the irradiation together with the mobile defects. A study of the dose dependence of the recovery above stage I is, therefore, essential for the identification of stage III in the different metals.

After electron irradiation the dose dependence of the high temperature recovery has been studied in Al [104,36,87], in Cu [105,36] and in Au [106,107]. For Pt, recent results [108] are shown in fig. 47. In all of these metals, a single well defined recovery peak has been observed in the differential isochronal annealing curves which shifts to lower temperatures with increasing initial defect density. In Pt, for example, the stage III peak in fig. 47 shifts from 690 to 480°K when the resistivity recovering in stage III increases from $\Delta\rho_{III} = 0.5$ to 428 n$\Omega \cdot$cm. The dose dependence of the high temperature annealing in Ni electron irradiated at 4.5°K is shown in fig. 48. Again stage III can be clearly recognized as a single recovery peak which

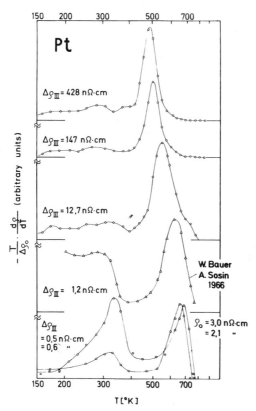

Fig. 47. Dose dependence of the high temperature recovery of Pt irradiated with 3 MeV electrons at 4.5°K. The resistivity recovering in the stage III is indicated by $\Delta\rho_{III}$ at the different curves. Data are taken from ref. [108], except the curve for $\Delta\rho_{III}$ = 1.2 n$\Omega$·cm which was taken from ref. [130].

shifts to lower temperatures with increasing dose. Although there is no doubt about the identification of stage III in Ni, it is also observed that the annealing structures below stage III seem to be influenced by the initial defect density. Additional experiments are needed to clarify this point.

After fast neutron damage the dose dependence of the high temperature recovery of Al has been investigated by several groups [109—111]. An example of the results is given in fig. 49 *. As can be recognized at low doses, stage III consists of two subpeaks, one at 190°K and the other one at 240°K. With increasing dose the

* Although the isochronal heating program was not the same in the different runs shown in figs. 49 and 50, the variation in dose is so large that a correction for the different effective heating rates does not change the principal features of the observed dose dependence.

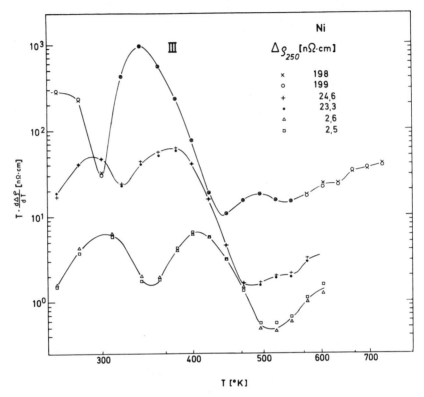

Fig. 48. Dose dependence of the unnormalized resistivity recovery at high temperatures of Ni irradiated with 3 MeV electrons at 4.5°K. The damage present after annealing at 250°K is indicated by $\Delta\rho_{250}$ for the different samples. Data are taken from ref. [39].

second subpeak shifts to lower temperatures whereas the position of the first one seems to be unchanged. At high defect densities both peaks merge into each other.

The existence of two subpeaks at low doses and their coincidence at higher doses has been observed for Al also by Frois and Dimitrov [111]. In addition to the dose dependence, activation energies have also been determined in these experiments by the slope method. For both subpeaks the same value of the activation energy has been observed [111]. Quite analogous to stage $I_D - I_E$, the low temperature peak may, therefore, be attributed to the correlated recombination of the stage III defect with its counterpart within the defect zones produced by fast neutrons, whereas the high temperature peak is due to uncorrelated recombination of the stage III defect at sinks outside of its native displacement zone. The correlated recombination process is characterized by a small number of diffusion steps due to the high local defect density in the interior of the zones whereas the number of

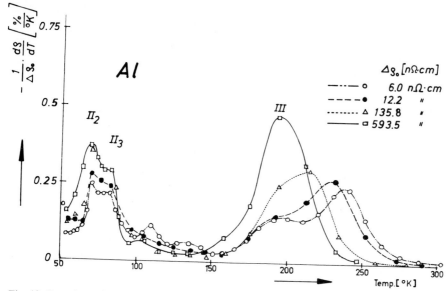

Fig. 49. Dose dependence of the isochronal recovery in Al irradiated with fast neutrons at 4.5°K to the indicated resistivity changes $\Delta\rho_0$. Data are taken from ref. [57].

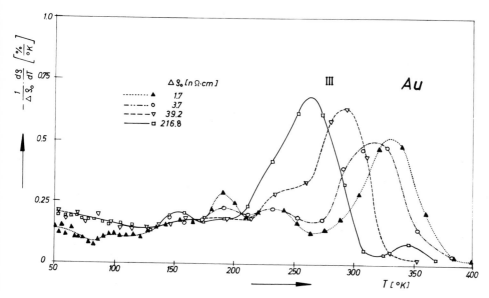

Fig. 50. Dose dependence of the isochronal recovery in Au irradiated with fast neutrons at 4.5°K to the indicated resistivity changes $\Delta\rho_0$. Data are taken from ref. [57].

steps for the uncorrelated recombination is large for low doses and decreases with increasing dose. Detailed studies of the reaction kinetics in neutron irradiated Al, as discussed in section III.3, confirm this interpretation.

Also, in the other fcc metals, fast neutrons produce displacement zones of high local defect density. Therefore, also, for these metals the existence of two subpeaks in stage III is to be expected at low doses. Such subpeaks have indeed been observed in Cu, Ag and Au at low neutron doses [58] (see figs. 42, 43 and 50). With increasing dose the high temperature peaks are found to shift to lower temperatures until both subpeaks coincide. For Au, as an example, this shift is shown in fig. 50. Contrary to Al, however, for the other fcc metals no measurement of the activation energies have been performed in the dose range where both subpeaks can be separated. Therefore, the inclusion of the low temperature subpeaks into stage III, while highly plausible, is not directly proved in these metals. For Cu and Ag, we have the additional difficulty that the strong increase in the recovery rate towards the end of stage II prevents a clear separation of the stage II and stage III recovery processes. For Cu, measurements of the activation energy outlined in section III.2 indicate, however, that at higher doses the recovery process is uniquely activated in a temperature region which also contains the low temperature subpeak observed at small doses.

After heavy charged particle irradiation Dworschak and Koehler [101] have investigated the dose dependence of the recovery in Cu. They observed that the recovery rate in the lower part of stage III, if normalized to the total defect density, was the same after increasing the irradiation dose by a factor of 10, whereas the normalized recovery rate in the main peak was enhanced on the average by a factor of 4. This again demonstrates that the stage III defect anneals by free migration and recombination with its counterpart and that correlated recovery is important in the initial part of stage III also after deuteron damage.

## III.2. Activation energies

For the identification of the stage III defect, a reliable determination of its activation energy for free migration is of extreme importance. Unfortunately, incorrect procedures for the evaluation of activation energies from the experimental data have been used in some of the experiments reported. This together with an underestimation of the possible systematic errors has generated a situation where there are some conflicting values for the activation energies reported in the literature.

In the first part of this section we will briefly review the different methods for activation energy measurements and discuss possible sources for systematic errors. In the second part a critical review of the experimental data will be endeavoured.

### III.2.1. *Summary of experimental methods*
The rate of resistivity change measured during the reaction of freely migrating

defects at sinks may be written in the general form

$$-\frac{d\Delta\rho}{dt} = -\frac{d\Delta\rho}{dc}\frac{dC}{dt} = \frac{d\Delta\rho}{dc} 4\pi D R_o^{III} c F(C,\{0\}) .$$ (23)

where $dC/dt$ is the number of Frenkel defects * annihilated per second and unit volume. $d\Delta\rho/dC$ measures the resistivity change which accompanies the annihilation of one Frenkel pair. $R_o^{III}$ denotes the reaction radius for annihilation of the mobile stage III defect at its antidefect. If the reaction is uniquely activated $-dC/dt$ is given by an expression of the type outlined in eq. (3), which contains the temperature only via the diffusion constant $D$ of the mobile defect. The rest of eq. (23) depends only on the instantaneous Frenkel defect density $C$ and the initial concentration and distribution of the vacancies and interstitials symbolized by $\{0\}$. Some typical examples for the form of this factor have been discussed in section I.2.1.

The measured resistivity change $\Delta\rho$ is made up from the contribution of all kinds of defects and defect clusters present in the sample. Since the concentrations of all these individual types of defects present in the sample are determined only by the initial condition of the distributions of vacancies and interstitials, $\{0\}$, and by the instantaneous concentration of Frenkel defects, $C$, a relation of the form

$$\Delta\rho = \Delta\rho(C, \{0\})$$ (24)

must exist. The simplest form would be $\Delta\rho = \rho_F C$ with $\rho_F = $ const. If, however, clustering of the mobile defect occurs simultaneously with recombination, the resistivity increment per Frenkel defect may be altered either because the resistivity contribution of the single defect is changed by the clustering process or because of deviations from Matthiessen's rule (see section I.2.2 for further discussion).

From a combination of eqs. (23) and (24) we obtain immediately the result that the rate of resistivity change can be expressed in the form

$$-\frac{d\Delta\rho}{dt} = \nu_o G(\Delta\rho, \{0\}) \exp(-U/kT) ,$$ (25)

where the factor $G$ does not contain the temperature explicitly.

Any determination of the activation energy $U$ is now based on a comparison of the recovery rates $d\Delta\rho/dt$ measured at different temperatures $T$ for identical values of $G$ in relation (25). For measurements at two different temperatures, the factors $G$ are identical only if $\Delta\rho$ and the initial damage state symbolized by $\{0\}$ are identical. From this requirement, two different procedures may be derived for the determination of $U$:

---

* Here again the term Frenkel defect is used to indicate the existence of equal numbers of vacancies and interstitials in the sample irrespective of their detailed configuration as single defects, pairs, clusters or defects trapped at impurities.

a) In the first procedure *one sample* is used which is subjected to sudden alterations of the annealing temperature, e.g., from $T_1$ and $T_2$ as illustrated in fig. 51. The activation energy is then obtained from the ratio of the slopes $S_1$ and $S_2$ of the annealing curve at point A in fig. 51. This so called "slope-change method" has the important advantage that the requirement of identical defect configurations at the two temperatures is fulfilled automatically. However, systematic errors may easily sneak in during the extrapolation of the slopes of the recovery curve towards the point A. Some improvement may be obtained by employing annealing programs with alternating temperatures [112].

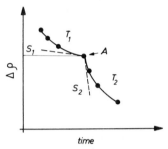

Fig. 51. Determination of activation energy by the slope change method. At point A the temperature is rapidly increased from a constant value $T_1$ to a new constant value $T_2$.

b) In the second procedure, *two samples* are used which are subjected to different time-temperature programs. A great variety of combinations of temperature programs may be envisaged. Two examples are shown in figs. 52 and 53 where two isothermals (method of cross-cut) and one isochronal with one isothermal (Meechan-Brinkman method) are combined. In the method of cross-cut the activation energy is found from the ratio of the two slopes $S_1$ and $S_2$ taken for equal values of $\Delta\rho$.

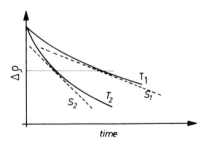

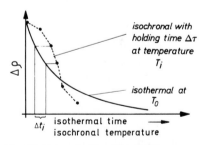

Fig. 52. Determination of activation energy from two isothermals at temperatures $T_1$ and $T_2$ (method of cross-cut).

Fig. 53. Determination of activation energy from isothermal at $T_0$ and isochronal with constant holding time $\Delta\tau$ (Meechan-Brinkman method).

In the Meechan-Brinkman method the activation energy is obtained through the relation

$$\ln \Delta t_i - \ln \Delta \tau = \frac{U}{k} \left( \frac{1}{T_o} - \frac{1}{T_i} \right) , \tag{26}$$

where $\Delta \tau$ is the constant holding time of the isochronal program, $T_o$ is the constant temperature of the isothermal and the $\Delta t_i$ are the time intervals which would have been needed at the isothermal temperature $T_o$ to obtain equal recovery increments as observed in the isochronal steps at temperatures $T_i$ (see fig. 53).

All methods using two samples have the great disadvantage that both samples must have identical initial defect states. Experience in the past has shown, that this condition is very stringent. For example, a mismatch of only 3% in the total amount of recovery of the isochronal and isothermal may cause systematic errors in the determination of $U$ of as much as 20%. Due to background annealing, in many cases, the resistivity values at which a given annealing stage begins and ends cannot be determined exactly (especially the limiting value $\Delta \rho(\infty)$ of the isothermal) and also the total amount of recovery in stage III often varies from sample to sample even for identical irradiation conditions, especially at low defect densities. Therefore, in spite of the high accuracy usually claimed, the discrepancies reported in the literature are not particularly surprising. The only possibility of obtaining more reliable activation energies appears to require better statistics by the use of a larger number of independent samples with irradiation histories that are as identical as possible.

### III.2.2. Review of experimental results

Tables 8–10 give a compilation of the activation energies reported in the literature for stage III of fcc metals. The first and second column of these tables contain the type of irradiation particles and the irradiation temperatures. The fourth and fifth column give the total resistivity increment recovering in stage III and the number of independent samples used for the activation energy measurements. The sixth column gives the method used for the activation energy determination. The information in columns 4, 5 and 6 may be used to estimate the reliability of the activation energies. All activation energy values obtained by methods requiring specific assumptions about the recovery kinetics in stage III have been omitted from tables 8–10. Examples of activation energy values not included are the values obtained by the Primak analysis [106,113,114] and the values obtained by the "second order method" for Al [115,116].

To date, the largest amount of data is available for aluminium. If the early value of 0.45 eV is discarded * the rest of the data in table 8 all support a value around

---

* If in the original paper of Sosin and Rachal [116], the isothermal used for the Meechan-Brinkman plot is shifted so that $\Delta \rho(\infty)$ increases by $0.2 \times 10^{-10}$ $\Omega \cdot$cm (only 2.5% of the total resistivity recovery in stage III!) the activation energy increases from 0.45 to 0.55 eV. This shift also corrects the data in such a manner that now the test: $\Delta t_i = \Delta \tau$ at $T_i = T_o$ (see eq. (26)) for internal consistency of the Meechan-Brinkman plot is satisfied.

Table 8

Activation energies for stage III recovery in aluminium

| Type of irradiation | Irradiation temperature (°K) | $U$ (eV) | $\Delta\rho_{III}$ (nΩ·cm) | Number of independent samples | Method | References |
|---|---|---|---|---|---|---|
| electrons 1 MeV | 20 | 0.61 ± 0.03 | 0.4 | 2 | Meechan-Brinkman | [115] |
| electrons 1 MeV | 10 | 0.58 | 0.5 | 10 | Meechan-Brinkman | [116] |
| electrons 1 MeV | 80 | 0.45 ± 0.01 | 0.8 | 3 | Meechan-Brinkman | [85] |
| electrons 2 MeV | 90 | 0.63 ± 0.04 | 1 | 7 | slope change | [104] |
| electrons 2 MeV | 90 | 0.61 ± 0.03 | 2 | 2 | alternate temperature | [104] |
| electrons 1.5 MeV | 100 | 0.58 ± 0.03 | 3 | | alternate temperature | [118,119] |
| electrons 1.5 + 1 MeV | 140 | 0.59 ± 0.03 | | | slope change | [117] |
| fast neutrons | 4 | 0.58 ± 0.02 | 36 | 8 | Meechan-Brinkman slope change cross-cut | [109] |
| fast neutrons | 80 | 0.55 | | 3 | cross-cut | [120] |
| fast neutrons | 80 | 0.59 ± 0.02 | 110 and 16 | 10 | Meechan-Brinkman cross-cut | [110] |
| fast neutrons | 80 | 0.56 ± 0.06 | 70 | 2 | slope change | [98] |
| fast neutrons | 80 | 0.58 ± 0.03 | 40 | | slope change | [99] |
| | | 0.59 ± 0.02 | | | Meechan-Brinkman | |

Table 9

Activation energies for stage III recovery in copper

| Type of irradiation | Irradiation temperature (°K) | $U$ (eV) | $\Delta\rho_{III}$ (n$\Omega\cdot$cm) | Number of independent samples | Method | References |
|---|---|---|---|---|---|---|
| electrons 1.2 MeV | 80 | $0.60 \pm 0.01$ | 0.6 | 2 | Meechan-Brinkman | [124] |
| electrons 1 MeV | 90 | 0.67 | 3 | 2 | Meechan-Brinkman | [11] |
| electrons 1.5 MeV | 100 | $0.71 \pm 0.03$ | 2 | 2 | slope change | [105] |
| electrons 1.5 MeV | 113 | $0.69 \pm 0.05$ | 2 | 2 | alternate temperature | [125] |
| α-particle 35 MeV | 120 | 0.72 | 120 | 4 | cross-cut | [126] |
| deuterons 12 MeV | 90 | 0.68 | 80 | several | slope change | [127] |
| deuterons 10 MeV | 80 | $0.71 \pm 0.04$ | 20 | 2 | slope change | [113] |
| fast neutrons | 4 | $0.72 \pm 0.03$ | 18 | 8 | Meechan-Brinkman cross-cut slope change | [123] |

Table 10

Activation energies for stage III recovery in gold, silver, platinum and nickel

| Metal, type of irradiation | Irradiation temperature (°K) | $U$ (eV) | $\Delta\rho_{III}$ (nΩ·cm) | Number of independent samples | Method | Reference |
|---|---|---|---|---|---|---|
| *Gold* | | | | | | |
| electrons 2 MeV | 80 | 0.80 ± 0.04 | 10 and 40 | 4 | Meechan–Brinkman | [107] |
| electrons 3 MeV | 100 | 0.85 ± 0.02 | 2–8 | 13 | slope change | [106,128] |
| deuterons 10 MeV | 80 | 0.80 ± 0.04 | 110 | 2 | slope change | [113] |
| gold ions 60 keV | 90 | 0.78 ± 0.05 | 100 | 2 | alternate temperature | [129] |
| *Silver* | | | | | | |
| deuterons 10 MeV | 80 | 0.67 ± 0.04 | 40 | 2 | slope change | [113] |
| *Platinum* | | | | | | |
| electrons 2 MeV | 90 | 1.36 ± 0.08 | 1.8 | 2 | Meechan–Brinkman | [130] |
| fast neutrons | 320 | 1.4 ± 0.10 | 540 | several | slope change | [131] |
| fast neutrons | 320 | 1.46 ± 0.05 | 540 | 2 | Meechan–Brinkman | [131] |
| *Nickel* | | | | | | |
| electrons 1.2 MeV | 90 | 1.03 ± 0.04 | 1.5 | 2 | Meechan–Brinkman | [132] |
| electrons 3 MeV | 280 | 1.03 ± 0.04 | 1.5 | 2 | Meechan–Brinkman | [133] |

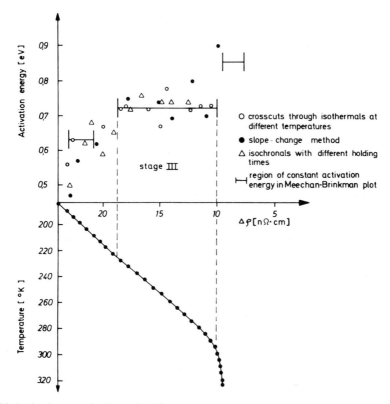

Fig. 54. Activation energies determined for Cu, neutron irradiated at 4.5°K to $\Delta\rho_0 \approx 40$ nΩ·cm, by different methods versus recovery in the stage II − stage III region. Lower plot: isochronal recovery curve of one of the samples ($\Delta\tau = 3$ min) used for the Meechan-Brinkman plot. Stage III is defined as that recovery region where the activation energy is found to be constant within experimental error. Data are taken from ref. [123].

0.59 eV. An important feature of the data listed in table 8 is that there is no systematic difference for the activation energies observed after electron irradiation at temperatures below and above stage I and after neutron irradiation. From this we have to conclude that for all the defect patterns described in section II.3 the same kind of freely migrating defects annihilates in stage III.

For copper, the data are less conclusive than for aluminium. If, however, the value of 0.60 of the earliest experiment is ignored, the rest of the data in table 9 support a common value for electron and heavy particle irradiated samples of around 0.71 eV. Although more experiments, especially after higher dose electron irradiation, would be desirable to substantiate the above conclusion, the present situation does not seem to justify the viewpoint [121,122] that there is a systematic difference between the activation energies observed after electron and heavy particle irradiation.

As mentioned in section II.2.2, in neutron irradiated copper the recovery rate in stage II increases steadily and merges continuously into stage III. Therefore, the extension of stage III to low temperatures is not very well defined. In order to clarify this point, a systematic study [123] of activation energies in the temperature range from 180 to 320°K has been performed using 8 copper samples irradiated simultaneously at 4°K to the same neutron dose. The results are shown in fig. 54 which contains the activation energies determined by different methods and the isochronal annealing curve belonging to one of the samples. The existence of a distinct recovery range where the activation energy is constant within experimental error is clearly recognized. This range of constant $U$ may be used to define the extent of stage III in neutron irradiated copper.

For gold and platinum the data listed in table 10 also seem to support the conclusion that there is no systematic difference in the activation energies observed after heavy particle and electron irradiation.

### III.3. Annealing kinetics

For a mathematical description of the recovery kinetics in stage III, the formalism outlined in section I.2.1 and eq. (23) may be used.

Aluminium shows complete recovery in stage III after all types of irradiation. Therefore, $C = \Delta\rho/\rho_F$ is probably a good approximation and eq. (23) may be used directly for an analysis of the experimental data. In fig. 55 the quantity

$$-\frac{1}{\Delta\rho}\frac{d\Delta\rho}{d[t\exp(-U/kT)]} = 4\pi R_o^{III} D_o F(\Delta\rho) \tag{27}$$

as obtained from different annealing experiments is plotted against $\Delta\rho$. A common value of $U = 0.58$ eV has been used for the reduction of the experimental data. Isothermals at different temperatures as well as isochronals can be utilized for this plot. In the latter case the effective heating rate approximation [112] is used to convert the time derivative in eq. (27) into a derivative with respect to temperature.

In the final part of the recovery, all of the curves shown in fig. 55 exhibit a linear relationship beteeen the total defect density and the annihilation probability $F$ of eq. (27). As discussed in section I.2.1.1 such a relationship is typical for the uncorrelated recombination of equal numbers of interstitials and vacancies (second order reaction). According to eqs. (27) and (6) the slope of the linear part of curves shown in fig. 55 may be used to infer the product $D_o R_o^{III}$. For electron damage above 80°K (defect pattern c in fig. 36) and neutron damage (defect pattern d in fig. 36) values of 0.5 and $0.4 \times 10^{14}$ atomic vol. sec$^{-1}$ are observed respectively. For the determination of these numbers, $\rho_F$ has been taken as $4 \times 10^{-6}$ n$\Omega\cdot$cm/at% Frenkel defects in Al [48]. With eq. (4a) and $\nu_o \approx 10^{14}$ sec$^{-1}$ one finally obtains values of $R_o^{III}$ around 2 atomic diameters. This value seems to be quite reasonable if

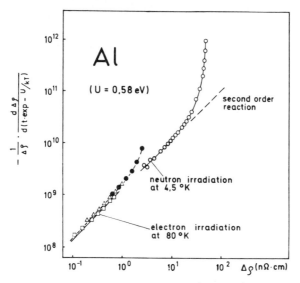

Fig. 55. Kinetic analysis of stage III in Al. The quantity $\dfrac{1}{\Delta\rho} \dfrac{d\Delta\rho}{d[t\exp(-U/kT)]}$ is plotted versus $\Delta\rho$ for isochronals and isothermals observed after irradiation with fast electrons at different temperatures and fast neutrons. Data are taken from ● ref. [117], △ ref. [104], □ ref. [85], ○ ref. [109]. A common value of $U = 0.58$ has been used for the evaluation.

migration of single vacancies to trapped interstitials is assumed for stage III. $R_o^{III}$ then constitutes the average contribution per interstitial to the total capture radius of an interstitial cluster for single vacancies *.

The deviation from the second order behaviour in the initial part of the recovery curves in fig. 55 may easily be explained by correlations in the initial arrangement of interstitials and vacancies. As discussed in section III.1 in neutron irradiated samples the correlated recombination of defects within the individual defect zones involves only small numbers of diffusion jumps. The strong initial increase of the recombination probability $F$ in the beginning of stage III, therefore, is not surprising.

All the other fcc metals investigated so far show up more complex kinetic behaviour in stage III than does Al. In Pt — although the recovery goes to completion in stage III — a kinetic behaviour is observed which can be approximated by a chem-

---

* In contrast to the good agreement among the data obtained by the different authors for 80°K electron irradiations the values of $D_o R_o^{III}$ which can be deduced from samples irradiated below 20°K differ appreciably. So Garr's and Sosin's data [115] yield $D_o R_o^{III} \approx 1.3 \times 10^{14}$ whereas the more recent data of Bauer [116] give $D_o R_o^{III} \approx 0.2 \times 10^{14}$ atomic vol. sec$^{-1}$. Therefore no safe conclusions are possible as to the influence of the different arrangements of the interstitials produced by irradiations below and above stage I on the magnitude of the mean reaction radii $R_o^{III}$ in stage III.

ical rate equation of the form (5) with an apparent reaction order of 2.5 [130] and 2.8 [131]. This deviation from the pure second order kinetics could indicate the possible influence of mutual interactions or interactions with impurities of the mobile stage III defects. However, it could also be attributed to a decrease of the mean effective reaction radius per Frenkel defect $R_0^{III}$ or to an increase in the effective contribution of one Frenkel pair to the electrical resistivity during the recovery in stage III.

For electron irradiated gold, Lee and Koehler [106] report that they are able to fit their recovery curves to second order behaviour assuming variable $\Delta\rho(\infty)$ over the whole recovery range. However, this formal second order fit seems to have little physical significance.

For copper, the annealing kinetics in stage III is complicated by the fact that incomplete recovery is observed in this stage (see section III.6). Thus we have to conclude that in addition to recombination, part of the mobile stage III defects form stable clusters in stage III. If the assumption is made that the resistivity per Frenkel pair is unchanged by the clustering of the mobile defects in stage III the formalism of section I.2.1.2 together with eq. (15) could be used to describe the reaction kinetics. As outlined in fig. 12 a characteristic feature of the reaction kinetics involving uncorrelated recombination plus clustering is, that the function $F$ in eq. (3) increases approximately linearly with $Z - Z(\infty)$. Contrary to this expectation, in the final part of stage III a behaviour has been observed in several experiments [105,123,124,101,113], which can be represented by a formal rate equation of the form

$$ -\frac{d[\Delta\rho - \Delta\rho(\infty)]}{d[t\,\exp(-U/kT)]} = \text{const} \cdot [\Delta\rho - \Delta\rho(\infty)]^2 , \qquad (28) $$

where $\Delta\rho(\infty)$ is the resistivity increment remaining above stage III. No physical interpretation of this result can be given. Even, if $[\Delta\rho - \Delta\rho(\infty)]$ would be taken as an approximate linear measure for the number of mobile stage III defects at the end of stage III *, the formal second order behaviour of eq. (28) would be inconsistent with any recovery model which allows for the observed survival of radiation induced defects above stage III. At the end of stage III when $\Delta\rho - \Delta\rho(\infty) \lesssim \Delta\rho(\infty)$ the last few mobile stage III defects face such an overwhelming number of possible reaction partners that the mean number of jumps until annihilation must approach a constant value. Therefore, first order and not second order kinetics is to be expected. The observed deviations from the expected first order behaviour at the end of stage III may indicate the importance of additional reactions like thermal detrapping of

---

* This assumption would require that at the end of stage III the number of freely migrating defects which join a cluster is a constant fraction of the number of freely migrating defects which recombine with the antidefects and that the resistivity contribution of the freely migrating defect is unaltered by the clustering process.

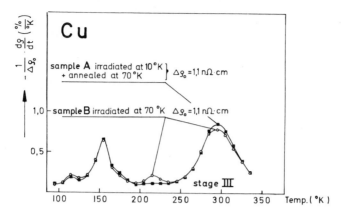

Fig. 56. Comparison of the recovery in Cu after irradiation with 1.3 MeV electrons at temperatures below and above stage I. Data are taken from ref. [90].

stage III defects from smaller clusters, etc. in copper. These detrapping reactions
would delay the decrease of the reaction rate at the end of stage III and therefore
could give the appearance of a higher order reaction.

From the observed kinetic behaviour of stage III in copper no conclusion can be
drawn about the possible influence of the primary defect arrangement. Nevertheless
Bauer and Sosin [90] were able to confirm directly that for electron irradiated copper the recovery in stage III is virtually the same for samples irradiated at temperatures below and above stage I (see fig. 56). Judging from the defect retention above
stage I, sample A in fig. 56, which was irradiated at low temperatures, contained a
defect pattern resembling type a) in fig. 36. For sample B irradiated at 80°K the observed dose dependence of the defect production rate indicates the existence of a
damage pattern resembling type c) in fig. 36. Unfortunately the doses employed in
the experiment were not high enough to ensure the existence of clusters of much
more than two trapped interstitials at impurities in the high temperature irradiation.
Nevertheless we may conclude from the observed agreement in the recovery that
the different initial defect arranegements in the two samples have no major influence on the recombination and clustering of the freely migrating stage III defects.

For stage III in nickel the experimental situation is similar to that outlined for
copper. Again incomplete recovery and a kinetic law of the form of eq. (28) is found
at the end of stage III [132,133]. As discussed above, both observations are inconsistent with each other, if, as usual, $\Delta\rho - \Delta\rho(\infty)$ is assumed to be a linear measure
for the number of freely migrating defects.

### III.4. The influence of impurities on the recovery in stage III

The influence of low concentrations of foreign atoms on the recovery in stage III has been studied most extensively for Al. After neutron damage the influence of elements like Mg, Si, Sn, Cu, Zn, Ag has been studied extensively by Dimitrov-Frois and Dimitrov [96–99] and by Ceresara et al. [93–95]. After electron irradiation the influence of Mg, Zn, Cu, Ag and Ga has been studied by Sosin and coworkers [85,115] and by Peters and Shearin [87]. The common results of all these investigations are the following.

1) The activation energies observed for the alloys seem to be the same, within experimental error, as those observed for pure aluminium. For neutron irradiated AlMg, AlAg and AlCu Dimitrov-Frois and Dimitrov [96,99] found $U = 0.59$ eV. For AlSi Ceresara et al. [94] report a value of 0.56 eV after neutron irradiation, whereas Garr and Sosin [115] find 0.64 eV for electron irradiated AlMg and AlGa. Since there is no systematic difference to the values listed in table 8 we have to conclude that the annihilation of the same kind of freely migrating defect is responsible for stage III in both pure and alloyed samples.

2) The addition of several elements like Ag, Zn, and Si in concentrations well above the irradiation induced defect densities shifts the recovery in stage III to lower temperatures. A similar enhancement of the recovery in the temperature range of stage III has been observed also in unirradiated quenched AlSi alloys [134]. The usual interpretation of this effect is that a vacancy can form a stable association with a silicon atom, and this complex is thought to be more mobile than the vacancy by itself.

3) For the alloying elements Sn, Mg, Si, Ag, Zn and Cu, present in larger concentrations, incomplete recovery is observed in stage III. The final recovery in these samples occurs at temperatures 50 to 100°K higher (depending on the element present) than stage III in the pure material, and with significantly higher activation energy (0.74 eV for AlMg [99] and 1.1 eV for AlSi [94]). Since a similar effect is observed also in quenched Al alloys, a possible interpretation is that the impurities enhance the formation of vacancy clusters which then dissolve at higher temperatures. It is also interesting to note that in some experiments on AlAg [115] and AlCu [87,135], and AlZn [136] an increase of the electrical resistivity in the final part of stage III has been observed after neutron or electron irradiation. This increase is typical for the formation of GP zones, a process for which migration of vacancies is essential.

For fcc metals other than Al, little systematic information is available on the influence of impurities in stage III. Only Greening and Koehler [137] have studied the recovery of dilute alloys of Cu, Ag and Au after proton irradiation. For CuBe and also AgBe little influence of the impurities on the recovery was observed. The activation energies were found to be the same within experimental error as in pure samples.

The recovery in Au, however, seems to be markedly altered by the addition of impurities like Mg and Al. Smaller activation energies and a shift of stage III to lower temperatures were observed [137]. Also, residual impurities seem to exert a similar influence on the recovery in stage III of electron irradiated Au [100,106, 128].

### III.5. The influence of quenched-in vacancies on the recovery of stage III

The recovery of irradiated, prequenched and annealed samples has been compared in several experiments for Al [138,116,118,119], Au [106] and Pt [108]. In all these experiments two recovery peaks were observed in the prequenched samples. Typical data are shown in fig. 57 for Pt. The two sets of data refer to two different ratios of quenched-in and radiation produced defects. The first peak in the prequenched samples is found at a somewhat lower temperature than stage III in unquenched samples containing the same irradiation produced defect density. This difference can be explained by the smaller number of jumps necessary for a stage III defect to annihilate at its antidefect in a prequenched sample compared with an unquenched sample. At the temperatures where all the radiation produced defects are annihilated, a minimum is reached in the recovery rate and the remaining excess vacancies recover in a separate annealing stage. This stage coincides approximately with the recovery stage in which the vacancies of an unirradiated quenched sample are found to disappear and is called stage IV in the usual notation.

In the two-interstitial model the clear separation of the recovery peaks III and IV in irradiated prequenched samples has been taken as evidence [116,118] that two different kinds of defects are annihilating in the two stages, namely, the converted interstitials in stage III and vacancies in stage IV.

On the other hand for Al [116] and Au [106] no significant difference in the activation energies for the two stages has been observed. For this reason, it seems possible that the same freely migrating defects could be responsible for stage III in irradiated as well as for stage IV in quenched Al, Au and Pt. These defects can then only be vacancies.

If vacancies are responsible for stage III *and* stage IV, the different kinds of sinks at which the vacancies annihilate must then account for the separation of the two stages: In this model stage III is then due to recombination of vacancies with trapped interstitials, present in equal initial concentration $C(0)$ in the form of di-interstitial or small clusters in pure unquenched samples. The characteristic time $\tau_{III}$ for this process is approximately

$$\frac{1}{\tau_{III}} = 2\pi D_{1V} R_o^{III} C(0) , \tag{29}$$

where $R_o^{III}$ denotes the recombination radius of vacancies at the trapped interstitials and $D_{1V}$ is the diffusion constant of the single vacancies.

344 W.SCHILLING et al.

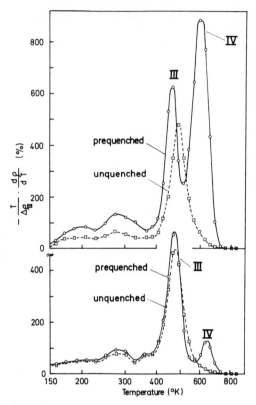

Fig. 57. Comparison of the high temperature recovery of annealed and prequenched Pt irradiated
with 3 MeV electrons at 4.5°K.

Upper curves: ○ prequenched, $\Delta\rho_{III}$ = 73 nΩ·cm, $\Delta\rho_Q$ = 120 nΩ·cm;
□ unquenched, $\Delta\rho_{III}$ = 147 nΩ·cm.

Lower curves: ○ prequenched, $\Delta\rho_{III}$ = 382 nΩ·cm, $\Delta\rho_Q$ = 59 nΩ·cm,
□ unquenched, $\Delta\rho_{III}$ = 428 nΩ·cm.

$\Delta\rho_Q$ is the quenched-in resistivity. The total resistivity recovery in the high temperature peak
found after pre-quenching equals $\Delta\rho_{III}$. The apparent enhancement of the recovery by prequenching for temperatures below 350°K is due only to the normalization. For the same reason,
the sizes of the high temperature peaks in the upper and lower plot cannot be compared directly.

As long as the annihilation radius for vacancies at interstitials is larger, or at least
not much smaller, than the reaction radius for di-vacancy formation, the possibility
of formation and more rapid diffusion of di-vacancies does not greatly influence the
reaction rate in stage III *.

* For example, in the extreme case that the binding energy of the di-vacancy is very large so that
the di-vacancies cannot dissociate before reaction at interstitials and if di-vacancies diffuse
much faster than single vacancies and if little interaction between di-vacancies and other
vacancies exists, the only modification to eq. (29) is that $R_o^{III}$ is replaced by $R_o^{III} + 2R_{2V}$
where $R_{2V}$ is the reaction radius for di-vacancy formation out of two single vacancies.

In contrast to the situation often faced in quenched metals, no local equilibrium in the formation and dissociation of di-vacancies can be established in irradiated samples. This is a consequence of the presence of interstitials as sinks in equal numbers to the vacancies in the irradiated samples: The average life-time of a vacancy is so small that the same vacancy has no chance to act several times as a partner for more rapidly diffusing di-vacancies. Therefore the mean time for removal of interstitials by vacancies — the primary process detected by electrical resistivity measurements — is still governed by the diffusion of the single vacancies and the activation energy measured for stage III should be equal to the activation energy for single vacancy diffusion.

Contrary to stage III the details of recovery of the vacancies in stage IV may be greatly affected by the mutual interaction of the vacancies, as is well known from annealing studies of purely quenched samples. In this case mainly two different annealing processes may be distinguished: Annihilation of the excess vacancies at fixed sinks like dislocations, grain boundaries etc. or precipitation of the excess vacancies into stable vacancy loops or voids. The characteristic times for the two reaction mechanisms are quite different and will be discussed separately.

a) For the annihilation of vacancies at dislocations the characteristic time is approximately given by [139,44]

$$\frac{1}{\tau_{IV}} = \frac{2\pi\Lambda}{-\ln(7\Lambda R_d^2)} D_{1V}\,\beta(C, T), \tag{30}$$

where $\Lambda$ is the dislocation density, $R_d$ the radius of the reaction cylinder for vacancy annihilation at a dislocation, $D^{1V}$ the diffusion constant of the single vacancies and $\beta$ an enhancement factor which takes into account the possibility of a vacancy to make part of its walk to the dislocation as a more rapidly diffusing di-vacancy. The enhancement factor $\beta$ depends both on the vacancy concentration $C$ and the temperature $T$.

If single vacancies and di-vacancies are in local thermal equilibrium with each other, the enhancement factor is given by [149,150]

$$\beta(C, T) = \frac{1 + 4C_{2V}D_{2V}/C_{1V}D_{1V}}{1 + 4C_{2V}/C_{1V}} \tag{31}$$

with

$$\frac{C_{2V}}{C_{1V}} = 6C_{1V}\exp(\Delta S/k)\,\exp(E_{2V}^{B}/kT), \tag{31a}$$

where $C_{2V}$, $C_{1V}$ and $D_{2V}$, $D_{1V}$ are the concentration and diffusion constants of the di-vacancies and single vacancies respectively. $\Delta S$ is the change in entropy due to di-vacancy formation out of two single vacancies and $E_{2V}^{B}$ the binding energy of the divacancy. For small vacancy concentrations due to its bimolecular character the divacancy formation is largely suppressed. If also $D_{2V}/D_{1V} < C_{1V}/C_{2V}$ the annihilation of the vacancies at the grain boundaries occurs mainly by single vacancy migration and $\beta \approx 1$. Such a situation probably prevailed in the experiments reported by Lee and Koehler [106] for Au and by Bauer [116] and by Budin and Lucasson [119] for Al. In these experiments similar activation energies have been observed for stage III and stage IV in pre-quenched electron irradiated samples. The separations of the recovery peaks III and IV corresponded to ratios for the mean numbers of jumps until annihilation in stage IV and stage III of around $10^3$ and $10^2$ for Al and Au, respectively, at initial defect densities of about $10^{-5}$. On the other hand from the values of $\tau_{III}$ and $\tau_{IV}$ given by eqs. (29) and (30) a theoretical estimate of the ratio of the mean number of jumps in stage III and IV can be given. If reasonable values for $R_o^{III}$ and $R_d$ are inserted one finds for $C(0) = 10^{-5}$ and dislocation densities $10^9$ cm$^{-2}$ that the vacancy has to make about $10^3$ times more jumps to annihilate at dislocations than at randomly distributed interstitials *. From this estimate one can conclude that the observed separation of the stages III and IV in the regime of single vacancy migration can easily be accounted for by the different sink geometries. For smaller dislocation densities the calculated ratio $\tau_{IV}/\tau_{III}$ would be even higher.

At larger vacancy concentrations the enhancement of the diffusion by partial di-vacancy formation becomes important. As discussed by Schumacher and Seeger [149] in this case the situation can often be characterized by the condition $C_{2V} \ll C_{1V}$ and $C_{2V}D_{2V} \gg C_{1V}D_{1V}$, i.e., the vacancy diffusion is governed by a relatively small number of, however, rapidly migrating di-vacancies. The effective activation energy observed in this case is given by the difference $E_{2V}^m - E_{2V}^B$ of the migration and binding energy of the di-vacancies instead of the migration energy $E_{1V}^m$ of the single vacancies. Recent investigations of Schumacher et al. [151] suggest that in Pt the concentrations of quenched-in vacancies to which the data of fig. 57 pertain are so high that the annealing of these vacancies in stage IV is greatly affected by the di-vacancy mechanism. Using the values of the frequency factors listed in table 2 of ref. [140] and $E_{1V}^m + E_{2V}^B - E_{2V}^m = 0.4$ eV the enhancement factor $\beta$ can be estimated to be about 7 for $T = 600°$K and $C(0) = 2 \times 10^{-4}$ vacancies/atom. The separation of the two peaks shown in fig. 57a, without correction for enhanced diffusion of vacancies, suggests a ratio of the mean number of jumps until annihilation in stage IV and stage III of about $2 \times 10^3$. This value, if corrected for the di-vacancy mechanism in stage IV, is in good agreement with a theoretical estimate of the ratio $\tau_{IV}/\tau_{III}$ (see eqs. (29) and (30)) at about 600°K using $\beta \approx 7$ and dislocation densities of about $3 \times 10^8$ cm$^{-2}$. Dislocation densities of the order of $10^8$ cm$^{-2}$ acting as sinks for the annealing of the excess vacancies are not too small to be unreasonable for the well annealed Pt samples used for this investigation. Therefore we have to conclude that in spite of the enhancement of the vacancy diffusion at

* For annihilation at the boundaries of subgrains of reasonable sizes the estimated number of jumps is even larger than for normal dislocation densities.

higher defect densities in the quenched samples the observed separation of the annealing stages III and IV can still be accounted for by the different sink geometries in both stages.

b) If the excess vacancies anneal by precipitation into homogeneously nucleated vacancy clusters the mean number of jumps for the removal of the single vacancies in stage IV would be of the same order of magnitude as in stage III. However, in this case, during the initial nucleation period mainly small vacancy clusters consisting of 3 or 4 vacancies will be formed by reaction of single vacancies and di-vacancies. If, as usually assumed, the electrical resistivity per vacancy is not changed very much by the formation of such small clusters these nucleation processes will not show up as a larger recovery stage in the residual resistivity. Later on, larger clusters will grow at the expense of the smaller ones which dissolve until thermally stable cluster sizes are achieved. Only during this process which occurs at higher temperatures and where most of the single vacancies disappear, the main recovery stage of the electrical resistivity will be observed. In this case the delay of the annealing of the electrical resistivity contribution per excess vacancy to higher temperatures would be responsible for the separation of the two annealing peaks in irradiated and quenched metals.

At present the question under what circumstances the quenched in vacancies primarily precipitate into larger loops or voids or anneal at fixed sinks like dislocations cannot be answered for sure. For Al, Pt and Au quenched from temperatures near the melting point large vacancy clusters have been observed after stage IV [151,152,153]. However, as outlined above, the observed separation of the annealing stage III in irradiated and stage IV in quenched Al, Pt and Au, within the vacancy model, can in any case be accounted for by the different kinds of sinks at which the vacancies anneal and it is not necessary to invoke two different kinds of defects recovering in the two stages.

## III.6. Defect retention above stage III

In contrast to Al and Pt, even the purest samples of the fcc metals, Cu, Ag, Au and Ni, do not show complete recovery at the end of stage III. If $\Delta\rho$ is normalized to the resistivity $\Delta\rho_{III}$, associated with the damage present at the beginning of stage III, about 50% of the damage in copper and silver is retained above stage III after neutron [84] and about 30% after proton irradiation [113]. For gold, about 30% and 17% of the damage is retained after neutron and proton irradiation, respectively. The fractional retention after neutron irradiation is almost independent of the irradiation dose [84]. After electron irradiation in copper [36,90, 124,140] and gold [106,107] incomplete recovery has been observed. However, the absolute value of the fractional retention seems to depend rather strongly on the impurity content of the samples at least at low irradiation doses. For very pure samples, at least in gold [106], there seems to be a tendency for almost complete

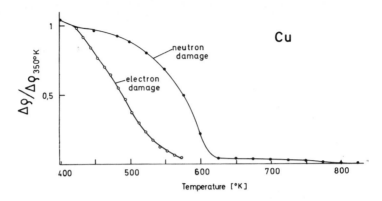

Fig. 58. Resistivity recovery above stage III of Cu electron irradiated at 80°K and neutron irradiated at 4.5°K. The recovery is normalized to the damage $\Delta\rho_{350}$ present after annealing at
350°K. $\Delta\rho_{350}$ was 0.35 n$\Omega$·cm for the electron and 12 n$\Omega$·cm for the neutron irradiated sample. Data are taken from refs. [124,145].

recovery in stage III. However, in copper, electron irradiated at 4°K to higher dose
levels, about 15% of the defects present in the beginning of stage III are retained.
This value increases to about 25% if the defects are introduced by irradiation above
stage I [124,140].

Relatively little information is available about the resistivity recovery above stage
III. For copper, recovery curves observed above 350°K after neutron and electron
irradiation are shown in fig. 58. One clearly recognizes that the final resistivity
recovery after neutron damage occurs at higher temperatures than after electron
damage. However, no reliable activation energy measurements for this final stage
seem to be available.

Direct information about the defects remaining above stage III may be obtained
by electron microscopic observations and indirect information from radiation hardening experiments. As discussed by Wilkens in these proceedings [141], both
vacancy and interstitial clusters have been observed above stage III in neutron as
well as high dose electron irradiated samples. (See also ref. [142].) During annealing in the temperature range above stage III, the mean size, especially of the vacancy
clusters, first increases and then the clusters disappear at temperatures where the
electrical resistivity and the critical shear stress are also observed to recover.

Nickel also shows considerable defect retention above stage III after electron as
well as neutron damage. The fractional resistivity retention (normalized to the
resistivity due to the damage present at the beginning of stage III) is about 30% and
60% respectively for electron and neutron damage. In the electron microscope, both
vacancy and interstitial clusters have been observed above stage III in neutron irradiated samples [143] and only interstitial clusters in electron irradiated samples
[144]. The recovery of the electrical resistivity above stage III is shown in fig. 59.

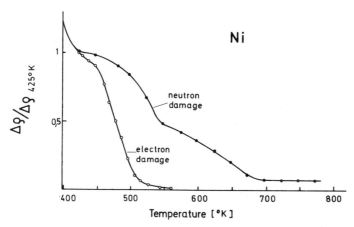

Fig. 59. Resistivity recovery above stage III of Ni electron irradiated at 270°K and neutron irradiated at 4.5°K. The recovery is normalized to the damage $\Delta\rho_{425}$ present after annealing at 425°K. $\Delta\rho_{425}$ was 9 n$\Omega$·cm for the electron and 20 n$\Omega$·cm for the neutron irradiated sample. Data are taken from refs. [133,145].

Whereas for electron irradiated samples [132,133] the recovery goes to completion in a single stage around 200°C (usually called stage IV), neutron irradiated samples show up an additional recovery stage around 330°C in which almost complete recovery of the electrical resistivity occurs. The different behaviour of the electron and neutron irradiated samples may be due to the influence of larger vacancy clusters formed by neutron damage and which are missing after electron damage.

## III.7. Recovery models for stage III

In this chapter, recovery models proposed for the interpretation of stage III will be outlined and compared with the experiments. In order to simplify the discussion, the experimental situation described in sections III.1—6 will be summarized into the following postulates:
1) Stage III is due to recombination of Frenkel defects which occurs by the free migration of a unique defect (see sections III.1—3).
2) The same defect is found to annihilate in stage III for all the different initial defect patterns outlined in fig. 36 (see sections III.2 and III.3).
3) In Al and Pt, complete recovery occurs in stage III, however, in Cu, Ag, Au, and Ni the mobile defect can form stable clusters. The extent of this clustering seems to depend critically on the nucleation conditions. This accounts for the difference between heavy particle and electron irradiation (see section III.6).
Although these postulates, on the whole, summarize the present experimental situa-

tion rather well, the assumption of a unique recovery process for the whole of stage III has been especially criticized by several authors [121,122,125,116]. However, in order to avoid the consideration of a multitude of possible interpretations, the following discussion will be limited to consideration of the consequences of the above postulates, since it is believed that these postulates are more firmly based on the present experimental evidence than any other alternate possibility.

On the basis of postulate 2) all models [121] which assume free migration of di-interstitials as the migrating entity can immediately be ruled out since the defect patterns pertaining to the experimental situations b) and c) of fig. 36 will contain very few di-interstitials and, as discussed in sections III.2 and III.3, in such samples stage III is the same as in samples pertaining to pattern a) in fig. 36 in which primarily di-interstitials are present.

For similar reasons, also the possibility that di-vacancy migration alone could account for stage III can be ruled out. In experimental situations pertaining to the defect patterns a to c in fig. 36 only very few di-vacancies will be present. However, the observed recovery in stage III has the same principal features as for defect patterns d and c of fig. 36, which may contain di-vacancies to a larger extent. Complete recovery as observed for Al and Pt is impossible if di-vacancies only could migrate in stage III.

Based on the observed dose dependence, it is also possible to rule out all models which involve thermal dissociation of di-interstitials or larger interstitial clusters. These processes would be purely first order and are inconsistent with the findings reported in section III.2. We therefore are left essentially with two models, the vacancy and the conversion-two-interstitial model which will be discussed in turn.

### III.5.1. *The vacancy model*

In this model, stage III is attributed to the migration of single vacancies which recombine with the trapped interstitials remaining after stage I. This model works well for the fcc metals aluminium and platinum. The activation energies measured for stage III are in good agreement with the migration energies for single vacancies deduced from quenching and equilibrium measurements [146]. This model also seems to be applicable for gold [80,106,147]. The discrepancy of 0.05 to 0.07 eV between the activation energies observed for stage III in gold and the values extracted for single vacancy migration from quenching and equilibrium measurements [146] is still a matter of discussion [106,147] and may be small enough to be removable by other choices in the parameters entering the intricate evaluation of quenching and equilibrium data. With aluminium, a direct proof for the vacancy model is available from the observation of the formation of GP zones during stage III in irradiated dilute alloys [87,115,135,136].

As outlined in section III.5 the possible formation and more rapid diffusion of di-vacancies does not complicate the annealing behaviour of stage III. This is due to the presence of an equal number of interstitials as sinks which prevent the establishment of a local equilibrium between single and di-vacancies as it may be found in quenched samples.

In many of the fcc metals vacancies produced by quenching experiments are known to coagulate at least partially into stable clusters or loops. Therefore complications for the recovery might be expected for irradiated samples whenever the defect pattern in the beginning of stage III contains vacancies primarily in form of clusters or more loose assemblies as is the case in neutron irradiated samples. In contrast to this a rather small influence of the primary defect pattern on the recovery in stage III has been observed experimentally. In order to understand this we have to assume that most of the vacancy clusters expected to be present in neutron irradiated samples in the beginning of stage III can dissolve without appreciably delaying the vacancy-interstitial recombination. A possible reduction of the cluster sizes by the capture of single interstitials released by the reactions of single vacancies with di-interstitials may help in this dissolution process.

Especially for aluminium and platinum, where complete recovery is observed in stage III, the dissolution process must outweigh a possible growth of vacancy clusters by capture of single vacancies.

For copper, silver and nickel the activation energies observed for stage III are too low to be compatible with the values presently proposed [146] for the migration of single vacancies. If this difference cannot be removed, e.g., by more reliable quenching experiments, the vacancy model must be abandoned for these metals.

However, there seems to exist some indirect evidence that in Cu some vacancy migration occurs in stage III. In radiation doping experiments performed by Wollenberger et al. [37,51] it has been observed that the initial damage rate at 80°K is much less reduced by doping with defects which have been annealed through stage III compared to doping with defects (corresponding to the same amount of $\Delta\rho_{dop}$) which have not been annealed in stage III. Thus we have to conclude, that the defects, present at the onset of stage III, are much more effective in annihilating freely migrating interstitials during electron irradiation at 80°K than the defects present above stage III. These findings, therefore, provide evidence that the vacancies present above stage III are coagulated into larger clusters with a reduced capture radius per vacancy for free interstitials. Also, preliminary electron microscopic observations of larger vacancy clusters above stage III in high dose electron irradiated copper samples [141,142] point towards vacancy clustering in stage III.

### III.5.2. *The conversion-two-interstitial model*

The basic idea of the conversion-two-interstitial model [50,148] is the assumption of a metastable configuration in which interstitials can migrate freely in stage I and the possibility for conversion of these interstitials into a stable configuration. This second configuration is thought to be immobile up to the temperature of stage III where it can migrate freely by thermal activation. The main advantage of this model is that it relieves the discrepancy between the activation energies observed for Cu, Ni and Ag in stage III and the values presently accepted for single vacancy migration from quenching and equilibrium measurements. In addition, it offers the possibility to interpret one of the internal friction and magnetic after-effect peaks ob-

served in Ni in the temperature range of stage III by reorientation of dumb-bell interstitials [40].

The interpretation of the experiments reported to date by the conversion-two-
interstitial model requires the following properties for the *metastable* interstitial.

a) The displacements resulting from electron irradiation can lead only to metastable interstitials (possible exceptions may be close pair configurations recovering
below stage $I_D$). This follows from the almost complete suppression of defect production at $80°K$ by quenched-in vacancies and from the suppression of defect retention above stage I by vacancy doping (see sections I.1.3.2 and I.1.3.3).

b) From the observed constant probability for interstitials to escape correlated
recombination (see section I.2.3), it follows that the metastable interstitial must be
able to undergo three dimensional diffusion. An alternate possibility would be that
electron irradiation produces a constant fraction of approximately one third of the
defects in the form of crowdion-interstitial pairs in a configuration in which the
migration line of the crowdion bypasses the vacancy such that correlated recombination is impossible.

c) Conversion of the meastable interstitials occurs either by interaction with
other interstitials (metastable or converted) or by interaction with impurities. In
the latter case, trapping of metastable interstitials and conversion only at higher
temperature must be assumed in order to have the possibility of de-trapping of
interstitials in the impurity substages of stage II. Thermal conversion of isolated
metastable interstitials can be excluded from damage rate measurements at temperatures up to the beginning of stage III [37] (see section I.2.3).

The *converted* interstitial must have the following properties to account for the
experimental findings available at present:

a) The converted interstitial must be immobile up to the temperatures of stage III.

b) Only a rather small attractive interaction can exist between converted interstitials and between impurities and converted interstitials. If this were not the case,
interstitial agglomerates could not dissolve readily in stage III and one would expect
quite a different annealing behaviour of samples containing the interstitials in the
different defect patterns outlined in fig. 36.

c) On the other hand, coagulation into stable clusters must be possible in stage III.
Otherwise the observed defect retention in form of stable interstitial clusters above
stage III, as is found in Cu and Ni, cannot be understood.

At present no final judgment as to the success or failure of the vacancy or the
conversion-two-interstitial model can be made. As outlined above, the simple
vacancy model satisfactorily accounts for the behaviour of stage III in Al, Pt and
probably Au, but runs into difficulties with Cu, Ag and Ni. The two-interstitial model, due to its great flexibility, can account for stage III in all the fcc metals considered. However, its plausibility suffers greatly from the number of necessary assumptions and the special properties which have to be conceived for the metastable and
stable form of the interstitials.

## Conclusion

Although this review of the current state of understanding of the recovery in irradiated metals, when compared with earlier surveys [121], may give the impression that progress in this area has been relatively slow, the authors feel that the recognition of the important parameters which determine the reactions of interstitials and vacancies has improved considerably.

In particular the realization of the great importance that the detailed defect arrangements play in determining the recovery behaviour is one of the most significant advances made in recent years. Future experiments designed to elucidate the details of these arrangements should therefore lead to decisive contributions to our understanding of the recovery mechanisms of irradiated metals. Also the present trend towards the increased use of methods more specific for the detection of differences in the defect configurations and particularly the measurement of several property changes in a single experiment promises significant progress.

Apart from these general considerations, the present survey points up the following specific areas where additional experimental work is critically needed.

In stage I, precise activation energy determinations are of extreme importance, especially in the substages $I_D$ and $I_E$ after electron damage. To date, only Corbett, Smith and Walker [3] have reported an unequivocal determination of the activation energy in stages $I_D$ and $I_E$ for electron irradiated Cu. Since the cardinal point concerning the present interpretation of stages $I_D$ and $I_E$ is the equality of the activation energies for these stages, a confirmation of the earlier result for Cu and systematic measurements for other electron irradiated metals would be highly desirable.

In addition to activation energy measurements, quantitative and systematic studies of the influence of doping agents on the defect retention above stage $I_E$ in electron irradiated metals would be of great value for the establishment of the nature of the trapping reactions by which interstitials manage to survive above stage I. The better these reactions are understood, the more reliably can predictions be made as to the details of the defect patterns which form the starting point for the higher annealing stages. A systematic study of the recovery of Frenkel pairs injected by a test irradiation into prequenched samples or samples which contain interstitials and vacancies from doping irradiations, and subsequent annealing treatments at different temperatures may yield quantitative figures for the interaction radii of interstitial clusters and vacancies with the freely migrating interstitials. Here again, aside from the early investigations of Corbett, Smith and Walker [3] on Cu, very few systematic measurements are available at present.

On the other hand, when the trapping and annihilation reactions of the free interstitials in stage $I_E$ are understood sufficiently, these free interstitials can be used as a probe for the investigation of more details of the defect patterns present after different doping treatments.

Another line of approach, the importance of which can hardly be overemphasized, is the investigation of the damage production rate during electron irradiation at temperatures above stage I in samples which contain defects from a preceding doping treatment. In these experiments the interstitials produced during the irradiation are so mobile and therefore have such a short life time that the instantaneous concentration of free interstitials is extremely low so that bimolecular reactions can be entirely ignored. Under these conditions, the free interstitials produced during the irradiation can survive only by being trapped at doping defects and therefore act directly as a probe for the trapping ability of the doping defects relative to the annihilation reaction. Experiments of this type give valuable information about the changes in the defect pattern during annealing. For a further discussion of this subject the reader is referred to the contribution of Wollenberger in this volume [37].

For stage III, aside from more reliable activation energy measurements, especially after electron damage, systematic investigations of the influence of the defect pattern on the recovery of this stage are greatly needed. Experiments of the type performed by Bauer and Sosin [9] (see also fig. 56), in which the recovery (and activation energies!) are compared for samples which were irradiated below and above stage I to doses such that di-interstitials dominate in one case and larger clusters of interstitials trapped around impurities in the other case would be of great help for the establishment of the types of reactions going on in stage III. In addition, the influence of the damage pattern on the defect retention above stage III deserves systematic investigation. Relatively little is known at present about the nucleation conditions for the formation of the clusters in which Frenkel defects survive above stage III.

Electrical resistivity studies concerning the recovery above stage III have been neglected in the past. Reliable activation energy measurements are entirely absent although they are surely required for a better understanding of the processes going on in these stages.

## Acknowledgements

The authors gratefully acknowledge the many helpful discussions with G.Duesing, W.Sassin, H.Wollenberger and especially the great help given by K.Schroeder and G.Leibfried during the preparation of the theoretical part of this review.

In addition we would like to thank T.S.Noggle for his assistance during the preparation of the final manuscript and for the many stimulating and clarifying discussions.

## References

[1] H.G.Cooper, J.S.Koehler and J.M.Marx, Phys. Rev. 97 (1955) 599.
[2] J.W.Corbett, R.B.Smith and R.M.Walker, Phys. Rev. 114 (1959) 1452.
[3] J.W.Corbett, R.B.Smith and R.M.Walker, Phys. Rev. 114 (1959) 1460.

[4] J.W.Corbett and R.M.Walker, Phys. Rev. 110 (1958) 767.
[5] G.W.Iseler, H.I.Dawson and J.W.Kauffman, Lattice Defects and Their Interactions, ed. R.R.Hasiguti (Gordon and Breach, New York, 1967) p. 654.
[6] H.I.Dawson, G.W.Iseler and J.W.Kauffman, Lattice Defects and Their Interactions, ed. R.R.Hasiguti (Gordon and Breach, New York, 1967) p. 681.
[7] G.W.Iseler, H.I.Dawson, A.S.Mehner and J.W.Kauffman, Phys. Letters 17 (1965) 212.
[8] H.I.Dawson and J.W.Kauffman, Phys. Letters 21 (1966) 488.
[9] H.I.Dawson, G.W.Iseler, A.S.Mehner and J.W.Kauffman, Phys. Letters 18 (1965) 247.
[10] H.M.Simpson, T.N.O'Neil, A.B.Pruitt, W.E.Faust and R.L.Chaplin, Phys. Letters 27A (1968) 559.
[11] C.J.Meechan, A.Sosin and J.A.Brinkman, Phys. Rev. 120 (1960) 411.
[12] J.A.Tesk, E.C.Jones and J.W.Kauffman, Phys. Rev. 133 (1964) A288.
[13] C.L.Snead, F.W.Wiffen and J.W.Kauffman, Phys. Rev. 164 (1967) 900.
[14] F.W.Wiffen, C.L.Snead and J.W.Kauffman, Phys. Letters 23 (1966) 22.
[15] C.L.Snead, F.W.Wiffen and J.W.Kauffman, Proc. of the Intern. Conf. on Solid State Physics Research with Accelerators, Brookhaven, 1967, BNL 50083 (C-52) p. 230.
[16] W.Bauer and W.F.Goeppinger, Phys. Rev. 154 (1967) 588.
[17] J.L.Oddou, Thesis, University of Grenoble, France (1967).
[18] P.Peretto, J.L.Oddou, C.Minier-Cassayre, D.Dautreppe and P.Moser, Phys. Stat. Sol. 16 (1966) 281.
[19] C.L.Snead and P.E.Shearin, Phys. Rev. 140 (1965) A1781.
[20] A.Sosin and K.R.Garr, Phys. Rev. 161 (1967) 664.
[21] R.L.Chaplin and H.M.Simpson, Phys. Rev. 163 (1967) 587.
[22] A.Sosin and H.H.Neely, Phys. Rev. 127 (1962) 1465.
[23] J.L.Oddou, C.Minier-Cassayre and P.Moser, Phys. Stat. Sol. 17 (1966) 793.
[24] K.Herschbach and J.J.Jackson, Phys. Rev. 158 (1967) 661.
[25] K.Herschbach and J.J.Jackson, Phys. Rev. 153 (1967) 694.
[26] J.J.Jackson and K.Herschbach, Phys. Rev. 164 (1967) 951.
[27] J.J.Jackson and K.Herschbach, Phys. Rev. 173 (1968) 664.
[28] J.J.Jackson and K.Herschbach, Phys. Rev. 170 (1968) 618.
[29] C.P.Flynn, Phys. Rev. 171 (1968) 682.
[30] D.Barb, G.Vogl, W.Vogl and H.Wenzl, to be published.
[31] R.L.Chaplin and P.E.Shearin, Phys. Rev. 124 (1961) 1061.
[32] J.W.Corbett and R.M.Walker, Phys. Rev. 115 (1959) 67.
[33] A.Sosin, Phys. Rev. 126 (1962) 1698.
[34] D.Keefer, J.C.Robinson and A.Sosin, Acta Met. 13 (1965) 1135.
[35] G.de Keating-Hart, R.Cope, C.Minier and P.Moser, Jül. Conf. 2 (Vol. I) 1968, p. 327.
[36] W.Sassin, Thesis, Technische Hochschule Aachen, Germany (1969).
[37] H.Wollenberger, this volume.
[38] G.Duesing, H.Hemmerich, D.Meissner and W.Schilling, Phys. Stat. Sol. 23 (1967) 481.
[39] G.Duesing, Thesis, Technische Hochschule Aachen, Germany (1969).
[40] H.Kronmüller, this volume.
[41] H.Mehrer, Jül. Conf. 2 (Vol. II) 1968, p. 643.
[42] A.Scholz, Phys. Stat. Sol. 14 (1966) 169.
[43] T.R.Waite, Phys. Rev. 107 (1957) 463, 471.
[44] G.Leibfried, Bestrahlungseffekte in Festkörpern (Teubner Verlag, Stuttgart, 1965) p. 268.
[45] K.Schroeder, Thesis, Technische Hochschule Aachen, Germany (1969).
[46] H.M.Simpson and R.L.Chaplin, Phys. Rev. 178 (1969) 1166.
[47] R.C.FLetcher and W.L.Brown, Phys. Rev. 92 (1953) 585.
[48] H.Wenzl, this volume.
[49] W.Frank, A.Seeger and G.Schottky, Phys. Stat. Sol. 8 (1965) 345.

[50] A.Seeger, this volume.

[51] F.Dworschak, H.Schuster, H.Wollenberger and J.Wurm, Phys. Stat. Sol. 29 (1968) 75, 81.

[52] R.M.Walker, Proc. of the Intern. School of Physics "E.Fermi", ed. D.S.Billington (Academic Press, New York, 1962).

[53] G.Leibfried, this volume.

[54] G.Burger, H.Meissner and W.Schilling, Phys. Stat. Sol. 4 (1964) 281.

[55] J.R.Beeler, Phys. Rev. 150 (1966) 470.

[56] G.Lück and R.Sizmann, Phys. Stat. Sol. 14 (1966) 507.

[57] G.Burger, Thesis, Technische Hochschule München, Germany (1965).

[58] G.Burger, K.Isebeck, J.Völkl, W.Schilling and H.Wenzl, Z. Angew. Phys. 22 (1967) 452.

[59] G.Burger, K.Isebeck, J.Völkl and H.Wenzl, J. Appl. Phys. 36 (1965) 3356.

[60] R.R.Coltman, C.E.Klabunde, D.L.McDonald and J.K.Redman, J. Appl. Phys. 33 (1962) 3509.

[61] P.Peretto, Thesis, C.E.N. Grenoble, France (1967).

[62] M.L.Swanson and G.R.Piercy, Can. J. Phys. 42 (1964) 1605.

[63] M.L.Swanson and G.R.Piercy, Phys. Letters 7 (1963) 97.

[64] M.L.Swanson, Phys. Stat. Sol. 23 (1967) 649.

[65] T.H.Blewitt, R.R.Coltman, C.E.Klabunde, D.K.Holmes and J.K.Redman, ORNL Report 2614 (1958) p. 67.

[66] E.Klement and H.Wenzl, Z. Angew. Phys. 24 (1968) 182.

[67] G.D.Magnuson, W.Palmer and J.S.Koehler, Phys. Rev. 109 (1958) 1990.

[68] K.Herschbach, Phys. Rev. 130 (1963) 554.

[69] D.Meissner, Diplomarbeit Technische Hochschule Munich (1963).

[70] R.R.Coltman, C.E.Klabunde and J.K.Redman, Phys. Rev. 156 (1967) 715.

[71] R.R.Coltman, C.E.Klabunde and J.K.Redman, Phys. Rev. 159 (1967) 521.

[72] G.Duesing, H.Hemmerich, W.Sassin and W.Schilling, Jül. Conf. 2 (Vol. I) 1968, p. 246.

[73] E.Klement, Thesis, Technische Hochschule Munich (1966).

[74] H.Knöll, Diplomarbeit, Technische Hochschule Munich (1964).

[75] T.H.Blewitt, R.R.Coltman, C.E.Klabunde and T.S.Noggle, J. Appl. Phys. 28 (1957) 639.

[76] J.B.Ward and J.W.Kauffman, Phys. Rev. 123 (1961) 90.

[77] W.Bauer, J.W.DeFord, J.S.Koehler and J.W.Kauffman, Phys. Rev. 128 (1962) 1497.

[78] W.Bauer and A.Sosin, Phys. Rev. 136 (1964) A255.

[79] T.H.Blewitt, R.R.Coltman, C.E.Klabunde and J.K.Redman, ORNL Report 3017 (1960) p. 21.

[80] J.S.Koehler, this volume.

[81] H.Wollenberger, private communication.

[82] A.Seeger, J. Phys. Soc. Japan 18, Suppl. III (1963) 260.

[83] R.A.Johnson, Phys. Rev. 145 (1966) 423.

[84] G.Burger, H.Meissner and W.Schilling, Phys. Stat. Sol. 4 (1964) 267.

[85] A.Sosin and L.H.Rachal, Phys. Rev. 130 (1963) 2238.

[86] K.R.Garr and A.Sosin, Phys. Rev. 162 (1967) 669.

[87] P.B.Peters and P.E.Shearin, Phys. Rev. 174 (1968) 691.

[88] D.G.Martin, Phil. Mag. 6 (1961) 839.

[89] A.Sosin, J. Phys. Soc. Japan 18, Suppl. III (1963) 277.

[90] W.Bauer and A.Sosin, Phys. Letters 24A (1967) 193.

[91] A.Sosin, Lattice Defects and Their Interactions, ed. R.R.Hasiguti (Gordon and Breach, New York, 1967) p. 235.

[92] D.G.Martin, Phil. Mag. 7 (1962) 803.

[93] S.Ceresara and T.Federighi, Phil. Mag. 10 (1964) 893.

[94] S.Ceresara, T.Federighi and F.Pieragostini, Phys. Stat. Sol. 11 (1965) 779.

[95] S.Ceresara, T.Federighi and F.Pieragostini, Phys. Letters 6 (1963) 152.

[96] C.Dimitrov-Frois and O.Dimitrov, Mem. Sci. Rev. Met. 65 (1968) 425.
[97] C.Frois and O.Dimitrov, Compt. Rend. Acad. Sci. Paris 263 C (1966) 1496.
[98] C.Frois and O.Dimitrov, Compt. Rend. Acad. Sci. Paris 264 C (1967) 1923.
[99] C.Dimitrov-Frois and O.Dimitrov, Jül. Conf. 2 (Vol. I) 1968, p. 290.
[100] W.Bauer, Phys. Letters 19 (1965) 180.
[101] F.Dworschak and J.S.Koehler, Phys. Rev. 140 (1965) A941.
[102] G.Burger, K.Isebeck, H.Meissner, W.Schilling and H.Wenzl, Phys. Letters 20 (1966) 124.
[103] A.van den Beukel, this volume.
[104] Y.N.Lwin, M.Doyama and J.S.Koehler, Phys. Rev. 165 (1968) 787.
[105] C.L.Budin, P. Lucasson and A.Lucasson, J. Phys. 26 (1965) 9.
[106] C.Lee and J.S.Koehler, Phys. Rev. 176 (1968) 813.
[107] W.Bauer and A.Sosin, Phys. Rev. 136 (1964) A474.
[108] G.Duesing and W.Schilling, Radiation Effects 1 (1969) 65.
[109] K.Isebeck, R.Müller, W.Schilling and H.Wenzl, Phys. Stat. Sol. 18 (1966) 427.
[110] S.Ceresara, T.Federighi, D.Gelli and F.Pieragostini, Nuovo Cimento 29 (1963) 1244.
[111] C.Frois and O.Dimitrov, Compt. Rend. Acad. Sci. Paris 258 (1964) 5647.
[112] F.Bell and R.Sizmann, Phys. Stat. Sol. 15 (1966) 369.
[113] F.Dworschak, K.Herschbach and J.S.Koehler, Phys. Rev. 133 (1964) A293.
[114] W.Primak, Phys. Rev. 100 (1955) 1677.
[115] K.R.Garr and A.Sosin, Phys. Rev. 162 (1967) 681.
[116] W.Bauer, Jül. Conf. 2 (1968) p. 275; and Rad. Effects 1 (1969) 23.
[117] R.Brugière and P.Lucasson, Phys. Stat. Sol. 24 (1967) K77.
[118] C.Budin and P.Lucasson, Interaction of Radiation with Solids (Plenum Press, New York, 1967) p. 497.
[119] C.Budin and P.Lucasson, Phys. Letters 16 (1965) 229.
[120] A.W.McReynolds, W.Augustyniak, M.McKeown and D.B.Rosenblatt, Phys. Rev. 98 (1955) 418.
[121] J.W.Corbett, Electron Damage in Semiconductors and Metals (Academic Press, New York, 1966) p. 235.
[122] J.W.Corbett, this volume.
[123] H.G.Haubold, Diplomarbeit, Technische Hochschule Munich (1963).
[124] C.J.Meechan and J.A.Brinkman, Phys. Rev. 103 (1956) 1193.
[125] R.Brugière and P.Lucasson, Phys. Stat. Sol. 30 (1968) K139.
[126] R.R.Eggleston, Acta Met. 1 (1953) 679.
[127] A.W.Overhauser, Phys. Rev. 90 (1953) 393.
[128] R.K.Sharma, C.Lee and J.S.Koehler, Phys. Rev. Letters 19 (1967) 1379.
[129] K.Wittmaack, Jül. Conf. 2 (Vol. II) 1968, p. 473.
[130] W.Bauer and A.Sosin, Phys. Rev. 147 (1966) 482.
[131] G.R.Piercy, Phil. Mag. 5 (1960) 201.
[132] A.Sosin and J.A.Brinkman, Acta Met. 7 (1959) 478.
[133] H.Mehrer, H.Kronmüller and A.Seeger, Phys. Stat. Sol. 10 (1965) 725.
[134] T.Federighi, Lattice Defects in Quenched Metals (Academic Press, New York, 1965) p. 217.
[135] F.Pieragostini, C.Ceresara and T.Federighi, Acta Met. 14 (1966) 450.
[136] S.Ceresara, T.Federighi and F.Pieragostini, Phil. Mag. 9 (1964) 623.
[137] D.A.Grenning and J.S.Koehler, Phys. Rev. 144 (1966) 439.
[138] T.Federighi, S.Ceresara and F.Pieragostini, Phil. Mag. 12 (1965) 1093.
[139] F.S.Ham, J. Phys. Chem. Solids 6 (1958) 335.
[140] G.Roth and V.Naundorf, Jül. Conf. 2 (Vol. I) 1968, p. 364.
[141] M.Wilkens, this volume.
[142] G.P.Scheidler and G.Roth, Jül. Conf. 2 (Vol. I) 1968, p. 391.

[143] A.Bourret and D.Dautreppe, Phys. Stat. Sol. 29 (1968) 283.

[144] A.Bourret, Jül. Conf. 2 (Vol. I) 1968, p. 377.

[145] M.Kleitner, Diplomarbeit, Technische Hochschule Munich (1965).

[146] A.Seeger, this volume.

[147] J.S.Koehler, this volume.

[148] W.Bauer, A.Seeger and A.Sosin, Phys. Letters 24A (1967) 195.

[149] A.Seeger and D.Schumacher, in: Lattice Defects in Quenched Metals (Academic Press, New York, 1965) p. 15.

[150] M.de Jong and J.S.Koehler, Phys. Rev. 129 (1963) 40.

[151] D.Schumacher, A.Seeger and O.Härlin, Phys. Stat. Sol. 25 (1968) 359.

[152] R.M.J.Cotterill, in: Lattice Defects in Quenched Metals (Academic Press, New York, 1965) p. 97.

[153] E.Ruedl, P.Delavignette and S.Amelinckx, in: Radiation Damage in Solids, Vol. I (IAEA, Vienna, 1962) p. 363.

## Discussion

*P.Lucasson:* Some years ago, I have done with Budin (C.Budin and P.Lucasson, Xème Colloque de Métallurgie, Saclay 1966, P.U.F., 1967; Interaction of Radiation with Solids, Plenum Press, 1967, p. 497) an investigation on aluminium, where we studied in detail the behaviour of aluminium after quenching, after irradiation and after quench and irradiation, in a wide range of defects concentration.

I should like to say first that in this kind of experiment in the stages III and IV temperature range, one has to be very careful about the quenching conditions. One may quench from low temperatures and at high quenching rates, and this will give a recovery stage shifted towards higher temperatures with a high activation energy. Or one may perform a slow quench from a high temperature, and this will shift the recovery stage towards low temperatures and give lower apparent activation energies. Thus, it is possible to obtain almost at will, some recovery, either in the stage III or in the stage IV temperature or energy ranges, thus apparently supporting one model of intersticialcies or the other.

Concerning the remark of Dr. Duesing (on quenched and irradiated platinum), I should like to mention that Budin and I had shown, in aluminium quenched from "high temperatures" (350°C) and then irradiated, that the effect of irradiation was to shift both the average recovery stage temperature of vacancy type defects *and* the corresponding activation energies towards higher values, compared to that of the only-quenched material. This could be readily explained by assuming that during both the electron irradiation and the stage III recovery process, divacancies produced by quenching are converted into single vacancies by reactions with interstitials $(V_2 + I \rightarrow V_1)$, thus increasing the single vacancy partial concentration in the vacancy type defects population. This process should actually happen in every metal, and particularly in platinum.

*W.Schilling:* As for the first remark, we have always used the same technique of quenching from air into water and we have observed that stage IV is shifted to lower annealing temperatures with increasing quenching temperatures. Our results agree closely with Jackson's quenching data who has explained the temperature shift by an increasing fraction of frozen-in divacancies.

As for the reduction of the fraction of quenched-in divacancies by irradiation, we have not observed a shift of stage IV due to irradiation. The stage III peaks we found after irradiation are slightly shifted to lower temperatures by prequenching. This fits Dr. Lucasson's observations. It can, however, be explained just as well by the smaller mean number of jumps to annihilation in prequenched samples.

*W.Frank:* How would you explain the enhancement of the small recovery stage slightly above 300°K in deuteron-irradiated platinum due to a prequenching treatment, as found by Jackson and Herschbach?

Moreover, I would like to comment on the fact that more than one peak can be introduced by one kind of impurity atoms in the temperature range of stage II. This may be explained by the release of crowdions which may be trapped in a spectrum of discrete distances by impurity atoms during their free migration in stage $I_E$.

*W.Schilling:* We have not observed such an enhancement in all 4 different runs where we compared the recovery of quenched and unquenched platinum after electron irradiation to various doses. However, we did find that the height of the recovery stage around 300°K observed by Jackson and Herschbach in a single experiment (and not in an earlier one) was very sensitive to residual impurities and disappeared at high doses. In addition, Jackson and Herschbach could not avoid a small amount of deformation when they remounted their samples at room temperature to another sample holder for further annealing.

*K.Isebeck:* We have investigated stage III in Al following a high dose neutron irradiation (Phys. Stat. Sol. 18 (1966) 427). A Meechan-Brinkman analysis revealed a simply activated process in stage III with an activation energy of 0.58 ± 0.03 eV over the *entire* recovery stage. An analysis of the reaction kinetics of isochronals and isothermals revealed a diffusion limited process due to correlated recovery of defects in the initial part of stage III. As the recovery increased, this process merged into a simple second order process.

It should be emphasized in this connection that apart from ordinary straight line tests a further criterion testing the validity of a certain kinetics was used. Stated briefly, we only accepted a certain straight line fit (e.g. $1/\Delta\rho$ versus $t$ for isothermals) if the ratio of the slopes *also* yielded an activation energy in agreement with the Meechan-Brinkman result, which is independent of any model based on reaction kinetics.

*H.I.Dawson:* I would like to make a statement regarding stage $I_E$ after electron irradiation. I do think the substructure of this stage is real, as it has been observed by several investigations. It is, however, superimposed on a background which seems to be due to random interstitial migration. This structure is not observed in Chaplin's curve, nor does one observe a substructure in $I_D$ in this case, while this has been observed in other electrical resistivity as well as in stored energy measurements. I may point out, however, that the way Chaplin has drawn his curve does not do justice to the claimed accuracy. If one takes this accuracy seriously and one connects the clusters of the data points, one observes that even in this work there is an indication for the $I_E$ substructure which is rather similar to that observed by the Northwestern group.

*J.A.Venables:* (1) You have left gold out of your scheme. What do yout feel you can say about stage I in gold?

(2) I have difficulty in visualizing the sink structure in the irradiated prequenched samples in stage III. Do you have electron micrographs which show a duplex structure which could account for the two peaks?

*W.Schilling:* (1) The recovery of gold in the low temperature region is discussed in detail in chapter I.7 of the written version of this review.

(2) We have not followed the recovery of prequenched irradiated samples by electron microscopic observation. Such experiments are in progress. For a more detailed discussion of the sink structure the reader is referred to chapter III.5 of the written version of this review.

*O.Dimitrov:* In your presentation, the requirements which any theory would have to fulfill rely on the state attained by the metal after the completion of each successive stage. For the case of stage II, you have assumed, for the 4°K electron irradiated impure metal, that no detrapping of interstitials from impurities occurs, but only local rearrangements. What are the bases for such an assumption?

*W.Schilling:* I have not excluded partial detrapping from impurities in stage II. However, if all interstitials would be released from their traps, complete recovery would be expected to occur in stage II and no stage III would be observed.

*R.J.Taylor:* I would be interested to know more details of the model involving moving to deeper traps near an impurity in stage II. It is suggested that an interstitial moves with an energy which is higher than its free migrating energy. This would normally occur if it was moving to a position of higher potential energy, and if this was so, it would preferentially stay where it was.

*W.Schilling:* The basic idea of the model discussed in detail, e.g., by A.Sosir. (in: Lattice Defects and Their Interaction, ed. R.R.Hasiguti (Gordon and Breach, New York, 1967) p. 233) is that an interstitial can be trapped near impurities in positions characterized by different binding energies. The deeper trap positions are though to be separated from the more shallow position by energy barriers which can be overcome only at higher temperatures. Therefore, the interstitial is first trapped in the shallow trap A and then can move to the deeper trap B upon thermal activation at higher temperatures. During this process it has also some chance to escape into unbound positions C.

*Wilkes:* Are all impurities equally effective as interstitial traps? Are traps equally effective in trapping vacancies also?

*W.Schilling:* From the fact that different types of foreign atoms yield quite different recovery in stage II, e.g., of alloyed aluminium, in my opinion one has to conclude that different types of impurities have different interactions with interstitials. Vacancies seem to be less affected by the same impurities which trap interstitials strongly. This may be concluded from the weak influence of impurities on the recovery of stage III, e.g., in aluminium or copper.

*O.Dimitrov:* I would like to add a comment on the influence of the nature of the foreign elements on the phenomena taking place in stage II of irradiated impure metals. Actually there have been a few experiments on the effect of various foreign elements in aluminium, in the range of concentrations below 0.1%. This influence can be reasonably well explained by considering the binding energy of the foreign element with interstitials to be mainly of elastic origin and related to the effective size effect of the element. We have shown that this explains the occurrence of an enhanced stage III for elements with a high binding energy, which retain the trapped interstitial up to the temperature range of stage III. [C.Dimitrov-Frois and O.Dimitrov, Mem. Sci. Rev. Met. 65 (1968) 425.]

# PHYSICAL PROPERTIES OF POINT DEFECTS
# IN CUBIC METALS

H.WENZL

*Physik-Department, Technische Hochschule München, Germany*

## 1. Introduction

In structural disordered crystals the atoms are permanently displaced more or less from their ideal positions. The whole arrangement is generally stabilized by potential barriers defined for movements of representative points in configuration space [1]. Even in metals irradiated at low temperature with a high dose of fast particles only few atoms in certain regions are permanently displaced from the ideal positions by large distances of the order of the interatomic separation. Such a localized arrangement of atoms not extending into the lattice in any direction is usually called "point defect". More precisely it can be called the "core field" of the defect comprising typically around 20 atoms. An atomistic treatment is necessary to find the influence of the core field on physical properties of the crystal. A few interatomic distances from the centre of the core field already, the atomic displacements are usually much smaller than the lattice parameter [2]. This region is called "Fernfeld" and extends to the surface of the sample. To describe the Fernfeld effects usually an elastic continuum model of the crystal is used in which the defect is replaced by an arrangement of double forces [3]. E.g., the core field governs the scattering of conduction electrons and thus the electrical resistivity, the Fernfeld gives rise to a volume change, and both Fernfeld and core field influence the elastic susceptibility.

The physical properties of the crystal can be separated into three groups:

a) Properties which are approximately proportional to the concentration or number of defects. E.g., the change of the residual electrical resistivity $\Delta\rho$ is equal to the product of the defect concentration $c_D$ and the resistivity per unit concentration of defects $\rho_D$, which is a specific defect property directly related to the experimental data. It is connected with the more fundamental scattering matrix elements for conduction electrons and thus with the scattering potential, which is based on the particle properties of the core field and the electron wave functions.

Similar physical properties to be discussed are: energy, volume, lattice parameter, elastic modulus, internal friction, neutron scattering cross section, heat conductivity, reciprocal high field Hall coefficient.

The defect concentrations and the different configurations induced by fast particle interaction are not well known until now [4]. The knowledge is better for metals quenched from high temperatures and best for the defects in equilibrium at high temperatures.

In most cases it is, therefore, necessary to combine different measurements to evaluate specific defect properties. Considerable weight must obviously be given to experiments in which the changes of two or more properties were measured simultaneously or by using different samples with identical treatment. In this review, ratios of the different property changes and the corresponding change of the electrical resistivity will be collected to establish at least values for the ratios of specific properties from the experimental data available.

Production of interstitials I and vacancies V by irradiation in a nuclear reactor is particularly suited for this purpose because the irradiation dose can be controlled with a relative accuracy [5] of $10^{-3}$ and the high defect concentrations necessary for most measurements [6] can be reached even in large samples [7] in reasonable time without serious cooling problems at liquid helium temperatures.

Due to the collision processes during particle irradiation, distance correlations between I and V arise. At high electron doses strong correlations between like defects are built up [8]. High doses of fast neutrons lead to a more homogeneous distribution of defects in "light" metals as aluminium; in "heavy" metals (gold, platinum) strong correlations between like defects exist already at low doses and do not seem to build up further during irradiations because each collision cascade destroys the existing and builds up new correlations [8,9]. Therefore, for reaching a high concentration of I and V, electron irradiation has no principle advantage and many practical disadvantages compared with neutron irradiation.

After irradiation at liquid helium temperature the total changes of the physical properties and the changes in annealing stage I will be used to determine Frenkel defect properties [10]. Generally, by measuring property changes in a single annealing stage, the specific properties of the corresponding defect configurations can be determined, although only mean values of property changes over several stages are usually available.

After quenching from high temperatures single and multiple vacancies are present [11]. The equilibrium concentration of V can be calculated from combined lattice parameter and length measurements and gives an upper limit of the total concentration quenched. The evaluation of specific vacancy properties from high temperature equilibrium measurements suffers from the uncertainty of the "base line" [12].

Usually high defect concentrations are necessary for accurate measurements. Therefore, possible interactions between the defects prevent exact determinations of the single defect properties, although the interaction of the defect core fields, which usually govern the behaviour, is usually negligible if the defects are several atomic distances apart; the interactions in the Fernfeld are generally small and will be neglected [13] *.

b) Another group of properties is independent of the concentration of the "predominant" defects and provides specific defect properties directly. Mainly transport properties belong to this group: low field Hall coefficient, relative change of the electrical resistivity in a magnetic field, change of thermopower per resistivity change, relative deviations from Matthiessen's rule.

By measuring the form of the temperature and pressure dependence of the equilibrium vacancy concentration and of the self diffusion coefficient, using a physical property of group a), the formation enthalpy, the volume change, and the activation volume of vacancies can be evaluated [15].

By analysing the kinetics of defect reactions, also using group a) properties, not only the activation enthalpy but also the core field symmetry and local vibrational properties can be studied [15,16].

c) Finally, physical properties exist which depend in a complicated way on the mean concentration and distribution of the defects in the sample, e.g. partly elastic neutron scattering, magnetic properties of superconductors, partly internal friction (interaction of defects with dislocations), critical shear stress [17].

In such cases specific defect properties cannot be defined. E.g., distance correlation functions can be used to describe the influence of the defects on the physical properties.

Only in few cases theories exist which are capable of predicting quantitatively the properties of the simplest types of defects. Even in the case of a simple metal like copper the energy or resistivity of vacancies or interstitials is uncertain by 50%. This uncertainty arises from the model of the defect and the lack of knowledge about the interatomic potentials, electron wavefunctions, and band structure.

To avoid becoming involved in theoretical uncertainties, specific defect properties will be defined which are related as directly as possible to the experimental data (e.g. resistivity per unit concentration). Such defect properties are usually very complex on a theoretical viewpoint.

Since it is not intended to collect experimental data only, relations between different defect properties and their connections with more fundamental solid state parameters will be mentioned where it is possible and useful.

* Interactions due to changes of lattice vibrations are not considered in [13] but may be important. See [14] for a discussion of defect interactions via Friedel oscillations.

## 2. Stored energy

### 2.1. Concepts

The change of the internal energy of a metal caused by point defects can be divided into two parts (in principle one has to use *enthalpies*, but the difference is negligible for the cases discussed in this chapter):

$$Q = C(E_D^S + E_D^V) = CE_D , \qquad (1)$$

where $Q$ is the heat release per atom due to disappearance of $C$ defects per atom, $E_D^S$ the contribution of the static disorder and $E_D^V$ that of the vibrations and thermal excitations to the stored energy per defect. Interactions between defects are neglected or, if the interaction energy is not negligible, a new defect type is defined (e.g. double vacancies etc.).

In the quasiharmonic model of lattice vibrations $E_D^V$ can be related to changes of the phonon spectrum $g(\omega)$ arising from the anharmonic parts of the lattice potential *.

Correspondingly $E_D^V$ contains two additive terms: the change of the zero point vibrational energy per defect $E_D^O$ and the change of the thermal energy at finite temperatures per defect $E_D^{th}$, which can be expressed by the change of the lattice specific heat $\Delta c$ (thermal energy per atom and °K):

$$E_D^V(T) = E_D^O + \frac{1}{C} \int_0^T \Delta c \, dT . \qquad (2)$$

Fig. 1 shows how these terms depend on the vibrational spectrum **.

According to thermodynamic relations $E_D^{th}$ is connected with the vibrational entropy of formation of the defects $S_D$ [18]. $S_D$ is temperature independent for temperatures above the Debye temperature.

The "static" part of the stored energy $E_D^S$ can be separated in a somewhat artificial but useful way into several additive terms. The contribution caused by changes of the ion positions in the core field must be treated atomistically and generally contains the overwhelming part of the stored energy, whereas the Fernfeld contribution can be treated by elasticity theory [13,19].

The stored energy per defect in the Fernfeld is related to the volume change per defect $v_D$ caused by distortions and is of the order of $v_D^2 G/10v_o$ if the core field contains about 40 atoms, where $v_o$ is the atomic volume and $G$ a typical elastic mo-

---

* In principle also changes of the excitations of the conduction electrons must be considered. The relative change of the coefficient of the electron specific heat is of the order of the relative volume change induced by the defects, which is roughly equal to the defect concentration. Therefore, the change of the electron thermal energy is of the order of $10^{-8}$ eV$(T/°K)^2$ for the metals under discussion and negligible (see table 1).

** The relative difference between the measured specific heat at constant pressure and that at constant volume, connected directly with the phonon spectrum, is $10^{-4}$ and negligible.

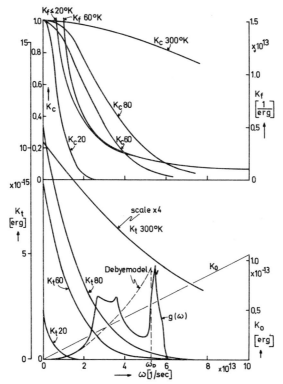

Fig. 1. Phonon density of states of aluminium $g(\omega)$ (arbitrary linear scale) as a function of the phonon frequency $\omega$ [140] and weighing factors for the evaluation of physical properties depending on the spectrum. Zero point vibrational energy per atom $E_0 = (1/N) \int K_0 \, g(\omega) \, d\omega$ ($N$ denotes the number of atoms), thermal energy per atom $E_t = (1/N) \int K_t g(\omega) \, d\omega$, specific heat $C = (1/N) \, k \int K_c g(\omega) \, d\omega$, Lamb-Mössbauer factor for the case where the mean square vibrational amplitude of the nucleus correponds to the overall phonon spectrum $f = \exp[-(R/3N) \times \int K_f g(\omega) \, d\omega]$, where $R$ is the recoil energy (see [134]) and $3N$ is the number of phonon modes.

dulus [13,14,20]. The contribution of the conduction electrons to $E_D^S$ can be separated into the following parts:

$$E_D^{S \ el} = -\tfrac{2}{5} \, \epsilon_F \, q \, \frac{v_D^{tot}}{v_0} + U + S \,, \tag{3}$$

where $v_D^{tot}$ is the total volume change by the defect, $q$ the valency of the metal, $\epsilon_F$ the Fermi energy [21,22,23]. The first term arises from the free electron approximation, the second term $U$ takes account of possible changes of the pseudo-potential; $U$ is unknown but probably small [23,24].

In addition the energy of the conduction electrons is changed due to local rearrangements in the core field, which shield the perturbing potential. In the free electron and Born approximation the energy change per defect caused by this shielding effect is $S = -\frac{2}{3} Z_{\text{eff}} \, \epsilon_F$, where $Z_{\text{eff}}$ is the effective local charge to be shielded (e.g., $Z_{\text{eff}} \approx -q$ for a vacancy, $Z_{\text{eff}} \lesssim +q$ for an interstitial; critical discussion see e.g. [21, 25]; for more general expressions see [22]). Thus $\epsilon_F \, q$ seems to be a natural unit in which to measure the electron part of the stored energy of defects, at least of vacancies [25]. A relation exists between the Debye temperature $\theta$ as a measure of the ion-ion interaction and the electronic part of the vacancy formation energy $E_V$ [25,26], namely

$$\theta = \text{const.} \; \frac{E_V^{\frac{1}{2}}}{M^{\frac{1}{2}} \, v_0^{\frac{1}{3}}} \; , \tag{4}$$

where $M$ is the atomic mass. Fig. 2 shows that eq. (4) is confirmed by experiment and can be used as a rule of thumb to determine unknown vacancy energies.

## 2.2. Copper

The energy of point defects is usually determined by measuring the heat release on a sample during warming up, where the heat release is caused by the annihilation of the defects (see fig. 5).

Fig. 3 presents an example of such a measurement after reactor neutron irradiation [27] at 4.6°K.

In fig. 4 all available measurements on low temperature irradiated samples are collected, which allow to calculate ratios of the heat release in the annealing stages and the corresponding decrease of the electrical resistivity $\Delta Q/\Delta \rho$.

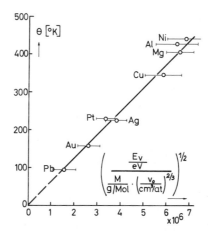

Fig. 2. Semiempirical relation between the formation energy of vacancies $E_V^F$, Debye temperature $\theta$, atomic mass $M$ and atomic volume $v_0$. According to this relation the different points should lie on a straight line.

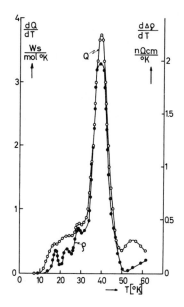

Fig. 3. *Copper.* Heat release and resistivity annealing during continuous warm-up (0.3°K/min) after reactor neutron irradiation at 4.6°K (total residual resistivity change $\Delta\rho_0 = 59\,n\Omega$ cm). Both samples, for heat release and for resistivity measurement, were treated together in a completely identical way in a differential heatflux calorimeter [27].

Remarks:

a) The values of blocks 1 and 6 in fig. 4 seem to be the most reliable ones, because they are based on several measurements with identical treatment of the samples used for the calorimetric and resistivity measurements *.

By using reactor neutron irradiation to introduce defects one can deal with thick samples, whereas in the case of foils, as used for electron irradiation, adsorption or desorption heats of gases at the surface of the samples nearly prohibit reliable calorimetric measurements.

b) According to the most reliable value of the energy-resistivity ratio in stage I (fig. 4)

$$\frac{\Delta Q}{\Delta\rho} = \frac{C_F\,E^F}{C_F\,\rho_F} = \left(\frac{4.6}{250} \pm 5\%\right)\ \frac{eV}{\mu\Omega\ cm}, \qquad (5)$$

---

* The old values of $\Delta Q/\Delta\rho$ for neutron irradiation of the Blewitt group [28] were approximately a factor of two lower than the values of other groups for deuteron irradiation (see fig. 4), which caused considerable confusion in literature [28–31]. The old Blewitt values are probably erroneous. They have recently been revised in new measurements of the same group [33].

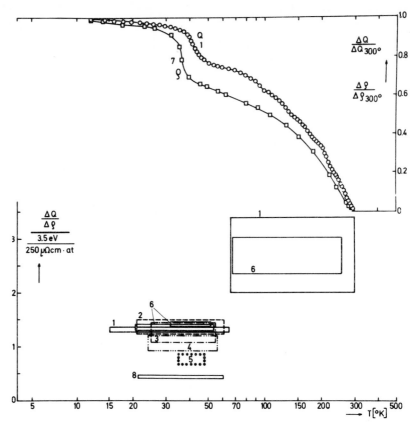

Fig. 4. *Copper.* Lower part: Ratio of heat release per atom $\Delta Q$ during a linear rise of temperature with time ($0(1°K/\text{min})$) and residual resistivity change $\Delta\rho$ after irradiation at low temperatures. The horizontal dimensions of the blocks indicate the temperature range of annealing used for calculating the ratio $\Delta Q/\Delta\rho$, the vertical dimensions the error quoted by the authors.

Characteristics of the different groups (reference, irradiation type, number of measurements, total residual resistivity change):

    (1) [94] reactor neutrons; 2; 16 $n\Omega$ cm;
    (2) [95] electrons; 1; 2 $n\Omega$ cm;
    (3) [30] deuterons; 2; 6 $n\Omega$ cm;
    (4) [96] electrons; 1; 5 $n\Omega$ cm;
    (5) [28] reactor neutrons; 2; 5 $n\Omega$ cm;
    (6) [27] reactor neutrons; 2; 60 $n\Omega$ cm;
    (7) [97] reactor neutrons; 41 $n\Omega$ cm;
    (8) [31] vapour deposition at 20°K.

In measurements (1) and (6) the ratio was calculated by using results on samples, which were treated together in a completely identical way.

Upper part: Stored energy during heating ($1°K/\text{min}$) and annealing of residual resistivity (10 min isochronals) normalized to total annealing between 4°K and 300°K and plotted as a function of annealing temperature. $\Delta Q_{300°K} = 43$ Wsec/Mol, corresponding resistivity change

$$\Delta\rho_{300°K} = 16.5 \ n\Omega \text{ cm, total resistivity change } \Delta\rho_{\text{tot}} = 41 \ n\Omega \text{ cm.}$$

where $C_F$ is the number of Frenkel defects (FD) per atom annihilated in stage I, $E_F$ the energy per FD in the stage I temperature region, $\rho_F$ the resistivity change per unit concentration of FD at $4°$K, $\Delta Q$ the heat release per atom in stage I, $\Delta\rho$ the corresponding resistivity decrease at $4°$K.

Larger values of the ratio $\Delta Q/\Delta\rho$ are observed above stage I (fig. 4), which could be explained if the resistivity change is comparatively small during the agglomeration of like defects in this temperature region [10]. But the results of the lattice parameter measurements contradict this explanation. The observed effect can also be explained by the temperature dependence of the FD-energy (see below).

c) Only few measurements of the influence of FD on the specific heat are known [27]. After reactor neutron irradiation at $4°$K and annealing at $20°$K or $60°$K the experiment showed $\Delta c/c(14°K) = O(0.05)$ for defects with $\Delta\rho \approx 20\,n\Omega$ cm $\hat{\approx} 10^{-4}$ FD/atom annealing above $60°$K (see also chapter 6 and fig. 5).

According to eq. (2) $E_F^{th}(20°K) = 0\,(10^{-2}\ \text{eV})$.

If the Debye model is used for an order of magnitude evaluation of the corresponding $E_F^0$ (see eq. (2) and fig. 1), $E_F^0 = 0\,(-1\ \text{eV})$, which is of the order of $E_F$ it-

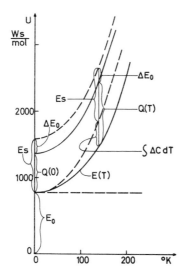

Fig. 5. *Copper*. Semischematic plot of different energies as a function of temperature: $E_s$ = static part of the stored energy, $\Delta E_0$ = change of the zero point energy due to defects, $Q(T)$ = heat release during annealing as a function of the annealing temperature, $\int_0^T \Delta c\,dT$ = change of thermal energy due to defects at the temperature $T$, $E_0$ = zero point energy of the defect free sample, $E(T)$ = vibrational thermal energy as a function of temperature without defects.

self (see table 1). But one must keep in mind that information about the change of the high frequency phonon modes, which enter with greater weighing factors, is not available.

A value $E_F^{th} > 0$ corresponds to a positive formation entropy $S_F^F$ (during isothermal production of the defects heat flows into the sample due to the softening of the phonon modes; see also table 1).

Obviously the overwhelming part of the theoretical statements about the relative stability of different defect types and also about the interaction energies may be misleading, because the vibrational energies are generally neglected in the theoretical calculations.

d) By means of equilibrium measurements at high temperatures the vacancy formation energy has been deduced [32] as $E_{1V}^F(T \gg \theta) = 1.17 \pm 0.11$ eV (see also table 1). Since the defect energies may depend on the temperature it is recommended to note the temperature range used for the determination and be careful in using these values at other temperatures.

## 2.3. Aluminium

In fig. 6 the ratio of the heat release during warming up after low temperature irradiation and the corresponding residual resistivity change is plotted for the stage I, II and III annealing region separately.

With the exception of the data of ref. [28], which are probably erroneous (see also chapter 2.2), all measurements agree. Reproducible changes of the specific heat could not be found ($|\Delta c|/c < 0.02$ for $\Delta \rho \approx 30$ n$\Omega$ cm, annealing above stage I [34]), although other evidence (see chapter 4) indicates a softening of the phonon modes at low frequencies due to irradiation.

The ratios in stages I, II and III are equal, which may be accidental, but it may be also taken as evidence for the weakness of the binding between interstitials, because interstitial clusters are probably involved in the annealing stages II and III [10]. All data pertaining to Frenkel defects, interstitials, and vacancies are collected in table 1.

## 2.4. Niobium

Fig. 7 presents ratios of stored energy and resistivity for niobium after 4°K reactor neutron irradiation [35]. Niobium is the prototype of a type II superconductor and therefore of special interest (see chapters 5 and 7). As in copper and iron [36] the ratios increase with increasing annealing temperature, a behaviour not yet understood. It may be due to the temperature dependence of the Frenkel defect energy.

For the temperature range from 4°K to 50°K the mean ratio is

$$\frac{\Delta Q}{\Delta \rho} = \left(\frac{8.4}{1000} \pm 10\%\right) \frac{\text{eV}}{\mu\Omega \text{ cm}}.$$

The value $E_F^F \approx 10$ eV would be consistent with the empirical relation valid for copper and aluminium, that the ratio of $E_F^F$ and the binding energy per atom $E^B$ is a

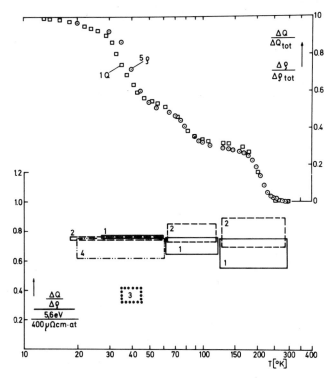

Fig. 6. *Aluminium.* Lower part: Ratio of heat release per atom $\Delta Q$ during warm-up (O(1°K/min)) and residual resistivity change $\Delta \rho$ after irradiation at low temperatures. Cf. caption of fig. 4 for further explanations.

      (1) [98] reactor neutrons; 3; 130 nΩ cm;
      (2) [34] reactor neutrons; 1;
      (3) [28] reactor neutrons; 1;
      (4) [95] electrons; 1;
      (5) [97] reactor neutrons; 135 nΩ cm.

Upper part: Stored energy during heating (1°K/min) and residual resistivity during isochronal annealing (10 min holding time), normalized to total changes, plotted as a function of annealing temperature; $\Delta Q_{tot}$ = 124 Wsec/Mol, corresponding resistivity change $\Delta \rho_{tot}$ = 135 nΩ cm.

constant (see table 1). Then $\rho_F \approx 1000 \, \mu\Omega$ cm per unit concentration of FD, which also agrees roughly with the general observation, that the ratio $\rho_F / \rho_\theta$, where $\rho_\theta$ is the resistivity at the Debye temperature, is a constant. The specific heat measurements resulted in $\Delta c / c (30°K) = 0.05 \pm 0.03$ for $\Delta \rho \approx 700$ nΩ cm ($\approx 5 \times 10^{-4}$ defects/atom) annealing above 100°K. Therefore, vibrational defect energies are probably as important as in copper and not negligible.

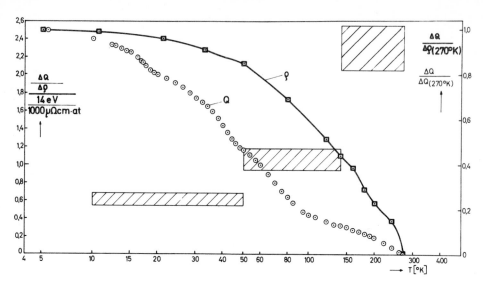

Fig. 7. *Niobium*. Blocks: Ratio of heat release per atom $\Delta Q$ during a linear rise of temperature with time $(0(1°K/min))$ and corresponding residual resistivity change $\Delta\rho$ after irradiation with reactor neutrons at $4.6°K$ [35] (cf. fig. 4 for further explanations).

Curves: Annealing of stored energy and residual resistivity change, normalized to total annealing between $4°K$ and $270°K$, plotted as a function of annealing temperature. $\Delta Q_{270°K} = 261$ Wsec/Mol, corresponding resistivity change $\Delta\rho_{270°K} = 167.7$ n$\Omega$ cm. Total resistivity change $\Delta\rho_{tot} = 222$ n$\Omega$ cm. As new measurements have shown [163], the details of the annealing curves sensitively depend on the content of desolved gases in the otherwise pure samples.

## 2.5. *Gold*

Resistivity and length change [37] and the release of stored energy [38] have been measured by different authors after quenching.

These experiments permit to determine the volume, resistivity, and energy of vacancies (see table 1), although systematic errors due to formation of double vacancies during the cooling-down process cannot be excluded. Results:

$$Q = 2 \frac{eV}{atom} \exp[-(0.97 \pm 0.10 \text{ eV})/kT] \ ,$$

$$\Delta\rho = (490 \pm 100)\,\mu\Omega \text{ cm} \exp[-(0.98 \pm 0.03 \text{ eV})/kT] \ .$$

According to equilibrium experiments [39]

$$C_V = e^1 \exp[-(0.94 \pm 0.09)eV/kT] \ ,$$

and

$$\frac{\Delta L}{\Delta \rho} = \frac{1}{330} \frac{1}{\mu\Omega\,\mathrm{cm}},$$

(see chapter 3).

Similar experiments on irradiated samples are not known (see also ref. [160]).

### 2.6. Iron

Resistivity change and stored energy release have been measured after electron and neutron irradiation [36]. The ratio of stored energy release and resistivity decrease in the main low temperature annealing stage around 100°K (called $I_D$ in [36]) is smaller for electron compared with reactor neutron irradiation by a factor of two. Before the reproducibility will have been checked, one should not take this difference too serious. According to the rules of thumb (table 1) and the remarks in chapter 2.2 the results after neutron irradiation are more reliable and are shown in table 1.

### 2.7. Conclusions

In table 1 all data are summarized together with some plausible relations (see also fig. 2) providing estimates for unknown quantities. It would be worthwhile to discuss the theoretical basis of these relations. A discussion of calorimetric methods, especially of the heat flux calorimeter, can be found in [35] (see also [28]).

## 3. Volume and lattice parameter change

### 3.1. Concepts

In cubic crystals with a random distribution of defects, the well known relations hold [39]:

$$\frac{\Delta V}{V} = 3\frac{\Delta l}{l} \equiv L = C_V - C_I + C_V \frac{v_V}{v_0} + C_I \frac{v_I}{v_0}, \tag{6}$$

where $\Delta V/V$ is the relative change of volume of a finite sample, $\Delta l/l$ the relative change of length of the sample due to a concentration $C_V$ and $C_I$ of interstitials and vacancies, $v_V$, $v_I$ are the volume changes of a finite sample due to the lattice distortions in the Fernfeld of a vacancy and an interstitial, respectively [40]. The lattice parameter is defined for a homogeneous distribution of defects only, for which a new reference lattice for the crystal can be defined [40,41]. The relative lattice parameter change $\Delta a/a$ is related to the lattice distortions by

$$3\frac{\Delta a}{a} \equiv A = C_V \frac{v_V}{v_0} + C_I \frac{v_I}{v_0}. \tag{7}$$

Table 1

Survey of physical properties discussed in this review. The lines 1–8 and 18 contain experimental values. The lines 21 and 22 show a certain relation between Frenkel defect properties and binding energy $E_B$ and resistivity at the Debye temperature $\rho_\theta$. These relations were used to postulate 21/Pt and 22/Fe. The numbers in the lines 11–17 and 19, 20 have the same order of magnitude for different metals and can also be used as a rule of thumb to estimate unknown data (for $c < 10^{-3}$). The values of 13/14 and 15/16/17 are related according to chapter 6. In rows 23–30 plausible and self-consistent defect properties are collected (see also refs. [157,158].

| Properties | Al | Cu | Ag | Au | Pt | Nb | W | Fe |
|---|---|---|---|---|---|---|---|---|
| 1 $\Delta Q/\Delta\rho$ (I) eV/$\mu\Omega$ cm | 3.8/400 | 4.6/250 | | | | 8.4/1000 | | 4.2/1000 |
| 2 $\Delta A/\Delta\rho$ (I) 1/$\mu\Omega$ cm | 1.6/400 | 1.9/250 | | $\Delta L/\Delta\rho$ (V): 1/330 | | | | |
| 3 $v_0 \Delta M_d/\Delta\rho$ (I) eV/$\mu\Omega$ cm | −140/400 | −150/250 | | | | | | |
| 4 $v_0 \Delta M_d/\Delta\rho$ (V) eV/$\mu\Omega$ cm | −16/220 | | | | −400/600 | | | |
| 5 $\Delta S_e/\Delta\rho$ (V) $\mu V$/$\mu\Omega$ cm °K | | | | −0.93 (200°K) | 0.64 (350°K) | | | |
| 6 $\Delta S_p/\Delta\rho$ (V) $\mu V$/$\mu\Omega$ cm °K | | | | −5.6 (40°K) | −0.92 (150°K) | | | |
| 6' $\Delta S_p/\Delta\rho$ (V) $\mu V$/$\mu\Omega$ cm °K | | | | −16.7 (20°K) | −1.84 (100°K) | | | |
| 7 $V_A/v_0$ | 1.3 | 0.91 | 0.90 | | | | | |
| 8 $S/k$ (V) | 0.75 | 0.5 ± 0.2 | 1.5 ± 0.5 | 1.2 ± 0.2 | | | | |
| 9 $a (I_n; V_{1,n})$ | | 0(0.04) | | | | | | |
| 10 $\beta (I_n; V_{1,n})$ | 0(0.1) | 0(0.1) | 0(0.1) | 0(0.1) | 0(0.1) | | | 0(0.1) |
| 11 $\Delta V/V C_F$ (F) | 1.6 | 1.9 | | | | | | |
| 12 $\Delta V/V C_V$ (V) | 1.0 | | | | | | | |
| 13 $\Delta M_d/M C_F$ (F) | −44 | −38 | | | −66 | | <0 | |
| 14 $\Delta M_d/M C_V$ (V) | −5 | | | | | | <−5 | |
| 15 $\Delta\theta_\rho/\theta_\rho C_V$ (V) | | | | 0(−10²) | | | | |

Table 1 (continued)

| Properties | Al | Cu | Ag | Au | Pt | Nb | W | Fe |
|---|---|---|---|---|---|---|---|---|
| 16 $\Delta\theta_\rho/\theta_\rho\,C\,(I_n; V_{1,n})$ | | 0(-10²) | | | | | | |
| 17 $\Delta\theta_D/\theta_D\,C\,(I_n; V_{1,n})$ | | 0(-10²) | | | | 0(-10²) | | |
| 18 $3\,\Delta p_{max}/\mathrm{tr}\,p\,(I)$ | 0(1/10) | | | | | | 0(1/5) | 0(1/5) |
| 19 $\Delta S_e/S_e\,C_V\,(V)$ | | | | -86 (200°K) | -20 (350°K) | | | |
| 20 $\Delta S_p/S_p\,C_V\,(V)$ | | | | -130 (30°K) | -70 (125°K) | | | |
| 21 $E_F/E_B\,(F)$ | 1.2 | 1.3 | | | | 1.3 | | 0.98 |
| 22 $\rho_F/\rho_\theta\,(F)$ | 100 | 125 | | | 75 | 120 | | 100 |
| 23 $E_F$ eV (F) | 3.8 | 4.6 | | | | 10 | | 4.2 |
| 24 $E_V$ eV (V) | 0.76 | 1.05 | 1.09 | 0.96 | | | | |
| 25 $v_F/v_o\,(F)$ | 1.6 | 1.9 | | | | | | |
| 26 $v_V/v_o\,(V)$ | 0 | -0.2 | -0.06 | -0.55 ± 0.10 | | | | |
| 27 $\rho_F$ (F) $\mu\Omega$ cm p.u.c. | 400 | 250 | | | 600 | 1200 | | 1000 |
| 28 $\alpha_F$ eV (F) | -140 | -150 | | | -400 | | | |
| 29 $\alpha_V$ eV (V) | -16 | | | | | | | |
| 30 $\rho_V$ (V) $\mu\Omega$ cm p.u.c. | 220 | 160 | 130 ± 70 | 150 ± 30 | | | | |

Remarks: The concentration is always in defects/atom. (F) = Frenkel defect, (V) = vacancy, (I) = stage I. The interstitial properties can be determined from rows 23–30 by subtracting the V- from the F-data. $I_n$, $V_n$ = multiple interstitials and vacancies. Instead of the number in 27/Fe also 1600 is used [69]. The values of line 8 are from [6,15,32,42,43], those of 10 from [97]. All errors range between 5% and 10% if not quoted. For influence of radiation induced defects on thermopower see [156].

The difference $A - L = C_I - C_V$ is already a semispecific property, which is zero only for defect reactions in which the number of lattice positions of the sample does not change. From equilibrium measurements of the lattice parameter and length as a function of temperature $v_V$ cannot be determined since the defect free value of the thermal expansion (the "base line") is not known accurately enough (see also [12]).

Further information on lattice distortions can be obtained by elastic scattering of neutrons, which react only on lattice disorder. The differential scattering cross section per unit solid angle extrapolated to zero scattering vector $\varkappa = \mathbf{k}' - \mathbf{k}$ ($\mathbf{k}'$,$\mathbf{k}$ neutron wave vector after and before scattering) is (see detailed discussion in [44])

$$\frac{d\sigma}{d\Omega}(\kappa \to 0) = a_{coh}^2 \left[ C_I \left(1 - \frac{v_I}{\gamma v_0}\right)^2 + C_V \left(1 + \frac{v_V}{\gamma v_0}\right)^2 \right] , \qquad (8)$$

where $\gamma = 3(1-v)/(1+v)$, $v$ is Poisson's ratio, and $a_{coh}$ is the coherent scattering length, which is known for many nuclei. If the defects would induce no distortions (i.e. $v_V = v_I = 0$), the sum $C_I + C_V$ could be determined directly by scattering experiments.

The angular dependence of the scattering cross section near the Bragg directions (Huang tails) is also related to $v_V, v_I, C_V$, and $C_I$, but in a different way [44].

Hence, for Frenkel defects ($C_V = C_I = C_F$) there are in principle three independent relations available for determining the three unknown quantities $C_F, v_V, v_I$. In practice it will be very difficult to get rid of the influence of defect correlations on the scattering intensity, especially near $\kappa \approx 0$ and $\kappa \approx \tau$ ($\tau$ is $2\pi$ times a reciprocal lattice vector).

The value of $v_V$ is related to the pressure dependence of the vacancy equilibrium concentration $C_V$ [15] by

$$\frac{\partial \ln C_V}{\partial p} = v_V + v_0 .$$

It is also part of the activation volume defined by the pressure dependence of the diffusion coefficient for a vacancy diffusion mechanism [45], namely

$$-\frac{\partial \ln (D/a^2 v)}{\partial p} = \frac{V_A}{kT} \qquad (9)$$

with

$$V_A = v_V + v_0 + v_m ,$$

where $v_m$ is the additional volume change in the "activated state"; probably $v_m \gtrsim 0$.

## 3.2. Aluminium

In fig. 8 the ratios of lattice parameter and volume changes and the corresponding

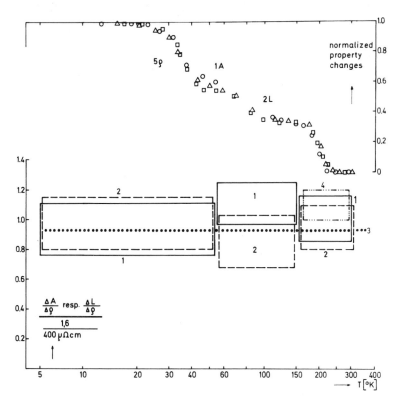

Fig. 8. *Aluminium.* Upper part: Isochronal annealing curves (10 min holding time) of residual resistivity $\Delta\rho$ and lattice parameter change $\Delta A$ (see eq. (7), measured at 10°K) and annealing curves of length change $\Delta L$ (eq. (6)), measured during warming up (0(1°K/min)), normalized to total changes plotted versus annealing temperature.
Lower part: Ratio of lattice parameter or length change and corresponding resistivity change for the three annealing stages (cf. fig. 4 for further explanations).

        (1) [99]  $A$; reactor neutrons; 330 nΩ cm;
        (2) [98]  $L$; reactor neutrons; 240 nΩ cm;
        (3) [28]  $L$; $a$-particles; 280 nΩ cm;
        (4) [100] $A$; reactor neutrons; 430 nΩ cm;
        (5) [97]  $\rho$; reactor neutrons.

residual resistivity change after low temperature irradiation are collected. The ratios agree with regard to different authors, different types of irradiation, different annealing stages, and also with regard to $L$ and $A$, although the experimental errors allow considerable differences (0(20%)) of the concentration of interstitials and vacancies annealing in the stages I, II and III.

This shows that combined $A$ and $L$ measurements require precision methods not yet available, before reliable conclusions about the value of $\Delta C_I - \Delta C_V$ during annealing can be drawn. It must be kept in mind, that also during agglomeration of equal defects * $\Delta A$ is equal to $\Delta L$ as long as the number of lattice positions in the sample does not change. A change of this number can be expected only for very large agglomerates, which collapse to Frank dislocation loops [46].

According to fig. 8,

$$\frac{v_F}{v_0 \, \rho_F} = \frac{\Delta A}{\Delta \rho}\bigg|_{st. \, I} = \left(\frac{1.6}{400} \pm 10\%\right) \frac{1}{\mu\Omega \, cm} \, . \tag{10}$$

In a series of experiments the elastic scattering cross section of sub-thermal neutrons on samples neutron irradiated at 4°K was measured [44,47] (fig. 9):

$$\frac{d\sigma/d\Omega \, (\kappa \to 0)}{\Delta \rho} = \left(\frac{117}{400} \pm 10\%\right) \frac{mb/sr}{\mu\Omega \, cm} \, . \tag{11}$$

By combining eqs. (6) and (7) (with $C_I = C_V$) and eqs. (10) and (11) a relation between $v_I$ and $v_V$ can be formulated, which is displayed in fig. 10.

The maximum value of $v_V$ is 0.3 $v_0$ according to measurements of the activation volume [45].

The smallest possible $v_V$ in fig. 10 is $-0.4 \, v_0$ assuming that the interstitials do not give rise to a resistivity change and that therefore $\rho_F \approx \rho_V \approx 220 \, \mu\Omega cm$ per vacancy/atom (table 1). Scattering interference between I and V, which could reduce $\rho_F$ even below $\rho_V$, can probably be neglected, because I and V cannot come closer than the spontaneous recombination volume allows (several atomic distances [92]).

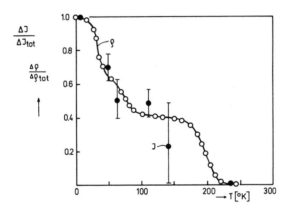

Fig. 9. *Aluminium.* Change of residual resistivity $\Delta\rho$ and neutron scattering intensity $\Delta I$ (extrapolated to zero scattering vector $\kappa$) during isochronal annealing (10 min holding time) plotted as a function of annealing temperature after neutron irradiation at 4.6°K, normalized to total changes $\Delta\rho_{tot} = 600 \, n\Omega \, cm$, $\Delta I_{tot} = 30$ impulses/min $\triangleq d\sigma/d\Omega = (0.18 \pm 10\%)$ mb/sr.

* The quantities $\Delta A$ and $\Delta L$ denote changes of $A$ and $L$ due to reactions of the defects.

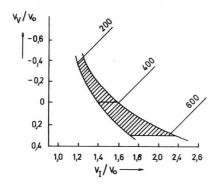

Fig. 10. *Aluminium*. Relation between the volume changes due to lattice distortions by vacancies ($v_V$) and by interstitials ($v_I$) according to eqs. (6), (7), (10) and (11). Parameter: Change of electrical resistivity per unit concentration of Frenkel defects $\rho_F$ ($\mu\Omega$ cm). The atomic volume is indicated by $v_0$. The area of presumable values for the lattice parameter and neutron scattering measurements is shaded. Lower and upper limits for $v_V/v_0$ are discussed in chapter 3.2.

According to the very large value of the activation volume [45] ($V_A = 1.3 v_0$) (see eq. (9)) and theoretical considerations [14], which show that the electron charge oscillations around the vacancy induce forces pushing the surrounding ions radially outwards, away from the vacancy, $v_V$ is probably $> 0$ with a maximum value $v_V = V_A$ (eq. (9)). For $0 < v_V < 0.3 \, v_0$ the range of the other values would be (fig. 10) $1.4 \, v_0 < v_I < 2.1 \, v_0$ and $400 < \rho_F < 600 \, \mu\Omega$ cm per unit concentration, i.e. $180 < \rho_I < 380 \, \mu\Omega$ cm p.u.c. In table 1 all defect properties deduced from these data are based on the assumption $\rho_V = 400 \, \mu\Omega$ cm p.u.c. The ratio $\rho_I/\rho_V \approx 2.0$ was extracted from a detailed analysis of the reaction kinetics of stage III after irradiation with and without prequenching [48]. But this value disagrees with the data in table 1 and is probably wrong, because the defect configurations and accordingly the reaction coefficients are different for the two different treatments [10], which was neglected in the analysis.

Only one experiment is known [49] where the influence of defects on the expansion coefficient has been studied between 20 and 80°K. Defects annealing above 100°K ($\Delta\rho \approx 100$ n$\Omega$ cm) after 4°K reactor neutron irradiation gave rise to an increase of the length of the sample which is roughly 30% larger at 80°K than at 10°K. This increase of the thermal expansion caused by the defects can be discussed in terms of a simple anharmonic potential [50,51], for which the thermal expansion coefficient depends on $gc/f^2$, where $f$ is the coefficient of the harmonic term (spring constant), $g$ is the coefficient of the anharmonic term in the expansion of the potential, $c$ the specific heat.

The spring constant $f$ is probably decreased by the presence of the defects (see chapter 4); $c$ is probably increased (see chapter 2). Both effects change the expansion coefficient in the sense observed. The value of $g$ may change, too (see also [52]).

### 3.3. *Copper*

In fig. 11 the experimental results of the ratios of lattice parameter and volume change and the corresponding residual resistivity change after low temperature irradiation are plotted. The apparent differences are probably due to systematic errors, which are likely to arise if the ratios are calculated using samples with not completely identical treatment.

The data of the blocks number 1 in fig. 11 are based on three independent measurements and are probably free of such errors. Therefore the respective ratios

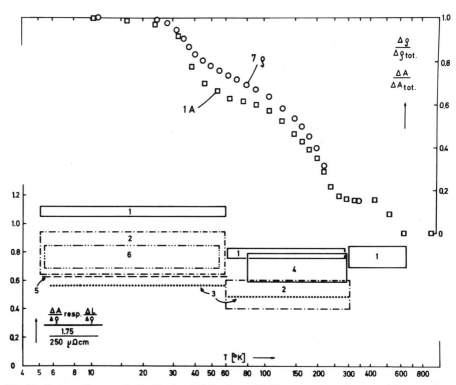

Fig. 11. *Copper.* Upper part: Residual resistivity $\Delta\rho$ and lattice parameter change $\Delta A$ (measured at 10°K) during isochronal annealing after neutron irradiation at 4.6°K, normalized to total changes, plotted as a function of temperature ($\Delta\rho_{tot}$ = 200 nΩ cm; $\Delta A_{tot}$ = (1.13 ± 0.05) $10^{-3}$). Lower part: Ratios of lattice parameter or length change and the corresponding resistivity change for the different annealing regions (cf. fig. 4 for further explanations).

(1) [101] $A$, reactor neutrons; 3 measurements, $\Delta\rho_{tot}$ = 100 nΩ cm;
(2) [102] $A$, deuterons, 1; 180 nΩ cm;
(3) [28] $L$, α-particles, 1; 50 nΩ cm;
(4) [103] $L$, reactor neutrons; 1; 205 nΩ cm;
(5) [104] $L$, deuterons; 1; 200 nΩ cm;
(6) [105] $L$, electrons; 1; 5 nΩ cm;
(7) [97] $\rho$, reactor neutrons; 200 nΩ cm.

seem to be the most reliable ones:

$$\left.\frac{\Delta A}{\Delta \rho}\right|_{\text{st. I}} = \frac{v_F}{v_o \, \rho_F} = \left(\frac{1.9}{250} \pm 5\%\right) \frac{1}{\mu\Omega \, \text{cm}} . \tag{12}$$

Length and lattice parameter changes on samples with identical treatment have been measured only once and in stage III only (fig. 11). $\Delta L$ and $\Delta A$ agree, although the experimental errors allow a 20% deviation favouring interstitial agglomeration into Frank dislocation loops.

As one can see in fig. 11,

$$\left.\frac{\Delta A}{\Delta \rho}\right|_{\text{st. I}} > \left.\frac{\Delta A}{\Delta \rho}\right|_{\text{st. II, III}} \approx \left.\frac{\Delta A}{\Delta \rho}\right|_{\text{st. V}} .$$

Together with the results on stored energy (chapter 2.2) this shows that (see [10])

$$\left.\frac{\Delta Q}{\Delta A}\right|_{\text{st. II, III}} > \frac{E_F}{v_F/v_o} .$$

Due to the lack of knowledge on the defect reactions further conclusions are not possible now.

The ratio for stage V pertains to I- and V-Frank loops disappearing there [9,53]. The experimental value above shows that the relative volume decrease during agglomeration of I or V is larger than the relative resistivity decrease.


## 4. Elastic susceptibility

### 4.1. Concepts

The reaction of the disordered lattice applying static or low frequency ($\omega \ll \omega_R$) dynamic stress can be described by the elastic modulus tensor $M$ ($\omega_R$ is the resonance frequency of the defect [19]). The elastic susceptibility $\chi$ of the defects is defined as the change of $M$ induced by the presence of the defects and is also a tensor of the same type as $M$ if the defects are distributed at random in the lattice [54]. Otherwise the cubic symmetry of the sample may be destroyed, resulting in more than three independent $\chi$-components [55]. Three different contributions to $\chi$ must be distinguished:

a) Defects can pin dislocations, which causes an increase of $M$. Experiments where these effects are important will not be discussed.

b) If crystallographically equivalent defect positions split in energy under the applied strain $\epsilon$ the defects redistribute themselves among the available positions with a certain relaxation time $\tau$. This gives rise to an additional length change and correspondingly to a modulus decrease. The "parelastic" susceptibility $\chi_p$ is defined as the difference between completely "relaxed" and "unrelaxed" modulus.

The relaxation is in general correlated with an internal friction, which can be used to evaluate the parelastic susceptibility [56]:

$$Q^{-1} = \tfrac{1}{2} \frac{1}{M} \chi_p(0,T) \frac{2\omega\tau}{1 + (\omega\tau)^2} \; , \tag{13}$$

where the reciprocal quality factor $Q^{-1}$ is $1/\pi$ times the logarithmic decrement of the sample vibrating with a frequency $\omega$ in a mode corresponding to the elastic modulus $M$, $\chi_p(0,T)$ is the parelastic susceptibility at zero frequency and temperature $T$. The relaxation time $\tau$ in general obeys an Arrhenius equation of the form $\tau = \tau_0 \exp(-H_R/kT)$, where $H_R$ is the activation enthalpy for the relaxation. On a more fundamental level the Fernfeld of the defects can be described in an elastic model, in which the core field is replaced by an arrangement of double forces defining the elastic dipole tensor $p$ [3,54,56].

For cubic crystals the volume change $v$ of a finite sample due to the lattice distortions of a defect, the compressibility $\kappa$, and the trace of the dipole tensor are related by [57]

$$v = \tfrac{1}{3} \kappa \operatorname{tr} p \; . \tag{14}$$

For a random distribution of $\langle 100 \rangle$-dumbbell interstitials (concentration $C$) in a polycrystalline sample vibrating under shear strain [58]

$$Q_{\max}^{-1} = Q^{-1}(\omega\tau = 1) = \frac{1}{2G} \chi_p(0,T_{\max})$$

$$\approx \frac{1}{G v_0} 3 \times 10^{-2} (\Delta p)^2 \frac{1}{kT_{\max}} C \; , \tag{15}$$

where $G$ is the polycrystalline shear modulus, $\chi_p$ the shear susceptibility, $\Delta p$ the difference of the two main dipole tensor components of the dumbbell, which is of the order of [3,56] 1 eV. The maximum value of the internal friction $Q_{\max}^{-1}$ is reached at the temperature $T_{\max}$, where $\omega\tau = 1$.

Eq. (15) is valid for the linear region only (splitting of energy levels $\Delta p \, \epsilon$ smaller than $kT$). If the nonlinear region ($\Delta p \, \epsilon > kT$) could be reached without destroying the sample by the large strain necessary a different relation between $Q_{\max}^{-1}$ and the unknowns $C$ and $\Delta p$ is valid (see e.g. [59]). In this case $C$ and $\Delta p$ could be evaluated directly from the experiment.

As long as this is not done and $C$ is unknown, it is necessary to use the relation

$$Q_{\max}^{-1} kT_{\max}/\Delta\rho \propto (\Delta p)^2/\rho_D \tag{16}$$

to establish at least ratios of the specific defect properties, where $\rho_D$ is the resistivity per unit concentration of defects giving rise to the internal friction maximum at the temperature $T_{\max}$. The strength of the interaction of the defects, which may cause self orientation without external strain, can be checked by plotting $1/\chi_p(0,T_{\max}) \propto 1/Q_{\max}^{-1}$ versus $T_{\max}$. Extrapolated from the linear region the corresponding straight line must pass through $T = 0$ if the interaction is negligible (see also [57]).

c) The elastic susceptibility is analogous to the electric susceptibility (see also section 6). Accordingly a "dielastic" susceptibility $\chi_d$ can be defined, a modulus change, which is caused by the change of the density and the atomic interaction potentials of the crystal due to the defects [54,55].

Formally the dielastic susceptibility $\chi_d$ can be related to an "elastic polarizability" $\alpha$ of the defects, which is a specific defect property:

$$\chi_d = \Delta M_d = c\,\alpha/v_o \ . \tag{17}$$

According to the theory of this effect [55] for a certain component of the tensors

$$\frac{\Delta M_d}{M} = \frac{c\alpha}{v_o M} = -c\left(\frac{v_D^{tot}}{v_o} + C.E.\right) \tag{18}$$

is valid, where $v_D^{tot}$ is the total volume change by one defect, $v_o$ the atomic volume, and C.E. indicates the contributions of the potential changes in the core field.

If the defects are not restricted to a certain configuration but can move in a limited range essentially without activation, the susceptibility would depend on the applied strain (nonlinear stress-strain relation).

The temperature and frequency dependence of the elastic susceptibility is in principle equivalent to that of the electric susceptibility of permanent electric dipoles in a dissipative medium (see also chapter 6).

The dielastic and parelastic susceptibility can be separated experimentally by measuring the temperature dependence of the internal friction and that of the elastic susceptibility at temperatures as low as possible (see fig. 12).

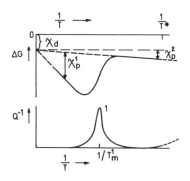

Fig. 12. Temperature dependence of the dynamic elastic modulus change $\Delta G$ due to two types of defects with a total dielastic susceptibility $\chi_d$ (temperature independent) and a parelastic susceptibility $\chi_p^1$ and $\chi_p^2$ due to the thermally activated relaxation of the two defect types respectively with different activation energies (schematic). The internal friction maximum 1 lies above the lowest temperature $T^*$ assumed to be available and can be observed $(Q_m^{-1}(1)$ $= \chi_p(0,T_m^1)/2G)$. If the vibrational frequency $\omega$ used for the measurements is much smaller than the resonance frequency $\omega_R$ of the defect core, $\chi_d$ is essentially the static susceptibility. If $\omega_R$ is very small $(\omega \gg \omega_R)$, $\chi_d$ should be zero. All scales are linear.

## 4.2. Aluminium

After reactor neutron irradiation at 4.6°K the internal friction and the dynamic shear modulus $G$ of polycrystalline samples have been measured [58,61]. In fig. 13 an example of the dependence of the internal friction on the temperature is presented. Equivalent internal friction maxima were found on polycrystalline samples after α-particle irradiation (3 MeV) at 20°K [60]. In all cases known the dielastic susceptibility is negative after irradiation; the defects give rise to a "softening" of the lattice. In fig. 14 the ratios of the di- and parelastic susceptibility and the corresponding resistivity changes are plotted for the neutron irradiation and annealing measurements, together with results of Young's modulus $Y$ measurements on polycrystalline samples after quenching, where also a decrease of the modulus was found [62] (indicated by V in fig. 14).

From fig. 14 one can deduce for Frenkel defect properties

$$\frac{\alpha_F^G}{\rho_F v_o} = \frac{\Delta G_d}{\Delta \rho}\bigg|_{st. I} = \left(\frac{-140}{400} \pm 10\%\right) \frac{eV}{v_o \, \mu\Omega \, cm} \tag{19}$$

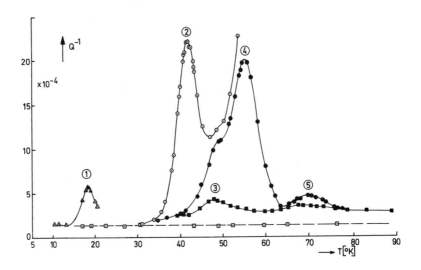

Fig. 13. Aluminium. Internal friction $Q^{-1}$ as a function of temperature after reactor neutron irradiation at 5°K. Total residual resistivity change 108 nΩ cm. Heating rate approx. 1°K/min. The different curves were measured after heating to different temperatures and cooling to 5°K (highest temperature before measurement: 5°K (△), 26°K (○), 58°K (●), 79°K (■), 326°K (□)). See also table 2. No indication of a thermally activated relaxation process below 5°K could be found (see fig. 12 for method used). Above 100°K reproducible internal friction maxima could not be found in the measurements [58].

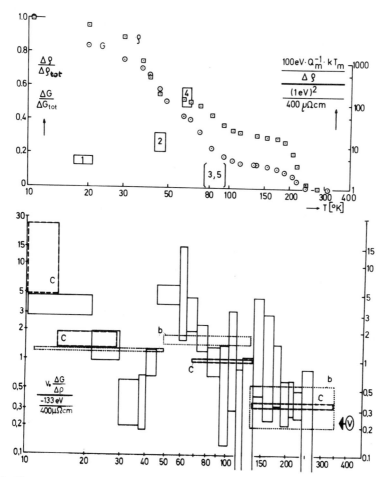

Fig. 14. *Aluminium.* Upper part: Residual resistivity change $\Delta\rho$ and dielastic modulus change $\Delta G_d$ as a function of annealing temperature after irradiation with reactor neutron at $4.6°K$ (holding time 2 min if not indicated otherwise), normalized to total changes ($\Delta\rho_{tot}$ = 140 nΩ cm, $\Delta G_{tot}$ = −0.0162 G). The horizontal dimensions of the blocks 1 to 5 indicate the temperature range in which the corresponding internal friction maxima disappear (see fig. 13), the vertical positions (the vertical range indicating the error) give formally the "anisotropy" of the relaxing defects, according to eqs. (15) and (16). E.g., for a polycrystalline sample with dumbbell interstitials with two different dipole tensor components, whose difference is 1 eV $(\Delta p)^2 = (1 \text{ eV})^2$, disappearing by recombination with vacancies ($\Delta\rho = c\,\rho_F = c\,400\,\mu\Omega$ cm, assuming $\rho_F = 400\,\mu\Omega$ cm per unit concentration), the ratio 100 eV $Q_{max}^{-1}\,kT_{max}/\Delta\rho$ would be $(1 \text{ eV})^2/400\,\mu\Omega$ cm.

Lower part: Ratio of dielastic modulus change and corresponding resistivity change for certain temperature ranges of annealing (see fig. 4 for further explanations; $v_0$ = atomic volume). Three different measurements have been used:

(a) $\Delta G_{d\,tot}\,v_0/\Delta\rho_{tot}$ = (−133/400 ± 5%) eV/$\mu\Omega$ cm, $\Delta\rho_{tot}$ = 140 nΩ cm (blocks without indication);

(b) $\Delta G_{d\,tot}\,v_0/\Delta\rho_{tot}$ = (−133/400 ± 5%) eV/$\mu\Omega$ cm, $\Delta\rho_{tot}$ = 220 nΩ cm;

(c) $\Delta G_{d\,tot}\,v_0/\Delta\rho_{tot}$ = (−120/400 ± 5%) eV/$\mu\Omega$ cm, $\Delta\rho_{tot}$ = 550 nΩ cm.

and for vacancy properties

$$\frac{\alpha_V^Y}{\rho_V v_0} = \frac{\Delta Y_d}{\Delta \rho} \approx \frac{-16}{220} \frac{eV}{v_0 \mu\Omega\, cm} \tag{20}$$

(eq. (17); see also table 1).

If interstitial-vacancy interactions are neglected

$$\alpha_F = \alpha_I + \alpha_V \tag{21}$$

and accordingly $\alpha_I \approx -124$ eV, $\alpha_V \approx -16$ eV, $\rho_F = 400\,\mu\Omega$ cm per unit conc. and $\rho_V = 220\,\mu\Omega$ cm per unit conc. Interstitials contribute nearly 90% to the total FD's susceptibility. Both, I and V, have a much larger elastic polarizability than foreign atoms in metals, for which [54] $\alpha = 0(-1$ eV$)$.

From the theory of the dielastic susceptibility it is obvious that the density change of the lattice cannot account for the observed effect (see eq. (18) and table 1).

Therefore, the change of the interatomic potentials in the core field is essential for an explanation. With the simple models used so far it was not possible to explain the enormous softening observed [55]. Maximum theoretical values for the shear modulus * are $\alpha_V \approx -20$ eV, $|\alpha_I| < \alpha_V$.

Since the observed susceptibility $\chi$ is independent of the strain $\epsilon$ ($10^{-4} < \epsilon < 10^{-5}$) it seems that the effect cannot be due to a change of the core field configuration under the applied stress (relaxation with negligible activation energy).

The close I–V pairs annealing in the low temperature part of stage I probably have a factor of ten larger polarizability than the single I and V recombining in the main $I_D$ subpeak. The large value of the ratio $|\Delta G_d|/\Delta\rho$ in the temperature region between stage I and II seems to be nonphysical and due to defect reactions with small corresponding resistivity changes, which are no longer a good measure of the concentration of defects (see also chapter 5.5).

The same anomaly is found in the ratio $Q_m^{-1} kT_m/\Delta\rho$ for the internal friction maxima 2 and 4 (fig. 14). The internal friction peak 1 (fig. 13), annealing in stage $I_A$ (fig. 14), is probably due to the relaxation of an interstitial interacting with a nearby vacancy, with which it recombines in stage $I_A$ [10]. Even at such low tem-

---

* Two older theories are known. One of them [63] applies the elasticity model also for the core field of the defects. Therefore, important contributions to $\chi$ due to the atomistic nature of the lattice are lost (see [55]). The sign of $a$ is introduced ad hoc by assuming that the applied strain changes the dipoltensor of the defect in the sense observed. The conclusion that an intimate relation between $a$ and the volume change by distortions $v$ exists is misleading. Only part of $a$ is directly connected with $v$ (see eq. (18)). The elastic model alone is not sufficient; the agreement between theory and experiment seems to be accidental. In the light of the lattice theory [55] the continuum elastic model does not give the sign and the order of magnitude of the dielastic susceptibility correctly, as claimed in the literature [65].

In another theory [133] the model used was oversimplified (neglect of relaxation and symmetry change of lattice); the results are in serious disagreement with all known experiments.

peratures the relaxation time has an Arrhenius form [61]; a self polarization discussed at the end of chapter 4.1 could not be observed.

Internal friction peak 2 (fig. 13) may be caused by the relaxation of the free interstitials [58,61], which disappear (fig. 14) during their long range diffusion (table 2) by recombining with vacancies or reacting with other interstitials [10], where they loose their ability to relax in the high temperature branch of stage $I_D$.

The other internal friction maxima 3, 4 and 5 are probably due to a relaxation of interstitials within groups of few interacting interstitials [10,60]. The relaxing interstitials disappear by rearrangement of these groups or "evaporation" of interstitials, which then diffuse through the lattice and recombine with vacancies or are trapped at interstitial clusters [10] in a configuration, where relaxation is no longer possible. The properties of the internal friction maxima in aluminium are summarized in table 2.

With eqs. (15) and (16), the assumption that all relaxing interstitials recombine with vacancies during the annealing ($\Delta\rho = C_I \rho_F$), and with the ratios $Q_m^{-1} kT_m/\Delta\rho$ of fig. 14, formally $(\Delta p)^2$ has roughly the values 4, 10 and 200 $(eV)^2$ for peaks 1, 2 and 4 respectively *.

From the theoretical value for the dipole tensor of the $\langle 100 \rangle$-dumbbell interstitial in copper [3] (in main axes,

$$(p_{ij}) \approx \begin{vmatrix} 14 & 0 & 0 \\ 0 & 14 & 0 \\ 0 & 0 & 16 \end{vmatrix} \text{ eV} \tag{22}$$

one expects $\Delta p \approx 2$ eV in rough agreement with the above value for peak 1 and also for peak 2, if one assumes that all interstitials present at the peak temperature are free and participate in the relaxation process (see table 2 and [61]).

In addition, an estimate on the basis of eq. (14) and table 1 gives $\text{tr} p \approx 38$ eV for peak 1 and 2, so that the value of eq. (22) seems to represent the correct order of magnitude for the interstitial dipoltensor in aluminium (see also chapter 5.5). Obviously the "anisotropy" $3 \Delta p/\text{tr} p$ of the interstitial is very small and the corresponding internal friction peak would have been difficult to detect were it not for the low observation temperature.

## 4.3. Copper

Defects induced by low temperature irradiation give rise to a "softening" of the lattice as in aluminium. The available measurements of the dielastic susceptibility

---

* The true resistivity change related to peaks 2, 3, 4 and 5 must obviously be smaller according to the above model, because the resistivity change is negligible for the reaction of interstitials with one another [64]. Therefore, the formal values of $(\Delta p)^2$ for peaks 2 and 4 are too large.

H.WENZL

Table 2

Some properties of the internal friction maxima in aluminium observed after fast neutron irradiation at 4.6°K (see fig. 13).

| Number | $T_m$ °K ($\nu = 64$ Hz) | $H_r^1$ meV | $H_r^2$ meV | $\log_{10} \tau_o$ sec | $H_a$ MeV | $\log_{10} n$ | $\frac{\Delta\rho}{\Delta\rho_o}$ |
|---|---|---|---|---|---|---|---|
| 1 | 18 | $35 \pm 9$ | $20 \pm 8$ | $14 \pm 3$ | $\cdot 63 \pm 8$ | 1 | 0.05 |
| 2 | 42 | $97 \pm 20$ | $80 \pm 25$ | $14 \pm 2$ | $115 \pm 15$ | 4 | 0.10 |
| 3 | 49 | $100 \pm 20$ | ? | $13 \pm 2$ | ? | ? | 0.10 |
| 4 | 55 | $135 \pm 25$ | $128 \pm 30$ | $15 \pm 2$ | $195 \pm 25$ | 1.8 | 0.02 |
| 5 | 70 | $180 \pm 40$ | $170 \pm 40$ | $16 \pm 2$ | ? | ? | 0.10 |

*Explanation of symbols:* $H_{r_2}^1$ is the activation enthalpy of relaxation obtained from the shift of the maximum temperature $T_m$ with a change of vibrational frequency $\omega$; $H_R^2$ is the activation enthalpy obtained from the half width; $\tau_o$ from $\omega\tau = 1$ at $T_m$ and $\tau = \tau_o \exp(H_R/kT)$; $H_m$ is the activation enthalpy for the annealing process, $n$ the corresponding number of jumps at the beginning of the annealing, $\Delta\rho/\Delta\rho_o$ the resistivity change related to the disappearance of the internal friction maxima. The values $H_m$ of peak 1 and 2 are equal to the activation enthalpy of resistivity annealing [6] in stages $I_A$ and $I_D$, respectively.

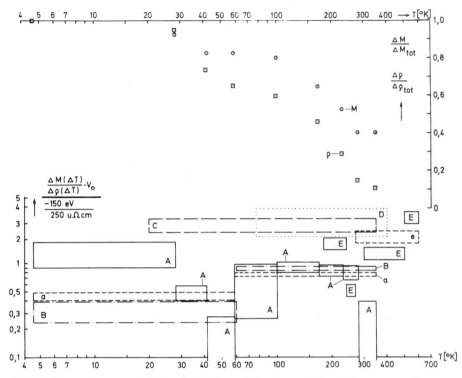

Fig. 15. *Copper.* Lower part: Ratio of dielastic modulus change $\Delta M_d$ and the corresponding resistivity change $\Delta\rho$ plotted for certain temperature ranges of annealing after irradiation at low temperatures (see also fig. 4 and 14).

(A,a) neutron irradiation [161], shear modulus, $\Delta M_{d\ tot}\ v_o/\Delta\rho_{tot} = (-6.15 \pm 2\%) \times 10^5$ eV/$\Omega$ cm;

(B,b) neutron irradiation [161], shear modulus, $\Delta M_{d\ tot}\ v_o/\Delta\rho_{tot} = (-5.8 \pm 2\%) \times 10^{-5}$ eV/$\Omega$ cm; for defects annealing above 350°K $\Delta M_d v_o/\Delta\rho = (-2.0 \pm 0.2) \times 10^6$ eV/$\Omega$ cm;

(C) $\alpha$-particles [66];

(D) electrons [106]; (E) electrons [67]. Especially in measurements (C) and (D) the systematic errors may be large due to the uncertainty of the resistivity change or the use of thin foils, whose vibrational modes very often are not stable [66].

Upper part: residual resistivity change ($\rho$) and dielastic modulus change ($M$) as a function of annealing temperature (measurement ($A$); 2 min holding time).

are collected in fig. 15 (see also [164] with $\Delta Y_d/Y \leqslant 80 C_F$). From the neutron irradiation data

$$\left.\frac{\Delta G_d}{\Delta\rho}\right|_{tot} = (-150 \pm 3)\frac{\text{eV}}{250\,\mu\Omega\text{ cm } v_o} = \frac{\alpha_F}{\rho_F\, v_o}. \qquad (23)$$

Two internal friction maxima have been found after neutron irradiation [161] at 4.6°K, one at 8°K, annealing in the low temperature part of stage $I_D$ (probably $I_C$),

Table 3

Some properties of internal friction maxima in copper at low temperatures after neutron irradiation [161] (number 1, 2, 57 c/sec) and proton irradiation [162] (number 2, 330 c/sec). Explanations see table 2. $T_a$ indicates the temperature range of annealing for 10 min half lifetime.

| Number | Frequency c/sec | $T_m$ °K | $Hr^1$ MeV | $Hr^2$ MeV | $\log_{10}\frac{\text{sec}}{\tau_0}$ | $T_a$ °K |
|--------|------|----------|-----------|-----------|----------|-----|
| 1 | 57 | 7.7 ± 0.1 | 11 ± 4 | 7 ± 2 | 8 ± 3 | 28–35 |
| 1 | 330 | 10.0 | 15 ± 2 | 10 ± 2 | 12 ± 1 | 28–35 |
| 2 | 57 | 34 ± 1 | | 31 ± 6 | 6 ± 2 | 36–40 |

the other at 34°K, annealing in the high temperature part of stage $I_D$ (both for a vibrational frequency of 57 c/sec; see table 3).

The peak at 8°K was also found after proton irradiation [162]. Measurements in the stage III region are discussed in ref. [56].

### 4.4. Platinum

In fig. 16 the dynamic dielastic susceptibility of defects induced by low temperature reactor irradiation can be seen. Again, point defects give rise to a softening of the lattice, which anneals during temperature increase in annealing stages corresponding to those of the electrical resistivity. Internal friction maxima have not been found between 4°K and 400°K [58]. According to fig. 16

$$\frac{v_0 \, \Delta G_d}{\Delta \rho}\bigg|_{st.\,I} = \left(\frac{-400}{600} \pm 20\%\right) \frac{\text{eV}}{\mu\Omega \, \text{cm}} = \frac{\alpha_F^G}{\rho_F} . \tag{24}$$

As in aluminium the defects annealing in the low temperature part of stage I, close I–V pairs, have a larger negative ratio and therefore probably a larger susceptibility than the single I and V (see also [10]).

At the high temperature end of stage I the ratio increases. This anomaly is probably unphysical and can be explained as in the case of aluminium as being due to defect reactions in this temperature range, which lead to a decrease of the negative susceptibility accompanied with a comparatively small resistivity decrease [10].

As in aluminium and copper the negative susceptibilities of Frenkel defects (table 1) are much larger than the theoretical values calculated using simple models ([55] and chapter 4.2).

### 4.5. Tungsten

Internal friction maxima have been studied after electron irradiation at 20°K using single crystals of different orientation [68]. The analysis showed that the free interstitial at temperatures around 30°K is probably a ⟨110⟩ split one with a stress

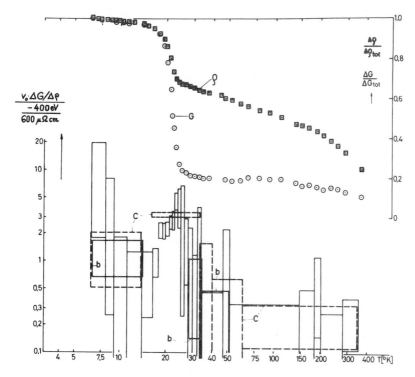

Fig. 16. *Platinum.* Upper part: Isochronal annealing curves (2 min holding time) of the residual resistivity change and the dielastic shear modulus change after irradiation with reactor neutrons at 4.6°K, plotted as a function of annealing temperature (see also fig. 14; polycrystal; $\Delta G_{d\,tot}/G = -0.0128 \pm 5\%$, $\Delta\rho_{tot} = 118$ nΩ cm).

Lower part: Ratios of dielastic modulus change and the corresponding resistivity change (analogous to fig. 14):

   (a) $\Delta G_{d\,tot}v_0/G = (-400/600 \pm 5\%)$ eV/μΩ cm, $\Delta\rho_{tot} = 70$ nΩ cm (letter (a) not indicated);

   (b) $\Delta G_{d\,tot}v_0/G = (-360/600 \pm 5\%)$ eV/μΩ cm, $\Delta\rho_{tot} = 70$ nΩ cm;

   (c) $\Delta G_{d\,tot}v_0/G = (-390/600 \pm 5\%)$ eV/μΩ cm, $\Delta\rho_{tot} = 118$ nΩ cm.

For defects annealing above 350°K, $\Delta G_d v_0/G = (-2.7 \pm 0.3) \times 10^5$ eV/Ω cm.

field anisotropy ($3\,\Delta p_{max}/\mathrm{tr}\,p$) of $\frac{1}{5}$. The dielastic susceptibility seems to be negative for Frenkel defects, but systematic measurements have not been performed.

### 4.6. *Iron*

Similar measurements as on tungsten have been performed on iron single and polycrystals after neutron and electron irradiation at 20°K and 77°K [36]. The freely migrating interstitial around 120°K is probably split in ⟨110⟩-direction with a similar stress field anisotropy as in tungsten and a negative dielastic susceptibility for Frenkel defects (measured at $\Delta\rho = 430$ nΩ cm)

$$\chi_d/G < -5 C_F . \tag{25}$$

## 5. Transport properties

We shall discuss transport properties of the conduction electrons (electrical resistivity tensor in zero and finite magnetic field, thermal conductivity, thermoelectric power), and briefly also phonon thermal conductivity (in connection with the phonon drag part of the thermoelectric power, and in superconductors). The theory is generally based on the Boltzmann equation, which is sufficient for the comparatively low defect concentration in irradiated or quenched metals (provided that many-body effects such as in the Kondo effect are not important) and which can be solved numerically [70,71].

### 5.1. Electrical resistivity in zero magnetic fields
### 5.1.1. Specific electrical resistivity of defects

For nonferromagnetic cubic crystals with a random distribution of defects, which may have a noncubic symmetry, the electrical resistivity is a scalar quantity *.

In the quasi-free electron model the change of the electrical resistivity in a sample with one type of defect scattering the conduction electrons is given by [73]

$$\Delta\rho = \frac{m^2 k_F N v_o}{ne^2 (2\pi)^2 \hbar^3} \; C \int_0^\pi |V_{k'k}|^2 (1-\cos\theta)\sin\theta \; d\theta = \rho_D \, C \; , \qquad (26)$$

where $C$ is the defect concentration, $\rho_D$ the resistivity change per unit concentration, $k_F$ the Fermi wave number, $n$ the number of conduction electrons, $m$ the effective mass, $N$ the number of atoms, $C|V_{k'k}|^2$ the rate of scattering from a state with wave-vector $\mathbf{k}$ into $\mathbf{k}'$ under the angle $\theta$, $V_{k'k}$ the corresponding matrix element.

Since the scattering rate due to structural defects is expected to change in the same way as the density of conduction electrons from metal to metal [78] the specific resistivity change $\rho_D$ is insensitive to $n$, as indeed is observed (table 1). $V_{k'k}$ can be calculated in the phase shift approximation, from which one can conclude qualitatively, that the specific defect resistivity is sensitive primarily to the local variation of the potential and not to its absolute magnitude [64,22]. Spread out potentials give a lower resistivity than concentrated ones. The electronic stored energy (see chapter 2) depends less on details of the potential than $\rho_D$ [22].

The value of $\rho_F$ is usually determined by measuring the rate of resistivity change during irradiation with electrons as a function of the electron energy. Reliable determinations of the displacement probability function [4] from these measurements have been possible in few cases only. Therefore, most of the published data

---

* If an external stress gives rise to a redistribution of defects as discussed in chapter 4, the resistivity becomes orientation dependent: piezoresistivity (see e.g. [72]).

of $\rho_F$ based on these measurements are not reliable, but can be taken as lowest possible values [4] (see table 1).

Since the rate of resistivity change may vary by 20% or more due to deviations from the Matthiessen rule (see below), one must be very careful to avoid systematic errors. Another method for obtaining $\rho_F$ was discussed in chapter 3.

The vacancy resistivity $\rho_V$ can be obtained by residual resistivity measurements after quenching (see table 1). This method is subject to systematic errors due to loss of vacancies and double vacancy generation during the rapid cooling process (see [74]).

The high temperature resistivity measurements suffer from the insufficient knowledge of the "base line" [12,32]. Furthermore, the value of $\rho_V$ may depend on temperature (see below and chapter 6).

In view of these uncertainties one can only estimate orders of magnitude for the defect resistivities. If one uses the resistivity at the Debye temperature $\rho_\theta$ as a measure of the electron scattering strength, the ratios $\rho_F/\rho_\theta$ and $\rho_V/\rho_\theta$ are expected to have roughly the same value for different metals (see table 1 and [75]). A model for more complicated scattering systems as usually present in the samples can be obtained by separating the defect population in the metal into single defects and complexes of point defects (e.g. close Frenkel pairs, double vacancies etc.) and regarding the electron phonon scattering separately. As a rule of thumb the resistivity changes only slightly during agglomeration of single to double or triple defects [22, 64,78]. Guided by the simplest approximation of a free electron gas the total resistivity can be separated in the following way:

$$\rho(T) = [\rho_{imp} + \sum C_i \rho_i(T) + \rho_T] + \Delta(\rho_{imp}, C_1\rho_1, \dots, \rho_T), \qquad (27a)$$

$$\delta \equiv \rho(T)_{defects} - \rho(T)_{annealed}, \qquad (27b)$$

where the terms in brackets represent Matthiessen's rule (MR) [76] and $\Delta$ is the deviation from MR due to the simultaneous presence (not interaction) of defects of different type i with specific resistivity $\rho_i(T)$ (if present alone), impurities ($\rho_{imp}$), and phonons ($\rho_T$). The phonon resistivity $\rho_T$ may be also changed by the defects.

## 5.1.2. Deviations from Matthiessen's rule

In most studies of defects in metals, where the electrical resistivity is used as a measure of the defect concentration, the MR is assumed to be valid. But if different defect configurations are present in the sample MR is violated, even in the residual resistivity range [77], except for the case of spherical scattering potential and Fermi surface *.

At higher temperatures additional deviations of MR occur due to the electron-phonon scattering processes. These deviations are usually neglected in the literature. If the sample contains essentially one defect type ($\rho_o \approx C\rho_D \gg \rho_{imp}$) the "Kohler rule" states [76]

$$\frac{\Delta}{\rho_o} = \frac{\alpha\beta \, (\rho_T/\rho_o)}{\alpha \, (\rho_T/\rho_o) + \beta} = f\left(\frac{\rho_T}{\rho_o}\right) \quad , \tag{28}$$

where the parameters $\alpha$ and $\beta$ are specific properties of the combined scattering system of defects and phonons; $\alpha$, $\beta$, and the form of the function $f$ are a measure of the difference of the scattering "anisotropy" of defects and phonons † [79,80].

The analog statements are valid for two different defect types 1 and 2, where $\rho_o$ and $\rho_T$ in the above formula must be replaced by $\rho_1$ and $\rho_2$.

Roughly, $\alpha$ and $\beta$ increase with increasing difference in scattering anisotropy of the two different scattering types under consideration. By measuring the dependence of $\delta/\rho_o$ on the defect concentration one can decide, whether the observed effect is due to a deviation from the MR ($\delta = \Delta = \rho_o \, f(\rho_T/\rho_o)$) or due to a change of the phonon dispersion relation by the defects and thus due to a change of the phonon resistance $\rho_T$ ($|\delta|/\rho_o$ for $\rho_T/\rho_o$ = const. increases with increasing defect concentration) or a superposition of both, as it is to be expected generally (see chapter 6 for further discussion of the defect influence on $\rho_T$): Fig. 17 gives a survey of the different effects.

Usually, deviations from the MR have been studied on alloys by comparing $\rho(T)$ of alloyed and pure samples. Systematic errors to uncertainty of the sample geometry, which must be known for an evaluation of the specific resistivity, may be large in these cases. For structural point defects $\delta$ can be measured more accurately because either $\rho(T)$ curves of the same sample in irradiated and annealed condition can be compared or different samples are compared in the residual resistivity region, where systematic errors of the geometry are not as important as at high tempera-

---

* Therefore, the resistivity change cannot be used as an unambiguous measure of the defect concentration. E.g. changes of the height of resistivity annealing stages after different treatments or a detailed analysis of the reaction kinetics by using resistivity measurements cannot be expected to reflect exactly the behaviour of the defect concentration.

† Scattering anisotropy exists if the scattering matrix elements depend either on the direction of the wavenumber vector of the electron before collision or on the scattering angle (direction or angle anisotropy).

Both anisotropies may be important, the direction anisotropy in the case of extremely non-cubic and small (compared with electron wavelength) defects, the angle anisotropy in the case of more spherical, extended defects. The phonon scattering shows a direction anisotropy (in relation to the crystal axis) in the temperature region below $\frac{1}{5} \theta$ ($\theta$ = Debye-temperature) [78].

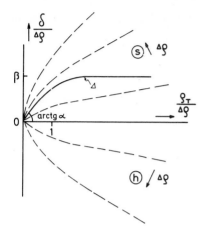

Fig. 17. Schematic temperature dependence of the deviation from the Matthiessen rule ($\delta = \Delta$) and the change of the thermal resistivity ($\delta = \Delta\rho_T$; dashed lines; see eqs. (27)). The temperature is measured by the defect free thermal resistivity $\rho_T$. The residual resistivity change due to defects $\Delta\rho$ is assumed to be large compared with the defect free residual resistivity $\rho_0$. The letters h and s indicate the behaviours for hardening or softening of the phonon modes due to the defects. The parameters $a$ and $\beta$ (see eq. (18)) may be temperature dependent [77,88]; the residual resistivity change $\Delta\rho \gg \rho_{imp}$.

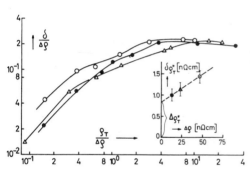

Fig. 18. *Copper.* Change of the temperature dependence of the electrical resistivity $\delta$ caused by reactor neutron irradiation at 4°K and annealing (10 min) at 150°K (between stages II and III). The temperature is measured by $\rho_T$ as in fig. 17, the residual resistivity changes corresponding to the different curves are (o) $\Delta\rho = 48$ n$\Omega$cm, ($\triangle$) 23 n$\Omega$cm, and (●) 13 n$\Omega$cm, the defect free residual resistivity is $\rho_0 \approx 0.5$ n$\Omega$cm. The inserted smaller figure indicates the dependence of $\delta$ for a constant value $\rho_T^* = 20$ n$\Omega$cm on the defect resistivity $\Delta\rho$. Since $\Delta\rho \gg \rho_T^*$ the deviation from the MR is $\Delta = a\rho_T^*$ (see eq. (28)), independent of $\Delta\rho$ (see also fig. 17). Accordingly $a \approx 0.04$ in this case.

tures [77]. The volume change by defects can be taken into account but is usually negligible.

The behaviour of $\delta$ has been studied by mixing the following scattering centers:

a) irradiation induced defects and phonons [77,85],

b) plastic deformation induced defects and phonons [77,81–83],

c) quenched-in vacancies and phonons [84],

d) plastic deformation induced and irradiation induced defects [77,86,87].

In all cases $\delta/\rho_0$ is positive and depends roughly on $\rho_T/\rho_0$ (or the corresponding $\rho_{irrad}/\rho_{deform}$ in case d)) as one expects from eq. (28), the maximum value of $\delta/\rho_0$ lying between 10% and 100%.

As an example the only known systematic study of type a and d behaviour on copper will be discussed now.

In fig. 18 the dependence of $\delta/\Delta\rho$ as a function of $\rho_T/\Delta\rho$ is presented for defects produced by irradiation with reactor neutrons at $4.6°K$ and annealing above $150°K$. To separate the influence of the deviations from MR $\Delta$ and the changes of the phonon-resistivity $(\Delta\rho_T)$ on [†] $\delta$ it is necessary to study the function $\delta/\rho_0 = F(\rho_T/\rho_0)$ at different defect concentrations.

One expects a completely different concentration dependence of $\Delta\rho_T$ and $\Delta$:

$$\Delta\rho_T\Big|_{\rho_T = \text{const}} \propto C, \qquad \frac{\Delta\rho_T}{\rho_T} = -n\,\frac{\Delta\theta_\rho}{\theta_\rho}, \qquad (29)$$

$$\Delta\Big|_{\rho_T = \text{const} \ll \rho_0} = \alpha\rho_T \quad \text{(independent of } C), \qquad (30)$$

where $\theta_\rho$ is the characteristic temperature in the Grüneisen relation [73,76] (see chapter 6), $n$ ranges from $6\,(T < \frac{1}{10}\theta_\rho)$ to $2\,(T > \theta_\rho)$.

On the basis of eqs. (29) and (30) the experiments presented in fig. 18 indicate for the single vacancies, multiple vacancies and multiple interstitials in the sample [10]

$$\frac{\Delta\theta_\rho}{\Delta\rho\,\theta_\rho} = 0\left(-\frac{10^2}{250\,\mu\Omega\,\text{cm}}\right) \quad \text{for} \quad \Delta\rho < 100\,\text{n}\Omega\,\text{cm}, \qquad (31)$$

where $\Delta\rho$ is the residual resistivity change ($\Delta\rho \approx \rho_0$ in the case discussed); the defects cause a softening of the phonon spectrum in agreement with the specific heat measurements (chapter 2.2). In addition, the MR is violated:

$$\alpha = 0(0.01), \qquad (32a)$$

$$\beta = 0(0.1). \qquad (32b)$$

Both parameters are roughly independent of the defect concentration (see [77] for a detailed discussion).

To illustrate the phenomena, the deviations of MR can be formulated in a simple two band model of the conduction electrons. The Fermi surface (fig. 19) is separated into two parts, the "neck" regions with total area $A_N$, Fermivelocity $v_N$ and relaxation time $\tau_N$ and the "belly" region with $A_B$, $v_B$, $\tau_B$, where $A_N v_N/A_B v_B \approx 0.2$ [88] (for a critical discussion of the relaxation time approximation see [73, 78,89]). In this model [88]

$$\alpha = \frac{(d-p)^2}{p(1+d)^2} \quad \text{and} \quad \beta = \frac{(d-p)^2}{d(1+p)^2}, \qquad (33)$$

where

$$d \equiv \frac{A_N\,v_N\,\tau_N}{A_B\,v_B\,\tau_B}\bigg|_{\text{defects}} \qquad (34a)$$

[†] $\delta = \Delta\rho_T + \Delta$.

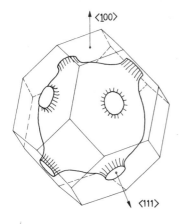

Fig. 19. Fermi surface FS of copper and boundaries of the first Brillouin zone BZ [76]. The electrons in states near the contact regions of the FS with the BZ are called neck electrons, those in states at the spherically shaped regions are called belly electrons.

and

$$p \equiv \frac{A_N v_N}{A_B v_B} \frac{\tau_N}{\tau_B}\bigg|_{\text{phonons}} \tag{34b}$$

are the ratios of the relaxation times pertaining to pure defect or pure phonon scattering, respectively. The formulae show clearly the dependence of $\alpha$ and $\beta$ on the difference of the scattering properties of defects and phonons.

One expects [88] for phonons $(T < \theta)$ $p \gtrsim 0.1$, for spherical defect clusters (small angle scattering) $d < 0.2$, for isotropic scattering at single point defects $d \approx 0.2$.

To explain the experimental values (eqs. (32a) and (32b)) the defects present after neutron irradiation at 4.6°K and annealing at 150°K must have $d \approx 0.03$ (if $p \approx 0.1$). The value of $\beta$ increases and, accordingly, that of $d$ decreases further during annealing in the temperature region of stages II and III (fig. 26), where the agglomerates grow and single defects disappear [10] *.

Next, we shall discuss properties of a mixture of type d [77,93]. Pure copper samples were plastically deformed at 300°K. After different annealing treatments at higher temperatures they were irradiated at 4.6°K with reactor neutrons. The initial resistivity change can be written

$$\Delta\dot\rho(t \to 0) = \rho_D \dot C [1 + \alpha + K(0)] , \tag{35}$$

where $\rho_D$ is the specific resistivity per unit concentration of radiation induced defects, $\dot C$ the production rate of defects per lattice atom in the dislocation free sample, $\alpha$ the MR deviation parameter according to eq. (28), now pertaining to the mixture

---

* The defects left in copper after annealing at about 350°K, i.e. Frank dislocation loops in ⟨111⟩-planes [53], seem to scatter "neck electrons" more strongly than "belly electrons" (the group velocity of neck electrons in general does not point into one of the ⟨111⟩-directions), which further lowers the ratio $\tau_N/\tau_B$ of the defects and thus $d$, with a corresponding increase of $\beta$ (see fig. 26).

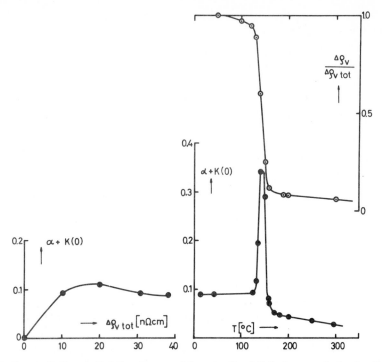

Fig. 20. *Copper*. Left part: Relative changes of the rate of resistivity increase during irradiation at 4.6°K with reactor neutrons $a + K(0)$ as a function of the resistivity change caused by plastic deformation at 20°C prior to the irradiation ($\Delta\rho_{V\,tot}$).
Right lower part: The dependence of $a + K(0)$ on annealing after plastic deformation ($\Delta\rho_{V\,tot}$ = 38 nΩ cm $\gg \rho_0$) prior to irradiation.
Upper part: Corresponding annealing curve after plastic deformation alone (10 min isochronals).
All measurements were performed at 4.6°K.

of radiation induced and plastic deformation induced defects; $K(0)$ takes account of the increase of the defect production rate, e.g. by the "Leibfried mechanism" (scattering of focussed collisions at dislocations) [77]. Fig. 20 presents a survey of the behaviour of $\alpha + K(0)$ as a function of the resistivity due to plastic deformation *.

The curves in fig. 20 reflect essentially the behaviour of $\alpha$ for the different treatments, since presumably $K(0)/\alpha \ll 1$ [77]. Plastic deformation at 300°K produces point defects, probably in the form of agglomerates ($d_1 \leqslant 0.2$) and dislocations [88] ($d_2 \approx 0.01$), whereas irradiation at 4.6°K produces mainly point defects ($d_3 \approx 0.2$). The increase of the specific property $\alpha$ after partial anneal of the deformed sample before irradiation shows a change of the predominant defect configuration in the deformed sample.

* Similar effects were observed on platinum [87], but the explanation for those data is based solely on $K(0)$; $\alpha$ is neglected, which does not seem to be justified (see also [77]).

Either dislocations rearrange to give a more pronounced scattering anisotropy of a kind, which leads to a smaller $d$, or point defects disappear, which causes a decrease of the effective $d_{\text{plastic.def.}}$ ($d_2 < d_1$) and accordingly an increase of $\alpha$ (see fig. 20) *.

Many problems in connection with deviations from MR could be settled if another physical property, e.g. stored energy or lattice parameter, would be used as an indication of the defect concentration instead of the resistivity. But usually these methods cannot compete with the accuracy of the resistivity measurements.

### 5.2. Thermal conductivity

#### 5.2.1. Concepts

In metals heat is conducted by electrons and phonons, which can be scattered by defects [76]. The corresponding part of the thermal resistivity per unit concentration of defects can be defined for each heat carrier type separately. The temperature dependence of the phonon heat resistivity can be used to study the wavenumber dependence of the phonon scattering cross section, the dominant wavenumber being approximately proportional to the absolute temperature. The various lattice defects have each a characteristic wavelength dependence of the phonon scattering and accordingly give rise to a characteristic temperature dependence of the phonon heat resistivity [76,107,108,118]. The wavenumber dependence of the electron scattering cannot be exploited in such experiments, because the wavenumbers of the electrons participating in the conduction process are nearly temperature independent.

#### 5.2.2. Electron thermal conductivity

Usually the contribution of the conduction electrons to the thermal resistivity is dominant and can be measured easily **.

The specific thermal resistivity of the conduction electrons per unit concentration of defects $W_D$ is related to the corresponding electrical resistivity $\rho_D$ by the Wiedemann-Franz law [76,109]

$$\frac{\rho_D}{W_D T} = L , \tag{36}$$

where $L$ is the Lorenz number. If in addition to the defects also phonons participate in the scattering processes the thermal resistivity can be treated in a similar way as the electrical resistivity in chapter 5.1. Then the Wiedemann-Franz law is usually violated for temperatures below the Debye temperature [110].

---

* Deviations from the law $\Delta\dot{\rho} = \Delta\dot{\rho}(0) (1 - \Delta\rho/\Delta\rho_S)$ ($\Delta\rho_S$ = extrapolated saturation resistivity change) observed in many metals during fast particle irradiation, especially in the low dose range [91,92], are probably also caused mainly by deviations from the MR (corresponding to the parameter $\beta$) and not to changes of the defect production mechanism [77].
** E.g., in pure copper at 4°K the electronic conductivity is about a factor of 100 larger than the phonon conductivity.

### 5.2.3. Phonon thermal conductivity

In superconductors the electron conductivity decreases with decreasing temperature below the critical temperature $T_c$ whereas the phonon conductivity may even increase due to the decreased phonon-electron scattering. Therefore, measurements at temperatures sufficiently below $T_c$ allow to exploit the powers of the phonon conductivity measurements. In fig. 21 measurements on niobium are presented to show the general behaviour and the orders of magnitude [112,113]. To allow a reasonable analysis temperatures below 1°K must be reached, which was not the case in the studies known. Unfortunately, pure niobium has a comparatively large electronic heat conductivity even below $T_c$; therefore, the analysis of phonon conductivity is a difficult task (see also ref. [159]).

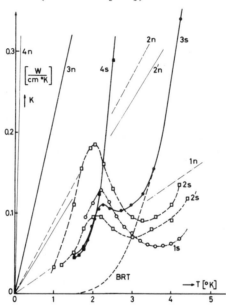

Fig. 21. *Niobium.* Thermal conductivity $K$ as a function of temperature $T$, for samples with different treatment, in the superconducting (s) and normal conducting state (n, measurement in a magnetic field $H \approx 10$ kOe; upper critical field $H_{c2} \approx 3$ kOe, critical temperature 9.2°K). The different curves are for the following samples:

    (1) Single crystal, ratio of room temperature to residual resistivity (rrr) 22.5 [141], annealed;
    (2) Single crystal [112], annealed;
    (2′) Sample (2), irradiated with reactor neutrons at room temperature [112];
    (3) Polycrystal, rrr 60 [113], annealed;
    (4) Polycrystal, rrr 1300 [113], annealed.

The dashed curve BRT indicates the theoretical temperature dependence of the electron thermal conductivity alone (sample 3) [142]. The peak of $K$ around 2°K is due to the increased phonon heat transport in the superconducting state. It is very difficult to detect it in the pure samples (4s). The decrease of $K$ from (2s) to (2′s) is caused by the scattering of phonons at larger defect clusters. Much smaller changes are to be expected by the Rayleigh scattering at single defects.

Obviously in practice this technique is not a convenient tool for metals. For a study of the phonon-defect scattering measurements of the phonon drag thermoelectric force seem to be more suitable (see chapter 5.3).

### 5.3. Thermoelectric force
### 5.3.1. Concepts

The absolute thermoelectric force (TEF) $S$ is defined by $\mathbf{E} = S\, \text{grad}\, T$, where $\mathbf{E}$ is the electric field induced by the temperature gradient under the condition that the electric current density is zero [76]. It can be divided into two parts:

$$S = S_e + S_p \; . \tag{37}$$

The electron diffusion TEF $S_e$ is due to the change of the electron distribution in the sample under the action of the temperature gradient and the scattering processes [70,131]. The quantity $S_e$ is a measure of the dependence of the electron scattering cross section and the area of the Fermi surface on the energy. The phonon drag TEF $S_p$ is caused by the interaction of electrons and phonons. Its magnitude and sign depend on the details of the electron and phonon scattering processes [114—116]. It can be used to investigate the wavelength dependence of the phonon-defect scattering even in those cases, where the heat conduction of the electrons overwhelms that of the phonons. Generally, the TEF can be used to investigate the scattering potentials of defects.

At low temperatures ($\rho_o \gg \rho_T$) the change of $S_e$ due to defects, $\Delta S_e$, is a specific property, independent of the defect concentration [115]. It is given by

$$\Delta S_e = S_e^d - S_e^p \; , \tag{38}$$

i.e. the difference between defect and phonon scattering ($\rho_o$ is the defect resistivity, $\rho_T$ the phonon resistivity, $S_e^d$ the TEF for pure defect scattering centers, $S_e^p$ the TEF for electron scattering at phonons).

At high temperatures ($\rho_o \ll \rho_T$)

$$\Delta S_e / \rho_o = (S_e^d - S_e^p)/\rho_T \; , \tag{39}$$

where $\Delta S_e \rho_T / \rho_o$ is now a specific property.

At low temperatures ($\tau_{id} \gg \tau_{pd}$), the ratio $S_p/\rho_o$, at high temperatures ($\tau_{id} \ll \tau_{pd}$) the ratio $\Delta S_p/\rho_o$ is a specific property of the defects ($1/\tau_{id} = 1/\tau_{pe} + 1/\tau_{pp}$, $\tau_{pe}$ is the relaxation time for phonon-electron, $\tau_{pp}$ that for phonon-phonon, $\tau_{pd}$ that for phonon-defect scattering (see e.g. [115,121,122]), and $\Delta S_p$ is the change of the phonon drag TEF.

### 5.3. Gold

The temperature dependence of the TEF before and after quenching [116] is shown in fig. 22. At $200°K$

$$\frac{\Delta S_e}{\Delta \rho} = -0.93 \, \frac{\mu V}{\mu \Omega \, \text{cm} \, °K} \; , \tag{40}$$

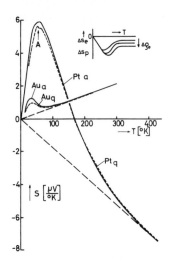

Fig. 22. Thermoelectric force of pure, annealed platinum ($Pt_a$) and gold ($Au_a$) and of quenched samples ($Pt_q$, $C_V \approx 5 \times 10^{-4}$; $Au_q$, $C_V \approx 10^{-4}$) as a function of temperature [115,116]. The sign A indicated an anomaly ascribed to resonance scattering of phonons at vacancies. At low temperatures $S_p$ contributes significantly and gives rise to the peak in the TEF. Therefore, $\Delta S_e$ can be evaluated only by extrapolating the measured TEF from high enough temperatures ($T > 200°K$, but see [117]), where $S_e$ dominates. This procedure is not always possible for defects annealing already at lower temperatures. This disadvantage of the $\Delta S_e$-measurements is shared by the study of the deviations from the Matthiessen rule (see chapter 5.2). Positive $S_e(Au)$ is anomal and due to contact of the Fermi surface with Brillouin zone boundaries [119], positive $S_p$ implies mainly Umklapp electron-phonon scattering. The small inserted figure indicates schematically the dependence of the change of $S_e$ and $S_p$, caused by defects with residual resistivity change $\Delta\rho_0$, as a function of temperature.

where $\Delta\rho$ is the residual resistivity change due to vacancies (similar values were evaluated in [120]).

The theoretical value for vacancies is in close agreement with the experiment [70]:

$$\frac{\Delta S_e}{\Delta\rho} = -0.82 \frac{\mu V}{\mu\Omega\, cm\, °K} \cdot \tag{41}$$

The experimental values for the change of the phonon drag TEF are

$$\frac{\Delta S_p}{\Delta\rho} \approx -5.6 \frac{\mu V}{\mu\Omega\, cm\, °K} \quad \text{at } 40°K\,, \tag{42}$$

$$\frac{\Delta S_p}{\Delta\rho} \approx -16.7 \frac{\mu V}{\mu\Omega\, cm\, °K} \quad \text{at } 20°K\,. \tag{43}$$

The reduction of $S_p$ by vacancies is normal. For a Rayleigh type phonon-vacancy scattering one expects $1/\tau_{pV} = a\,\omega^4$ where $\tau_{pV}$ is the phonon-vacancy relaxation-time, $\omega$ the phonon frequency. The experimental result reads [116]

$$\frac{a}{\Delta\rho} \approx 1.0 \times 10^{-41} \frac{\sec^3}{\mu\Omega\,\text{cm}} \, . \tag{44}$$

Comparison with theory shows that the phonons are scattered by vacancies predominantly through the strain field associated with the vacant lattice site and that the contribution of the mass difference term is negligible.

5.3.3. Platinum
In fig. 22 the temperature dependence of the TEF in defect-free platinum is shown. From the quenching experiments the following specific vacancy properties can be evaluated ($\Delta\rho$ is the residual resistivity change due to the vacancies) [115]:

$$\frac{\Delta S_e}{\Delta\rho} = 0.64 \pm 0.06 \frac{\mu V}{\mu\Omega\,\text{cm}\,°K} \text{ at } 350°K \, , \tag{45}$$

$$\frac{\Delta S_p}{\Delta\rho} = -0.92 \pm 0.05 \frac{\mu V}{\mu\Omega\,\text{cm}\,°K} \text{ at } 150°K \, , \tag{46}$$

$$\frac{\Delta S_p}{\Delta\rho} = -1.84 \pm 0.08 \frac{\mu V}{\mu\Omega\,\text{cm}\,°K} \text{ at } 100°K \, . \tag{47}$$

Anomalies of the temperature dependence of $\Delta S_p$ could be explained by assuming a resonance scattering of phonons at the vacancies according to

$$\frac{1}{\tau_{pV}} = \frac{a\,\omega^4}{(1-\omega^2/\omega_R^2)^2 + \frac{1}{4}\pi^2(\omega/\omega_R)^2} \, ,$$

where $\omega_R$ is the resonance frequency of the defect (see also chapter 6). Comparison with the experiments gave $\omega_R \approx 0.29\,\omega_D$, where $\omega_D$ is the Debye frequency and

$$\frac{a}{\Delta\rho} = (5.43 \pm 0.24) \times 10^{-42} \frac{\sec^3}{\mu\Omega\,\text{cm}} \, . \tag{48}$$

As in gold the last value is comparatively large and indicates the importance of the distortions and change of force constants around the vacancy in the phonon scattering process.

5.4. Hall-effect
5.4.1. Concepts
The Hall coefficient $R$ depends on the shape of the Fermi surface and of the scattering potentials for the conduction electrons [119,70,122].
It is necessary to distinguish between the Hall coefficient at high ($\omega\tau \gg 1$) and

low ($\omega\tau \ll 1$) magnetic fields ($\omega$ = cyclotron frequency, $\tau$ = relaxation time). Only the high-field Hall coefficient $R_\infty$ is an unambiguous measure of the concentration of conduction electrons, independent of the scattering potentials. If all electron orbits are closed $R_\infty$ is independent of the crystal orientation [123]

$$R_\infty = \frac{1}{(n_- - n_+)e} \, , \tag{49}$$

where $n_+$ and $n_-$ are the densities of conduction electrons with hole like and electron like orbits respectively (for a detailed discussion see e.g. [90]) and $e$ is the electron charge.

If each defect traps $f$ electrons ($\Delta n = fc$, where the change of the total electron density is $\Delta n = \Delta(n_- - n_+)$) the ratio

$$\frac{\Delta\left(\dfrac{1}{R_\infty}\right)}{\Delta\rho} = \frac{f}{\rho_D} \tag{50}$$

is a specific defect property where $\rho_D$ is the resistivity change per unit concentration of defects *.

Much more important for the study of defects is the *low* field Hall coefficient $R_o$. $R_o$ is independent of the crystal orientation in cubic crystals with a random distribution of the defects:

$$R_o = \frac{r}{ne} \, , \tag{51}$$

where $n$ is the density of the conduction electrons and $r$ is a parameter sensitive to the shape of the Fermi surface and the scattering potentials (usually $r \neq 1$) [125]. In the relaxation time model [90]

$$r = n\,\frac{12\pi^3}{e}\,\frac{\int \bar{K}l^2 \, dS}{[\int l \, dS]^2} \tag{52}$$

($\bar{K} = \frac{1}{2}(1/R_1 + 1/R_2)$ is the mean curvature at a certain region of the Fermi surface with area $dS$. $R_1$ and $R_2$ are the radii of curvature in the "main cuts" of this region, $l$ is the mean free path for the conduction electrons with states within $dS$ and related to the corresponding Fermi velocity $v(\mathbf{k})$ and the relaxation time $\tau(\mathbf{k})$ by $l = v\tau$, where $\mathbf{k}$ is the wavenumber vector ending at $dS$).

---

* Complications arise if the defects induce a redistribution of electron states in $k$-space in such a way that new Brillouin zones come into play [90]. Structural defects can also change the Fermi surface due to the relative density change (scaling factor in the rigid band model) and due to the change in the pseudo-potentials, which may be caused by the density change. In the case of copper, and probably also for the other metals under discussion, the corresponding relative changes of the Hall coefficient and of the magnetoresistance (to be discussed in chapter 5.5) are of the order of the defect concentration [90,124].

The quantity $r$ is independent of the defect concentration if only one type of defects is present or if one type is predominant and is directly a specific property of these defects.

Areas of low curvature on the Fermi surface, which may be important for the conductivity, may contribute very little to $R_0$. The integration over the Fermi surface makes $R_0$ very sensitive to the **k**-dependence of the mean free path and therefore to the details of the scattering potential.

### 5.4.2. Aluminium

After reactor neutron irradiation at $4.6°K$ the high field Hall coefficient $R_\infty$ is altered within experimental error only ($|\Delta n|/\Delta \rho < 0.1$ $(1/\mu\Omega \, cm))$ [90,143] which is not very conclusive and could only be improved by using magnetic fields larger than 50 kOe). The concentration of conduction electrons can be taken as constant for the interpretation of the influence of the radiation induced defects on the low field Hall coefficient $R_0$, which can be seen in fig. 23. (The field dependence of $R$ is shown in fig. 27.)

Foreign atoms at $4.6°K$ and phonons above the Debye temperature usually give rise to nearly isotropic scattering (isotropic $\tau$) and therefore nearly isotropic mean free path $l$ (assuming the Fermi velocity to be isotropic). Then the regions with large negative and positive curvature on the Fermi surface FS probably compensate themselves (see fig. 24), the values of $r$ and, therefore, $R_0$ are gouverned by the large areas with the same curvature as the spherical FS in the free electron approximation; accordingly $R_0 \gtrsim 3$ electrons/atom (see fig. 23 and eq. (51) with $r = 1$).

The Frenkel defects change $R_0$ to a slightly positive value. The "average" scattering potential of the interstitials must reduce the mean free path of the electrons with states on part $A$ or $C$ of the FS (fig. 24) much more than those with states on part B.

A comparison of the $\langle 100 \rangle$-, $\langle 110 \rangle$-, and $\langle 111 \rangle$-dumbbell configuration of the interstitial [3] shows, that probably only the $\langle 100 \rangle$-dumbbell interstitial provides the anisotropy required for the scattering cross section (taking always the average over the 3 resp. 6 or 4 possible crystallographic orientations of the three interstitial types) [90]. The vacancy and also the hypothetical interstitial in the centre of the unit cube probably behave as the foreign atoms and, therefore, do not change $R_0$. At the end of stage I, $R_0$ changes rather abruptly to negative values again which indicates that the defects surviving stage I give rise to nearly isotropic scattering of the conduction electrons (fig. 23; see also [10]).

### 5.5. Magnetoresistance
### 5.5.1. Concepts

The increase of the residual electrical resistivity of a non-magnetic metal in an external magnetic field $H$, $\Delta \rho_0(H) \equiv \rho_0(H) - \rho_0(0)$ is caused by the deviations of the Fermi surface and/or the scattering potential from a spherical shape [130,76]. Therefore, the magnetoresistance — like the Hall coefficient — can be used to explore details of the defect potentials.

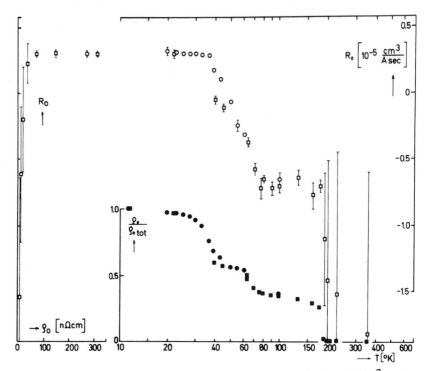

Fig. 23. *Aluminium*. Left part: Low field Hall coefficient $R_0$ for $H/\rho_0(0) = 4 \times 10^7$ kOe/$\Omega$ cm ($\omega\tau \approx 10^{-2}$) as a function of the residual resistivity $\rho_0$ during irradiation with reactor neutrons at 4.6°K.

Right part: $R_0$ and $\rho_0/\rho_{0\,tot}$ as a function of the annealing temperature after the irradiation ($\rho_{0\,tot} = 300$ n$\Omega$ cm). Each point corresponds to a measurement at 4.6°K after 10 min annealing at the temperature $T$. Measurements on two different samples are indicated by circles and squares. The field dependence of the Hall coefficient is shown in fig. 27. The values of $R_0$ (and also of $R_\infty$) are obviously insensitive to the exact choice of $H/\rho_0(0)$ which is not the case for the magnetoresistance $\Delta\rho_0(H)/\rho_0(0)$, except for the saturation region at high magnetic fields. To avoid serious systematic errors or even completely unphysical results the change of $R$ must be evaluated by comparing measurements at equal values of $H/\rho_0(0)$! Similar measurements on copper have been performed recently [143].

For a cubic metal with one type of scattering center randomly distributed, the value of $\Delta\rho_0(H)/\rho_0(0) \equiv M$ is a unique function of $H/\rho_0(0)$ according to Kohler's rule [129,143]

$$\frac{\Delta\rho_0(H)}{\rho_0(0)} = f\left(\frac{H}{\rho_0(0)}\right) , \qquad (53)$$

where the form of $f(H/\rho_0(0))$ is sensitive to the form of the scattering potential. For weak magnetic fields ($\omega\tau \ll 1$) and in a quasifree electron model this is particu-

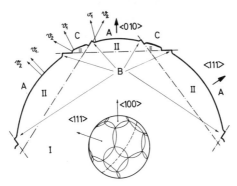

Fig. 24. The Fermi surface FS of aluminium is nearly spherical (small sphere) with anomalies along the lines where it cuts through the Brillouin zone boundaries (indicated by the rosette like lines in the small sphere). A view on the cut through the FS along the dashed line (the normal vector of the cut pointing into $\langle 110 \rangle$) is shown in part by the lines drawn around the sphere. The FS can be separated into several parts: electrons in states at the large spherical regions A, within the second zone (II) with small curvature, behave electron like in a small external magnetic field $\mathbf{H}$ (the position of the group velocity vector $\mathbf{v}$ at two times differing by the relaxation time $\tau$ for $\mathbf{H}$ normal to the cut are indicated:

$$v_1 = \mathbf{v}(t) , \qquad v_2 = \mathbf{v}(t + \tau)).$$

The small areas in the second zone near the zone boundary (B) have a large negative curvature. The corresponding electrons behave hole like in $\mathbf{H}$. The small areas C in the third zone (III) have large positive curvature with electron like behaviour in $\mathbf{H}$.

larly obvious in the approximation of a $\mathbf{k}$-dependent relaxation time where [126]

$$\frac{\Delta \rho_0(H)}{\rho_0(0)} = K' \left( \frac{eH}{\rho_0(0)} \right)^2 \frac{\overline{l^3}\,\overline{l} - (\overline{l^2})^2}{(\overline{l})^4} , \qquad (54)$$

$\overline{l^n}$ being a mean value of the $n$th power of the mean free path over the Fermi surface and $K'$ a constant, which depends on the Fermi surface (in rewriting the original equation [126] the relation $1/\rho_0(0) = \overline{l}/mK'$ has been used, where $m$ is the effective mass). The change of $M$, evaluated at a constant value of $H/\rho_0(0) \sim \omega \tau$ indicates changes of the variance of the mean free path over the FS and, therefore, changes of the defect configuration *.

At high magnetic fields ($\omega \tau \gg 1$) the magnetoresistance $M_\infty$ saturates in the case of noncompensated metals with closed electron orbits [123] (e.g. aluminium; copper, excluding certain directions of the magnetic field in relation to the crystal axes). Contrary to the Hall coefficient the magnetoresistance $M_\infty$ depends on the type of scattering potential operative [130]. The change of $M_\infty$ ($H/\rho_0(0) = $ const)

* This can be demonstrated in a very general way by studying the influence of a combined electric and magnetic field on the distribution of occupied states in $k$-space near the Fermi surface [127,128].

can be used for qualitative discussions of the change of the predominant defect type without the danger of systematic errors as in the low field region (see [90]).

In an exact treatment the whole function $f(H/\rho_o(0))$ must be considered. Exact solutions of the corresponding Boltzmann equation have been derived [130] and, therefore, a determination of the scattering matrix elements from the experiments seems to become possible in the future (but see ref. [143]).

### 5.5.2. Copper

In fig. 25 the field dependence of the longitudinal magnetoresistance after reactor neutron irradiation at 4.6°K and the annealing behaviour is shown [143]. The value

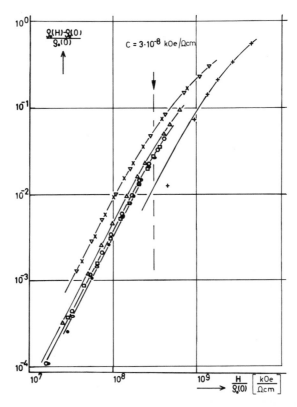

Fig. 25. *Copper.* Longitudinal magnetoresistance as a function of the magnetic field $H$ (Kohler plot) [143]. The different signs indicate different treatments of the sample (measurements always at 4.6°K):

(+) pure annealed polycrystalline sample, $\rho_o(0) = 1.8$ nΩ cm (grain diameter always much larger than electron mean free path);

(●) irradiated at 4.6°K with reactor neutrons, $\rho_o(0) = 137.8$ nΩcm;

(◓) 10 min anneal at 60°K, 97 nΩ cm;    (□) 120°K, 83 nΩ cm;

(◔) 150°K, 73.8 nΩ cm;    (△) 220°K, 42 nΩ cm;

(▽) 300°K, 22 nΩ cm;    (x) 350°K, 20.3 nΩ cm.

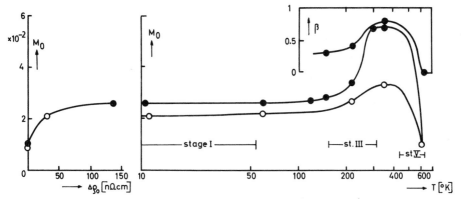

Fig. 26. *Copper.* Longitudinal magnetoresistance $M_0 = \Delta\rho_0(H)/\rho_0(0)$ for $H/\rho_0(0) = C$ according to fig. 25 ($\omega\tau \approx 0.2$).
Left part: behaviour during irradiation with reactor neutrons at 4.6°K.
Right part: behaviour of $M_0$ and the parameter $\beta$ (deviation from Matthiessen's rule) during iso-chronal annealing (10 min holding time at each temperature $T$). The values of $\beta$ belong to the ir-radiation with largest resistivity change and are probably systematically too large due to a super-imposed contribution from the change of the thermal resistivity.

of $M_0$ ($\omega\tau \approx 0.2$) remains constant during irradiation after an initial transient de-pending sensitively on the type of defects present before irradiation.

Single interstitials disappear in stage I without change of $M_0$. The quantity $M_0$ increases during stage III (see fig. 26), where large interstitial I and vacancy V-agglo-merates are building up, mainly in the form of small $\langle 111\rangle$-Frank dislocation loops (see chapter 5.1.2 and [10]).

The variance of the electron mean free path over the Fermi surface may increase by an increase of small angle scattering [132] to be expected during the growth of the agglomerates and by an increased scattering cross section for electrons with **k**-vectors near the neck region of the Fermi surface (fig. 19) compared with that of the belly electrons. Because the neck electrons move mainly in directions different from the six $\langle 111\rangle$-directions, the last behaviour is to be expected from simple geo-metrical arguments [90].

### 5.5.3. Aluminium

In fig. 27 the transverse magnetoresistance measured after reactor neutron irradi-ation at 4.6°K is shown.

The magnetoresistance $M_0$ ($\omega\tau \approx 10^{-2}$) is the same for foreign atoms (probably mainly iron) and Frenkel defects (fig. 28), which means that the variance of the electron mean free path $l$ over the Fermi surface is the same for foreign atoms and FD, although the scattering potential must be quite different (see chapter 5.4.2).

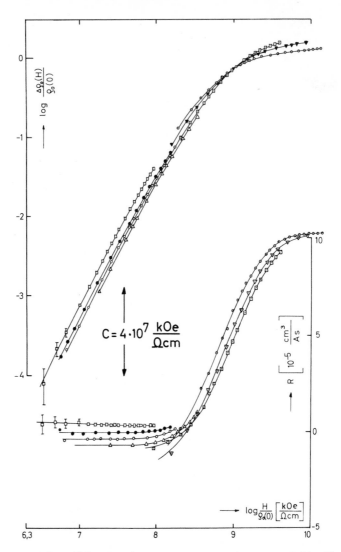

Fig. 27. *Aluminium.* Hall coefficient $R$ and transverse magnetoresistance $\Delta\rho_0(H)/\rho_0(0)$ as a function of magnetic field $H$ (Kohler plot; $\rho_0(0)$ = residual resistivity with $H = 0$). The low field Hall coefficient $R_0$ in fig. 23 and the low field magnetoresistance in fig. 28 were obtained by using the value on the vertical cut at $H/\rho_0(0) = C$, $(\omega\tau \approx 10^{-2})$. The different symbols indicate the following treatments of the polycrystalline sample (grain diameter $\gg$ electron mean free path):

   (□) irradiation with reactor neutrons at 4.6°K, $\rho_0(0)_{tot}$ = 311 nΩ cm;
   (●) 10 min annealing at 40°K, 184 nΩ cm;
   (○) 64°K, 157 nΩ cm;        (△) 90°K, 109 nΩ cm;
   (⊡) 190°K, 74 nΩ cm;       (▽) 210°K, 3.3 nΩ cm;
   (⊙) 354°K, 0.21 nΩ cm

(completely annealed, defect free residual resistance). All measurements were performed at 4.6°K

[143].

The defect reactions during annealing in stage I as discussed in chapter 5.4.2 induce a considerable reduction of $M_0$ ($\omega\tau \approx 10^{-2}$) and, therefore, of the variance of $l$ (fig. 28). Thus $M_0$ ($\omega\tau \approx 10^{-2}$) for vacancies and interstitial agglomerates is even lower than for foreign atoms, an unexpected result, whose detailed explanation must wait until details of the Fermi surface of aluminium are better known. On the other hand, the increase of the high field value $M_\infty$ during agglomeration can very well be understood in terms of the increase of small angle scattering [132] to be expected for increasing size of the scattering centers.

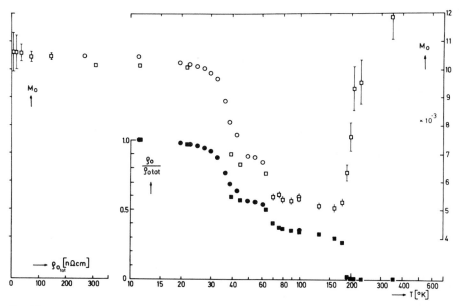

Fig. 28. *Aluminium.* Low field transverse magnetoresistance $M_0 = \Delta\rho_0(H)/\rho_0(0)$ for $H/\rho_0(0)$ = $C$ according to fig. 27 ($\omega\tau \approx 10^{-2}$).
Left part: behaviour during irradiation with reactor neutrons at 4.6°K with total resistivity change $\rho_{0\,tot}$.
Right part: behaviour of $M_0$ and $\rho_0/\rho_{0\,tot}$ during isochronal annealing (10 min holding time). Squares and circles correspond to two different measurements (see also fig. 23). All measurements were performed at 4.6°K.

## 6. Defects and lattice vibrations

### 6.1. *Concepts*

In the Debye model the influence of defects on the lattice vibrations are described by a change of the Debye temperature $\theta$. Relations exist between, e.g., the thermal energy $E_t$, the specific heat $c$, the elastic modulus $G$, the Debye-Waller factor [44], the Lamb-Mössbauer factor $f$, the vibrational electrical resistivity $\rho_T$, the quadratic Doppler-shift * of a Mössbauer-line [134], which are widely used to interrelate the defect induced changes of the physical properties depending on the lattice vibration. For $T$ = const $\ll \theta$

$$\frac{\Delta C}{C} \approx -3 \frac{\Delta \theta}{\theta} \approx -\frac{3}{2} \frac{\Delta G}{G} \approx \frac{\Delta E_t}{E_t} \approx -3 \frac{\Delta f}{f} \tag{55}$$

and

$$\rho_T T = F(T/\theta_\rho) = \rho_T' \ T' = F(T'/\theta_\rho') \quad \text{for} \quad T/\theta_\rho = T'/\theta_\rho' \ , \tag{56}$$

where $\Delta f/f$ is the relative change of the Lamb-Mössbauer factor for the case $f \ll 1$, $F(T/\theta_\rho)$ is Grüneisen's function [73,136], $\rho_T$ is the thermal resistance of the defect free, $\rho_T'$ of the disturbed lattice, $\theta_\rho$ and $\theta_\rho'$ the respective characteristic temperatures roughly equal to the Debye temperature [136].

But these relations may be misleading, because the realistic vibrational spectrum deviates from the Debye spectrum (see fig. 1) and the lattice defects usually do not only induce on overall shift of the spectrum, which could roughly be described by a change of the Debye temperature, but may give rise to resonance and localized vibrational modes [19,137,138]. The physical properties mentioned above depend with different weighing functions on the different phonon modes (see fig. 1) and, therefore, may change in a completely different way than expected from eq. (55). If a defect gives rise to a resonance mode whose frequency $\omega_R$ is much smaller than the maximum phonon frequency $\omega_m$ the vibrational behaviour can be described by a frequency dependent "elastic polarizability" $\alpha(\omega,T)$ (see chapter 4) in analogy to the electric polarizability (see also [19,54]).

## 6.2. Platinum

As shown in chapter 5.3.3 vacancies give rise to a resonance vibrational mode.

Increased mean square vibrational amplitudes of atoms in the neighbourhood of interstitial-vacancy pairs were detected with the Mössbauer effect [135]. The I–V pairs were produced by irradiating platinum with neutrons at 4.6°K, giving rise to the reactions

$$^{196}\text{Pt}(n,\gamma) \ ^{197}\text{Pt} \xrightarrow[T_{\frac{1}{2}} = 18\,\text{h}]{\beta} \ ^{197}\text{Au}^* \xrightarrow[T_{\frac{1}{2}} = 1.9 \times 10^{-9}\,\text{s}]{\gamma_M} \ ^{197}\text{Au} \ .$$

The recoil energy of the neutron capture $\gamma$ (max. approx. 150 eV) is capable of producing an I–V pair. In addition, the activated $^{197}$Au, deposited in the neighbour-

---

* The quadratic Doppler shift $v_q$ depends on the thermal $E_t$ and zero point $E_0$ vibrational energy [144]. The relative change of $v_q$ due to defects is equal to the relative change of the total vibrational energy $E = E_0 + E_t$: $\Delta v_q/v_q = \Delta E/E$ (see also fig. 1). For $T \ll \theta$ the change of $v_q$ depends on $E_0$ only ($E_0 \gg E_t$) and thus on the behaviour of the high frequency phonon modes mainly. In the Debye model and for $T \ll \theta$: $\Delta v_q/v_q = \Delta E_0/E_0 = \Delta \theta/\theta$.

hood of the Frenkel defect, emits a 77 keV $\gamma_M$ used for Mössbauer resonance absorption experiment. The defects cause a decrease of the Lamb-Mössbauer factor: $f$(irrad. at 5°K)/$f_0$ (annealed at 700°K) = 0.8 ± 0.05, independent of the residual resistivity change in the range of accurate measurements available ($20 < \Delta\rho < 150$ nΩcm). The change of $f$ anneals completely in stage I around 30°K, where the close I–V pairs recombine [10] (see fig. 29).

The Lamb-Mössbauer factor is related to the mean square vibrational amplitude $\langle x^2 \rangle$ of the nucleus emitting the $\gamma_M$-ray with wavenumber $k$ (in this case $k = 3.7 \times 10^9$ 1/cm)

$$f = \exp(-k^2 \langle x^2 \rangle / 3) \tag{57}$$

and from the observed effect

$$\Delta f/f_0 \,(4.6°K) \approx -\Delta\langle x^2 \rangle / \langle x_0^2 \rangle = -0.19 \pm 0.05 \ ,$$

where $f_0 = 0.24$, $\langle x_0^2 \rangle = 30 \times 10^{-20}$ cm$^2$ at 4.6°K.

From chapter 4 and table 1 the dielastic modulus change caused by Frenkel defects with $\Delta\rho = 15$ nΩcm would be $\Delta G_d/G \approx -0.002$, which is two orders of magnitude smaller than expected on the basis of the Debye model (eqs. (55)). For the measurement of $\Delta G_d/G$ vibrations with a frequency around $10^2$ Hz have been used, with which the resonance modes giving rise to the change of $f$ and having a frequency $\omega_R = 0\,(10^{13}$ Hz) (chapter 5.4.4 and [135]) cannot be detected.

The temperature dependence of $f$ in the temperature range below the annealing stage I seems to confirm the existence of such a resonance mode [135].

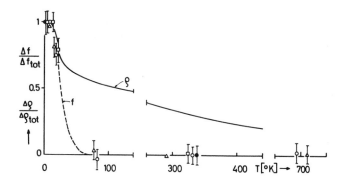

Fig. 29. *Platinum.* Relative change of the Lamb-Mössbauer-factor $\Delta f/\Delta f_{tot}$ (77 keV – $\gamma$ of $^{197}$Au) and of the residual resistivity $\Delta\rho/\Delta\rho_{tot}$ as a function of annealing temperature (10 min holding time) after irradiation with reactor neutrons at 4.6°K. Measurement always at 4.6°K. Total resistivity change [97] $\Delta\rho_{tot} = 7.8$ nΩ cm. The values of $\Delta f_{tot}/f_0$ with $f_0 = 0.24$, are
(o) −0.10 ± 0.07,   (□) −0.13 ± 0.06,   (△) 0.19 ± 0.05.

By irradiating the absorber in a resonance absorption experiment, and measuring the corresponding change of the Lamb-Mössbauer factor, the influence of defects on the overall vibrational spectrum could be studied (see fig. 1).

### 6.3. Gold and other metals

By measuring the temperature dependence of the electrical resistivity of gold after quenching-in vacancies and after annealing [84] a change of the characteristic temperature $\theta_\rho$ (eq. 56) was found: $\Delta\theta_\rho/\theta_\rho = 0(-100\,C_V)$, where $C_V$ is the vacancy concentration (see table 1).

In copper similar changes are caused by Frenkel defects and agglomerates of I and/or V (see chapters 2.2 and 5.1.2, table 1). Generally, structural point defects seem to cause a "softening" of the phonon modes.

In fig. 18 an anomalous "hump" can be observed in the curves at $\rho_T/\Delta\rho_0 \approx 10$, which cannot be described by eq. (28). Such anomalies were also observed in Mg-Pb alloys and explained by scattering of electrons at resonance modes [145].

## 7. Irradiation effects in superconducting niobium

### 7.1. Goodman-Gorkov relations

The upper critical field $H_{c2}$ of niobium, a type II superconductor, depends on the Ginzburg–Landau parameter $\kappa$ $(H_{c2} = \kappa\sqrt{2}H_c)$; $\kappa$ is related to the resistivity in the normal state $\rho_n$ $(\mu\Omega\,cm)$ by [147]

$$\kappa = \kappa_0 + 7.5 \times 10^{-3}\sqrt{\gamma}\rho_n \,, \tag{58}$$

where $\gamma$ is the coefficient of the electronic specific heat in erg/cm$^3$ ($^\circ$K)$^2$ and $\kappa_0$ is the parameter in the pure substance. The value of $\rho_n$ can be changed easily by irradiation induced defects, which seems to be especially useful for the region around $\kappa = 1/\sqrt{2}$, where the superconductive behaviour changes from type I to II. Defect induced changes of the thermodynamic critical field $H_c$ can be measured indirectly by the changes of the critical temperature $T_c$, whereas the hysteresis effects in the magnetization curves prevent a direct determination of $H_c$ (see below).

Interstitials and vacancies produced by fast neutron irradiation at $4.6^\circ$K give rise to a linear change of $H_{c2}$ with $\rho_n$ $(0.01 < \rho_n < 1.2\,\mu\Omega\,cm)$ with the slope [146] $\partial H_{c2}/\partial\rho_n = (1.56 \pm 2\%)$ kOe/$\mu\Omega$ cm.

Essentially the same value is found for oxygen or nitrogen impurities and in theory [146]. Thus eq. (58) is not sensitive to the type and also the distribution of scattering centers (the distribution of Frenkel defects is extremely inhomogeneous at low neutron doses, see fig. 30 and [146]).

The critical temperature $T_c$ seems to be slightly reduced by Frenkel defects [148]: $\Delta T_c/\Delta\rho = 0(-(1/10)^\circ K/\mu\Omega\,cm)$, where $\Delta\rho$ is the normal resistivity due to the defects.

## 7.2. Pinning of the fluxline lattice

The defects interact with fluxlines in the mixed state of superconductors and prevent the establishment of the thermodynamic equilibrium.

This causes hysteresis effects in the magnetization curves [146,149] and in the field dependence of thermal conductivity [113,141]. A survey of the effects observed after neutron irradiation at 4.6°K is presented in fig. 30. From "minor"

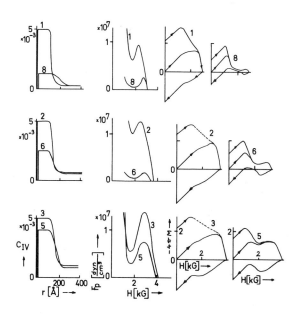

Fig. 30. Niobium [146]. Right column: Magnetic hysteresis curves: The difference of internal and external magnetic field $4\pi M$ of long niobium samples as a function of a longitudinal external field $H$ at 4.6°K (plotted is only the right part $H \geqslant 0$ of the total hysteresis curve; the virgin curve starts at $H = 0; M$ = magnetization). The different numbers pertain to different irradiation and annealing treatments (see fig. 31). Before irradiation the annealed and degassed sample was hysteresis-free (residual resistivity ratio 800).

Middle column: Dependence of the pinning force per unit volume $F_p$ on the external field $H$ ($H$ is of the order of the local internal field $B$ related to $F_p$ for the region of the curves drawn). The "peak effect" (maximum of $F_p$) is not yet understood [146,155]).

Left column: Qualitative plots of the distance correlation densities of interstitials and vacancies for the different treatments: $C_{IV}$ = mean concentration of interstitials at a distance $r$ from a vacancy. The peak at low distances is due to the strong correlation of I and V in the defect nests produced by the collision cascades during neutron irradiation. For $r \gg$ nest-diameter = 0(100 Å) the value of $C_{IV}$ corresponds to the mean concentration of Frenkel defects [16].

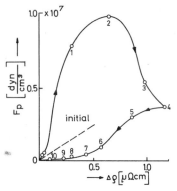

Fig. 31. *Niobium* [146]. Pinning force $F_p$ at the minimum of the $F_p$-$H$-curves in fig. 30 (middle column) as a function of the residual resistivity change due to point defects. Irradiation at 4.6°K with fast neutrons: curve 0–1–2–3–4.

Lower curve: $F_p$ after irradiation to point 4 and 10 min anneal at 21°K (5), 57°K (6), 80°K (7), 126°K (8), 166°K (9), 300°K (10) (compare fig. 7). Dividing $F_p$ by the density of fluxlines $n \approx 10^{10}$ 1/cm² corresponding to the local internal field $B \approx 2 \times 10^3$ $G$, the pinning force per unit length of a fluxline $f_p$ can be calculated formally ($F_p = nf_p$). At a total neutron irradiation induced resistivity change of 10 nΩ cm the pinning force on 1 cm fluxline per defect nest is of the order of $10^{-6}$dyn, if the fluctuations of the local concentration of defect nests are considered and each fluxline contributes to the pinning.

Explanation of symbols: $H_r^1$ is the activation enthalpy of relaxation obtained from the shift of the maximum temperature $T_m$ with a change of vibrational frequency $\omega$; $H_r^2$ is the activation enthalpy obtained from the half width; $\tau_0$ from $\omega\tau = 1$ at $T_m$ and $\tau = \tau_0 \exp(H_r/kT)$; $H_m$ is the activation enthalpy for the annealing process, $n$ the corresponding number of jumps at the beginning of the annealing, $\Delta\rho/\Delta\rho_0$ the resistivity change related to the disappearance of the internal friction maxima. The values $H_m$ of peak 1 and 2 are equal to the activation enthalpy of resistivity annealing [6] in stage $I_A$ and $I_D$.

magnetic hysteresis curves the forces acting between the fluxlines and the defects can be determined [146] (see also [151]). These pinning forces $F_p$ depend sensitively on the distribution of defects in the sample (see fig. 30 and 31). Fig. 31 shows the extremely nonlinear dependence of $F_p$ on the mean defect concentration measured by the normal resistivity change $\Delta\rho$. This dependence is very different from that of the critical shear stress, which is a measure of the interaction of dislocations with defects [17]. At the maximum value of $F_p$ in fig. 31 only 20% of the sample is filled with defects, counting the core field volumes only. Since $F_p$ is given by the local gradient of the fluxline energies caused by the fluctuations of the local superconductivity properties, these fluctuations have reached their maximum values at a comparatively low defect concentration. Probably the proximity [152] effect is operative to bend down $F_p$ at comparatively low irradiation doses.

The elementary process of the pinning is not yet clear. Recently the stress state of the lattice was incorporated into an extended Ginzburg-Landau theory, so that at least a sound phenomenological theory seems to become available [153]. The behaviour of defects in the fluxline lattice [154,151] may turn out to be essential for a solution of the pinning problem.

# References

[1] G.H.Vineyard, J. Phys. Chem. Solids 3 (1957) 121.
[2] M.Doyama and R.M.J.Cotterill, in: Lattice defects and their interaction, ed. R.R.Hasiguti (Gordon and Breach, New York, 1967).
[3] A.Seeger, E.Mann and R.v.Jan, J. Phys. Chem. Solids 23 (1962) 639.
[4] H.Wollenberger, this volume.
[5] K.Böning and H.Wenzl, Forschungsreaktor München, Report 92 (1967), to be published.
[6] J.W.Corbett, Electron radiation damage in semiconductors and metals (Academic Press, New York, 1966) p. 45.
[7] H.Meissner, W.Schilling and H.Wenzl, EuroNuclear 2 (1965) 277.
[8] G.Lück and R.Sizmann, Phys. Stat. Sol. 6 (1964) 263; 5 (1964) 683.
[9] P.Sigmund, G.Scheidler and G.Roth, Conference on "Solid State Research with accelerators", Brookhaven 1967, BNL 50083 (C-52);
    K.Dettmann, Phys. Stat. Sol. 10 (1965) 269;
    K.Schröder, Diplomarbeit, Technische Hochschule Aachen, 1966.
[10] W.Schilling, this volume.
[11] "Lattice defects in quenched metals", eds. R.M.Cotterill, M.Doyama, J.J.Jackson and M. Meshii (Academic Press, New York, 1965); and this volume.
[12] M.Hoch, this volume.
[13] R.Siems, Berichte der Kernforschungsanlage Jülich Nr. 545, 1968.
[14] J.Friedel, this volume.
[15] A.C.Damask and G.J.Dienes, Point defects in metals (Gordon and Breach, New York, 1963);
    A.Seeger and H.Mehrer, this volume.
[16] H.Wenzl, Thesis, Technische Hochschule München, 1966.
[17] J.Diehl, this volume.
[18] G.H.Vineyard and G.J.Dienes, Phys. Rev. 93 (1954) 265;
    H.B.Huntington, G.A.Shirn and E.S.Wajda, Phys. Rev. 99 (1955) 1085;
    G.Schottky, A.Seeger and G.Schmidt, Phys. Stat. Sol. 4 (1964) 439.
[19] W.Ludwig, Springer Tracts Vol. 43 (Springer Verlag, Berlin, 1967).
[20] Y.Quéré, Défauts ponctuels dans les métaux (Masson, Paris, 1967).
[21] E.Mann, Phys. Stat. Sol. 11 (1965) 753 and 767.
[22] A.Seeger, Journ. Phys. Radium 23 (1962) 616.
[23] R.v.Jan, J. Phys. Chem. Solids 29 (1968) 561.
[24] K.Böning, Thesis, Technische Hochschule München, 1968.
[25] N.H.March and B.Oli, in: Calculations of the properties of vacancies and interstitials, ed. A.D.Franklin (Nat. Bureau of Standards Miscell. Publ. 287, Washington, D.C., 1967) p. 69.
[26] K.Mukherjee, Phil. Mag. 12 (1965) 915.
[27] F.Losehand, Diplomarbeit, Technische Hochschule München, 1968; to be published.
[28] T.H.Blewitt, in: Radiation damage in solids, ed. D.S.Billington (Academic Press, New York, 1962) p. 630;
    M.W.Lucas and T.H.Blewitt at the "Conference on point defects in metals", Reading 12–13 April 1967.
[29] Vacancies and other point defects in metals (The Institute of Metals, London, 1958) p. 54.
[30] A.Granato, Phys. Rev. 111 (1958) 740;
    A.V.Granato and T.G.Nilan, Phys. Rev. 137 (1965) A1233, A1250.

[31] W.Mönch and W.Sander, Z. Physik 157 (1959) 149.

[32] R.O.Simmons, J. Phys. Soc. Japan 18 Suppl. II (1963) 172.

[33] T.H.Blewitt, A.C.Klank, T.Scott and M.Lucas, Jül. Conf. 2 (Vol. I) 1968, p. 339.

[34] J.v.Stebut, Diplomarbeit, Technische Hochschule München, 1967.

[35] F.Rau, Thesis, Technische Hochschule München, 1967; to be published.

[36] H.Bilger, V.Hivert, J.Verdone, J.L.Leveque and J.C.Soulie, Jül. Conf. 2 (Vol. 2) 1968, p. 251;
     H.Bilger, private communication.

[37] J.E.Bauerle and J.S.Koehler, Phys. Rev. 107 (1957) 1493.

[38] W.DeSorbo, Phys. Rev. 117 (1960) 444.

[39] R.O.Simmons, in: Radiation damage in solids, ed. D.S.Billington (Academic Press, New York, 1962) p. 568.

[40] J.D.Eshelby, in: Solid State Physics, Vol. 3, eds. F.Seitz and D.Turnbull (Academic Press, New York, 1956) p. 79.

[41] K.Fischer and H.Hahn, Z. Physik 172 (1963) 172.

[42] A.Seeger, Phys. Letters 12 (1964) 176.

[43] G.Schottky, A.Seeger and G.Schmidt, Phys. Stat. Sol. 4 (1964) 439.

[44] W.Schmatz, this volume.

[45] M.Beyeler and Y.Adda, J. Phys. 29 (1968) 345.

[46] Theory of crystal defects, ed. B.Gruber (Academia Prague, 1966) pp. 167 and 275.

[47] J.–P.Niklaus, W.Schmatz, R.Simson and H.Wenzl, Z. Angew. Phys. 24 (1968) 313;
     R.Simson, Thesis, Technische Hochschule München 1968; to be published.

[48] C.Budin and P.Lucasson, in: 10e Colloque de métallurgie, ed. G.Chaudron (Presses Universitaires, Paris, 1966) p. 227.

[49] A.Sepp, private communication.

[50] G.Leibfried, in: Handbuch der Physik, Vol. VII/1, ed. S.Flügge (Springer, Berlin, 1955) p. 273.

[51] C.Kittel, Introduction to solid state physics (Wiley, 1967).

[52] K.Fischer, Z. Physik 155 (1959) 59; 157 (1959) 198.

[53] M.Rühle, Phys. Stat. Sol. 19 (1967) 263;
     M.Rühle and M.Wilkens, Phil. Mag. 15 (1967) 1075.

[54] E.Kröner, Phys. Kondens. Materie 2 (1964) 262.

[55] M.Pistorius and W.Ludwig, Jül. Conf. 2 (Vol. 2) 1968, p. 558;
     Calculation of the properties of vacancies and interstitials, ed. A.D.Franklin (Natl. Bureau of Standards Misc. Publ. 287, Washington, D.C., 1967) p. 151.

[56] H.Kronmüller, this volume.

[57] A.S.Nowick and W.R.Heller, Adv. Physics 12 (1963) 251.

[58] V.Fischer, Diplomarbeit, Technische Hochschule München 1968; to be published.

[59] G.Alefeld, Z. Physik 170 (1962) 249.

[60] M.Riggauer, Thesis, Technische Hochschule München, 1968; to be published.

[61] F.Kerscher, Thesis, Technische Hochschule München, 1968, to be published.

[62] R.C.Folweiler and F.R.Brotzen, Acta Met. 7 (1959) 716.

[63] J.Melngailis, Phys. Stat. Sol. 16 (1966) 247.

[64] L.C.R.Alfred, Phys. Rev. 152 (1966) 693.

[65] J.Friedel, in: Physique des basses températures, eds. C.DeWitt, B.Dreyfus and P.G.DeGennes (Gordon and Breach, New York, 1962) p. 562.

[66] D.König, J.Völkl and W.Schilling, Phys. Stat. Sol. 7 (1964) 591.

[67] G.Roth and V.Naundorf, Jül. Conf. 2 (Vol. I) 1968, p. 364.

[68] J.A.DiCarlo, C.L.Snead Jr. and A.N.Goland, BNL 12807; to be published.

[69] P.Lucasson and R.M.Walker, Phys. Rev. 127 (1960) 52.

[70] A.Seeger and E.Mann, in: Calculation of the properties of vacancies and interstitials, ed. A.D.Franklin (Nat. Bureau of Standards Misc. Publ. 287, Washington, D.C., 1967) p. 75.

[71] A.Rau, Thesis, Universität München, 1968.
[72] B.S.Berry and J.L.Orehotsky, Phil. Mag. 8 (1964) 467.
[73] H.Jones, in: Handbuch der Physik, Vol. 19, ed. S.Flügge (Springer, Berlin, 1956);
     H.Bross, in: Festkörperprobleme, Vol. 5 (Vieweg, Braunschweig, 1966).
[74] R.W.Balluffi, R.W.Siegel, K.H.Lie and D.N.Seidmann, this volume.
[75] R.M.Walker, J. Phys. 24 (1963) 476.
[76] J.M.Ziman, Electrons and phonons (Clarendon Press, Oxford, 1960).
[77] B.Lengeler, Thesis, Technische Hochschule Aachen, 1968;
     H.Kreuzer, Diplomarbeit, Technische Hochschule München, 1966.
[78] H.Bross, in: Moderne Probleme der Metallphysik, Vol. 1, ed. A.Seeger (Springer, Berlin, 1965).
[79] H.Bross, Z. Naturforsch. 14a (1959) 560.
[80] H.Bross and A.Seeger, J. Phys. Chem. Solids 4 (1958) 161.
[81] K.Rösch, F.Bell and R.Sizmann, Jül. Conf. 2 (Vol. I) 1968, p. 444.
[82] E.Krautz and H.Schultz, Z. Naturforsch. 12a (1957) 710; 9a (1954) 125; Abhandlungen
     der Braunschweigischen Wissenschaftl. Gesellschaft Vol. 8, 1956;
     H.Schultz, Z. Angew. Physik 9 (1957) 465;
     W.Boas and J.F.Nicholas, Austr. J. Phys. (1953) 116;
     P.G.Klemens, Australian J. Phys. (1953) 122.
[83] M.Löffler, Diplomarbeit, Technische Hochschule München, 1966.
[84] R.R.Conte, J.Dural and Y.Quéré, Jül. Conf. 2 (Vol. I) 1968, p. 235.
[85] G.D.Magnuson, W.Palmer and J.S.Koehler, Phys. Rev. 109 (1958) 199.
[86] M.L.Swanson and G.R.Piercy, Can. J. Phys. 42 (1964) 1605.
[87] J.J.Jackson and K.Herschbach, Phys. Rev. 170 (1968) 618.
[88] J.S.Dugdale and Z.S.Basinsky, Phys. Rev. 157 (1967) 552.
[89] H.Bross, Phys. Kondens. Materie 3 (1965) 349.
[90] K.Böning, Thesis, Technische Hochschule München, 1968; to be published.
[91] G.Burger, H.Meissner and W.Schilling, Phys. Stat. Sol. 4 (1964) 281.
[92] G.Duesing, H.Hemmerich, W.Sassin and W.Schilling, Jül. Conf. 2 (Vol. I) 1968, p. 246.
[93] K.Fischer, Phys. Kondens. Materie 6 (1967) 171.
[94] D.Heeger, Diplomarbeit, Technische Hochschule München, 1966.
[95] H.Wollenberger, Diskussionstagung über atomare Fehlstellen und Strahlenschädigung,
     Schliersee, Sept. 1965, unpublished.
[96] C.J.Meechan and A.Sosin, Phys. Rev. 113 (1959) 422.
[97] H.Wenzl, unpublished.
[98] W.Schilling and P.Tischer, Z. Angew. Phys. 22 (1967) 56;
     K.Isebeck, F.Rau, P.Tischer, K.Sonnenberg, W.Schilling and H.Wenzl, Phys. Stat. Sol. 17
     (1966) 259.
[99] U.Himmler, H.Peisl, A.Sepp, W.Waidelich and H.Wenzl, Z. Angew. Phys. 23 (1967) 8;
     Jül. Conf. 2 (Vol I) 1968, p. 343.
[100] A.Sepp, unpublished.
[101] U.Himmler, A.Sepp, H.Peisl, W.Waidelich and H.Wenzl, Phys. Rev. Letters 19 (1967)
      956; Jül. Conf. 2 (Vol. I) 1968, p. 343.
[102] R.O.Simmons and R.W.Balluffi, Phys. Rev. 109 (1958) 1142.
[103] U.Himmler, Thesis, Technische Hochschule München, 1968.
[104] R.Vook and C.Wert, Phys. Rev. 109 (1958) 1529.
[105] R.Hanada and J.W.Kauffman, Appl. Phys. Letters 12 (1968) 42.
[106] H.Diekamp and A.Sosin, J. Appl. Phys. 27 (1956) 1416.
[107] A.Seeger, H.Bross and P.Gruner, Disc. Faraday Soc. 38 (1964) 69.
[108] H.Bross, Phys. Stat. Sol. 2 (1962) 481.
[109] H.Bross and A.Seeger, J. Phys. Chem. Solids 4 (1958) 161.

[110] J.Lauterwein, Diplomarbeit, Technische Hochschule München, 1965.

[111] H.M.Rosenberg, Low temperature Solid State Physics (Clarendon, Oxford, 1965).

[112] K.Mendelssohn and H.Montgomery, Phil. Mag. 1 (1956) 718;
      K.Mendelssohn, J. Phys. Soc. Japan 18, Suppl. II (1962) 17.

[113] E.Schmidbauer, Thesis, Technische Hochschule München, 1969.

[114] M.Bailyn, Phys. Rev. 157 (1967) 480.

[115] R.P.Huebner, Phys. Rev. 146 (1966) 490.

[116] R.P.Huebner, Phys. Rev. 135 (1964) A1281.

[117] R.J.Gripshover, J.B.VanZytoeld and J.Bass, Phys. Rev. 163 (1967) 598.

[118] M.V.Klein, Phys. Rev. 141 (1966) 716.

[119] The Fermi Surface, eds. W.A.Harrison and M.B.Webb (Wiley, New York, 1960).

[120] J.Polák, Czech. J. Phys. B13 (1963) 616; B14 (1964) 176.

[121] R.Fletscher and J.S.Dugdale, in: Proceedings of the Xth international conference on low
      temperature physics, Vol. III, ed. M.–P.Malkow (Moscow, 1967) p. 246.

[122] Conference on electron mean free paths in metals, ETH Zürich, Sept. 1968, to be pub-
      lished in Phys. Kondens. Materie.

[123] E.Fawcett, Adv. Physics 13, No. 50 (1964) 139.

[124] R.v.Jan, J. Phys. Chem. Solids 29 (1968) 561.

[125] R.S.Allgaier, Phys. Rev. 165 (1968) 775.

[126] A.Sommerfeld and H.Bethe, Elektronentheorie der Metalle (Springer, Berlin, 1967).

[127] S.Winkler, Thesis, Technische Hochschule München, 1967.

[128] D.Langbein, Z. Physik 172 (1963) 358.

[129] M.Kohler, Ann. Phys. 32 (1938) 211.

[130] A.Seeger, Phys. Letters 20 (1966) 608;
      A.Seeger, E.Mann and K.Clausecker, Phys. Stat. Sol. 24 (1967) 721.

[131] E.Mann, A.Seeger and G.Thierer, Z. Physik 193 (1966) 295.

[132] A.B.Pippart, Proc. Roy. Soc. A282 (1964) 464.

[133] G.J.Dienes, Phys. Rev. 86 (1952) 228.

[134] U.Gonser, this volume.

[135] J.Weiser, Thesis, Technische Hochschule München 1966;
      W.Vogl, Diplomarbeit, Technische Hochschule München, 1968.

[136] M.Blackman, in: Handbuch der Physik, Vol. VII/1, ed. S.Flügge (Springer, Berlin, 1955).

[137] J.M.Lifshitz and A.M.Kosevich, Rep. Progr. Phys. XXIX, part I (1966) 217;
      A.A.Maradudin, in: Solid State Physics, Vol. 18, eds. F.Seitz and D.Turnbull (Academic
      Press, New York, 1966) p. 274.

[138] Localized excitations in solids, ed. R.F.Wallis (Plenum Press, New York, 1968).

[139] W.Bauer, J.W.DeFord, J.S.Koehler and J.W.Kauffmann, Phys. Rev. 128 (1962) 1497;
      G.D.Magnuson, W.Palmer and J.S.Koehler, Phys. Rev. 109 (1958) 1990;
      D.Bowen and G.W.Kodeback, Acta Met. 1 (1953) 649;
      K.Herschbach, Phys. Rev. 130 (1963) 554.

[140] G.Gilat and R.M.Nicklow, Phys. Rev. 143 (1966) 487.

[141] E.Umlauf, Z. Physik 206 (1967) 415.

[142] I.G.Bardeen, G.Rickayzen and L.Tewordt, Phys. Rev. 113 (1959) 982.

[143] K.Böning, B.Lengeler, J.–M.Welter and H.Wenzl, Jül. Conf. 2 (Vol. I) 1968, p. 405;
      J.–M.Welter, Thesis, Technische Hochschule München, 1969.

[144] H.Wegener, Der Mössbauereffekt (Bibliographisches Institut, Mannheim, 1965).

[145] Y.M.Kagan and A.P.Zhernow, Soviet Physics JETP 23 (1966) 737;
      Localized excitations in solids, ed. R.F.Wallis (Plenum Press, New York, 1968) p. 14.

[146] H.Berndt, N.Kartascheff and H.Wenzl, Z. Angew. Phys. 24 (1968) 305.

[147] L.P.Gorkov, JETP 10 (1960) 998;
      B.B.Goodman, I.B.M., J. Res. and Dev. 6 (1962) 63.

[148] J.Kopainsky, Diplomarbeit, Technische Hochschule München, 1967;
      F.Sernetz, Diplomarbeit, Technische Hochschule München, 1968.
[149] R.H.Kernohan and S.T.Sekula, ORNL-Report 67–62, to be published in Phys. Rev.
[150] J.Friedel, P.G.DeGennes and J.Matricon, Appl. Phys. Letters 2 (1963) 199.
[151] H.Träuble and U.Essmann, J. Appl. Phys. 39 (1968) 4052.
[152] E.g., P.Fulde and W.Mormann, to be published in Phys. Kondens. Materie;
      K.Maki, Physics 1 (1964) 21.
[153] A.Seeger and H.Kronmüller, Phys. Stat. Sol. 27 (1968) 371;
      R.Labusch, Phys. Rev. 170 (1968) 470.
[154] P.G.DeGennes, Superconductivity of metals and alloys (Benjamin, New York, 1966)
      p. 91.
[155] H.Conrad, L.Rice, E.L.Fletscher and F.Vernon, Mater. Sci. Eng. 1 (1967) 360.
[156] C.A.Domenicali and F.A.Otter, Phys. Rev. 95 (1964) 1134;
      G.Burger, K.Isebeck, J.Völkl, W.Schilling and H.Wenzl, Z. Angew. Phys. 22 (1967) 452.
[157] H.Schultz, Mater. Sci. Eng. 3 (1968/69) 189.
[158] J.Diehl, in: Moderne Probleme der Metallphysik, vol. 1, ed. A.Seeger (Springer, Berlin,
      1965).
[159] P.G.Klemens and L.Tewordt, Rev. Mod. Phys. 36 (1964) 118.
[160] K.Isebeck, Phys. Stat. Sol. 8 (1965) 577.
[161] K.Ehrensperger, Diplomarbeit, Technische Hochschule München (1969).
[162] R.Nielsen and J.R.Townsend, Phys. Rev. Letters 21 (1968) 1749;
      J.R.Townsend, J.A.DiCarlo, R.Nielsen and A.Stabell, Acta Met. 17 (1969) 425.
[163] F.Rau and H.Wenzl, to be published.
[164] S.Okuda and T.Nakanii, in: Radiation damage in reactor materials (IAEA, Vienna, 1969)
      Report No. SM-120/A-3.

## Discussion

*U.Gonser:* In your Mössbauer experiment with the isotope [197]Au you observe after irradiation a change in the recoil-free fraction (change in $x^2$) and you interprete your results in terms of a low frequency mode. Such mode should change the mean square velocity $(v^2)$, thus giving rise to a shift, a Mössbauer parameter which is normally easier to observe than the change in the recoil-free fraction.

*H.Wenzl:* At a constant temperature in the range of low temperatures $(T > 0)$ the change of the quadratic Doppler shift is a measure of the change of the vibrational energy of the lattice due to defects. Therefore it is sensitive to changes of the phonon spectrum at high frequencies mainly, whereas the proposed low frequency mode would not give rise to a line shift outside the experimental error.

# PART 4

## POINT DEFECTS
## IN COLD-WORKED FCC METALS

# POINT DEFECTS IN COLD WORKED FCC METALS

A.van den BEUKEL

*Laboratorium voor Metaalkunde, Technische Hogeschool, Delft, The Netherlands*

Dedicated to Prof. Dr. M.J.Druyvesteyn

## 1. Introduction

About 20 years ago the experimental investigations on point defects in metals started with the pioneering experiments of Druyvesteyn and coworkers on copper, cold worked at liquid air temperature. The first result, obtained by Molenaar and Aarts [1] is shown in fig. 1. The electrical resistivity of a copper wire was measured as a function of plastic strain at liquid air temperature. At a certain point the experiment was interrupted by annealing the wire at room temperature. This treatment causes a decrease of the resistivity, called recovery, whereas the stress-strain curve was unaffected. Since plastic deformation is expected to produce dislocations and point defects of both the vacancy and interstitial type, and the mechanical properties are hardly affected by the recovery, it was ascribed to the annealing out of point defects.

When the specimen is warmed up gradually, the resistivity drop appears to occur in several more or less clearly separated recovery stages. The discussion of these stages is the main subject of this paper. The first isochronal annealing experiments [2,3] revealed the existence of two clear recovery stages (later on labeled II and III respectively [4]), which were tentatively attributed to the annealing out of interstitials and vacancies, respectively. There was, however, no positive evidence supporting this interpretation: It was based on the fact that two types of point defects were expected to be present and two recovery stages were observed, whereas according to theory single interstitials were predicted to be more mobile than single vacancies.

Later on measurements of the recovery spectrum of cold worked fcc metals revealed that the situation is more complicated than suggested by the early results. In many cases the two main recovery stages showed some substructure. Further there is evidence for a small third stage (stage IV). Moreover it has appeared to be very difficult (and in fact impossible up till now) to set up experiments which identify the point defects in cold worked metals beyond doubt. Therefore the interpretation

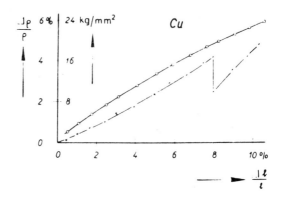

Fig. 1. Stress-strain curve (o o o) and increase of resistivity (x x x) versus plastic strain for Cu, cold worked at liquid air temperature [1]. For $\epsilon = 8\%$ the experiment was interrupted by annealing the specimen at room temperature.

of the recovery spectrum after cold working needs data on the properties of vacancy and interstitial type defects obtained from other sources, such as equilibrium, quenching and irradiation experiments. For this reason the results of such experiments have to be considered in this paper. A few points will be mentioned here.

Equilibrium measurements (Simmons and Balluffi, see the review by Balluffi et al. [5]) have succeeded in determining the formation energies of vacancies $E_{1V}^{F}$ for a number of fcc metals in agreement with the results of quenching experiments. Combination of the values observed with the known activation energies for self-diffusion provides the activation energies of migration of single vacancies $E_{1V}^{M}$. The activation energies observed during annealing of quenched metals are usually lower than $E_{1V}^{M}$, because, even if only single vacancies should have been quenched in, the vacancies spend part of their time as members of more mobile vacancy clusters (di-vacancies, tri-vacancies etc.). This mutual interaction of vacancy type defects during the annealing of quenched metals has made it extremely difficult to interpret the annealing data uniquely. For instance, numerous experiments on quenched Au have not resulted in generally accepted values of simple parameters such as the migration and binding energies of di-vacancies. In one respect the irradiation experiments have been more successful. In electron irradiation it is expected that vacancy-interstitial pairs are formed with varying distances. The recovery spectrum is dominated by a large stage, labeled I, at low temperatures ($\approx 10-60°$K). It is generally agreed that in the first and major part of this stage recombination of close Frenkel pairs occurs, whereas in the final part free migration of single interstitials takes place. However, different opinions exist on the *kind* of interstitial which is mobile in stage I. According to one group of authors it is the $\langle 100 \rangle$ split interstitial (sometimes called "dumbbell"), being the stable interstitial configuration as predicted by theory. In this scheme no free migration of single interstitials occurs above

stage I (1 interstitial model). A second group of authors argues that the free interstitial mobile in stage I is the metastable $\langle 110 \rangle$ crowdion, whereas the stable
$\langle 100 \rangle$ split interstitial becomes mobile in stage III (2 interstitial model).

From the foregoing it will be clear that at the present time very few undisputed
data of vacancy and interstitial type defects is available. This makes the interpretation of the recovery spectrum of cold worked metals rather uncertain. On the other
hand the recovery phenomena after cold working could be more simple than after
irradiation or quenching in the following respects:

1) The fact that stage I is almost absent after cold working shows that at least
one type of single interstitial produced in irradiation is absent in cold worked
metals.

2) In deformed metals the number of dislocations present is so large that they
act as the main sinks and mutual interaction of point defects is less important. For
a regular dislocation network the average number of jumps of the point defects to
reach a dislocation in random walk is of the order

$$n_j \approx \frac{1}{\Lambda b^2} \approx \frac{10^{15}}{\Lambda} , \tag{1}$$

where $\Lambda$ is the dislocation density and $b$ the interatomic distance. (The number of
jumps is smaller when the diffusion is assisted by the dislocation stress fields and
larger when the dislocation distribution is inhomogeneous.) The point defect concentrations annealing out are of the order of $10^{-5} - 10^{-4}$ for degrees of deformations between 5 and 50%. The corresponding dislocation densities are $\approx 10^{10} -
10^{11}$ cm$^{-2}$. Therefore the average number of jumps for arriving at a dislocation is
of the same order of magnitude as the number of jumps for meeting another point
defect.

In this context another point is of interest. From quenching data * it can be
estimated that a di-vacancy in Au makes about $10^5$ jumps at 300°K before disso-
ciating. This means that for dislocation densities larger then $10^{10}$ cm$^{-2}$ a di-vacancy
will probably arrive at a dislocation before it dissociates. If di-vacancies are formed
in plastic deformation (for instance by boiling off from a vacancy row) one expects to observe a recovery stage due to diffusion of di-vacancies to dislocations.

3) The influence of impurities on the annealing out of point defects can also be
reduced by the presence of dislocations. For severely cold worked metals
$\Lambda \approx 10^{11} - 10^{12}$ cm$^{-2}$, and $n_j \approx 10^4 - 10^3$, whereas the impurity concentrations
in the pure metals used are $\approx 10^{-5}$.

In this paper first the production mechanisms of point defects by plastic deformation will be discussed and compared with experimental data. Subsequently the
experimental methods used to get information on the recovery processes will be reviewed prior to the discussion of the experimental evidence. Finally, changes of the

---

* For this purpose one needs the value of $E_{1V}^M - E_{2V}^M + E_{2V}^B$ which for Au is $0.30 \pm 0.05$ eV [6,
7].

elastic constants, the mechanical properties and the internal friction which occur during annealing and are thought to be due to interactions between dislocations and point defects are discussed in the last chapter.

It will not be attempted to give a complete review of the older data. For complete reviews up to 1962 the reader is referred to the papers by Balluffi et al. [5] and by Clarebrough et al. [8].

## 2. Production of point defects by plastic deformation

Many models have been proposed for the formation of point defects by moving dislocations. They are based either on the mutual annihilation of dislocations others than screws or on the non conservative motion of jogs in dislocations with a strong screw component. These models (up to 1962) have been reviewed by Balluffi et al. [5], who conclude that a number of models are available to explain defect production either as isolated defects or in the form of rows or platelets. We shall restrict the discussion to some recent papers on this subject.

A problem often treated is, whether the point defects produced are vacancies or interstitials or both. If the moving jogs were formed by the intersection of a moving dislocation with a stationary forest dislocation, vacancies and interstitials will be produced in approximately equal numbers. It has been shown by Cottrell [9] that, if the predominant intersections are between two moving dislocations, the jogs should be mainly of the interstitial producing type. This conclusion has been confirmed by Zsoldos [10], who finds, however, that the vacancy production is not negligible in this case.

When the dislocations are split into partials, constriction of the partials at the jog and their behaviour under an applied stress have to be considered. It has been concluded by Hirsch [11] that an applied stress tends to constrict an interstitial producing jog, making it glissile, whereas the vacancy producing jogs will be extended and remain sessile. For that reason point defects formed by low temperature deformation should be predominantly vacancies. Hirsch' analysis has been extended by Weertman [12]. He examines the role of partial dislocations attached to a double stacking fault. He concludes that vacancies and interstitials are formed in approximately equal numbers. Pfeffer, Schiller and Seeger [13] argue that Hirsch and Weertman consider long jogs only, and that the theory cannot be applied to jogs of atomic dimensions (elementary jogs). These authors develop an atomistic theory of these elementary jogs, which can dissociate as well as complete dislocations. They show that both vacancies and interstitials can be produced by a non-conservative motion of dissociated elementary jogs. Further it comes out that point defect production will increase with decreasing stacking fault energy.

Friedel [14] doubts whether point defect production by the moving jog mechanism should be important in plastic deformation. He argues that for the rather small dislocation velocities observed during cold work the jogs should move along the dislocation to parts having edge character rather than produce point defects. According to Friedel in cubic crystals a more important mechanism of point defect production occurs each time a mobile dislocation loop cuts through an attractive tree of the dislocation forest. This model has been worked out in detail by Saada [15], and it has the great advantage that it allows a quantitative comparison with experimental results.

When a mobile loop meets an attractive tree, the reaction of Hirsch [16] will occur, and the loop will be divided in two parts separated by an immobile junction dislocation. If the Burgers vector of the tree is not parallel to the slip plane of the loop, the two parts of the loop will be in different slip planes. They subsequently bow out until they meet and recombine over a certain length, resulting in a row of point defects of length $x$. It is shown that $x$ is proportional to the size of the dislocation network $l$:

$$x = Al \, . \tag{2}$$

It is then easily derived that the concentration of point defects produced is given by

$$C \cong \frac{A}{G} \int_0^\epsilon \sigma \mathrm{d}\epsilon \, , \tag{3}$$

where $G$ is the shear modulus and $\sigma$ and $\epsilon$ are the plastic stress and strain respectively. Therefore, the point defect concentration produced by cold working would be proportional to the work done.

This prediction appears to be in reasonable agreement with a number of experimental results, collected in table 1. To obtain the point defect concentrations from

Table 1

Validity of Saada's relation $C = \dfrac{A}{G} \displaystyle\int_0^\epsilon \sigma \mathrm{d}\epsilon$.

| Metal | Method | $\epsilon$ (%) | $\rho_V, E_{1V}^F$ | $A$ | Ref. |
|---|---|---|---|---|---|
| Cu | resistivity | 0–6 | 1.5 $\mu\Omega$ cm/% | 0.06 | 17 |
| Cu | resistivity | 0–140 | 1.5 $\mu\Omega$ cm/% | 0.05 | 18 |
| Cu | stored energy | 43–66 | 1 eV | 0.07 | 19 |
| Ag | stored energy | 49–63 | 1 eV | 0.06 | 19 |
| Ag | resistivity | 0–8 | 1.5 $\mu\Omega$ cm/% | 0.10 | 17 |
| Au | resistivity | 0–10 | 1.5 $\mu\Omega$ cm/% | 0.10 | 17 |
| Al | resistivity | 0.–20 | 3 $\mu\Omega$ cm/% | 0.05 – 0.07 | 20, 21 |
| Al | resistivity | 0–70 | 3 $\mu\Omega$ cm/% | 0.09 | 22 |

stored energy or resistivity measurements one has to estimate the formation energy
of the point defects or the resistivity per percent point defects. The values chosen
are given in the table and can be in error, of course, by a factor of 2. For Cu, Ag and
Au the total decrease of resistivity or release of stored energy prior to the recrystallization was taken to be due to point defects. For the two results on Al, the contributions of point defects and dislocations to the resistivity were not separated. It
was assumed that 55% of the total increase in resistivity during low temperature deformation is due to point defects. The proportionality between $C$ and $\int \sigma d\epsilon$ is valid
in the deformation ranges given in the table.

The calculated values of the proportionality factor $A$ are shown in the table *.
They are all in the range 0.05–0.10. According to the physical interpretation of $A$
this would mean that the length of the point defect rows is of the order of 5–10%
of the dislocation network size.

The number of experimental results suitable for a comparison with Saada's relation is still limited. The reason is that before the publication of Saada's thesis it was
usual to describe the produced point defect concentration $C$ as a function of $\epsilon$
alone. The results were fitted to a formula of the form $C = a \epsilon^p$. A variety of $p$-
values between 1 and 2 were found, most of them being about 1.5 (see e.g. Van
Bueren [4] ). Saada's relation accounts for this variety in an elegant way: It is due to
the different shapes of the stress-strain curves. The predominance of the $p \approx 1.5$ result comes from the fact that in many cases the stress-strain curve has an approximately parabolic form. In the experiments of Blewitt et al. [18] $p = 2$ was
observed, due to the almost linear stress-strain curve.

Finally we mention a somewhat different approach by Feltham [23] . His model
is that plastic deformation produces a cell structure of dislocations, the cell size decreasing with increasing degree of cold work. Point defects are produced by non-
conservative motion of intersection jogs. The result is, that the ratio of point defect
concentration $C$ and dislocation density $\Lambda$ is constant during the deformation:

$$\frac{C}{\Lambda} \approx 20 b^2 . \tag{4}$$

Feltham compares this result with experimental results of Kovacs et al. [24] on
Ag and Yoshida et al. [25] on Al and finds agreement of the observed $C/\Lambda$ ratio
with the calculated $20 b^2$ within a factor of 10 **. Further it is clear from the data
of Yoshida et al. [25] that the $C/\Lambda$ ratio is far from constant for $\epsilon$ between 4 and
14%. The same is concluded by Kovacs and Nagy [26] from their measurements on
Ag and Au. On the other hand Peiffer observes in Al [27] and Cu [28] that the re-

---

* Several $A$-values given in the table differ from those reported in the quoted papers. Some
authors [17,22] have used Youngs modulus instead of the shear modulus $G$ in formula (3).
This has been corrected. Some errors in the calculations of the quoted papers have also been
removed.
** The better agreement claimed by the author is due to errors in the calculation.

sistivity increase associated with point defects is proportional to the increment associated with dislocations. This author explains this result as follows: According to Kuhlmann-Wilsdorf and Wilsdorf [29] jogs are formed because of lattice vibrations along the dislocation lines. This being a statistical process, the probability of jog formation will be proportional to the total dislocation line length. If point defects are formed by non-conservative motion of jogs, the point defect concentration produced is expected to be proportional to the dislocation line length.

*Summary*. Many models are available to account for the production of point defects of both vacancy and interstitial type in plastic deformation by dislocation mechanisms. The most satisfactory one in view of its quantitative agreement with experimental results in Saada's model, predicting that the point defect concentration produced is proportional to the work done.

## 3. Sources of information on the recovery processes

In this chapter first the isochronal recovery spectra obtained after low temperature cold working of the fcc metals Cu, Ag, Au, Pt, Ni, Al, Pd and Rh will be reviewed. The subdivision of the spectra in so-called recovery stages will be discussed. It will be shown that the recovery spectra of all the metals considered are quite analogous, which results in a proposal to revise the current labelling of the recovery stages for cold worked Pt. Furthermore the value of the information obtained from the reported annealing kinetics and activation energies will be discussed. Finally a number of experimental techniques will be reviewed which have been used in order to identify the recovery processes after cold working.

### 3.1. *Isochronal recovery*

Isochronal recovery measurements on cold worked metals have been mainly carried out for the *electrical resistivity*. The technique is as follows: After deformation at low temperature the specimen is warmed up step by step, the sucessive temperature intervals being equal. At each temperature the sample is kept for a fixed time, whereafter it is cooled down to a low temperature (e.g. liquid nitrogen or helium) where the resistivity $\rho$ is measured. The plot of $\rho$ obtained after annealing at temperature $T$ versus $T$ is called an isochronal. It often reveals several more or less clearly separated steps or stages. The isochronals are often presented in a differentiated form, so that the steps become peaks.

A related technique is to warm up the specimen continuously at a constant rate. This method is especially suitable for the measurement of the release of *stored energy* during recovery. In these experiments the heat flow going to the sample is measured in two subsequent heating runs. In the second run the heat flow to the annealed specimen is measured and the heat flow generated in the specimen due to the annealing out of lattice defects is obtained by subtraction of the two results.

The resulting curve has naturally the differentiated form because in this experiment the heat flow is measured, which is proportional to the time derivative $dU/dt$ of the energy $U$, whereas $dU/dt \sim dU/dT$ because $dT/dt$ is constant. For simplicity we shall call the $dU/dT$ versus $T$ curves resulting from stored energy experiments isochronals as well.

The recovery stages or peaks observed in isochronals are, of course, not characterized by fixed temperatures. The peak temperatures will depend on the warming up rate. In both types of isochronals discussed the warming up rates $\alpha$ are usually of the order of $1°K/min$. If $\alpha$ is varied by a factor of 2, the peak shifts are of the order of $5°K$. Further the peak temperatures usually shift to lower values with increasing defect concentrations annealing out.

In figs. 2–7 the results are shown of isochronal recovery measurements on Al, Au, Pt, Ni, Ag and Cu, all after heavy plastic deformation at $78°K$ (for Al at $20°K$). In the three resistivity isochronals (Al, Pt, Ni) the last peak, called stage V, is due to recrystallization and will not be considered further. The remainder of the recovery spectrum is seen to be more or less clearly divided in two main parts in all cases. The two main recovery ranges have been called stage II and III respectively, with the exception of Pt, where they have been labelled III and IV respectively, without clear reasons.

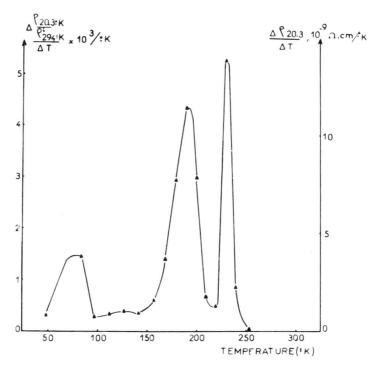

Fig. 2. Resistivity isochronal of Al, heavily cold worked at $20.3°K$ [30].

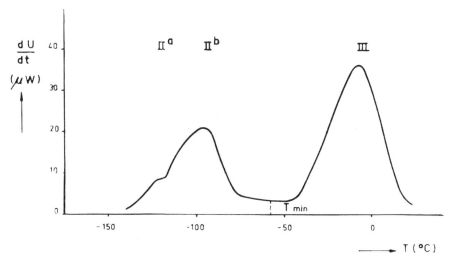

Fig. 3. Stored energy release in Au, heavily cold worked at 78°K [19].

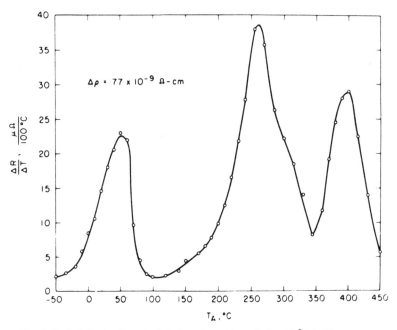

Fig. 4. Resistivity isochronal of Pt, heavily cold worked at 78°K [31].

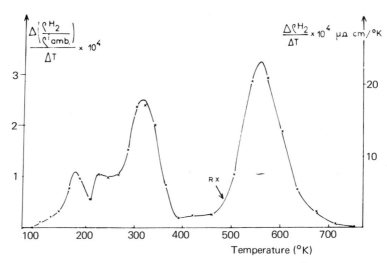

Fig. 5. Resistivity isochronal of Ni, heavily cold worked at 78°K [32].

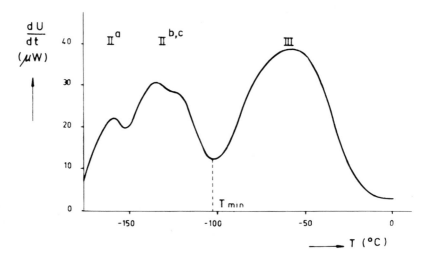

Fig. 6. Stored energy release in Ag, heavily cold worked at 78°K [19].

The correspondence of the recovery spectra of Pt and Au is demonstrated in fig. 8, where the temperature scale for Au has been multiplied by a factor of 1.95 (being somewhat larger than the ratio of the melting temperatures of Pt and Au: 1.53). The isochronal for heavily deformed Pt observed by Jackson [31] and reproduced in fig. 4 is in full agreement with results of Piercy [33] and Menting [34]. For small de-

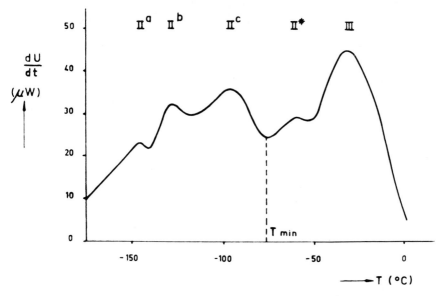

Fig. 7. Stored energy release in Cu, heavily cold worked at 78°K [19].

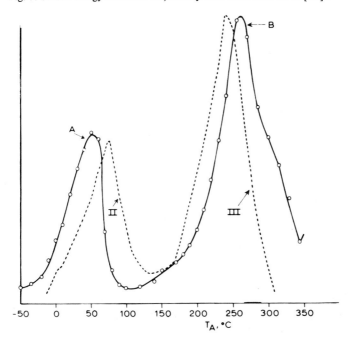

Fig. 8. Comparison of the recovery spectra of heavily cold worked Pt (full line) [31] and Au (dashed line) [19]. The temperature scale for Au has been multiplied by a factor of 1.95.

grees of deformations of about 5%, Menting and also Miura et al. [35] find a small recovery between 80 and 120°K, which they call stage II [†]. In the present view this recovery belongs to the "stage I" region, which in some other fcc metals is found below 78°K, being a small and rather continuous recovery of the order of 5% of the total recovery. This is in agreement with the fact illustrated before in fig. 8, that the recovery spectra of Pt and Au are similar if the temperature scale for Au is multiplied by a factor of about 2. It is concluded that no compelling reason exists for the current deviating nomenclature of the two main recovery stages in cold worked Pt and it is proposed to label these stages in agreement with those of the other fcc metals, namely as II and III respectively. From now on this nomenclature will be used in this paper. The same conclusion has been drawn independently by Schilling (this volume) with respect to the comparable stages in irradiated Pt. An analogous recovery spectrum, consisting of two main parts has been reported for Rh [36] and Pd [37].

For Al, Pt, Au and Ag stages II and III are clearly separated. For Cu and Ni the separation is somewhat arbitrary. The stored energy spectrum for Cu shown in fig. 7 is in good agreement with the observations of Henderson and Koehler [38] on the stored energy and of Verel [39] on the electrical resistivity. Only the small substage preceding stage III and called II* is absent in Henderson and Koehler's results. The fine structure observed in stage II in Cu and Ni is quite analogous as can be seen by comparing figs. 9 and 7. Stage II * is again present in Ni, in agreement with the observations of Merklen and Dimitrov [32] on the resistivity shown in fig. 5. The double peak $II^b$, $II^c$ found in the stored energy (fig. 9) is not resolved in the resistivity measurements (fig. 5, first peak). In the stored energy spectrum of Al also a small substage is observed [19] preceding stage III, which may correspond to stage II*.

It will be clear from the isochronals discussed that in many cases the stages II and III cannot represent singly activated processes. In stage II a fine structure is often resolved. Stage III, especially in Ag, is too broad to be due to a single process. The complexity of stage III has been demonstrated by the experiments of Dawson [40] on Cu, Ag and Au after deformations between 1 and 10%. As an example Dawson's results on Au are shown in fig. 10. For small deformations three different substages b, c and d can be distinguished in the stage III range, which merge into stage III for larger deformations. The same was found for Ag (fig. 11). For Cu, Dawson's results suggest that stage III is built up of two processes, b and c, whereas the third one, stage d lies in the range between 100 and 200°C, which is usually called stage IV. It is possible that for Cu substage b must be identified with the substage II* mentioned before. An interesting feature of Dawson's results is that for the smallest deformations in Au and Ag (but not in Cu) only one recovery stage, namely stage d is observed.

---

[†] Menting already suggests that his labelling of the recovery stages might be wrong.

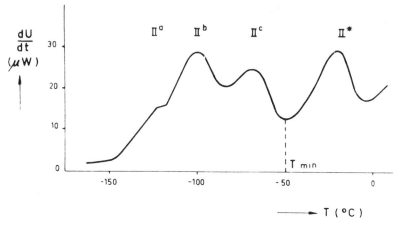

Fig. 9. Stored energy release in the stage II region of Ni, heavily cold worked at 78°K [19].

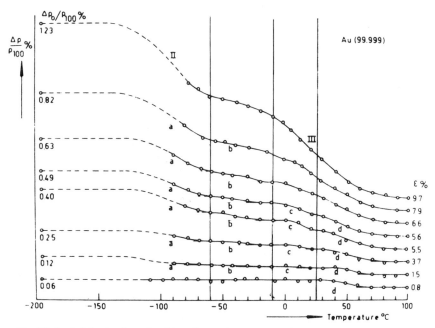

Fig. 10. Resistivity isochronals of Au after various degrees of plastic deformation [40].

For intermediate deformations (of the order of 10%) the recovery is rather continuous, especially in Cu and Ag. Also in Ni the isochronal observed by Spark [41] for $\epsilon = 15\%$ is more continuous than those observed after heavily cold working (fig. 5, see also Kressel et al. [42]). In general the recovery stages seem to be better resolved for heavy than for intermediate deformations. This could be due to the fact

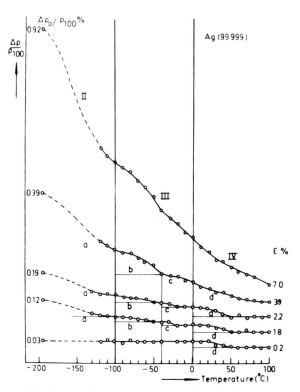

Fig. 11. Resistivity isochronals of Ag after various degrees of plastic deformation [40].

that in heavily cold worked metals interactions between point defects and impurities become unimportant, as argued in the introduction.

The low temperature plastic deformations discussed have been mainly carried out at 78°K. A number of investigators observed that after cold working at 4.2°K between 4.2 and 78°K a small continuous recovery occurs of the order of a few percent of the total defect resistivity. This has been reported by Meechan and Sosin [43] for Cu, Au and Ni, by Buck [44] for Cu, by Swanson [45] and Swanson and Quenneville [46] for Al and by Okuda and Takamura [47] for Au. The latter two pairs of authors report that the recovery in this range is considerably increased when the initial dislocation density is increased. They suggest that the continuous recovery in this range is due to rearrangements of dislocations, which is supported by an observation of Okuda [48], who finds that in this range a plastic after effect occurs. The recovery in this temperature range is sometimes called stage I, analogous to the prominent stage observed in this temperature region after irradiation. It is far from certain, however, that the annealing mechanism is the same in the two cases. At any rate this stage I recovery in cold worked metals is of minor importance and it shall not be discussed further.

Mainly in Cu and Ni after stage III and prior to recrystallization some recovery, called stage IV is observed. This stage will be discussed separately in chapter 4.

Isochronal annealing measurements are very suitable to get an overall picture of the recovery spectrum. They can also be used to estimate the point defect concentrations produced. For a precise calculation the point defects responsible for the different stages should be known as well as their contributions to energy and resistivity. However, both from theoretical estimates and results from quenching and irradiation experiments it has become probable that the formation energies and resistivities of vacancy and interstitial type defects do not differ by much more than a factor of 2. Therefore a reasonable estimate of the point defect concentration produced in cold working can be made. It comes out that the concentrations are of the order of $10^{-6}$, $10^{-5}$ and $10^{-4}$ for degrees of deformation of 1, 10 and 100% respectively.

Isochronal annealing experiments are not useful in determining the nature of the annealing processes. In the next sections experimental efforts aimed to clarify this problem will be discussed.

## 3.2. Activation energies

Comparison of the annealing results of cold worked metals with those of the same quenched and irradiated metals will be mainly restricted to the activation energies observed. At first sight this seems to be a rather hopeless task, because the reported activation energies are essentially *effective* values, which usually do not represent a single atomic jump process. For quenched Au, for instance, activation energies have been reported between 0.55 and 0.95 eV, whereas no generally accepted values of the migration energies of mono- and di-vacancies exist. On the other hand, if one collects the reported values of the activation energies in quenched Au, it appears that the overwhelming majority lies in the range $0.70 \pm 0.05$ eV, whatever that may mean. This corresponds very well to the activation energies observed in stage III of cold worked Au. If such a correspondence appears to occur generally in the fcc metals discussed, this shall be considered as an argument in favour of diffusion of vacancy type defects in stage III.

In view of the interpretation of stages III and IV after cold working an important question is the accuracy of literature values for the migration energies of single vacancies $E_{1V}^{M}$ as deduced from other sources. In an annealing experiment after quenching it is not very probable to meet an activation energy corresponding to the migration energy of single vacancies, because the vacancies annealing out spend part of their time as members of more mobile vacancy clusters. As argued in the introduction, in this respect the situation in cold worked metals (if single vacancies are present) is more favourable, because the mutual interaction of vacancy defects is restricted by the large dislocation density. As self-diffusion is generally considered to be due mainly to single vacancies, the relation between the activation energy for self-diffusion $Q$ and the formation and migration energies of single vacancies should be

$$Q = E_{1V}^{F} + E_{1V}^{M} . \tag{5}$$

Table 2

Activation energies for self-diffusion ($Q$), formation energies of vacancies ($E_{1V}^F$) and their differences $Q - E_{1V}^F = E_{1V}^M$.

| Metal | $Q$ (eV) | Ref. | $E_{1V}^F$ (eV) | Ref. | $Q - E_{1V}^F = E_{1V}^M$ (eV) |
|---|---|---|---|---|---|
| Pt | $2.96 \pm 0.06$ | 49 | $1.51 \pm 0.04$ | 31 | $1.42 \pm 0.10$ |
|    | $2.89 \pm 0.04$ | 50 | | | |
| Al | $1.44 \pm 0.10$ | 51 | $0.76 \pm 0.04$ | 52 | $0.68 \pm 0.14$ |
| Cu | $2.05 \pm 0.04$ | 53 | $1.14 \pm 0.06$ | 54 | $0.91 \pm 0.10$ |
| Ag | $1.91 \pm 0.01$ | 55 | $1.08 \pm 0.05$ | 51 | $0.85 \pm 0.08$ |
|    | $1.96$ | 56 | | | |
| Au | $1.81 \pm 0.02$ | 57 | $0.95 \pm 0.05$ | 51 | $0.83 \pm 0.10$ |
|    | $1.83$ | 56 | | | |
|    | $1.75 \pm 0.02$ | 58 | | | |
| Ni | $2.9 \; \pm 0.1$ | 59 | – | | – |

$E_{1V}^F$ has been determined either from quenching or from equilibrium experiments. Values of $E_{1V}^M$ derived from this relation are given in table 2.

In the last years there is some discussion on the question whether $E_{1V}^M$ is temperature dependent or not. Based on self-diffusion data of Al and Au, Stoebe and Dawson [60] have argued that $E_{1V}^M$ decreases with decreasing temperature. The evidence is not conclusive, however (see Seeger, this volume). In this context it is interesting to note that the $Q$-value of $1.75 \pm 0.02$ eV for self-diffusion in Au reported by Ermert et al. [58] in the temperature range 286–412°C is distinctly lower than the values found at high temperatures (table 2). Recently two theoretical papers on this subject were published. Nowick and Dienes [61] argued that for temperatures well above the Debye temperature $\theta$ the temperature dependence of $Q$ is negligibly small. Flynn [62] presented a new theory of the diffusion-jump process in monatomic crystals. The large atomic displacements causing diffusion jumps were treated as a summation of phonon amplitudes, where the Debye approximation of the phonon spectrum was used. The most important result in connection with the present discussion is represented in fig. 12. The calculated effective migration energy for single vacancies is seen to decrease considerably as a function of $T/\theta$ when $T/\theta$ becomes smaller than 2.

### 3.3. Annealing kinetics

The annealing kinetics after cold working have been mainly investigated in the stage III range. As argued before dislocations are expected to play an important part as sinks for point defects in cold worked metals. When the initial distribution of point defects is homogeneous it has been derived [63], that for random diffusion

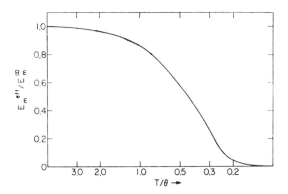

Fig. 12. Migration energy of single vacancies as a function of temperature according to Flynn's [62] theory.

of the point defects to a regular network of dislocations the defect concentration must decay exponentially after an initial transition period. This is usually *not* observed in stage III after cold working.

As an alternative it has been proposed by Wintenberger [64] that the point defects do not diffuse randomly but under the influence of the stress field of the dislocations. In this case the point defect concentration should decay with time according to

$$C = C_0 \exp(-t/\tau)^p , \qquad (6)$$

where $p = 0.5$ for vacancies. The derivation of this formula was somewhat tentative. Later on it has been shown by calculations of Bullough and Newman [65] that the initial stages of vacancy annealing to dislocations should satisfy (6). If eq. (6) is valid, a plot of log log $C_0/C$ versus log $t$ should give a straight line with slope 0.5. Wintenberger has shown that the isothermals for quenched and subsequently cold worked Al can be described in this way. From the constant $\tau$ the dislocation density $\Lambda$ can be calculated. He finds that $\Lambda$ increases linearly with the degree of deformation, which seems to be reasonable. It has been found by Frois [30] and also by Ceresara et al. [66] that the annealing kinetics in stage III of heavily cold worked Al satisfy (6) with $p$ between 0.4 and 0.5. The calculated dislocation densities are between $10^{11}$ and $10^{12}$ cm$^{-2}$. Finally Cuddy [67] showed that stage III annealing in a number of bcc metals (Fe, Mo, W, Nb) also can be described by eq. (6) with $p$ between 0.4 and 0.5.

Recently, Balluffi and Seidman [68] argued, however, that diffusion of vacancies to dislocations cannot be expected to be described by (6). The diffusion flow consists of two terms: Stress assisted diffusion and diffusion due to concentration gradients. The authors calculate that at more than a few atomic distances from the dislocations the second term dominates over the first. Therefore the contribution of the first term should be negligible, unless the dislocation densities are extremely large or the elastic interaction between vacancies and dislocations is considerably stronger than predicted by theory. Due to the domination of the concentration gradient term first order kinetics must be expected. The deviations found experimentally can be explained by inhomogeneous dislocation distributions, giving rise to a spectrum of $\tau$ values. It has also been shown by Peretto et al. [69] and by Dawson [40] that a series of first order processes with a spectrum of $\tau$ values can result in kinetics of apparently higher order.

On the other hand, a second group of authors, e.g. [70–72], submit their stage III data to a test for second order kinetics. A positive result is regarded as a support for the interpretation of stage III as a bimolecular recombination of moving interstitials with vacancies. For such a process the point defect concentration changes with time according to

$$\frac{C_o}{C} - 1 = K_1 t , \tag{7}$$

where $K_1$ is a reaction constant. The test consists of plotting $1/C$ versus $t$, which must give a straight line. In a number of cases a straight line can be drawn through a substantial part of the data points, whereas often deviations are found at the initial and final parts of the plot.

The deviations at the end are hardly surprising. The second order test requires that $C_o$, the total defect concentration annealing out in the stage considered, is known very accurately (within 5% if the test must yield a straight line in the range $C/C_o$ between 1 and $\frac{1}{3}$). This involves a serious limitation especially for the analysis of the recovery stages after cold working, because in this case the stages are separated rather badly. (In fact, it must be considered a miracle that the $1/C$ verus $t$ plot can be straight even when the reaction is really second order.) Several authors (e.g. Stals and Nihoul [73], Sosin and Brinkman [74]) observed that the initial kinetics can be described by a second term, to be added to (7), namely

$$\frac{C_o}{C} - 1 = K_2 t^{0.5} \tag{8}$$

in agreement with Waite's [75] calculations on bimolecular reaction kinetics for short times. The term originates from the interstitials being within a distance $r_o$ from a vacancy where they "feel" the stress field of the vacancy. The analysis of Stals and Nihoul for Nb yields $r_o \approx 10b$. An objection against the second order reaction in stage III and its interpretation seems to be that the dislocations must be ruled out as important sinks for point defects. Other complications with respect to the reaction order of bimolecular processes have been treated by Nihoul and Stals [76]. These authors show that considerable deviations from second order will occur, when the initial concentrations of vacancies and interstitials are not exactly equal, but differ by only 10%. This situation is very well possible in cold worked metals.

It can be easily understood why an annealing process which obeys eq. (6) can be approximately described by second order kinetics (eq. (7) and (8)) and vice versa. If the exponential in (6) is expanded for $p = 0.5$, the first two terms are proportional to $t^{0.5}$ and $t$ respectively, just as in the case of Waite kinetics. It has been shown, however, [77] that the two cases can be distinguished by measuring the reaction kinetics for different defect concentrations.

The confusion is nicely demonstrated by two papers presented to the Jülich conference, both dealing with the reaction kinetics in stage III of cold worked Pt. Miura et al. [35] show that a plot of $\Delta\rho/\Delta\rho_o$ versus $t^{0.5}$ yields straight lines for their isothermals, in agreement with eq. (6). On the other hand, Rösch et al. [78] studied the reaction kinetics of this stage by isochronal step annealing measurements (for the details the reader is referred to ref. [78]). The result is that the stage can be described for a large part by a second order reaction.

At the present time no choice can be made. It is even dubious whether the choice is confined to the two types of kinetics discussed. An assumption in all models is that in stage III *one* single thermally activated process takes place which is far from certain. And even if it could be proved that stage III is a simple second order process, the interpretation is not unique. It has been shown by Corbett [79] and Damask and Dienes [80] that release of impurity trapped interstitials and their subsequent recombination with vacancies can give rise to second order kinetics. Even in quenched metals, containing only vacancy type defects, second order kinetics is sometimes observed (Doyama and Koehler [81] in Ag, Federighi [52] in Al, Kino and Koehler [7] in Au).

In conclusion it must be said that at the present time the reported annealing kinetics of the cold work stage III do not provide sound arguments for the interpretation. It is even dubious whether in this case the study of annealing kinetics is useful at all.

## 3.4. *Special experimental techniques*

In this section, a number of experimental methods will be reviewed which have been used to study annealing of cold worked metals in order to contribute to the identification of the point defects involved. A review of the results obtained will be mainly postponed to the next chapter. Only in those cases where the method has *not* been successful the results will be mentioned in this section.

### 3.4.1. Mechanical and magnetic relaxation experiments

This topic is treated extensively by Kronmüller in this volume. The aim of the technique is to detect point defects or small point defect clusters having non-cubic symmetry in cubic crystals. When a unidirectional elastic stress is applied preferred positions of lower energy are created for the point defects considered into which they will jump after the stress has been applied. This will give rise to an elastic after-effect or, when an alternating stress is applied, to an internal friction peak analogous to the Snoek peak of C atoms in $\alpha$-iron. It has been argued by Seeger et al. [82] that the dumbbell interstitial in fcc metals will cause such effects due to its tetragonal symmetry. Under the influence of the stress the dumbbell-axis can rotate $90°$ to an energetically more favourable $\langle 100 \rangle$ direction. If the activation energy for the rotation is lower than for the jump from one interstitial position to another, the damping could be observed prior to the annealing out of the dumbbells. Further it can be predicted that in single crystals the observed damping will depend on the crystal orientation.

In magnetic materials the point defects considered will be oriented with respect to the magnetostrictive stresses. When a fully magnetized metal containing dumbbells is quickly demagnetized, the dumbbells reorient themselves each in their own ferromagnetic domain. This causes a decrease of the Bloch wall mobility, which will be detected as a decrease of the initial susceptibility as a function of time. Effects of this kind have been investigated by the Stuttgart and Grenoble groups on irradiated and cold worked Ni, Fe, Co and Ga. Some of the results will be discussed further on.

### 3.4.2. Ordering and clustering phenomena

When a homogeneous binary alloy is quenched from a high to a low temperature, in general the atoms will show a tendency to redistribute themselves over the lattice in order that the free energy should be lowered. The redistribution can involve either an increase of the number of unlike neighbours per atom (ordering) or a decrease (clustering), dependent on the alloy system considered. Both types of processes have been observed to occur in temperature ranges which are much too low to be understood by an extrapolation of the high temperature diffusion coefficients. The explanation is that the annealing out of the quenched in vacancies provides the atomic mobility required for the redistribution process.

From these experiments it has become clear that for several alloy systems an increase of order is accompanied by an increase of the electrical resistivity which is considerably larger than the decrease due to the annealing out of the excess vacancies (e.g. Korevaar [83] (AuCu) and Van der Sijde [84] (AuAg)). The same is true for the initial stages of the clustering process (e.g. Federighi [52] for a number of Al alloys). If these alloys are plastically deformed at low temperatures and subsequently annealed, and if in one of the recovery stages a relatively large increase of the electrical resistivity is observed, this will be considered as a strong indication that during the annealing ordering or clustering occurs. When this process is observed in the same temperature range as in the quenching experiments the conclusion is obvious that it is caused by vacancy type defects. An example is shown in fig. 13, representing the isochronal recovery of Au (7.5% Cu) after cold working at $78°$K (Korevaar [83]). Stages II and III are clearly resolved. The temperature ranges of both stages in the alloy and in pure Au correspond very well. Stage II is a decrease of the resistivity both in the alloy and pure Au, whereas in stage III of the alloy an increase of the resistivity is observed, which is ascribed to an increase of short range order.

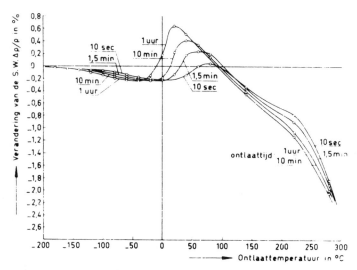

Fig. 13. Resistivity isochronal of Au (7.5% Cu) after plastic deformation at 78°K [83].

For an observable ordering to be attained, each atom of the alloy must have jumped about once. In other words

$$n_j C_V \approx 1 , \tag{9}$$

where $n_j$ is the number of jumps of an excess vacancy prior to annihilation. If the vacancies are annihilated at a regular network of dislocations, we have seen that

$$n_j \approx \frac{10^{15}}{\Lambda} . \tag{9a}$$

It follows from (9) and (9a) that

$$\frac{\Lambda}{C_V} \approx 10^{15} \text{ cm}^{-2} . \tag{10}$$

For a degree of deformation of 10%, $\Lambda$ is about $10^{10}$ cm$^{-2}$, whereas the point defect concentration calculated from the resistivity decrease in stage III of pure Au is about $10^{-5}$, so that the condition for observable ordering is roughly satisfied.

It must be noted that the assignment of the ordering processes observed after cold working to vacancy type defects is not beyond doubt. In principle, diffusion of dumbbell interstitials or "normal" interstitials migrating by the interstitialcy mechanism can give rise to ordering as well. It has been argued by Brinkman et al. [85] that in CuAu alloys the latter process will not contribute much to the ordering because of the size difference between the Cu and Au atoms. It was pointed out that a Au atom in an interstitial position will be transformed into a Cu interstitial, but that the reverse requires a considerably higher energy. The same may be the case for an asymmetrical Au-Cu dumbbell. Whatever may be true of it, up till now a clear proof of the contribution of interstitial type defects to atomic redistribution processes in alloys has not been given, whereas for vacancies the question has been settled beyond doubt. (Recently Ermert et al. [58] reported experimental evidence indicating that interstitials do play a part in the radiation enhanced self-diffusion of Au.) For the moment we shall consider the observed ordering and clustering phenomena as evidence for vacancy type diffusion, but it must be kept in mind that the argument is not conclusive.

### 3.4.3. Point defect-dislocation interactions

In cold worked metals the dislocations provide the most obvious sinks for the excess point defects annealing out. There is substantial experimental evidence from measurements of the internal friction, the elastic constants and the flow stress that point defects indeed arrive at the dislocations during the recovery of cold worked metals. These results, which can be commonly called "pinning phenomena", will be discussed separately in chapter 5. They strongly suggest that after arrival at the dislocations the point defects keep their identity for some time before they are definitively absorbed.

### 3.4.4. Prequench experiments

In some cases recovery experiments have been carried out on cold worked metals which had been quenched prior to the deformation. Such experiments are only meaningful if the recovery is studied in a temperature range where the quenched-in vacancies are immobile, that is to say in the stage II region. If the recovery is enhanced in the quenched specimen compared to the unquenched one, this indicates that the defect annealing out is of a vacancy-annihilating type.

### 3.4.5. Simultaneous measurements of two physical properties

To a first approximation, both the extra resistivity $\Delta\rho$ and the extra internal energy $\Delta U$ associated with point defects are proportional to the defect concentration. When in a certain annealing stage both properties are measured on the same specimen or on two identical specimens the ratio $\Delta U/\Delta\rho$ will be characteristic for the annealing process considered. For cold worked Cu two determinations of $\Delta U/\Delta\rho$ have been carried out. Loretto et al. [86] find for the range of stage II and III together: $\Delta U/\Delta\rho = 5.5$ cal/g $\mu\Omega$ cm. Van den Beukel [19] reports values of 3.4 and 3.0 cal/g$\mu\Omega$ cm for stage II and III, respectively. These values are in the same range as observed in irradiated Cu, namely between 3 and 7 cal/g $\mu\Omega$ cm. For vacancies in Cu, $E_{1V}^F \approx 1.15$ eV [54], whereas $\Delta\rho$ per percent vacancies is about $1-1.5$ $\mu\Omega$ cm, resulting in $(\Delta U/\Delta\rho)_{vac} \approx 3-4.5$ cal/g$\mu\Omega$ cm. For interstitials the formation energy is probably about twice that for vacancies, whereas the resistivity per percent should be about the same for vacancies and interstitials. Therefore it cannot be excluded that more precise measurements of $\Delta U/\Delta\rho$ may be helpful, but the data reported up to now are not of much use.

Simultaneous measurements of the electrical resistivity and the thermoelectric power $S$ in stage III of cold worked Au have been carried out by Begemann and Van der Wekken [87]. The result is $\Delta S/\Delta\rho = -1.2 \pm 0.4$ V/$^\circ$K $\Omega$ cm, to be compared with a value of $-0.90 \pm 0.03$ V/$^\circ$K $\Omega$ cm reported by Huebener [88] for quenched Au. The values correspond within the limits of accuracy, but these limits are rather wide. Moreover it is not known whether the $\Delta S/\Delta\rho$ values for interstitial and vacancy type defects are substantially different.

### 3.4.6. Annealing under an elastic stress

It has been observed by Berghout [89] that isothermal recovery in stage III of cold worked Cu was accelerated when an elastic tensile stress was applied to the specimen. According to Berghout the diffusion coefficient of point defects is enhanced by the elastic dilatation of the lattice. He calculated the decrease of the vacancy migration energy due to this effect and found a reasonable agreement with the experimental results. This explanation cannot be correct, however, because Van Allrer [90] has shown that the recovery is also accelerated when a specimen which was initially annealed under an elastic tensile stress is unloaded. The interpretation of these phenomena is not yet clear. It has been suggested by Balluffi et al. [5] that the stress moves the dislocations from regions depleted of point defects to defect-rich regions, giving rise to a temporary acceleration of the annealing process.

### 3.4.7. Data from theory and experiments other than cold working

In the introduction it was already pointed out that recovery experiments on cold worked metals alone do not provide sufficient information for the identification of the recovery stages. One needs data on the properties of vacancy and interstitial type defects resulting from equilibrium, quenching and irradiation experiments and also from theoretical calculations. A review of these data is outside the scope of this paper. Therefore only the relevant results will be introduced in the next chapter each time they are considered useful in clarifying the situation.

## 4. Discussion of the recovery stages

### 4.1. Stage II

This stage has been investigated in much less detail than stage III. An exception is Pt, probably because in this metal stage II is situated near room temperature and because it has been labelled III up to now. In Cu, Ni and Ag the stage shows a fine structure (see figs. 6, 7, and 9), whereas in Al, Au and Pt (see figs. 2, 3, and 4) it is much better defined. Activation energies observed in the stage II range have been collected in table 3.

The following interpretations of stage II annealing have been proposed:
1) Release of impurity trapped interstitials [79].
2) Recombination of close interstitial-vacancy pairs [72].

Table 3
Activation energies observed in stage II after cold working.

| Metal | $E_{II}$ (eV) | Ref. |
|-------|--------------|------|
| Au | 0.29 | 2 |
|    | 0.28 | 19 |
|    | 0.3–0.4 | 83 |
|    | 0.44 | 91 |
| Pt | 0.73 | 33 |
|    | 0.72 | 31 |
|    | 0.66 ± 0.06 | 34 |
|    | 0.70 ± 0.05 | 35 |
| Al | 0.22 ± 0.02 | 30 |
| Cu | 0.20 – 0.25 | 2 |
|    | 0.44 | 92 |
| Ag | 0.18 | 2 |
| Ni | 0.35 ± 0.05 | 32 |
|    | 0.60 ± 0.10 (stage II*) | 32 |
|    | 0.54 (stage II*) | 42 |

3) Annealing out of di-vacancies or larger vacancy clusters [38].

4) Rearrangements of dislocations [94].

5) Rearrangements within point defect strings [91,93].

6) Migration or break up of di-interstitials or larger interstitial agglomerates [19].

1) In the annealing spectrum of irradiated metals between stages I and III a rather continuous recovery is observed, which is called stage II. This recovery has been shown to be rather impurity sensitive and consequently it has been often ascribed to *release of interstitials trapped by impurities* during free migration in stage I (see e.g. Corbett [79]). According to other authors [72] in this range recombination of close Frenkel pairs occurs with increasing separation between the interstitial and the vacancy. Neither of these explanations can be correct for the cold work stage II, at least for heavy deformations. In heavily cold worked metals the point defect concentrations annealing out are of the order of $10^{-4}$, to be compared with impurity concentrations of $10^{-5}$ in the pure metals used. Moreover, the estimated number of jumps for a point defect to arrive at a dislocation is about $10^3-10^4$. Therefore ascribing stage II to a release of impurity trapped interstitials requires a preceding stage of at least the same magnitude, which has not been observed. *It is concluded that stage II is at least partially due to intrinsic defects.* The same conclusion has been reached by Dworschak and Koehler [95] for heavily proton irradiated Cu. Also Schilling (this volume) concludes that after heavy irradiations in

stage II intrinsic defects anneal out. In fact, the activation energy spectra determined by Dworschak et al. [96] for irradiated Cu and Au following Primak's [97] method are closely analogous to the stored energy spectra of cold worked Cu and Au. This can be seen by comparing figs. 3 and 7 with figs. 14 and 15. It is somewhat dubious, however, whether such a comparison is allowed. For Pt, the resistivity isochronal reported by Jackson [31] resembles to a large extent that observed by Duesing (see Schilling, this volume) on heavily electron irradiated Pt. In all cases stage II represents a smaller fraction of the total recovery in the irradiation than in the cold work experiments.

2) About 25–50% of the total point defect concentration anneals out in stage II. If this is ascribed to *"close" pair recombination,* this would mean that vacancy-interstitial attraction should not be negligible at distances as large as 30–40 atomic distances for defect concentrations of $10^{-5}$ and random distributions of vacancies and interstitials. This seems to be extremely improbable. Moreover, stage II should be a strongly increasing fraction of total recovery with increasing degree of deformation, which is usually not observed.

3) *Divacancies,* sometimes proposed as a stage II candidate, can be safely ruled out because the di-vacancy migration energies, although not precisely known, are almost certainly too large for the stage II region. Almost nothing is known about the mobility of *tri-vacancies* and larger vacancy clusters. Two remarks can be made, however. First, in Au, quenched in liquid He-II by Schumacher [98], no trace of recovery has been observed in the stage II range. Secondly, although it is usually not very safe to call on assistance of theory, an exception can possibly be made for Johnson's calculations of the mobilities of vacancy clusters in Ni [99]. This author

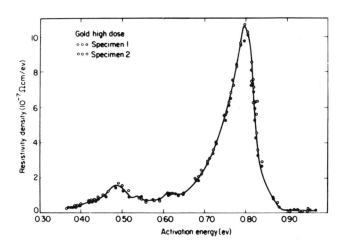

Fig. 14. Activation energy spectrum observed during the recovery of Au, following proton irradiation at 80°K [96].

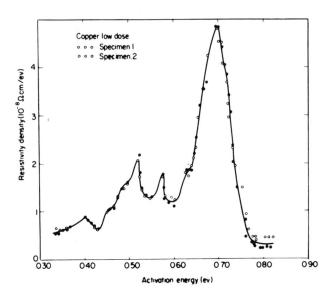

Fig. 15. Activation energy spectrum observed during the recovery of Cu following proton irradiation at 80°K [96].

finds values of 1.3 and 0.9 eV for the migration energies of single and di-vacancies, respectively, in good agreement with the values derived from quenching experiments (e.g. [100,101]). According to Johnson the migration energies of larger vacancy clusters are between 0.9 and 1.3 eV, being much too high for the stage II region.

4) *Rearrangements of dislocations* occurring in stage II have been suggested by Nowick [94], to account for the results of internal friction measurements. In a direct experiment Reits et al. [102] have shown that rearrangements of dislocations indeed occur in the stage II region. The main result is shown in fig. 16. A Ni wire, deformed in torsion at 78°K, exhibits a plastic after effect when it is warmed up to 0°C (curve B). The recovery of the electrical resistivity was measured simultaneously (curve C). It is seen that in the first part, where a considerable plastic after effect occurs, the resistivity does hardly change, whereas the resistivity stage II is accompanied by a retardation of the after effect. It is concluded that the resistivity stage II cannot be explained by a rearrangement of dislocations. On the contrary: The dislocation motion responsible for the after effect is clearly hindered by the point defects migrating in stage II. This conclusion is in accordance with the interpretation of related phenomena to be discussed in chapter 5.

5) *Rearrangements within point defect strings* have been proposed by Schumacher and Seeger [91] and by Schumacher [93] to account for stage II. In the opinion of these authors single interstitials become mobile and recombine with vacancies in stage III, so that nearly all the point defects produced by the deforma-

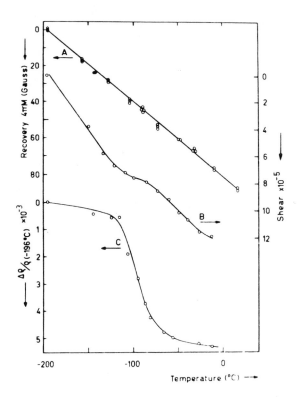

Fig. 16. Plastic after effect (curve B) and recovery of the resistivity (curve C) in Ni, cold worked at 78°K [102].

tion disappear in stage III. It will be clear that according to this view in stage II nothing important can happen. The proposed interpretation of stage II is contrary to the experimental results in two respects: a) Prequenching has been shown to in-fluence stage II annealing (see point 6), this section). b) Point defects *do* arrive at the dislocations during stage II, as is clearly shown by the experiments to be discus-sed in chapter 5. Moreover, the energy released during stage II and III is of the same order of magnitude [19]. This would mean that the energy of the point defects re-orienting in stage II is lowered by an amount of the order of their formation energy (or even more, as not all of the point defects will take part in the reorientation process). This seems to be rather improbable.

6) Simply by a lack of alternatives we are inclined to explain stage II recovery in terms of *migration or break up of interstitial agglomerates*. This does not seem un-reasonable, because according to most models, point defects are produced in rows. There are also some experimental indications that the stage II defect is of the inter-stitial type. First, it has been observed by Swanson in Al [45] and by Jackson in Pt

[31] that stage II recovery was enhanced when the specimen had been quenched prior to the deformation. Secondly, in irradiated Ni a magnetic after effect has been observed by Peretto et al. [69], which anneals out in stage II and is ascribed by the authors to di-interstitials. According to Johnson's calculations [99] on Ni, the migration energy of a di-interstitial corresponds to the stage II range, whereas the binding energy is too high to allow a dissociation. Calculations of Bennemann and Tewordt [103] of the binding energy of a di-interstitial in Cu indicate that dissociation in stage II is possible. A detailed interpretation of the fine structure observed in stage II is, however, not possible at the present time.

The interpretation of stage II recovery in terms of migration or break up of small interstitial agglomerates has been proposed in 1963 by Van den Beukel [19], based on the same kind of argumentation as presented here. In the literature on irradiation effects the stage has been called sometimes "garbage annealing". It has been usually ascribed to point defect-impurity interactions. It has now become clear (see Schilling, this volume) that stage II after high dose irradiation and severe cold working are quite analogous and the interpretation given by Schilling is in accordance with that proposed here. On the other hand, it has been shown [19] that impurities can influence the deformation stage II. In these experiments the impurity concentration was about $10^{-3}-10^{-2}$, being at least a factor of 10 larger than the point defect concentration, a situation comparable with that after low dose electron irradiation of "pure" specimens. It comes out that due to the impurities the recovery has a more continuous character and is shifted to somewhat higher temperatures. Smaller impurity concentrations do not much affect the recovery. It has been shown by Buck [44] that stage II recovery in heavily cold worked Cu single crystals is not different in 99.98 and 99.999% pure material.

Finally a complication must be mentioned which is met for rather small degrees of deformation. It has been observed by Schumacher and Seeger [91] for Au and by Dawson [104] for Au, Ag and Cu that the resistivity isochronals show one or more *rising* portions in the stage II range. According to Schumacher this effect is due to rearrangements within point defect strings, whereas Dawson argues that impurities are involved. Rising portions in the resistivity isochronals have also been found in the stage III and IV range of deformed Ni by Spark [41] and by Hellenthal and Lotter [105]. The latter authors (private comm.) argue that these effects are due to internal stresses.

*Summary:* Stage II in heavily cold worked fcc metals is probably due to intrinsic point defects. Most interpretations proposed in the literature can be rejected with a high degree of probability. The one remaining is the migration or break up of interstitial agglomerates. Some experimental evidence supports this interpretation.

## 4.2. *Stage III*

### 4.2.1. Review of experimental results

(a) Structure in stage III

As discussed in chapter 3, stage III shows a two- or threefold fine-structure in Au, Ag and Cu after *small* deformations. For Au (fig. 10) the three substages merge into stage III for deformations of $\approx 10\%$. Substage b seems to become relatively less important with increasing degree of deformation. For $\epsilon = 10\%$ the centre temperature of stage III is $\approx 300°$K. After heavy deformations (fig. 3) a well defined stage III is observed, centered at $\approx 260°$K. (This has also been reported by Schüle et al. [72] and by Dawson [40].) If this shift of $\approx 40°$K to lower temperatures should apply to individual substages, this would mean that substage b in heavily deformed Au shifts into the stage II range. In this case stage III after heavy deformations should consist of substages c and d. The same applies to Ag. In this case the width of stage III after heavy deformations (fig. 6) suggests more clearly that the stage does not consist of a single process, which is confirmed by activation energy measurements (see below). An objection against the idea that stage b shifts away from the stage III range with increasing degree of deformation is the fact that both for Ag and Au the centre temperature of stage b does hardly change when the degree of deformation increases from 1 to 10% (fig. 10 and 11). Therefore an alternative possibility is as follows: The centre temperature of stage b is constant. For heavy deformations the contribution of stage b becomes negligible for Au, whereas for Ag it remains important. This suggestion is supported by a comparison of figs. 10 and 11, indicating that stage b represents a more important fraction of stage III in Ag than in Au.

Let us now compare stage III of Cu, Ag and Au found after *heavy* deformations. For Cu (fig. 7) the clear stage III peak is preceded by a small substage, labelled II*. Comparison of this result with stages III of Au and Ag (fig. 3 and 6) suggests that the Cu result is intermediate between Au and Ag: In Au stage II* is absent, in Cu it is present but small compared to the main stage III peak, whereas in Ag it is considerably larger and merges with the remainder of stage III into one broad peak. This suggestion implies that the single stage III peak in Au must be compared with the main peak in Cu and the second part of the broad peak in Ag, which is in agreement with the results of activation energy measurements to be discussed below.

In Ni a substage preceding stage III analogous to stage II* in Cu has been observed by van den Beukel [19] and by Merklen and Dimitrov [32] (figs. 5 and 9). In Al stage III is well defined and rather narrow (fig. 2); again in the stored energy spectrum [19] a small preceding substage has been found. Finally in Pt (fig. 4) stage III is a pronounced peak; a "shoulder" on the high temperature side indicates that more than one process may be active. For small degrees of deformation between stages II and III in Pt a small substage has been observed by Miura et al. [35].

*Summary:* In all the metals considered a pronounced stage III peak is observed after heavy deformations. In some cases it is preceded by a small substage (Cu, Ni, perhaps Al); in other cases (Au, Pt) this does not occur; in Ag this substage is probably a substantial part of the broad stage III. The relation between the fine structure observed after low degrees of deformation and the results after heavy deformations is not yet clear.

(b) Activation energies

The activation energies reported for stage III of cold worked fcc metals have been collected in table 4. Some remarks should be made.

For Cu Dawson [40], using the slope change method, finds that in the first and smaller part of the stage, corresponding to substage b, the activation energy increases continuously from 0.5 to 0.7 eV. In the second part, corresponding to substage c, $E_{III}$ is constant: $0.72 \pm 0.03$ eV. The somewhat lower value reported by Ramsteiner et al. [70] has been determined by the Meechan-Brinkman method and will repre-

Table 4
Activation energies observed in stage III after cold working.

| Metal | $E_{III}$ (eV) | Ref. |
|-------|----------------|------|
| Au | $0.71 \pm 0.02$ | 72 |
|    | $0.65 \pm 0.04$ | 83 |
|    | $0.69 \pm 0.06$ | 2 |
| Pt | 1.4 | 33 |
|    | $1.38 \pm 0.05$ | 31 |
|    | $1.35 \pm 0.05$ | 78 |
| Al | $0.57 \pm 0.04$ | 30 |
|    | $0.57 \pm 0.01$ | 66 |
| Cu | $0.64 \pm 0.04$ | 70 |
|    | $0.68 \pm 0.04$ | 89 |
|    | $0.67 \pm 0.07$ | 92 |
|    | $0.5 - 0.7$ (first part) | 40 |
|    | $0.72 \pm 0.03$ | 40 |
| Ag | 0.65 | 2 |
|    | $0.60 \pm 0.05$ | 71 |
|    | $0.2 - 0.5$ (first part) | 40 |
|    | $0.55 \pm 0.02$ (second part) | 40 |
| Ni | $0.92 \pm 0.04$ (pure) | 106 |
|    | $0.86 \pm 0.03$ (pure) | 42 |
|    | $1.0 \pm 0.1$ (pure) | 32 |
|    | $1.09 \pm 0.04$ (impure) | 106 |
|    | $1.09 \pm 0.05$ (impure) | 107 |
|    | $1.1 \pm 0.1$ (impure) | 74 |
|    | $0.98 \pm 0.08$ (impure) | 108 |

sent an average activation energy. The same happens in Ag [40]. In the first part of stage III activation energies between 0.2 and 0.5 eV were found, whereas in the second part the value is fairly constant: 0.55 eV. The value of 0.60 ± 0.05 eV reported by Ramsteiner et al. [71] belongs to the second part, because the deformation temperature was −40°C in this experiment. The $E_{III}$-values found in Au can be summarized by 0.69 ± 0.06 eV, corresponding to the results of the slope change method [40] except in the small early part of the stage where a few lower values were found. For Pt Jackson [31] reports that the observed 1.38 ± 0.05 eV is unique for the whole stage. With exception of a few values at the beginning the results of Frois [30] obtained for Al by the slope change method (0.57 ± 0.04 eV) correspond to the 0.57 ± 0.01 eV reported by Ceresara et al. [60].

For Ni it has been shown by Simson and Sizmann [106] that $E_{III}$ is rather impurity dependent. For 99.8% pure Ni a value of 1.09 ± 0.04 is found in correspondence with the values reported by Sosin and Brinkman [74] and by Schumacher et al. [107], both on impure Ni. For 99.999% in pure Ni $E_{III}$ = 0.92 ± 0.04 eV [106], in agreement with the 0.86 ± 0.03 eV reported by Kressel et al. [42] for Ni of the same nominal purity. Therefore the best value of $E_{III}$ for pure Ni seems to be about 0.89 ± 0.05 eV.

(c) Ordering and clustering

Resistivity increases interpreted as to be due to increases of short range ordering or to clustering have been observed in stage III of the following cold worked alloys: Au (7.5% Cu) [83]; Au (4.6% Cu) [40]; Au (3.6% Ag) [40]; Cu (3.9% Au) [40]; Ag (15.4% Au) [40]; Al (2.4 and 10% Zn) [109,110]. Illustrations are given for an ordering Au(Cu) alloy and a clustering Al(Zn) alloy in figs. 13 and 17 respectively. Dawson [40] has investigated which of the substages observed in stage III after small deformations is responsible for the ordering process. One of the results is shown in fig. 18, which compares the isochronals of pure Au, a Au(Cu) and a Au(Ag) alloy. The recovery spectra of the alloys and the pure metal are seen to be quite analogous. The ordering effect appears to be confined to the range of substages c and d, whereas stage b is a decrease of the resistivity in both the alloys and the pure Au. In Cu(Au) two separate increases of the resistivity were found in temperature ranges corresponding to stages c and d in pure Cu. In Ag(Au) also two increases of the resistivity were observed which in this case, however, correspond to the temperature ranges of stages b and d in pure Ag. Therefore the relation between the substages and the ordering processes does not seem to be completely clear at the present time.

(d) Special experiments on Ni

The results of internal friction and magnetic after effect measurements on irradiated and cold worked Ni are reviewed by Kronmüller in this volume. Some of the results will be mentioned here very briefly. It has been shown by Kronmüller et al. [111] that stage III in neutron irradiated Ni is accompanied by the disappearance of a magnetic after effect. In cold worked Ni Seeger et al. [82] observed a magnetic after effect and an internal friction peak which also annealed out in stage III. The

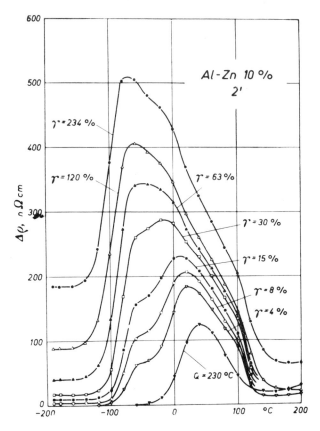

Fig. 17. Resistivity isochronals of Al (10% Zn) after various degrees of plastic deformation at 78°K [110].

relaxation times $\tau$ observed in the irradiation and cold working experiments can be commonly described [112] by $\tau = \tau_0 \exp(E^R/kT)$ where the relaxation energy $E^R = 0.87 \pm 0.03$ eV and $\tau_0 = 10^{-13.6}$ sec. In the irradiated Ni the relaxation effect anneals out with an activation energy of $1.02 \pm 0.03$ eV. The authors argue that these effects cannot be ascribed to a vacancy type defect (e.g. the di-vacancy), because in this case the reorientation and the migration energy must be the same. The relaxation effects are ascribed to rotation of the ⟨100⟩ split interstitial (dumbbell). This interpretation is supported by the experiments of Seeger and Wagner [113] on deformed Ni single crystals, indicating that the relaxation phenomena are caused by a defect having ⟨100⟩ symmetry. The internal friction peaks can be described by a single relaxation process and correspond to defect concentrations of about $10^{-5}$ for $\epsilon = 15\%$ in tension.

Magnetic relaxation processes in irradiated and cold worked Ni have also been studied by the Grenoble group (Peretto, Dautreppe, Moser, Oddou, Minier-Cassayre

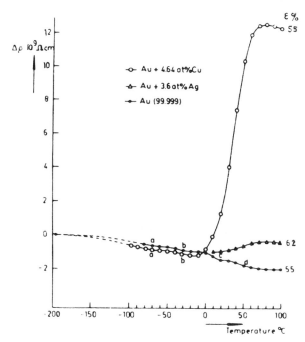

Fig. 18. Resistivity isochronals of Au, Au (4.6% Cu) and Au (3.6% Ag) after plastic deformation at 78°K [40].

[69,114] ). These authors observed a magnetic after effect in electron irradiated Ni [114], which anneals out in stage $I_E$ and can be ascribed to interstitials as well. They also found a magnetic after effect both in cold worked and irradiated Ni, which anneals out in stage III [69]. They argue that this effect is due to the reorientation of interstitials on the edges of interstitial platelets in the (111) planes.

In this context some results of Hellenthal and Lotter [105] can be mentioned. These authors investigated the recovery of the resistivity and the magnetoresistance of Ni cold worked at 78°K. The magnetoresistance was measured with the aid of an alternating magnetic field. The main result is shown in fig. 19. The isochronal recovery of the magnetoresistance was followed between 20 and 300°C, involving stages III and IV. At each annealing temperature the sample was annealed for 10 min while in an alternating magnetic field and subsequently for 10 min while in a constant magnetic field. After each treatment the sample was cooled to 78°K where the magnetoresistance was measured. The general result of the annealing treatment is a rather continuous increase of the magnetoresistance. However, the second annealing treatment in a constant magnetic field gives rise to a decrease of the magnetoresistance. The authors interpret this effect as follows: In the constant magnetic field an orientable point defect (e.g. the dumbbell) is oriented with respect to

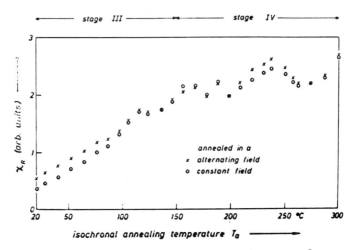

Fig. 19. Isochronal recovery of the magnetoresistance of Ni, deformed at 78°K, in an alternating and a constant magnetic field [105].

the local magnetization. At the measuring temperature of 78°K the oriented point defects cause a stabilization of the local magnetization, which is observed as a decrease of the magnetoresistance. This effect disappears after annealing between 75 and 100°C (stage III) which is ascribed to the annealing out of the orientable point defects.

### 4.2.2. Discussion

(a) General remarks

In the preceding sections a great deal of attention has been given to the fine structure observed in stage III of Cu, Ag and Au after small degrees of deformation. It is very well possible, however, that this complexity is less important than it seems to be. The reason is that the point defect concentrations annealing out in substages b, c and d are of the order of $10^{-6}$, being smaller by a factor of 10 than the impurity concentrations in the pure metals used. Moreover the number of jumps of a point defect to arrive at a dislocation is estimated at about $10^6$ (formula (1), taking $\Lambda = 10^9$ cm$^{-2}$). Therefore impurities, if ever, are expected to play an important part in these particular annealing experiments. Especially substage b is a promising candidate for being ascribed to point defect-impurity interactions. The stage II defects have ample opportunity to travel from one impurity trap to another until they find the deepest one, from which they could be released in stage b. The narrowness of the stage can be explained by the reasonable assumption that the deepest traps are provided by a special kind of impurity. The relatively constant centre temperature can be understood also: The annealing out of the trapped defects is mainly determined by their first jump. The absence of ordering effects due to stage b (with one possible exception) corresponds to the fact that the stage II defects do not give rise to ordering either. Further in all cases stage b is only present when stage II is present (see figs. 10 and 11). Finally, the fact that stage b is clearly more important in Ag and Cu than in Au is what should be intuitively expected if oxygen is the specific impurity involved (it has been found by Quéré [115] that 99.999% pure Johnson and Mattey Ag contains an oxygen concentration of $2 \times 10^{-5}$).

The conclusion is at hand that for an investigation of intrinsic point defects in cold worked metals heavy deformations must be preferred. In that case the point defect concentrations annealing out are $\approx 10^{-4}$ and the dislocation densities $\approx 10^{11}$ cm$^{-2}$, so that $n_j \approx 10^4$ (formula (1)), which strongly reduces the influence of impurity concentrations of $10^{-5}$. As discussed before, after heavy deformations stage III is a well defined annealing stage in Au, Pt and Al; it consists of a main peak preceded by a small one in Cu and Ni; only in Ag stage III is probably complex, but it has been argued in section 4.2.1(a) that the high temperature part is probably comparable with the "true" stage III of the other fcc metals.

The observed ordering and clustering effects point to a vacancy type diffusion in stage III and invite to a comparison with results obtained from quenching experiments. Further, in the annealing spectrum after irradiation of the fcc metals considered a stage labelled III has been observed which has to be compared with the corresponding cold work stage.

(b) Comparison with quenching results

In table 5 the activation energies reported for the cold work stage III have been collected, together with those found for the irradiation stage III and after quenching. Each value represents an average over the available data. The values of $E_{III}$(def.) have been derived from table 4. For irradiated Pt [116] and Ag [96] only one value is available. The remaining values of $E_{III}$(irr.) have been derived from refs.

Table 5

Average activation energies (in eV) observed in stage III after deformation and irradiation and after quenching (for comments see the text).

| Metal | $E_{III}$ (def.) | $E$ (quench.) | $E_{III}$ (irr.) |
|-------|------------------|----------------|-------------------|
| Au | $0.69 \pm 0.06$ | $0.70 \pm 0.05$ | $0.76 \pm 0.10$ |
| Pt | $1.38 \pm 0.05$ | $1.33 \pm 0.08$ | $1.36 \pm 0.08$ |
| Al | $0.57 \pm 0.04$ | $0.57 \pm 0.10$ | $0.59 \pm 0.04$ |
| Cu | $0.68 \pm 0.05$ | $0.70 \pm 0.15$ | $0.69 \pm 0.05$ |
| Ag | $0.60 \pm 0.05$ | $0.57 \pm 0.03$ | $0.67 \pm 0.04$ |
| Ni | $0.89 \pm 0.05$ | $0.85 \pm 0.15$ | $1.02 \pm 0.03$ |

[96,117–120] for Au, refs. [30,121–125] for Al, refs. [96,126–129] for Cu and refs. [74,111] for Ni. If a reported activation energy was clearly outside the range covered by the other ones it has been omitted.

The values of $E$ (quench) in the table need some comments. For Au numerous determinations of $E$ have been carried out, the results varying between 0.55 and 0.95 eV. However, for vacancy concentrations between $10^{-4}$ and $10^{-6}$ the overwhelming majority of the reported values lies in the range $0.70 \pm 0.05$ eV (e.g. [130, 131,132]). According to Koehler (this volume) about 0.9 eV is observed in the purest Au for high quenching rates, in contradiction to Siegel [133], who finds 0.7 eV under these conditions also. The predominant value of 0.7 eV is usually interpreted as the migration energy of di-vacancies, although it cannot be excluded that it represents the single vacancy migration energy.

For Pt the situation seems to be more simple. The $1.33 \pm 0.08$ eV is obtained [31,134,135] only if the quenched in vacancy concentration is not too large. The observed $E$-values decrease to about 1 eV with increasing concentration. The 1.33 eV is in good agreement with the migration energy of single vacancies expected from $Q - E_{1V}^{F}$ (table 2).

For Al a very wide range $(0.3 - 0.7$ eV) of activation energies after quenching have been reported (e.g. [52]). The value in the table only covers a majority. There is, however, a remarkable agreement among different reviewers [52,120,136] in assigning a value of about 0.60 eV to single vacancy migration.

For Cu the average of $0.70 \pm 0.15$ eV has been obtained from the following values: $0.55 \pm 0.05$ eV [137]; $0.77 \pm 0.10$ eV [127]; $0.80 \pm 0.06$ eV [127]; $0.71 \pm 0.04$ eV [54]. The latter value has been obtained after quenching from a CO-atmosphere. It has been argued by Clarebrough et al. [138] and confirmed by Wright and Evans [54] that this quenching method is the best one up till now in avoiding oxygen contamination. Therefore the value of $0.71 \pm 0.04$ eV is probably the best one available for quenched Cu at the present time. It is clearly lower than the $0.91 \pm 0.10$ eV derived from the relation $E_{1V}^{M} = Q - E_{1V}^{F}$ (table 2) and for this reason it is thought [54] to be more representative for di-vacancy than for single vacancy migration.

For quenched Ag a dominant activation energy of $0.57 \pm 0.03$ eV has been reported by several authors [81,115,139]. For the same reasons as for Cu this value is interpreted as the di-vacancy migration energy. Moreover, for low quenching temperatures [115] or by a pulse heating technique [81] in quenched Ag an activation energy of $\approx 0.85$ eV is found, which corresponds very well to what is expected for the migration energy of single vacancies (table 2). In the next section (stage IV) we shall return to this point.

Finally the recovery behaviour of quenched Ni, analogous to that of cold worked Ni, has been shown to be rather impurity dependent [100,101,140]. The annealing of the purest Ni exhibits a main stage in the temperature range corresponding to stage III. The following activation energies have been reported: 0.72 eV [100]; $0.85 \pm 0.05$ eV [101]; $1.0 \pm 0.1$ eV [141]. For Ni $E_{1V}^{M}$ cannot be estimated from

$Q - E_{1V}^F$, because $E_{1V}^F$ is not known. As $Q \approx 2.9$ eV, in analogy with the other fcc metals $E_{1V}^M$ is expected to be about $1.3 - 1.4$ eV. Further it has been shown by Seeger (this volume) that the high temperature diffusion data of Ni can be described by a sum of single and di-vacancy contributions if $E_{1V}^M$ and $E_{2V}^M$ are chosen as about 1.47 eV and 0.82 eV, respectively. This also indicates that the 0.85 eV found in quenched Ni represents di-vacancy migration.

Comparing the $E_{III}$(def.) values with the $E$ (quench) values in table 5 and taking into account the foregoing discussion it can be concluded that a good agreement exists between $E_{III}$(def.) and the dominant activation energies observed after quenching. This is regarded as a support for the interpretation of stage III in terms of vacancy type defects. The evidence points to di-vacancies in Cu, Ag, Au and Ni and to single vacancies in Al and Pt. The assignment of stage III to vacancy type defects is in agreement with the ordering and clustering phenomena observed in related alloys. It would be rather satisfactory, if no irradiation experiments had been done.

(c) Comparison with irradiation results

In table 5 the activation energies reported for the irradiation stage III are given. With the possible exception of Ag and Ni they agree reasonably with the $E_{III}$(def.) values. For Pt and Al the common assignment of the stage to single vacancies seems to be obvious. For Au the spread of $E_{III}$(irr.) is rather wide. The highest value of $0.86 \pm 0.08$ eV has recently been reported by Koehler (this volume) for electron irradiated Au and ascribed to single vacancies, because this value corresponds to the highest ones observed in quenched Au. If this interpretation is correct we notice that for Au the $E_{III}$(def.) of 0.7 eV is clearly lower than $E_{III}$(irr.). The former value could be ascribed to di-vacancies (preceding section). An analogous situation seems to exist in Ag and Ni. For both metals $E_{III}$(def.) can be ascribed on good grounds to di-vacancies; in both metals $E_{III}$(irr.) is somewhat larger, but (and here the "stage III dilemma" comes in) at first sight not large enough to be ascribed to single vacancies as was possible for Pt, Au and Al.

The stage III dilemma is best illustrated when the results of electron irradiated Cu are considered. The main problem is as follows. If stage III after low dose electron irradiation should be due to vacancy type defects, these could only be single vacancies, homogeneously distributed in the lattice in concentrations between $10^{-6}$ and $10^{-5}$. If the low temperature value of $E_{1V}^M$ is given by $Q - E_{1V}^F$, the result for Cu is $E_{1V}^M = 0.91 \pm 0.10$ eV, being clearly higher than the observed 0.7 eV. The decrease of the activation energy cannot be ascribed to di-vacancy formation, because at the stage III temperature a vacancy having $E_{1V}^M = 0.91 \pm 0.10$ eV makes far too few jumps to meet another vacancy during the time of the experiments. The same probably applies to Ni.

A possible way out of this difficulty is to drop the assumption of a temperature independent $E_{1V}^M$. In this respect the results of Flynn's calculations represented in fig. 12 are of interest. In table 6 the approximate centre temperatures of stage III $(T_{III})$ are given and also the ratio's $T_{III}/\theta$. The value of $E_{1V}^M(T_{III}/\theta)/E_{1V}^M(\infty)$ can be

Table 6
Migration energies of single vacancies at the centre temperature of stage III ($T_{III}$), calculated
from Flynn's [62] theory.

| Metal | $\theta$ ($^\circ$K) | $T_{III}$ ($^\circ$K) | $T_{III}/\theta$ | $E_{1V}^M(T_{III})$ (eV) |
|-------|-----|-----|-----|--------------|
| Pt | 229 | 520 | 2.3 | $1.40 \pm 0.10$ |
| Au | 165 | 260 | 1.6 | $0.78 \pm 0.10$ |
| Al | 418 | 210 | 0.5 | $0.40 \pm 0.07$ |
| Cu | 339 | 250 | 0.7 | $0.67 \pm 0.07$ |
| Ag | 225 | 220 | 1.0 | $0.73 \pm 0.07$ |
| Ni | 456 | 350 | 0.8 | $1.10 \pm 0.08$ |

derived from fig. 12 and combination with the values of $E_{1V}^M(\infty)$ in table 2 yields
$E_{1V}^M(T_{III})$. The results are shown in table 6. For Ni, $E_{1V}^M(\infty)$ has been chosen as
1.4 ± 0.1 eV. It is seen that in this way the stage III problem for Cu is removed.
Also for Ni and Ag the calculated $E_{1V}^M(T_{III})$ correponds to the activation energies
observed in the irradiation stage III (table 5). On the other hand the low value of
$E_{1V}^M(T_{III})$ for Al creates a new problem.

Another possible solution of the stage III problem is the so-called "2 interstitial
model", first introduced by Meechan, Sosin and Brinkman [128]. In this model it
is proposed that the free migrating interstitial in stage I of irradiated metals is the
⟨110⟩ crowdion, whereas in stage III a second type of interstitial, the ⟨100⟩ split
interstitial or dumbbell becomes mobile. The merits of this model with respect to
the interpretation of the irradiation results will not be discussed here at large; the
reader is referred to recent review papers dealing with this subject (e.g. Corbett
[79], Schilling (this volume), Kronmüller (this volume)).

The evidence supporting the dumbbell interpretation of stage III after cold working has been mentioned in section 4.2.1.(d) . It comes from mechanical and magnetic relaxation experiments on cold worked Ni, indicating that in stage III a defect
anneals out having the required ⟨100⟩ symmetry. The assignment of this effect to
dumbbells seems to be obvious but not compelling in view of the following objections that can be raised:

1) The magnetic after effect annealing out in stage $I_E$ after irradiation [114] can
be ascribed to dumbbells as well. According to Corbett [79] the assignment of this
effect to crowdions meets the difficulty that a (metastable) crowdion changing its
axis will very probably convert to a ⟨100⟩ split interstitial.

2) The after effect annealing out in stage III may be due to impurity trapped
interstitials [79], which provide the required anisotropic defects as well. It has
been argued [142] that this should be contradictory to the fact that the internal
friction peaks can be described by a single relaxation process. This argument does

not apply, however, if only one special type of impurity is involved. In this respect it would be useful to repeat the internal friction experiments on very heavily cold worked pure Ni, for instance by wire drawing. In such experiments point defect concentrations of $10^{-3} - 10^{-4}$ anneal out in stage III, being almost certainly larger by an order of magnitude than the concentration of any kind of impurity present.

3) If the suggested interpretation of stage II recovery, the break up or migration of small interstitial agglomerates, is correct, this involves a serious difficulty to the 2 interstitial model. It is clear that release of an interstitial from a cluster requires a larger activation energy than the migration energy of the interstitial. Further, theoretical calculations [99] indicate that the migration energy of di-interstitials is larger than that of single interstitials. In both cases single interstitial migration is expected to occur below stage II, in accordance with the 1 interstitial models. If the proposed interpretation of stage II is not correct, the 2 interstitial model (in order to be really a model) should provide a satisfactory alternative.

*Summary:* The main points of the discussion of stage III recovery can be summarized as follows:

1) Heavy deformations are preferable for the study of intrinsic point defects produced in plastic deformation.

2) In heavily cold worked Au, Pt and Al a well defined stage III is observed. In Cu and Ni the dominant stage III peak is preceded by a small substage. In Ag the high temperature part of the broad stage III peak probably corresponds to stage III of the other fcc metals.

3) Comparison of the activation energies observed after quenching and in the deformation stage III suggests a vacancy interpretation of stage III. The evidence points to single vacancies in Pt and Al and to di-vacancies in Au, Cu, Ni and Ag. The vacancy interpretation is supported by the ordering and clustering phenomena observed in related alloys.

4) The irradiation and cold work stages III of Pt and Al can be commonly attributed to single vacancies. For Ag, Ni and Au there is some doubt whether the cold work and irradiation stages III represent the same annealing porcess in view of the somewhat higher activation energies observed in the latter. The most elegant way out is ascribing the irradiation stage III to single vacancies in all cases, but this is not without problems.

5) Some authors have proposed that a second type of interstitial, the ⟨100⟩ split interstitial, becomes mobile in stage III, in order to solve some difficulties in the interpretation of irradiation data. The interpretation of recovery data of cold worked fcc metals do not need this assumption. The "stage III dilemma" must be solved in the field of irradiation experiments from which it originates.

## 4.3. Stage IV

Sometimes after stage III and prior to the recrystallization a more or less clear and usually rather small recovery has been observed in cold worked fcc metals, which has been called stage IV. Activation energies found in this range show some correspondence with the values of $E_{1V}^M$ listed in table 2, which were obtained by equating $E_{1V}^M$ to $Q - E_{1V}^F$. For this reason the stage – if present – has often been attributed to the annealing out of single vacancies. In the following the experimental evidence on stage IV will be discussed with special attention to the single vacancy interpretation.

1) In cold worked Au and Al a separate stage IV has not been observed. It is generally agreed that if in these metals single vacancy diffusion occurs, this happens in the stage III range. A number of authors (e.g. Sosin and Garr [143]) who identify stage IV with single vacancy migration express this as follows: Stage IV is overlapped by stage III.

2) In Ag essentially the same situation occurs. What is called stage IV is not clearly separated from stage III but only the tail of it, as is illustrated in fig. 11 showing Dawson's [40] isochronals for cold worked Ag. "Stage IV" is a rather continuous recovery. Between 40 and 80°C (representing only a part of stage IV in fig. 11) Dawson carried out three activation energy determinations by the slope change method, giving 0.94, 0.85 and 1.04 eV. Therefore his assignment of $E = 0.89 \pm 0.05$ eV to stage IV seems to be weakly founded. Ramsteiner et al. [71] claim to observe in Ag a rather sharply defined stage IV centered at about 60°C. However, from an inspection of their "isochronals" it appears that in the "stage IV" temperature range the density of data points is strongly increased in all the curves presented. These authors report an activation energy of 0.88 ± 0.04 eV between 30 and 80°C. Finally Kamel and Attia [144] observed an activation energy of 0.7 eV between 25 and 50°C in cold worked Ag.

From table 2 it is seen that for Ag $E_{1V}^M$ as found from $Q - E_{1V}^F$ is 0.85 ± 0.08 eV, corresponding to what is sometimes found after quenching [71,81,115]. From the foregoing discussion it is concluded, that the existence of a well defined stage IV in cold worked Ag with an activation energy equal to the migration energy of single vacancies has not been established.

In this context another feature of fig. 11 must be considered. It is seen that the continuous stage IV recovery develops gradually from a rather sharp stage d, found at the smaller deformations. For the smallest deformations this stage is even the only one observed. It is centered at about 300°K. The defect concentration annealing out in this case is about $10^{-6}$. The estimated number of jumps of a vacancy to reach a dislocation is larger than $10^6$. Further it has been shown by Quéré [115], that the oxygen concentration in the used Johnson and Mattey Ag is about $10^{-5}$ and that a strong binding energy exists between vacancies and oxygen in Ag. Therefore, if we assume that stage d is due to single vacancies, the oxygen atoms are the most probable sinks for the vacancies and the number of jumps is about $10^5$. Taking this number and substituting it in

$$n_j = AZvt \, \exp(-E/kT) \tag{11}$$

with $AZv = 10^{14 \pm 1}$, $t = 300$ sec and $T = 300°$K, $E = 0.70 \pm 0.06$ eV. This corresponds to: a) The value of Kamel and Attia [144] found in cold worked Ag in the same temperature range. b) The $0.67 \pm 0.04$ eV reported by Dworschak et al. [96] for stage III of irradiated Ag. c) The $0.73 \pm 0.07$ eV from table 6, representing $E_{1V}^M$ for Ag at low temperatures, obtained from Flynn's calculation of the temperature dependence of $E_{1V}^M$.

In conclusion, the evidence of the recovery in the tail of stage III, usually called stage IV, provides in cold worked Ag some arguments in favour of single vacancy diffusion with a migration energy of either 0.85 eV or 0.70 eV. The arguments are, however, far from conclusive.

3) As argued before, the stage in Pt usually called stage IV should preferably be labelled III. The observed activation energies point to single vacancy migration. The stage is followed immediately by the recrystallization stage V, so that stage IV is absent just as in Al and Au.

4) Between 100 and 200°C in cold worked Cu some recovery has been observed which is usually called stage IV. Reported activation energies in this range vary between 1 and 1.3 eV [70,145,146]. The recovery has a continuous character. According to Berghout [89] the activation energy increases continuously from 0.7 to 2 eV. In their review papers Balluffi et al. [5] and Clarebrough et al. [8] conclude that rearrangements of dislocations play an important part in this recovery range. On the other hand, Ramsteiner et al. [70] claim to observe a unique activation energy of $1.05 \pm 0.05$ eV in this range which they compare to the $1.08 \pm 0.03$ eV found by Ramsteiner et al. [137] in quenched Cu. They ascribe these observations to free migration of single vacancies. This conclusion is supported by Dawson's [40] experiments on a cold worked Cu(Au) alloy, exhibiting ordering in this temperature range. There are, however, some objections. It has been shown by Clarebrough et al. [138] and confirmed by Wright and Evans [54] that in quenched Cu recovery between 100 and 200°C is strongly reduced when the quench is performed in a reducing CO atmosphere, indicating that this recovery stage is possibly due to oxygen contamination. Moreover, the activation energies reported by Schüle et al. and by Ramsteiner et al. are higher than the $E_{1V}^M = 0.91 \pm 0.10$ from table 2, indicating that in the temperature range of stage IV release of oxygen trapped vacancies may occur. This would not be in conflict to the ordering evidence observed in the Cu(Au) alloy.

5) In cold worked Ni, a clear separate recovery stage labelled IV has been found near 250°C by several investigators. ([8,42,74,106–108].) The reported activation energies vary between 1.3 and 1.6 eV. It has been shown by Clarebrough et al. [8], that for the purest Ni used (99.96%) stage IV is absorbed by stage V for high degrees of deformation. In 99.999% pure Ni stage IV is absent, as has been shown by Simson and Sizmann [106], by Merklen and Dimitrov [32] and by Bridges and Ball [147]. The latter authors report that addition of $5 \times 10^{-4}$ carbon *produces* a stage IV recovery. They ascribed this effect to diffusion of C in Ni, in agreement with the known activation energy for this process. In this context the results of Kressel et al. [42] who do find a stage IV in cold worked 99.999% Ni are an exception.

In quenched Ni the results are similar. Mughrabi and Seeger [100] and Scherrer et al. [101] only observe recovery in the stage IV range ($E$ = 1.4 eV) if the material is not very pure.

Stage IV in cold worked Ni is usually attributed to migration of single vacancies. Although $E_{IV}^M$ for Ni is not known, the $Q$ value of 2.9 eV suggests that $E_{IV}^M$ is about 1.4 ± 0.1 eV (at least at high temperatures), which is in the stage IV range. The impurity dependence of the stage was fitted by Simson and Sizmann [106] in the framework of the 2-interstitial model in the following way: In stage III freely migrating interstitials recombine with immobile vacancies. If vacancies and interstitials were present in equal numbers after stage III nearly all the point defects have disappeared. In impure Ni part of the interstitials migrating in stage III are trapped by impurities, leaving a number of vacancies which anneal out in stage IV. The authors find support for this interpretation in their observation that stage III is increasing and stage IV is decreasing in magnitude with increasing purity. This observation has not been confirmed by Bridges and Ball [147], however. Moreover, the impurity dependence of the recovery behaviour of quenched Ni seems to be difficult to explain.

In view of the discussion given it must be concluded that it is premature to identify stage IV in cold worked Ni with free migration of single vacancies.

*Summary:* In cold worked Al, Pt and Au stage IV has not been observed. In Ag the recovery range usually called stage IV can be regarded as a part of stage III. The attribution to single vacancies is uncertain. The separate stage IV observed in Cu and, more clearly, in Ni is not free from suspicion to be related with impurities. In general, the existence of a stage IV due to single vacancy migration in cold worked fcc metals is far from established.

## 5. Interaction between dislocations and point defects

### 5.1. Introduction

When a point defect arrives at a dislocation it can give rise to so called pinning phenomena: due to the interaction between a point defect and a dislocation, the motion of the dislocation in its slip plane will be hindered when a stres is applied. The subject is treated in the paper by Sosin (this volume) and here only results on cold worked fcc metals will be briefly summarized.

As proposed by Koehler [148], Mott [149] and Friedel [150], dislocations will bow out under the influence of an applied elastic stress, which results in an extra elastic strain and thus in a decrease of the elastic moduli. The dislocation contribution to the elastic strain is reduced when point defects arrive and pin the dislocations, which causes an increase of the elastic moduli. Point defect pinning can also give rise to an increase of the flow stress (source hardening). Due to the interaction between dislocations and point defects, in the internal friction spectrum relaxation peaks are expected, each peak being due to a specific point defect-dislocation interaction. The mechanism is thought to be the following [151]: A dislocation line containing a pinning point has a certain probability to break away from the pinning point with the help of thermal energy. When the dislocation has broken away the point defect left behind will be attracted to the dislocation and try to pin it down again before the dislocation has returned to its original position. When the frequency of the break-away and repinning process coincides with the external vibrational frequency of the specimen, a relaxation peak will appear *.

All three types of pinning effects have been studied after cold working at 78°K, mainly on Cu, Au and Al.

## 5.2. Internal friction measurements

After cold working at 78°K in Cu and Au three internal friction peaks have been observed between 78°K and room temperature, called $P_1$, $P_2$ and $P_3$. These peaks have been studied in detail by Hasiguti and coworkers [151,152]. One of the results on Au is shown in fig. 20. The main results can be summarized as follows:

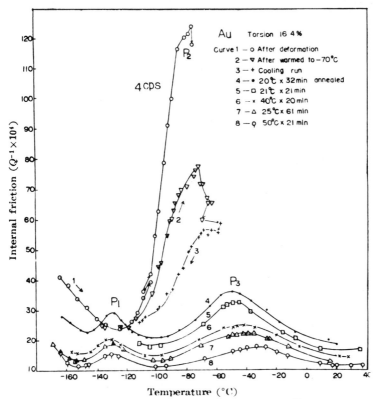

Fig. 20. Internal friction peaks in Au, cold worked at 78°K [151].

* Effects of this kind must be well distinguished from the Granato-Lücke damping, due to breaking away of dislocations from immobile pinning points.

1) When after deformation at 78°K the specimen is warmed up to room temperature a peak $P_2$ is observed, centered at 150 and 180°K for Cu and Au, respectively. This peak grows and decays at the peak temperature, this being the temperature range of stage II.

2) After annealing at room temperature (the stage III range) $P_2$ has disappeared and two new peaks, $P_1$ and $P_3$ are found. These peaks decay again after prolonged annealing at room temperature.

3) The frequency factors of the relaxation processes are of the order of $10^9 - 10^{10}$ sec$^{-1}$. The peaks are characterized by activation energies between 0.2 and 0.4 eV.

4) The peak heights are reduced by a small additional deformation.

5) The growth and decay of $P_2$ is accompanied by a decrease respectively an increase of the Bordoni maximum.

Most of the experimental results have been recently confirmed by Grandchamp et al. [153]. The peaks can be satisfactorily explained by assuming an interaction between dislocations and point defects. The growth of the peaks coincides with the point defect recovery stages. The evidence indicates that in stage III two different types of point defects arrive at the dislocations, tentatively interpreted by Hasiguti et al. as single and di-vacancies. The observed frequency factors point to dislocation vibrations. The decay of the peaks is ascribed to the annihilation of the point defects for instance by pipe diffusion. For detailed considerations on the mechanism of the relaxation the reader is referred to papers by Hasiguti [154], Koiwa and Hasiguti [155] and Schiller [156]. Variations of the height of the Bordoni peak during the point defect recovery stages have also been studied by Baxter and Wilks [157] and by Völkl et al. [158], both on cold worked Al. These authors also observed a decrease of the Bordoni maximum followed by an increase during annealing between 90 and 250°K. The dislocations responsible for the maximum are pinned by the arrival of point defects and subsequently depinned due to the disappearance of the point defects.

Damping phenomena related to those discussed here have been reported by Niblett and Wilks [159], Swartz [160], Walz [161] and Baxter and Wilks [162].

### 5.3. Modulus effects

It has been first observed by Köster [163] on Al that the internal friction decreases and the elastic modulus increases with time after deformation at room temperature. Analogous phenomena have been reported by Smith [164] on Cu, deformed between room temperature and 100°C. It has been shown by Granato et al. [165] that these results can be described quantitatively by a model based on diffusion of point defects to dislocations, giving rise to pinning. The early stages of the pinning process could be described by a Cottrell-Bilby $t^{\frac{2}{3}}$ dependence.

The effects of annealing on the elastic moduli have also been studied on polycrystalline Cu, Ag and Au after plastic deformation at 78°K. The deformation

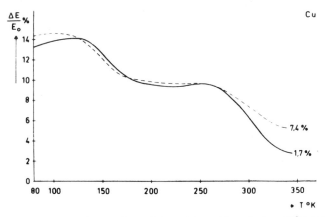

Fig. 21. Recovery of Young's modulus of Cu, cold worked at 78°K [168].

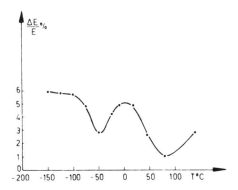

Fig. 22. Recovery of Young's modulus of Au, cold worked at 78°K [153].

causes a decrease of the shear modulus $G$ (Druyvesteyn et al. [166], Brouwer and Groeneboom [167]) and of Young's modulus $E$ (Lems [168], Brouwer and Groeneboom [167]) by 10–20%. During isochronal annealing both $E$ and $G$ increase again. For Cu and Au the increase occurs in two stages, corresponding to the stages II and III observed in the stored energy and resistivity. The difference is that after stage II the $\Delta E$ isochronal exhibits a rather large horizontal part (see fig. 21), which is absent in the stored energy and resistivity isochronals. The isochronal of Brouwer and Groeneboom on Cu shows a rising part just after stage II, indicating that a net depinning occurs. The depinning following stage II is present more clearly in the results of Grandchamp et al. [153] on Au, shown in fig. 22. These results fully agree with those discussed before in connection with the Hasiguti peak $P_2$. The stage II defects arriving at the dislocations cause pinning effects, which vanish again due to the annihilation of the point defects. Subsequently the pinning is renewed by the arrival of the stage III point defects. The annihilation of the stage II defects can occur either by pipe diffusion or by the stage III defects eating them up. The latter explanation is favoured by the observation of Grandchamp et al. [153], that the growth of $P_3$ is related to the decay of $P_2$. We note that if a pinning interstitial is annihilated by a di-vacancy a single vacancy remains, leaving the amount of pinning unchanged.

## 5.4. The flow stress effect

When a low temperature stress-strain curve is interrupted by removing the stress partially and when it is continued after a certain time $t_a$ at the same or a higher temperature $T_a$, a small increase of the flow stress, $\Delta\sigma$, is observed, which is a function of $t_a$ and $T_a$. This effect has been found for the first time by Blewitt [169] on Cu and later on by Westwood and Broom [170] on Al and Cu, by Takamura and Miura [171] on Cu, by Birnbaum and Tuler [172–174] on Cu, by Takamura et al. [175] on Au and by Aaron and Birnbaum [176] on Al. The effect has been studied most extensively by Birnbaum and coworkers; their results will be discussed briefly.

After cold working at 78°K the increase of the flow stress $\Delta\sigma$ for Cu passes through a maximum as a function of annealing time at a fixed annealing temperature (fig. 23). The height of the maximum increases and $(t_a)_{max}$ decreases with increasing $T_a$. This temperature and time dependence of the pinning process suggests that it is caused by a diffusion process. Birnbaum analyses the results by means of the following model: The pinning point defects migrate to the dislocations according to a Cottrell-Bilby $t^{\frac{2}{3}}$ law, which he claims to observe in the early stages of the pinning process. Subsequently the point defects disappear by migration along the dislocations to existing jogs. The migration energies of the two processes are different, $E$ and $E'$ respectively. The result of the analysis is that $E \approx 0.1$ eV and $E' \approx 0.05$ eV in the temperature range of stage II. These values correspond to tremendously large numbers of jumps, contradictory to the basis of the $t^{\frac{2}{3}}$ law, which describes stress assisted diffusion of interstitials to dislocations. The $E$ values found in this way will be rather sensitive to the model used and must be viewed with some caution. Moreover, Birnbaum's plot of $\Delta\sigma$ versus $t^{\frac{2}{3}}$ gives a straight line, which does not pass through the origin. If we plot the data points as ln $\Delta\sigma$ versus log $t$ we obtain a reasonable straight line passing through the origin, the slope being $\frac{1}{3}$ (whatever that may mean).

Qualitatively, however, the $\Delta\sigma$ results agree with the damping and modulus phenomena discussed before. It can be seen in fig. 23 that for the higher annealing temperatures $\Delta\sigma$ after having passed through the maximum increases again, indicating that after the arrival and disappearance of the stage II defects, pinning is taken over by the arrival of the stage III defects.

## 5.5. Concluding remarks

The results of the three types of experiments discussed provide strong and con-

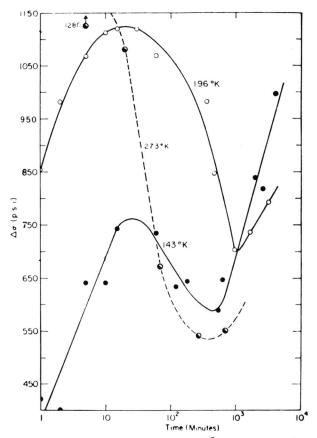

Fig. 23. Increase of the flow stress of Cu, measured at 78°K, versus time of annealing at the temperatures indicated [174].

sistent evidence for diffusion of point defects to dislocations in the two main recovery stages after cold working. They do not answer the question how large a fraction of the point defects annealing out is annihilated at the dislocations. In fact, it has been calculated by Schiller [156] that the Hasiguti relaxation peaks can be accounted for by bulk concentrations of point defects of about $10^{-10}$. The same conclusion has been reached by Lems [168], who shows that for the modulus effects observed a bulk point defect concentration of about $10^{-9}$ is sufficient. The reason is that if point defect concentrations of this magnitude are collected at the dislocations (density of the order of $10^{10}$ cm$^{-2}$) the point defect concentration along the dislocations becomes about $10^{-3}$, or about one point defect per dislocation line on the average. This is consistent with the results of van den Beukel and Brouwer [177] who showed that impurity concentrations of the order of $10^{-3}$ along the dislocation lines reduce the modulus effect by about the same amount as observed during the recovery of intrinsic point defects.

The foregoing does not mean, however, that only a very small fraction of the point defects annealing out really arrives at the dislocations. The actual number of pinning points is the result of two diffusion flows: The flow of point defects towards the dislocations and the flow of point defects along the dislocations to their final sinks. If it is assumed, for instance, that both diffusion flows obey first order kinetics with characteristic times $\tau_1$ and $\tau_2$ respectively, it can be shown easily that the actual number of pinning points is a fraction $\tau_2/\tau_1$ at most of the total point defect concentration annealing out. This fraction can be small if the migration energy of the point defects along the dislocations is smaller than in the bulk, or if the distance between the sinks along the dislocations is small compared to the dislocation network size.

Experiments of the kind discussed do not contribute much to the identification of the point defects involved. They all agree in indicating that at least two and possibly three different types of point defects play a part in the recovery range of stages II and III.

## 6. Conclusions

At the end of each chapter a summary of the discussion has been presented. The author feels some hesitation to repeat them here and call them "conclusions", because some of them are not conclusive. The method of discussion was somewhat similar to that used in the court of justice: Due to the lack of direct proof, arguments and counter-arguments were weighted against each other in order to come to a decision beyond reasonable doubt. What is considered reasonable depends on the judge. Therefore it is emphasized that the following "conclusions" are not definitively established; they represent a description and interpretation of the experimental data which is the most reasonable one in the authors opinion. The reader is strongly advised to appeal to a higher court by carrying out sophisticated experiments or by fighting the author's arguments.

1) Many models are available to account for the production of vacancy and interstitial type point defects by plastic deformation. The most satisfactory one in view of its quantitative agreement with experimental results is Saada's model, predicting that the point defect concentration produced is proportional to the work done in plastic deformation.

2) For the study of point defects in cold worked metals, *high* degrees of deformation are to be preferred mainly because in this case the influence of impurities will be strongly reduced.

3) The recovery spectrum after low temperature deformations of the fcc metals considered (Al, Au, Pt, Ni, Ag, Cu) consists of two main stages, labelled II and III in all cases. For Pt this implies a revision of the current nomenclature.

4) Stage II, at least in heavily cold worked fcc metals, is due to intrinsic point defects. The best interpretation is that stage II is due to migration or break up of interstitial agglomerates.

5) In heavily cold worked Au, Pt and Al a well defined stage III is observed. In Cu and Ni the dominant stage III peak is preceded by a small substage. In Ag the high temperature part of the broad stage III peak probably corresponds to stage III of the other fcc metals.

6) Comparison of the activation energies observed after quenching and in the deformation stage III suggests a vacancy interpretation of stage III. The evidence points to single vacancies in Pt and Al and to di-vacancies in Au, Cu, Ni and Ag. The vacancy interpretation is supported by the ordering and clustering phenomena observed in related alloys.

7) Evidence for the existence of a stage IV mainly comes from experiments on Cu and Ni. The evidence indicates that stage IV is influenced by impurities.

8) Experiments on the influence of annealing on the internal friction, the elastic constants and the flow stress provide strong and consistent evidence for diffusion of point defects to dislocations in the two main recovery stages after cold working.

## Acknowledgements

The author wishes to express his gratitude to Prof. Dr. M.J.Druyvesteyn, Prof. Dr. P.Penning, Ir. C.M.van Baal and Dr. H.I.Dawson for helpful discussions. He is indebted to Professor Penning for providing time to accomplish this review.

## References

[1] J.Molenaar and W.H.Aarts, Nature 166 (1950) 690.

[2] J.A.Manintveld, Thesis, Delft, 1954; Nature 169 (1952) 623.

[3] M.J.Druyvesteyn and J.A.Manintveld, Nature 168 (1951) 868.

[4] H.G.Van Bueren, Imperfections in crystals (North-Holland, Amsterdam, 1961).

[5] R.W.Balluffi, J.S.Koehler and R.O.Simmons, in: Recovery and recrystallization of metals, ed. L.Himmel (Interscience, New York, 1962) p. 1.

[6] M.de Jong and J.S.Koehler, Phys. Rev. 129 (1963) 40.

[7] T.Kino and J.S.Koehler, Phys. Rev. 162 (1967) 632.

[8] L.M.Clarebrough, M.E.Hargreaves and M.H.Loretto, in: Recovery and recrystallization of metals, ed. L.Himmel (Interscience, New York, 1962) p. 63.

[9] A.H.Cottrell, in: Dislocations and mechanical properties of crystals, eds. J.C.Fisher et al. (Wiley, New York, 1957) p. 509.

[10] L.Zsoldos, Phys. Stat. Sol. 3 (1963) 2127.

[11] P.B.Hirsch, Phil. Mag. 7 (1962) 67.

[12] J.Weertman, Phil. Mag. 8 (1963) 967.

[13] K.H.Pfeffer, P.Schiller and A.Seeger, Phys. Stat. Sol. 8 (1965) 517.

[14] J.Friedel, Dislocations (Pergamon Press, Oxford, 1964) p. 273.

[15] G.Saada, Thesis, Paris, 1960; Acta Met. 9 (1961) 166, 965.

[16] P.B.Hirsch, in: Internal stresses and fatigue in metals, eds. G.M.Rassweiler and W.L.Grube (Elsevier, Amsterdam, 1959) p. 139.

[17] H.J.Dawson, Thesis, Delft, 1964; Physica 31 (1965) 342.

[18] T.H.Blewitt, R.R.Coltman and J.K.Redman, in: Defects in crystalline solids (The Physical Society, London, 1955) p. 369.

[19] A.van den Beukel, Thesis, Delft, 1962; Acta Met. 11 (1963) 97.

[20] C.A.Pistorius, Physica 27 (1961) 149.

[21] G.Saada, Physica 27 (1961) 657.

[22] S.Ceresara, H.Elkholy and T.Federighi, Phys. Stat. Sol. 8 (1965) 509.

[23] P.Feltham, Phys. Stat. Sol. 6 (1964) 235.

[24] I.Kovacs, E.Nagy and P.Feltham, Phil. Mag. 9 (1964) 797.

[25] S.Yoshida, T.Kino, M.Kiritani, S.Kabemoto, H.Maeta and Y.Shimomura, J. Phys. Soc. Japan 18, Suppl. II (1963) 98.

[26] I.Kovacs and E.Nagy, Phys. Stat. Sol. 3 (1963) 726.

[27] H.R.Peiffer, J. Appl. Phys. 29 (1958) 1581.

[28] H.R.Peiffer, Acta Met. 11 (1963) 435.

[29] D.Kuhlmann-Wilsdorf and H.G.F.Wilsdorf, Acta Met. 10 (1962) 584.

[30] C.Frois, Thesis, Paris, 1965; Acta Met. 14 (1966) 1325.

[31] J.J.Jackson, in: Lattice defects in quenched metals, eds. R.M.J.Cotterill et al. (Academic Press, New York, 1965) pp. 467, 478.

[32] P.Merklen and O.Dimitrov, Mém. Sci. 63 (1966) 871.

[33] G.R.Piercy, Phil. Mag. 5 (1960) 201.

[34] L.C.Menting, Physica 30 (1964) 407.

[35] S.Miura, J.Takamura and N.Ogasa, Jül. Conf. 2 (Vol. I) 1968, p. 429.

[36] J.G.M.van Kuijk, Physica 30 (1964) 398.

[37] W.Köster and H.P.Kehrer, Z. Metallk. 56 (1965) 1761.

[38] J.W.Henderson and J.S.Koehler, Phys. Rev. 104 (1956) 626.

[39] D.J.Verel, Physica 29 (1963) 562.

[40] H.I.Dawson, Thesis, Delft, 1964; Acta Met. 13 (1965) 453.

[41] I.J.Spark, Acta Met. 15 (1967) 424.

[42] H.Kressel, D.W.Short and N.Brown, Acta Met. 15 (1967) 525.

[43] C.J.Meechan and A.Sosin, J. Appl. Phys. 29 (1958) 738.

[44] O.Buck, Phys. Stat. Sol. 2 (1962) 535.

[45] M.L.Swanson, Can. J. Phys. 42 (1964) 1890.

[46] M.L.Swanson and A.F.Quenneville, Appl. Phys. Letters 10 (1964) 179.

[47] S.Okuda and J.Takamura, Phys. Letters 25A (1967) 239.

[48] S.Okuda, J. Appl. Phys. 34 (1964) 3107.

[49] C.V.Kidson and H.Ross, Proc. Int. Conf. Radio-isotope Sci. Paris 1 (1957) 185.

[50] F.Cattaneo. E.Germagnoli and F.Grasso, Phil. Mag. 7 (1962) 1373.

[51] Average of various data, see J.W.Corbett, Electron radiation damage in semicondutors and metals (Academic Press, New York, 1966) p. 266.

[52] Average of various data, see T.Federighi, in: Lattice defects in quenched metals, eds. R.M.J. Cotterill et al. (Academic Press, New York, 1965) p. 217.

[53] A.Kuper, H.Letaw, L.Slifkin, E.Sonder and C.T.Tomizuka, Phys. Rev. 96 (1954) 1224; 98 (1955) 1870.

[54] P.Wright and J.H.Evans, Phil. Mag. 13 (1966) 521.

[55] C.T.Tomizuka and E.Sonder, Phys. Rev. 103 (1956) 1182.

[56] W.C.Mallard, A.B.Gardner, R.F.Bass and L.Slifkin, Phys. Rev. 129 (1963) 617.

[57] S.M.Makin, A.H.Rowe and A.D.Le Claire, Proc. Phys. Soc. B70 (1957) 545.

[58] U.Ermert, W.Rupp and R.Sizmann, Jül. Conf. 2 (Vol. I) 1968, p. 30.

[59] Average of various data, see H.Bakker, Phys. Stat. Sol. 28 (1968) 569.
[60] T.G.Stoebe and H.I.Dawson, Phys. Rev. 166 (1968) 621.
[61] A.S.Nowick and G.J.Dienes, Phys. Stat. Sol. 24 (1967) 461.
[62] C.P.Flynn, Phys. Rev. 171 (1968) 682.
[63] P.Penning, Philips Res. Repts. 14 (1959) 337.
[64] M.Winterberger, Thesis, Paris, 1958; Acta Met. 7 (1959) 549.
[65] R.Bullough and R.C.Newman, J. Phys. Soc. Japan 18, Suppl. III (1963) 27.
[66] S.Ceresara, H.Elkholy and T.Federighi, Phil. Mag. 12 (1965) 1105.
[67] L.J.Cuddy, Acta Met. 16 (1968) 23.
[68] R.W.Balluffi and D.N.Seidman, Phil. Mag. 17 (1968) 843.
[69] P.Peretto, D.Dautreppe and P.Moser, Phys. Stat. Sol. 13 (1966) 325.
[70] F.Ramsteiner, W.Schüle and A.Seeger, Phys. Stat. Sol. 7 (1964) 937.
[71] F.Ramsteiner, W.Schüle and A.Seeger, Phys. Stat. Sol. 2 (1962) 1005.
[72] W.Schüle, A.Seeger, D.Schumacher and K.King, Phys. Stat. Sol. 2 (1962) 1199.
[73] L.Stals and J.Nihoul, Phys. Stat. Sol. 8 (1965) 785.
[74] A.Sosin and J.A.Brinkman, Acta Met. 7 (1959) 478.
[75] T.R.Waite, Phys. Rev. 107 (1957) 463.
[76] J.Nihoul and L.Stals, Phys. Stat. Sol. 17 (1966) 295.
[77] A.van den Beukel, Scripta Met. 2 (1968) 327.
[78] K.Rösch, F.Bell and R.Sizmann, Jül. Conf. 2 (Vol. I) 1968, p. 444.
[79] J.W.Corbett, Electron irradiation damage in semiconductors and metals (Academic Press, New York, 1966).
[80] A.C.Damask and G.J.Dienes, Point defects in metals (Gordon and Breach, New York, 1963).
[81] M.Doyama and J.S.Koehler, Phys. Rev. 127 (1962) 21.
[82] A.Seeger, P.Schiller and H.Kronmüller, Phil. Mag. 5 (1960) 853.
[83] B.M.Korevaar, Thesis, Delft, 1960; Acta Met. 6 (1958) 572.
[84] B.van der Sijde, Physica 29 (1963) 559.
[85] J.A.Brinkman, C.E.Dixon and C.J.Meechan, Acta Met. 2 (1954) 38.
[86] M.H.Loretto, M.E.Hargreaves and L.M.Clarebrough, J. Austr. Inst. Met. 8 (1963) 127.
[87] S.H.A.Begemann and C.J.van der Wekken, Acta Met. 15 (1967) 1461.
[88] R.P.Huebner, Phys. Rev. 135A (1964) 1281.
[89] C.W.Berghout, Thesis, Delft, 1956; Acta Met. 6 (1958) 613.
[90] G.van Aller, Thesis, Delft, 1962; Acta Met. 10 (1962) 1061.
[91] D.Schumacher and A.Seeger, Phys. Letters 7 (1963) 184.
[92] R.R.Eggleston, J. Appl. Phys. 23 (1952) 1400.
[93] D.Schumacher, Scripta Met. 2 (1968) 209.
[94] A.S.Nowick, Acta Met. 3 (1955) 312.
[95] F.Dworschak and J.S.Koehler, Phys. Rev. 140 (1965) 941.
[96] F.Dworschak, K.Herschbach and J.S.Koehler, Phys. Rev. 133 (1964) A293.
[97] W.Primak, Phys. Rev. 100 (1955) 1677; J. Appl. Phys. 31 (1960) 1524.
[98] D.Schumacher, Thesis, Stuttgart, 1965; Phys. Letters 19 (1965) 367.
[99] R.A.Johnson, Phys. Rev. 152 (1967) 629.
[100] H.Mughrabi and A.Seeger, Phys. Stat. Sol. 19 (1967) 251.
[101] S.Scherrer, G.Lozes and B.Deviot, Jül. Conf. 2 (Vol. II) 1968, p. 167.
[102] D.Reits, R.W.Starreveld and H.J.de Wit, Phys. Letters 16 (1965) 13.
[103] K.H.Bennemann and L.Tewordt, Z. Naturforsch. 15a (1960) 772.
[104] H.I.Dawson, Physica 31 (1965) 1046.
[105] W.Hellenthal and U.Lotter, Jül. Conf. 2 (Vol. I) 1968, p. 456.
[106] P.Simson and R.Sizmann, Z. Naturforsch. 17a (1962) 596.
[107] D.Schumacher, W.Schüle and A.Seeger, Z. Naturforsch. 17a (1962) 228.

[108] F.Bell, Acta Met. 13 (1965) 363.
[109] S.Ceresara, Phil. Mag. 17 (1968) 1299.
[110] S.Ceresara and T.Federighi, Phil. Mag. 18 (1968) 301.
[111] H.Kronmüller, A.Seeger and P.Schiller, Z. Naturforsch. 15a (1960) 740.
[112] A.Seeger, H.Kronmüller, H.Rieger, H.E.Schaefer and F.J.Wagner, Phys. Letters 16 (1965) 110.
[113] A.Seeger and F.J.Wagner, Phys. Stat. Sol. 9 (1965) 583.
[114] P.Peretto, J.L.Oddou, C.Minier-Cassayre, D.Dautreppe and P.Moser, Phys. Stat. Sol. 16 (1966) 281.
[115] Y.Quéré, J. Phys. Soc. Japan 18, Suppl. III (1963) 91.
[116] W.Bauer and A.Sosin, Phys. Rev. 147 (1966) 482.
[117] R.A.Wullaert and J.W.Kauffman, Bull. Am. Phys. Soc. 6 (1961) 157.
[118] J.W.Kauffman, Conference on recovery in metals, Delft, 1962.
[119] W.Bauer and A.Sosin, Phys. Rev. 136 (1964) 474.
[120] J.S.Koehler, this volume.
[121] T.Federighi, S.Ceresara and F.Pieragostini, Phil. Mag. 12 (1965) 1093.
[122] K.Isebeck, R.Müller, W.Schilling and H.Wenzl,  Phys. Stat. Sol. 18 (1966) 427.
[123] Y.M.Liwin, M.Doyama and J.S.Koehler, Phys. Rev. 165 (1968) 787.
[124] C.Budin and P.Lucasson, in: Interaction of radiation with solids, ed. A.Bishay (New York, 1967); Phys. Letters 16 (1965) 225.
[125] W.Bauer, Jül. Conf. 2 (Vol. I) 1968, p. 275.
[126] A.W.Overhauser, Phys. Rev. 90 (1953) 393.
[127] C.Budin, P.Lucasson and A.Lucasson, J. Phys. 26 (1965) 9.
[128] C.J.Meechan, A.Sosin and J.A.BRinkman, Phys. Rev. 120 (1960) 411.
[129] D.O.Thompson, O.Buck, R.S.Barnes and H.B.Huntington, J. Appl. Phys. 38 (1967) 3051.
[130] J.W.Kauffman and M.Meshii, in: Lattice defects in quenched metals, eds. R.M.J.Cotterill et al. (Academic Press, New York, 1965) p. 77.
[131] J.A.Ytterhus, R.W.Siegel and R.W.Balluffi, in: Lattice defects in quenched metals, eds. R.M.J.Cotterill et al. (Academic Press, New York, 1965) p. 679.
[132] C.G.Wang, D.N.Seidman and R.W.Balluffi, Phys. Rev. 169 (1968) 553.
[133] R.W.Siegel, see discussion of J.S.Koehler's paper, this volume.
[134] J.Polak, Phys. Stat. Sol. 21 (1967) 581.
[135] D.Schumacher, A.Seeger and O.Härlin, Phys. Stat. Sol. 25 (1968) 359.
[136] A.Seeger, this volume.
[137] F.Ramsteiner, G.Lampert, A.Seeger and W.Schüle, Phys. Stat. Sol. 8 (1965) 863.
[138] L.M.Clarebrough, R.L.Segall, M.H.Loretto and M.E.Hargreaves, Phil. Mag. 9 (1964) 377.
[139] L.J.Cuddy and E.S.Machlin, Phil. Mag. 7 (1962) 745.
[140] S.Scherrer, H.Octor and B.Deviot, Compt. Rend. Acad. Sci. Paris 261 (1965) 3571.
[141] M.Wuttig and H.K.Brinkman, Acta Met. 14 (1966) 58.
[142] A.Seeger, see Panel discussion, this volume.
[143] A.Sosin and K.R.Garr, Acta Met. 15 (1967) 1250.
[144] R.Kamel and E.A.Attia, Acta Met. 9 (1961) 1047.
[145] D.Bowen, R.R.Eggleston and R.H.Kropshott, J. Appl. Phys. 23 (1952) 630.
[146] P.Jongenburger, unpublished.
[147] P.J.Bridges and C.J.Ball, Phil. Mag. 15 (1967) 1107.
[148] J.S.Koehler, in: Imperfections in nearly perfect crystals (Wiley, New York, 1952) p. 197.
[149] N.F.Mott, Phil. Mag. 43 (1952) 1151.
[150] J.Friedel, Phil. Mag. 44 (1953) 444.
[151] R.R.Hasiguti and S.Okuda, Acta Met. 11 (1963) 257.
[152] M.Koiwa and R.R.Hasiguti, Acta Met. 11 (1963) 1215.
[153] P.A.Grandchamp, W.Benoit, B.Bays and B.Vittoz, Jül. Conf. 2 (Vol. II) 1968, p. 517.

[154] R.R.Hasiguti, Phys. Stat. Sol. 9 (1965) 157.
[155] M.Koiwa and R.R.Hasiguti, Acta Met. 13 (1965) 1220.
[156] P.Schiller, Phys. Stat. Sol. 5 (1964) 391.
[157] W.J.Baxter and J.Wilks, Acta Met. 11 (1963) 979.
[158] J.Völkl, W.Weinländer and J.Carsten, Phys. Stat. Sol. 10 (1965) 739.
[159] D.H.Niblett and J.Wilks, Phil. Mag. 2 (1957) 1427.
[160] J.C.Swartz, Acta Met. 10 (1962) 450.
[161] E.Walz, Phys. Stat. Sol. 7 (1964) 953.
[162] W.J.Baxter and J.Wilks, Acta Met. 10 (1962) 175.
[163] W.Köster, Z. Metallk. 32 (1940) 282; 39 (1948) 1.
[164] A.D.N.Smith, Phil. Mag. 44 (1953) 453.
[165] A.V.Granato, A.Hikata and K.Lücke, Acta Met. 6 (1958) 470.
[166] M.J.Druyvesteyn, O.E.Z.Schannen and E.C.J.Swaving, Physica 25 (1959) 1271.
[167] A.J.Brouwer and C.Groeneboom-Eygelaar, Acta Met. 15 (1967) 1597.
[168] W.Lems, Physica 28 (1962) 445; 30 (1964) 445.
[169] T.H.Blewitt, Phys. Rev. 91 (1953) 1115.
[170] A.R.C.Westwood and T.Broom, Acta Met. 5 (1957) 77.
[171] J.Takamura and S.Miura, J. Phys. Soc. Japan 17 (1962) 237.
[172] H.K.Birnbaum and F.R.Tuler, J. Appl. Phys. 32 (1961) 1403.
[173] H.K.Birnbaum, J. Appl. Phys. 33 (1962) 750.
[174] H.K.Birnbaum, J. Appl. Phys. 34 (1963) 2175.
[175] J.Takamura, K.Furukawa, S.Miura and P.A.Shingu, J. Phys. Soc. Japan 18, Suppl. III
      (1962) 8.
[176] H.B.Aaron and H.K.Birnbaum, Acta Met. 13 (1965) 205.
[177] A.van den Beukel and C.Brouwer, Phil. Mag. 17 (1968) 453.

## Discussion

*S.Ceresara:* I have one remark on the interpretation of stage II in cold worked Al.
The isochronal annealing curves of Al (10% Zn) (fig. 17) indicate that in the latter
part of stage II [the so-called stage II$^b$, ranging from 95 to 160°K (T.Federighi, S.
Ceresara and F.Pieragostini, Phil. Mag. 12 (1965) 1093] a defect producing Zn clustering is mobile. It has been pointed out [S.Ceresara and T.Federighi, Phil. Mag. 18
(1968) 301] that this defect could be identified as a multiple vacancy type defect,
such as the divacancy. It is also stressed that this defect is not present after neutron
irradiation since no Zn clustering below stage III is observed when the same alloy is
neutron irradiated at 78°K [S.Ceresara, T.Federighi and F.Pieragostini, Phil. Mag. 7
(1962) 623].

*A.v.d.Beukel:* In pure cold worked Al stages II and III are well-defined peaks
(fig. 2) centered at 75 and 190°K, respectively, and separated by a small and continuous recovery. If the stages are defined in this way it will be clear from fig. 17 that
in stage II of Al (10% Zn) no clustering has been observed. In fact the data you refer to indicate that both single and di-vacancies are mobile in the stage III region, in
accordance with the view presented in the paper.

*H.I.Dawson:* I would like to make a general remark on the experimental determination of the order of reaction kinetics. This is usually determined by verifying whether a linear relationship exists between some function of $\Delta\rho$ and the annealing time. While it is true that if the particular kinetic equation holds one will obtain a linear relationship, the reverse is not necessarily true, and one must be careful in drawing conclusions from such analysis.

*A.v.d.Beukel:* In general this remark is, of course, correct. If, however, the $f(\Delta\rho)$ versus $t$ plot should yield a straight line for 100% of the $\Delta\rho$ annealing out, it is very improbable that the kinetics would differ from the kind tested. The problem is that usually the plots are only partially straight. Statements often met in the literature, such as "the process is second order for the initial, middle or final 50%" must not be taken too serious, because few plots exist which do not allow the drawing of a straight line through approximately 50% of the data points. In particular, the use of double logarithmic paper is very helpful in obtaining straight lines.

*M.Wuttig:* Concerning the remark of the author that stage IV in Ni might be connected with carbon impurity I would like to comment, that the quenching experiments by Wuttig and Birnbaum (J. Phys. Chem. Solids 27 (1966) 225) would confirm this suspicion.

*J.W.Corbett:* Let me ask concerning your remark about stage II being intrinsic. It is my recollection that some authors have irradiated doped samples and found impurity dependent effects. Would you agree that in some experiments stage II can contain impurity dependent processes?

*A.v.d.Beukel:* Stage II after low dose irradiations is undoubtedly influenced by impurities. The arguments presented for stage II being intrinsic apply to heavily cold worked metals. In this case the point defect concentrations annealing out in stage II are larger than the impurity concentrations by a factor of 10. After high dose irradiations intrinsic defects probably take part in stage II annealing. The question is discussed in detail in chapter 4.1.

*W.Bauer:* I have only a short remark on the measurement of activation energies in stages III or IV after electron irradiation. Although the nature of the damage is clearly simpler than after cold work there is evidence, in Al for example, that more than one annealing process is taking place and the kinetics are complex. Therefore the value of the measured activation energy has to be examined with some care.

*R.Bullough:* I would like to comment on observations of kinetics of the form $C/C_0 = \exp(-t/\tau)^{0.5}$ in stage III. I do not think observation *proves* that vacancies are migrating to dislocations under the influence of the stress field of the dislocations. If the stress field was important then only in the early stages could the kinetics possibly have this form; at later times it should become first order. I would suggest that such kinetics probably mean that sinks other than dislocations are also involved. If, however, only the dislocations are involved, then a saturation condition is necessary which, for vacancies, is hard to understand.

*J.Nihoul:* Your statement that stage III is usually too broad to be explained by a singly activated reaction order, is probably based on the assumption of pure first or second order. I wonder whether you considered the fact that a broad receovery stage can be caused by a changing reaction order, from high values to about 2, e.g., as one would expect for a bimolecular diffusion controlled process if significant interactions are involved.

*A.v.d.Beukel:* For small degrees of deformation stage III is seen to develop from two or three substages (figs. 10 and 11). For high degrees of deformation stage III in Al, Pt and Au is narrow enough to be described approximately by a singly activated process. In Cu and Ni it is preceded by the substage II*. Only in Ag stage III is a rather broad stage. It seems somewhat artificial to fit the isochronal to the kinetics you propose just for the case of Ag. In my paper it is argued that stage III in Ag is really build up of several processes, which is mainly based on activation energy observations.

*W.Hellenthal:* Our measurements of the recovery of magnetization processes, as observed by magnetoresistance in Ni after low tensile straining, showed superpositions of orientable and other recovery effects contributing sometimes even simultaneously to the physical quantity used, thus directly revealing that quite a variety of processes has to be considered around stage III recovery after plastic deformation.

# PART 5

# SPECIAL EXPERIMENTAL TECHNIQUES AND RESULTS

# STUDIES OF POINT DEFECT CLUSTERS BY TRANSMISSION ELECTRON MICROSCOPY

M.WILKENS

*Institut für Physik am Max-Planck-Institut für Metallforschung, Stuttgart, Germany*

## 1. Introduction

Initially, the increased application of electron transmission microscopy to the problems of solid state physics was, to a large degree, concerned with the investigation of the dislocation structure and distribution in deformed crystals. The rather rapid progress in this specialized field was due, at least to some extent, to the fact that soon after the first early work [1, 2] the Cambridge group published, in a series of papers, their approach to the theory of diffraction contrast [3,4]; this included the application to some "simple" types of lattice defects such as straight dislocations [3,5] and extended stacking faults [6,7]. In the meantime these contrast calculations have been used with great success for the explanation of many special dislocation configurations. This holds even for the interpretation of the more complicated contrast figures from vacancy agglomerates in quenched and annealed metal specimens (dislocation loops [8], stacking fault tetrahedra [9]), as long as their diameters are larger than, or comparable with, the extinction length.

In the following years another topic of fundamental interest, namely the study of the defect structure in particle-irradiated crystals, was introduced and created considerable interest. Although we are now sure that many of the defects produced by particle irradiation may be described in terms of "dislocation loops" with or without included stacking faults, the "classical" rules for the contrast from straight dislocations and extended stacking faults cannot be applied, since these loops are frequently smaller than the lateral width of the contrast line from straight dislocations. Therefore for many years the rather uncertain expressions "black dots" or "black spots" have been used to describe the apparently unspecific contrast from these small lattice defects [10]. (In this context "small" means small compared with the extinction length.) Furthermore, whereas in the case of quenched and annealed metal crystals it is clear, for other physical reasons, that even the small defects, observed on the micrographs, may be interpreted as vacancy agglomerates, in the case of radiation damage the vacancy or interstitial nature of the small defect clusters, is not known *a priori*. This is true, since due to the law of "conservation of mass" during the primary events of particle irradiation an equal number of vacancies and interstitials are produced. Consequently, the study of the irradiation damage structure raised the question as to whether the observed defects are of vacancy or interstitial type.

For "large" point defect agglomerates (larger than, or comparable with the extinction length) this question could be solved in many cases by a more or less sophisticated application of the "classical" properties of dislocation contrast. The desire to achieve a correct interpretation of the contrast from small defects gave a new impetus to the study of the diffraction contrast from small defect clusters. Recently considerable progress has been made in the theoretical interpretation of the contrast formation and in the corresponding experimental procedures. This progress has resulted in an essentially improved understanding of the structure of radiation damage and consequently, gives a better basis for an understanding of the mechanisms of radiation damage formation.

The present paper attempts to give a survey of this recent development. The first part of the paper deals with the basic principles of the interpretation of the diffraction contrast from point defect agglomerates. The information, which may be derived by electron transmission microscopy, is commented upon critically. The second part of the paper contains a survey of experimental results. Since in the case of quenched crystals the vacancy nature of the agglomerates observed is in general not in question, and since in the case of radiation damage it is the differentiation be-between vacancy and interstitial type defects which is of considerable interest, the second part of the review is restricted to the experimental results of radiation damage. For further details of the experimental procedures and especially of experimental results on reactor materials the reader is referred to the review article of Rühle [144].

## 2. Some remarks on the theory of diffraction contrast

Well-defined contrast images are obtained in general only under the so-called two-beam diffraction conditions; this means that the primary electron beam (described by a plane wave) suffers strong Bragg reflection from only one set of lattice planes (denoted by the corresponding diffraction vector $\mathbf{g}$). Under two-beam condition the electron beam propagates inside the crystalline foil in the form of two Bloch waves with slightly differing wave vectors $\mathbf{k}$. The difference $\Delta\mathbf{k}$ of these two wave vectors is equal to the reciprocal of the extinction length $\xi_g$ which is a parameter characteristic of the substance and of the reflecting planes under consideration. $\Delta|\mathbf{k}|^{-1} = \xi_g$ holds exactly if the direction of the primary beam satisfies exactly the Bragg condition. However, for deviations from the Bragg condition, measured by the excitation error $s = g \cdot \Delta\theta$ ($\Delta\theta$ = deviation angle of the primary beam from the Bragg angle $\theta_B$) the "effective" extinction length is given by $\xi_{eff} = \xi_g(1 + (s \cdot \xi_g)^2)^{-\frac{1}{2}}$ [11,12,4].

Micrographs taken under two beam conditions with $s \cong 0$ are called "dynamical" images ("dynamical" contrast conditions). Micrographs taken under the condition $(|s| \cdot \xi_g) > 1$ or under unspecified many-beam conditions with no preferentially excited reflection will be called "kinematical" images ("kinematical contrast conditions).

Any kind of lattice inhomogeneity or lattice defect, which modifies the local diffraction conditions, gives rise to contrast on the micrographs. There are several different idealized types of inhomogeneities:

(i) A locally varying strain field, e.g. in the vicinity of a dislocation or a dislocation loop.

(ii) A planar defect, like the boundary faces of a stacking fault tetrahedron, between perfect regions of the crystal foil.

(iii) An empty void inside the foil.

(iv) A local change of the extinction length $\xi_g$, e.g. inside a coherent precipitate in a supersaturated alloy. This type of lattice defect is, however, of minor interest in the present paper.

The diffraction contrast on the micrographs especially from defects of type (i) is not a simple geometrical image of the lattice defect. It is necessary therefore to differentiate carefully between the observable image position of the contrast on the micrographs and the image position of the defect itself, which is generally not known.

In order to calculate the diffraction contrast the column approximation is usually applied. This was first introduced by Hirsch, Howie and Whelan [3] and assumes that the scattering angle $2\theta_B$ between the primary (or transmitted) and the reflected (or scattered) beam is negligible. Since for low order reflections $\theta_B$ is of the order of $1°$, this approximation is expected to be valid. For a justification see Jouffrey and Taupin [13] and Howie and Basinski [14]. In the column approximation the intensity at a given point on the micrograph is determined solely by the diffraction conditions in the corresponding infinitesimally narrow "column" (inside the foil) parallel to the electron beam.

For defects of types (ii) and (iv), which, under ideal conditions, are not accompanied by inhomogeneous lattice strains, the contrast may be calculated by means of the well-known diffraction solutions of an ideal undistorted lattice, matching the general solutions inside the undistorted parts of a column by appropriate boundary conditions at the internal surfaces between the defect and the surrounding matrix (as well, of course, as at the external surfaces of the foil). This can easily be carried out using scattering matrix as introduced by Howie and Whelan [4] and by Gevers, Amelinckx and coworkers [15].

The contrast calculation for defects of type (i) generally requires the numerical integration of differential equations. Several formulations of the differential equations have been derived, which describe the scattering by means of either (i) plane waves (Howie and Whelan [4], Takagi [16], Taupin [17]), (ii) Bloch waves of an undistorted reference lattice (Howie [18], Wilkens [19]) or (iii) modified Bloch waves (Wilkens [20]). An essential advantage of the equations of type (ii) as compared with the equations of type (i) is that they may be treated analytically in a Born first approximation for various types of lattice defects [19, 14]. This facilitates a better and quicker understanding of the influence of specific parameters of the

lattice defect and of the diffraction conditions on the contrast formation. Furthermore, the time required for the numerical integrations is reduced. The differential
equations of type (iii) are especially useful for the calculation of the contrast due
to slowly varying strain fields [21–23].

A critical property of the diffraction contrast is the anomalous absorption, expressed by the ratio $q = \xi_g/\xi_g'$, where $\xi_g'$ means the "anomalous absorption length".
Although $q = 0.1$ (a value first derived by Hashimoto, Howie and Whelan [7] from
the visibility of stacking fault fringes) has been used with success for quantitative
contrast interpretations by several authors [24–28], there is some evidence that for
low order reflections, e.g. of copper, $q$ is better approximated by 0.07 or even less
[29,30]. This discrepancy has not yet been quantitatively resolved.


## 3. Contrast from large dislocation loops

For dislocation loops with diameters $d \gtrsim \xi_g$, the main properties of the loop
contrast may be understood in terms of the usual dislocation contrast. Hence the
Burgers vector $\mathbf{b}$ of the loop is easily determined by the $\mathbf{g} \cdot \mathbf{b} = 0$ criterion for vanishing contrast.

If the foil is imaged with an excitation error $s \neq 0$, the image position of a dislocation does not coincide with the centre of the contrast profile (Hirsch, Howie and
Whelan [3,4]). As a simple rule it appears that the contrast line will be shifted to
that side of the dislocation position on which the lattice bending (due to the dislocation strain field) reduces locally the excitation error $s$.

This property of dislocation contrast was first used by Groves and Kelly [31],
and in a slightly modified form by Mazey, Barnes and Howie [32], to differentiate
between loops of vacancy and interstitial types. The method is outlined in the
original papers and also in the book of Hirsch and coworkers [33]. Only the basic
principles will be indicated here.

If the loop habit plane is inclined to the image plane (i.e. neither parallel nor perpendicular), those two parts of the loop, which are most steeply inclined to the
image plane, give rise to a weaker and thinner contrast line as compared with the
other parts of the loop arcs which extend approximately parallel to the image plane
[3]. Thus, the line through the two weak parts of the loop contrast runs parallel
to the trace of the image plane with the loop habit plane. If we now define the
positive direction of the normal $\mathbf{n}$ of the loop habit plane in such a way, that $\mathbf{n}$
always makes an acute angle with the direction of $\mathbf{k}_0$ (= wave vector of the incident
electron beam), then we may differentiate between two loop plane orientations:

(i) $\mathbf{g} \cdot \mathbf{n} > 0$ ;
(ii) $\mathbf{g} \cdot \mathbf{n} < 0$.

Which of these two orientation types occurs for a specific loop under consideration
may be determined by tilting experiments with high tilting angles, and observing
the change of the projected loop width. From the above mentioned fundamental

property of dislocation contrast it follows that the loop contrast line lies, for $s \neq 0$, either "inside" (called case (a)) or "outside" (case (b)) of the projected loop position.

Which of these two cases (a) or (b) occur may be determined by changing either the sign of $s$ with fixed diffraction vector $\mathbf{g}$ [31], or by changing from $\mathbf{g}$ to $-\mathbf{g}$ with fixed sign of $s$ [32]. This latter procedure is more successful, especially in thick foils, since here the transmitivity is low for negative values of $s$.

Combining cases (i) and (ii) for the loop plane orientation with cases (a) and (b) for the position of the loop contrast and assuming $s > 0$, the following simple rule allows for a differentiation between vacancy and interstitial loops.
(i) + (b) and (ii) + (a) : vacancy loops
(i) + (a) and (ii) + (b) : interstitial loops.
This simple rule works correctly only if the loop Burgers vector $\mathbf{b}$ is perpendicular to the loop habit plane. If, however, $\mathbf{b}$ contains a shear component $\mathbf{b}_s$ parallel to the loop plane, errors in the application of the above rule may happen, if $\mathbf{b}_s$ has the proper direction and is large enough to change the sign of $\mathbf{g} \cdot \mathbf{b}$ compared to the corresponding sign of $\mathbf{g} \cdot \mathbf{b}_n$, $\mathbf{b}_n$ = component of $\mathbf{b}$ parallel to $\mathbf{n}$. Therefore, for a correct analysis not only the differentiation between "inside" and outside" contrast and the determination of the inclination of the loop habit plane but also the determination of the direction of the Burgers vector (irrespective of sign) is needed. For details see Maher and Eyre [34].

Also for partial dislocations, by which a stacking fault area is terminated, the contrast is laterally shifted as determined by the $(\mathbf{g} \cdot \mathbf{b})s$ sign. Therefore the method is applicable for stacking fault loops as well, compare e.g. Mazey and Barnes [35].

A semi-empirical approach to some special properties of the contrast from perfect dislocation loops with diameters $d \approx \xi_g$ has been attempted by Bell and Thomas [36].


## 4. Contrast from small point defect clusters with $d \ll \xi_g$

For agglomerates too small to be resolved geometrically on the micrographs, a more detailed interpretation of the contrast is necessary. Historically, the evolution of the interpretation technique was strongly influenced by the experimental and theoretical investigations of the contrast from small coherent precipitates with either a positive or negative volume misfit, according to which the surrounding lattice is distorted. Since the calculations of the dynamical contrast by Ashby and Brown [24] have been particularly widely used, it is expedient to begin this chapter in the section 4.1 with a short review of their results. In section 4.2 we refer to contrast calculations from small strain centres, especially small dislocation loops, which are unresolved on the micrographs. The connection between the apparently each other excluding results of section 4.1 and 4.2 is outlined in section 4.3. Section 4.4 deals with some remarks on the contrast from small stacking fault tetrahedra. Voids and fission tracks are treated in sections 4.6 and 4.6 respectively. Section 4.7 summarizes experimental methods for applying the theoretical results of this chapter. In section 5 some remarks are made concerning the reliability of the interpretation of the contrast due to small defect clusters.

### 4.1. Anomalous images from large spherical inclusions

Ashby and Brown [24] have shown, in agreement with earlier "kinematical" contrast calculations of Phillips and Livingston [37], that for spherical inclusions approximately in the middle of the foil cross section a "coffee-bean"-like contrast is expected, which sometimes resembles the "double arc" contrast of a dislocation loop inclined to the foil plane. The two dark, approximately elliptically shaped parts of the contrast figure are separated by the "line of no contrast" which always extends perpendicular to the operating diffraction vector $g$.

On the other hand, if the inclusion lies within a range of approximately one (or a little more) extinction length from one of the two foil surfaces, anomalously wide images are expected which consist of a white part on the side of the line of no contrast and a dark part on the other side. For the following, we define a vector $l$, pointing from the black to the white part of the black-white contrast (on positive prints). We will differentiate between the *orientation* of $l$ with respect to $g$, irrespective of the sign, and of the *sign* of $l$, depending on whether $l$ makes an acute $(g \cdot l > 0)$ or an obtuse $(g \cdot l < 0)$ angle with $g$. Using this definition the authors [24] found from their calculations that the orientation of $l$ is always parallel to $g$ and that on darkfield images the sign of $l$ is positive for inclusions with negative volume misfit (inclusion of "vacancy type") and negative for those with positive volume misfit ("interstitial type"). According to the symmetry rules for strain contrast formation [4,38], the sign of $l$ is on bright field images the same as for dark field images for inclusions close to the top surface and is reversed for those close to the bottom surface.

These properties of the black-white contrast (occasionally denoted as the Ashby-Brown rule) have been used with success to determine the sign of the volume misfit of spherical and of non-spherical inclusions [25]. However, later contrast calculations demonstrated that the Ashby-Brown rule is valid only for the special case of inclusions with a rather large volume misfit, whereas the contrast due to small strain centres is much more complicated.

### 4.2. Contrast due to small strain centres, especially dislocation loops

Essmann and Wilkens [39] have studied experimentally the dynamical contrast of the so-called "black dots" in neutron irradiated copper. They have observed that, under dynamical two-beam conditions, some of the black dots display a characteristic contrast image consisting of a black and a white tail. Examples are presented in figs. 1 and 2. In contrast to the observations on spherical inclusions the orientation of the vector $l$, as defined above, was fixed and in general not parallel to $g$. It was found that $l$ was nearly always parallel to a $\langle 111 \rangle$-direction or parallel to a projec-

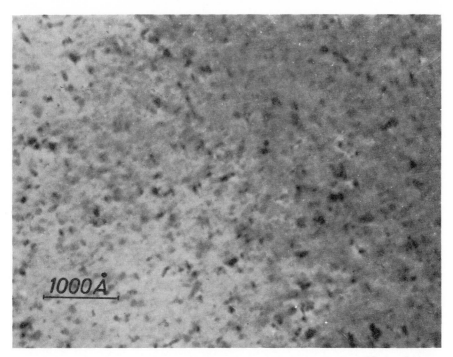

Fig. 1a. Small Frank dislocation loops in neutron irradiated copper. $\phi = 6 \times 10^{17}$ n/cm$^2$, $T_{irr} =$ 80°C, foil plane $\approx$ (001), kinematical contrast. The black-white streaks $l$ are parallel or anti-parallel to **g** in fig. 1b and at 45° or 135° to **g** in fig. 1c as expected for **b** parallel to $\langle 111 \rangle$, see section 4 2.

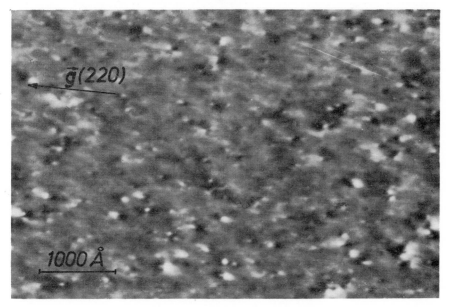

Fig. 1b. Dynamical contrast, bright field.

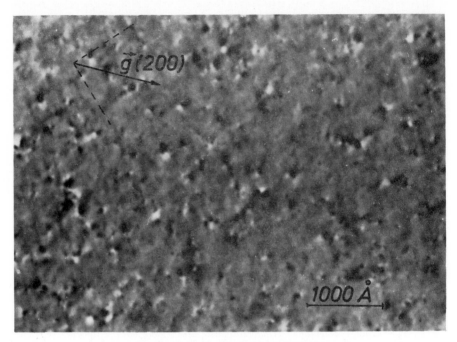

Fig. 1c. Dynamical contrast, bright field.

tion of a ⟨111⟩-direction onto the image plane. From this observation they made the
intuitive assumption that the fixed l-direction corresponded to a preferential direction (or of its projection) of the defect clusters and that the dots in neutron irradiated copper were due to Frank sessile dislocation loops with Burgers vectors parallel to ⟨111⟩. Stimulated by these experiments, Rühle, Wilkens and Essmann [40],
and Rühle [26] performed detailed contrast calculations for small dislocation loops,
which were later confirmed and to some part extended by McIntyre and Brown
[41,42]. The essential results are summarized under the following items.

(i) A loop oriented with $\mathbf{g} \cdot \mathbf{b} \neq 0$ and with its centre close to one of the foil surfaces reveals, under dynamical contrast conditions (excitation error $s = 0$), a black-
white contrast. The black-white vector l is independent of the direction of $\mathbf{g}$ and
parallel or anti-parallel to the Burgers vector $\mathbf{b}$ or its projection onto the image plane.
According to McIntyre and Brown small, but not significant deviations of the orientation of l are expected, if $\mathbf{b}$ or its projection is not parallel to $\mathbf{g}$.

(ii) The sign of l as defined above depends (a) on the actual distance of the loop
centre from the neighbouring foil surface, and (b) on whether the loop is of vacancy
or interstitial type. The results of the calculations are summarized schematically in
fig. 3.

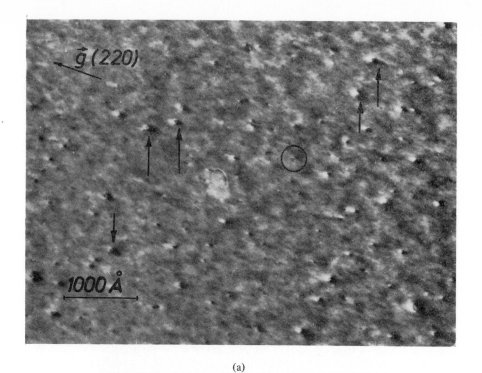

(a)

(b)

Fig. 2. Small Frank dislocation loops of vacancy type in copper irradiated with 100 keV $O^-$ ions, foil plane $\approx$ (001), bright field. The distances of the loop centres to the irradiated foil surface are less than 80 Å [26,128]. With respect to the directions of l see the caption of fig. 1 and section 4.2. Notice the fine structure of the black-white separation line of the indicated loops. The peculiar black-white contrast figure enclosed by a circle was explained by Rühle [26] as due to a Frank loop of special diameter with its centre just at the boundary between the layers L1 and L2. In fig. 2a a thin gold layer was evaporated on the iron-irradiated foil surface for the stereo measurements, see section 4.5.

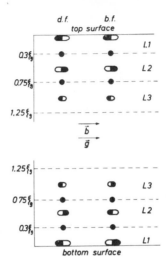

Fig. 3. Schematic plot of the depth oscillations of the black-white contrast from small dislocation loops of vacancy type. The contrast figures are drawn at that depth position at which the
loop centres were assumed. d.f. = dark field, b.f. = bright field. The direction of **g** is indicated.
For loops of interstitial type the black and white contrast parts must be interchanged.

(iii) If we divide the regions near the surfaces of the foil into layers L1, L2, ... as
indicated in fig. 3 the result is that the sign of $(\mathbf{g} \cdot \mathbf{l})$ changes for a given loop type,
if the loop centre changes from one layer to the adjacent layer, thus leading to
"depth oscillations" of the black-white contrast. The thickness of the layer L1
amounts to about $0.3 \, \xi_g$ (in a slightly simplified calculation $\approx \frac{1}{4}\xi_g$), whereas the
inner boundaries of the subsequent layers L2, L3, ... correspond to distances of
$\frac{3}{4}\xi_g, \frac{5}{4}\xi_g, ...$ to the adjacent foil surface. The sign of $\mathbf{g} \cdot \mathbf{l}$ in the first layer on either
surface agrees with the prediction of above mentioned Ashby-Brown rule.

(iv) The depth oscillations of the black-white contrast are damped by the
anomalous absorption which depends on the ratio $\xi_g/\xi_g'$. For $\xi_g/\xi_g' = 0.1$ (as frequently used [7,24,26]) the black-white contrast is expected to be observable only
for loops in the first two (or three) layers. For smaller values of $\xi_g/\xi_g'$, the observable depth oscillations extend deeper inside the foil.

(v) The contrast, for loops in the middle region of the foil, i.e. outside the region
of observable black-white contrast, consists of a black dot without a characteristic
geometric structure.

(vi) If loops which are near the surface are imaged with an excitation error
$s \neq 0$, the black or white tail of the black-white contrast is enhanced depending,
especially for dark field images, upon the sign of $s$ and upon whether the loops are
close to the top or the bottom surface. This property is in accordance with previous
general theoretical predictions of Wilkens [19] (see also Bell and Thomas [43]).

(vii) For loops with $\mathbf{g} \cdot \mathbf{b} = 0$ only a very weak contrast is calculated which is due to the displacement field component transverse to $\mathbf{b}$ (residual contrast, Querkontrast). Therefore, the well-known $\mathbf{g} \cdot \mathbf{b} = 0$ extinction rule for the determination of $\mathbf{b}$ may be applied, although care is necessary.

(viii) The line of no contrast (which for dislocation loop is better called black-white separation line) coincides with the trace of the loop habit plane with the image plane only for loops perpendicular to the image plane. Generally the shape of the line of no contrast depends strongly on the inclination of the loop habit plane with respect to the image plane and on the actual image conditions. (For a detailed discussion see Rühle [26].) Therefore, in general, the line of no contrast cannot be used to determine the loop habit plane or the loop Burgers vector, as has frequently been assumed [44–46].

(ix) Under $s = 0$ conditions the 20% image width (for definition see [24]), measured perpendicular to the black-white direction $\mathbf{l}$, amounts to about 1.2 of the actual projected loop diameter.

(x) For large excitation errors $s(|s| \gg \xi_{\mathbf{g}}^{-1})$, which corresponds approximately to the kinematical diffraction, the black-white contrast is suppressed and only a black dot contrast remains for all loop positions over the foil cross section. The black dot diameter (at the 20% image width) corresponds approximately to the projected loop width.

(xi) For small spherical strain centres most of the above results remain unchanged. The essential difference is that the orientation of $\mathbf{l}$ is according to the symmetry of the strain centre, always parallel to $\mathbf{g}$. Since no extinction rule like $\mathbf{g} \cdot \mathbf{b}$ exists, spherical strain centres are visible as black-white contrast for all diffraction vectors $\mathbf{g}$, as far as the strain centres lie in one of the depth layers suitable for black-white contrast formation.

### 4.3. The influence of the traction-free surface of the contrast formation

The transition from the black-white contrast due to spherical or non-spherical strain centres *with* depth oscillations of the sign of $\mathbf{g} \cdot \mathbf{l}$ (type $\alpha$, section 4.2) to the black-white contrast *without* depth oscillations (type $\beta$, section 4.1) was studied by McIntyre and Brown [41] and by Chik, Wilkens and Rühle [23]. Both groups found that the transition from type ($\alpha$) to type ($\beta$) is due to the neighbouring traction-free surface which modifies the strain field of the strain centre. This happens in such a way that the black-white contrast of type ($\alpha$) is, to a first approximation, linearly [23] superimposed by an additional black-white contrast of type ($\beta$). Both types of black-white contrast are *in phase* for strain centres located in layers with odd numbers, L1, L3,... (Hence for these layers the signs of $\mathbf{g} \cdot \mathbf{l}$ are not changed.) Consequently, they are *in antiphase* for strain centres in layers with even numbers, L2, L4... . Which of the two types of black-white contrast prevails and remains observable on the micrographs depends on the dimensionfree normalized misfit parameter

$$P = \Delta V \cdot g / \xi_{\mathbf{g}}^2 \cdot \pi \,,$$

where $\Delta V$ represents the volume misfit of the strain centre, such that $\Delta V = b R_L^2 \pi$ for a Frank dislocation loop, and $\Delta V = 4\pi \epsilon R_s^3$ for a spherical inclusion. $R_L$ and $R_s$ are the radii of the loop and the inclusion respectively. $3\epsilon$ is the relative volume misfit $\Delta V/V$ of the inclusion. The most important question is what occurs for strain centres in the second layer L2, since due to the anomalous absorption the black-white contrast, for layers with higher even numbers, can scarcely be observed.

From the calculations it emerged that the lateral extension of the black-white contrast of type $(\beta)$ increases with increasing misfit parameter $P$ more rapidly than that of type $(\alpha)$. McIntyre and Brown [41] concluded from their numerical contrast calculations that the reversal of the sign of $\mathbf{g} \cdot \mathbf{l}$ in the layer L2, compared to the sign in the layer L1, will no longer be observable if $P$ exceeds about 1. This holds approximately for both spherical inclusions and dislocation loops. However, this numerical value for the critical misfit parameter is not very reliable, since the authors used for the image strain field, which serves the neighbouring surface traction free, the approximation of infinitesimally small strain centres. Chik, Wilkens and Rühle [23] derived for spherical strain centres similar critical values for $P$ by numerical as well as analytical approaches to the contrast calculations.

From the above-mentioned calculations it may be concluded that for strain centres with $P \ll 1$ the black-white contrast oscillates with the depth position of the strain centre (for exception see below), whereas for $P \gg 1$ the depth oscillations are suppressed *. Consequently, the Ashby-Brown rule is valid only in the latter case.

Experimental observations on the precipitations of cobalt from a supersaturated copper matrix [24,41], demonstrated that for spherical inclusions $P > 1$ is in fact a possible configuration. Considering dislocation loops we put for an estimate $\mathbf{g} \cdot \mathbf{b} = 1$ (low order reflexion) then the condition $P > 1$ means $R_L > \xi_g$. This is not compatible for loops with centres in the critical layer L2, since the inner boundary of L2 is only 0.75 $\xi_g$ apart from the surface. Furthermore, loops of such a size are in general directly resolved on the micrographs. We conclude therefore that for unresolved dislocation loops $(R_L \ll \xi_g)$ the depth oscillations of the black-white contrast should at any rate be expected. For loops with a misfit parameter $P \approx 1$ further contrast calculations which, with respect to the elastic boundary conditions, are not restricted to the infinitesimal loop approximation are desirable.

Apart from the condition $P \gg 1$ there is another case, for which the Ashby-Brown rule seems to be applicable. If the geometric size of the defect is rather extended and if the misfit volume is small, the black-white contrast of type $(\alpha)$ is weak and practically superimposed by the unspecific, in general black image of the defect itself. In this case only the extremely extended black-white contrast of type $(\beta)$ for defects very close to one of the surfaces exceeds the geometric extension of the defect [23]. It appears that stacking fault tetrahedra are examples for such a defect type, compare section 4.5.

* Of course, if $P$ is too small, the black-white contrast becomes too weak to be observable, see [23].

A physical interpretation of the different types of black-white contrast was given by Chik, Wilkens and Rühle [23]. The black-white contrast with depth oscillations (type α) was explained as being due to a distortion induced "interband scattering" between the two Bloch waves involved in the actual two-beam diffraction condition. Thus, the black-white depth oscillations resemble, to some extent, the stacking fault fringes or the black-white zig-zag contrast of dislocations, intersecting the foil. On the other hand, the black-white contrast of type (β) without depth oscillations was identified as being due to "intraband-scattering" of that Bloch wave, which suffers anomalously weak absorption. This intraband scattering (although it is in fact not a "scattering" but rather a steady movement of the Bloch wave tie points on their dispersion branches during the paths of the Bloch waves through the weakly bent crystal foil [20,22,23]) is induced by a peculiar type of deformation of the reflecting planes close to a traction-free surface, if there is a spherical or non-spherical strain centre just beneath.

## 4.4. Black-white contrast from stacking fault tetrahedra

The strain produced in the lattice surrounding a stacking fault tetrahedron is much less than that resulting from a Frank loop, which contains the same number of point defects (either vacancies or interstitials). Consequently the diffraction contrast image of a small stacking fault tetrahedron resembles more closely the geometric shape than, for instance, the contrast image of a small Frank loop. In fact, stacking fault tetrahedra down to sizes of less than 50 Å have been identified, on well focused micrographs, by their characteristic shape. Since for stacking fault tetrahedra with edge lengths smaller than the extinction length of the operating diffraction vector no fringes are observable, it is only possible to differentiate between tetrahedra of interstitial or vacancy type by means of the black-white contrast which is produced by their strain fields.

Up to the present time, only Brown [47] and Chik [48] have treated the contrast phenomena from stacking fault tetrahedra, which are too small to be identified by their fringes in any detail. If in a foil with an orientation which deviates only slightly from a (001)-orientation a tetrahedron is imaged by a g-vector of {220}-type, the image reveals a well resolved line of no contrast perpendicular to g, which corresponds to the ⟨110⟩-edge of the tetrahedron perpendicular to g. Brown [47] has explained this characteristic line of no contrast by means of the symmetry property of the strain field of a tetrahedron. For reflexions different from g = {220} no such well defined line of no contrast is observed nor is it expected [48].

Tetrahedra of medium sizes (≈ 200 Å), which are truncated by one of the foil surfaces, may be identified by their "truncated" images. According to Chik [48] these tetrahedra reveal, under dynamical two-beam conditions, a pronounced black-white contrast with the orientation of l always approximately parallel to g. This is expected as a result of the higher symmetry of a tetrahedral strain centre, as compared with the extremely unidirectional strain field of a dislocation loop. On dark-field images of quenched and annealed gold, Chik found that the signs of

$\mathbf{g} \cdot \mathbf{l}$ are always positive, thus indicating the validity of the Ashby-Brown rule for this special case (black-white contrast of type ($\beta$), see section 4.3). If the stacking fault tetrahedra were very small ($\lesssim$ 50 Å), Chik observed a weak black-white contrast on some of the tetrahedra for $\mathbf{g} = \{220\}$ but not for $\mathbf{g} = \{111\}$ or $\{200\}$. Such different behaviour depending on the diffraction vector is reasonable, since the extensions of the black-white tails and consequently, for a fixed size of the tetrahedra, the visibility of the black-white contrast is controlled by the extinction length ($\xi_{220} \approx 1.5 \, \xi_{200} \approx 2 \, \xi_{111}$) (see Ashby and Brown [24]).

## 4.5. *Experimental methods of discriminating between strain centres of vacancy or interstitial type*

If a defect agglomerate reveals, under dynamical two-beam conditions, a black-white contrast it is, according to the above summarized theoretical results firstly necessary to examine whether the observed black-white contrast is of type ($\alpha$) (with depth oscillations) or of type ($\beta$) (without depth oscillations). If one is sure, from some other reason, that the defect type under consideration is equally distributed over the foil cross section (condition (i)) and if dark field images reveal only one sign of $\mathbf{g} \cdot \mathbf{l}$ (condition (ii)), the Ashby-Brown rule may be applicable and the observed sign of $\mathbf{g} \cdot \mathbf{l}$ determines whether the agglomerate is of vacancy type (negative volume misfit, $\mathbf{g} \cdot \mathbf{l} > 0$) or of interstitial type (positive volume misfit, $\mathbf{g} \cdot \mathbf{l} < 0$). If, however, either of these two conditions are violated one should be aware that the black-white contrast observed is of type ($\alpha$). (That the condition (ii) is insufficient to confirm the applicability of the Ashby-Brown rule was demonstrated by Diepers and Diehl [49,50] by their investigations of the damage in copper foils after the impact of 4 keV-argon ions.) In this case it is necessary to localize the depth position inside the layer L1, L2 of those defect agglomerates which give rise to the black-white contrast under dynamical conditions. Several methods have been proposed and examined experimentally.

(i) Consider micrographs of the same foil area under different dynamical two-beam conditions with $\mathbf{g}$-vectors of different extinction lengths. The thicknesses of the layers L1, L2.. are changed and thus some of the agglomerates may change their layer and, consequently, change the sign of the product $\mathbf{g} \cdot \mathbf{l}$. Thus the type of the agglomerate may be derived, at least for those agglomerates which have changed their $\mathbf{g} \cdot \mathbf{l}$-signs from one to the other micrograph. However, this method requires a preliminary knowledge of the numbers of layers (2 or 3, see section 4.2) which give rise to black-white contrast.

A change of the "effective" extinction length $\xi_{eff} = \xi_g (1 + (s \cdot \xi_g)^2)^{-\frac{1}{2}}$ may also be obtained by using the same diffraction vector $\mathbf{g}$, but with different excitation errors $s$. However, this method is rather restricted, since the black-white contrast disappears for values of $s$ large compared with $\xi_g^{-1}$. Method (i) has been experienced for instance by Bell, Maher and Thomas [46] on vacancy agglomerates in quenched aluminium. However, their results were not conclusive, compare also Rühle [26].

(ii) Changing the extinction length of a given diffraction vector **g** by changing the accelerating voltage of the electron beam. However, due to the unavoidable systematic high-order reflections the resultant two-beam extinction lengths are rather insensitive to the voltage actually applied. Perhaps the new high voltage microscopes with accelerating voltages up to 1 MV may have more success in varying, for a given g-vector, the resultant two-beam extinction length sufficiently.

(iii) So far the best technique seems to be that of stereo-microscopy. Since the first layer L1 of the depth oscillations had a thickness of about $0.25-0.3 \, \xi_g$, the stereo-technique is applicable if an accuracy of about $\pm 0.1 \, \xi_g$ can be achieved. Diepers and Diehl [49,50] were the first to demonstrate that this is possible (see also the error discussions of the stereo-technique by Nankivell [51], Rühle [26], and Diepers [50]). To obtain the necessary accuracy some special precautions should be observed. Under dynamical conditions the "structure" of the black-white contrast is very sensitive to the actual diffraction conditions. Therefore the pair of stereo-micrographs must be taken under kinematical diffraction conditions. (Calculations showed that under kinematical contrast conditions the shape and position of the black dot is much less sensitive to the actual image conditions and that the image position of the black dot corresponds in fact quite well to the image position of the agglomerate.) In order to measure the distance of the agglomerate to the next foil surface it is necessary to make the foil surface visible on the stereo-micrographs. In the method of Diepers the surface is marked by the evaporation of a very thin layer of gold onto the transmission specimens (after having taken the dynamical images to identify the black-white contrast). If the amount of hold evaporated is sufficiently small the layer consists of small islands with diameters of the order of 50 Å; these are easily recognized in the optical stereo-viewer. By considering the amount of gold evaporated it emerged that these islands have a maximum thickness of about 10 Å. Thus, the surface layer is defined in the stereo-viewer by the gold islands with an accuracy of better than 10 Å.

## 4.6. Contrast from fission tracks

Under special conditions, high energy fission fragments produce continuous damage along their paths through the lattice, thereby giving rise to streak-like contrast phenomena. The "core"-structure of the fission tracks may be idealized for contrast calculations as cylindrically extended inclusions with diameter smaller than, or comparable with the extinction length and with positive or negative volume misfit.

Chadderton [52] has calculated the contrast from such a model. As is expected from the general properties of strain contrast, the calculated contrast profiles for "strain"-cylinders parallel to the foil surface resemble very closely those of small spherical inclusions, if one takes account of the linear extension of the inclusion under consideration. The depth dependence of the contrast may then be studied by following the contrast along the path of the cylinder, especially for cylinders which penetrate the foil under a small angle. In this way, the contrast of fission tracks, which penetrate the foil under a small angle, should demonstrate directly the depth oscillations of the black-white contrast. This is in fact true, as Chadderton has also shown experimentally. From the sign of the black-white contrast on dark field micrographs at those parts of the fission track contrast where the track penetrates the foil surface, the sign of the volume misfit of the track core may be deduced. Theoretically, both signs of volume misfit are possible, depending on the energy of the fission fragment or on the mechanism for energy loss during the path of the fragment [52].

### 4.7. *Voids (cavities)*

In an idealized model it is assumed that the matrix surrounding the voids is unaffected by the void. For this model the contrast has been calculated in detail by Ashby and Brown [24] and by Landuyt, Gevers and Amelinckx [53] (see also Hirsch and coworkers [33]).

Under pure dynamical image conditions ($s = 0$) the void is equivalent to a locally reduced thickness of the foil, irrespective of the depth position of the void inside the foil. This means that, especially in "thick" foils, the contrast is expected to be always brighter than the matrix. (A "thick" foil is meant if as a consequence of the anomalous absorption almost only the weakly absorbed Bloch wave reaches the exit surface of the foil.)

Although obviously no application has been published, it is probably this property of the void contrast, which allows for a differentiation between small voids and small stacking fault tetrahedra. The contrast of the latter is in general black (or black-white, see section 4.4) even under dynamical image conditions.

In the case of $s \neq 0$, the void contrast may be brighter or darker than the environment, depending on the depth position of the void inside the foil, on the thickness of the void and on the value of the excitation error $s$.

The basic approximation of the above mentioned contrast calculations, i.e. that the surrounding matrix is unstrained by the void, is not very sensitive for voids with diameters of several 100 Å or larger since the above mentioned characteristic properties of the void contrast should be at any rate observable. However, for small voids with $d \lesssim 100$ Å it is not at all clear whether or not the contrast due to a strained surrounding matrix (strained by surface tension or by a gas of high pressure, gathered into the void) overwhelms the specific void contrast properties, see for instance Brown and Mazey [54].

Voids may be formed by the agglomeration of supersaturated vacancies. Kiritani and coworkers [54–56] have studied the formation of voids in quenched and annealed gold and aluminium. (According to their recent results voids are formed, instead of glissile or sessile dislocation loops, if the specimens are annealed and quenched under special atmospheric conditions [56].) Furthermore, voids have been extensively studied in a variety of substances after irradiation with α-particles. If the specimens are subsequently annealed, the α-particles, which were stopped inside the specimen, tend to agglomerate and form helium bubbles [57] (see also [144]). Because of the extremely small solubility of He in most solids, these bubbles are presumably under high internal pressure [54].

## 5. Some remarks on the reliability of the experimental results

### 5.1. *Quantitative measurements of defect sizes*

In the case of large, well resolved dislocation loops there are some uncertainties in the loop size measurements due to the lateral shift of the dislocation contrast. However, the change in the loop contrast by change of the sign of $(\mathbf{g}\cdot\mathbf{b})s$ from "inside" to "outside" or vice versa gives a rough estimate of the true (projected) loop size. In general a single specimen contains loops with different Burgers vectors and with different loop planes. This means that loops with "inside" and "outside" contrast are on the average equally probable. Therefore, for large loops a systematic error in the loop size measurements, even under unspecific $(\mathbf{g}\cdot\mathbf{b})s$ diffraction conditions, is not expected.

The situation, however, is not so simple in the case of small unresolved loops (black dots). Here the measurement is based only on the relation between the true loop size and the calculated contrast width. So far no method of independent control is known. Furthermore, the sizes of the black dots on the micrographs depend to a certain extent on the film processing and printing conditions as well as on the "measuring technique" of the individual experiments. The latter points may give rise to a considerable scattering of the measured values of the black dot sizes up to ± 30%. For all quantitative comparisons this error source, which is difficult to control, should be taken into account. However, the accuracy is much greater, if only data, derived from the same film developing and printing conditions and measured by the same person, are compared.

### 5.2. *Determination of the defect shape*

Large dislocation loops, with or without enclosed stacking faults, are easily identified by the $\mathbf{g}\cdot\mathbf{b}$ dependence of the contrast of their surrounding dislocations. A similar situation holds for large stacking fault tetrahedra. For defects with diameters small compared with $\xi_g$ an unambiguous identification is more difficult. If the black-white streak vector $\mathbf{l}$ is always observed parallel to $\mathbf{g}$, irrespective of the direction of $\mathbf{g}$, the defect strain field should be spherically symmetric. However, this condition is obviously not very restrictive, since $\mathbf{l}$ always parallel to $\mathbf{g}$ has been found also for small stacking fault tetrahedra (with tetrahedral rather than spherical symmetry).

If one observes the vector $\mathbf{l}$ to be fixed to a certain crystallographic direction (or to its counter direction) it is now well established by contrast calculations that this direction corresponds to a preferential direction of the defect displacement field (or to its projection onto the image plane). The model used in section 4.2, in which the defect is represented by a single dislocation loop, is obviously the simplest one to account for the preferential displacement field direction. At least two other models can be imagined:

(i) The defect consists of a flat ellipsoidal void, with the two large axes constituting the "habit plane" of the defect, whereas the third short axis determines the main displacement field direction.

Such flat ellipsoidal voids have been found in copper after special quenching and annealing treatments by the technique of small angle X-ray scattering [58]. However, due to the lack of any small angle scattering effects in copper after neutron irradiation [26] (compare also with nickel [59]) this model is disregarded.

(ii) The defect consists of a number of small "sub-loops" all of which have the same Burgers vector **b**. The planes of the sub-loops are aligned with each other due to their mutual elastic interaction.

The long range strain field of such an "ensemble" of sub-loops is not expected to be critically dependent on the internal structure of the ensemble. Thus, a resultant black-white streak **l** parallel to **b** is expected. On the other hand, the short range strain field, and consequently the contrast near to the separation line between the black and the white parts of the contrast figure, is certainly strongly sensitive to the ensemble structure. For instance in neutron or ion irradiated copper the small defects have been identified as Frank loops on {111}-planes. If the {111}-loop habit plane lies parallel to the electron beam (i.e. perpendicular to the image plane), the black-white separation line is observed to be straight and sharply defined (within the electron optical resolution) rather than diffuse as expected for the model of a loosely distributed ensemble of sub-loops. Therefore such a model is rather unlikely but cannot be disregarded completely.

There is also another uncertainty with regard to the Burgers vector of the small sessile dislocation loops. These loops are obviously due to the agglomeration of single point defects. Agglomerates which consist of multiple vacancy layers parallel {111} have been frequently observed, especially in quenched and annealed high purity aluminium [60]. It is therefore possible that the Burgers vectors of the Frank loops in irradiated fcc metals are not equal to $\frac{1}{3} \langle 111 \rangle$, as assumed [26], rather than equal to an integer multiple of this smallest partial Burgers vector.

In neutron and ion irradiated copper the Frank loops inclined to the image plane sometimes display a characteristic fine structure of their black-white separation line, see fig. 2 and Rühle [26]. It is hoped that a theoretical interpretation of this fine structure (which as yet has not been produced) may allow the length of the Burgers vector to be determined.

### 5.3. Differentiation between vacancy and interstitial loops

For small loops the differentiation depends critically upon whether the depth position of the loops inside the foil can be measured with sufficient accuracy. For a demonstration of the accuracy obtainable by the technique of stereo microscopy we refer here to the results of Rühle and Wilkens [61] on neutron-irradiated copper. In the histogram of fig. 4 the data on 240 loops with diameters smaller than 50 Å are presented. The number of analysed loops is plotted as a function of the depth position at which the loops were found by stereo microscopy. The number of loops are plotted above or below the abscissa depending on whether the **g · l**-product of their corresponding black-white contrast figures on dynamical images are of positive or negative sign. It is obvious that the sign changes with depth position. At

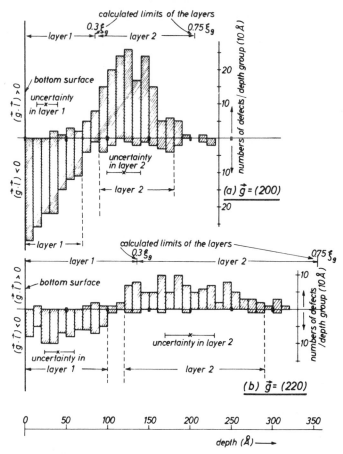

Fig. 4. Results of the stereo analysis of the black-white contrast figures from Frank loops with $d \lesssim 50$ Å in neutron-irradiated copper [61]. The number of black-white dots with $\mathbf{g} \cdot \mathbf{l} > 0$ and $\mathbf{g} \cdot \mathbf{l} < 0$ are plotted against the distance of the defect centre from the bottom surface of the transmission foil (bright field, positive prints). The depth oscillations of the sign of $\mathbf{g} \cdot \mathbf{l}$ is clearly demonstrated. Thus, the Frank loops analysed by ref. [61] are mainly of vacancy type.

least two layers with a rather unique sign of $\mathbf{g} \cdot \mathbf{l}$ can be distinguished. Since (dynamical) bright field images have been used for the sign determination and since loops close to the bottom surface have been stereo-measured, it was concluded from fig. 4 that the overwhelming majority of the small Frank loops in neutron-irradiated copper are of vacancy type. The layer thicknesses as indicated by the sign changes correspond fairly well to the calculated values, if one corrects the two-beam extinction lengths of the two reflections (002) and (022) used for higher-order reflections. The estimated measuring errors of the loop depth position are indicated in the figure. They are in fact of the order of the width of the overlap regions between the first and the second layer, thus indirectly indicating that the estimation of the measurement errors is realistic and that the depth position determination of small defect clusters, by means of the stereo-technique, is sufficiently accurate to differentiate between vacancy and interstitial type defects.

So far, the calculations of the black-white contrast for small dislocation loops are confined to two cases, characterized by the "shear angle" $\varphi$ between the loop Burgers vector $\mathbf{b}$ and the loop plane normal $\mathbf{n}$ ($0 \leqslant \varphi < \pi/2$). In the first case, which is most important for small loops in irradiation-damaged fcc metals, $\mathbf{b}$ was assumed to be parallel to $\mathbf{n}$ (pure Frank loops, $\varphi = 0$). In the second case, $\mathbf{b} = \frac{1}{2}$ [110] and $\mathbf{n} = (111)$ was assumed, corresponding to $\varphi = 35°$. In the latter case the thicknesses of the layers L1,L2... of unique signs of $\mathbf{g \cdot l}$ were found to have the same values as for $\varphi = 0$, i.e. the shear component of $\mathbf{b}$ perpendicular to $\mathbf{n}$ has practically no influence on the sign of $\mathbf{g \cdot l}$. It is, however, expected that there is a change in the sign of $\mathbf{g \cdot l}$ or a change of the layer thicknesses, if $\varphi$ becomes larger. To understand why this is so, let us imagine a pure shear loop with $\mathbf{b \cdot n} = 0$. From our knowledge of the general properties of diffraction contrast formation [19,23] there is no reason, why such a pure shear loop of proper orientation should not give rise to black-white contrast with depth oscillations, similar as pure edge loops do. A formal application of the analysis outlined in section 4.5 would thus give rise to wrong results since a pure shear loop is neither of vacancy nor of interstitial type. Consequently, deviations from the rules of section 4.2 are expected to occur, if $\varphi$ approaches $\pi/2$. Contrast calculations to clear up this open question, which may be important for the interpretation of the small-loop contrast in other than fcc metals, are in progress.

## 6. Experimental observations of radiation damage in metal crystals (introduction)

If a particle of mass $M_1$ and kinetic energy $E$ hits a lattice atom of mass $M_2$ energy is transferred with a maximum value $E_m$ when a head-on collision occurs. For neutrons and ions $E_m$ is given by

$$E_m = \frac{4M_1 M_2}{(M_1 + M_2)^2} E .$$

For electrons (mass $m$) the relativistic expression should be used which yields with $m/M_1 \ll 1$

$$E_m = \frac{2(E + 2mc^2)}{M_2 c^2} E \qquad (c = \text{velocity of light}) .$$

With respect to the primary damage structure (i.e. the damage immediately after the impact without subsequent thermally controlled diffusion) there are two critical values of $E_m$, which we denote by $E_d$ and $E_c$. $E_d$ defines the minimum transferred energy which is necessary to produce stable Frenkel pairs (with a probability of 0.5);

for close-packed metals $E_d$ is of the order 20 eV [63]. Thus, taking copper as an example electron irradiation damage may occur only for electron energies above about 0.5 MeV. $E_c$ denotes the energy transfer necessary to produce displacement cascades (with a probability of 0.5) [63–66]. According to Seeger [64] these displacement cascades consist in their centre of a depleted zone of high-vacancy concentration. The interstitials are shot out of the zone into the surrounding lattice by channelling or collision chains. From theory $E_c$ is estimated to be of the order of 1–10 keV [66].

Irradiation under the condition $E_m < E_d$ produces practically no stable damage. For $E_d < E_m < E_c$, mainly isolated Frenkel pairs are created which may or may not agglomerate subsequently into defect clusters depending on secondary circumstances such as temperature, dose, rate of irradiation, impurity content etc. If $E_m$ exceeds $E_c$, the probability of formation of displacement cascades increases rapidly, which should facilitate the nucleation of defect clusters. Due to their extremely wide energy spectrum, irradiation by fast reactor neutrons does not constitute a simple experiment for investigating the damage formation for either $E_m < E_c$ or $E_m > E_c$. For this purpose irradiation with mono-energetic ions or electrons is more suitable. In the former case the condition $E_m \lessgtr E_c$ is controlled by the primary ion energy. In the case of electron irradiation all experiments up to the present time have been performed under the condition $E_m \ll E_c$.

Nevertheless, it is proposed to begin the second part of this paper with a survey of the observations of neutron irradiation damage, because the techniques for analysing the contrast from small defect clusters were to a large extent developed as a result of the study of neutron irradiation damage. The damage structure due to electron and ion bombardment will be treated in subsequent sections.

The experimental results will be discussed under the following fundamental topics.

(1) Size distribution function of the point defect clusters for a given type and dose of irradiation.

(2) Dependence of the size distribution and of the total density of point defect clusters on radiation dose.

(3) Shape of the agglomerates, e.g. dislocation loops, stacking fault tetrahedra, voids, etc...

(4) Differentiation between vacancy and interstitial type defects.

(5) Dependence of the items (1)–(4) on internal irradiation parameters such as type of irradiation, temperature of irradiation, impurity contents, etc...

(6) Annealing behaviour of the defects.

Up to the present, no complete answer to all these questions has been obtained for any metal. However, in some cases the answers are sufficiently complete to allow fairly definite conclusions to be drawn concerning the mechanisms of radiation damage.

## 7. Fast neutron irradiation damage

### 7.1. *Copper*
7.1.1. Size distribution and dose dependence

After some preliminary examinations by Silcox and Hirsch [67] the density and size distribution of the visible defect clusters in neutron-irradiated copper were systematically studied in a series of papers by Makin, Whapham, Minter and Manthorpe [68–70] for irradiation doses between $6 \times 10^{17}$ and $4 \times 10^{18}$ fast neutrons/cm$^2$, $E > 1$ MeV. Using micrographs taken under kinematical image conditions the authors obtained for all doses a size distribution function $P(d)$ with the highest value for the smallest size group (defects with diameters $d$ up to 25 Å) and steadily decreasing with increasing defect sizes $d$. This sloping type of $P(d)$ was later confirmed by Scheidler, Makin, Minter and Schilling [71] and by Rühle [26,72]. According to Scheidler et al. the experimental data may be fitted within the experimental accuracy by an exponential function,

$$P(d) = P(0) \cdot \exp(-d/d_o) \, ,$$

where the parameters $P(0)$ and $d_o$ allow for a simple characterization of $P(d)$. Although both groups agree in so far as $d_o$ (in the order of 25–50 Å) decreases with decreasing irradiation temperature, $T_{irr}$, their absolute values for $P(0)$ and $d_o$ are significantly different.

There are several reasons why the experimental results obtained from different research groups are difficult to compare quantitatively: (i) The fast neutron energy spectra of different reactors may differ from each other. (ii) The quoted irradiation doses may refer either to all neutrons with energies $E > 1$ MeV or to those with $E > 0.1$ MeV. In particular the latter holds for irradiation experiments in the Forschungsreaktor München-Garching. (iii) Other reasons for quantitative discrepancies lie at least partly in the responsibility of the experimentalists. A different developing and printing technique for the micrographs and a different technique for counting and measuring the small defect clusters may yield considerably different results. Further, it is possible that the impurity content of the specimen may influence the quantitative data.

In contrast to the above mentioned results Crump III [73a] has recently obtained peaked as opposed to steadily decreasing $P(d)$ functions with a pronounced peak at about 50 Å ($\phi$ between $1 \times 10^{17}$ and $1 \times 10^{19}$ n/cm$^2$). The discrepancy between these and the other results is not yet resolved.

Koppenaal, Yeh and Cotterill [73b] have compared the defect size distributions in neutron-irradiated copper and dilute copper alloys qualitatively. The authors found that alloying with a few percent of aluminium is sufficient to reduce the density of the large defects ($d \gtrsim 100$ Å) considerably, while the density of the smaller defects remains essentially unchanged.

According to Makin, Whapham and Minter [69] small defect clusters with diameters $d \lesssim 50$ Å obey a fairly linear relationship between the volume density

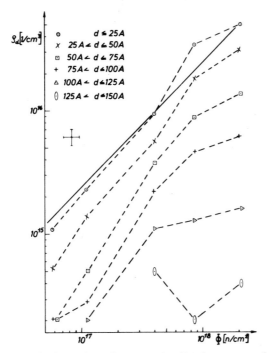

Fig. 5. Loop density per size interval, $\rho_d$, in neutron-irradiated copper as a function of the irradiation dose $\phi$ ($T_{irr} = 80°C$). Data according to Rühle [26]. The slope of the full line in the double logarithmic plot represents proportionality between $\rho_d$ and $\phi$. The indicated error marks correspond to a ±20% uncertainty of both $\phi$ and $\rho_d$.

$\rho_d$ * and the irradiation dose (up to $\phi = 4 \times 10^{18}$ n/cm²). For the larger defects the dose dependence was weaker than linear. In fig. 5 the corresponding data of Rühle [26] are collected, which extend over a larger dose range than the data of ref. [69]. The linear dose dependence of $\rho_d$ of the small defect clusters with $d \lesssim 75$ Å and the tendency for saturation for the larger clusters is obvious.

If for a constant dose $\phi$ the irradiation temperature $T_{irr}$ is changed from 300°C to 4.2°K, the total cluster density $\rho_t$ increases only by a factor of 2 (microscopy observation at room temperature) [71], indicating that the cluster formation is not strongly temperature-dependent.

### 7.1.2. Defect type

In the first paper on neutron irradiation damage in copper, Silcox and Hirsch [67] were able to identify defect clusters with diameters larger than 200 Å as perfect dis-

---

* The lower subscripts d and t discern between the density per size interval and the total density of all clusters.

location loops with Burgers vector $\mathbf{b} = \frac{1}{2} \langle 110 \rangle$. Makin and coworkers [68–70] concluded from the different annealing behaviour of the small ($d < 50$ Å) and the large
($d > 50$ Å) defect clusters that the former defects were presumably of vacancy type
and the latter of interstitial type. According to the authors [70] this interpretation
was corroborated by the similar observations of Barnes and Mazey [57] in α-particle
irradiated copper and by the loop analysis of Mazey, Barnes and Howie [32], the latter
identified the large loops in α-particle irradiated aluminium as of interstitial type.

A direct proof of the loop nature of the small unresolved black dots was first
given by Essmann and Wilkens [39] and Rühle, Wilkens and Essmann [41,26].
Making use of the properties of the black-white contrast figures on dynamical
images they concluded the small black dots were due to Frank-type dislocation
loops with $\mathbf{b}$ parallel to $\langle 111 \rangle$-directions. Only about 5% of the small loops were
found to have a $\langle 110 \rangle$-type Burgers vector.

As outlined in sections 4.2 and 4.7, the differentiation between small vacancy
and interstitial loops requires the determination of the depth position of the loops
inside the transmission foils. This has been done by Rühle and Wilkens [26,61] who
applied the technique of stereo electron microscopy. Their experimental results are
summarized in fig. 4 which has already been discussed in section 5. Accordingly,
the small Frank loops in neutron-irradiated copper are mainly of vacancy type.
(With respect to later results of Rühle and coworkers [74,75] – see below – it
should be emphasized here that in this first work [26,61] only loops with diameters
between 30 and 50 Å were stereo-analysed, since – according to experience – the
stereo technique is easiest to apply in this loop size range. This restriction was not
stated in the original papers.

In subsequent papers, several authors repeated the stereo experiments on neutron-irradiated copper. In striking contrast to Rühle's results, McIntyre [76] found
only interstitial loops (see also McIntyre and Brown [42]), whereas Crump III
[77] agreed with Rühle in finding only vacancy loops. Bourret and Dautreppe
[78] irradiated copper specimens under special atmospheric conditions: They observed either only interstitial loops or only vacancy loops; depending upon whether
the specimens were irradiated in an atmosphere of purified helium gas or in an
oxidizing atmosphere.

After publication of these controversial results, which may have aroused the
suspicion as to whether or not the stereo technique were sufficiently reliable for
the determination of the depth positions of the clusters, Häussermann, Rühle, Rapp
and Wilkens [74,75] repeated the experiments taking special precautions. Two
batches of high-purity copper specimens, both annealed before irradiation for
20 hours at 1070°C in $H_2$, were prepared. The first batch was irradiated in liquid
helium at 4.2°K, the second one (similar as in ref. [26,61]) at 80°C in a slightly
oxidizing atmosphere. Care was taken not to analyse only loops of a narrow size
range as in ref. [26,61]. Loops with diameters between 15 and 150 Å were included
in the stereo-measurements. The results derived from a total number of 150 loops
are summarized in fig. 6. (Since the number of loops analysed per size interval was

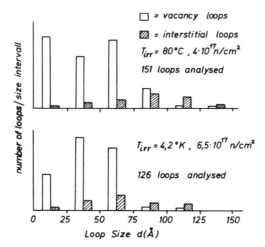

Fig. 6. Vacancy and interstitial type loops in neutron-irradiated copper as a function of the loop diameter $d$ (Rühle, Häussermann, Rapp and Wilkens [74,75]).

not proportional to the corresponding volume density $\rho_d$, the histogram in fig. 6 does not resemble the true size distribution function). Accordingly, loops with diameters $d$ below a critical value $d^*$ of the order of 75 to 100 Å are mainly of vacancy type, whereas loops with $d > d^*$ are mainly of interstitial type. Of course, the two types are not sharply separated.

This result was found in both specimen batches, which indicates that the mechanism for the loop formation is not very sensitive to the irradiation atmosphere (as had been assumed by Bourret and Dautreppe [78]) and not sensitive to the irradiation temperature. (This holds in so far as the microscopic observations are performed at room temperature.) It should be mentioned here that vacancy loops are found in just that size range which obeyed a linear dose dependence of their volume density, see fig. 5. Consequently, one may assume that the vacancy loops are nucleated by the primary damage events such as, e.g., displacement cascades or depleted zones.

The above mentioned discrepancies between the results of ref. [76–78] in comparison to the recent results [74,75] may be tentatively explained as follows: It is possible that different authors have stereo-measured mainly loops of rather restricted but different size intervals (see the discussion of McIntyre's [76] results by Rühle and Wilkens [61]) and that the "transition" size $d^*$ depends on the impurity content and on other parameters of the irradiation procedure.

Using the results summarized in fig. 6 and the corresponding size distribution functions, the total numbers of point defects agglomerated into visible agglomerates were calculated. It emerged that the numbers of agglomerated vacancies and inter-

stitials were about equal within the experimental uncertainty [74,75]. This appears
to be rather satisfactory, since it has been shown that in low temperature irradiated
specimens an equal number of vacancies and interstitials annealed out when the
specimens were warmed up to room temperature [79a,b]. (Under the assumption
that the observed size distribution can be extrapolated down to $d = 0$ Å the number
of point defects agglomerated into loops too small to be visible on the micrographs
comes out to be negligible.)

Finally, we may refer once more to the earlier works of Barnes and Mazey [57]
and of Makin and Manthorpe [70]. The more indirect conclusions of these authors
on the vacancy nature of the small unresolved defect clusters are now confirmed
by the interpretation of the diffraction contrast itself. Furthermore, the latter
method resulted in the larger, but still unresolved loops being of interstitial type.
This fits well with the reasoning of the above mentioned authors regarding the
interstitial nature of the large, resolved loops.

### 7.1.3. Annealing experiments

The annealing behaviour of the damage structure was first studied by Makin and
Manthorpe [70]. As an essential result it emerged that after annealing the specimens at about 300°C the "large" loops disappeared much more rapidly than the
small ones. Similar experiments were performed by Rühle, Häussermann, Rapp and
Wilkens [74,75]. Copper foils (75 $\mu$ thick), irradiated at 4.2°K, were annealed for
one hour at 305°C either (i) in a reducing atmosphere, consisting of 92% $N_2$ and
8% $H_2$ or (ii) in a dynamical vacuum of better than $10^{-4}$ Torr. In both cases $\rho_t$
was reduced to about $\frac{1}{3}$ of the "as-irradiated" values. However, the loop density in
the two surface layers, about 100 Å thick, of the transmission foils was smaller
than in the mean. This holds especially for loops with diameters $d \gtrsim 75$ Å. The number of ⟨110⟩-type loops was remarkably increased. It is assumed that in the annealed
bulk material the ⟨110⟩-type loops are even more abundant and that it is just these
glissile loops that had been swept out by the surface image forces, during the transmission foil preparation. Furthermore, in agreement with ref. [70], small stacking
fault tetrahedra were observed.

Whereas in case (i) the size distribution remained "exponential" (although
broadened) and the small loops remained preferentially of vacancy type, after annealing treatment (ii) the size distribution became peak-shaped with the maximum
at about 50 Å, and vacancy and interstitial loops were found with about equal
number in all size intervals.

It is clearly demonstrated by these annealing experiments that even for copper
the annealing atmosphere must be carefully controlled (see also the annealing
studies of the electrical resistivity of nickel by Mughrabi and Seeger [80]).

### 7.2. Nickel

First attempts at observing the damage structure in neutron-irradiated nickel were
reported by Greenfield and Wilsdorf [81], who did not succeed in observing any

damage structure unless the specimens (irradiated at 70°C) were annealed at 200°C. However, Bell [82], Brimhall, Kissinger and Mastel [59], Rühle [26], and Bourret and Dautreppe [83] found a black dot structure even in the as-irradiated specimens with a volume density comparable to that in copper (for comparable irradiation doses). Also the defect size distribution came out to be similar to that of copper [26,83]. The dose dependence of the density $\rho_d$ specified for different size intervals was studied by Bourret and Dautreppe [83]. Although the authors have published only "interpolated" curves rather than individual $\rho_d$-values, it appears that the dose dependence is not as simple as in neutron-irradiated copper (doses between some $10^{17}$ n/cm$^2$ and some $10^{18}$ n/cm$^2$, data not explicitly stated in the paper, $T_{irr}$ = 78°K, observation at room temperature): The density of defects with diameters smaller than 40 Å increases slower than linear with dose, whereas the reverse was found for defects larger than 40 Å. The type of the defects ($\lesssim$ 100 Å) were identified by means of their black-white contrast on dynamical images as being Frank-type loops [59,26,83]. Using the method of changing the diffraction vector (see section 4.5) Brimhall and coworkers [59] and Rühle [26] concluded that the loops were mainly of vacancy type. Bourret and Dautreppe [83] applied the more reliable stereo technique and found mainly interstitial loops. Although the latter authors stereo-analysed only loops with diameters > 40 Å, they believed that this result should be valid for the Frank loops of all size groups. However, in view of the recent results of Rühle and coworkers [74,75] on neutron-irradiated copper there is some doubt as to whether this holds also for loops with $d$ < 40 Å.

In addition to the Frank loops, Bourret and Dautreppe observed another defect type with diameters down to 15 Å and with the following contrast properties: The black-white streak vector l turned on dynamical images always parallel (or anti-parallel) to g. On kinematical images these dots revealed rather well defined triangular shapes, which were just the same as expected for tetrahedrally shaped defects of course, for the orientation of the transmission foils. Accordingly these defects are probably either stacking fault tetrahedra or tetrahedral voids. The authors favoured the second interpretation (without "diffraction" proof), since under this assumption about the same number of single vacancies and single interstitials, agglomerated into visible defects, were counted. However, their reasoning is open to objections (see section 4.7) as long as the interstitial nature of the small Frank loops with $d \lesssim 40$ Å has not been confirmed.

Bourret and Dautreppe [83] included in their work a study of the annealing behaviour of the damage structure. This is of considerable interest, since for nickel the annealing stage III lies at about 80–100°C, i.e. well above room temperature. Here, only one of their observations will be reported. After annealing the bulk specimens at 125°C the number of point defect agglomerated into the Frank loops (which the authors assumed to be only of interstitial type) increased by a factor of 1.5, followed by a decrease after annealing at higher temperatures. In the interpretation favoured by the authors [83] this is explained by conservative climb and coagulation of the interstitial loops including a high number of extremely small loops too small to be visible on the micrographs. We will return to this interpretation in section 8.3.

### 7.3. Platinum

Ruedl, Delavignette and Amelinckx [84,85] studied the neutron irradiation damage in platinum foils which were mechanically thinned by beating before irradiation. For neutron doses up to $10^{18}$ n/cm$^2$ ($T_{irr} = 78°$K) they observed a comparatively low density of black dots and resolved loops, the density was sometimes enhanced near dislocations and grain boundaries. Rühle, Häussermann, Rapp and Wilkens [75] irradiated bulk specimens of platinum (foils of 75 $\mu$m thickness, $T_{irr} = 80°$C, $\phi = 8 \times 10^{17}$ n/cm$^2$, polishing as described in ref. [86]). In contrast to ref. [84,85], the authors [75] found a defect cluster density and size distribution comparable with copper. The black-white streaks on dynamical images indicated, similarly as in copper and nickel, a high number of small dislocation loops with Burgers vector **b** parallel to $\langle 111 \rangle$. However, in contrast to copper, the number of loops with **b** parallel to $\langle 110 \rangle$, presumably perfect loops with $\mathbf{b} = \frac{1}{2} \langle 110 \rangle$, was considerably higher (about 40%). According to preliminary stereo-measurements, the majority of the small loops were identified as vacancy loops. But the small number of 24 loops, so far analysed, do not enable definite conclusions to be drawn. Apart from the dots, which were uniquely identified as being due to dislocation loops, a small number of black dots with diameter $\lesssim 50$ Å were observed, which turned on dynamical images their black-white vector **l** always parallel to **g** and which do not reveal any crystallographic structure other than a somewhat diffuse structure even on well focussed (kinematical) images. According to the latter observation it is improbable that these dots are due to stacking-fault tetrahedra. A stereo analysis of four of the defects resulted in vacancy type defects. Their atomistic nature is not as yet well understood. Perhaps they are identical with the zones with high concentrations of point defects, especially vacancies, which were detected by Attardo and Galligan [87] on field ion micrographs from neutron-irradiated platinum.

### 7.4. Gold

The neutron irradiation structure was recently examined in detail by Eades [88]. According to Norris [89] who quotes Eades' results mainly vacancy loops were found.

### 7.5. Aluminium

Silcox [90] irradiated aluminium with doses up to $10^{20}$ n/cm$^2$. No damage structure was observed on inspection of the transmission foils at room temperature. This lack of any visible damage structure at room temperature agrees well with the complete recovery at room temperature of the critical shear stress after low temperature irradiation (compare refs. [91,92]). However, Brimhall and Mastel [93] found as rather complex dislocation network ($\phi = 10^{20}$ n/cm$^2$). It is fairly certain that this dislocation network is not due to the spontaneous damage events during irradiation but to diffusion and subsequent agglomeration of single point defects, produced during irradiation.

## 7.6. Molybdenum

Black dots and large resolved dislocation loops have been found not only in fcc metals but also in bcc metals. The damage structure in molybdenum was examined by several authors [94–101]. However, most of the papers have dealt with the nature of the large loops which were mainly observed after "low temperature" irradiation ($T_{irr} \lesssim 100°C$) and subsequent annealing at temperatures $T_{an} \gtrsim 600°C$ or after high temperature irradiation ($T_{irr} \gtrsim 600°C$). No systematic investigations of the size distribution and the dose dependence of the volume density of the defects have so far been reported.

A high density of small black dots were found by Mastel and Brimhall [97] ($T_{irr} = 40°C$) and by Rao and Thomas [98]. Studying the black-white contrast figures of the small defects on dynamical images the latter authors stated that the dots are due to dislocation loops. Their black-white contrast analysis, resulting in **b** parallel to ⟨111⟩ and the loop plane parallel to {110}, was based on the assumption that the black-white streak vector **l** and the "line of no contrast" extend perpendicular to the loop plane and to the Burgers vector **b** respectively. According to section 4.2 this assumption is not justified. Instead of this, the observed streak directions **l** are comparable with **b** parallel to ⟨110⟩ (see also section 7.7).

With respect to the large, well resolved loops, all authors are agreed that the loop Burgers vectors are of $\frac{1}{2}$⟨111⟩-type. Especially after high temperature annealing or high temperature irradiation (see above) the loop habit planes are closely oriented to {111}, resulting in loops of pure edge type. There are some disagreements between the different authors, as to whether the large loops are of vacancy or interstitial type. In the earlier papers mainly interstitial type loops were found, whereas in recent papers, Maher, Eyre and Downey [101,102] have identified vacancy type loops as well. The annealing behaviour of the damage structure, produced by irradiation below 100°C, was studied by Downey and Eyre [95] and by Brimhall, Mastel and Bierlein [100]. There was no detectable change in the defect density and the size distribution for annealing temperatures $T_{an}$ below 600°C. For $T_{an}$ above 600°C the small defects disappeared much more rapidly than the large loops.

According to Mastel and Brimhall [97] and Eyre [104] the formation of large loops is strongly favoured by a high level of carbon impurities.

## 7.7. Niobium

The defect structure of niobium after neutron irradiation was first described by Tucker and Ohr [103]. After irradiating high purity foils at a temperature of about 50°C with $2 \times 10^{18}$ n/cm$^2$ ($E > 1$ MeV) they counted a total volume density $\rho_t$ of $5 \times 10^{15}$ defects/cm$^3$. The defect sizes ranged between 20 Å (lower resolution limit) and about 100 Å.

Huber, Rühle and Wilkens [74,104] studied $\rho_t$ for doses $\phi$ of between $2 \times 10^{17}$ and $2 \times 10^{18}$ n/cm$^2$ ($E > 0.1$ MeV, $T_{irr} = 80°C$). The results are plotted in fig. 7. Although there is a rather large scatter, the points are fairly well compatible with a relation $\rho_t$ proportional to $\phi$. In the experiments of Rühle [26] and Huber, Rühle

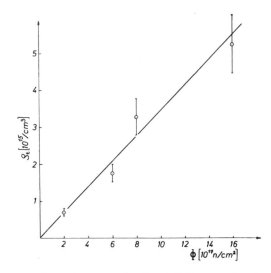

Fig. 7. Density $\rho_t$ of defect clusters in neutron-irradiated niobium as a function of the irradiation
dose $\phi$ (Huber, Rühle and Wilkens [104]).

and Wilkens [74,104] the copper and niobium specimens were irradiated in the same
position in the Forschungsreaktor München. Furthermore in both cases the same
printing and counting technique was applied. Therefore the corresponding $\rho_t$-values
allow for a more quantitative comparison, see section 7.1.1. It is noticeable that for
equivalent irradiation doses the cluster densities in copper are higher by a factor of
about 10 than in niobium. Huber, Rühle and Wilkens [104] irradiated two niobium
specimens with the same dose ($\phi = 6 \times 10^{17}$ n/cm$^2$) but at different temperatures
(80°C and 4.2°K respectively). In the latter case $\rho_t$ was higher by a factor of about
two compared with the former case. A similarly weak temperature dependence of
$\rho_t$ was found in copper (section 7.1.1). The size distribution [104], as shown in
fig. 8 is similar as found in, e.g., neutron-irradiated copper (maximum value at the
smallest size group with $d \leqslant 25$ Å), although for the higher doses a shallow maximum
at $d = 50$ Å may be assumed. The size distribution measured by Ohr, Tucker and
Wechsler [105] displays a pronounced peak at $d = 80$ Å. This peak-shaped curve is
not necessarily in contradiction to the results of Huber, Rühle and Wilkens [104],
since the former authors investigated specimens which were annealed after irradiation for 1 hour at 300°C.

Studying the black-white contrast streaks on dynamical images, Tucker and Ohr
[103] concluded that the defects were due to dislocation loops. The observed streak
directions l were taken as evidence for loop Burgers vectors parallel to ⟨100⟩, ⟨110⟩
and ⟨111⟩. According to Huber et al. [104] these three types of Burgers vectors occur with about equal probability. The latter authors applied the stereo-technique to

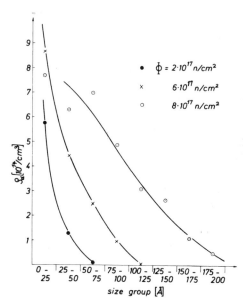

Fig. 8. Size distribution function of defect clusters in neutron-irradiated niobium, $T_{irr} = 80°C$ (Huber, Rühle and Wilkens [104]).

a total number of 250 loops. Vacancy and interstitial loops were found in all size groups with a slight excess of interstitial loops. This holds for $T_{irr} = 80°C$ and $4.2°K$ as well, see fig. 9.

## 7.8. Tungsten

A first examination of the defect structure was carried out by Lacefield, Moteff and Smith [106] and by Rau, Moteff and Ladd [107]. In specimens irradiated at 70°C and subsequently annealed at 400°C with some $10^{18}$ n/cm² only small black dots with average sizes of about 25–50 Å could be detected. For $\phi = 6 \times 10^{18}$ n/cm² the volume density of the black dots came out to $\rho_t = 1.4 \times 10^{16}$/cm², a value which is compatible with the $\rho_t$-values found in niobium, see section 7.7 and fig. 7. Rau [108] irradiated tungsten up to a comparatively high dose of $1.5 \times 10^{21}$ n/cm². After a subsequent annealing of the specimens at 1100°C he observed large well resolved loops ($d > 1000$ Å), which he identified as pure edge loops ($\mathbf{b} = \frac{1}{2}\langle 111 \rangle$) of vacancy type. This result should be compared with those obtained on post-irradiation annealed molybdenum, where mainly (large) interstitial type loops have been found, see section 7.6.

## 7.9. Vanadium

Rau and Ladd [109] studied vanadium after irradiation with $5 \times 10^{19}$ n/cm² ($E > 1$ MeV, $T_{irr} = 70°C$). In the as-irradiated condition a high density of small dots

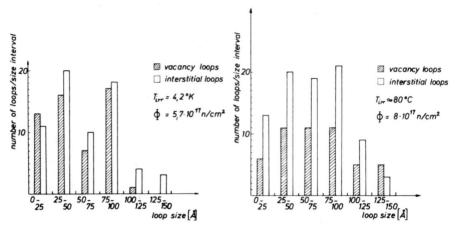

Fig. 9. Vacancy and interstitial type loops in neutron-irradiated niobium as a function of the
loop diameter $d$ (Huber, Rühle and Wilkens [104]).

($d \lesssim 50$ Å) was observed. Annealing of the as-irradiated specimens at various temperatures between 330°C and 1175°C resulted in a density decrease and coarsening
of the defect structure, which consisted finally of large, well resolved loops. These
loops were identified as probably being of interstitial type.

### 7.10. Rhenium

Brimhall and Mastel [110,111] were concerned with a more detailed analysis of
the nature of the black dots in neutron-irradiated rhenium ($T_{\text{irr}} = 550$°C,
$\phi = 1.5 \times 10^{19}$ n/cm$^2$ ($E > 1$ MeV), $\rho_t \approx 1 \times 10^{16}$ clusters/cm$^3$). By inspection of
the black-white contrast streaks on dynamical images the loop Burgers vector $\mathbf{b}$
was found to be always parallel to $\langle 11\bar{2}0 \rangle$, which indicated that the loop planes
were not parallel to the basal plane. The application of the stereo technique to
about 100 loops with diameters $d$ between 40 and 100 Å resulted in a majority of
interstitial loops. However, the authors stated that this must not be representative
for the loops with $d < 40$ Å. In this context we refer to a paper by Bernstein and
Gulden [112] who looked for the damage structure in zirconium irradiated with
150 keV Kr$^+$ ions. The black dots in the as-irradiated specimens were not analysed.
However, after a post-irradiation annealing well resolved loops on prismatic planes
with $\mathbf{b}$ parallel to $\langle 11\bar{2}0 \rangle$ were found and identified as interstitial loops.

## 8. Electron irradiation damage

### 8.1. Copper

Makin, Whapham and Minter [69] were the first to use electron transmission
microscopy techniques for electron irradiation damage in copper ($E = 3$ MeV, irra-

diation at room temperature). However, they did not succeed in observing any visible defects. Recently, the experiments were repeated by Sigmund, Scheidler and Roth [113] and by Scheidler and Roth [114]. Copper foils were irradiated at temperatures between 120°K and 320°K with 3 MeV-electrons. The irradiation doses ranged between $5 \times 10^{18}$ and $3 \times 10^{20}$ e$^-$/cm$^2$ (current density = 0.5 mA/cm$^2$). In variance with the negative results of Makin and coworkers [69], the electron microscopy investigations (in all cases at room temperature) resulted in a typical radiation damage structure, consisting of black dots with a size distribution function of "exponential" type, see section 7.1. For $T_{irr}$ = 130°K and 230°K the $d_o$ values obtained ranged between 20 and 35 Å, depending upon the irradiation temperature and the impurity content of the copper specimens (two batches of specimen with purities 99.999% Cu and 99.99% Cu were compared). These $d_o$ values are of the same order, as has been found in neutron-irradiated copper, see section 7.1. However, the dose dependence of the total volume density $\rho_t$ of the visible defects is quite different to that after neutron irradiation. Between the doses $\phi = 5 \times 10^{18}$ e$^-$/cm$^2$ and $3.2 \times 10^{20}$ e$^-$/cm$^2$ $\rho_t$ varied between $4 \times 10^{15}$ and $3.2 \times 10^{16}$ defects/cm$^3$, following closely a $\phi^{\frac{1}{2}}$-law. Furthermore, in contrast to neutron irradiation, in the purer specimen $\rho_t$ was strongly influenced by the irradiation temperature. Between $T_{irr}$ = 120°K and 250°K $\rho_t$ decreased linearly with increasing $T_{irr}$ by a factor of 5.5. Up to $T_{irr}$ = 320°K a further decrease (linear with $T_{irr}$, but with reduced slope) by a factor of 2 was observed. For the specimens with 99.99% Cu the temperature variation of $\rho_t$ was less pronounced, resulting in higher $\rho_t$-values at $T_{irr}$ higher than 120°K.

The defect nature was studied by Häussermann, Rühle, Scheidler and Roth [115], using specimens (99.999 % Cu), which were pre-annealed and electron-irradiated at 120°K under the same conditions as in ref. [114]. As a result, it emerged that the defects are Frank sessile dislocation loops, as expected from the analogy to neutron irradiation damage. However, in contrast to the latter, vacancy and interstitial loops were found in all size groups with approximately equal numbers (a total number of 90 loops with diameters between 15 and 100 Å were analysed).

Very recently, Makin [116] reported that the electron beam in the Cambridge high voltage microscope (maximum voltage 750 kV) is capable of producing visible electron irradiation damage in copper transmission foils, when the foils are in situ inside the microscope. If the electron beam is optimally focussed on the specimen plane (diameter of the illuminated area $\cong 5\,\mu$), the beam current density reaches values in the order of 1 A/cm$^2$, which exceeds the current density in conventional electron accelerators by a factor of $10^3$ or even more. According to Makin there exists a critical voltage $V_c$ between 450 and 500 kV. For acceleration voltages $V_a > V_c$ the damage in the transmission foil was formed after few minutes of irradiation (at room temperature). For $V_a < V_c$ no damage was observed even after long irradiation times. The observed value for $V_c$ is in fairly good agreement with theoretically expected values, based on a displacement energy $E_d$ of about 20 eV. In comparison with the results of Makin and coworkers [69] and of Scheidler and coworkers [113,114], it is concluded that in the case of electron irradiation the production of visible defects is not only controlled by the integrated irradiation dose but also favoured by the extremely high current density achievable in the high voltage microscope. Studying the damage formation in polycrystalline copper specimens Makin [116] found that the critical voltage $V_c$ is sensitive to the grain orientation with respect to the incident electron beam. This indicates that the displacement energy for Frenkel pair formation is dependent on the angle of incidence of the striking particle as was predicted by Gibson, Goland, Milgram and Vineyard [117].

## 8.2. Gold, niobium, platinum

In the paper of Scheidler and Roth [114], some preliminary transmission microscopy results, obtained from electron-irradiated gold, niobium and platinum, are reported. In all these cases, black dots were observed after irradiation doses between $10^{19}$ and $10^{20}$ e$^-$/cm$^2$. In gold, in addition to the black dots (presumably Frank loops) tetrahedrally shaped defects could be identified, which the authors interpreted as due to stacking fault tetrahedra (see, however, sections 7.2 and 4.7).

## 8.3. Nickel

Bourret and Dautreppe [83,118] irradiated nickel foils (70 μm thick) between −40°C and +10°C with 2 MeV and 3 MeV electrons (doses $\phi$ between $1 \times 10^{19}$ and $5 \times 10^{19}$ e$^-$/cm$^2$). The electron microscopy observations were made at room temperature. The size distribution of the defects (black dots) and the dose dependence of the defect density $\rho_t$ are more complicated than in the case of electron-irradiated copper. There exists a critical dose $\phi_c$ slightly above $2 \times 10^{19}$ e$^-$/cm$^2$. For $\phi < \phi_c$ practically no damage was observed, whereas for $\phi > \phi_c$ the values for $\rho_t$ turned out to be of the same order of magnitude as in copper. The size distribution curve displayed a maximum at about 50 Å rather than a simple steadily decreasing ("exponential") form as in the case of copper [114]. The defects were identified as Frank loops. Application of the stereo-technique revealed that all analysed loops (number not stated) were of interstitial type, irrespective of their sizes (40 Å < $d$ < 120 Å). No vacancy clusters could be observed. In order to decide whether or not single interstitials are mobile below stage III (at about 80–100°C), two specific experiments were carried out. In the first experiment, a bulk specimen (70 μ thick), containing vacancy loops (by any pre-irradiation treatment not stated in the paper) with an exponential size distribution function, were irradiated at −30°C with $8.7 \times 10^{19}$ e$^-$/cm$^2$. The microscopic inspection at room temperature of the subsequently thinned foils showed an increase in the density for loops with $d < 70$ Å and a decrease for $d > 70$ Å. In the interpretation of Bourret and Dautreppe [83, 118] the increase for $d < 70$ Å is due to freshly nucleated interstitial loops whereas the decrease for $d > 70$ Å is due to a shrinking of the vacancy loops by absorption of freely migrating interstitials. This explanation should be confirmed by careful loop type determinations (vacancy or interstitial type) after irradiation. In the second experiment nickel specimens, irradiated below room temperature, were annealed for one hour at 100°C. Inspecting thin foils of the specimens before and after the annealing treatment it emerged that the total number of point defects, agglomerated into the visible loops, increased during annealing by a factor of about 2 or more. At the same time the mean loop diameter $\bar{d}$ increased. According to the authors this may be explained in two ways: (i) by conservative climb and coagulation of those interstitial loops, which before annealing were too small to be visible on the micrographs. However, this suggestion has the following weaknesses: In order to account for the increase in the number of interstitials, agglomerated into visible loops, there must be in the as-irradiated specimens an extremely high density of small, not imaged loops ($d \lesssim 15$ Å). So far there exists no evidence for such a high peak below 20 Å in the size distribution function. Further, even if a coagulation of such small invisible loops occurs, one should expect a decrease rather than an increase of the mean loop diameter $\bar{d}$. (ii) In the second explanation proposed by Bourret, both observations can be accounted for by the assumption of a high background of interstitials, which are immobile in the as-irradiated specimens and which become mobile at 100°C to migrate either to vacancies, resulting in a mutual annihilation, or to the interstitial loops already present, resulting in an increase of $\bar{d}$ and the total number of interstitials, agglomerated in visible defect clusters.

## 9. Ion irradiation damage

The ion damage experiments may be subdivided into two groups depending upon whether the maximum energy transferred, $E_m$, lies below or above the threshold energy $E_c$ for displacement cascade formation. Recent experiments with ions of low or medium energy, which belong to the first group, were mainly performed in order to produce self-interstitials and to study their annealing behaviour. These experiments will not be considered in detail here, since they are more closely related to the contribution of Venables [119]. Consequently, we will deal here mainly with papers, which are relevant for the understanding of the formation of displacement cascades.

### 9.1. Identification of defect cluster type
Up to the present time damage by heavy ions with high energies has been investigated mainly in fcc metals. For ion doses low enough to produce isolated defect clusters without mutual overlapping (doses $\phi \lesssim 10^{12}$ ions/cm$^2$) these clusters appear with diameters $d \lesssim 150-200$ Å. This means that their crystallographic nature is, in most cases, not resolved on the micrographs. However, based on the interpretation of the black-white contrast on dynamical images, it is now well established that the defect clusters are in the majority dislocation loops of Frank sessile type and with minor frequence of perfect loops [26,120–123]. In an earlier paper, Hesketh and Rickards [124] applied the $\mathbf{g} \cdot \mathbf{b} = 0$ extinction criterion for dislocations to the

small "black dots" in copper, irradiated with 150 keV $Zn^+$-ions. By this criterion they attempted to discriminate between small loops and three-dimensional clusters. From statistical considerations they arrived at the conclusion that the majority of the defects are three-dimensional clusters rather than loops. However, as pointed out in section 4.2, this method appears to be unreliable.

Howe, McGurn and Gilbert [45] have studied the damage structure due to irradiation with 100 keV $O^-$-ions. Using a low temperature specimen stage in a Siemens Elmiskop I the specimens (Al, Cu, Au) were ion-irradiated inside the microscope and subsequently investigated at temperatures below 30°K. Even at such low temperatures the observed damage consisted mainly of small Frank loops. From this experiment it may be argued that also the Frank loops observed at room temperature in neutron or high energy ion-bombarded specimens are created not by long-range diffusion but rather by an athermal collapse of mechanically unstable depleted zones in the centre of the displacement cascades.

## 9.2. Defect size

In gold foils, irradiated with various kinds of particles, Merkle [125–127] has found that the mean diameter of the defect clusters increases with increasing transferred energy ($10 \text{ keV} < E_m < 100 \text{ keV}$). This is easy to interpret as due to an energy dependence of the sizes of the depleted zones. If, however, $E_m$ exceeded about 100 keV, the clusters split into a number of closely spaced sub-clusters, indicating a splitting of the large cascades into a number of sub-cascades in agreement with the calculations of v. Jan [65,66].

In copper foils Merkle did not observe a similar energy dependence of the defect sizes; this is in contrast to Rühle and Wilkens [26,128], according to whom the Frank loops in copper produced by 100 keV $O^-$-ions are on the average larger by a factor of two than those produced by 40 keV $O^-$-ions. However, both authors agree that the defect sizes are not dose-dependent, which means that defects, once created by a displacement cascade, do not grow during subsequent irradiation.

## 9.3. Differentiation between clusters of vacancy and interstitial type

The penetration depth of heavy ions in close packed metals is, for not too high energies, of the order of 1000 Å or less. Irradiation experiments with heavy ions are therefore in most cases performed on transmission foils, which were prepared either electrolytically from thicker sheets or by evaporation and epitactic growth. Due to the small penetration depth the ion damage is expected to lie more or less in the close vicinity of that foil surface through which the ion beam penetrates into the foil. If the distance of the defect clusters to the adjacent foil surface is smaller than about one quarter of the extinction length, and if they consist solely of interstitial or solely of vacancy type, then the black-white contrast figures on dynamical images are expected to reveal a unique sign of their $\mathbf{g} \cdot \mathbf{l}$-products. Such a unique sign of $\mathbf{g} \cdot \mathbf{l}$ has been observed in several cases (e.g. Howe, McGurn and Gilbert [45], Merkle [120,125]) and has lead the authors to the conclusion that the defects are mainly of vacancy type (see the critical comments on this argument in section 4.5). However the more reliable defect type determinations of Rühle and Wilkens [26,128], and Norris [89], which were based on the application of the stereo technique, confirmed the vacancy nature of the defects produced by the impact of highly energetic heavy ions.

In the experiments of Diepers, Diehl and Hertel [50,129] copper and gold foils were irradiated parallel to $\langle 100 \rangle$ or $\langle 110 \rangle$ with $Ar^+$-ions of 1 keV or 5 keV energy. The Frank loops, which appeared in a narrow layer at a distance of 100–200 Å from the irradiated surface, were mainly identified as being due to the agglomeration of interstitials. According to the authors these interstitials were shot into the lattice by focussing chains induced at the surface by the incident $Ar^+$-ions and athermally converted into the loops. Obviously the transferred energies $\lesssim E_m \cong 5$ keV were too small to produce depleted zones for a spontaneous agglomeration of vacancies large enough to be visible on the micrographs.

In this context, the paper of Jouffrey [130] which is concerned with 4 keV $Ar^+$ irradiation of gold foils should be mentioned. The author interpreted the observed small defect clusters as due to vacancy loops at distances $< 50$ Å from the irradiated surface. However, no stereo-measurements for the depth position determination were applied. Therefore, Jouffrey's experiments, which are in striking contrast to the results of Diepers [50], should be repeated for confirmation.

A similar change from vacancy to interstitial type clusters with changing transferred energies is observed in the case of light ion irradiation. In the experiments of Barnes and Mazey [57], copper was irradiated with 38 MeV $\alpha$-particles ($E_m = 8$ MeV). The defect structure resembled, to some extent, that of fast neutron-irradiated copper. By indirect arguments the authors concluded that the small unresolved defect clusters were of vacancy type, whereas the comparatively few larger ones, which appeared as loops on the micrographs, were of interstitial type. By analogy with neutron-irradiated copper, it may be assumed that the small unresolved clusters are in fact Frank sessile loops of vacancy type, which are presumably produced by displacement cascades. On the other hand, Mazey and Barnes [35] irradiated copper foils with 60 keV $H^+$-ions ($E_m = 4$ keV). Although $E_m$ is of the same order as in the experiments of Diepers and coworkers [50,129] the damage structure is expected to be different, since the penetration depth of 5 keV $Ar^+$ and 60 keV $H^+$ ions in copper amounts to about 40 Å and 7000 Å respectively [50,35]. Nevertheless, in partial agreement with ref. [50], Mazey and Barnes observed mainly large ($\gtrsim 1000$ Å) faulted loops of interstitial type on {111}-planes, which were obviously grown by diffusion (irradiation between 70°C and 300°C).

Extremely low ion energies were used in the experiments of Brandon and Bowden [131,132] (100 eV, $Ar^+$-ions on copper) and Thomas and Balluffi [133] (270 eV $Au^+$ and $Ar^+$-ions on gold). In both papers interstitial loops, which intersected the surface, were found. However, Thomas and Balluffi only succeeded in finding an appreciable density of these interstitial clusters if the foil surface were contaminated with impurities or irradiated with $Ar^+$ instead of $Au^+$ ions. Obviously in the range of extremely low ion energies, impurities play an important role in the nucleation of interstitial agglomerates.

## 9.4. *Dose dependence*

The area density of defect clusters in gold foils produced by high energy ions or fission fragments ($E_m \geqslant 10$ keV) is proportional to the irradiation dose. This was found by Merkle [127] and by Van Vliet and Chadderton [134]. For cluster densities higher than some $10^{11}/cm^2$ saturation effects become predominant, presumably due to an increased overlapping of adjacent clusters.

Within the region of linear dose dependence a "cross section" $\sigma$ for the formation of clusters large enough to be visible on the micrographs, may be defined. Merkle [125–127] has studied the dependence of $\sigma$ on the maximum transferred energy $E_m$ with $E_m$ between 10 keV and 40 MeV. In the case of gold the $\sigma(E_m)$-curve displayed a well defined maximum at $E_m \approx 24$ keV and a $1/E_m$ decrease for $E_m \gg 24$ keV. Making the assumption that the defect clusters are directly produced by displacement cascades, which is strongly favoured by many other evidences, Merkle was able to interpret the observed $\sigma(E_m)$-curve quantitatively. He concluded that in gold there exists a threshold energy $E_c$ of the order of magnitude of 34 keV for the formation of displacement cascades, all of which are large enough to produce a visible defect cluster on the micrograph. This value for $E_c$ was later confirmed by Noggle [135] *. Similar experiments of Merkle [125] with copper did not yield unique results. He concluded that in copper apparently only a fraction of 10% of the displacement cascades is capable of producing visible agglomerates. See, however, the discussion of Rühle [26].

The damage formation in aluminium is different from that in heavier metals such as nickel, copper or gold. Beevers and Nelson [136] irradiated Al foils with $H^+$ and $Xe^+$ ions of 85 keV energy. For $H^+$ the maximum transferred energy $E_m$ is less than 10 keV. Consequently no displacement cascades are expected. There was in fact evidence that the observed damage structure was due to long range diffusion of single point defects. However, even in the case of $Xe^+$ irradiation ($E_m = 50$ keV) the doses necessary for producing appreciable damage were higher by a factor of about 100 than the doses for a comparable damage in nickel or copper. This was demonstrated more directly by Norris [123], who compared the damage in aluminium and nickel after irradiation with 150 keV $Xe^+$ ions. Although he found vacancy loops close to the irradiated surface in the aluminium foils, the production rate was orders of magnitude less than in nickel. Thus, one may argue that in aluminium the formation of displacement cascades, resulting in a spontaneous agglomeration of vacancies, needs considerably higher transferred energies than in the noble metals and nickel.

---

* Note added in proof: Compare, however, the recent results of Högberg and Nordén [145]. Studying heavy-ion irradiation on gold, the authors found in a similar way as Merkle that $E_c$ range in the order of 10 keV.

## 9.5. *Channelling and depth distribution of the defect clusters*

Ruedl, Delavignette and Amelinckx [84,85] observed that the irradiation of platinum with fission fragments resulted in an enhanced damage at coherent twin boundaries. This was interpreted as evidence for the existence of either collision chains or channelling of knocked-on atoms, abruptly stopped at the twin boundaries, which are unable to act as sinks for single point defects. Similar observations in neutron-irradiated nickel were reported by Brimhall and Mastel [137]. A more direct proof of channeling was presented by Noggle [135]. This author irradiated gold transmission foils with an extremely narrow collimated beam of 51 MeV $I^+$-ions. If the beam direction coincided within 0.5° with a ⟨110⟩-direction, the damage production was lower by a factor of about ten than for beam directions far away from ⟨110⟩. This is easy to understand, since ions, which propagate along the ⟨110⟩-channels through the entire foil, have only a small chance of producing displacement cascades. Recently, Schober and Balluffi [138] demonstrated that 40 keV $Au^+$ ions may also channel along ⟨100⟩ in gold. Their experimental evidence was based on the observation of de-channeling of the $Au^+$ ions at stacking faults. Similar observations have been done by Merkle [139].

Diepers, Diehl and Hertel [50,129] determined the depth distribution of the defect clusters in copper and gold foils after irradiation with 1 keV and 5 keV $Ar^+$ ions. When the specimens were irradiated parallel to ⟨100⟩, a single peaked depth distribution function was found. Irradiation parallel to ⟨110⟩ resulted in a double peaked distribution. This difference is expected if the clusters are due to ⟨110⟩-collision chains. For ⟨100⟩-irradiation all ⟨110⟩-directions not perpendicular to the beam direction are equivalent, whereas for ⟨110⟩-irradiation the collision chains may propagate either parallel to the beam or at an angle of 60°.

A peculiar damage in aluminium, irradiated parallel to ⟨110⟩ or ⟨111⟩ with 50 keV $Al^+$ or $Cu^+$ ions was reported by Hendriksen and coworkers [140]. The damage consisted of interstitial loops (diameter $\lesssim$ 200 Å) which were aligned over several 1000 Å along a ⟨110⟩ direction. The authors assumed that these loop rows were nucleated in an early stage of irradiation with the help of some channeling mechanisms.

Norris [141] measured the depth distribution of the defect clusters in gold and nickel after irradiation with $Hg^+$ or $Au^+$ ions of energies between 80 and 150 keV. It emerged that the mean distance of the agglomerates from the irradiated foil surface (100–200 Å) amounted to 50% (gold) or 30% (nickel) of the theoretically derived mean ion penetration depth. These figures were found to be independent of both the ion energies used and the irradiation temperature (either 80°K or 295°K).

## 10. Final remarks

### 10.1. *Interpretation of the diffraction contrast*

The first part of the paper summarizes the main details of our present knowledge on the formation of the diffraction contrast, particularly from those defect clusters which are too small to be resolved geometrically on the micrographs. Many of the theoretically predicted properties of the diffraction contrast have been verified experimentally. Thus it is demonstrated that the theory of diffraction contrast as developed in the present approximation permits the interpretation of the contrast images from clusters with diameters down to 20 Å.

For such small point defect clusters the interpretation technique based on the properties of the black-white contrast has been found to be extremely useful. From the theoretical point of view two questions are still open:

(i) So far the depth oscillations of the black-white contrast figures have been explicitly verified only for Frank loops in fcc metals, i.e. for loops of pure edge type. However, it appears probable that among the small loops as observed in radiation damaged bcc metals there are also other than pure edge configurations. Therefore calculations of the depth positions, at which the sign of the black-white contrast inverts, are desirable also for more general loops.

(ii) In the so far published calculations of the black-white contrast from dislocation loops of finite sizes the elastic boundary conditions at the near-by foil surface have been allowed for only in an approximate way, assuming an infinitesimally small image stress centre. This is a good approximation for loops with diameters $d$ small compared with the extinction length $\xi_g$. However, if $d$ is of the order of magnitude of or larger than about $\frac{1}{2} \xi_g$, such an infinitesimally small image stress centre might no longer be a good description. One expects that the thickness at least of the first layer of the black-white oscillations would be affected in an improved treatment.

Another open problem associated with perfect dislocation loops with $d \approx \frac{1}{2} \xi_g$ is that sometimes they are apparently "resolved" on the micrographs as "double arc" contrast. At present the relation of this type of contrast to the loop size is not known. A theoretical treatment of the contrast from these "just resolved" loops with full allowance for the elastic boundary conditions would be very useful.

## 10.2. *Application to point defect clusters*

The second part of the paper is concerned with the electron microscopical investigations of the structure of radiation damage in metals. There are several aspects for which electron microscopy may contribute valuable informations, e.g.:

(i) The primary structure of defect clusters due to the impact of particles of kinetic energies high enough to produce displacement cascades or depleted zones. Here the term "primary" means that the defect cluster in mind should not be influenced by any long-range diffusion of point defects.

(ii) The correlation of the different annealing stages to the thermally activated mobility of special types and configurations of point defects.

(iii) The quantitative interpretation of irradiation-sensitive physical properties in terms of concentration and configurations of point defect agglomerates.

It has been shown that (i) is most easily investigated by means of ion-irradiation experiments. In fact, valuable informations on the structure of the depleted zones have already been obtained. Considerable progress in the near future is expected.

For the studies of question (ii) electron irradiation experiments are most suitable. However, as long as the electron microscopic observations are performed at room temperature, conclusive results can at best be obtained for those metals for which the critical annealing stage III occurs above room temperature. Low temperature irradiation combined with low temperature observations (without warming up of the specimens between irradiation and observation) will be essential for further progress in this field.

With respect to question (iii) only the increase in the critical shear stress of fcc single crystals due to neutron irradiation will be mentioned here. For more than ten years considerable theoretical efforts have been made by several groups in order to obtain a quantitative understanding of this striking phenomenon for which point defect agglomerates are essential (see Diehl [142]). However, most of these theoretical attempts involve adjustable parameters connected with the defect structure. A notable exception to this is a recent paper by Frank, Rühle and Saxlowa [143]. These authors achieved a quantitative explanation of the temperature dependence of the critical shear stress of neutron-irradiated copper which did not involve any free parameters. Instead, quantitative data on the type, concentration and size distribution of the defect clusters as evaluated by electron transmission microscopy were used. By this example it is demonstrated that a quantitative evaluation of the defect structure, e.g., in particle-irradiated crystals may yield results which can be incorporated with success into the interpretation of other physical phenomena.

## Acknowledgements

The author is indebted to Professor A.Seeger for encouraging him to write the present paper. Furthermore, many helpful discussions with the author's colleagues Dr. M.Rühle, Dipl.-Phys. F.Häussermann and Dipl.-Phys. P.Huber are gratefully acknowledged.

## References

[1] W.Bollmann, Phys. Rev. 103 (1956) 1588.
[2] P.B.Hirsch, R.W.Horne and M.J.Whelan, Phil. Mag. 1 (1956) 677.
[3] P.B.Hirsch, A.Howie and M.J.Whelan, Phil. Trans. Roy. Soc. (London) A252 (1960) 499.
[4] A.Howie and M.J.Whelan, Proc. Roy. Soc. A263 (1961) 217.
[5] A.Howie and M.J.Whelan, Proc. Roy. Soc. A267 (1962) 206.
[6] M.J.Whelan and P.B.Hirsch, Phil. Mag. 2 (1957) 1121, 1303.
[7] H.Hashimoto, A.Howie and M.J.Whelan, Phil. Mag. 5 (1960) 967; Proc. Roy. Soc. A269 (1962) 80.
[8] P.B.Hirsch, J.Silcox, R.E.Smallman and K.H.Westmacott, Phil. Mag. 3 (1958) 897.
[9] J.Silcox and P.B.Hirsch, Phil. Mag. 4 (1959) 72.
[10] D.W.Pashley and A.E.B.Presland, Phil. Mag. 6 (1961) 1003.
[11] H.A.Bethe, Ann. Phys. (Germany) 85 (1928) 55.
[12] R.D.Heidenreich, J. Appl. Phys. 20 (1949) 993.

[13] B.Jouffrey and D.Taupin, Phil. Mag. 16 (1967) 703.

[14] A.Howie and Z.S.Basinski, Phil. Mag. 17 (1968) 1039.

[15] R.Gevers, P.Delavignette, H.Blanck and S.Amelinckx, Phys. Stat. Sol. 4 (1964) 383.

[16] S.Takagi, Acta Cryst. 15 (1962) 1311.

[17] D.Taupin, Bull. Soc. fr. Miner. Cristallogr. 87 (1964) 469.

[18] A.Howie, Proc. Roy. Soc. A271 (1963) 268.

[19] M.Wilkens, Phys. Stat. Sol. 6 (1964) 939.

[20] M.Wilkens, Phys. Stat. Sol. 13 (1966) 529.

[21] M.Wilkens and M.Rühle, Proc. 6 Intern. Congress for Electron Microscopy, Kyoto, Vol. I, (1966) p. 77.

[22] M.Wilkens, M.Rühle and F.Häussermann, Phys. Stat. Sol. 22 (1967) 689.

[23] K.P.Chik, M.Wilkens and M.Rühle, Phys. Stat. Sol. 23 (1967) 113.

[24] M.F.Ashby and L.M.Brown, Phil. Mag. 8 (1963) 1083.

[25] M.F.Ashby and L.M.Brown, Phil. Mag. 8 (1963) 1649.

[26] M.Rühle, Phys. Stat. Sol. 19 (1967) 263, 279.

[27] F.Häussermann and M.Wilkens, Phys. Stat. Sol. 18 (1966) 609.

[28] J.W.Steeds, Phil. Mag. 16 (1967) 785.

[29] C.J.Humphries and P.B.Hirsch, Phil. Mag. 18 (1968) 115.

[30] M.Wilkens and H.Ruf, to be published.

[31] G.W.Groves and A.Kelly, Phil. Mag. 6 (1961) 1527; 7 (1962) 892.

[32] D.J.Mazey, R.S.Barnes and A.Howie, Phil. Mag. 7 (1962) 1861.

[33] P.B.Hirsch, A.Howie, R.B.Nicholson, D.W.Pashley and M.J.Whelan, Electron Microscopy of Thin Crystals (Butterworths, London, 1965).

[34] D.M.Maher and B.L.Eyre, Proc. 4th European Reg. Conf. on Electron Microscopy, Rome, Vol. I (1968) p. 373.

[35] D.J.Mazey and R.S.Barnes, Phil. Mag. 17 (1968) 387.

[36] W.L.Bell and G.Thomas, Phil. Mag. 13 (1966) 395.

[37] V.A.Phillips and J.D.Livingston, Phil. Mag. 7 (1962) 969.

[38] C.J.Ball, Phil. Mag. 9 (1964) 541.

[39] U.Essmann and M.Wilkens, Phys. Stat. Sol. 4 (1964) K53.

[40] M.Rühle, M.Wilkens and U.Essmann, Phys. Stat. Sol. 11 (1965) 819.

[41] K.G.McIntyre and L.M.Brown, J. Phys. Radium 27 (1966) C3—178.

[42] K.G.McIntyre and L.M.Brown, Symposium on the Nature of Small Defect Clusters, Harwell, AERE Report R 5269, (1966) p. 351.

[43] W.L.Bell and G.Thomas, Phys. Stat. Sol. 12 (1965) 843.

[44] W.Bell, D.M.Maher and G.Thomas, Lattice Defects in Quenched Metals (Academic Press, New York and London, 1965) p. 739.

[45] L.M.Howe, J.F.McGurn and R.W.Gilbert, Acta. Met. 14 (1966) 801.

[46] W.L.Bell, D.M.Maher and G.Thomas, Symposium on the Nature of Small Defect Clusters, Harwell, AERE Report R 5269 (1966) p. 314.

[47] L.M.Brown, Symposium on Electron Microscopy, Modena 1963, Ed. Paolo Buffa, CNR Roma (1964).

[48] K.P.Chik, Phys. Stat. Sol. 16 (1966) 685.

[49] H.Diepers and J.Diehl, Phys. Stat. Sol. 16 (1966) K109.

[50] H.Diepers, Phys. Stat. Sol. 24 (1967) 235, 623.

[51] J.F.Nankivell, Optik 20 (1963) 171.

[52] L.T.Chadderton, Proc. Roy. Soc. A280 (1964) 110.

[53] J.van Landuyt, R.Gevers and S.Amelinckx, Phys. Stat. Sol. 10 (1965) 319.

[54] L.M.Brown and D.J.Mazey, Phil. Mag. 10 (1964) 1081.

[55] M.Kiritani, Y.Shimomura and S.Yoshida, J. Phys. Soc. Japan 19 (1964) 1624.

[56] M.Kiritani, A.Sato, Y.Shimomura and S.Yoshida, Proc. 6th Intern. Congress for Electron Microscopy, Kyoto, Vol. I (1966) p. 341.
[57] R.S.Barnes and D.J.Mazey, Phil. Mag. 5 (1960) 1247.
[58] A.Seeger, V.Gerold and M.Rühle, Z. Metallkde. 54 (1963) 493.
[59] J.L.Brimhall, H.E.Kissinger and B.Mastel, J. Appl. Phys. 37 (1966) 3317.
[60] W.J.Tunstall and P.J.Goodhew, Phil. Mag. 13 (1966) 1259.
[61] M.Rühle and M.Wilkens, Phil. Mag. 15 (1967) 1075.
[62] A.Seeger, in: Handbuch der Physik, Ed. S.Flügge, Vol. VII, 1 (Springer, Berlin-Heidelberg-Göttingen, 1955) p. 383.
[63] A.Brinkman, Am. J. Phys. 24 (1956) 246.
[64] A.Seeger, Proc. of the 2nd Geneva Conf. on Peaceful Use of Atomic Energy 6 (1958) 250.
[65] R.van Jan, Phys. Stat. Sol. 6 (1964) 925.
[66] R. van Jan, Phys. Stat. Sol. 8 (1965) 331.
[67] J.Silcox and P.B.Hirsch, Phil. Mag. 4 (1959) 1356.
[68] M.J.Makin, A.D.Whapham and F.J.Minter, Phil. Mag. 6 (1961) 465.
[69] M.J.Makin, A.D.Whapham and F.J.Minter, Phil. Mag. 7 (1962) 285.
[70] M.J.Makin and S.A.Manthorpe, Phil. Mag. 8 (1963) 1725.
[71] G.P.Scheidler, M.J.Makin, F.J.Minter and W.F.Schilling, Symposium on the Nature of Small Defect Clusters, Harwell, AERE Report R 5269 (1966) p. 405.
[72] M.Rühle, Phys. Stat. Sol. 26 (1968) 661.
[73a] Private communication of F.R.Young Jr.
[73b] T.J.Koppenaal, W.C.T.Yeh and R.M.J.Cotterill, Phil. Mag. 13 (1966) 867.
[74] M.Rühle, F.Häussermann, P.Huber and M.Wilkens, 4th European Reg. Conf. on Electron Microscopy, Rome Vol. I, (1968) p. 377.
[75] M.Rühle, F.Häussermann, M.Rapp and M.Wilkens, to be published.
[76] K.G.McIntyre, Phil. Mag. 15 (1967) 205.
[77] J.C.Crump III, Bull. Am. Phys. Soc. 13 (1968) 462.
[78] A.Bourret and D.Dautreppe, Phys. Stat. Sol. 24 (1967) K174.
[79a] R.O.Simmons and R.W.Balluffi, Phys. Rev. 109 (1958) 1142.
[79b] R.Vook and C.Wert, Phys. Rev. 109 (1958) 1529.
[80] H.Mughrabi and A.Seeger, Phys. Stat. Sol. 19 (1967) 251.
[81] I.G.Greenfield and H.G.F.Wilsdorf, J. Phys. Soc. Japan 18, Suppl. III (1963) 20.
[82] F.Bell, Acta Met. 13 (1965) 363.
[83] A.Bourret and D.Dautreppe, Phys. Stat. Sol. 29 (1968) 283.
[84] E.Ruedl, P.Delavignette and S.Amelinckx, Radiation Damage in Solids (Vienna, 1962) p. 363.
[85] E.Ruedl and S.Amelinckx, J. Phys. Soc. Japan 18, Suppl. III (1963) 195.
[86] C.T.J.Ahlers and R.W.Balluffi, J. Appl. Phys. 38 (1967) 910.
[87] M.J.Attardo and J.M.Galligan, Phys. Rev. 161 (1967) 558.
[88] J.Eades, Ph.D. Thesis, Cambridge, 1967; Phil. Mag. 19 (1969) 47.
[89] D.I.R.Norris, Berkeley Nucl. Labs. Report RD/B/N 1172 (1968); Phil. Mag. 19 (1969) 527.
[90] J.Silcox, Proc. Europ. Reg. Conf. on Electron Microscopy Delft, Vol. I (1960) p. 362.
[91] J.Diehl and W.Schilling, Proc. of the 3rd UN Intern. Conf. PUAE, Vol. IX, (1965) p. 72.
[92] G.Burger, H.Meissner and W.Schilling, Phys. Stat. Sol. 4 (1964) 267.
[93] T.K.Bierlein and B.Mastel, J. Appl. Phys. 33 (1962) 2873.
[94] P.R.B.Higgins and A.C.Roberts, J. less-common Metals 6 (1964) 472.
[95] M.E.Downey and B.L.Eyre, Phil. Mag. 11 (1965) 53.
[96] J.D.Meakin and I.G.Greenfield, Phil. Mag. 11 (1965) 277.
[97] B.Mastel and J.L.Brimhall, Acta Met. 13 (1965) 1109.
[98] P.Rao and G.Thomas, Acta Met. 15 (1967) 1153.
[99] B.L.Eyre and M.E.Downey, Metal. Sci. J. 1 (1967) 5.

[100] J.L.Brimhall, B.Mastel and T.K.Bierlein, Acta Met. 16 (1968) 781.

[101] D.M.Maher and B.L.Eyre, Phil. Mag. 17 (1968) 1.

[102] B.L.Eyre and M.E.Downey, Proc. 6th Intern. Congress for Electron Microscopy, Kyoto, Vol. I (1966) p. 385.

[103] R.P.Tucker and S.M.Ohr, Phil. Mag. 16 (1967) 643.

[104] P.Huber, M.Rühle and M.Wilkens, to be published.

[105] S.M.Ohr, R.P.Tucker and M.S.Wechsler, Trans. Jap. Inst. Met. 9, Suppl. (1968) 187.

[106] K.Lacefield, J.Moteff and J.P.Smith, Phil. Mag. 13 (1966) 1079.

[107] R.C.Rau, J.Moteff and R.L.Ladd, J. Nucl. Mater. 24 (1967) 164.

[108] R.C.Rau, Phil. Mag. 18 (1968) 1079.

[109] R.C.Rau and R.L.Ladd, in press.

[110] J.L.Brimhall and B.Mastel, Phil. Mag. 12 (1965) 419.

[111] J.L.Brimhall and B.Mastel, Phys. Stat. Sol. 27 (1968) K89.

[112] I.M.Bernstein and T.D.Gulden, Symposium on the Nature of Small Defect Clusters, Harwell, AERE Report R 5269 (1966) p. 441.

[113] P.Sigmund, G.P.Scheidler and G.Roth, Proc. Intern. Conf. on Solid State Physics with Accelerators, Brookhaven, BNL 50083 (1967) p. 374.

[114] G.P.Scheidler and G.Roth, Jül. Conf. 2 (Vol. I) 1968, p. 391.

[115] F.Häussermann, M.Rühle, G.P.Scheidler and G.Roth, Phys. Stat. Sol. 32 (1969) K103.

[116a] M.J.Makin, Proc. 4th Europ. Reg. Conf. on Electron Microscopy, Rome, Vol. I (1968) p. 33.

[116b] M.J.Makin, Phil. Mag. 18 (1968) 637.

[117] J.B.Gibson, A.N.Goland, M.Milgram and G.H.Vineyard, Phys. Rev. 120 (1960) 1229.

[118] A.Bourret and G.J.Thomas, Jül. Conf. 2 (Vol. I) 1968, p. 377.

[119] J.A.Venables and G.J.Thomas, this volume.

[120] K.L.Merkle, L.R.Singer and R.K.Hart, J. Appl. Phys. 34 (1963) 2800.

[121] R.V.Hesketh and G.K.Richards, Phil. Mag. 13 (1966) 1069.

[122] M.M.Wilson, Proc. 4th Europ. Reg. Conf. of Electron Microscopy, Rome, Vol. I (1968) p. 365.

[123] D.I.R.Norris, Berkeley Nuclear Laboratories, Report RD/B/N 668 (1966); Symposium on the Nature of Small Defect Clusters, Harwell, AERE Report R 5269 (1966) p. 433.

[124] R.V.Hesketh and G.K.Richards, Proc. Roy. Soc. A 289 (1966) 353.

[125] K.L.Merkle, Phys. Stat. Sol. 18 (1966) 173.

[126] K.L.Merkle, J. Appl. Phys. 38 (1967) 301.

[127] K.L.Merkle, Proc. of the AIME Conference on Radiation Effects (1965) p. 173.

[128] M.Rühle and M.Wilkens, Proc. 6th Intern. Congress for Electron Microscopy, Kyoto, Vol. I (1966) p. 379.

[129] J.Diehl, H.Diepers and B.Hertl, Canad. J. Phys. 46 (1968) 647.

[130] B.Jouffrey, Bull. Soc. Fr. Miner. Cristallogr. 87 (1964) 557.

[131] P.B.Bowden and D.G.Brandon, Phil. Mag. 8 (1963) 935.

[132] D.G.Brandon and P.B.Bowden, J. Nuclear. Mat. 9a (1963) 348.

[133] L.E.Thomas and R.W.Balluffi, Phil. Mag. 15 (1967) 1117.

[134] D.Van Vliet and L.T.Chadderton, Phil. Mag. 16 (1967) 275, 291.

[135] T.S.Noggle, Proc. 6th Intern. Congress for Electron Microscopy, Kyoto, Vol. I (1966) p. 367.

[136] C.B.Beevers and R.S.Nelson, Phil. Mag. 8 (1963) 1189.

[137] J.L.Brimhall and B.Mastel, J. Appl. Phys. 38 (1967) 3027.

[138] T.Schober and R.W.Balluffi, Phys. Stat. Sol. 27 (1968) 195.

[139] K.L.Merkle, private communication.

[140] L.Hendriksen, A.Johansen, J.Koch, H.H.Andersen, T.Leffers and R.M.J.Cotterill, Canad. J. Phys. 46 (1968) 641.

[141] D.I.R.Norris, Berkeley Nucl. Labs. Report RD/B/N 1171 (1968), Phil. Mag. 19 (1969) 653.
[142] J.Diehl, this volume.
[143] W.Frank, M.Rühle and M.Saxlowa, Phys. Stat. Sol. 26 (1968) 671.
[144] M.Rühle, Proc. of the Symp. on Radiation Damage in Reactor Materials, Vienna, 1969, in press.
[145] G.Högberg and H.Nordén, Phys. Stat. Sol. 33 (1969) K71.

# INTERSTITIALS IN F.C.C. METALS

J.A.VENABLES and G.J.THOMAS

*School of Mathematical and Physical Sciences,*
*University of Sussex, Falmer, Brighton, Sussex, UK*

## 1. Introduction

Interstitials are elusive. Despite a large amount of work over the past 15 years, very few properties of interstitials are known with any certainty. In particular, there is a dispute as to whether two different kinds of interstitials exist in f.c.c. metals. The configuration of the interstitial (or interstitials) is not certain: neither is the migration energy. And the mechanism of their production is sufficiently uncertain to hamper quantitative discussion of the damaged state of metals.

One of the reasons for this confusion is undoubtedly that interstitials are more difficult to produce and observe than vacancies. They are not the defects in equilibrium at high temperatures, and in a normal irradiation experiment interstitials and vacancies are produced in equal numbers, with an often complex (and unknown) initial spatial distribution. Also most experiments employ techniques (e.g. resistivity, stored energy, internal friction) which detect both vacancies and interstitials and small clusters indiscriminately. These techniques (especially resistivity) are employed because they have high accuracy and sensitivity, but a qualitative check on the models proposed on the basis of such experiments is often lacking.

A typical resistivity experiment is as follows. A well annealed sample is irradiated at low temperature with protons, deuterons, neutrons or perhaps, most satisfactorily, with electrons of a few MeV energy. A change in resistivity $\Delta\rho$ is measured due to the irradiation, and this may be correlated with damage theory. After irradiation the specimen is annealed at successively higher temperatures and the resistivity recovers to the initial value in more or less well-defined stages. These stages have been characterised I–V in increasing order of temperature. By use of fairly detailed models of what is happening, activation energies can be measured for each of the stages. The hope is then that each activation energy is characteristic of a certain defect process, and the theoretical problem is to assign the correct defect process to each stage.

Interstitials have been assigned to both stage I ($\lesssim 60°$K in Cu, Ag, Al, Pt...) and to stage III ($\lesssim 0°$C in Cu, Ag, Au...). In the 1-interstitial model [1] free interstitial migration occurs at the high temperature end of stage I, the so-called stage $I_E$. This interstitial is the only stable interstitial and is presumed to have the split $\langle 100 \rangle$ configuration. In the 2-interstitial model [2] the stable interstitial has this same configuration but is assigned to stage III. The migration of another (metastable) interstitial is assigned to stage I; this interstitial is thought to be the crowdion, or split $\langle 110 \rangle$ interstitial. The possibility that the crowdion may convert into the stable $\langle 100 \rangle$ interstitial [3] gives an added complexity to an already more complicated model. Undoubtedly, the 1-interstitial model is to be preferred on the grounds of simplicity. But because of several apparently conflicting experimental results, and also possibly because of the complexity of the 2-interstitial model, this model has been difficult to disprove conclusively.

In this paper we review experiments which are different in one or two ways from the normal irradiation experiments. The first difference in the experiments considered is that the detection technique used should be specific to interstitials. The second difference is that the irradiation should produce only interstitials and no vacancies. The satisfaction of both these conditions should provide ideal experiments for testing theories of the properties of interstitials. In the following sections we describe experiments which have made some progress towards this goal and discuss how they have influenced our ideas about interstitials in f.c.c. metals.


## 2. Techniques for detecting interstitials

So far there is no technique available which, it is generally agreed, specifically detects isolated interstitials in metals. Consequently, no information exists on the configuration of the interstitial. In this respect research in metals is far behind semiconductors and insulators where spectroscopic and E.P.R. techniques can identify a specific defect configuration non-destructively. Even in silicon, using these superior techniques, the Si interstitial has never been seen [4]. Indeed, it has been demonstrated fairly convincingly that the Si interstitial moves below 4°K, and ends by displacing an impurity into an interstitial position [5]. So it is not quite certain that isolated interstitials are ever stable, though the arguments for a stage I interstitial in Cu, Ag, Al and Pt seem convincing. In Au, however, it may well be that isolated interstitials migrate at the lowest temperatures [6].

In metals most of these specific detection techniques see where the interstitial *was*. In section 4 we discuss the observation of interstitial clusters, and their formation from isolated interstitials. In section 5 experiments concerning the absorption of interstitials by vacancies and vacancy clusters are reviewed. In section 6 we describe experiments which use low energy ion bombardment to produce interstitials, but use non-specific techniques such as resistivity, and internal friction to detect them. And in section 7 we mention Field Ion Microscopy and channelling, either of which may provide the best hope of studying interstitials in the future. Isolated interstitials have already been claimed to have been seen using the FIM [7,59,60], and it remains to be seen whether what has been observed can be unambiguously identified. If it can, then there is little doubt that this technique, the most direct of all direct observation techniques, will solve the problems of interstitial atoms which have been with us for more than 15 years. But, firstly, in section 3, we examine techniques which attempt to produce only isolated interstitial atoms.

## 3. Techniques for producing pure interstitial damage

To study interstitials by themselves, ideally one would have techniques for producing interstitials only, i.e. for producing pure interstitial damage. To date, this has been attempted in two different ways, by low energy ion bombardment and by channelling.

### 3.1. *Low energy ion bombardment*

In a low energy ion bombardment experiment, the aim is to produce the damage event at the surface of the material. The interstitial is then thought to be produced by means of a focussed replacement collision sequence (r.c.s.) and the vacancy and the ion initiating the damage are left at the surface. If the range of the r.c.s. is long then experiments can be done with these interstitials which are not completely dominated by the proximity of the surface. In practice this means that experiments with high atomic number metals are likely to be more successful than with metals of low atomic number; but, since r.c.s. ranges are $\approx 100$ Å, the experiments must be done on fairly thin films in any case.

Whether or not pure interstitial damage is obtained depends on the combination of ion and target material, on the ion energy, and on the cleanliness of the surface. The best combination would undoubtedly be a bombardment with ions of the same material as the target, at an energy just above threshold for producing an r.c.s., in a degassed U.H.V. system. But such experiments are only in the planning stage, and in practice there are several technical difficulties, so that usually a compromise has had to be made. Just above threshold the r.c.s. range may be small, and also the available ion current usually falls off dramatically at these low energies. Secondly, *in situ* experiments in electron microscopes cannot be done under these conditions using present-day techniques. The compromise has, so far, been *either* to use slightly higher energy (target) metal ions and transfer to an electron microscope if required [8], *or* to use gas ions which can be produced *in situ* [9,10]. In no case yet have the experiments been done in a U.H.V. system.

For the damage event to occur at the surface the range of the ions must be about one atomic distance. Extrapolation of the ranges of high energy ions to lower energies suggests that this may well be the case for heavy ions of similar mass to the target atoms for energies about 100 eV. For example, 500 eV Xe atoms in W have a mean "range" [11] of $\approx 5$ Å, and 1% of the ions travel 15 Å in a $\langle 100 \rangle$ direction. The "range" of 500 eV $Au^+$ ions in Au should be similar. However, it is in just this low energy range ($\approx 100$ eV) that the sticking coefficient of gas ions increases dramatically [12]. So, at the lowest energies it is still possible (see section 4) that some of the experiments which have been done were influenced by the embedded gas ions. It would be very interesting to know if the threshold for producing interstitials coincides with this rise in sticking coefficient or if the two phenomena are unrelated.

Some of the experiments with low energy gas ions (see section 5) and the experiments with low energy (target) metal ions are not open to this objection. However, only at the very lowest energies are the vacancies produced truly at the surface and again these may have an effect (section 4), especially in stabilizing contamination knocked in from the surface. But in the experiments which measure the properties of interstitials several hundred Ångstrøms below the surface (section 5.2), the exact processes going on in these first few layers at the surface can hardly be important.

The interstitial is thought to be deposited at the end of the range of a replacement collision sequence [13]. This range has been discussed extensively in theory [14–16], but has been deduced from experiment only indirectly from sputtering experiments [17–19], and in one set of experiments to be discussed in section 4 [19–21]. There is a need for measuring this r.c.s. range and its dependence on material, temperature and energy. In particular, the lack of this knowledge hampers the discussion of the initial damaged state of a metal after all types of irradiation.

Theoretically [16], the range of a "simple" r.c.s. depends on the focussing energy $E_f^{hkl}$ for focussing along $\langle hkl \rangle$, the final energy at which replacement occurs, $E_r$, the rate of loss of energy $-dE/dx$ (assumed equal to $\alpha E$), and the energy $E$. Then, the range is approximately given by $R = (1/\alpha) \ln (E_0/E_r)$ for $E_0 < E_f$, where $E_0$ is the initial energy. Assuming $\alpha$ is largely determined by lattice vibrations, Nelson et al. [15] have estimated the ranges as a function of temperature. Their calculations for Au are shown in fig. 1. The range determining factor $(1/\alpha)$ is proportional to the mean square displacement of the target atoms (mass $m$) and hence to $(\theta_D^2 m/T)$ at high temperatures and $(m\theta_D)$ at low temperatures, where $\theta_D$ is the Debye temperature, and is weakly dependant on $E_f^{hkl}$. The focussing energy $E_f^{hkl}$ is greatest for $\langle 110 \rangle$ close packed rows and depends on the constants in the assumed (Born-Mayer) potential, such that it is largest for atoms with large ion cores. On this basis, one can calculate that the maximum ranges in Cu and Al at low temperature might be expected to be smaller than those for Au by factors of about 3 and $> 6$, respectively. These factors have not been determined experimentally.

The efficiency with which a r.c.s. is produced has been considered by Leibfried [14]. He obtained the probability $p$ of focussing in a given direction $\langle hkl \rangle$ as

$$p \approx (b/D_{hkl}) \ln (E_f^{hkl}/E_0),$$

where $D_{hkl}$ is the collision chain spacing and $b$ is the constant in the Born-Mayer potential $A\,e^{-r/b}$. For a (100) surface of a crystal which has 4 possible $\langle 110 \rangle$ simple focussing directions the probability of an ion forming an r.c.s. after hitting an atom in the first and second layers in the surface is of order $8p$. For $E_0 \approx \frac{1}{2}E_f^{hkl} \approx 150$ eV

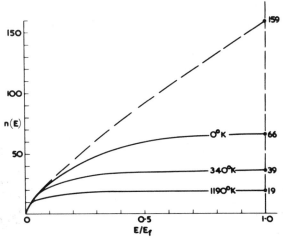

Fig. 1. The number of collisions, $n(E)$ made by a replacement collision sequence as a function of temperature for Au [15]. [Courtesy of the authors and Philosophical Magazine].

and $(b/D_{110}) \approx \frac{1}{15}$, which may be suitable values for Au [16], the probability of forming an r.c.s. would be in the region of 0.1. Low energy ion bombardment experiments [9,22] seem to indicate values as high as this.

Thus, low energy ion bombardment is an efficient way, and at present the only way, of producing relatively pure interstitial damage. Because of this, all experiments using this technique are reviewed in sections 4, 5 and 6.

### 3.2. Channelling

Channelling may, in future, be used to produce pure interstitial damage. For example, if a 40 keV $Au^+$ channels in Au it may come to rest in the channel some 4000 Å below the surface [23]. In this case the only damage produced is the interstitial. However, a 40 keV $Au^+$ which was not channelled would produce roughly 400 Frenkel pairs and it is obvious that very perfect channelling is required to reduce this number to zero. It is also not clear theoretically if a channelled ion will come to rest without producing displacements near the end of its track, especially in the case of identical channelled and lattice atoms [56]. Experimentally, it is observed that most channelled ions meet a violent end. For instance, Schober and Balluffi [24] showed (for a room-temperature irradiation) there was an almost 1—1 correspondence between channelled ions and observable defects in the electron microscope.

Some interesting results have been reported by Davies et al. [25]. With several different species of ions in tungsten, a "supertail" is observed which has been shown convincingly [26] to be due to interstitial diffusion of the ions. In the latest work the "supertail" contains about 10% of the embedded ions at 30°K. If, as assumed, these are ions which have been deposited in the channel without displacements then the technique shows promise as an efficient means of producing pure interstitial damage. The fact that this "supertail" has not been observed in f.c.c. metals [23,25] is strong evidence that interstitials in f.c.c. metals (both self- and impurity-interstitials) diffuse by an interstitial mechanism. Interstitialcy migration cannot be detected by these radio-tracer methods.

The advantage of producing interstitials by channelling is firstly that interstitials can be produced at greater depths than by low energy ion bombardment and that the experiments are less sensitive to surface contamination. Secondly, the various techniques which have been used in conjunction with channelling, such as Rutherford scattering of protons, or p—x reactions have great sensitivity and may be made specific to atoms in specific positions [27]. By experiments of this kind we may well be able to determine the configuration of the interstitial as well as its migration energy.

However, at the present, the use of channelling combined with a non-specific detection technique such as resistivity [28] cannot be used to deduce interstitial properties, such as the nature of stage III. Only once we are sure that no other defects besides interstitials are produced will such experiments throw any new light on these problems.

## 4. Observation of interstitial clusters in the electron microscope

Brandon and Bowden [29] were the first to observe interstitial clusters in the transmission electron microscope after low energy ion bombardment. They showed that Au, Cu, Ni and Pt [30] bombarded with 100 eV $Ar^+$ ions to a dose of about $10^{16} - 10^{17}$ ions $cm^{-2}$ contained defect clusters. These clusters were shown to be interstitial in character and very near to the bombarded surface, using the contrast calculations for small inclusions of Ashby and Brown [31]. They also showed that the clusters were mostly dislocation loops with a Burgers vector in the plane of the foil, and that some of them were glissile. On these grounds they could show definitely that the loops were composed of self-interstitials and *not* of argon, though they could have been nucleated by injected argon.

Bowden and Brandon also showed that there was a transition in the appearance of these loops as the bombardment temperature was varied between −30°C to +30°C in Au and Cu, namely, in the region of stage III. At the lower end of this range the loops formed right up to the edge of a tapered specimen but at the higher end of the loops only formed in the thicker parts of the specimen. Thus the width of this "denuded zone" was temperature dependent and as seen in fig. 2, surprisingly well defined. The conclusion that this implied that the stage III defect is an interstitial [29] was a natural one, though as they pointed out, this conclusion depends on how the clusters are nucleated. If the nucleation is homogeneous then stage III interstitials are necessarily indicated, but if surface contamination or interstitial trapping by injected argon is involved, the interstitials themselves could be diffusing fast throughout this temperature range around 0°C.

Fig. 2. Low energy ion damage in Cu and the "denuded zone" at the edge of the foil. The specimen was given a dose of 1.5 $\times 10^{17}$ 100 eV Ar$^+$ ions cm$^{-2}$ at 27°C. Dark field micrograph, $g$ = 220 [29]. Bar length is 1000 Å. [Courtesy of P.B.Bowden and J. Nucl. Mat.].

In Pt [30] they showed that a denuded zone was not formed in the same temperature range. Although previous authors have suggested that stage III in Pt is about 0°C [32,33], vacancy motion is at a much higher temperature [33]. At this conference, Schilling [57] suggested that this 0°C stage had been wrongly assigned, and that stage III was between 500–700°K. If this is accepted, the discrepancy between the ion bombardment experiments on Pt and the other metals disappears.

Jouffrey and Castaing [34] observed similar effects in Au bombarded with 4 keV Ar$^+$ ions. On warming these samples to 250°C the loops disappeared and gas bubbles formed. Apart from the fact that gas is obviously embedded in the sample in this case, the damage appeared very similar to the lower energy bombardments [29].

Ogilvie, Saunders and Thomson [35] observed similar clusters after irradiation in a plasma system to very high doses ($\approx 10^{20}$ ions cm$^{-2}$). They were able to measure the threshold for the production of this damage by He, Ne, Ar and Xe ions. The values for Ne, Ar and Xe bombardments gave consistent threshold values of energy transferred of 21.6 ± 1.3, 25 ± 8 and 19.7 ± 1 eV respectively, though the values for He$^+$ was anomalously low. If we assume that in a plasma system double charged ions are responsible for the damage the threshold values of about 40 eV compare very well with bulk values of 33–36 eV after electron-irradiation [43]. In more recent work they [58] bombarded crystals of different orientations and found different threshold energies which indicated that the interstitials were produced by ⟨110⟩ focussed replacement sequences as described in section 2. Ogilvie et al. [35] also showed that the interstitial clusters annealed at temperatures which depended on the bombarding gas. The temperature was greatest after He$^+$ bombardment ($>$ 400°C) and least after Ar$^+$ and Xe$^+$ bombardment (250–280°C), which suggested that at least the He$^+$ ions and maybe the other also penetrated the surface.

Recently, however, Thomas and Balluffi have bombarded Au with low energy Au$^+$ ions. They have shown that almost no interstitial clusters are formed in the temperature range −30°C to 100°C when special precautions are taken to keep the surface clean. On the other hand when surface contamination is present, interstitial clusters are formed, and they can be formed up to at least 100°C. As the temperature is lowered below −30°C to −90°C, more clusters form but their density was still below that in the Ar$^+$ bombardments. They, however, still observed the "denuded zone" with Ar$^+$ ions.

As Thomas and Balluffi had independent evidence that interstitials are still produced after Au$^+$ bombardment, this work shows that the interstitial clusters are nucleated heterogeneously, and that the interstitial clusters have no necessary connection with the problem of the assignment of stage III. After Ar$^+$ ion bombardment, however, the temperature dependence of the "denuded zone" is very marked and fairly reproducible [8,9,29]. The profile of this denuded zone has been calculated on a homogeneous nucleation model by Venables and Balluffi [9] but because of the Au$^+$ bombardment results this model is obviously incorrect. It is quite possible that the clusters are mechanically unstable in the tapered foil near the edge of the specimen [8], but so far a satisfactory explanation of why this effect should be temperature dependent in just this range around 0°C has not been given.

Because these interstitial clusters are nucleated heterogeneously, the fascinating results of Diehl and Diepers [19,20,21] should also not be used to imply anything about interstitial migration. They may very well, however, tell us a great deal about interstitial production. Diehl and Diepers used stereo-electron microscopy to observe the depth distribution of interstitial clusters in Au and Cu produced by 1 and 5 keV Ar$^+$ bombardment. In Cu and Au foils with a (100) orientation they observed a single peak in the depth distribution. However, in Cu foils with a (110) orientation two distinct peaks were observed. Almost the only way to explain these two peaks is to say that the interstitial clusters are formed near the end of the focussed replacement sequence range and that there are two different types of ⟨110⟩ sequences produced in a (110) foil: one normal to the surface and one at 60° to it. The two peaks will then be separated in depth by a factor of two, as observed.

So far the distributions have been measured at 5 keV in Cu and Au (100) at temperatures ≲ 130°K and at 300°K and Cu (110) at ≲ 130°K at both 1 and 5 keV. These results are shown in fig. 3. The distributions all have the same half-width, with the possible exception of Au (100) at 300°K. The peak positions have to be corrected for the mean penetration of the argon ions and a surface contamination layer [20] before the range of the ⟨110⟩ collision sequences can be evaluated.

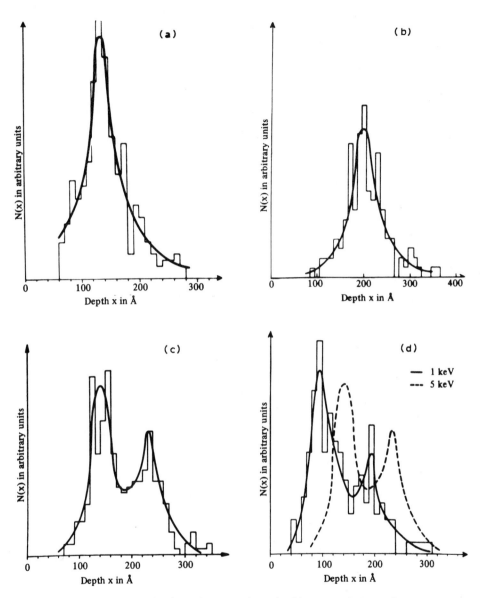

Fig. 3. Depth distributions of $Ar^+$ ion damage as determined by stereo-electron microscopy [21].

a) (100) Cu, $1.5 \times 10^{15}$ 5 keV $Ar^+$ ions $cm^{-2}$ at room temperature.
b) (100) Au, $0.5 \times 10^{15}$ 5 keV $Ar^+$ ions $cm^{-2}$ at $\lesssim 130°K$.
c) {110} Cu, $1.6 \times 10^{15}$ 5 keV $Ar^+$ ions $cm^{-2}$ at $\lesssim 130°K$.
d) {110} Cu, $3 \times 10^{15}$ 1 keV $Ar^+$ ions $cm^{-2}$ at $\lesssim 130°K$.
    Dashed curve is identical with fig. 3c.

When this is done, these ranges are given as 245, 210 and 205 Å in Cu at $\lesssim 130°$K using the (100) and 2 (110) peaks observed; 127 Å in Cu (100) at 300°K, and 240 and 206 Å in Au (100) at $\lesssim 130°$K and 300°K respectively.

At energies of 1 and 5 keV some of the $Ar^+$ ions will almost certainly channel in (100) and (110) foils to depths greater than the ranges measured in Diehl and Diepers' experiments [21]. Therefore if injected argon or impurities nucleated the clusters they will be formed near to the point where the interstitials are deposited, provided that there is enough injected argon, or impurities, present and that the binding energies involved are high enough. If this is the case, nothing can be said from these experiments about the migration energy of interstitials. The condition that the observed depth distribution should not be broadened because of interstitial migration is not very restrictive: for the distributions of fig. 3, $2 \times 10^{-4}$ atom fraction of trapping sites would be sufficient. Depending on how one extrapolates the higher energy data of Kornelsen et al. [11], the $Ar^+$ ion concentration in Au after a 5 keV bombardment to a dose of $3 \times 10^{15}$ ions $cm^{-2}$ could be as large as this down to depths of between 200 and 1500 Å.

Two other points are worth mentioning. Firstly, Thomas and Balluffi [38] have very recently bombarded Au with $Au^+$ ions of energies above 3 keV. In all cases they observed vacancy clusters up to doses of $3 \times 10^{14}$ ions $cm^{-2}$. They did not observe interstitial clusters. As the energy was reduced the vacancy clusters became smaller and eventually invisible. Secondly, unlike the clusters observed by Diehl and Diepers, those observed in the very low energy ion irradiations [29,9,22] ($\approx 100$ eV) all seem to have the same black-white contrast under dynamical conditions, which implies [39] that they are all within the first 0.3 of an extinction distance of the surface (or about 70 Å for Au). The present authors have re-checked that this is so in 300 eV $Xe^+$ ion bombardments of Au, using both contrast theory and also stereomicroscopy. These results imply that in the low energy case interstitials are generated at the end of a collision sequence and then migrate nearer to the surface before forming the clusters.

In summary, we feel that the observations of interstitial clusters have given valuable information about the threshold energy for producing focussed replacement sequences and interesting results about the length of these sequences. Deductions about the migration energy of interstitials have, however, been misleading, and the exact mechanism for the formation of the clusters in gas-ion bombarded foils remains unclear.

## 5. Observations of the effects of interstitials on quenched-in vacancies

We consider two types of experiment which give specific information about interstitials, using quenched-in vacancies. The first observes the difference in a property (e.g. resistivity) between annealed and pre-quenched materials after irradiation. The second type observes the effect on quenched-in vacancy clusters in the electron microscope during and after irradiation. In both cases the extra vacancies are sinks for interstitials, and low temperatures bombardment and annealing experiments have been used to investigate interstitial migration.

## 5.1. Resistivity experiments on irradiated quenched metals

Swanson and Piercy [40] n-irradiated quenched Au and Al, and investigated the resistivity recovery in stage I. They found enhancement of recovery at the end of stage I for Al and (to a lesser extent) throughout stage I for Au. Bauer and Sosin [41] e-irradiated quenched Au and Bauer and Goeppinger [42] also irradiated quenched Pt. In the case of Pt the data is particularly convincing that the recovery is enhanced at the end of stage I in the quenched samples and they ascribe this to free interstitial migration in stage $I_E$ at about 28°K. This data is shown in fig. 4. In the case of Au the recovery in stage I is as usual much less than in Pt, but also no significant differences occur on annealing between annealed and pre-quenched

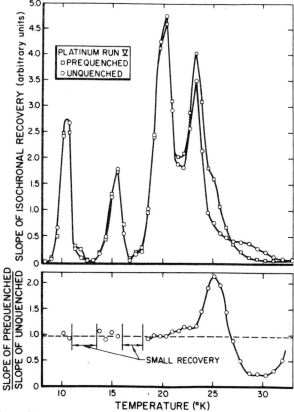

Fig. 4. Comparison of the annealing spectrum observed after electron-irradiation of unquenched and prequenched platinum samples. The recovery in the prequenched sample is enhanced in the region of stage $I_E$ at around 25°–28°K [42]. [Courtesy of W.Bauer and Phys. Rev.].

samples. This experiment seems to have two interpretations. Either interstitials are immobile up to stage III, as the authors [41] then suggested, or the interstitials are mobile during irradiation at $13°$K. In the latter case, it might well be that the only major difference between the two samples would be in the damage rate. Decreases in the damage rate has been measured in Pt at $90°$K [44] and decreases of up to a factor of 20 have been found in pre-quenched samples. Unfortunately the damage rate in quenched Au has not yet been measured accurately at low temperature. If interstitials are still mobile below stage I the damage rate should be much reduced. Even in unquenched samples it is unaccountably low [43,45], and Corbett [6] has suggested that this is because the interstitial in Au is mobile throughout stage I.

### 5.2. Electron-microscope observations on quenched vacancy clusters

Visible vacancy clusters can be produced by quenching and annealing, especially in Au and Al. These clusters act as sinks for interstitials, and have been shown to disappear during irradiation. Almost all the work has been done on gold, where the vacancy tetrahedra are very convenient to observe, and the effects of the bombardment are readily measurable. Two irradiation experiments with high energy particles established that tetrahedra disappear during bombardment. Cotterill and Jones [46] showed that irradiation with $10^{13}$ 3 MeV $\alpha$-particles cm$^{-2}$ at about $50°$C caused almost all of the tetrahedra present to disappear. As vacancies and interstitials are mobile at this temperature (on any model so far proposed), no information was obtained about interstitial mobility. However, it was thought that interstitials arrived primarily by diffusion rather than by defocussing of r.c.s. The tetrahedra collapsed rather abruptly and did not shrink visibly before collapse. Howe, McGurn and Gilbert [47]) bombarded similar foils with 100 keV O$^-$ ions *in situ* in an electron microscope. Moreover, they were able to do this at temperatures $\lesssim 20°$K. The vacancy tetrahedra were still removed at this low tempersture, as shown in the sequence of fig. 5. On warming the bombarded foils no changes in the appearance of the damage took place and the tetrahedra did not shrink further. Between $200°$K and $295°$K however, *some* tetrahedra did either disappear, collapse or shrink. This was the only indication of any annealing processes taking place below $300°$K.

Howe et al. [47] thought that the removal of the tetrahedra at $20°$K could be due to the direct defocussing of r.c.s. However, this leads to an estimate of the r.c.s. range of $\approx 2000$ Å which is about 10 times longer than measured by other techniques [17,21]. This, combined with the absence of any pronounced annealing, might suggest that the interstitial is already mobile at $20°$K.

This work was followed by three sets of experiments on low energy ion bombardment of quenched gold films [9,8,22]. Venables and Balluffi [9] performed 200 eV Ar$^+$ ion irradiations *in situ* in an electron microscope. They reported that tetrahedra disappeared after irradiation at room temperature but that after low temperature bombardment (down to $140°$K) most of the tetrahedra remained in the foil. Moreover, they reported that tetrahedra disappeared on warming through a narrow range of temperature around $0°$C. This last key observation, combined

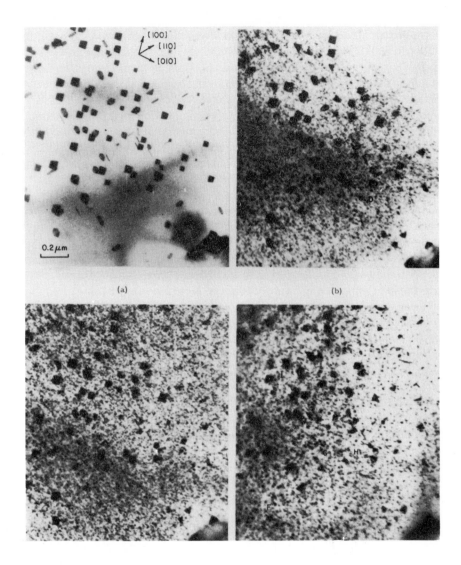

Fig. 5. The removal of vacancy tetrahedra in gold after irradiation with 100 keV O⁻ ions below 20°K in an electron microscope [47].
a) Before irradiation.
b) Same area after 1.8 × 10¹³ O⁻ ions cm⁻². At A, B and C the tetrahedra are in various stages of collapse. At D and E they have been annihilated.
c) Further collapse and annihilation after 2.2 × 10¹³ ions cm⁻².
d) After warming to room temperature and recooling to 200°K. Further collapse and annihilation has occurred in regions F to I. [Courtesy of L.M.Howe and Acta Met.].

with the "denuded zone" observations discussed in section 4, led them to the conclusion that a stage III interstitial was responsible for both phenomena.

Thomas and Balluffi [8] irradiated Au foils containing tetrahedra with 270 eV $Au^+$ ions and observed the foils subsequently in the electron microscope. In these experiments they showed that many of the tetrahedra really shrink after bombardment and that the loss of vacancies this shrinkage represents was independent of bombardment temperature between 183°K and 373°K. However, the specimens bombarded at 183°K were only observed at room temperature. They reported that there were no effects of annealing on the tetrahedra which had been bombarded at 223°K and transferred into a cold stage in the microscope. Two runs with 180 eV $A^+$ ions at 223°K gave the same results. They therefore felt that the results of Venables and Balluffi should be disregarded and that all their own observations could be explained by interstitials which were very mobile at 183°K. Some of their observations are shown in figs. 6 and 7, and the proportion of vacancies annihilated as a function of foil thickness is shown in fig. 8.

The present authors [22] have been repeating the previous work [9] using a superior technique. Foils of Au containing tetrahedra have been bombarded *in situ* in the liquid helium stage with a low energy r.f. gas ion source [48]. Initially stereo-pairs of the tetrahedra were taken. Tilts of 5 to 10° enabled us to position the tetrahedra in depth with an error which was much less than the tetrahedra size of between 200–500 Å. Bombardments were made with $Xe^+$, $Ar^+$ or $Ne^+$ ions of a few hundred volts energy (in most cases 300 eV $Xe^+$) to doses of $3 \times 10^{16}$ ions $cm^{-2}$, the same as Thomas and Balluffi [8]. Pictures taken after irradiation and subsequent annealing were then compared with the initial stereo-pair. The depth distributions of the change of the edge length of the tetrahedra, $\Delta L$, were obtained for various bombardment and annealing treatments. Some of these distributions are shown in fig. 9. It can be seen from fig. 9(a) and (c) that the depth distribution of $\Delta L/L_0$, where $L_0$ is the mean edge length of the tetrahedra, is similar after bombardments at 77°K and 283°K. The 77°K histogram shows that tetrahedra can be affected over 1000 Å below the bombarded surface. Unless the r.c.s. range is very long, as mentioned before, the interstitials must have arrived by diffusion at this temperature. Further experiments are now in progress to extend these measurements to lower temperatures, and we should be able to see if interstitials in Au are still mobile at 10°K. In any case, this work extends and generally supports the work of Thomas and Balluffi [8], that interstitials in Au are mobile below stage III, and contradicts the major conclusions of Venables and Balluffi [9].

However, we *do* see pronounced changes to the tetrahedra on warming [22]. An example of a bombardment at 77°K followed by an anneal to 210°K is shown in fig. 10. After bombardment only the tetrahedra near the bombarded surface appear to be affected in this particular case, and some of these are "moth eaten". Annealing to about 200°K produces many more "moth eaten" tetrahedra and a wide variety of final tetrahedra configurations. In fig. 10(c) some of these are particularly striking and clear and the change in $\Delta L/L_0$ is plotted for another 77°K specimen in

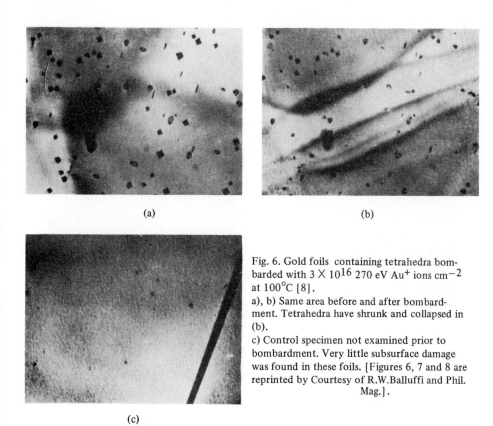

(a)

(b)

(c)

Fig. 6. Gold foils containing tetrahedra bombarded with $3 \times 10^{16}$ 270 eV Au$^+$ ions cm$^{-2}$ at 100°C [8].
a), b) Same area before and after bombardment. Tetrahedra have shrunk and collapsed in (b).
c) Control specimen not examined prior to bombardment. Very little subsurface damage was found in these foils. [Figures 6, 7 and 8 are reprinted by Courtesy of R.W.Balluffi and Phil. Mag.].

fig. 9(d). It is because it is difficult to estimate the "$\Delta L$" for these tetrahedra that the fraction of tetrahedra affected, $p_a$, is also plotted in fig. 9. The effects on warming seem to take place at lower temperatures than those reported by Venables and Balluffi [9], in the same range as Howe et al. [47], and at or below the lowest temperatures investigated by Thomas and Balluffi [8]. The effects are not caused by dislocation motion as has been suggested [8], and are not confined to the large tetrahedra of fig. 10. Tetrahedra in specimens bombarded at 250°K and 283°K (figs. 9(b) and (c)) showed no changes in warming to room temperature. Thus we feel sure the warming results previously reported [9] were real, though the reported temperature range was too high and too precisely specified. In particular the combination of the annealing effects on the tetrahedra and the "denuded zone" of damage now looks much less convincing evidence for a stage III interstitial.

We feel there may be a common thread which explains most of these apparently conflicting observations with vacancy tetrahedra. The removal of tetrahedra is a two-stage process. The interstitial must first arrive at the tetrahedron (by diffusion),

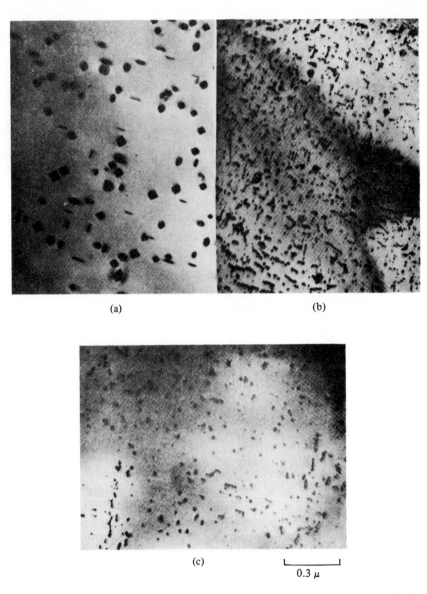

(a)     (b)

(c)

0.3 μ

Fig. 7. Foils bombarded at −30°C to same doses as fig. 6 [8]. (a), (b) Before and after bombardment. (c) Control specimen. In (b) and (c) the subsurface damage is very sparse, and from the
contrast is estimated to be within 100 Å of the surface.

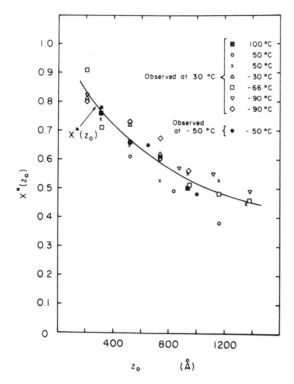

Fig. 8. Fraction of vacancies lost X* ($z_0$) from all tetrahedra throughout foil of thickness $z_0$. The data shown indicates that X* ($z_0$) was independent of temperature in the range $-50°C$ to $100°C$ and that if changes occurred on warming the samples bombarded at $-90°C$ they must have occurred between $-90°C$ and $-50°C$.

and the probability is high that it will arrive at one of the four stacking fault faces. In order for the tetrahedron to *shrink as a tetrahedron* [8] the interstitial must be able to move across the face to where the tretrahedron's vacancy-like regions are. Such a region might well be a ledge-line [49], as absorption of interstitials there would allow the stacking fault to shrink. Alternatively, if there are no ledge lines initially the interstitial would have to migrate to an edge or a corner and initiate such a line.

If interstitials are not mobile across the face of the tetrahedron, or if many interstitials arrive simultaneously, so that interstitial cluster formation is possible, the tetrahedron may not be able to shrink uniformly. In this case the vacancy-like region would be along the edges and the interstitials and/or small clusters would be randomly distributed across the four faces of the tetrahedron. If this situation persisted till large numbers of interstitials had arrived, the configuration would eventually become mechanically unstable and the tetrahedron would collapse catas-

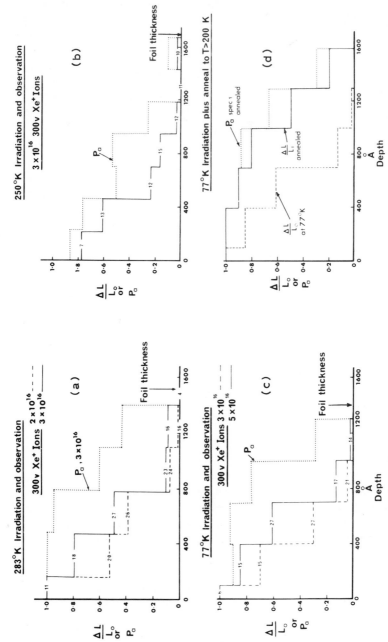

Fig. 9. Depth distributions of the fractional change in edge length of tetrahedra, $\Delta L/L_0$, and the proportion of tetrahedra affected, $p_a$, after 300 eV Xe$^+$ ion bombardment at various temperatures [22]. The numbers in the histograms are the number of tetrahedra measured.
a) 283 K irradiation and observation.
b) 250 K irradiation and observation. In a) and b) no changes were observed in these distributions on warming to room temperature.
c) 77 K irradiation and observation.
d) 77 K irradiation plus anneal to $T > 200$ K.

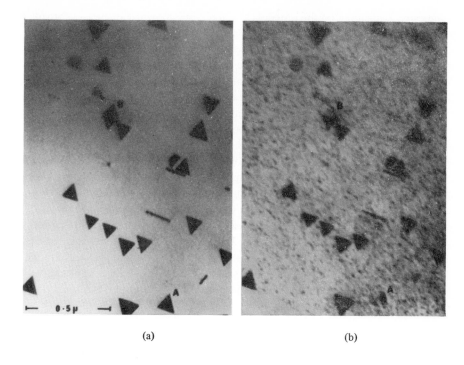

(a)                                          (b)

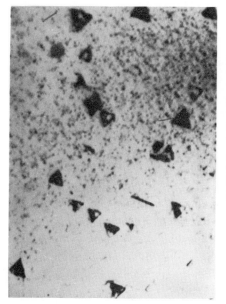

(c)

Fig. 10. An example of the effect of annealing
tetrahedra subjected to low energy ion bombardment at low temperatures [22].
a) One of the stereo-pair taken before irradiation.
b) After $3 \times 10^{16}$ 300 eV $Xe^+$ ions $cm^{-2}$ at
$77^\circ K$, observed at $77^\circ K$. The affected tetrahedra
A and B are close to the bombarded surface.
c) After annealing to $210^\circ K$. Many more tetrahedra are affected. Most of the tetrahedra do
not shrink, but appear "moth-eaten".

trophically. Depending on the numbers of interstitials absorbed at the time of collapse, the resulting defect could be either a smaller Frank loop, a perfect vacancy loop, a "moth-eaten" tetrahedron, or even, conceivably, an interstitial type defect. We feel that we have observed several of these possibilities [22].

We also feel that this model can account for many of the apparent discrepancies. Cotterill and Jones [46] observed sudden collapse of tetrahedra which had preserved their shape up to the last moment, while Thomas and Balluffi [8] observed mostly uniform tetrahedron shrinkage (above 223°K). In α-irradiation [46] many interstitials would arrive almost simultaneously from nearby displacement spikes and make interstitial cluster formation probable on the faces of the tetrahedron. Thus these tetrahedra would tend to collapse after a certain number of interstitials had arrived, whereas in low energy ion bombardment they arrive singly, and the tetrahedra can shrink, at least at temperatures $\gtrsim 223$°K. As mentioned above, we have observed that tetrahedra do not anneal on warming in bombardments carried out at above 250°K. In bombardments at 77°K, the tetrahedra can eventually be eliminated to a considerable depth by a sufficiently long bombardment. On annealing many more of the tetrahedra are affected and have the "moth-eaten" appearance shown in fig. 10. Typically, this happens at around 200°K, and in this respect our results parallel those of Howe et al. [47].

## 6. Observations of effects of low energy ion bombardment using non-specific detection techniques

### 6.1. Resistivity

Bowden [36] has observed the resistivity of thin Au foils during and after 200 eV $Ar^+$ ion bombardment. The latter part of the bombardment shows a linear rise which is due primarily to sputtering. When the bombardment stops, the resistance decreases in a long decay which extends for many times the bombardment time. These curves have been repeated by Venables [37] and are remarkably insensitive to bombardment temperature in the range −90°C to about 120°C. The curves do not show any marked changes in the stage III region, and it is possible that they are caused by gas diffusing out of the surface layers [37], in a manner similar to the desorption spectra obtained by Kornelson [12]. In any case, it is apparent from these experiments that gas ion bombardment produces a masking effect on the resistivity which makes the experiment unsuitable for detecting interstitials. However, assuming the total size of the decay at the lowest temperature (180°K) is due to the migration of single interstitials, we can put an upper limit to the time interstitials remain as singles in the foil. Thus, if the decay at 180°K is $\approx 1.4 \times 10^{-3}$ for a beam of $8 \times 10^{13}$ ions/cm$^2$, this lifetime is less than 1.5 sec, implying an activation energy of less than 0.3 eV. (The efficiency of interstitial production was estimated from tetrahedra removal experiments, and we assumed a reasonable resistivity of 1.5 $\mu\Omega$ cm/ at % interstitials).

Further resistivity work is in progress using low energy $Au^+$ ions to bombard Au thin films [50]. This experiment should allow us to see whether low energy ion bombardment produces a stage III defect. If it apparently does not, we shall be able to set very stringent limits on the proportion of such defects produced. Also we shall be able to extend these measurements to at least $10°K$ in an attempt to see whether interstitials in gold have even been slowed down sufficiently to be observed!

## 6.2. *Internal friction*

Loebach, Bowden and Birnbaum [10] have observed internal friction in Au bombarded with 300 eV $Ar^+$ ions between 80 and $373°K$. They view the internal friction changes as arising from both dislocation pinning from migrating interstitials and dislocation loop production close to the surface. Because the latter dominates at low temperatures it is difficult to use this data as definite evidence that the interstitials don't move at $80°K$. However, Buckley [51] has apparently shown, using 90 eV $Ar^+$ ions and a very sensitive internal friction detection technique, that there are two pinning stages, one at $40°K$ and another at $240°K$. In view of the correspondence of these temperatures to stage I and stage III, respectively, and the extreme sensitivity of internal friction techniques [52] it is clear this experiment should be repeated, using the lowest energy (and preferably metal) ions feasible, at temperatures down to $4°K$.

## 7. Other techniques

The remaining techniques which are specific to interstitials in metals are field-ion microscopy and channeling. Both of these were reviewed in separate papers at this conference.

Channelling is a very attractive technique both because of the possibility of producing pure interstitial damage and also because of the sensitivity and selectivity of the detection techniques which can be used. As mentioned in section 3, the absence of a "super-tail" in the channelling distributions of f.c.c. metals [23,25] probably represents the best evidence that interstitials in this structure diffuse via an interstitialcy mechanism. The F.I.M. is a most challenging technique, with Attardo and Galligan's [7] claim that single interstitials were seen in n-irradiated Pt and that these interstitials annealed out around 0°C. The number of "interstitials" seen was $\approx 10^{-4}$ atom fraction, was much greater than the number of impurities, and were concentrated around vacancy-rich "depleted zones", and appeared to be elongated along ⟨100⟩. A picture of an "interstitial" in Pt is shown in fig. 11. Although interstitials may be detected using the F.I.M., one is hardly likely to observe the equilibrium configuration.

At this conference it was clear that there is still a lot to be learned about the contrast to be expected from "interstitials". Petroff and Washburn [59] reported the

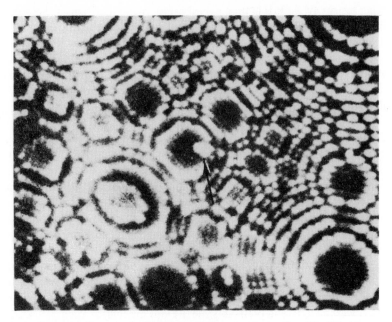

Fig. 11. An "interstitial" as seen by Field Ion Microscopy of n-irradiated Pt [7]. [Courtesy of
J.M.Galligan and Phys. Rev.].

appearance of both single and double bright spots as bombarded Ir was annealed
through stage I, similar to previous experiments on W [60]. Stage III was not investigated. Whether the single and double spots necessarily implied single and di-interstitials was not certain. Moreover, Schilling's suggestion [57], that stage III in Pt is
not around $0°C$, gave rise to doubts about the interpretation of the reported
F.I.M. work [7].

## 8. Discussion and conclusions

What can the experiments we have discussed tell us about interstitials? There
seem to be two separate questions requiring answers. Firstly, are there two different
types of interstitials migrating in stage I and III in the typical f.c.c. metals, Cu, Pt,
Al, Ag..., or only one type migrating in stage I? Secondly, is the "untypical" metal
Au only untypical in that stage I is at too low a temperature to be detected, or is
there no long range migration in Au at low temperatures?

The experiments discussed in sections 1 certainly indicate long range-migration
in stage I in Pt [42], and the experiments reported in section 5.2 seem to indicate
long range migration in Au below stage III [8,22,47]. The one provison for this
second statement is that replacement collision sequences in Au should be much

shorter than 2000 Å for it to be true. As discussed in section 2 and section 5.1, this is confidently expected to be so, although a direct measurement of the r.c.s. range would be extremely helpful. Whether or not this fast moving interstitial in Au moves *below* stage I, may be discovered in the future by ion bombardment experiments of the types described in section 5.2 and section 6.

Surprisingly, the question of whether interstitials migrating in stage III *also* exist is more difficult to answer. However, once it has been shown that interstitials in Au also move at low temperature, the motivation for this model is not so strong. In many cases at least the upper part of stage III has been ascribed to single vacancy migration. The fact that the activation energies deduced for stage III after a high energy irradiation are usually less than that for vacancy migration but greater than that for divacancy migration [53] is hardly surprising as the vacancies are almost certainly produced in localized groups. The number of jumps to annihilation in stage III is often very small [53]. Evidence was given at this conference that the sink density in stage III is high. Pulsing experiments [54] do not rule against divacancies in stage III if the binding energies of a divacancy is high [55].

In addition, the more recent experiments reported in section 4 and section 5.2 [8,22] suggest strongly that interstitials which migrate in stage III are not produced in large numbers during low energy ion bombardment. If they were, one would expect that the scale of subsurface damage would be different above and below stage III, even with clean surface conditions. If stage III interstitials were produced in large proportion in such experiments, they should also prevent the stage I interstitials from reaching the tetrahedra at low temperatures. It has also been argued on the basis of electron irradiation experiments, that if stage III interstitials are produced, their production rate is very low.

The one strong piece of evidence remaining in favour of the existence of a stage III interstitial is the F.I.M. work described in section 7. However, this evidence would be much strengthened if the same defects could be produced with low energy ion irradiation and observed quantitatively. The reason is that with low energy ion irradiation the interstitials are produced one at a time, and with an approximately known efficiency (section 2 and section 5). The "interstitials" which were observed [7] around each depleted zone in n-irradiated Pt were all produced at the same time. Thus the probability of them forming di-interstitials and interstitial clusters is purely a geometrical problem and is independent of the migration energy of the interstitials. If the interstitials were produced one at a time and the number of "interstitials" seen was comparable with the known production efficiency, and these interstitials disappeared in stage III, then the argument for a stage III interstitial would be pretty conclusive. Meanwhile, the suspicion must remain that what has been observed [7] are not single interstitials.

In conclusion, we feel that the evidence at present remains weighted in favour of there being only one type of interstitial which migrates in stage I or below. However, there are several experiments in progress at present which could put this hypothesis on a much firmer foundation. New types of experiments are needed to investigate the configuration of the interstitial, and to give further insight into the interstitial production mechanism.

## Acknowledgement

We are indebted to many colleagues who have commented on parts of the manuscript and to many others who have allowed reproduction of their material, both published and unpublished. We are also obliged to the E.O.A.R. (Brussels) for a maintenance grant under grant No. AF-EOAR 65–61.

## References

[1] R.O.Simmons, J.S.Koehler and R.W.Balluffi, Radiation Damage in Solids (IAEA, 1962) p. 155.
[2] A.Seeger, Radiation Damage in Solids (IAEA, 1962) p. 101.
[3] W.Bauer, A.Seeger and A.Sosin, Phys. Letters 24A (1967) 195.
[4] J.W.Corbett, Solid State Physics, Supplement 7 (1966) p. 78.
[5] G.D.Watkins, in: "Radiation Damage in Semiconductors" (Academic Press, 1965) p. 97; Santa Fe Conference on Radiation Effects in Semiconductors (1967) paper 49R.
[6] J.W.Corbett, Solid State Physics, Supplement 7 (1966) p. 254.
[7] M.J.Attardo and J.M.Galligan, Phys. Rev. 161 (1967) 558; Phys. Rev. Letters 17 (1966) 1173.
[8] L.E.Thomas and R.W.Balluffi, Phil. Mag. 15 (1967) 1117, 1137.
[9] J.A.Venables and R.W.Balluffi, Phil. Mag. 11 (1965) 1021, 1039.
[10] D.C.Loebach, P.B.Bowden and H.K.Birnbaum, Acta Met. 16 (1968) 997.
[11] E.V.Kornelsen, R.Brown, J.A.Davies, B.Domeij and G.R.Piercy, Phys. Rev. 136 (1964) 849.
[12] E.V.Kornelsen, Can. J. Phys. 42 (1964) 364;
     E.V.Kornelsen and M.K.Sinha, Can. J. Phys. 46 (1968) 613.
[13] R.H.Silsbee, J. Appl. Phys. 28 (1957) 1246.
[14] G.Leibfried, J. Appl. Phys. 30 (1959) 1388.
[15] R.S.Nelson, M.W.Thompson and H.Montgomery, Phil. Mag. 7 (1962) 1385.
[16] M.W.Thompson, The Interaction of Radiation with Solids (1964) p. 102.
[17] M.W.Thompson, Phil. Mag. 18 (1968) 377.
[18] J.B.Sanders and M.W.Thompson, Phil. Mag. 17 (1968) 211.
[19] H.Diepers and J.Diehl, Phys. Stat. Sol. 16 (1966) K109.
[20] H.Diepers, Phys. Stat. Sol. 24 (1967) 235, 623.
[21] J.Diehl, H.Diepers and B.Hertel, Can. J. Phys. 46 (1968) 647.
[22] G.J.Thomas and J.A.Venables, to be published.
[23] L.M.Howe and D.A.Channing, Can. J. Phys. 45 (1967) 2467.
[24] T.Schober and R.W.Balluffi, Phys. Stat Sol. 27 (1968) 195.
[25] J.A.Davies, L.Eriksson and J.L.Whitton, Can. J. Phys. 46 (1968) 573.
[26] J.A.Davies and P.Jespersgard, Can. J. Phys. 44 (1966) 1631.
[27] H.J.Matzke and J.A.Davies, J. Appl. Phys. 38 (1967) 805.
[28] K.Wittmaack, Jül. Conf. 2 (Vol. 2) 1968, p. 473.
[29] P.B.Bowden and D.G.Brandon, Phil. Mag. 6 (1961) 707.
     Disc. Farad. Soc. 31 (1961) 70; Phil. Mag. 8 (1963) 935; J. Nucl. Mat. 9 (1963) 348.

[30] D.G.Brandon, P.B.Bowden and A.J.Baker, Properties of Reactor Materials and the effect of Radiation Damage (Butterworth, 1961), p. 120.

[31] M.F.Ashby and L.M.Brown, Phil. Mag. 8 (1963) 1083, 1649.

[32] J.J.Jackson, Lattice Defects in Quenched Metals (Academic Press, 1965) p. 467.

[33] W.Bauer and A.Sosin, Phys. Rev. 147 (1966) 482.

[34] R.Castaing and B.Jouffrey, J. Microscopie 1 (1962) 201;
B.Jouffrey, J. Microscopie 2 (1963) 45.

[35] G.J.Ogilvie, J.V.Saunders and A.A.Thomson, J. Phys. Chem. Solids 24 (1963) 247.

[36] P.B.Bowden, unpublished work.

[37] J.A.Venables, Conference Abstract, Point Defects in Metals, Reading, 1967.

[38] R.W.Balluffi, private communication.

[39] M.Rühle, M.Wilkens and U.Essmann, Phys. Stat. Sol. 11 (1965) 819;
M.Rühle, Phys. Stat. Sol. 19 (1967) 263, 279.

[40] M.Swanson and G.R.Piercy, Phys. Letters 7 (1963) 97.

[41] W.Bauer and A.Sosin, Phys. Rev. 136 (1964) A255.

[42] W.Bauer and W.F.Goeppinger, Phys. Rev. 154 (1967) 588.

[43] W.Bauer and A.Sosin, Phys. Rev. 135 (1964) A521.

[44] G.Duesing, H.Hemmerich, D.Meissner and W.Schilling, Phys. Stat. Sol. 23 (1967) 481.

[45] W.Bauer and W.F.Goeppinger, Phys. Rev. 154 (1967) 584.

[46] R.M.J.Cotterill and M.W.Jones, J. Phys. Soc. Japan 18 Suppl. III (1963) 158; Phil. Mag. 10 (1964) 535.

[47] L.M.Howe, J.F.McGurn and R.W.Gilbert, Acta Met. 14 (1966) 801; Appl. Phys. Letters 3 (1963) 125; Letters 4 (1964) 99.

[48] J.A.Venables, D.J.Ball and G.J.Thomas, J. Sci. Inst. 1 (1968) 121.

[49] D.Kuhlmann-Wilsdorf, Acta Met. 13 (1965) 257.

[50] L.D.Reed, W.H.Robinson and J.A.Venables, to be published.

[51] S.N.Buckley, Conference Abstract, Point Defects in Metals, Reading, 1967.

[52] D.O.Thompson, O.Buck, R.S.Barnes and H.B.Huntingdon, J. Appl. Phys. 38 (1967) 3051.

[53] F.Dworschak, K.Herschbach and J.S.Koehler, Phys. Rev. 133 (1964) A293.

[54] F.Dworschak and J.S.Koehler, Phys. Rev. 140 (1965) A941.

[55] C.G.Wang, D.N.Seidman and R.W.Balluffi, Phys. Rev. 169 (1968) 553.

[56] H.H.Anderson and P.Sigmund, Nucl. Inst. Meth. 38 (1965) 238.

[57] W.Schilling, this volume.

[58] G.J.Ogilvie, to be published in Austral. J. Phys.

[59] P.Petroff and J.Washburn, Jül. Conf. (Vol. 2) 1968, p. 485.

[60] M.K.Sinha and E.W.Müller, J. Appl. Phys. 25 (1964) 1256.

# FIELD ION MICROSCOPY OF POINT DEFECTS

## E.W.MÜLLER

*Department of Physics, The Pennsylvania State University,*
*University Park, Pennsylvania, USA*

## 1. Introduction

The field ion microscope (FIM) is the only microscopical device capable of imaging the individual atoms as the building blocks of metal crystals. By displaying the atomic structure of the specimen the lattice defects also become visible. Thus the instrument appears to be uniquely suitable for the study of point defects which remain beyond the reach of transmission electron microscopy. Although only the surface is imaged, the bulk structure of the crystal can be viewed when the specimen is gradually dissected by controlled, atom-by-atom or layer-by-layer field evaporation. All observational operations are carried out at cryogenic temperatures to preclude self annealing. With these basic techniques fully developed a decade ago [1—3], it remains to be shown why progress in the study of point defects has been so slow and what are the main obstacles that are gradually being overcome towards a more productive application.

## 2. Problems of image formation

It is readily seen that the highly magnified, radial projection on a distant screen of the nearly perfect, hemispherical tip cap by ions of the image gas, usually helium, should represent the distribution of ionization probability over the surface. Ionization as a tunneling effect is expected to rise steeply with the local field strength above the single surface atom. By constructing a ball model and assuming that the local degree of protrusion above an imaginary hemispherical envelope determines the field strength, one can expect that atoms protruding too much would be removed during the initial field evaporation tip shaping process, and that at a slightly reduced applied voltage the remaining surface would produce atomic image spot brightnesses according to the degree of geometrical protrusion [1]. As has been shown by Moore [4], this image criterion may be formulated quantitatively by considering only those atoms to image whose center lie within a thin hemispherical shell of $\frac{1}{20}$ to $\frac{1}{5}$ atomic spacing thickness. Indeed, a close agreement between a computer plot based on this geometrical model and a real FIM image is obtained, where the crystal hemisphere exhibits many facets representing the low-index poles and their concentric ledges. This computer model has been particularly useful in the interpretation of the geometrically somewhat complex intersection of dislocations with the surface [5,6].

However, there are a number of image details that cannot be explained by a purely geometrical approach. If this would suffice, all metals of the same lattice structure, such as b.c.c., f.c.c., or h.c.p. should produce identical FIM patterns. Actually, there is a pronounced chemical specificity in the regional brightness as well as in the brightness of individual atomic sites due to the effect of electronic conditions, and these factors must be particularly investigated in the study of point defects.

Once one has confidence in the imaging of point defects, determination of their density distribution should be straight forward if it would be certain that the stress of the applied field, equivalent to a negative, nearly hydrostatic pressure of the order of $10^{11}$ dynes/cm$^2$ would not introduce new problems. It is realized that the applicability of field ion microscopy is limited by the condition that the metal specimen can stand the field stress to which it must be exposed for the tip shaping field evaporation process [7]. Fortunately, the hydrogen promotion effect of field evaporation [1] allows one to reduce the evaporation field. Once the perfect field evaporation end form has been obtained without plastic deformation, imaging at a lower field no more presents a problem, as instead of helium other, easier to ionize image gases such as neon or hydrogen may be used. Additionally, the novel hydrogen promotion of field ionization of helium [8] can further expand the list of accessible metals. It is comforting to see that a metal as soft as gold [9] may be imaged without plastic deformation, and that for all metals the field evaporation end form is nearly independent of the field evaporation rate. To test the stability of a surface site we have evaporated as slowly as one atom every 1000 seconds, which would mean a monolayer within one year. Employing the new atom-probe FIM [10, 11] we have also evaporated 10 monolayers within a nanosecond pulse, which is 18 orders of magnitude faster and amounts to a rate of one meter of metal evaporating in a second.

One can estimate that the negative field pressure does not cause the formation of vacancies. The concentration of vacancies in equilibrium at pressure $p$ and temperature $T$ is

$$C_{1V}(p,T) = \exp(-E_{1V}^{F}/kT) \, ,$$

where $E_{1V}^{F}$ is the energy of formation. Calculating $(dC_{1V}/dp)_{T}$ and integrating from $p_o$ to the field-induced pressure $p$ one obtains,

$$C_{1V}(p,T) = C_{1V}(p_o,T) \exp[(p-p_o) \, \Delta V_V/kT] \, ,$$

which gives a completely negligible concentration due to a negative pressure of $10^{11}$ dynes/cm$^2$ and any reasonable volume of formation $\Delta V_V$. Similarly one can show that the typical 3% elastic increase of the lattice volume of the tip [12] does not affect the vacancy diffusivity to any great extent. Less certain remains the effect of the negative pressure upon the diffusivity of interstitials, particularly at sub-surface sites which offer easy relaxation.

It may be stated at this time that irradiation and annealing experiments have established the visibility of interstitials as bright spots, and of vacancies as empty lattice sites [1, 2]. The problem haunting the field ion microscopist is the abundant appearance of such image spots under circumstances that preclude their interpretation as true point defects. We cannot overlook the occurrence of artifacts [13] and must learn to discriminate them from genuine point defects.

Extra bright spots appearing on the field evaporation endform of pure, well annealed metals have been explained as atoms bound at a reduced-coordination site and stabilized against field evaporation by an increased polarization [14]. They appear on well defined zone lines, giving several metals a quite characteristic FIM pattern. They also show up more randomly at one side of the {112} planes of tungsten, around {237}, and are all over the place on niobium [8], making an image interpretation of the latter metal an unrewarding task. Extra bright spots may also indicate impurity interstitials, such as oxygen in tantalum [15] or iridium [16], or are caused by some corrosive process following the adsorption of residual gases such as CO or N$_2$ [17–19].

On the other hand, there are also "invisible" atoms at lattice sites where they should be easily recognizeable [20]. The problem is to decide whether such a site is really empty, that is either an intrinsic vacancy or one caused by preferential evaporation [21], or whether the local ionization probability above a still present atom is reduced to near zero [22]. Preferential field evaporation may either be a property of a specific net plane, such as {012} on platinum [23] and also on tungsten, or it may be promoted by the presence of a gas like hydrogen or neon in the imaging helium [24]. There are also situations where present atoms are simply invisible in spite of a geometrically regular site, such as the alternating ledges around the basal plane of h.c.p. crystals [25] and the invisible cobalt atoms in Pt-Co alloys [20, 26].

The ionization probability above a single surface atom is primarily a matter of local field strength, which is equivalent to the surface charge density. This charge density may not only be caused by the externally applied voltage and the local geometry, but also by a "chemical" or valency transfer of electronic charge from the considered atom to a neighbor [22]. In the light of this interpretation, the bright spots due to impurity or self interstitials are probably less indicative of a protrusion of relaxed surface atoms, but rather of an electron deficiency in the top atoms. A further refinement of the imaging process suggests a preferred ionization of the helium image gas into an extended, empty and directional orbital of the surface atom [25]. With an interstitial below the surface atom, the latter will have to

provide a bonding electron to the interstitial, thereby emptying an outwardly extended orbital for preferential ionization of the helium image gas.


## 3. Quenched-in vacancies

I should like to present some examples of observations of point defects. Ten
years ago [27] I field-evaporated 72 consecutive (012) layers of quenched Pt, found
5 vacancies among the 8500 inspected atomic sites and calculated an energy of formation of 1.15 eV, by putting the quenching temperature into the Boltzmann factor.
This result became questionable when in 1964 Pimbley et al. [23] observed in long
field evaporation sequences much higher vacancy concentrations, up to 2%, at the
(012) plane of well annealed Pt. This clearly suggests that these vacancies are artifacts due to random field evaporation. Recently Fortes and Ralph [28] came to the
same conclusion with iridium, where they found no significant difference in vacancy
counts of annealed material and neutron irradiated samples with $10^{14}$ and $10^{17}$ nvt,
the defect concentration being about $2 \times 10^{-4}$ counted on the {110} planes, and
five times higher on high index planes.

The problem with vacancy counting arises from the fact that close packed planes,
such as (001) and (111) in the f.c.c. lattice, and (011) in the b.c.c. lattice, can ordinarily not be resolved by the FIM. Thus vacancy counts must be made either along
the edges of net plane rings, which is very inaccurate, or on less densely packed
crystallographic regions, of which (012) on f.c.c. and (111) on b.c.c. are best
suited. Very long evaporation sequences, each time taking away only a fraction of a
net plane, are necessary. In an "open" net plane, moreover, the binding energy of an
atom inside the plane is not sufficiently higher than the binding energy of an atom
at the net plane edge in order to assure that field evaporation progresses from the latter sites only. An accurate calculation of the binding energy or the evaporation field
at these critical sites is presently not possible because of the limitation of the pair-
wise binding concept and the uncertainty of the contribution of surface polarization
by the field.

When vacancies are produced by in-situ irradiation, the density of surface vacancies is, of course, much larger than the bulk concentration, as the binding energy of
surface atoms is lower. In fact, as the applied field approaches the evaporation
field, the surface binding energy at the kink sites goes to zero. Thus, when irradiation is performed while the observational field is on, a larger number of surface
vacancies is created by the arrival at the surface of relatively small impulses due to
focusing collisions. This, however, should not affect the bulk concentration of defects which in the case of single vacancies can be reliably counted when exposed to
the surface. Great caution should be exercised in the interpretation of multiple
point defects and their specific configuration, as the field may rearrange the surface
atoms and preferentially evaporate low coordination atoms in diffuse clusters.

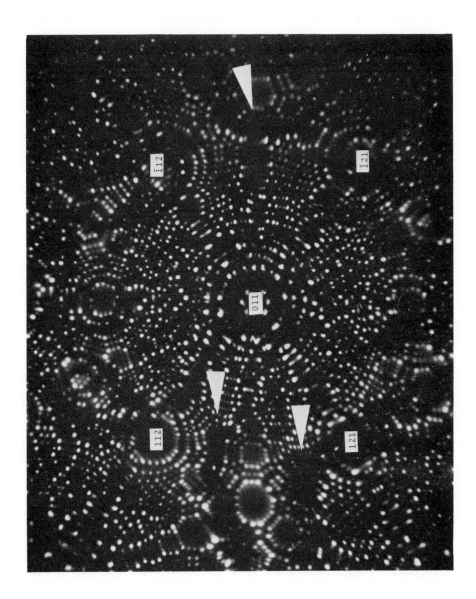

Fig. 1. Vacancies and voids in a tungsten tip heated to near the melting point by a 10 nanosecond laser pulse. The first two surface layers have been removed.

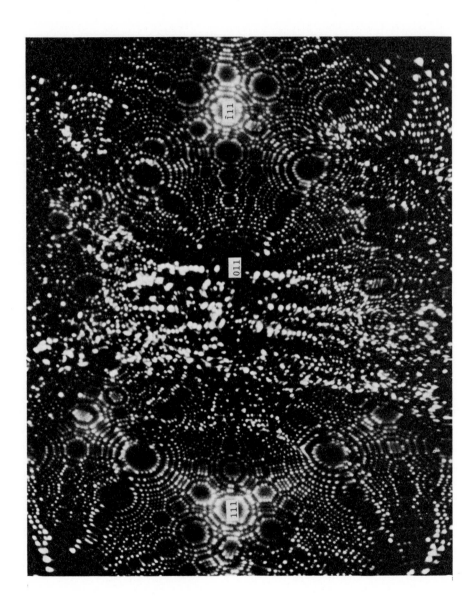

Fig. 2. Tungsten crystal after in-situ mechanical deformation by contacting a tungsten plate.

Another ambiguity may arise from the possibility of artifact vacancies due to impurity gas promoted field evaporation [19,24]. The appearance of atomic cleanliness of a field evaporated Pt surface may be deceiving. A few residual gas atoms, preferably nitrogen and hydrogen, may diffuse over the surface from the tip shank, which is always contaminated, even in an ultra high vacuum system. That such contamination atoms, although invisible, may react corrosively with a metal atom inside a net plane has been indicated by the atom-probe FIM [10]. It thus appears that the problem of vacancy counts on f.c.c. metals is still an open question. The best material is probably iridium, as its evaporation field is so high that most corrosive impurity atoms are desorbed.

The same advantage is offered by tungsten, but because of the very large formation energy, quenched-in vacancies have not been reliably observed. On tungsten in the form of a 0.025 mm diameter wire quenched from near the melting point at an initial rate of $500\,000°$/sec (in helium at atmospheric pressure, $20°C$) I inspected one hundred (111) layers and also the very regular vicinity of (112) and could not detect vacancies above the limiting accessible concentration of $10^{-4}$. The crystal did show line defects which might have acted as sinks. The concentration limit was merely given by a lack of patience, as no more than 20 000 atom sites were inspected. By contrast, Attardo and Gallighan [29] recently checked $8 \times 10^5$ sites in their study of irradiated tungsten, so that concentrations below $10^{-5}$ could be observed. A very fast temperature rise, within $10^{-8}$ sec, and a quenching rate estimated to be above $10^7$ °/sec, can be obtained by in-situ irradiation of a tungsten tip with a $Q$-spoiled laser [30]. While no establishment of a vacancy equilibrium may be expected in the short heating period, the anormous thermal stress formed 100 Å deep cracks or voids, with a few smaller vacancy clusters discernable (fig. 1).

Mechanical deformation of tungsten and of iridium by in-situ contacting of FIM tips [31] produces slip bands and complex defect structures, but no recognizable single vacancies further away from the gross defects (fig. 2). Seeing such structures one cannot help but wonder why annealing experiments following mechanical plastic deformation do give activation energies associated with single vacancy migration.

## 4. Low-energy particle irradiation

The most convenient way of producing point defects in FIM specimens is by in-situ irradiation [1,2]. Low energy helium or neon ions can be made impinging on the tip by reversing the polarity and drawing a small electron current from the tip, which then is being cathode sputtered by the gas ions produced. The bombardment energy is very inhomogeneous and the impact direction quite random. Vacancies and interstitials, some paired, are seen as a result of low density bombardment, while a larger dose produces shallow dislocation loops extending some 10 to 20 atomic layers deep when the bombardment is done at 78 or $21°K$ (fig. 3).

Larger energies can be imparted to the specimen atoms by the impact of heavier ions of intermediate energy. When the imaging gas contains some neon, negative

Fig. 3. Shallow dislocation loops, interstitials and vacancies caused by low energy helium ion bombardment (cathode sputtering) of a tungsten tip.

Fig. 4. Rhenium crystal in [0001] orientation bombarded by 20 keV negative ions released from an aluminum cathode shield. Single interstitials near the pole, damage clusters at larger angles from the $c$-axis.

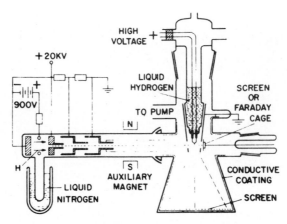

Fig. 5. FIM with a helium atom gun.

ions are released from the cathode in normal FIM operation, and large damage clusters of an amorphous structure are seen to appear, having a diameter of 20 to 50 Å and a depth of not more than 20 Å at 20 keV energy.

When this kind of bombardment is done on [0001] oriented Re tips, the resulting damage near the basal plane consists of single interstitial spots only, while further away from the $c$-axis the damage consists of shallow, 20 to 50 Å wide amorphous regions (fig. 4). The single interstitial mode may be due to channeling parallel to the $c$-axis.

The experiment by which the typical damage was most clearly shown was made in 1960 on tungsten with the instrument [2,32] shown in fig. 5, which consists of a Penning discharge and an ion beam focussing electrode system. Charge exchange in the path produces a neutral helium atom beam of 20 keV energy which was made to impinge on the tungsten tip at a rate of one to 30 atom hits per sec. By turning the tip axially, various crystallographic directions of impact can be chosen. The damage consisted of surface vacancies and interstitials, and of depleted zones of 20 to 60 Å diameter containing some 10 to 30 vacancies and some bright spots (fig. 6a, b). It is not clear whether these zones are not somewhat enlarged by preferred field evaporation of the atoms that had been displaced to low-coordination sites, an explanation that has also been proposed for the vacancy clusters seen by Attardo and Galligan [29]. About one half of the number of knock-on atoms that received 50 eV energy inside the tip volume produced one displacement visible at the surface, and the appearance of a considerable fraction of the total damage at the side of the tip away from the source indicates a long range of channeling, or focusing of energy. Impact directions normal to the [111] zone, that is along close packed atom chains, give a surface damage 2.5 times greater than with a bombardment direction normal to the [001] zone. At 20 keV helium beam energy and

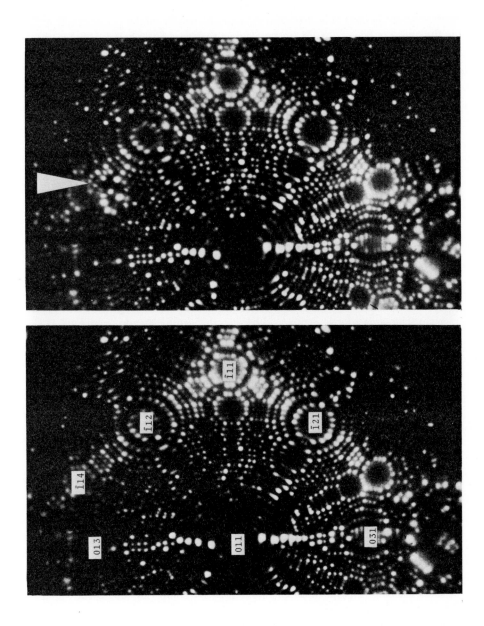

Fig. 6. (a) Section of a tungsten tip of 350 A radius. (b) Same tip after bombardment (from the top) by 20 keV helium atoms. A damage spike of 65 A diameter appeared on the 113 plane. There are also 14 single interstitials or displaced metastable atoms, and 12 surface vacancies.

bombardment in the [111] direction the damage density on the entrance side and on the opposite side of the tip are equal when the tip radius is below 500 Å, indicating the long range of channeling. When the bombarding beam was turned off, some bright interstitial spots continued to come out at the surface for about 2 sec, indicating some mobility at 21°K. When this had ceased, more interstitials came out upon increasing the applied field, and more so upon warming the specimen above 50°K. An abundance of arrivals was noted between 85 to 95°K, and then the supply from the interior was exhausted. This seems to represent the first direct observation of the mobility of interstitials in the annealing stage I of tungsten. When the tip had been bombarded with the field off, a subsequent gradual increase of the field made new interstitials appear at the surface at 21°K, presumably indicating a field stress enhanced activation of interstitial diffusivity.

## 5. Alpha-particle and proton irradiation

Interstitial migration in tungsten in the same temperature range was also observed as a result of α-particle bombardment [1,2], which can very conveniently be performed by placing a polonium source of a few millicurie strength near the specimen tip. The same arrangement was subsequently used by Brandon and Wald [33]. The bright spots observed must be self interstitials, as the probability of trapping α-particles within the small tip volume is very small. The surface damage consists of about 5 to 30 vacancies and interstitial spots appearing within a small region of the tip, of the order of 20 to 50 Å diameter (fig. 7). Simultaneously with the appearance of such a cluster there might be another smaller one popping out at a region of the tip far removed from the main disturbance, indicating that the primary knock-on event has actually occurred deep inside the tip volume. The surface effects then are essentially due to the arrival of either focusing or channeling events. In a recent re-examination of the α-bombardment experiments the latter mechanism was preferred by Bowkett [34] on the grounds of insufficient range of the focuson.

The range of focusing over a distance of at least 150 Å at 21°K can be seen in the example of fig. 8 (a,b) where a primary α-particle collision event took place somewhere near the center of the eleventh atomic layer below the top (001) plane of a platinum crystal. On one side of the eleventh net plane ring there are two surface vacancies created by the event, and on the opposite side, exactly in the [010] direction, there is one atom missing. Such rare surface events can be readily found by using the color superposition technique [35] for comparing the "before" and "after" field ion micrographs.

The bulk damage exposed by controlled, high-voltage pulse field evaporation, is much less than would be expected by the amount of surface damage. When the field is on during bombardment, a small focussed energy may field evaporate a surface atom to produce a vacancy, and some of the bright spots may not be true interstitials but rather surface atoms displaced into a low-coordination metastable site.

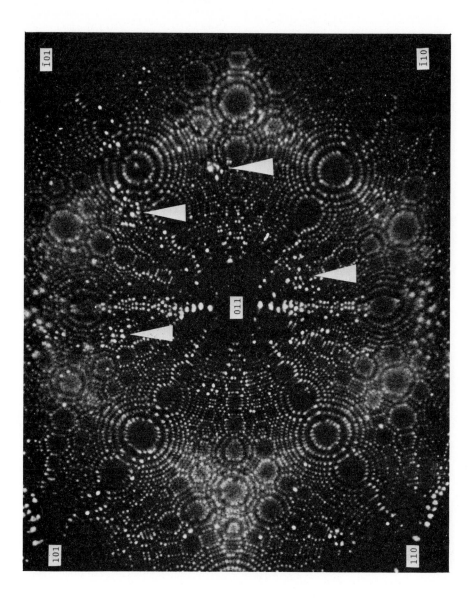

Fig. 7. Damage spikes and interstitials due to $a$-bombardment of tungsten
(two independent primary events).

E.W.MÜLLER

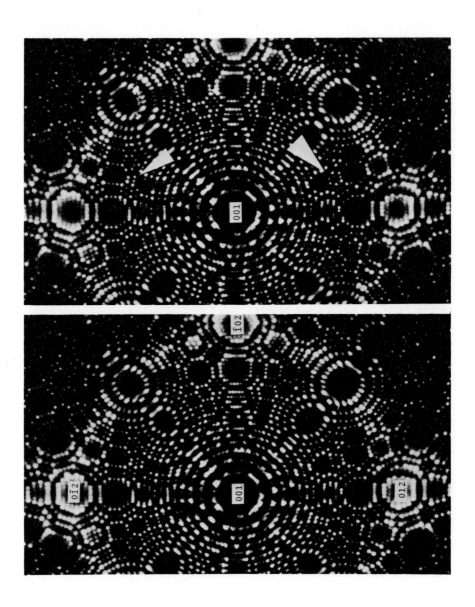

Fig. 8a,b. Single primary event of α-irradiation of a platinum tip at 21°K. Removal of surface atoms (at arrows) by focusons.

Genuine interstitials are, however, evident by their appearance of the surface after the bombarding event, with the migration enhanced by the field stress or a small temperature increase in an annealing experiment. In a long time α-irradiation experiment of the author a tungsten tip at 78°K was exposed for 340 hours to α-particles which should have produced some 1000 primary knock-on events. After subsequent removal of about 3 heavily disordered surface layers there were hardly any interstitials in the bulk, but a large number of voids and dislocation loops indicated an aggregation of vacancies. A platinum tip irradiated at room temperature, showed most of the damage annealed out, with occassional clustered, precipitate like inclusions.

The author (unpublished, 1963) also irradiated 0.1 mm diameter single crystal tungsten wires with protons of 6 MeV, using the Florida State University tandem accelerator. The range is such that most of the damage was expected near the wire axis, so that the subsequently fabricated tips should reveal the effects. Many voids were seen that had probably been formed during 3 weeks of room temperature annealing prior to the inspection. The fracture rate of this material was large, indicating brittleness.

In-situ proton irradiation at cryogenic temperatures was carried out by Petroff and Washburn [36] and reported at this conference [37]. Their tip irradiation geometry is the same as in the earlier Sinha and Müller helium atom beam experiment [2, 32]. An all-metal ultra high vacuum FIM provides a lower background pressure to permit tip irradiation without applied field, and the beam source is the 88″ Berkeley cyclotron. The 10 MeV protons can impart about ½ as much energy to a heavy metal atom than the 5.4 MeV α-particles used in the earlier experiments described above. It is assuring to see that the effects of proton irradiation observed at the surface of iridium tips are so similar to the effects of α-particles, and even of the 20 keV helium beam. Single vacancies, small diffuse vacancy clusters, and interstitials represent the low temperature damage. Petroff and Washburn also see bright interstitial spots emerge at the surface when the irradiated tip is gradually warmed up, in this case at a lower temperature range from 15°K to 42°K, and they confirm the effect of a field increase upon the diffusion to the surface. Thus it is evident that annealing stage I of iridium, as is the case with tungsten, is due to interstitial migration. Petroff and Washburn further suggest that stage II, above 40°K, is due to annihilation of vacancies by mobile interstitials that are being released from traps. Pairs of bright spots are tentatively interpreted as di-interstitials, although they may also simply represent two surface atoms displaced to metastable sites.

## 6. Neutron bombardment damage

Because of experimental difficulties neutron irradiation of FIM specimens has only been carried out at ambient reactor temperature. Numerous single vacancies and clusters of vacancies have been seen in molybdeum irradiated [38] with a dose of 2 × 10$^{19}$ nvt. Obviously, the interstitials have all been annealed out at room temperature in the month-long period which the material required to loose its activity from transmutation by thermal neutrons. Preliminary accounts of extensive studies of neutron damage in tungsten have been given by Bowkett et al. [39] and for damage in platinum and tungsten by Attardo and Galligan [40,41]. The latter also found interstitials besides the vacancies in highly pure tungsten specimens. Changes in the concentration of the defects after annealing at 400°C through stage III recovery, combined with the observation of rapid decrease of the vacancy concentration at 700°C, suggest that the stage III annealing mechanism in tungsten is due to single interstitials migrating to and being annihilated at vacancies

Next to tungsten, iridium is the most convenient material for field ion microscopy. Fortes and Ralph [42] neutron-irradiated iridium, but had to limit the dose to 10$^{14}$ nvt because of the high activity produced by transmutation. Single vacancy counts were unreliably low, but spherical depletion zones as well as clusters collapsed to dislocation loops were evident. The loops, lying in (111) planes, require an original vacancy cluster of 250 missing atoms.

## 7. Conclusion

The usefulness of the field ion microscope for the study of point defects is definitely established with the identification of the moving entities in annealing and irradiation experiments with some b.c.c. and f.c.c. refractory metals. So far, the h.c.p. metals have been neglected, and further work is particularly required in the improvement of reliability of single vacancy counts and the elimination of artifact effects. The mechanism of image formation of sub-surface interstitials must be more firmly established. It is hoped that the novel technique of the atom-probe FIM will contribute in this direction by identifying the chemical nature of impurity interstitials. The main difficulties, certainly not unsurmountable, lie in the need of time consuming data collection and in the interpretation of the image details in defect aggregates.

## References

[1] E.W.Müller, Advances in Electronics and Electron Physics, Vol. 13 (Academic Press, New York, 1960) p. 83.
[2] E.W.Müller, Proc. Fourth Intern. Symp. Reactivity of Solids (Elsevier, Amsterdam, 1960) p. 682.
[3] E.W.Müller, Proc. Intern. Congr. Electron Microscopy, Berlin 1958, Vol. 1 (Springer-Verlag, Berlin, 1960) p. 820.
[4] A.J.W.Moore, J. Phys. Chem. Solids 23 (1962) 907.

[5] S.Ranganathan, K.M.Bowkett, J.J.Hren and B.Ralph, Phil. Mag. 12 (1965) 841.
[6] R.C.Sanwald, S.Ranganathan and J.J.Hren, Appl. Phys. Letters 9 (1966) 393.
[7] E.W.Müller, Bull. Am. Phys. Soc. II 9 (1964) 104.
[8] E.W.Müller, S.Nakamura, O.Nishikawa and S.B.McLane, J. Appl. Phys. 36 (1965) 2496.
[9] S.B.McLane, E.W.Müller and O.Nishikawa, Rev. Sci. Instr. 35 (1964) 1297.
[10] E.W.Müller, S.B.McLane and J.A.Panitz, Rev. Sci. Instr. 39 (1968) 83.
[11] E.W.Müller, S.B.McLane and J.A.Panitz, Electron Microscopy, Proc. 4th Regional European Conference on Electron Microscopy, Rome 1968, Vol. 1, p. 161.
[12] K.D.Rendulic and E.W.Müller, J. Appl. Phys. 38 (1967) 2070.
[13] E.W.Müller, in: Field Ion Microscopy, Eds. J.Hren and S.Ranganathan (Plenum Press, 1968) p. 88.
[14] E.W.Müller, Surface Sci. 2 (1964) 484.
[15] S.Nakamura and E.W.Müller, J. Appl. Phys. 36 (1965) 2535.
[16] M.A.Fortes and B.Ralph, 14th Field Emission Symposium (NBS Washington D.C., 1967).
[17] G.Ehrlich, Disc. Faraday Soc. 41 (1966) 7.
[18] W.M.H.Sachtler and A.A.Holscher, Disc. Faraday Soc. 41 (1966) 29.
[19] J.F.Mulson and E.W.Müller, J. Chem. Phys. 38 (1963) 2615.
[20] T.T.Tsong and E.W.Müller, Appl. Phys. Letters 9 (1966) 7.
[21] H.N.Southworth and B.Ralph, Phil. Mag. 14 (1966) 383.
[22] E.W.Müller, Surface Sci. 8 (1967) 462.
[23] W.T.Pimbley, C.A.Speicher, M.J.Attardo, J.M.Galligan and S.S.Brenner, Phys. Letters 23 (1966) 194.
[24] O.Nishikawa and E.W.Müller, J. Appl. Phys. 35 (1964) 2806; Surface Sci. 12 (1968).
[25] Z.Knor and E.W.Müller, Surface Sci. 10 (1968) 21.
[26] T.T.Tsong and E.W.Müller, J. Appl. Phys. 38 (1967) 3531.
[27] E.W.Müller, Z. Physik 156 (1959) 399.
[28] M.A.Fortes and B.Ralph, 15th Field Emission Symposium, Bonn, 1968.
[29] M.J.Attardo and J.M.Galligan, Phys. Stat. Sol. 16 (1966) 449.
[30] E.W.Müller and S.B.McLane, 12th Field Emission Symposium, Penn. State University, 1965.
[31] E.W.Müller and O.Nishikawa, Proc. Seminar on Electric Contact Phenomena, Illinois Institute of Technology Chicago, 1967, p. 181; also in ASTM Special Techn. Publ. No. 431, p. 67, Philadelphia, 1968.
[32] M.K.Shina and E.W.Müller, J. Appl. Phys. 35 (1964) 1256.
[33] D.G.Brandon and M.Wald, Phil. Mag. 6 (1961) 1035.
[34] K.M.Bowkett, PhD Thesis, Cambridge 1966.
[35] E.W.Müller, J. Appl. Phys. 21 (1957) 1.
[36] P.Petroff and J.Washburn, Rev. Sci. Instr. 39 (1968) 317.
[37] P.Petroff and J.Washburn, Jül. Conf. 2, Vol. 2, 1968, p. 485.
[38] E.W.Müller, J. Phys. Soc. Japan 18 (1963) Suppl. II p. 1;
     D.G.Brandon, M.Wald, M.J.Southon and B.Ralph, ibid. p. 324.
[39] K.M.Bowkett, J.Hren and B.Ralph, 4th European Regional Conference Electron Microscopy, Prague, 1964, Vol. 1, p. 191.
[40] M.J.Attardo and J.M.Galligan, Phys. Rev. Letters 14 (1965) 671.
[41] M.J.Attardo and J.M.Galligan, Phys. Rev. 161 (1967) 558.
[42] M.A.Fortes and B.Ralph, Phil. Mag. 14 (1966) 189.

*Note:* The discussion of this paper is given after the subsequent paper by J.M.Galligan (see p. 586).

# FIELD ION MICROSCOPE STUDIES OF DEFECTS *

J.M.GALLIGAN

*Brookhaven National Laboratory, Upton, New York, USA*

## 1. Introduction

Recovery processes in crystals, which are associated with point defects, take place at fairly sharp temperatures and occur with comparatively simple kinetics [1]. In spite of this no fully accepted interpretation of many aspects of the recovery spectra of many metals has been given. For example, in the recovery spectrum of aluminum [2] − quenched or electron irradiated − there is a major recovery stage in a narrow temperature range. This stage can apparently be resolved into two substages but, again, there is no agreement on which defect migrates in this recovery stage.

In contrast to aluminum, platinum [3] and tungsten [4] have widely spaced recovery spectra, which should allow a distinction between the vacancy and interstitial recovery models. Similarly the purity of platinum and tungsten are comparable to, if not greater than, other common metals. In addition, and most significantly, it is relatively "easy" to obtain information on point defect concentrations by using field ion microscopy [5].

The technique of field ion microscopy has the distinct advantage over other techniques that it is able to record directly defects and that it allows determinations of defect concentrations. Also, some rather unique calibration experiments can be undertaken with the field microscope, in which some specifically known defects can be introduced and observed.

Experimental observations of defects in the field ion microscope, which attempt to relate in situ recovery steps to macroscopic recovery stages must consider the question of surfaces. It has been our experience that there is not a one to one relationship between macroscopic recovery stages and recovery stages observed in in situ field ion microscope experiments. In addition, it is extremely important for any experimental investigation, which uses field ion microscopy, to undertake extensive blank experiments in order to utilize fully and correctly the instruments capabilities.

* This work was performed under the auspices of the U.S. Atomic Energy Commission.

576 J.M.GALLIGAN

An important, additional capability of the field ion microscope, which is of interest to defect studies, is that of field evaporation [5]. Field evaporation is the technique of removing atoms from a specimen tip, which allows a determination of bulk concentration of defects. Such a counting technique consists of field evaporation, imaging the freshly revealed surfaces, recording the image and repeating the cycle. This technique has been used extensively in our studies, and it will be illustrated below.

The experiments we wish to discuss are concerned with point defects and point defect recovery stages in irradiated platinum and tungsten. The experiments have a bearing on what defects are involved in the recovery stages of these metals.

## 2. Experimental procedure

In the present investigation of defects in crystals, it is important to specify the purity and heat-treatment of specimens prior to irradiation. Furthermore, since we are studying the removal of defects by annealing treatments, artifacts such as radioactive decay schemes will not be of importance. For example, the appearance of interstitial atoms can not be correlated with radioactive decay schemes, since such time constants are independent of temperature and pressure.

### 2.1. Platinum

The platinum used in the present experiment was a special lot, laboratory grade material with a reported purity greater than 99.999%. The material was obtained from Englehard Industries, Inc. Prior to examination in the field ion microscope, the material was heated to 1300°C for various times. The heating was done in helium atmosphere, since platinum, which is heated in air, is known to dissolve oxygen [6]. Repeated examination of this material in a field ion microscope (fig. 1) was undertaken to assess the concentration of interstitial defects present in the annealed material. In these examinations the atom fraction of self-interstitials in the as-annealed material is less than one part in $10^5$.

### 2.2. Tungsten

The starting material for this investigation was General Electric undoped 218 tungsten and tungsten wire drawn from zone-refined stock. The latter was purchased from Westinghouse Co., Lamp Division, Bloomfield, New Jersey. These materials were examined repeatedly by standard field ion microscope techniques. In the work on the undoped 218 tungsten, about $9 \times 10^5$ atoms were indirectly examined. In the work on the wire obtained from a zone refined crystal, approximately $1 \times 10^5$ atoms were examined. In each investigation with different materials, blank experiments were always carried out to measure the background noise present in the experiment. On the planes examined and reported in this paper, the noise level was not measurable. In the case of the G.E. 218 wire, for example,

LOW TEMPERATURE FIELD ION MICROSCOPE

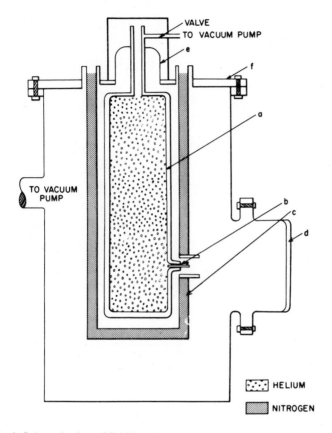

Fig. 1. Schematic view of field ion microscope used in present investigation.

this means that the vacancy concentrations are considerably below one vacant lattice site in $10^5$ atomic sites.

## 3. Experimental results and discussion

### 3.1. *Calibration experiments*

It is of interest to consider two previous calibration experiments, one by Sinha and Müller [7] and a second by Attardo and Galligan [8]. In the experiments by Sinha and Müller tungsten specimens were bombarded by energetic metastable atoms and direct recording of the damage was made. The defects observed were extra

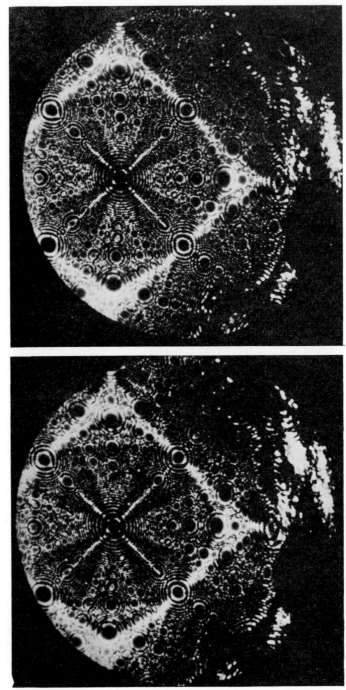

Fig. 2a. A platinum tie before bombardment. b. Same platinum tip after bombardment, showing extra bright spots.

bright spots and missing atoms (fig. 2). This experiment serves as a prototype calibration experiment and shows that interstitials (bright spots) and vacancies (missing atoms) can be observed in the field ion microscope. Attardo and Galligan have used another in situ technique, also introduced by Müller, to bombard a platinum tip in the field ion microscope. Again, these authors have observed interstitials and vacancies in the bombarded platinum and this serves as a calibration experiment. An additional calibration experiment, this time performed by Galligan [9], serves as a further independent calibration experiment. In this experiment a tungsten wire was quenched from the melting point in a superfluid helium bath, in the same way as used by Schultz [10]. Field ion microscope specimens were made from this quenched material and only missing atoms were observed. This serves as a calibration experiment for vacancies and this experiment also eliminates the possibility that "extra bright spots" could be identified as vacancies. A final calibration experiment which can be mentioned is that of Petroff and Washburn [11], who have field evaporated individual atoms from an irradiated iridium surface and counted the number of atoms associated with such bright spots. They find one more atom than the number of lattice sites and this, again, identifies extra bright spots with interstitial atoms. We have repeated this experiment and have found this conclusion to be true in platinum. The full confirmation of experiments such as those of Petroff and Washburn must await though quantitative measurements with Müllers atom probe [12].

### 3.2. Irradiation experiments

#### 3.2.1. Stage III recovery

In *platinum*, irradiations were performed *above* and *below* stage III, where we use the temperature range attributed by Jackson and Herschbach [3] to stage III. The observations made in platinum irradiated at $100°K$ (below stage III) and warmed through stage III are the following:

   a. Extra bright spots are present prior to stage III but not after stage III (fig. 3).

   b. The extra bright spots have a major axis along a [100] direction, which is expected for a split interstitial in a face-centered cubic lattice [13].

It is of interest to remark that the impurity levels in the platinum used in this experiment excludes the possibility that the extra bright spots are due to impurities or that a trapping of defects at impurities occurs. These observations, in conjunction with the above-mentioned calibration experiments, show quite clearly that split interstitials are removed in stage III in platinum.

In the case of *tungsten*, the material has been similarly irradiated below and above stage III and the following observations made.

   a. The bright spots are present prior to stage III but not after stage III (fig. 4). It might also be remarked that we did not observe such bright spots when we operated the field ion microscope at $80°K$.

   b. The major axis of the bright spot defects is [110] which, again, is the predicted major axis of the split interstitial in the body-centered cubic lattice.

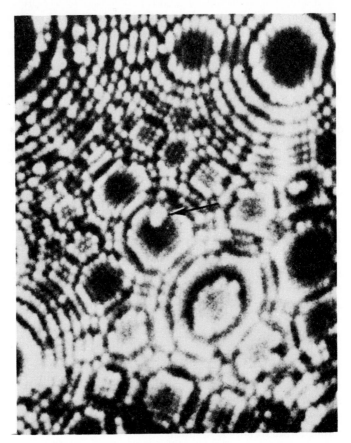

Fig. 3. Interstitial atoms in neutron irradiated platinum. These interstitial atoms disappear during stage III annealing.

c. The migration of substitutional impurities would require a vacancy to move.
Since vacancy motion is not observed, substitutional impurities can thus be excluded from contributing to stage III recovery. Also, the impurity interstitial levels
(about 5 ppm) are too low to account for stage III. Furthermore, impurity interstitial
atoms are not detectable in tungsten by standard field ion microscope techniques.

These arguments show quite conclusively that a self-interstitial atom is removed
in stage III in tungsten. In addition, though, the observed vacancy concentration is
also lowered in stage III in tungsten, which is only consistent with an interstitial
annihilating a vacancy, if the vacancy does not move (fig. 5).

### 3.2.2. Stage IV recovery

In neutron irradiated *platinum* the following observations were made. After annealing in the temperature range where according to quenching experiments vacan-

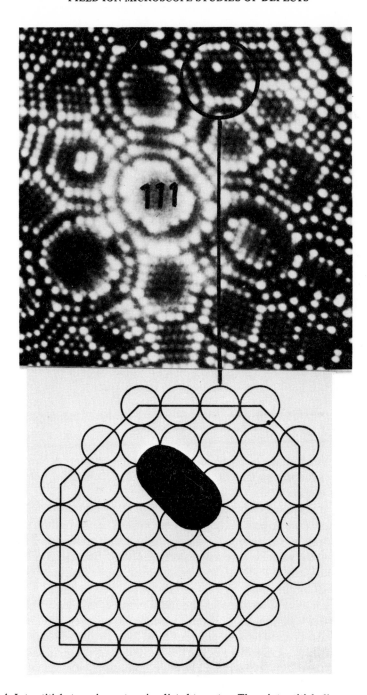

Fig. 4. Interstitial atoms in neutron irradiated tungsten. These interstitials disappear during stage III annealing.

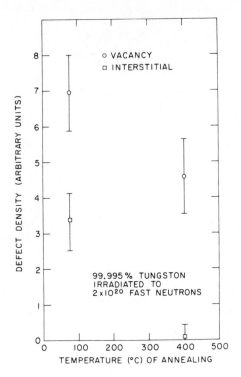

Fig. 5. Concentration of interstitial and vacancy defects as a function of annealing temperature in neutron irradiated tungsten.

cies are known to move, the concentration of small defect clusters decreases and vacancy dislocation loops grow (fig. 6). This can only be accounted for in terms of vacancies moving in stage IV.

*Tungsten* — as mentioned above — was irradiated at a temperature above stage III (400°C) and the vacancy concentration was determined (fig. 7). In this figure the vacancy concentration is compared for specimens irradiated *above* and *below* stage III. If in tungsten the vacancy were mobile in stage III, no vacancies should be left after an irradiation at 400°C. Hence this measurement shows that vacancies are *not* mobile in stage III in tungsten.

A sufficient and conclusive argument on the mobility of vacancies is given by the experiments of Jeannotte [15]. Jeannotte irradiated tungsten to a fast neutron flux of $\approx 10^{18}$ nvt. Specimens were prepared from these irradiated wires and examined in the field ion microscope. The irradiated wires were then heated to temperatures near 900°C for varying times and the vacancy concentration was determined. To this end, a new technique was developed to for counting the number of atomic sites. This technique involves a calibration of the number of atoms in a

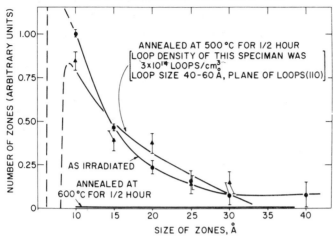

Fig. 6. Change in the size distribution of vacancy clusters as a function of annealing temperature in neutron irradiated platinum.

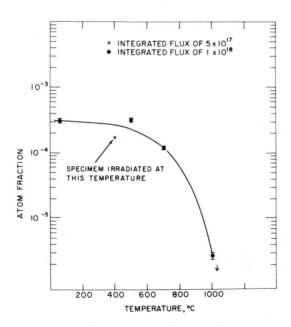

Fig. 7. A comparison of the vacancy concentration in neutron irradiated tungsten. The point at 400°C is a measurement based on a specimen irradiated at 400°C, which is clearly above stage III in tungsten.

given tip as a function of the average radius of the tip. The statistical uncertainty of this measurement was found to be negligible for the number of tips and sites examined. The latter number, for example, was approximately $9 \times 10^5$.

In the temperature range near 900°C, the observed vacancy density showed a monotonic decrease with time (fig. 8). These data were then compared to various orders of reactions, and the best fit of the data was found for first order kinetics (fig. 9). The activation energy for the process, obtained on the basis of this data, was 3.3 eV. This activation energy was determined from the ratio of the annealing rates at 870° and 900°C. The slopes used were obtained mathematically by means of a weighted linear regression, the weighting factor being based on the actual number of observed vacancies. The error associated with this measurement is quite small. An interval of 0.2 eV for example, has a 95% confidence level.

Another interesting comparison is a consideration of the number of jumps a vacancy would make in stage III if it moved with an energy of motion of 3.3. eV. The number of jumps $n_j$ is given by

$$n_j = Azvt \exp(-E_M/kT) ,$$

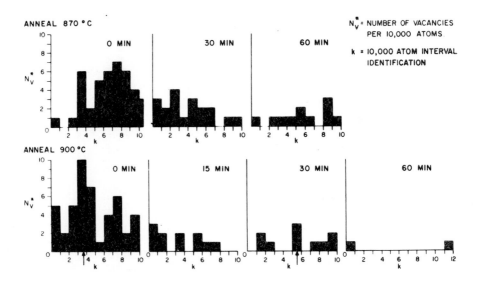

Fig. 8. Vacancy distribution in neutron irradiated tungsten as a function of time at various annealing temperatures.

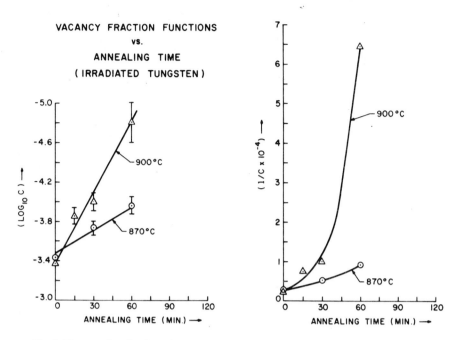

Fig. 9. Vacancy fraction functions versus annealing times for irradiated tungsten.

where

$z$ = the coordination number of the lattice

$A$ = an entropy factor ($\approx 10$)

$\nu$ = the frequency of atomic vibration ($\approx 10^{13}$ sec$^{-1}$)

and $k$ is Boltzmann's constant. For 1 sec annealing time the mean number of jumps at 700°K is found to be negligible. If on the other hand we take as energy of motion of vacancies the difference of the activation energy of self-diffusion (Andelin, Knight and Kahn [16]) and the energy of formation of a vacancy (Schultz [10]) then, again, the number of jumps a vacancy makes at 700°K is negligible.

## References

[1] H.G.van Bueren, Imperfections in Crystals (North-Holland Publishing Co., Amsterdam, 1960).
[2] A.Sosin and K.R.Garr, Phys. Rev. 162 (1967) 681.
[3] J.J.Jackson and K.Herschbach, Phys. Rev. 173 (1968) 664.
[4] H.Schultz, Acta Met. 12 (1964) 649.
[5] E.W.Müller, Advances in Electronics and Electron Physics, Vol. 13 (1960) 84.

[6] E.W.Müller, private communication.

[7] M.K.Sinha and E.W.Müller, J. Appl. Phys. 35 (1964) 1256.

[8] M.J.Attardo and J.M.Galligan, Phys. Rev. 161 (1967) 558.

[9] J.M.Galligan, unpublished results.

[10] H.Schultz, Lattice Defects in Quenched Metals (Academic Press, New York, 1965) p. 761.

[11] P.Petroff and J.Washburn, Jül. conf. 2 (Vol. 2) 1968, p. 485.

[12] E.W.Müller, 15th Field Emission Symposium, 1968.

[13] A.Seeger, P.Schiller and H.Kronmüller, Phil. Mag. 5 (1960) 853.

[14] J.J.Jackson, Lattice Defects in Quenched Metals (Academic Press, New York, 1965) p. 467.

[15] D.Jeannotte, Ph. D. Thesis, Columbia University, New York, 1967.

[16] R.L.Andelin, J.D.Knight and M.Kahn, Trans. A.I.M.E. 233 (1965) 19.

## Discussion

*J.R.Beeler Jr.:* It is interesting to note the striking similarity between the low temperature defect state depicted in Professor Müller's FIM micrographs for an atomic collision cascade and that shown in fig. 10 which comes from our computer experiments on collision cascades in metals at liquid helium temperature. One sees the same over-all spatial dimensions, the same general deployment of vacancy clusters and interstitials and the same defect density in the computer experiment ·damage state as that observed by Professor Müller. We have also noticed the production of two disjoint damage centers as a consequence of a single primary event as did Professor Müller. This comparison indicates that the damage state configuration revealed in the FIM using the field evaporation technique is perhaps quite similar to that produced by a collision cascade in the bulk. In this regard we find in computer experiments that the main perturbation of the bulk damage state which occurs as successive atom planes are evaporated away is merely the conversion of metastable vacancy configurations into the form of the most stable configuration.

*R.S.Nelson:* The reason for more damage at the surface may result from the fact that the effective displacement energy is perhaps only ~ 5 eV as against ~ 25 eV within the bulk.

*P.Wilkes:* In all the field ion images one always sees the surface. One may evaporate to see the bulk, but at any instant one examines the surface. Two points may then be made: 1. The frequency will not be the same. The formation energy of defects is expected to be different on the surface than in the interior. Counts of the surface defects will then not be typical of densities in the bulk 2. The nature of defects will be different, e.g. relaxations round a defect will be different at a surface than in the interior. They consequently will not look the same. I do not think that distinctions between crowdions etc. are meaningful under FIM conditions.

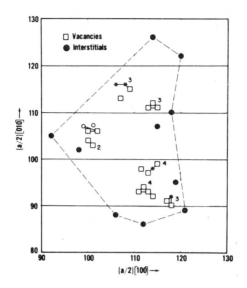

Fig. 10. (Discussion of papers by E.W.Müller and J.M.Galligan) Computer simulation of collision cascades in metals at liquid helium temperature.

*E.W.Müller:* I have pointed out in the paper that the energy of formation of a surface vacancy is much less than that of a bulk vacancy. I agree that relaxation effects preclude detailed interpretations of surface configurations.

*A.D.LeClaire:* I agree with Dr. Wilkes, but I think there are other difficulties, too. The technique would seem, if I understood it correctly, to reveal atoms most readily where field gradients are largest, i.e. on edges or steps and other special positions on the surface. It seems then that when, for example, counting defect concentrations in the way Dr. Müller described, one may be sampling quite *un*typical areas of the surface and therefore arrive at quite misleading results even for surface concentrations. (This is quite apart from whether surface concentrations in any case are representative of the bulk properties).

*E.W.Müller:* By performing the field evaporation process in sufficiently small steps, a reliable cross section through the bulk can be obtained. Choosing a specific, well resolved net plane for counting does not select an unspecific volume element, as in the interior this plane is not distinguished from other regions.

*Y.Quere:* In fig. 8 of your paper (p. 570, two damaged regions at the ends of a close-packed direction), what makes you think that channeling (rather than focussing) is responsible for the observed event?

*E.W.Müller:* I indicated in my paper, that I should prefer the *focussing* mechanism, but unambiguous experimental evidence is lacking.

# STUDIES OF POINT DEFECTS AND DEFECT CLUSTERS
# BY SMALL-ANGLE AND DIFFUSE SCATTERING
# OF X-RAYS AND NEUTRONS

## W.SCHMATZ

*Institut für Festkörper- und Neutronenphysik, Kernforschungsanlage Jülich, Germany*

## 1. Introduction

Scattering of X-rays or neutrons by interstitials, vacancies or clusters of such defects can be developed into a method of large potentialities. Especially, information on the local configuration of defects and atoms around defects can be obtained. Because of severe experimental difficulties only modest progress has been achieved during the past years. Nevertheless, considerable efforts are underway and it is worthwhile to outline theory, results and experimental techniques.

The scattering is described by the double differential scattering cross section per atom, $d^2\sigma/d\Omega\,d\omega$, per unit solid angle $d\Omega$ and per unit energy transfer $\hbar\,d\omega$ for a given momentum transfer $\hbar\varkappa$ and energy transfer $\hbar\omega$. $\varkappa$ is the difference between the wave vectors $k_0$ and $k_1$ before and after the scattering process respectively. The absolute values $k_0$ and $k_1$ are $2\pi/\lambda_0$ and $2\pi/\lambda_1$, where $\lambda$ is the wavelength.

Neutron- and X-ray-scattering are formulated within the same theoretical framework. In the first Born approximation $d^2\sigma/d\Omega\,d\omega$ for a monoatomic substance without spin and isotope incoherence is proportional to the scattering function $S$:

$$\frac{d^2\sigma}{d\Omega\,d\omega} = a^2\,\frac{k_1}{k_0}\,S(\varkappa,\omega)\,; \tag{1}$$

$a$ is the neutron or X-ray scattering length for a single atom. $S$ is the Fourier transform to the space-time correlation function $G(\mathbf{r},t)$ of the scattering system [1,2]:

$$S(\varkappa,\omega) = \frac{1}{2\pi}\int G(\mathbf{r},t)\,e^{i(\varkappa\cdot\mathbf{r}-\omega t)}\,d\mathbf{r}\,dt\,. \tag{2}$$

In the classical limit $G(\mathbf{r},t)$ gives the probability of finding the center of any atom at $\mathbf{r}_0 + \mathbf{r}$ at time $t_0 + t$ if the center of an atom was at $r_0$ at time $t_0$ *.

---

\* X-ray measurements give the correlation function between electron-densities. In eqs. (1) and (2) the same $a$ has been used for every atom. There may for instance be slight differences in the values of $a$ for an interstitial atom or an atom on a regular lattice site.

For polyatomic substances, $a$ and $G(\mathbf{r},t)$ in eqs. (1) and (2) have to be replaced by different scattering lengths and correlation functions $G_{\mu\nu}(\mathbf{r},t)$, where $G_{\mu\nu}$ denotes the correlation function between atoms of species $\mu$ and $\nu$.

With neutrons one can measure momentum and energy transfer and thus $S(\varkappa,\omega)$ or $G(\mathbf{r},t)$ is obtained. For X-rays the energy transfers are too small to be measured. One has the integrated scattering function for a fixed $\varkappa$, namely

$$\frac{d\sigma}{d\Omega}(\varkappa) = a^2 \int S(\varkappa,\omega) \, d\omega = a^2 \int G(\mathbf{r},0) \, e^{i\varkappa\cdot\mathbf{r}} \, d\mathbf{r} \,. \tag{3}$$

Thus we get $G(\mathbf{r},0)$, the instantaneous correlation function.

With the definition of a long-time asymptotic value $G(\mathbf{r},\infty)$, which exists in crystals if atoms are not diffusing, one can split $G(\mathbf{r},t)$ into

$$G(\mathbf{r},t) = G(\mathbf{r},\infty) + G'(\mathbf{r},t) \tag{4}$$

where $G'(\mathbf{r},t)$ tends to zero for $t \to \infty$. Substitution of (4) into (2) gives the elastic part of $d^2\sigma/d\Omega \, d\omega$

$$\frac{d\sigma}{d\Omega}(\varkappa)_{\mathrm{el}} = a^2 \, I(\varkappa) \,, \tag{5}$$

where

$$I(\varkappa) = \int G(\mathbf{r},\infty) \, e^{i\varkappa\cdot\mathbf{r}} \, d\mathbf{r} \,. \tag{5a}$$

For ideal crystals, $G(\mathbf{r},\infty)$ is periodic and elastic scattering occurs only at reciprocal lattice points $\tau_{hkl}$. Between Bragg-peaks, $I(\varkappa)$ is different from zero only for disordered crystals. This is the reason why small defect concentrations of the order of $10^{-3}$ or less can be observed by scattering techniques.

Information on defect concentration, lattice distortion, short range order and clustering can be extracted from $I(\varkappa)$ as will be discussed in the next chapter. Experiments with neutrons give directly $I(\varkappa)$ if energy selection is provided. For X-ray-scattering the contribution of $G'(\mathbf{r},t)$, called thermal diffuse scattering, can be subtracted approximately using the values of the undistorted crystal. However, $G'$ may also be modified by introducing defects in the scattering system. For crystals containing defects, inelastic neutron scattering is just beginning to explore $S(\varkappa,\omega)$ [3].

Experimental difficulties due to low scattering intensities and severe background problems will be discussed in the last chapter. Considerations on scattering intensities show that even with these difficulties, optimized scattering experiments at low defect concentrations should give high information rate. The development and use of high intensity sources and of multidetector arrangements are the most important factors.

## 2. Scattering theory

### 2.1. General features of elastic scattering

For a polyatomic substance the elastic scattering cross section per atom is given by

$$\frac{d\sigma}{d\Omega}(\varkappa)_{el} = \frac{1}{N} \sum_{i,j=1}^{N} a_i \, e^{-w_i} a_j \, e^{-w_j} \, e^{i\varkappa \cdot (\mathbf{r}_i - \mathbf{r}_j)} . \tag{6}$$

$\mathbf{r}_i$ is the thermally averaged position vector of the center of atom $i$, $a_i$ its scattering length and $e^{-w_i}$ the Debye-Waller-factor. $N$ is the number of atoms in the system. $e^{-w_i}$ may be different for atoms in disturbed positions and at regular lattice sites [4]. In principle this can be observed by comparing Debye-Waller-factors for diffuse scattering and for Bragg-peaks. In this sense, elastic neutron scattering would inherently be a supplementary technique to Mössbauer-resonance-absorption experiments. In the following we assume that $e^{-w_i}$ is equal for atoms of one element.

For neutron scattering, eq. (6) must be averaged with respect to the statistical distribution of different isotopes and spin states of the compound nuclei. In this case,

$$\left(\frac{d\sigma}{d\Omega}\right)_{el} = \left(\frac{d\sigma}{d\Omega}\right)_{coh,\,el} + \left(\frac{d\sigma}{d\Omega}\right)_{inc,\,el} \tag{7}$$

$$= \frac{1}{N} \sum_{i,j} \bar{a}_i \, \bar{a}_j \, e^{-w_i} \, e^{-w_j} \, e^{i\varkappa \cdot (\mathbf{r}_i - \mathbf{r}_j)} + \sum_{\nu=1}^{\nu_0} c_\nu \, e^{-2w_\nu} \, (\overline{a_\nu^2} - \overline{a_\nu}^2).$$

$\nu$ denotes the summation index for the different elements in the scattering system and $C_\nu$ the respective concentrations ($\sum C_\nu = 1$). $\bar{a}_i$ is the coherent scattering length of the element situated at the position $\mathbf{r}_i$. In most cases $\bar{a}_i$ is known within an accuracy of the order of one percent [5]. From measurements of the refractive index it can be determined even more accurately [6]. As an advantage over X-ray measurements, $a$ is here independent of $|\varkappa|$. To date, incoherent scattering cross sections $4\pi(\overline{a^2} - \overline{a}^2)$ are known rather inaccurately [5]. Measurements have been made only in special cases where the incoherent scattering is very large or required determination in studies of defect scattering [7–9].

For X-rays, equation (7) can also be used with $\bar{a}_i$ as the product of atomic form factors, electron scattering length and polarization factor. The second term in (7) is zero. We disregard any dependence of the atomic form factor on its special atomic environment and introduce instead of $\bar{a}_i \, e^{-w_i}$ the scattering length $f_i$. Furthermore, we use the probability $P_{\mu\nu}(\mathbf{r}, \infty) = P_{\mu\nu}(\mathbf{r})$ of finding the center of any atom of species $\nu$ at position $\mathbf{r}_0 + \mathbf{r}$ if an atom of species $\mu$ is at position $\mathbf{r}_0$ and obtain

$$\frac{d\sigma}{d\Omega}(\varkappa)_{\text{coh, el}} = \frac{1}{N} \sum_{i,j=1}^{N} f_i f_j \, e^{i\varkappa \cdot (\mathbf{r}_i - \mathbf{r}_j)} = \sum_{\mu,\nu=1}^{\nu_0} c_\mu f_\mu f_\nu \int P_{\mu\nu}(\mathbf{r}) \, e^{i\varkappa \cdot \mathbf{r}} \, d\mathbf{r}.$$

$$(8)$$

## 2.2. *Point defect scattering*

If there is no lattice distortion around defects then $P_{\mu\nu}(\mathbf{r})$ is a sum of $\delta$-functions $\delta(\mathbf{r} - \mathbf{r}_n)$, where $\mathbf{r}_n$ is a lattice vector *. Short range order, long range order and clustering are described by probability coefficients $\alpha_{\mu\nu}(\mathbf{r}_n)$. In this case (compare fig. 1a and 1b),

$$P_{\mu\nu}(\mathbf{r}) = \sum_n \alpha_{\mu\nu}(\mathbf{r}_n) \, \delta(\mathbf{r} - \mathbf{r}_n) \,,$$

$$(9)$$

with

$$\int \delta(\mathbf{r} - \mathbf{r}_n) \, d\mathbf{r} = 1 \,.$$

$$(9a)$$

Summation in (9) can be extended to infinite $\mathbf{r}_n$'s if Bragg-peaks are not considered quantitatively. Otherwise, (9) has to be multiplied with the self-convolution of the particle size function (see e.g. ref. 10). Equation (8) and (9) are extensively discussed in text books and review articles [10,11]. We want to point out that according to (9) the diffuse scattering is periodic in reciprocal space if the $\varkappa$-dependence of $f$ is omitted.

In the special case of random distribution of substitutional defects, $\alpha_{\mu\nu}$ is constant and equal to $C_\nu$ for $\mathbf{r}_n \neq 0$ and equal to $\delta_{\mu\nu}$ for $\mathbf{r}_n = 0$. In this case the diffuse scattering cross section is $(\overline{f^2} - \overline{f}^2)$ and called Laue monotonic scattering. For a binary alloy this reduces to

$$\left(\frac{d\sigma}{d\Omega}\right)_{\text{coh, el}} = C(1-C)(f_2 - f_1)^2 \,.$$

$$(10)$$

For point defects, such as interstitials, one has to consider the lattice distortion. Atoms surrounding a single defect in an infinite medium are displaced from ideal lattice sites by $s_n(\mathbf{r}_n)$ (fig. 2). $\mathbf{r}_n$ is the distance vector in the ideal lattice. For small concentrations of randomly distributed defects (characterized by subscript 2), with the assumption of linear superposition of the $s_n$, one obtains in first approximation

---

* If interstitials are present, additional sublattices and correlation functions between them must be introduced, e.g. ref. [11].

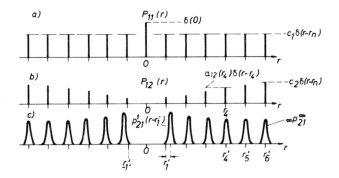

Fig. 1. One-dimensional correlation function $P_{\mu\nu}$ for a substitutional defect:
    a) randomly distributed defects in an undistorted lattice;
    b) clustering in an undistorted lattice;
    c) random defect distribution with lattice distortion, causing an expansion around the defect.

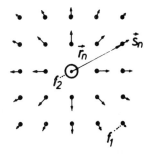

Fig. 2. Displacement field around a single substitutional defect.

[12–16] ($\mathbf{r}'_n$ is the averaged lattice vector of the distorted lattice *):

$$\frac{d\sigma}{d\Omega}(\varkappa)_{\text{coh, el}} = C|(f_2 - f_1) + i f_1 \varkappa \cdot \mathbf{s}(\varkappa)|^2 , \tag{11}$$

where

$$\mathbf{s}(\varkappa) = \sum_{n=1}^{\infty} \mathbf{s}_n(\mathbf{r}_n)\, e^{i\varkappa \cdot \mathbf{r}'_n} . \tag{11a}$$

---

\* In [15] ideal lattice vectors instead of average distorted lattice vectors have been used and lead to additional peaks very near to the Bragg-peaks. Experimental evidence for these satellite peaks [17] from fast neutron irradiated BeO is not convincing because the observed extra-peak can also be explained by clustering.

For the derivation of (11), Huang [12] and Borie [13] have implicitly used the correlation functions $P_{\mu\nu}(\mathbf{r})$. Due to the lattice distortions $\mathbf{s}_n(\mathbf{r}_n)$ of all defects, the δ-functions of $P_{\mu\nu}$ have to be replaced by broadened functions $p_{\mu\nu}^\infty(\mathbf{r}-\mathbf{r}_n')$ except for $\mathbf{r}_n' = 0$ (fig. 1c). $p_{\mu\nu}$ approaches a final profile $p_{\mu\nu}^\infty(\mathbf{r}-\mathbf{r}_n')$ with increasing $\mathbf{r}_n'$. The Fourier transform of $p_{\mu\nu}^\infty$ gives an additional Debye-Waller-factor for Bragg-reflections. The width of $p_{\mu\nu}$ increases with $\mathbf{r}_n'$. For statistically distributed substitutional defects there is $\int p_{\mu\nu}^n(\mathbf{r}-\mathbf{r}_n')\,d\mathbf{r} = c_v$ as above for $\delta(\mathbf{r}-\mathbf{r}_n)$. The centers of the $p_{\mu\nu}^n$ are displaced from the average lattice vectors $\mathbf{r}_n'$ by a distance proportional to $\mathbf{s}_n(\mathbf{r}_n)$. Considering terms up to first order and a part of second order one obtains eq. (11). If defects cause strong lattice distortions higher order terms have to be included.

The distortion caused by a single defect can be described by "virtual forces" $\mathbf{f}_n$. The $\mathbf{f}_n$'s are acting on the atoms of an ideal crystal and give together with the lattice forces described by the displacements and the coupling parameters of the ideal crystal the same displacement field as the defect (fig. 3). With this approach, Kanzaki [18] and more generally Eisenriegler [16] obtain

$$\phi(\varkappa) \cdot \mathbf{s}(\varkappa) = \mathbf{f}(\varkappa) \tag{12}$$

with

$$\mathbf{f}(\varkappa) = \sum_{n=1}^{n_0} \mathbf{f}_n(\mathbf{r}_n)\, e^{i\varkappa \cdot \mathbf{r}_n'} . \tag{12a}$$

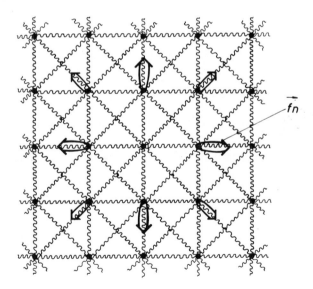

Fig. 3. Virtual forces of first and second nearest neighbours applied to an ideal lattice.

$\phi(\varkappa)$ is the dynamical matrix of the ideal crystal in harmonic approximation. This is known for instance from one-phonon-neutron scattering. As an example, in a symmetry direction of a monoatomic cubic crystal one has

$$\Phi(\varkappa) = m \begin{vmatrix} \omega_L^2 & 0 & 0 \\ 0 & \omega_{T_1}^2 & 0 \\ 0 & 0 & \omega_{T_2}^2 \end{vmatrix} \tag{13}$$

where $\omega_L$ and $\omega_T$ are the longitudinal and transversal phonon frequencies respectively. $\phi(\varkappa)$, $\mathbf{f}(\varkappa)$ and $\mathbf{s}(\varkappa)$ are periodic in the reciprocal lattice, whereas the scattering cross section $d\sigma/d\Omega$, because of $\varkappa \cdot \mathbf{s}(\varkappa)$ in eq. (11), on the average is an increasing function with $|\varkappa|$.

The $\mathbf{f}_n$'s are rapidly decreasing with distance from the defect, whereas the $\mathbf{s}_n$'s are proportional to $1/r_n^2$ only. This and the application of $\phi(\varkappa)$ is the advantage for using eq. (12). One can hope that with (12) $\mathbf{f}(\varkappa)$ can directly be determined from scattering experiments as a proper defect description.

For the special case of a dumb-bell interstitial and a vacancy in copper the "virtual forces" have been extracted by Eisenriegler [16] from near neighbour displacements, calculated by Seeger, Mann and v.Jan [19], using the phonon frequencies for Cu [20]. The scattering cross sections in symmetry directions have been calculated. Fig. 4 shows as an example the values for the [110] direction. The hump for the dumb-bell interstitial originates from interference of the atomic form factors $(f_2-f_1)$ with $if_1\varkappa\mathbf{s}(\mathbf{k})$. It seems possible that the hump may change if higher order terms in eq. (11) are included.

For the long wavelength limit, characterized by

$$|\mathbf{q}| \ll 2\pi/a \qquad \text{with} \qquad \mathbf{q} = \varkappa - \tau_{hkl} \tag{14}$$

(a lattice parameter, $\tau_{000}$ included in definition (14)), one obtains a quantitative relation between the differential scattering cross section and macroscopic quantities [16].

In symmetry directions of cubic crystals, for $\phi(\mathbf{q})$ values, $\omega_i = v_i q$ can be used where the $v_i$ are the sound velocities. In other directions $\phi(\mathbf{q})$ can be calculated also from elastic constants [21,22].

Equation (12a) expanded into a power series with respect to $\mathbf{q}\mathbf{r}_n$ gives in first order approximation

$$\mathbf{f}(\mathbf{q}) = i \sum_{n=1}^{n_o} \mathbf{f}_n(\mathbf{r}_n)(\mathbf{q}\cdot\mathbf{r}_n) = i\,\mathbf{P}\mathbf{q} \tag{15}$$

with

$$\sum_{n=1}^{n_o} \mathbf{f}_n(\mathbf{r}_n) = 0.$$

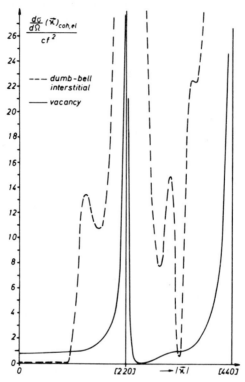

Fig. 4. Calculated scattering cross sections for point defects in copper in first order approxima-
tion. For $f_2$ in eq. (11) $2f_1 \cos (\varkappa \cdot \mathbf{l}_i/2) - f_1$ is used with $\mathbf{l}_i$ as the distance vector of the two
atoms of the dumb-bell. The cross section is averaged over the three possible [100] directions.

$\mathbf{P}$ is the double force tensor of the point defect (see e.g. [23]). A simple type of $\mathbf{P}$
for a cubic crystal is

$$\begin{vmatrix} A & 0 & 0 \\ 0 & B & 0 \\ 0 & 0 & B \end{vmatrix}$$

for a cartesian coordinate system coinciding with the principal axes of $\mathbf{P}$.
With eqs. (13), (12) and (11) one obtains in the long wavelength limit

$$\frac{d\sigma}{d\Omega}(\varkappa)_{\text{coh, el}} = C\{(f_2 - f_1) - f_1 \, (\tau_{hkl} + \mathbf{q}) \, \Phi^{-1}(\mathbf{q}) \, \mathbf{Pq}\}^2$$

$$= C\{f_L(\varkappa) - f_D(\varkappa)\}^2 \,, \tag{16}$$

where the first term in brackets is defined as the Laue scattering length and the second one as the displacement scattering length. The cross section must be averaged if there is a distribution of orientation axes of anisotropic defects. $f_D$ shall be discussed for special cases:

(i) Isotropic defect $(A = B)$ in isotropic medium:
From eqs. (10), (12) and (15)

$$f_D(\varkappa) = f_1(\tau_{hkl} + q) \frac{A \, q}{m \, v_L^2 \, q^2} \, , \tag{17}$$

where $v_L$ is the longitudinal sound velocity. According to elasticity theory [24]

$$\frac{A}{m \, v_L^2} = \frac{\Delta V}{\gamma \Omega} \, , \tag{17a}$$

where $\Delta V$ is the volume change per defect caused by distortion in a finite medium and $\Delta V/\gamma$ the same quantity in an infinite medium. $\gamma$ is equal to $3(1-\nu)/(1+\nu)$ with $\nu$ as Poisson's ratio. $\Omega$ is the atomic volume. Eq. (17) can also be derived from

$$s_n(r_n) = \frac{\Delta V}{4\pi\gamma} \frac{r_n}{r_n^3} \quad \text{with} \quad s(q) = i \frac{\Delta V}{\gamma \Omega} \frac{q}{q^2} \, . \tag{18}$$

For the special case $\tau = 0$ one obtains

$$\frac{d\sigma}{d\Omega}(\varkappa)_{\text{coh, el}} = C \left\{ (f_2 - f_1) - f_1 \frac{\Delta V}{\gamma\Omega} \right\}^2 , \quad |\varkappa| \ll 2\pi/a \, . \tag{19}$$

Assuming an interstitial with $f_L = f_2 - f_1 = f_1$ and $\Delta V/\gamma\Omega$ approximately unity, almost no scattering remains for small $\varkappa$'s. This situation holds for the calculated scattering cross section in fig. 4, whereas for the vacancy $(\Delta V$ small) little influence is seen *. Eq. (19) can be understood in the way that excess scattering density introduced by $(f_2 - f_1)$ is diminished or increased by outward or inward shift of material surrounding the defect.

Near the Bragg-peaks we obtain

$$\frac{d\sigma}{d\Omega}(\varkappa \to \tau_{hkl})_{\text{coh, el}} = C \left\{ (f_2 - f_1) - f_1 (\tau_{hkl} + q) \frac{\Delta V q}{\gamma\Omega q^2} \right\}^2 . \tag{20}$$

If $q$ is parallel to $\tau_{hkl}$ and approaching zero the cross section goes to infinity as $1/q^2$ ** and is proportional to the distortion volume squared.

---

* The anisotropy of the dumb-bell interstitial and of the copper host lattice does not appreciably change this general remark.
** For a crystal of finite size $D$ this singularity is smeared out into a region of $1/D$ diameter in reciprocal space. No infinity remains.

Therefore in this region an interstitial has a very high cross section as compared to a vacancy (fig. 4). If the distortion term $f_D$ is comparable to $f_L$ the cross section is assymetric with respect to the Bragg-peak, because $\tau_{hkl} \cdot \mathbf{q}$ changes sign in passing through the Bragg-peak.

(ii) Isotropic defect in anisotropic medium:
   For $\mathbf{q}$ parallel to [100], [110] or [111] directions in an anisotropic cubic crystal, eq. (17) can be used further with corresponding longitudinal sound velocities for the different directions. The cross section implies the anisotropy of the host lattice.

(iii) Anisotropic defect in anisotropic medium:
   One may hope that the scattering pattern reveals directly the anisotropy of defects. This is true if the defects are oriented mainly along one of their possible directions and even for random distribution of orientations if the double force tensor is strongly anisotropic. There is approximately a 10% deviation from the isotropic defect scattering pattern if the anisotropy $\eta = (A-B)/B$ is 30%. For $\eta < 1$ this deviation is approximately proportional to $\eta^2$. Anisotropic scattering patterns have been computer-calculated from $s_n$ for carbon interstitials in iron [25]. The host lattice has been assumed as isotropic and changes in the numerical results are to be expected from the rigorous treatment presented here.
   The scattering cross sections derived so far are only valid for very dilute solid solutions, because defect interaction must be expected at high concentrations. Until now, scattering cross sections similar to eq. (11) have mainly been applied to cases of highly concentrated alloys:

$$\frac{d\sigma}{d\Omega}(\varkappa)_{\text{coh, el}} = C(1-C)\left\{(f_2-f_1) + i\bar{f}\varkappa\bar{s}(\varkappa)\right\}^2 , \tag{21}$$

where $\bar{s}$ is an appropriate average of the shifts of the $p_{\mu\nu}^n$ [26]. This is a reasonable approach because with $\bar{s} \to 0$ the Laue monotonic scattering is obtained. But $\bar{s}$ is no longer a pure defect property. Nevertheless, it is also of considerable interest for our subject, to what extent scattering patterns of highly concentrated alloys can be described with eq. (21) since in the low concentration limit the pure defect properties should be obtained. For highly concentrated binary alloys, Borie introduced in addition to $\bar{s}(\varkappa)$ the $\alpha_{\mu\nu}^n$ explained above [26]. Another refinement in this direction has been made by Krivoglaz [14] for the condition of thermal equilibrium, where the defect interactions and the $\alpha_{\mu\nu}^n$'s are closely connected.

2.3. *Small angle scattering*
   Clusters of defects give usually a strong increase of the scattering cross section at small $\varkappa$-values. Equation (8) can also be used to describe such phenomena. For monoatomic substances this gives:

$$\frac{d\sigma}{d\Omega}(\varkappa)_{\text{coh, el}} = f^2 \int P(\mathbf{r}) \, e^{i\varkappa \cdot \mathbf{r}} \, d\mathbf{r} = f^2 \int \widehat{\rho(\mathbf{r})\rho(\mathbf{r})} \, e^{i\varkappa \cdot \mathbf{r}} \, d\mathbf{r} , \qquad (22)$$

where $P(\mathbf{r})$ according to the definition above is denoted as the self-convolution of the atomic density $\rho(\mathbf{r})$. As for small angle scattering, $d\sigma/d\Omega$ is only of interest in a small region around the origin of the reciprocal lattice (linear dimension $\kappa_0$) $\rho(\mathbf{r})$ can be smeared out with a function of width $1/\kappa_0$ without appreciable error *. Scattering at small particles is treated extensively for X-rays in textbooks [28] and proceedings [29] and for neutrons in [27] and [30]. Only three special cases, namely voids, dislocation loops and defect cascades shall be discussed here. For point defect clusters, because of their low concentration, the mean density is nearly the same as for ideal crystals. This allows one to replace $\rho(\mathbf{r})$ in eq. (22) by the density difference $\Delta\rho(\mathbf{r})$. Further if there is no correlation between the defect clusters, the scattering cross section can be written as

$$\frac{d\sigma}{d\Omega}(\varkappa)_{\text{coh, el}} = n_{\text{cl}} f^2 \int \widehat{\Delta\rho_{\text{s}}(\mathbf{r}) \, \Delta\rho_{\text{s}}(\mathbf{r})} \, e^{i\varkappa \cdot \mathbf{r}} \, d\mathbf{r}$$

$$= n_{\text{cl}} f^2 \, |\int \Delta\rho_{\text{s}}(\mathbf{r}) \, e^{i\varkappa \cdot \mathbf{r}} \, d\mathbf{r}|^2 , \qquad (23)$$

where $n_{\text{cl}}$ is the number of clusters relative to the number of atoms. $\Delta\rho_{\text{s}}(\mathbf{r})$ is the atomic density difference for a single cluster.

Assuming spherical voids of radius $R$ and of unique size one obtains from (23) in Guinier's approximation [28]

$$\frac{d\sigma}{d\Omega}(\varkappa)_{\text{coh, el}} = n_{\text{cl}} \, n_{\text{v}}^2 \, e^{-\kappa^2 R^2/5} = C_{\text{V}}' \cdot n_{\text{V}} \, e^{-\kappa^2 R^2/5} \qquad (24)$$

where $n_{\text{v}}$ is the number of vacancies clustered into one void and $C_{\text{V}}'$ the concentration of clustered vacancies. Further it can be shown that

$$\int \frac{d\sigma}{d\Omega}(\varkappa)_{\text{coh, el}} \, d\varkappa = n_{\text{cl}} f^2 \, n_{\text{V}} = C_{\text{V}}' f^2 . \qquad (25)$$

Equation (25) is independent of the special shape or size of the voids. Therefore, with the integrated scattering cross section around the origin of reciprocal lattice the concentration of clustered vacancies can be obtained even if there is a size and/ or shape distribution. From (24) and (25), experiments can determine $C_{\text{V}}'$, $n_{\text{V}} \cdot C_{\text{V}}'$ and $R$, and therefore the assumption above can be checked.

Scattering of edge-dislocation loops is treated by Seeger et al. [31,32] with linear elasticity theory for isotropic and anisotropic mediums and with second order elas-

---

* In the case of polyatomic substances instead of $f\rho$ for neutrons [27] a density of scattering lengths and for X-rays [28] the electron density is used.

ticity theory for an isotropic medium. Edge dislocation loops of random orientation distribution gives for $\kappa\rho_0 < 2$ a scattering cross section [31]

$$\frac{d\sigma}{d\Omega}(\varkappa)_{\text{coh, el}} = n_{\text{loop}} \cdot f^2 \left(\frac{1-2\nu}{1-\nu}\right)^2 \frac{8\pi^2}{15} \frac{b^2 \rho_0^4}{\Omega^2} e^{-3\kappa^2 \rho_0^2/14} . \qquad (26)$$

$b$ is the Burgers vector, $\nu$ Poisson's ratio, $\Omega$ the atomic volume and $\rho_0$ the loop radius. For $\kappa\rho_0 > 4$, we expect a $\kappa^{-3}$-dependence, which is the general asymptotic scattering law for dislocations [33]. The scattering of loops is much less than the scattering of voids of similar size for equal concentrations of clustered vacancies in each case. A similar anisotropy for $\varkappa \to 0$ as discussed for point defects is obtained if the anisotropy of the material is taken into account [31]. Second order elasticity theory does not change the numerical result of eq. (26) very much [32].

Another important example which up to now can be described only qualitatively is the small angle scattering pattern to be expected for fast neutron or electron irradiated metals. After spontaneous recombination, a defect cascade may look similar to the sketch in fig. 5. According to eq. (20), assuming $\Delta V/\gamma\Omega \approx 1$ for interstitials, and 0 for vacancies and neglecting anisotropy effects, essentially only the scattering of vacancies remains. The selfconvolution of $\Delta\rho_s$ (eq. (23)) can be extracted from fig. 5 and its Fourier transform looks like fig. 6a. With overlapping of cascades at high doses, the diffuse scattering (large $\varkappa$'s) will grow more rapidly than the small angle scattering. It is, however, not clear as to what occurs in the intermediate region.

For low dose electron irradiation, vacancies are statistically distributed. At high doses a tendency for clustering may appear because of irradiation annealing [34] and therefore a slight small angle scattering (fig. 6b).

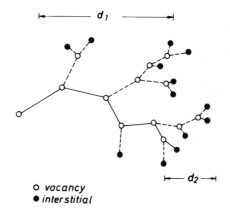

o *vacancy*
● *interstitial*

Fig. 5. Schematic sketch of a cascade with subcascades. $d_1$ and $d_2$ are roughly the correlation distances of the cascade and of the subcascade respectively.

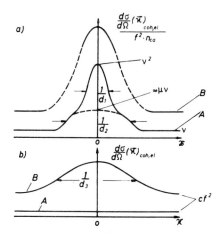

Fig. 6. Scattering cross sections at small $\varkappa$-values (qualitatively):
   a) A: For cascades (fig. 5) in small concentration. $n_{ca}$ = cascades per cm$^3$, $\nu$ number of vacancies per cascade and $\mu$ rough mean value for the number of vacancies in a subcascade.
   B: roughly expected scattering cross section for high cascade concentration. (B and A are different in ordinate scale).
   b) A: very low defect concentration after electron irradiation.
   B: high defect concentration, $d_3$ may be in the order of 4–8 lattice parameters.


# 3. Experimental results

## 3.1. *Point defect scattering*
   In the following we discuss existing experiments. In some cases we try to extract a sensitivity from the data. This sensitivity is defined by

$$\pm \Delta \frac{d\sigma}{d\Omega} = \pm \Delta C f_1^2 \qquad (27)$$

as the error-equivalent vacancy concentration $\Delta C$ of the experiment *, $f_1$ being the scattering length of the host lattice.
   At the Munich research reactor (FRM), point defects in fast-neutron irradiated aluminium have been studied [35,36]. The experimental set-up and the cryogenic technique for sample transfer at 4°K have been described [35]. Single crystals of about 5 cm$^3$ volume have been irradiated in the FRM low temperature irradiation facility to high doses. The scattering cross section has been measured with seven counters simultaneously. Background of about a factor 30 higher than the defect scattering has been eliminated by cycling measurements with and without sample and by measurements before irradiation and after annealing at 300°K. Defect scattering cross sections measured are shown in fig. 7.

* For this definition, vacancies without lattice distortion are assumed.

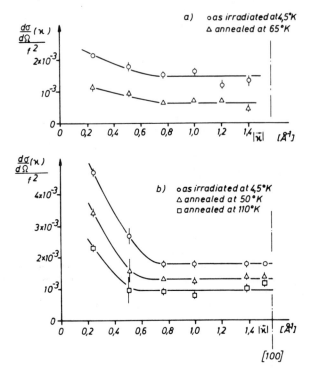

Fig. 7. Elastic coherent defect scattering cross section after fast-neutron irradiation [36]
  a) neutron dose $D(E > 1 \text{ MeV}) = 4.5 \times 10^{19} \text{ cm}^{-2}$ and
  b) $7.85 \times 10^{19} \text{ cm}^{-2}$.

   The dose dependent increase of $d\sigma/d\Omega$ at small $\varkappa$'s must probably be explained by correlation effects between vacancies. It is similar to the theoretically expected behaviour for electron irradiation as discussed above. For $|\varkappa| > 0.6 \text{ Å}^{-1}$ the ratios of the defect cross sections and the residual electrical resistivities of similar irradiated and annealed samples is constant within 10%. We therefore believe there is strong evidence that correlation effects are not important in this $\varkappa$-region and that we can use the formulas for statistically distributed point defects. With this assumption and by comparing fig. 4 with fig. 7 we feel justified to use the values between $0.6 \text{ Å}^{-1}$ and $1.4 \text{ Å}^{-1}$ as the long-wavelength limit for statistically distributed vacancies and interstitials.
   For this condition, the cross section is given by

$$\frac{d\sigma}{d\Omega}(\varkappa)_{\text{coh, el}} = C_F \cdot f_1^2 \left\{ \left(1 - \frac{\Delta V_V}{\gamma\Omega}\right)^2 + \left(1 - \frac{\Delta V_I}{\gamma\Omega}\right)^2 \right\}, \qquad (28)$$

$\Delta V_V$ and $\Delta V_I$ being the volume change of the vacancy and interstitial respectively, $C_F$ the Frenkel-defect concentration. Together with lattice parameter measurements [37] under similar conditions, for which

$$\frac{\Delta a}{a} = \tfrac{1}{3}\, C_F \left( \frac{\Delta V_V}{\Omega} + \frac{\Delta V_I}{\Omega} \right), \tag{29}$$

there are three unknown quantities, $C_F$, $\Delta V_V$ and $\Delta V_I$ connected with two equations. In fig. 8 values of $\Delta V_I/\gamma\Omega$ and $\Delta V_V/\gamma\Omega$ are shown which are compatible with these two experiments. We can further limit the possible range of values here by considerations of the limits for reasonable values of the resistivity as discussed by Wenzl [38].

For an exact determination, a third relation is necessary. This could be, for example, the cross section at the Huang tails

$$\frac{d\sigma}{d\Omega}(\boldsymbol{\varkappa} \to \tau_{hkl}) = C_F\, \frac{\tau_{hkl}^2}{q^2} \left\{ \left( \frac{\Delta V_V}{\gamma\Omega} \right)^2 + \left( \frac{\Delta V_I}{\gamma\Omega} \right)^2 \right\}. \tag{30}$$

It can be expected that the interstitials will give the main contribution in (29). However, clustering similar to that of vacancies would lead to a severe deviation from eq. (30). Therefore it seems that the best region for study of scattering by single interstitials is between the Bragg-peaks at high values of $|\boldsymbol{\varkappa}|$ (fig. 4).

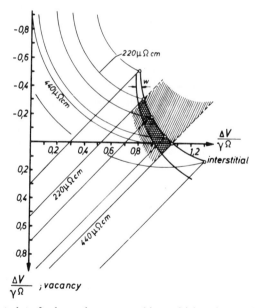

Fig. 8. Self-consistent plot of volume change around interstitials and vacancies in aluminium. Circles are given by eq. (28) (neutron scattering), straight lines by eq. (29) (lattice parameter measurements). Parameter is the residual resistivity per Frenkel-pair. Width W is due to the error of the neutron measurements. Crossed-hatched region ref. [36], single-hatched ref. [35].

With polycrystalline lead-bismuth alloys we have tested eq. (19). The coherent scattering lengths are known very well [5], the volume change per additional Bi-atom was determined by density measurements and the scattering cross section measured. Constant cross-sections obtained for 0.25, 0.5 and 0.75 Å$^{-1}$ were assumed to be representative for the long wavelength limit. As shown in table 1, the experiment gives the same values as the calculated cross sections, whereas the values with $f_L$ alone are quite different. Anisotropy of the lead has been corrected for.

The investigation of Pb-Bi is being extended to single crystals [39]. A preliminary result is shown in fig. 9 where for $|\varkappa| = 0.35$ Å$^{-1}$ the scattering cross section is plotted as a function of the $\varkappa$-direction. Considerable anisotropy is resolved, which qualitatively is in agreement with eq. (17) replacing $v_L$ by different sound velocities $v_{L,j}$ for different $\varkappa$-directions. The statistical error in this experiment corresponds to a vacancy concentration of $\pm 3 \times 10^{-5}$.

In diffuse X-ray scattering, the highest sensitivity up to now has been reported by Levelut and Guinier [40]. Their special scattering device for a $\varkappa$-range of 0.2...0.5 Å$^{-1}$ is sensitive to a vacancy concentration $\pm 5 \times 10^{-4}$. Experiments with polycrystalline alloys give agreement with Laue scattering for rapidly and slowly cooled Al−0.45 at% Cu, for Al−6.4 at% Ga and for very diluted Al-Zn alloys. For Au in Cu, a distortion term $\Delta V/\gamma\Omega \approx 0.2$ can be derived ($C \to 0$) from the experimental data. A value $\Delta V/\gamma\Omega \approx 0.25$ has been reported by Borie for Cu−25 at% Au. Contrary to the measurements of Levelut and Guinier [40] we have found for a rapidly quenched Al−1.5 at % Cu alloy a distortion contribution at small $|\varkappa|$'s with $\Delta V/\gamma\Omega = -0.28 \pm 0.03$. Alloy work for checking eq. (19) or more generally (20) should be continued for establishing a reliable basis in this field.

Full scattering patterns in large regions of reciprocal space are obtained in numerous cases for highly concentrated alloys. We refer to several reviews [26,41,42], which give a rather complete account of recent work. However, we want to summarize a few important points of these studies. (i) Huang scattering has been observed in many cases and in the correct order of intensity. Fig. 10 gives

Table 1

Disorder scattering cross sections for polycrystalline lead-bismuth alloys in units of $10^{-27}$ cm$^2$/steradian.

| at % Bi | $C(1-C)f_L^2$ * | $C(1-C)(f_L-f_D)^2$ * | Experiment |
|---|---|---|---|
| 3 | 0.30 | 0.85 | 0.85 ± 0.15 |
| 7 | 0.55 | 1.90 | 1.70 ± 0.15 |
| 10 | 0.80 | 2.70 | 2.75 ± 0.15 |
| 13 | 0.95 | 3.35 | 3.35 ± 0.15 |

* Calculated values.

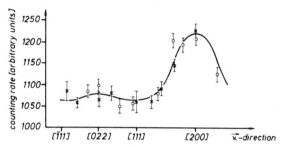

Fig. 9. Anisotropic scattering cross section for small $\varkappa$'s on a Pb–4 at% Bi single crystal. $\kappa \perp [01\bar{1}]$. $|\varkappa| = 0.35$ A$^{-1}$. o and x points from independent measurements. Sound velocity in [100] direction 2200 m/sec, in [110] and [111] direction 2500 m/sec.

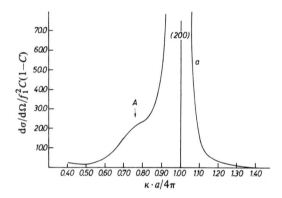

Fig. 10. Asymmetric Huang-tail due to size effect of a 60 at% Au – 40 at% Ni alloy [43]. With $f_{Ni}-f_{Au} < 0$ and $(\Delta V/\gamma\Omega)_{Ni} < 0$ the cross section $(d\sigma/d\Omega)$ is larger for $\mathbf{q}$ antiparallel $\tau_{200}$, eq. (20). Hump at A is due to clustering a lattice parameter.

an example for asymmetric Huang tails. (ii) Analyzing techniques have been developed to the point that clustering and short range order can be separated from displacement scattering. Moss [43] has demonstrated this for a Ni–25 at% Au alloy. (iii) Thermal diffuse scattering is a limitation on the accuracy of elastic diffuse scattering, because lattice dynamics of the alloys are not known and correction must be made within approximations [26].

For Huang scattering near Bragg-peaks there is no conclusive result for low concentrations and randomly distributed point defects. A rather sensitive experiment has recently been reported for $\gamma$-irradiated LiF [44]: Whereas the colour center concentration is changed only of the order of $10^{-6}$, very well-developed Huang tails could be observed (fig. 11). We would like to suggest that clustering of defects is responsible for the Huang scattering in this case, since the sensitivity limit is estimated to be ($10^{-4}$ to $10^{-5}$) when the scattering of randomly distributed point defects

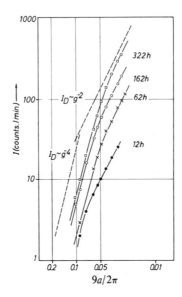

Fig. 11. Huang-tail near (400) reflection for $\gamma$-irradiated LiF [44]. If the change in slope at approximately $(9a/2\pi) = 0.05$ is interpreted as clustering a size of 50 Å would result.

give rise to an intensity approximately 10% of that due to thermal diffuse scattering. That clustering gives rise to very strong Huang tails can also be seen in experiments on fast neutron irradiated copper crystals [45]. In this case, diffuse scattering occurs close to the Bragg-peaks which is a factor of 3 above the scattering of unirradiated crystals. As the measurements have been made very near the Bragg-peaks and nearly perfect crystals have been used, one certainly must be cautious in applying the first Born approximation to this result. For very small $|\mathbf{q}|$'s treatment with the dynamical theory seems to be necessary [46].

Concluding the chapter on the elastic diffuse scattering experiments, mention should be made of some related neutron scattering studies. The first defect studies using neutrons were made with transmission experiments, where $\int (d\sigma/d\Omega)\,d\Omega$ was observed before and after fast neutron irradiation. Graphite [47], $Al_2O_3$ [48] and quartz single crystals [49,50] have been studied with this technique. This method has in some cases a remarkable sensitivity. Scattering experiments have been reported for irradiated MgO [51], BeO [52] and graphite [53]. A specially developed device has been used by Low and coworkers [54] at Harwell for the study of ferromagnetic alloys. Magnetic moment distributions were studied [55,56]. Magnetic scattering is dependent on the $\varkappa$-direction relative to the direction $\mathbf{M}$ of magnetization: if $\varkappa \| \mathbf{M}$ the magnetic scattering is zero in first order and maximal for $\varkappa \perp \mathbf{M}$. In this way background can be cancelled out. It is possible that this method can also be used for studies of point defects in ferromagnetic materials.

## 3.2. *Small angle scattering experiments*

Only a few small angle scattering experiments on point defect clusters in metals have been performed. This is due to the fact that experiments must be done with techniques that avoid double Bragg-scattering.

In quenched copper, voids of approximately 25 Å diameter have been observed by X-ray small angle scattering [57,58]. The experimental results are consistent with the assumption of spherical or slightly oblate voids. Only for samples quenched with a speed between $10^4$ °C/s and $5 \times 10^4$ °C/s and appropriate aging ($T$ between 20 and 80°C) a measurable intensity is obtained. At lower quenching rates the quenched-in vacancy concentration is too small. At higher rates, the vacancies cluster into loops and therefore have much less scattering power [58]. Concentrations of the order of $10^{-5}$ quenched-in vacancies have been observed.

In fast-neutron irradiated copper, small dislocation loops have been observed by means of neutron small angle scattering, where double Bragg-scattering is avoided by use of long wavelength neutrons. After preliminary experiments [59] it was shown that mainly large loops with a diameter of 80 Å are seen in small angle scattering [60]. The intensity is in agreement with the expected value from transmission electron microscope studies [66] extrapolated to the high doses used for the scattering samples. The sensitivity of this experiment was approximately the same as obtained in the X-ray experiment described above.

## 4. Discussion of experimental problems

### 4.1. *Background scattering*

The principle background contributions in X-ray studies are due to Compton, thermal diffuse and fluorescence scattering, and in neutron studies are due to incoherent elastic and inelastic scattering.

For individual atoms the ratio of Compton to coherent scattering is rapidly increasing with $|\varkappa|$ (fig. 12). Therefore scattering at small $|\varkappa|$'s is favourable. There is little information on the largest background to signal ratio which can be tolerated, however from our experience with neutrons we believe that effective studies are possible with ratios upto approximately 30:1. Accuracies of 10% or perhaps even 3% should be obtainable. Under these conditions, a vacancy concentration of $10^{-3}$ (reference line in fig. A) is measurable in a large region of reciprocal space. Large $\varkappa$-values are desirable because the spatial resolution with regard to $s_n$ or $f_n$ is increasing with extension of the reciprocal space explored. Compton scattering can be separated by monochromators in the scattered beam approximately at $|\varkappa| > 2 Å^{-1}$, if $\Delta\lambda/\lambda \approx 10^{-4}$.

The cross sections for incoherent elastic neutron scattering $4\pi f_{inc}^2$ due to isotope and/or spin disorder are very different for the elements. There are a few metals with very small ratios $f_{inc}^2/f_{coh}^2$ (fig. 12). Most of the values range between 0.01 and 0.5. Some metals such as Au or Ag are even above 0.5 and accordingly not favor-

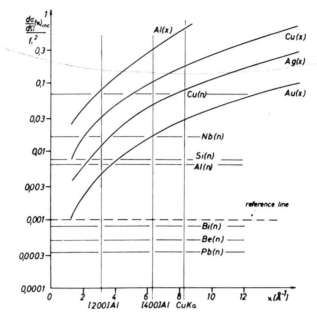

Fig. 12. Compton scattering of X-rays and elastic incoherent scattering of neutrons.

able materials for these studies. Scattering by crystals of a single isotope should be considered in some cases ($^{56}$Fe, $^{60}$Ni).

For the discussion of the inelastic background caused by thermal vibrations we use the coherent one-phonon-scattering cross section of the ideal crystal:

$$\frac{d^2\sigma}{d\Omega\,d\omega} = f^2 \frac{k_1}{k_0} \sum_i \frac{\hbar^2(\boldsymbol{x}\cdot\mathbf{n}_i)^2}{2m\hbar|\omega_i|} \left(\frac{1}{e^{(\hbar\omega_i/kT)}-1} + (\tfrac{1}{2}\pm\tfrac{1}{2})\right)\delta(\omega-\omega_i)$$

$$(31)$$

$$\boldsymbol{x} = \boldsymbol{\tau}_{hkl} + \mathbf{q}_i\,; \qquad \hbar\omega = (k_0^2 - k_1^2)\frac{\hbar^2}{2m_0}\,.$$

$\omega_i$ and $\mathbf{q}_i$ are the phonon-frequencies and phonon wave-vectors respectively. $\mathbf{n}_i$ is the polarization vector and $m_0$ the neutron mass.

Fig. 13 shows $d^2\sigma/d\Omega\,d\omega$ for X-rays integrated over $\omega$ using experimentally known dispersion curves [61]. Similar to Compton scattering there is an excellent background situation for small $|\boldsymbol{x}|$'s; $d^2\sigma/d\Omega\,d\omega$ is inversely proportional to the atomic mass $m$, thus for heavy elements the contribution of thermal diffuse scattering is smaller. Some quantitative values are given in table 2.

Cooling of the sample is especially effective for Huang scattering (fig. 13). For a given $q$, $kT$ should be smaller than $v_L\,q$. With this condition the thermal diffuse

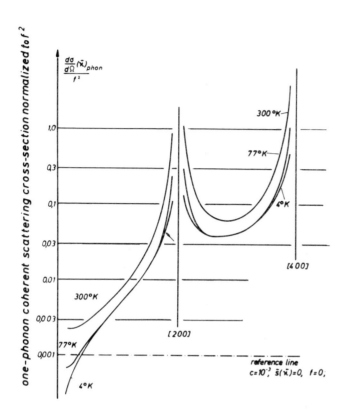

Fig. 13. X-ray thermal diffuse scattering for Al. $\varkappa$ parallel to [100]. Abscissa is $|\varkappa|$.

scattering is proportional $1/q$ whereas the Huang scattering caused by distortion is proportional to $1/q^2$. For instance, with a defect concentration of $10^{-3}$ and $\varkappa \parallel q$ for $q = (1/30) \, \tau_{hkl}$ a distortion of $\Delta V/\gamma\Omega \approx 0.2$ gives the same scattering as the thermal diffuse background ($v_L = 2000$ m/s). Since Huang- and thermal diffuse scattering are proportional $\varkappa^2$ high index of reflections are preferable in most cases.

For neutrons, inelastic one-phonon scattering with energy-gain can be avoided by low sample temperatures ($\hbar\omega/kT \gg 1$) and scattering with energy loss is minimized by the use of a sufficiently low neutron energy. This can be inferred from total energy and momentum-conservation included in eq. (31). Fig. 14 gives an example.

Table 2

Thermal diffuse scattering normalized to $f^2$ at (100) and (300) reciprocal lattice points at $4°K$ calculated with eq. (31) and with known values of $\hbar\omega_L$ ($\varkappa \parallel [100]$).

|          | Al    | Cu      | Nb      | Pb      |
|----------|-------|---------|---------|---------|
| (100)    | 0.005 | $0.003_5$ | $0.003_5$ | $0.002_3$ |
| (300)    | 0.045 | 0.031   | 0.031   | 0.021   |

Phonon creation cannot be avoided at high neutron energies, but a rough time-of-flight separation may be sufficient. An additional smooth multiphonon background [62,63] must be considered for experiments at elevated temperatures and/or high $\varkappa$-values.

Further difficulties arise from double scattering processes, parasitic scattering at slits, windows and other parts of the scattering device and scattering at condensation layers on the sample. For X-rays, fluorescence scattering and surface roughness or distortion must be especially considered, whereas with neutrons, hydrogen impurities in the sample can create difficulty. Usually these background contributions can be suppressed below the intrinsic background discussed above. Examples of this are given for diffuse X-ray scattering [26,40], for X-ray small angle scattering [64,65,57] and for neutron small angle scattering [27].

The allowable background ratio is connected with the required statistical accuracy. We call $t$ the time necessary to obtain the defect scattering rate $I_1$ with statistical accuracy $\rho = \Delta I_1/I_1$ and call $I_B$ the background rate, then we have

$$t = \frac{1}{\rho^2 I_1} 2\left(2\frac{I_B}{I_1} + 1\right). \tag{32}$$

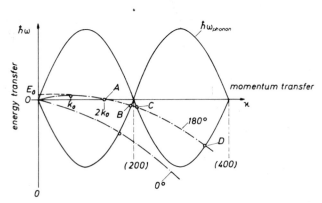

Fig. 14. Energy- and momentum conservation diagram for $0°$ and $180°$ degree scattering as limiting cases (schematically). At $A$ elastic scattering. Scattering at $B$, $C$ and $D$ is vanishing as $T \rightarrow 0$.

We see from this, that with a background to signal ratio of 30 : 1, a factor of 120 increase in time is necessary compared to the ideal case of zero background.

## 4.2. Intensity considerations

The counting rate $I_1$ can be discussed from the intensity formula

$$I_1 = L(\lambda)\, e^{-\mu(\lambda)D}\, D\, \frac{d\sigma}{d\Omega}(\varkappa)\, N_s\, \Delta\Omega_o\, \Delta\Omega_1\, F \ . \tag{33}$$

Eq. (33) holds for a scattering experiment in transmission and with circular geometry as sketched in fig. 15a. $L(\lambda)$ is the luminosity of the X-ray or neutron source, $N_s$ the number of atoms per $cm^3$. To obtain optimum intensity, all contributions to the final resolution width should be comparable in magnitude (fig. 15a and 15b). Therefore, for the desired resolution $\Delta\kappa$ one must optimize the solid angles of the incident and scattered beams and obtains

$$\Delta\Omega_o = \Delta\Omega_1 = \frac{\pi}{4}\frac{\Delta\kappa^2}{k_o^2}\ ; \qquad \Delta\Omega_o \Delta\Omega_1 \sim \lambda^4\, \Delta\kappa^4\ . \tag{34}$$

For neutrons the wavelength resolution must simultaneously be fixed. This is already assumed in eq. (33).

Optimizing $I_1$ further with respect to $D$ and $\lambda$ ($D_{opt} = 1/\mu(\lambda)$) one finds that for neutrons, long wavelengths should be used, e.g. for small angle scattering 7–10 Å, for diffuse scattering within the first Brillouin-zones 4–7 Å and if larger $\varkappa$-values are desired than $k_o$ should be about $\kappa_{max}/2$. This is because luminosity of neutron sources is rapidly decreasing with decreasing wavelength [67]. For X-rays $\lambda^4/\mu(\lambda)$ is a slowly increasing function with $\lambda$, therefore the excellent luminosity $L(\lambda)$ obtainable with copper anodes is decisive. Luminosities of 2–4 × $10^{16}$ quantas/sec $cm^2$ steradian are obtainable. Neutron values are much smaller (table 3) but large sample areas and thicknesses tend to compensate for this disadvantage. The optimum specimen thickness, $D_{opt}$, for neutrons in most cases lies between a few mm and several cm, while for X-rays $D_{opt}$ ranges from a few $\mu$ to a few 100 $\mu$.

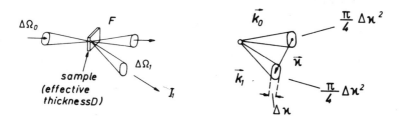

Fig. 15a. Resolution in experimental space. b. Resolution in reciprocal space.

Table 3

Luminosity of neutron sources for different thermal neutron flux $\phi_{th}$ n/sec cm$^2$: $L(\lambda) \lambda^4/\lambda_0^4$ with $\lambda_0 = 1.54$ Å is given, which can be compared to $L(\lambda) = 2 \ldots 4 \times 10^{16}$ for a CuK$_a$ source.

| Wavelength | | 7 Å | 4 Å | 1.8 Å |
|---|---|---|---|---|
| Resolution $\dfrac{\Delta\lambda}{\lambda}$ | | 0.2 | 0.1 | 0.04 |
| $\phi_{th} = 10^{13}$ | b) | $4.2 \times 10^{11}$ * | $1.7 \times 10^{11}$ | $4.2 \times 10^{10}$ |
| $\phi_{th} = 10^{14}$ | a) | $4.2 \times 10^{12}$ ** | $1.7 \times 10^{12}$ | $4.2 \times 10^{11}$ |
| | b) | $4.2 \times 10^{13}$ | $1 \times 10^{13}$ | – |
| $\phi_{th} = 10^{15}$ | a) | $4.2 \times 10^{13}$ | $1.7 \times 10^{13}$ | $4.2 \times 10^{12}$ |
| | b) | $4.2 \times 10^{14}$ | $1 \times 10^{14}$ | – |

a) Facility without and b) facility with cold neutron source.

* and ** luminosity for experiments fig. 7 and fig. 9 respectively.

With fixed $\varkappa$, $\Delta\varkappa$ and $\lambda$, a further optimization means enlarging the sample area $F$. Normally, for X-ray scattering in transmission, thin foils of only a few mm$^2$ area are employed due to the difficulties in foil preparation. For X-ray reflection scattering larger areas are possible. With neutrons, sample areas are as large as available, normally ranging between 2 and 20 cm$^2$. Since the sources are normally smaller than the sample areas for X-rays and larger or equal for neutrons, the experimental techniques are quite different.

For X-rays, focussing techniques are necessary. The most significant quantities of X-ray scattering equipment are shown in fig. 16. The acceptance angle of the focussing system can vary between $10^{-2}$ for total reflecting mirrors, $10^{-2}$ to $10^{-4}$ for mosaic crystals and $10^{-4}$ or less for ideal crystals. For high resolution work a small acceptance angle and a small source area can be used. With bent or double-bent monochromators in this case large sample areas can be illuminated using relatively short distances [26, 68].

A typical scattering device for low resolution X-ray work is shown in fig. 17. If a $\Delta\varkappa$ of $10^{-1}$ Å$^{-1}$ would be sufficient, it is possible, in principle, at this reduced resolution to increase the intensity by a factor of 100 compared to the device in fig. 17. To do this, the source area, monochromator dimensions and distances of the device must necessarily be enlarged, keeping sample area and its distance to the focal spot constant.

With neutrons, high resolution can be achieved by using large distances, e.g. in small angle scattering overall length of collimator and flight-path can be about 3 m to 40 m. Similar difficulties as in the X-ray work arise when one wishes to optimize

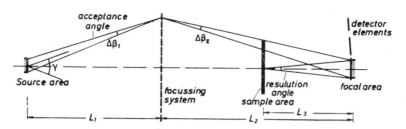

Fig. 16. Schematic sketch of a focussing system. Maximum values for $\gamma$ are 0.1 radian for X-rays and roughly 0.03 radian for neutrons. Acceptance angles $\Delta\beta$ can be kept small if $L_1$ and $L_2$ are enlarged.

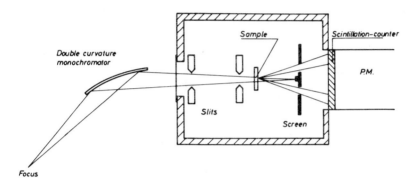

Fig. 17. Scattering system used by Levelut and Guinier [39]. Source area 1 mm$^2$, sample area 2–3 mm$^2$, $\Delta\kappa \approx 3 \times 10^{-2}$ Å$^{-1}$, overall length 50 cm, LiF crystal monochromator.

low resolution neutron experiments. Primary beams used today have an angular resolution of $2 \times 10^{-2}$ Å$^{-1}$, which in principle can be focussed onto smaller sample areas by large focussing systems with reduction in the angular resolution of the system. Further in low resolution work there is a gap in monochromator systems with wavelength resolution $\Delta\lambda/\lambda$ between 15% and 2%. For $\Delta\lambda/\lambda$ greater than 15% mechanical velocity selectors are used and for $\Delta\lambda/\lambda < 2\%$ mosaic crystals are employed. We conclude that a significant improvement in the experimental conditions can be obtained with optimized systems.

Use of multidetector systems offer good possibilities of additional improvement. Phototechniques available both for X-rays and neutrons [70,71] can be used if accuracy need not be high, e.g. in some cases for small angle and Huang scattering. Counters are necessary for accuracy better than 3%. Large arrays of single counters are normally used in neutron work. For X-rays, semiconductor counters fulfill the requirement of small geometrical dimensions. Single proportional counters with resistance wire can be used as multidetector system either with two outputs and

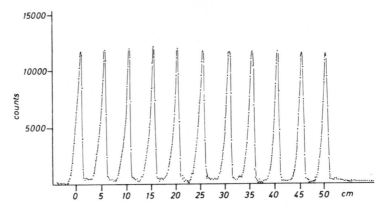

Fig. 18. Spatial resolution of a localizing $BF_3$ proportional counter with resistance wire [74].
Calibration curve with 5 cm distance of a 2 mm broad neutron beam.

pulse division [72] or with one output and delay-line-technique [73]. By such
techniques already 40 spatial resolution units can be given by one counter (fig. 18).
Similar techniques are also possible with solid state detectors. Crossed anode-
cathode systems are in preparation at various laboratories, for X-rays on semi-
conductor- and for neutrons on proportional counter or ionization chamber-
basis [69]. With 20 anodes times 20 cathodes one obtains 400 channels. On-line-
computers are necessary for an appropriate data handling of such systems.

From the above considerations we conclude that there are good prospects for
more extensive studies of defects in crystals by means of scattering techniques.

## Acknowledgements

The author wishes to thank Mr. Eisenriegler for clearifying discussions on the
theoretical aspects and Drs. Haubold, Springer and Schilling for discussions on
special topics of the field.

I am indebted to the colleagues which have contributed with unpublished experimental results.

## References

[1] L.Van Hove, Physica 24 (1958) 404.
[2] A.Sjölander, in: Thermal Neutron Scattering, ed. P.A.Egelstaff (Academic Press, London,
     1965).
[3] Inelastic Scattering of Neutrons in Solids and Liquids, 1 and 2 (IAEA, Vienna, 1968).
[4] U.Gonser, this volume.
[5] D.J.Hughes and R.B.Schwartz, Neutron Cross Sections, 2nd ed. (BNL 325, 1958).

[6] L.Koester, Z. Physik 182 (1965) 328.

[7] R.Scherm and W.Schmatz, Z. Naturforsch. 19a (1964) 354.

[8] R.Niklaus, R.Simson, W.Triftshäuser and W.Schmatz, Z. Physik 190 (1966) 295.

[9] R.Scherm, Nukleonik, in press.

[10] A.Guinier, X-ray Diffraction (W.H.Freeman and Company, San Francisco and London, 1963).

[11] H.Jagodzinski, in: Fortschritte der Strukturforschung mit Beugungsmethoden, ed. R.Brill (Vieweg und Sohn, Braunschweig, 1964) p. 167.

[12] K.Huang, Proc. Roy. Soc. (London) A190 (1947) 102.

[13] B.Borie, Acta Cryst. 10 (1957) 89; 12 (1959) 280.

[14] M.A.Krivoglaz, Fiz. Metal. Metallored. 9 (1960) 641; 12 (1961) 465; Sov. Phys. JETP 34 (1958) 139.

[15] D.T.Keating, J. Phys. Chem. Solids 29 (1968) 771.

[16] E.Eisenriegler, in: Jül. Conf. 1 (1967) p. 172.

[17] S.B.Austermann and K.T.Miller, Phys. Stat. Sol. 11 (1965) 241.

[18] H.Kanzaki, J. Phys. Chem. Solids 2 (1957) 24.

[19] A.Seeger, E.Mann and R.v.Jan, Phys. Chem. Sol. 23 (1961) 639.

[20] G.Squires, in: Inelastic Scattering of Neutrons in Liquids and Solids (IAEA, Vienna, 1963) p. 71.

[21] G.Leibfried, Encyclopedia of Physics, Vol. VIII, 1.

[22] K.Mika, Phys. Stat. Sol. 21 (1967) 279.

[23] A.Seeger, Phys. Stat. Sol. 1 (1961) 670.

[24] J.D.Eshelby, Solid State Physics 3 (1956) 79.

[25] A.N.Goland and D.T.Keating, J. Phys. Chem. Solids 29 (1968) 785.

[26] C.J.Sparks and B.Borie, Local atomic arrangements studied by X-ray-diffraction (Metallurgy Society Conferences 36 (Gordon and Breach, New York, 1966) p. 5.

[27] J.Christ, W.Schilling, W.Schmatz and T.Springer, Z. Angew. Phys. 18 (1965) 259.

[28] A.Guinier and G.Fournet, Small Angle Scattering of X-rays (John Wiley and Sons Inc., New York, London, 1955).

[29] Small-angle X-ray scattering, ed. H.Brumberger (Gordon and Breach, New York, 1967).

[30] T.Springer and W.Schmatz, Bull. Soc. fr. Mineral. Cristallogr. 90 (1967) 428.

[31] A.Seeger and M.Rühle, Ann. Physik 11 (1963) 216.

[32] A.Seeger and P.Brand, in: Small-angle X-ray scattering, ed. H.Brumberger (Gordon and Breach, New York, 1967) p. 383.

[33] A.Seeger and E.Kröner, Z. Naturforsch. 14a (1959) 74.

[34] G.Lück and R.Sizmann, Phys. Stat. Sol. 14 (1966) 507.

[35] J.P.Niklaus, R.Simson, W.Schmatz and H.Wenzl, Z. Angew. Phys. 24 (1968) 313.

[36] R.Simson, Dissertation Technische Hochschule München (1968).

[37] U.Himmler, H.Peisl, A.Sepp, W.Waidelich and H.Wenzl, Z. Angew. Physik 23 (1967) 8.

[38] H.Wenzl, this volume.

[39] A.M.Levelut and A.Guinier, in: Small-angle X-ray scattering, ed. H.Brumberger (Gordon and Breach, New York, 1967) p. 351;
A.M.Levelut, Thesis, Faculté des Sciences d'Orsay, Université de Paris (1968).

[40] H.Schumacher, private communication.

[41] S.C.Moss, in: Local atomic arrangements studied by X-ray diffraction, Metallurgy Society conferences 36 (Gordon and Breach, New York, 1966) p. 95.

[42] L.H.Schwartz, in: Local atomic arrangements studied by X-ray diffraction, Metallurgy Society Conferences 36 (Gordon and Breach, New York, 1966) p. 123.

[43] S.C.Moss and B.L.Averbach, in: Small-angle X-ray scattering, ed. H.Brumberger (Gordon and Breach, New York, 1967) p. 335.

[44] H.Peisl, H.Spalt and W.Waidelich, Phys. Stat. Sol. 23 (1967) K75.

616 W.SCHMATZ

[45] T.O.Baldwin, F.A.Sherill and F.W.Young Jr., J. Appl. Phys. 39 (1968) 1541.
[46] A.M.Afanasev, Yu.Kajan and F.N.Lukhovskii, Phys. Stat. Sol. 28 (1968) 287.
[47] J.J.Antal, R.J.Weiss and G.J.Dienes, Phys. Rev. 90 (1955) 1081.
[48] J.J.Antal and A.N.Goland, Phys. Rev. 112 (1958) 103.
[49] E.W.J.Mitchell and P.T.Wedepohl, Phil. Mag. 3 (1958) 1280.
[50] K.Baierlein, Phys. Stat. Sol. 7 (1964) 415.
[51] D.G.Martin, AERE Report 5521.
[52] D.G.Martin, Report AERE Report 4914.
[53] D.G.Martin and R.W.Henson, Phil. Mag. 9 (1964) 659.
[54] G.G.Low, Inelastic Scattering of Neutrons in Solids and Liquids 1 (IAEA, Vienna, 1965) p. 413.
[55] M.F.Collins and G.G.Low, Proc. Phys. Soc. 86 (1965) 535.
[56] G.G.Low and M.F.Collins, J. Appl. Phys. 34 (1963) 1195.
[57] V.Gerold, A.Seeger and M.Rühle, Z. Metallk. 54 (1963) 493.
[58] V.Gerold, in: Small-angle X-ray scattering, ed. H.Brumberger (Gordon and Breach, New York, 1967) p. 277.
[59] W.Schilling and W.Schmatz, Phys. Stat. Sol. 4 (1964) 95.
[60] B.Kaiser, unpublished.
[61] R.Stedmann and G.Nilson, in: Inelastic Scattering of Neutrons (IAEA, Vienna, 1965) p. 211.
[62] K.E.Larson, U.Dahlborg and D.Jovic, in: Inelastic Scattering of Neutrons (IAEA, Vienna 1965) p. 117.
[63] A.Sjölander, Arkiv Fysik 14 (1958) 315.
[64] O.Kratky, in: Small-angle X ray scattering, ed. H.Brumberger (Gordon and Breach, New York, 1967) p. 63.
[65] U.Bonse and M.Hart, in: Small-angle X-ray scattering, ed. H.Brumberger (Gordon and Breach, New York, 1967) p. 121.
[66] M.Wilkens, this volume.
[67] H.Maier-Leibnitz and T.Springer, Ann. Rev. Nucl. Sci. 16 (1966) 207.
[68] B.E.Warren, J. Appl. Phys. 25 (1954) 814.
[69] Charpak et al., Nucl. Instr. Methods 62 (1968) 262.
[70] S.P.Wang, C.G.Shull and N.V.Philipps, Rev. Sci. Instr. 33 (1962) 126.
[71] M.Ernst, J. Christ and W.Schmatz, Nukleonik 9 (1967) 29.
[72] K.Sistemich, K.H.Lauterjung, B.Schimmer and W.Kuhlmann, Nucl. Instr. Methods 40 (1966) 118.
[73] C.J.Borkowski and M.K.Kopp, Rev. Sci. Instr. 39 (1968) 1514.
[74] K.Abend, H.D.Müller, W.Schmatz and J.Schelten, in: International Conference on Nuclear Electronic, Versailles (1968), in press.

## Discussion

*R.Bullough:* Concerning the theoretical calculation of the displacement around a split interstitial, I would like to know if changes in the force constants in the immediate neighbourhood of the dumbbell have been allowed for and, if so, how reliable do you consider the local force constants to be? I recommend the explicit separation of the force constant charges from the force array combination. This separation is not done in the Kanzaki formalism which is probably acceptable for the analysis of a vacancy, but is very dubious for the split interstitial.

*E.Eisenriegler:* In the present formulation all defect influences (including changes in the force constants) are assumed to be involved in the $f_n$'s. In the explicit calculation of Seeger, Mann and v.Jan, potentials are used which take into account the electronic contribution to the potential only in a very approximate way.

*H.Wenzl:* What information can one derive from measurements of the Debye-Waller factor (elastic) and how are the experimental possibilities?

*W.Schmatz:* The mean square displacement of the defect due to thermal vibration is in principle obtained by diffuse elastic neutron scattering. In incoherent elastic neutron scattering, as for instance from hydrogen atoms, the Debye-Waller factor is determined directly. For coherent elastic scattering one has to start the calculation again with eq. (7) and must take into account also the possible change of $e^{-w_i}$ of the atoms surrounding the defect. There is little hope at the present to detect in diffuse scattering a change of Debye-Waller factor (caused by thermal vibration) at low defect concentrations because high $x$-values and/or high temperatures are necessary. With very-high-flux reactors, however, such experiments should be tried.

*A.N.Goland:* In answer to Dr. Wenzl's question concerning Debye-Waller factors, I should like to say that a recent theory by Keating shows that the artificial temperature factor from which one deduced mean-square displacements due to strain only multiplies the Bragg (coherent) scattering terms and not the diffuse term. Therefore, one must measure changes in integrated intensities of Bragg reflections to determine mean-square displacements.

*W.Schmatz:* It seems that measurements of the artificial temperature-factor – in other words the Debye-Waller factor caused by static lattice distortions – should also be tried with neutron scattering because inelastic scattering surrounding the Bragg-peak can be separated.

*J.Bass:* X-ray scattering occurs only in the region of the specimen surface. Can you obtain reliable measurements of defect properties in the bulk material using X-rays?

*W.Schmatz:* For point defects and point defect clusters a 100000 Å thick specimen as used in X-ray transmission scattering work is already a bulk material. Surfaces must be very clean and undistorted, of course.

# THE APPLICATION OF ANOMALOUS X-RAY TRANSMISSION TO THE STUDY OF POINT DEFECTS AND DEFECT CLUSTERS *

F.W.YOUNG Jr., T.O.BALDWIN and P.H.DEDERICHS

*Solid State Division, Oak Ridge National Laboratory, Oak Ridge, Tennessee, USA*

## 1. Introduction

One of the consequences of the availability of nearly perfect crystals has been a renewed interest in dynamical diffraction effects. Since long-range strain fields due to dislocations, etc., are negligible in these crystals, dynamical diffraction can be used to investigate point defects, defect clusters, and small dislocation loops. These latter defects cannot be imaged by X-ray topographic techniques because of their short-range strain fields, but can be investigated by integrated intensity measurements of anomalous X-ray transmission (Borrmann transmission). Patel and Batterman [1] observed two orders of magnitude decrease in Borrmann intensity upon clustering of impurity oxygen atoms in dislocation free silicon crystals. In a series of papers Efimov and co-workers [2] have reported their investigations of the effect of impurities, vacancies, and clusters of them on Borrmann intensities through nearly perfect germanium crystals. Maruyama [3] also investigated impurity effects but found less sensitivity than that reported by Efimov. Collela and Merlini [4] investigated the effects of fast neutron irradiation on anomalous transmission through silicon and germanium and reported no changes for a fast neutron dose $\approx 10^{20}/cm^2$. More recently, Baldwin and Thomas [5] have found changes by factors of two after irradiation of silicon and germanium with $4 \times 10^{19}$ fast neutrons/cm$^2$. In the only quantitative studies on metal crystals to date, Baldwin et al. [6] found that changes in Borrmann intensities of several orders of magnitude resulted from irradiation with $4 \times 10^{19}/cm^2$ fast neutrons. The range in the magnitude of intensity changes observed by these several authors would suggest that the exact form of the defects, i.e., whether as point defects or as clusters, is most important for a quantitative understanding.

While there have been many studies of the defects produced by irradiation with nuclear particles, it is apparent that sufficient information concerning these defects

* Research sponsored by the U.S. Atomic Energy Commission under contract with Union Carbide Corporation.

is still not available. In particular, more information concerning the geometry of the defects and of their environment in the lattice is needed. Since irradiation (particularly fast neutron) introduces a statistical array of defects and the clusters of these defects are suited to investigation by electron microscopy, irradiated nearly perfect crystals are appropriate for quantitative measurements and for testing theoretical treatments of the effect of defects and their clusters on Borrmann X-ray intensities.

The dynamical theory for intensities anomalously transmitted through perfect crystals [7] is well understood. Recently Dederichs and others [8–11] generalized the dynamical scattering theory to include crystals containing statistically distributed point defects. In this paper we outline the theory for crystals containing point defects, small defect clusters, and loops and compare this theory with observed intensity changes resulting from fast neutron irradiation of nearly perfect copper crystals.

## 2. Dynamical theory for crystals with "statistical" defects

The simplest defect which one can imagine is the thermal motion of the lattice atoms and several authors have treated this case [12–15]. The theory considers only the mean elastic or "coherent" wave; that is, it describes only those processes for which the final crystal state is identical with the initial one or, in other words, where finally no phonons have been excited. All other processes lead to phonon excitations. Due to the transfer of the phonon momentum, the corresponding inelastic or diffuse waves do not normally satisfy the Bragg condition and are therefore irrelevant for those experiments which measure only Bragg reflected intensities.

The same theory can also be applied to other defects, such as statistically distributed point defects [8–11] and small defect clusters [16]. Here one has to assume that the measured intensity depends not on the accidental microscopic defect configurations but only on macroscopic quantities such as the average defect densities and their pair correlations, etc. Therefore, one has to average over all the possible microscopic defect configurations. Significant deviations from such an average intensity are not expected for crystals with point defects or many small clusters.

As for the thermal case, we assume that for the Bragg reflected intensities we can restrict ourselves to the coherent wave, which is that part of the total wave which interferes with the incident wave and which is given by the average of the total wave $\psi$ over all the possible microscopic defect configurations leading to the same macroscopic situation. The diffuse waves are scattered by an oblique angle and normally do not satisfy the Bragg condition. Therefore, in the Borrmann case they are normally absorbed and have no chance to penetrate a thick crystal. The hypothesis that all the Bragg intensities are given by the coherent wave clearly breaks down for large defect clusters of the order of an extinction length, for then the diffuse waves are scattered by a very small angle and partially satisfy the Bragg condition, leading to "line broadening" in the Bragg case. Unfortunately, a dynamical theory taking this effect into account is not yet available. Therefore, we restrict ourselves to point defects and small clusters whose radii are small compared with the extinction length.

Furthermore, we will treat here only scalar waves. For X-rays the theory is just the same except for some simple polarization factors. As derived in references [9,14], the scattering of the coherent wave can be described by an effective potential $U$, which to a good approximation is given by

$$U \cong \langle V \rangle + \{ \langle VgV \rangle - \langle V \rangle g \langle V \rangle \}; \qquad g = \frac{1}{E_k + i\epsilon - H_o} \tag{1}$$

Here

$$V(\mathbf{r}) = V'(\mathbf{r}) + i\, V''(\mathbf{r}) = \sum_n v\,(\mathbf{r} - \mathbf{R}^n)$$

is the complex potential between the electron and the atoms of the defect crystal whose imaginary part $V''(\mathbf{r})$ describes the atomic absorption (photoelectric effect for X-rays, atomic excitations for electrons). $g$ is the free electron Green's function. The first term $\langle V \rangle$ is the average of the lattice potentials over the defect configuration, and its imaginary part gives directly the *photoelectric absorption*. The second term represents the correction of $U$ due to the diffuse waves. Because of particle conservation any increase of the diffuse incoherent waves must lead to a decrease of the coherent wave, or more precisely, to an absorption. Therefore, the imaginary part of the second term gives us directly the *"diffuse scattering absorption"*.

Due to the averaging process, the effective potential $U$ has the periodicity of the "average lattice". As is well known, point defects and defect clusters produce a homogeneous lattice expansion, as does anharmonicity in the temperature case. In the following we refer always to the periodicity of the expanded lattice.

## 2.1. Isolated point defects

In so far as the scattering process is concerned, point defects in the crystal act in two ways. First, they represent additional scattering centers (or holes for vacancies), and second, they displace their neighboring lattice atoms from their equilibrium positions and thus change the scattering at these atoms. In this section we consider the absorption that results from single impurity interstitials, self interstitials, and vacancies.

In continuum theory, assuming an isotropic medium, the displacement field of an "isotropic" point defect is $\mathbf{t(r)} = A\mathbf{r}/r^3$, where $A$ is related to the volume change $\Delta V$ by $\Delta V = 4\pi A\, 3(1 - v)/(1 + v)$. In a straightforward way one can calculate the photoelectric absorption due to the defects, using the approximation $U \simeq \langle V \rangle$ [9]. For impurity interstitials one obtains for the anomalous photoelectric absorption in the Borrmann case

$$\mu_{PE} = \frac{1}{k}(v_0'' - v_h'' e^{-L_h}) + C_I \frac{1}{k}(v_0^{I''} - \cos(h \cdot R^I) \cdot v_h^{I''} e^{-L_h^I}) \tag{2a}$$

$$\cong \mu_0 L_h + \mu_0^I C_I (1 - \cos h \cdot R^I) \quad \text{for} \quad L_h \ll 1, \quad v_0'' \cong v_h'', \ldots \tag{2b}$$

This result holds also if the impurities are clustered. Here $h$ is the reciprocal lattice vector, $k = 2\pi/\lambda$, and $v_h''$ and $v_h^{I''}$ are essentially the imaginary part of the atomic scattering factor of the lattice atoms and impurities, respectively, and are connected with the normal absorption $\mu_0$ by $\mu_0 = v_0''/k$. $C_I$ is the concentration of interstitials, and $R^I$ is the equilibrium position of the impurities in the unit cell. $L_h$ is a Debye-Waller factor due to the static displacements of the lattice atoms, being analogous to the thermal Debye-Waller factor. For randomly distributed point defects $L_h$ is given by [9]:

$$L_h \equiv L_h^0 = C_I \sum_n \{1 - \cos h \cdot t^n\} \cong C_I \sum_n \tfrac{1}{2}(h \cdot t^n)^2 \approx C_I \frac{2\pi}{3} \frac{A^2 h^2}{V_c \rho_c}, \tag{3}$$

where $t^n = t(R^n)$. For the last very rough approximation the sum has been replaced by an integral. $\rho_c$ is a cut-off distance of the order of the defect ion radius, and $V_c$ is the atomic volume.

According to eq. (2), the absorption consists of two parts. The first, described by $L_h$, is the photoelectric absorption of the lattice atoms which are displaced into the space between the reflecting lattice planes and therefore absorb the Borrmann wave more strongly. The second is the photoelectric absorption of the impurity interstitials themselves. This contribution is largest if the interstitials are located in the middle between the reflecting planes ($\cos h \cdot R^I = -1$) where they absorb the Borrmann wave most strongly. This term shows a characteristic h-dependence and practically disappears for $\cos h \cdot R^I = 1$, when the interstitials are lying exactly in the reflection planes. This absorption would be even more important if one could choose the X-ray energy to be near the absorption edge of the impurities. Then the impurity absorption would be enlarged by a factor of 6 to 8.

For self interstitials, eq. (2) simplifies because $\mu_0^I = \mu_0$. If the interstitials have no definite position in the unit cell, but can occupy more or less each position, $\cos h \cdot R^I$ is on the average zero. For statistically distributed vacancies only the photoelectric absorption of the lattice atoms is important. This is normally smaller than for the interstitials due to the smaller volume change $\Delta V$, which enters in $L_h$ quadratically.

The absorption due to diffuse scattering can also be calculated from the imaginary part of the second term in $U$. For X-rays, this term is very small and gives, for example, for Cu a correction of only a few percent to the photoelectric absorption [9]. But for electrons this absorption is more important [8].

## 2.2. Effects of defect clustering

In the preceding section we assumed that the point defects were randomly distributed. Now we will discuss the effects on absorption which can occur if point defects are clustered together. We will see that such effects can be quite large. In order to do this, we have to know something about the displacement fields of such defect aggregates. Because calculations from first principles are not available, we make two models for defect clustering.

*Cluster model:* We assume that the point defects are clustered together such that their displacement fields simply superimpose on each other. This would be the case for a very loose cluster with a small defect concentration. For the displacement fields of the point defects we still use the continuum expression $t(\mathbf{r}) = A\mathbf{r}/r^3$. Due to the superposition assumption, the volume change does not depend on the defect clustering. Furthermore, we will assume that the cluster centers are statistically distributed and that the clusters have spherical symmetry.

*Loop Model:* For high defect densities the point defects of a cluster may collapse into a flat disc and form a dislocation loop. Then, from continuum theory, the displacement field in the asymptotic region $r \geqslant 2R_o$ is [17]

$$t(\mathbf{r}) = \frac{bR_o^2}{8r^2} \left\{ \frac{1 - 2v}{1 - v} (2\mathbf{b}^o(\mathbf{b}^o \cdot \mathbf{e}) - \mathbf{e}) + \frac{3}{1 - v_*} \mathbf{e}(\mathbf{b}^o \cdot \mathbf{e})^2 \right\} \qquad (4)$$

with $\mathbf{b}^o = \mathbf{b}/|\mathbf{b}|$, $\mathbf{e} = \mathbf{r}/r$, and $v = \frac{1}{3}$ for Cu, where $\pi R_o^2 = F$ is the surface area of the not necessarily circular loop. $\mathbf{b}$ is the Burgers vector, assumed to be perpendicular to the loop plane and defined as positive for interstitial loops and negative for vacancy loops. The volume change due to a loop is given by $\Delta V = bF$, a result independent of the loop form and of the degree of anisotropy. Also in this model we assume that the loops are distributed at random.

The main difference between the two models is that in the cluster model we neglect any nonlinear relaxation process of the interacting point defects, whereas this is taken into account in the loop model. Further, the cluster is assumed to have spherical symmetry, whereas the loop is highly anisotropic. For the loops the absolute magnitude of the displacement is the same for vacancies and interstitials, while for the clusters vacancies normally cause smaller displacements than do interstitials. In both models the asymptotic displacement field of an aggregate of $n_{cl}$ defects is proportional to $n_{cl}/r^2$, which is most important for the following.

### 2.2.1. *Photoelectric absorption (Debye-Waller factor)*

As in the case of randomly distributed point defects, the photoelectric absorption of point defect aggregates, calculated from the imaginary part of the first average term $\langle V \rangle$ in eq. (1), consists of two parts: the photoelectric absorption of the defects themselves and the absorption of the displaced lattice atoms. In the *cluster model* eq. (2) still holds, and the direct defect absorption expressed by the last term does not change at all if the impurities are clustered. On the other hand, the indirect absorption via the displaced lattice atoms, which according to eq. (2b) is given by $\mu_o \cdot L_\mathbf{h}$, can increase remarkably due to the increase of the total lattice displacement.

Assuming the displacement s of a lattice atom to be Gaussian distributed, we get for the *Debye-Waller factor*

$$L_h = \tfrac{1}{2} \langle (\mathbf{h} \cdot \mathbf{s})^2 \rangle = \tfrac{1}{6} h^2 \langle s^2 \rangle \tag{5}$$

for cubic crystals. In the cluster model s is the sum of all the displacements $\mathbf{t}_i$ due to all defects $i = 1 \ldots N_d$. Assuming, moreover, that we have $N_{cl}$ clusters, each containing $n_{cl}$ defects ($N_d = N_{cl} n_{cl}$) and that the cluster radii are very small, then

$$\langle s^2 \rangle = \sum_{i,j=1}^{N_d} \langle \mathbf{t}_i \cdot \mathbf{t}_j \rangle = n_{cl} \sum_{i=1}^{N_d} \langle \mathbf{t}_i^2 \rangle = n_{cl} N_d \langle \mathbf{t}_1^2 \rangle = N_{cl} n_{cl}^2 \langle \mathbf{t}_1^2 \rangle \tag{6}$$

because the displacement $\mathbf{t}_j$ of all the defects in the cluster of defect $i$ is the same and because each defect gives on the average the same contribution. We see that $n_{cl}$ enters quadratically, which is due to the "coherent" displacement addition of the defects in the same cluster, whereas $N_{cl}$ enters linearly, which is due to the "incoherent" addition of the displacements of the different clusters. If the defects are randomly distributed, we get $\langle s^2 \rangle = N_d \langle \mathbf{t}_1^2 \rangle$, because now all displacements add incoherently. Therefore we see that under the above assumption $\langle s^2 \rangle$ increases due to clustering by a factor $n_{cl}$.

Actually, this formula is an overestimation of the clustering effect because we have assumed the cluster radius $R_{cl} \approx 0$. For clusters with finite radius, this coherent displacement addition is only correct for atoms far outside the clusters, because only the asymptotic displacement of the cluster is proportional to $n_{cl}$. Inside the cluster the displacements add more or less incoherently. A more realistic calculation gives therefore [16]

$$L_h \cong L_h^o + \tfrac{1}{6} C_d \frac{4\pi A^2 h^2 n_{cl}}{V_c R_{cl}}, \qquad C_d = C_{cl} n_{cl} \tag{7}$$

where $R_{cl}$ is an average cluster radius and $L_h^o$ is the Debye-Waller factor for statistically distributed point defects (eq. (3)). The increase in the Debye-Waller factor is essentially given by $n_{cl} \cdot \rho_c / R_{cl}$.

For the *Debye-Waller factor* of randomly distributed *dislocation loops*, we get analogously to eq. (3) [18,16]

$$L_h = C_L \sum_n \{1 - \cos \mathbf{h} \cdot \mathbf{t}_n^L\} \cong C_L \int \frac{d\mathbf{r}}{V_c} \{1 - \cos \mathbf{h} \cdot \mathbf{t}^L (\mathbf{r})\} \tag{8}$$

where $C_L$ is the loop density. Because the displacements $\mathbf{t}^L$ of the loops are quite large ($\approx b$), the cosines cannot be expanded. In general one can show that the function $\mathbf{t}(\mathbf{r})$ of a loop with an average radius $R_0$ is only a function of the reduced coordinate $\mathbf{r}/R_0$: $\mathbf{t}(\mathbf{r}) = \tau (\mathbf{r}/R_0)$, where now $\tau$ depends only on the orientation and the shape of the loop, but not on the size. Therefore $L_h$ is proportional to $R_0^3$, i.e.,

$$L_h = C_L \frac{R_0^3}{V_c} \int d\tilde{\mathbf{r}} \{1 - \cos \mathbf{h} \cdot \tau(\tilde{\mathbf{r}})\} . \tag{9}$$

Taking into account that the number $n_L$ of defects forming a loop is proportional to $(R_o/a_o)^2$, we have $L_h \approx C_d R_o/a_o \approx C_d n_L a_o/R_o$ with $C_d = C_L n_L$. Therefore, if point defects form a loop, the Debye-Waller factor increases by a factor of $R_o/a_o \approx n_L a_o/R_o$, and so does the photoelectric absorption of the lattice atoms. The enhancement factor is essentially the same as in the cluster case.

The remaining integral in (9) cannot be done in general due to the complicated displacement field $\tau(r)$. Following Krivoglaz [18], we replace $\tau(r)$ by the asymptotic expression for $r \gtrsim 2R_o$, an approximation which is allowed for $hb \gg 1$ but which is a surprisingly good approximation also for moderate values of $hb$. Considering that we may have loops on $\{111\}$ and/or $\{110\}$, we must average (9) over all the cubic equivalent planes. Thus, $L_h$ depends only slightly on the direction of $h$ and is given approximately by

$$L_h \approx C_L \frac{R_o^3}{V_c} \frac{(hb)^{\frac{3}{2}}}{2}. \qquad (10)$$

Characteristically, the $h$-dependence, resulting from the large displacements of the loop, is much less than the "normal" $h^2$-behaviour.

### 2.2.2. Diffuse scattering absorption

The absorption due to the diffuse waves has to be calculated from the second term in eq. (1). It consists also of two parts, one due to the diffuse scattering at the defects themselves and one due to the diffuse scattering at the displaced lattice atoms. As for the photoelectric absorption, the latter is the most important, and that only will be considered here. This is essentially determined by the correlation $\langle s_i^n s_j^{n'} \rangle$ of the displacements of different atoms $n$ and $n'$, in contrast to the Debye-Waller factor dependance on $\langle (s^n)^2 \rangle$. For $|R^n - R^{n'}| \gg R_{cl}$ the increase in these correlations due to clustering is essentially a factor $n_{cl} \cdot a_o/R_{cl}$, as for the Debye-Waller factor. But the long range correlations for $|R^n - R^{n'}| \gg R_{cl}$ increase much faster directly proportional to $n_{cl}$, because they are determined by the asymptotic displacement fields of the clusters. They cause a very strong diffuse scattering near the Bragg reflections, which gives rise to an extra absorption. This absorption can be calculated straightforwardly from the imaginary part of the second term in eq. (1). The Fourier coefficients $I_{hh'}$ of this imaginary potential [9,14] can be given as a surface integral over the Ewald sphere $k'^2 = k^2$:

$$I_{hh'} = -\pi \frac{V_c}{(2\pi)^3} \frac{1}{2k} \int_{k'^2 = k^2} dF_{k'} v_{k+h-k'} v_{k+h'-k'}$$

$$\times \sum_{n-n'} e^{i(k-k') (R^n - R^{n'})} \langle (k+h-k') \cdot s^n (k+h'-k') \cdot s^{n'} \rangle. \qquad (11)$$

For the *cluster model* we get from this

$$I_{hh'} = -\pi \frac{V_c}{(2\pi)^3} \frac{C_d}{2k} \int_{k'^2 = k^2} dF_{k'} \, v_{k+h-k'} \, v_{k+h'-k'}$$

$$\times (k+h-k') \cdot \tilde{t}(q) \, (k+h'-k') \cdot \tilde{t}(q) \, \{1 + \tilde{g}(q)\} \qquad (12)$$

with

$$\tilde{t}(q) = \sum_n e^{iq \cdot R^n} \, t(R^n) \simeq i \frac{4\pi A}{V_c} \frac{q}{q^2} \,, \quad \tilde{g}(q) = \sum_n e^{iq \cdot R^n} \, g(R^n)$$

and $k' - k = h + q$, $h$ is a reciprocal lattice vector, defined so that $q$ lies always in the first Brillouin zone. $g(R^n - R^{n'})$ is the conditional probability of finding a defect at position $R^n$ if one knows already that there is a defect of the *same* cluster at point $R^{n'}$. For $q \ll 1/R_{cl}$, we have therefore $\tilde{g}(q) \simeq (n_{cl} - 1) \approx n_{cl}$, the number of particles in one cluster, whereas $\tilde{g}(q)$ is very small compared to this for $q \gg 1/R_{cl}$. For randomly distributed point defects we have $\tilde{g}(q) \equiv 0$ and only the factor 1 remains. The enhancement factor $\tilde{g}(q) \approx n_{cl}$ is most important for these regions of the integration, for which the remaining strain factors $(k+h-k') \cdot t(q)$ have a divergence. Otherwise the enlargement of the integrand in a very small area cannot lead to a substantial enlargement of the integral $I_{hh'}$. In the two-beam case $(0,h)$ the coefficients $I_{00}, I_{hh}, I_{0h}$, and $I_{h0}$ are important. For instance, the $I_{00}$ integral has a $1/q^2$ divergence near $k' \simeq k+h$, which is due to the well known strong tails of the diffuse scattering near the Bragg reflections. For large clusters $(n_{cl} \gg 1)$ the only important contribution to $I_{00}$ comes therefore from this region. The coefficient $I_{hh'}$ turns out to be equal to $I_{00}$, whereas the coefficients $I_{0h}$ and $I_{h0}$ are an order of magnitude smaller because they have only a $1/q$ divergence. They will be neglected in the following. Therefore, we get for the absorption due to diffuse scattering

$$\mu_{D.S.} = -\frac{1}{k} I_{00} = C_d \, \pi \frac{A^2}{V_c} \, v_h^2 \frac{h^2}{k^2} \cos^2 \theta_B \cdot n_{cl} \cdot \ln \frac{1}{R_{cl} q_c} \,. \qquad (13)$$

Due to dynamical effects [9,14] the $1/q^2$ divergence has been cut off for $q < q_c = v_h/h$. Because of $I_{0h} \simeq 0$, this absorption is the same for the two Block waves on the different branches of the dispersion surfaces. Moreover, the absorption changes only very slightly, if the Bragg condition is not exactly fulfilled. In this case $q_c$ has to be replaced by $q_0$, the smallest $q$ value which can occur; $q_0 = ||k+h| - k|$. This absorption decreases therefore logarithmically with the excitation error, as long as $q_0 < 1/R_{cl}$, and is essentially zero otherwise.

According to eq. (3), $\mu_{D.S.}$ is proportional to $C_d \, n_{cl} = C_{cl} n_{cl}^2$ and is therefore very sensitive to clustering. Whereas for isolated point defects $\mu_{D.S.}$ is negligible compared with the photoelectric absorption, in the case of clustering it can be comparable to even much larger than the photoelectric absorption, depending on the cluster size. Moreover, it shows a different wavelength dependence, being proportional to $\lambda^2$ for small Bragg angles.

For *dislocation loops* we get a formula similar to (12). Only $C_d$ must be replaced by the loop concentration $C_L$, and $\tilde{t}(g)$ by the Fourier transform $\tilde{t}^L(q)$ of the loop displacement field, whereas $g(q) = 0$. For small $q$ we can evaluate $\tilde{t}^L(q)$ from the asymptotic expression in eq. (4). As in the cluster case we have very intense diffuse scattering near the Bragg reflection, which gives rise to an extra absorption. The calculations are similar to the cluster case, but more lengthy, and will be presented elsewhere [16]. If we assume, that the loops can occupy all planes and that no directions are preferred, we get finally (for $\nu = \frac{1}{3}$)

$$\mu_{D.S.} = C_L \, b^2 R_0^4 \, h^2 v_h^2 \, \frac{1}{k^2 V_c} \ln \frac{1}{q_c R_0} \times (0.104 + 0.098 \cos^2 \theta_B ). \qquad (14)$$

In analogy to the cluster expression (13), $\mu_{DS}$ is proportional to $C_L R_0^4 \approx C_L n_L^2 = C_d n_L$. Therefore, it is also very sensitive to clustering and increases for increasing $R_0$ much faster than the photoelectric absorption (10), which is proportional to $C_L R_0^3$. Whereas for very small loops the diffuse scattering absorption is negligible compared with the photoelectric absorption, the diffuse absorption becomes much more important for larger loops. The dependence of $\mu_{D.S.}$ for loops on the wavelength ($\approx \lambda^2$) and on the deviation from the Bragg condition is just the same as in the cluster case.

We have assumed the clusters or loops to have a uniform radius in a given crystal; in the general case of a distribution of cluster or loop radii, the proper moments of the radii must be used in calculations.

## 3. Comparison of theory with experimental data

We now compare the existing experimental data with the theory outlined above. First we calculate the changes in anomalous X-ray transmission which would result from point defects in copper. Then, since most of the experimental studies to date on point defects have been concerned with the effects of various kinds of impurities on anomalous X-ray transmission, we compare these results with the point defect model. We conclude with a more complete discussion of the effects of fast neutron irradiation on copper, silicon and germanium.

In these calculations we express the change in intensity resulting from the presence of defects in terms of an effective absorption coefficient $\mu^*$: $R_{HD} = R_{H_0} e^{-\mu^* t}$, with $\mu^* = \mu_{P.E.} + \mu_{D.S.}$. The expressions for point defects, clusters, and loops are given in eqs. (2, 3, 7, 10, 13, 14).

### 3.1. Point defects
It is necessary to have independent estimates of both the concentration of defects and the displacements of the atoms around the defects. The former can be obtained from electrical resistivity measurements, the latter from measurements of the change in lattice parameters resulting from a known number of defects or

from calculations of the displacements around a defect in the lattice. It should be remembered that all the values so obtained are of limited accuracy.

We only consider interstitial point defects since vacancies make no direct contribution to absorption and the lattice displacements around a vacancy are much less than those around an interstitial. And as stated in the theory section we neglect diffuse scattering for point defects. For copper, from the calculations of Seeger, Mann and v. Jan [19], Dederichs has computed the Debye-Waller factor $L_h$ and self-absorption term for the body centered and split forms of the interstitials for $\langle 111 \rangle$ and $\langle 220 \rangle$ reflections:

|  | Body centered | | Split | |
|---|---|---|---|---|
| h | $\langle 111 \rangle$ | $\langle 220 \rangle$ | $\langle 111 \rangle$ | $\langle 220 \rangle$ |
| $L_h/C_I$ | 1.8 | 4.4 | 2.7 | 4.65 |
| $1 - \cos h \cdot \mathbf{R}^I$ | 2 | 0 | 1.3 | 1.25 |

$C_I$ is the fractional concentration of interstitials. The calculated values of $\exp(-\mu^*t)$ for representative concentrations and crystal thicknesses are given in table 1 for maximum and minimum effects. Hence, to observe a change of intensity $> 1\%$ ($\langle 220 \rangle$ reflection) $C_I$ must be $\gtrsim 10^{-4}$ (equivalent to an irradiation with $\approx 10^{19}$ electrons/cm$^2$). At $C_I = 10^{-4}$ there would be a 2% difference between the split and body centered cases ($\langle 220 \rangle$ reflection). An experiment to test this calculation is currently in progress at University of Illinois [20]. Since impurity interstitials in copper generally would be atoms of lower atomic number $\mu_o^I < \mu_o^{Cu}$, and impurities would be expected to be less effective than self-interstitials, except in the special cases for which the X-ray wave-length corresponds to the absorption edge of the impurity.

For silicon and germanium less is known about the strength A of the defects than in the case of metals. For interstitial configurations in the body centered positions, the self absorption terms $\cos \mathbf{h} \cdot \mathbf{R}^I = 1$ for $\langle 220 \rangle$ reflections. Hence $\mu_{P.E.} = \mu_o L_h$. From electron irradiation of silicon and germanium [21] it appears that A should be quite small, but this must be considered as qualitative since the exact concentration

Table 1
Calculated values of intensity decreases due to point defects.

| | $e^{-\mu^*t}$ | | |
|---|---|---|---|
| | $\langle 220 \rangle$ | | $\langle 111 \rangle$ |
| $\mu_o t$ | $C_I = 10^{-5}$ | $C_I = 10^{-3}$ | $C_I = 10^{-3}$ |
| 40 | 0.997 | 0.79 | 0.86 |
| 100 | 0.994 | 0.55 | 0.70 |

is unknown. An estimate of $A$ for impurities can be obtained from lattice parameter measurements. Using the value for Poissons ratio $\nu = 0.27$ for Ge and 0.38 for Si, for Ge $4\pi A/V_c = 1.7 \, (\Delta a/a) \, (1/C)$ and for Si $4\pi A/V_c = 2.7 \, (\Delta a/a) \, (1/C)$. From published values of $\Delta a/a$ for various concentrations C [22] of Ni in Ge and C or As in Si we obtain:

$$\text{Ni in Ge} \qquad \frac{4\pi A}{V_c} \approx 0.1$$

$$\text{C or As in Si} \qquad \frac{4\pi A}{V_c} \cong 0.7 \; .$$

The Ni is thought to be interstitial, the C and As substitutional. Hence the value of

$$\left. \frac{4\pi A}{V_c} \right|_{\text{Impurities in Si or Ge}} < \left. \frac{4\pi A}{V_c} \right|_{\text{Cu in Cu}} \cong 1 \; ,$$

and the effect of single isolated impurities in silicon and germanium is less than that for interstitials in copper. We conclude that various studies [2] made of the effect of impurities on anomalous transmission cannot be interpreted in terms of a statistical distribution of point defects. Also the results attributed to vacancies and vacancy clustering in germanium [2] seem completely inconsistent with this theory in that large differences in anomalous transmission intensities observed were attributed to single vacancies.

## 3.2. Clusters

Baldwin and Thomas [5] have recently reported the effects of fast neutron irradiation at room temperature on anomalous transmission in silicon and germanium crystals. Regions of disorder of diameter 20–50 Å have been observed in electron microscopic studies of crystals so irradiated [23,24]. At the stage at which these clusters annealed (electron microscopic observations) about half of the total decrease in Borrmann intensity resulting from the irradiation was recovered. From an extrapolation of the published results we estimate $10^{17}/\text{cm}^3$ clusters were produced by the irradiation with $4 \times 10^{19}$ neutrons/$\text{cm}^2$ $(E > 0.6 \text{ MeV})$. From lattice parameter measurements on the same samples [25] we obtain $AC = 1.5 \times 10^{-4}$, and, taking $\rho_c = 1.2 \text{ Å}$, $V_c = 22 \, A_0^3$, $d = 2 \text{ Å}$, and a constant density of defects within the clusters so that $R_{cl} \approx R_0$, then $\mu_{\text{P.E.}} \cong 0.35 \text{ cm}^{-1}$. Since little or no wavelength dependence was observed $\mu_{\text{D.S.}} \ll \mu_{\text{P.E.}}$; hence $\mu^* \approx 0.35 \text{ cm}^{-1}$. The measured value of $\mu^*$ was about $3 \text{ cm}^{-1}$.

It has been suggested that similar disordered regions produced from heavy ion irradiation are "amorphous" [26]. If we assume that this is true here and that the regions are spherical and randomly oriented, the atomic defect fraction can be calculated:

$$\tfrac{4}{3}\pi \frac{R_o^3}{V} N_{cl} \cong 6.5 \times 10^{-3} = C \ \text{(assuming } R_o = 25 \ \text{Å)} .$$

Assuming that the self absorption term dominates, $\mu_{P.E.} = \mu_o C (1 - \cos \mathbf{h} \cdot \mathbf{R}^l) = \mu_o C$, or $\mu_{P.E.} = 2.3 \ \text{cm}^{-1}$. However, since the estimated defect concentration $C$ is so large, this apparent agreement may be fortuitous. An important consequence of the suggestion that these regions are 'amorphous' would be that $\mu^*$ would be independent of $h$. Although this point has not been checked it appears that measurements of the $h$ dependence of $\mu^*$ can give important information about the actual defect arrangement within the disordered region.

Probably the most complete experimental information that exists on the effect of 'clusters' on anomalous transmission is the data of Baldwin, Sherrill, and Young [6] on fast neutron irradiation of copper. Although experimental values of $\Delta a/a$ and electron microscopy observations on the same crystals for which X-ray intensity measurements were obtained indicate that those defect clusters were predominantly small dislocation loops, we apply the cluster model to the experimental data from crystals irradiated with $1.4 \times 10^{18}$ fast neutrons/cm$^2$. In the same crystal the number of defects observed by electron microscopy was $2.8 \times 10^{16}$/cm$^3$ † and the moments obtained from the size distribution are listed in table 2. The concentration of defects in the clusters is unknown and we assume $C_d = 1 \times 10^{-4}$ (this value is rather arbitrary; however, it allows a numerical comparison between this calculation for clusters and the one below for loops). If we also assume half the clusters are interstitial and a constant defect density within a cluster so that $R_{cl} \approx R_o = 14 \ \text{Å}$ for this calculation, we can compute $\mu^*$ using eqs. (7) and (13). We find for $\langle 111 \rangle$ reflections, $\mu_{P.E.} = 1.2 \ \text{cm}^{-1}$ and $\mu_{D.S.} = 0.2$ and $0.8 \ \text{cm}^{-1}$, giving $\mu^*$ (calc.) = 1.4 and 2.0 cm$^{-1}$ for Mo and CuK$_\alpha$ respectively, to be compared with the experimental values of $\mu^*$ of 4.8 and 8.0 cm$^{-1}$. The agreement between theory and experiment is only fair. Although a better fit could be obtained with a judicious choice of $C_d$, for the reasons indicated above it is probable that the loop model is a more realistic one.

Table 2
Concentration and moment data for two neutron irradiations ($E > 0.6$ MeV).

|  | $1.4 \times 10^{18}$/cm$^2$ | $1 \times 10^{19}$/cm$^2$ |
|---|---|---|
| $C_L$ | $2.8 \times 10^{-7}$ | $6.4 \times 10^{-7}$ |
| $R_o$ and higher moments | $R_o = 20$ | 18 |
|  | $R_2 = 28$ | 25 |
|  | $R_3 = 36$ | 33 |
|  | $R_4 = 44$ | 40 |

† The reader should note that these more recent values are somewhat higher than those quoted previously in ref. [6]. We thank J.C.Crump, for the electron microscopic observations.

### 3.3. Loops

The electron microscopy and lattice parameter measurements indicate that the defects existing in these copper crystals are dislocation loops of both interstitial and vacancy nature. Note that, in contrast to clusters, loops of either nature produce the same effect on X-ray intensities. The data for two irradiations $1.4 \times 10^{18}$ and $1 \times 10^{19}$ neutrons/cm$^2$ are given in table 2; some of the same crystals used for X-ray measurements and other crystals irradiated in the same experiments were used

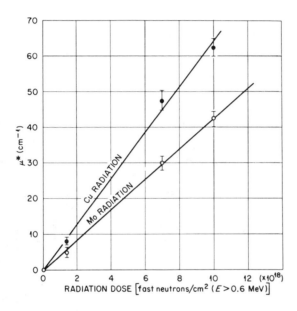

Fig. 1. A plot of the anomalous absorption coefficient $\mu^*$ versus fast neutron dose for both CuK$_a$ and MoK$_a$ wavelengths. The difference between the curves gives a rough estimate of the diffuse scattering absorption. $hkl = 111$.

for these microscopic observations. It should be noted that the number and size distribution in table 2 is different from those reported elsewhere for similar irradiations [6,27]. The experimental values of $\mu^*$ as a function of neutron dose for CuK$_\alpha$ and MoK$_\alpha$ are shown in fig. 1. The calculated and experimental values for $\mu^*$ are given in table 3 †; the $\mu^*$ (meas.) are in good agreement with $\mu^*$ (calc.) for the lower doses, but a factor of four larger than the calculated values for the higher doses.

* The experimental values for the $1.0 \times 10^{19}$ dose represent new data heretofore unpublished, whereas the $1.4 \times 10^{18}$/cm$^2$ data is taken from ref. [6]. The authors would like to thank J.E. Thomas for making some of these measurements.

These calculations are much less ambiguous than those for clusters since no assumptions about point defect concentrations are needed, but it would be possible to obtain a better numerical fit by making small adjustments in the tail of the distribution curve of the loops. And the known experimental uncertainties in the number and size of the loops might make such adjustments plausible. But the relative magnitude of $\mu_{D.S.}$ (calc.) apparently is already too large; we estimate that $\mu_{D.S.}$ should be $\lesssim \mu_{P.E.}$ for CuK$_\alpha$(note $\mu^*$ (meas.) for copper is less than twice $\mu^*$ (meas.) for MoK$_\alpha$). Therefore, any adjustments in only the tail of the loop distribution for better numerical fit between $\mu^*$ (calc.) and $\mu^*$ (meas.) would accentuate this discrepancy in $\mu_{D.S.}$. The discrepancy in the dose dependence points up the differences in the X-ray and the electron microscope evidence. The former indicates a linear dependence of $\mu^*$ on dose, fig. 1; the latter indicates a smaller increase in loop density with dose, table 2. The X-ray evidence would suggest that the loop densities which were observed with the electron microscope might be too small. On the other hand, it should be noted that the proper wave length dependence is predicted by this theory. Furthermore, with no data adjustment whatever, the magnitudes of the observed X-ray effects have been calculated from other unrelated experimental data (with their own rather large experimental uncertainties) for the same crystals.

From eqs. (7) and (10) it is apparent that $\mu^*$ varies as $h^2$ for the cluster model and as about $h^{\frac{3}{2}}$ for the loop model, hence intensity measurements for different reflections should serve to distinguish between the two cases. Integrated intensities measured for two wavelengths, 0.71 Å and 0.56 Å, and for several reflections are

Table 3

Calculated and measured values of $\mu^*$ (cm$^{-1}$) corresponding to the data in table 2. $hkl$ = 111.

|  | Loops | | | |
|---|---|---|---|---|
|  | $C_L = 2.8 \times 10^{-7}$ | | $C_L = 6.4 \times 10^{-7}$ | |
|  | Mo | Cu | Mo | Cu |
| $\mu_{P.E.}$ | 3.8 | 3.8 | 6.7 | 6.7 |
| $\mu_{D.S.}$ | 1.3 | 5.9 | 2.2 | 9.5 |
| $\mu^*$ | 5.1 | 9.7 | 8.9 | 16.2 |
| $\mu^*_{exp}$ | 4.8 | 8.0 | 42 | 62 |

presented in table 4. For loops the theoretical prediction is $L_{222}/L_{111} \approx 2.6 - 2.8$; for clusters, 4. The observed value of about 2.3 is in much better agreement with the loop model, strongly suggesting that loops are present.

Table 4
$\mu^*$ for different $hkl$ for $1.0 \times 10^{19}$ f.n./cm$^2$. $\mu^* \cong \mu_0(1 - e^{-L})$.

| | Crystal 633-2-20, $t_0 = 0.32$ mm, $\lambda = 0.71$ Å | |
|---|---|---|
| $hkl$ | $\mu^*$(cm$^{-1}$) | $L_{222}/L_{111}$ |
| 111 | $40 \pm 2$ | |
| 200 | 47 | 2.4 |
| 220 | 79 | |
| 222 | 88 | |
| | Crystal 633-2-10, $t_0 = 0.47$ mm, $\lambda = 0.56$ Å | |
| $hkl$ | $\mu^*$ | $L_{222}/L_{111}$ |
| 111 | 26 | 2.3 |
| 222 | 56 | |

3.4. *Larger loops and 'clusters'*

Although this theory does not apply for loops or clusters large with respect to an extinction length, observations of such large defects can be made via Borrmann topography, and intensity measurements might eventually provide us with the additional information needed to characterize them. Vacancy clusters and impurity clusters have been observed via topography and intensity measurements in semiconductors. In addition, it was found that vacancy clusters in copper appeared to have only a small influence on Borrmann intensities [28]. Some slight evidence for an increase in the Borrmann intensity was observed upon removal by annealing of the clusters shown in fig. 2. The exact nature of these clusters has not been determined in the electron microscope owing to the small density. It seems probable that the oxygen precipitation studied by Patel and Batterman [1] would fall into this size category.

However, recent work involving the effects of fast neutron irradiation of copper at 400°C has demonstrated that about $2 \times 10^6$/cm$^3$ 'defect regions' about 25 microns in diameter are produced by $10^{18}$ neutrons/cm$^2$ and they reduce the Borrmann intensities drastically [29]. The wavelength sensitivity is reversed from that observed for the much smaller clusters, i.e. the shorter wavelength X-ray intensities are reduced more than the longer ones. In this case, it appears clear that the diffuse scattering is scattered in the Bragg direction and the reflection is broadened. These clusters, for a given fast neutron dose, decrease the Borrmann intensity much more than that observed from the defects produced by irradiation at ambient temperature. Some typical 111 anomalous absorption coefficients for these crystals are

UC63

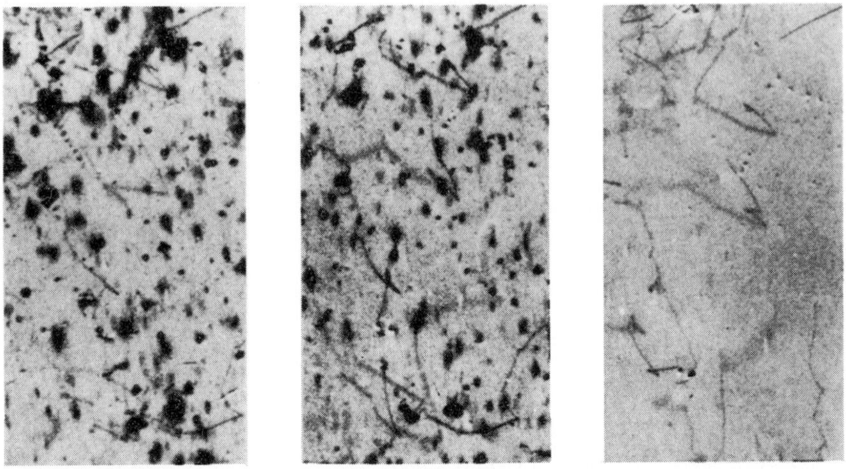

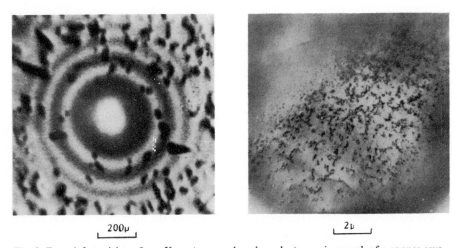

1.0 mm                        700°C                        900°C

Fig. 2. Topographs taken of a copper crystal after various stages of annealing of large 'vacancy clusters'. Little or no change in intensity resulted from the complete removal of the clusters.

200μ                                            2μ

Fig. 3. From left to right, a Lang X-ray topograph and an electron micrograph of a copper crystal irradiated to a dose of $1.0 \times 10^{18}/cm^2$ fast neutrons at about 400°C. The electron micrograph demonstrates the detailed structure of even the smallest black spots shown in the topograph.

40 cm$^{-1}$ ($\lambda = 0.71$ Å) and 30 cm$^{-1}$ ($\lambda = 1.54$ Å) for an irradiation dose of about $1 \times 10^{18}$ f.n./cm$^2$, and topographs of the defect regions are shown in fig. 3.

## 4. Conclusions

Considerable progress has been made in the development of the dynamical theory for crystals with statistical arrangements of small defects, extending the range of defect sizes for which the Borrmann technique can be applied. This technique is one of the few available for which defects can be studied in the bulk state but has the obvious limitation that crystals of low dislocation densities are needed. The theory for small clusters and loops can explain at least semi-quantitatively the experimental observations. It would appear that additional experiments are needed, particularly with regard to characterizing the defects introduced by the irradiation damage, so that a more rigorous check of the theory can be made.

## References

[1] J.R.Patel and B.W.Batterman, J. Appl. Phys. 34 (1963) 2716.
[2] O.N.Efimov and A.M.Elistratov, Soviet Phys. – Solid State 34 (1963) 2716;
    A.M.Elistratov and L.I.Datsenko, Soviet Phys. – Solid State 8 (1966) 648.
[3] S.Maruyama, J. Phys. Soc. Japan 20 (1965) 1399.
[4] R.Colella and A.Merlini, Phys. Stat. Sol. 14 (1966) 81.
[5] T.O.Baldwin and J.E.Thomas, J. Appl. Phys. 39 (1968) 4391.
[6] T.O.Baldwin, F.A.Sherrill and F.W.Young Jr., J. Appl. Phys. 39 (1968) 1541.
[7] For recent reviews see: B.W.Batterman and H.Cole, Rev. Mod. Phys. 36 (1964) 681;
    R.W.James, *Solid State Physics*, Vol. 15 (Academic Press, Inc., New York, 1963).
[8] C.R.Hall, P.H.Hirsch and G.R.Booker, Phil. Mag. 14 (1966) 979.
[9] P.H.Dederichs, Phys. Stat. Sol. 23 (1967) 377.
[10] M.Kuriyama, Phys. Stat. Sol. 24 (1967) 743; J. Appl. Phys. 39 (1968) 2162.
[11] E.A.Tikhonova, Sov. Phys. Sol. State 9 (1967) 394.
[12] Y.H.Ohtsuki, J. Phys. Soc. Jap. 19 (1964) 2285; 20 (1964) 314.
[13] Y.H.Ohtsuki and S.Yanagawa, J. Phys. Soc. Jap. 21 (1966) 326; 21 (1966) 502.
[14] P.H.Dederichs, Phys. Cond. Materie 5 (1966) 347.
[15] A.M.Afasanev and Yu.Kagan, Acta Cryst. A24 (1967) 163.
[16] P.H.Dederichs, to be published.
[17] F.Kroupa, Czech. J. Phys. B10 (1960) 284;
    T.D.Eshelby, Proc. Roy. Soc. A241 (1957) 376.
[18] M.A.Krivoglaz and K.P.Ryaboshka, Physics Metals Metallogr. 16 No. 5 (1963) 1.
[19] A.Seeger, E.Mann and R.N.Jan, J. Phys. Chem. Solids 23 (1962) 639.
[20] J.S.Koehler, private communication.
[21] F.L.Vook, *Radiation Damage in Semiconductors* (Dunod, Paris, France, 1965) p. 51.
[22] N.E.Moyer and R.C.Buschert, in: *Radiation Effects in Semiconductors*, ed. by F.L.Vook
    (Plenum Press, New York, 1968) p. 444;
    W.B.Pearson, ed., *Lattice Spacings and Structures of Metals and Alloys* (Pergamon Press, New York, 1958).

[23] G. den Ouden, J. Appl. Phys. 39 (1968) 4509.

[24] J.M.Pankratz, J.A.Sprague and M.L.Rudee, J. Appl. Phys. 39 (1968) 101.

[25] T.O.Baldwin, Phys. Rev. Letters 21 (1968) 901.

[26] J.R.Parsons and C.W.Hoelke, *Radiation Effects in Semiconductors*, ed. by F.L.Vook. (Plenum Press, New York, 1968) p. 339.

[27] M.Wilkens, this volume.

[28] T.O.Baldwin, A.Merlini and F.W.Young Jr., Phys. Rev. 163 (1967) 591.

[29] L.D.Hulett Jr., T.O.Baldwin, J.C.Crump, III and F.W.Young Jr., J. Appl. Phys. 39 (1968) 3945.

# CHANNELLING AND BLOCKING EFFECTS AS A TOOL FOR STUDYING DEFECTS IN METALS

R.S.NELSON

*Solid State Division, A.E.R.E., Harwell, Berkshire, U.K.*

## 1. Introduction

The phenomenon of "channelling" — the steering of fast ions along the open channels and planes of a crystal lattice so that their trajectories are constrained to travel in regions of low atomic density — has been known since about 1963 [1–3]. Even then, the possibility of using such a phenomenon to study defects in crystalline materials was recognised; for instance, Nelson and Thompson observed a significant reduction in the channelling of $He^+$ ions through thin Au foils due to the presence of radiation damage.

Since these original experiments the majority of effort has been directed towards understanding the channelling phenomenon itself, rather than its possible use as a tool in the study of defects. However, over the last two years or so a number of experiments have demonstrated the potentialities of the technique.

In this paper we will first outline the basic concepts which give rise to the crystallographic effects which occur when a beam of protons or charged particles interacts with a crystal lattice, and then illustrate how such effects can be used as a new powerful tool for studying defects in crystalline solids.

## 2. The influence of the crystal lattice on proton trajectories

### 2.1. *Incident beam*

Let us first consider the trajectories of protons incident parallel to a close-packed atomic row as shown in fig. 1. Those protons which have impact parameters greater than a critical distance of approach to the channel wall, $z_{min}$, have their trajectories constrained to within the channel and oscillate from side to side, never penetrating closer to the rows than $z_{min}$, e.g. protons A and B. On the other hand those protons which have impact parameters less than $z_{min}$ to the row, such as protons C and D, suffer a deflection which cannot be contained by the opposite channel wall and consequently undergo random collisions until they come to rest.

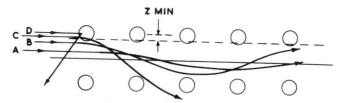

Fig. 1. Proton trajectories incident parallel to a close-packed row.

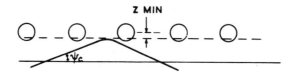

Fig. 2. The critical angle for channelling.

The incident beam is therefore effectively split into two parts differentiated by their ability to penetrate closer than a critical impact parameter to the atoms of the solid. We shall call these the channelled and random components, respectively.

From fig. 2 it is evident that there exists a critical angle of incidence $\psi_c$ which just allows the channelled trajectories to be contained. It is this angle, called the critical channelling angle, which is most easily determined experimentally. We must, therefore, relate $\psi_c$ to $z_{min}$, and to do this we must make certain assumptions regarding the interaction potential. It is a useful approximation to describe the scattering as resulting from the interaction between the moving particle and some average potential for a row or a plane. In the case of a row we may write the average potential for an ion a distance $z$ from the row as

$$\bar{U}_R(z) = \frac{1}{d} \int_{-\infty}^{\infty} V\{(x^2 + z^2)^{\frac{1}{2}}\} \, dx \, , \tag{1}$$

where $V(r)$ is the ion atom potential and $d$ is the separation of atoms in the row. Nelson and Thompson [1] used a Bohr potential for the interaction in the case of protons, and found that the average potential increased rather quickly as the channel wall was approached. The minimum distance of approach to the row can then be defined such that the transverse energy component just equals the average row potential at $z_{min}$. Thus for a particle of energy $E$, incident at $\psi_c$, we have for small angles

$$\bar{U}_R(z_{min}) = E\psi_c^2 \, . \tag{2}$$

In more general treatments, Erginsoy [4] and Lindhard [5,6] suggested that as the significant impact parameters were of the order of the screening distance of a Thomas-Fermi potential of the form

$$V(r) = \frac{Z_1 Z_2 e^2}{r} \phi_0 (r/a_{\text{TF}}) \tag{3}$$

such a potential would be more appropriate ($Z_1$ and $Z_2$ are the charge numbers of the incident particle and struck atom, respectively, $e$ is the electronic charge, $a_{\text{TF}} = 0.46(Z_1^{2/3} + Z_2^{2/3})^{-1/2}$ Å and $\phi_0 (r/a_{\text{TF}})$ is the Fermi function tabulated by Gombas [7]). In Lindhard's approximation the average potential then reduces to

$$\overline{U}_R (z) = \frac{Z_1 Z_2 e^2}{d} \ln \left\{ \left( \frac{a_{\text{TF}} C}{z} \right)^2 + 1 \right\}. \tag{4}$$

with $C \approx \sqrt{3}$. Further, as in the case of particle velocities in excess of $Z_1^{2/3} e^2/h$ the absolute minimum distance of approach, before penetration of the row occurs, is likely to be close to the Thomas-Fermi screening distance, we can substitute $a_{\text{TF}}$ for $z_{\text{min}}$ in eq. (4) to obtain

$$\psi_c \approx \left( \frac{2 Z_1 Z_2 e^2}{dE} \right)^{\frac{1}{2}}. \tag{5}$$

The critical angle $\psi_c$ therefore defines the condition under which an incident particle can become channelled. If then we direct a well collimated proton beam at an angle of incidence smaller than $\psi_c$ to a major axis of a single crystal we should expect a significant fraction of the beam to become channelled. In a perfect crystal this channelled fraction will remain aligned nearly parallel to the crystal axis, and will penetrate considerably deeper than the non-channelled fraction which is scattered by a series of statistically independent collisions to larger angles. This effect is simply demonstrated if we allow an energetic proton beam to pass through a thin single crystal foil onto a fluorescent screen or a photographic plate. For instance, fig. 3 shows the blackening recorded on X-ray film when a 3 MeV proton beam has passed through a 10 $\mu$m Si crystal parallel to the ⟨1 1 1⟩ axis. The well defined central spot corresponds to the channelled fraction whilst the general background corresponds to that component which has undergone random collisions. In addition, energy analysis of the transmitted protons shows that the energy lost by the channelled fraction is about half that lost by the random non-channelled fraction.

An alternative way of demonstrating channelling is by monitoring the back scattered fraction when thick single crystal target is rotated in a beam of protons. We know that large angle scattering can occur only when a proton suffers a close encounter with a lattice atom, i.e. from those collisions which have impact parameters very much smaller than $z_{\text{min}}$. Thus, whenever the incident beam is aligned to within the critical angle for channelling, the back scattered fraction must pass through a minimum. Fig. 4 shows the results of such an experiment specifically designed to illustrate this effect.

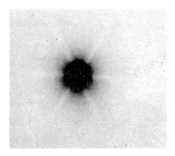

Fig. 3. Pattern recorded in X-ray film produced by a 3 MeV proton beam emerging along the ⟨111⟩ axis of a 10 μm Si crystal.

Besides the half-width at half minimum, which is a measure of the critical angle, another important characteristic feature of such an experiment is the actual magnitude of the dip. From our previous considerations we have stated that the channelled fraction can be defined as that fraction of the incident beam which enters the crystal so as to suffer collisions with impact parameters greater than $z_{min}$ to the channel walls. On the other hand the non-channelled fraction may be simply estimated to be that fraction which have impact parameters less than $z_{min}$. Thus under perfect alignment only those protons incident on an area $\pi a_{TF}^2 N_s$ within unit area of the crystal can enter the random beam, where $N_s$ is the number of atoms exposed to the incident beam per unit area. If $N_0$ is the number of atoms per cm$^3$, $N_s$ is given approximately by $N_0 d$, and so the fraction corresponding to the minimum yield or dip is

$$\chi = \pi a_{TF}^2 N_0 d . \tag{6}$$

Equation (6) suggests that the dip should be between one or two percent, whereas in actual practice the experimental minima are usually about 3%. However, this difference can be readily understood if such effects as thermal vibration and surface contamination are properly accounted for.

*2.2. Scattered beam*

We have already demonstrated that the incident beam is effectively resolved into two components. In general, the non-channelled scattered beam undergoes statistically independent atomic collisions in its passage through a crystalline solid and suffers an energy loss which is identical to that exposed for an amorphous material. However, the regular nature of the crystal lattice can in fact influence the spatial distribution of particles within this random component. For instance, if instead of rotating the crystal relative to the incident ion beam we keep the crystal fixed and rotate a detector in the path of the scattered protons, one obtains a structure having a crystallographic behaviour. Such an experiment was first performed by Tulinov

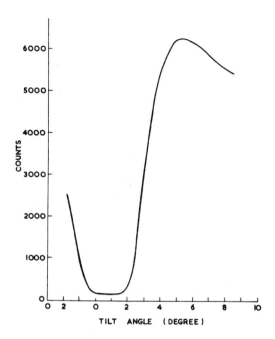

Fig. 4. Reduction in scattering yield which occurs when a W crystal is rotated in a proton beam.

[8]. Protons with an energy of 3 MeV were scattered from the surface layers of a tungsten single crystal. Those protons scattered with an energy in excess of 80% of the maximum were recorded for different angular positions of the detector, which explored a 10° cone of angles about a direction corresponding to the ⟨111⟩ axis of the crystal. Fig. 5 shows the result and clearly demonstrates a significant reduction in yield for the scattered beam energies in the direction of a close-packed row.

This phenomenon — which has been called "blocking" — is clearly similar to channelling and we may understand its origin as follows. Consider a row of atoms each separated by a regular distance $d$ (fig. 6). Suppose an energetic proton suffers a large angle collision with atom A, and is elastically scattered towards its nearest neighbour B close to the line of centres. Then, provided the proton passes sufficiently close to the nucleus of atom B, it will be deflected further away from the row. Further small angle scattering will occur at atoms C and D and so on until the protons trajectory eventually emerges from the row at some angle $\psi$. This will occur for every collision which scatters protons in the direction of the row, with the result that the probability of protons emerging close to the row axis is very small. In the case of a particle starting effectively at a lattice site, as in the case for blocking phenomena, Lindhard [6] has calculated the critical

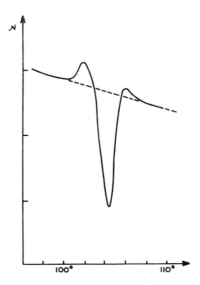

Fig. 5. Angular distribution of scattered protons from a W crystal at 3 MeV (after Tulinov, 1965).

blocking angle as follows. Let us initially assume that the particle is emitted at an angle $\phi$ from an atom residing in a row, which has no thermal vibration. Then, if one assumes that the scattering from the average potential occurs after the particle has travelled a distance $d/2$, we can write from the conservation of energy perpendicular to the row

$$E\psi^2 = E\phi^2 + \bar{U}_R(\phi d/2) .$$

(7)

Substituting for $U_R$ and solving for the minimum angle of emission $\psi$, Lindhard finds that to a good approximation

$$\psi_{min} = \psi_c .$$

(8)

This immediately infers that the critical angles for channelling and blocking are identical, and such a hypothesis has in fact been checked experimentally.

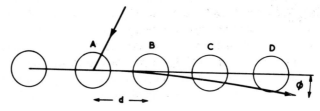

Fig. 6. Illustration of the blocking effect.

## 3. The study of defects in crystals

### 3.1. *Point defects and dislocations*

We have shown that the channelled component of a beam incident on a single crystal suffers a restricted range of impact parameters such that distances of approach to a channel wall are always less than $z_{min}$. Consequently, any atom which is displaced from its equilibrium position in a perfect lattice can interupt a channelled trajectory and result in its being scattered into the random component. In other words, the fraction of the original beam which remains channelled during its passage through a crystal depends on the density of defects within the crystal.

In the context of the present paper it is our intention to concentrate on the influence of point defects rather than extended defects such as dislocation lines. However, if it is our aim to use channelling to study the annealing of point defects in irradiated metals, we must remember that defect clusters and dislocation loops are often produced during irradiation and it may be difficult to separate the dechannelling effect of single defects such as interstitials from that of such extended defects. To date no experiments have been performed which set out to systematically study the dechannelling produced by defects in metals over a wide range of temperature. In fact, the only reported work is that of Gibson et al. [9], where the orientation dependence of proton back scattering from Cu was measured as a function of increasing bombardment with 250 keV $Cu^+$ ions at room temperature. The $\langle 110 \rangle$ minimum in the back scattered yield was found to rise steadily from about 10% to 20% of the normal yield after a dose of $\sim 5 \times 10^{14}$ $Cu^+$ ions $cm^{-2}$, after which it remained unchanged even for a ten-fold increase in bombardment dose. Electron microscopy of ion bombarded Cu shows that during such an irradiation with $Cu^+$ ions at room temperature, as the dose is increased, the damage evolves by the growth of isolated defect clusters into well resolved loops and eventually saturates to form an entangled dislocation network. Therefore, the above-mentioned experiment clearly shows that the presence of such dislocation damage can readily be detected by channelling techniques.

Returning now to point defects, it is clear from our knowledge of defects such as interstitials that experiments must be performed at very low temperatures where even close-pairs are stable. This in itself presents a major experimental problem as it necessitates the construction of a versatile goniometer, accurate to something less than 0.05°, which can be operated at liquid helium temperatures.

In principle two methods can be used: firstly, monitoring the change in the channelled fraction which emerges from a thin single crystal foil; and secondly, monitoring the change in the minimum yield of back scattered particles. The first case, although probably the most sensitive, suffers from the disadvantage that it is extremely difficult to obtain good defect free thin single crystal foils. In addition to this, the fact that damage and thermal changes cause bending of thin foils makes such a technique rather unattractive. In the back scattering case, large rigid crystals can be used, and this is clearly preferable. Perhaps the major limitation is sensitivity, for as we have already seen the minima are at best only about 1/50 of the normal yield. Even if we use the technique of double alignment (i.e. firing the incident beam down a channel and detecting the scattered particles in a blocking direction) the largest reduction in intensity would be about equal to the square of just one reduction, e.g. $\approx 5 \times 10^{-4}$. This automatically infers that in order to detect interstitials their concentration must be at least $\gtrsim 10^{-3}$. At such a concentration some clustering could easily have occurred even at liquid helium temperature and it might therefore be difficult to inambiguously detect the presence and annealing behaviour of single interstitials.

### 3.2. Impurity defects

Perhaps the most exciting use of channelling techniques is the ability to detect and locate the atomic positions of impurity atoms in crystals. For instance, if the foreign atom is located substitutionally within the host lattice, its probability of interacting with the incident beam is significantly reduced under condition of channelling. On the other hand, if the impurity atom is located in an interstitial position, even a well channelled beam will not necessarily be prevented from "seeing" it. In fact the chance of interaction with the impurity relative to the non-channelled case may well be enhanced. However, we must use an unambiguous method of detecting the impurity atoms.

If the impurity is somewhat heavier than the atoms constituting the host lattice, one method of detecting impurities that has been used, employs energy analysis of the scattered protons and provides an immediate distinction, for protons are scattered with a smaller energy loss from heavy atoms than from light atoms. Eriksson et al. [10] have used such a technique to examine the position of antimony implanted into silicon as follows. Chemically polished single crystal slices of silicon were implanted with $\approx 10^{15}$ Sb$^+$ ions/cm$^2$ at 40 keV, and at 400°C so as to reduce radiation damage. The energy spectrum of scattered protons at 1 MeV was then measured under both channelling and non-channelling conditions as illustrated in fig. 7. It is seen that the yields from both silicon and antimony are significantly reduced when the incident beam is aligned with the $\langle 111 \rangle$ axis of the silicon lattice. It was concluded that under these conditions of the order of 80% of the implanted antimony occupies isolated substitutional sites. The remainder might remain as interstitials or most likely are trapped in the vicinity of dislocations where the local atomic disorder would influence the channelling.

A more universal technique is to study the impurities by their nuclear reaction yields or by their characteristic X-ray production. Eriksson et al. [11] have made use of the reactions $^7$Li(p,$\alpha$) $^4$He and $^{11}$B(p,$\alpha$) $^8$Be to explore the usefulness of this technique by studying the fate of implanted lithium and boron in silicon. As expected, they found that lithium was predominantly interstitial and boron predominantly substitutional. The possibility of using characteristic X-rays has been examined by Cairns and Nelson [12] and as this technique is perhaps the most universal we will discuss it in some detail.

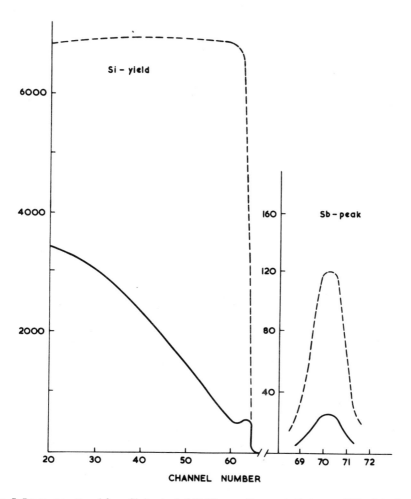

Fig. 7. Protons scattered from Sb implanted Si. The result suggests that some 80% of the Sb atoms are substitutional with the lattice (after Eriksson et al., 1967).

Unlike X-ray production during electron bombardment, protons excite only the characteristic transitions within the inner shells, and it is therefore possible to detect impurity concentrations of less than 1 in $10^6$. It is now well established that the yield of characteristic X-rays from a single crystal under proton bombardment is strongly orientation dependent. This clearly arises from the fact that the impact parameter for inner shell excitation can be somewhat less than the closest distance of approach to a channel wall. Thus whenever a well collimated proton beam is incident parallel to a channelling direction the production of X-rays will be somewhat lower than that observed under non-channelling conditions (fig. 8).

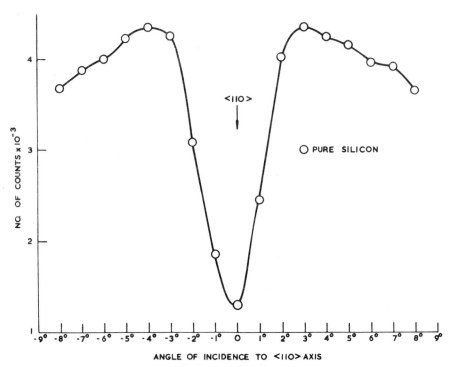

Fig. 8. Variation in Si X-ray yield as the ⟨110⟩ axis of a Si crystal is rotated about a 100 keV proton beam.

If then an impurity atom is occupying a substitutional site its X-ray yield will also pass through a minimum whenever the proton beam is channelled within the host lattice. On the other hand, if the impurity is sitting interstitially in the lattice, whenever the proton beam is channelled, the probability of exciting its X-ray will be increased over that for corresponding to random trajectories. An example of the potential of this technique is shown in fig. 9 where it is readily apparent that antimony sits as a substitutional impurity in silicon.

## 4. Conclusions

It is now quite evident that channelling and blocking phenomena will play an important role in many fields of materials research. However, it seems that although the possibility of studying intrinsic point defects such as interstitials exists theoretically, it is by no means a simple matter, both from the experimental viewpoint and from the inability to unequivocally interpret the results. On the other hand, the use

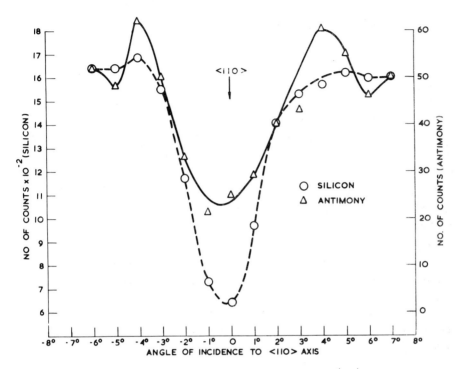

Fig. 9. Variation in Sb and Si X-ray yields during a rotation about the ⟨110⟩ axis indicating that a substantial fraction of Sb lies substitutionally.

of these new techniques to study the atomic configuration of impurity atoms and their solubilities is already a reality.

## References

[1] R.S.Nelson and M.W.Thompson, Phil. Mag. 8 (1963) 1677.
[2] J.A.Davies, G.R.Piercy, F.Brown and M.McCargo, Phys. Rev. Letters 10 (1963) 399.
[3] M.Lutz and R.Sizmann, Phys. Letters 5 (1963) 113.
[4] C.Erginsoy, Phys. Rev. Letters 12 (1965) 366.
[5] J.Lindhard, Phys. Letters 12 (1964) 126.
[6] J.Lindhard, Mat. Fys. Medd. Dan. Vid. Selsk. 34, No. 14 (1965).
[7] P.Gombas, Die Statistische Theorie der Atome (Springer Verlag, Wien, 1949).
[8] A.F.Tulinov, Dokl. Akad. Nauk SSSR 162 (1965) 546.
[9] W.M.Gibson, J.I.Andersen and E.Uggerhøj, Proc. Symp. on Rad. Effects in Semiconductors, Toulouse, 1967.
[10] L.Eriksson, J.A.Davies, J.Denhartog, J.Mayer, O.J.Marsh and R.Markarious, Appl. Phys. Letters 10 (1967) 323.

[11] L.Eriksson, J.A.Davies, J.Denhartog, Hj.Matzke and J.L.Whitton, Can. Nucl. Techn. 5
     (1966) 40.
[12] J.Cairns and R.S.Nelson, Phys. Letters 27A (1968) 14.

## Discussion

*K.Isebeck:* Is it possible for channelled atoms to follow a curvature of the lattice, which may be due to the strain field of a dislocation?

*R.S.Nelson:* Yes, it is possible that a channelled atom may follow such curvatures, but this would result in an increased channelled amplitude and perhaps eventual de-channelling.

*U.Gonser:* Do you have difficulties in the interpretation of the experimental results due to imperfections and relaxations on the surface which might partially block the channels?

*R.S.Nelson:* Yes, in some special cases.

*J.W.Corbett:* Concerning the (p,X-ray) experiments it might be helpful to note that the new semiconductor detectors will simplify the experiment since the detectors can be used to directly energy-analyze the X-rays.

*R.S.Nelson:* This is only the case for well separated X-ray energies. If we are looking for say 1 part in $10^4$, then such detectors could not resolve X-rays with close energies. In this case we are forced to use a crystal spectrometer.

# INVESTIGATION OF INTERSTITIALS AND VACANCIES IN METALS USING MÖSSBAUER SPECTROSCOPY

## U. GONSER

*Science Center, North American Rockwell Corporation, Thousand Oaks, California*

## 1. Introduction

In this paper the point of observation is the nucleus. We ask the question what information via nuclear resonance techniques can be obtained due to the presence of vacancies and interstitials. Mössbauer spectroscopy seems particularly applicable in the studies of lattice defects because (1) it allows singling out the resonance atoms, (2) the technique is non-destructive, (3) specific nuclear and atomic states can be measured in contrast to some other techniques (magnetic susceptibility, magnetization, X-rays, etc.) where macroscopic averages are observed. In general, lattice defects of transient and stationary nature will influence the physical properties: charge density, spin arrangements, spin density, lattice symmetry, atomic force constants, etc. and thus will give rise to changes in the resonance spectrum. One might distinguish between proximity effects where the property of the local perturbation in the environment of the defect is probed by the resonating atom and bulk effects.

## 2. Mössbauer parameters

Mössbauer's discovery had its 10th anniversary this year. While the first resonance observation [1,2] was made with the isotope $^{191}$Ir, the breakthrough and the realization of the wide applicability became apparent with the observation of the resonance effect in the nucleus $^{57}$Fe. Nature was kind to provide one of the most important elements — iron — with the nucleus with favorable properties for Mössbauer spectroscopy. Up to now — with only a few exceptions — the application of Mössbauer spectroscopy in regard to lattice defects was accomplished with this isotope. This might change in the future, especially when resonance data of various nuclei obtained by Coulomb excitation, nuclear reaction, and ion implantation techniques are analyzed in terms of lattice defects.

Table 1

| Effect | Formulation | Derived quantity | Schematic representation of observation |
|---|---|---|---|
| Isomer shift | $\delta = C \dfrac{\delta R}{R}[\,\lvert\psi_A(0)\rvert^2 - \psi_S(0)\rvert^2]$ | $\lvert\psi_A(0)\rvert^2, \lvert\psi_S(0)\rvert^2$ | |
| Nuclear Zeeman effect | $E_m = -g\,\mu_n m_I H_{eff}$ | $H_{eff}$ | |
| Quadrupole splitting | $E_Q = \pm\tfrac{1}{4}e^2 qQ(1+\tfrac{1}{3}\eta^2)^{\frac{1}{2}}$ | $q$ | |
| Second order Doppler shift | $\delta_R = \dfrac{\overline{v^2}}{2c^2}E_\gamma$ | $\overline{v^2}$ | |
| Line width | $\Gamma = \dfrac{\hbar}{\tau_{eff}}$ | $\tau_{eff}$ | |
| Recoil-free fraction | $f = \exp - \langle x^2\rangle k^2$ | $\langle x^2\rangle$ | |

The important Mössbauer parameters are summarized in table 1. More detailed information is found in refs. [3–11]. In the first and second column, the various effects and their formulations are listed. Column 3 contains the quantity one normally derives from the spectra. In column 4 a schematic representation is shown of the observed spectra for $^{57}$Fe with the effects indicated by the arrows. Thus, the isomer shift, $\delta$, is a measure of the electron density at the absorber or source nuclei, $\lvert\psi_A(0)\rvert^2$ and $\lvert\psi_S(0)\rvert^2$; the nuclear Zeeman effect measures the effective internal magnetic field $H_{eff}$ and nuclear $g$ factors; from the quadrupole splitting the electric field gradient (EFG) $q$ can be derived; the second-order Doppler shift is related to the mean square velocity $v^2$ which, of course, is a function of temperature; the line width is related to the lifetime of the excited state or an effective relaxation time $\tau_{eff}$; and the recoil-free fraction — that is, the intensity of the Mössbauer line — is a function of the mean square displacement $\langle x^2\rangle$. In table 1 the symbols have the following meaning: $C$ — constant for a given isotope, $R$ — nuclear radius, $\delta R = R_{excited} - R_{ground}$, $g$ — gyromagnetic ratio, $\mu_n$ — nuclear magneton, $m_I$ — magnetic quantum number, $e$ — charge of the electron, $Q$ — nuclear quadrupole moment, $\eta$ — asymmetry parameter, $c$ — velocity of light, $E_\gamma$ — $\gamma$-ray energy, $\hbar$ — Planck's constant divided by $2\pi$, $k$ — wave number of the $\gamma$-ray.

Of course, the scheme in table 1 is rather simplified. In actual Mössbauer spectra effects are superimposed. For instance, if a nuclear Zeeman effect and quadrupole interaction are simultaneously present, the angle between the principal axes of the EFG and the spin has to be specified in order to calculate the expected spectrum. Also, the relative line intensities of the hyperfine interactions are influenced by the lattice anisotropy, by polarization effects, preferred orientations (texture), etc. With this short introduction, let us examine specific cases.

The examples presented in this paper are restricted to Mössbauer spectroscopy. However, it should be mentioned that other nuclear resonance techniques, particularly NMR, are complimentary in nature [12–18]. Local susceptibility measured by the Knight shift and spin lattice relaxation time have yielded information on defects in metals. NMR has the advantage that it is not restricted to radioactive isotopes of convenient half life.

## 3. Selected examples of interstitial and vacancy investigations by Mössbauer spectroscopy

### 3.1. *Carbon interstitials in iron*

The α-Fe resonance spectrum exhibiting a nuclear Zeeman effect as seen in fig. 1 has become a symbol in Mössbauer spectroscopy and is also used frequently as a convenient velocity calibration. As we incorporate an impurity atom in the magne-

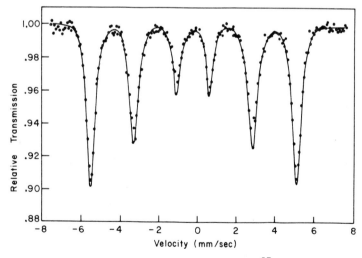

Fig. 1. Mössbauer transmission spectrum of α-Fe obtained with a $^{57}$Co-Cu source. Absorber and source were kept at room temperature.

tic matrix, the charge distribution and spin density in the environment will change. The result of this perturbation is a complex Mössbauer spectrum with structure. The appearance of satellites in the hyperfine spectra can be associated with distinct near neighbor interaction. The decomposition of the pattern can be accomplished by correlating the various superimposed spectra to the various shells surrounding the impurity atom (nearest neighbor, next nearest neighbor, etc.). Analyses of this type were carried out on α-Fe with the substitutional impurities V, Cr, Mo, Al, Ti, Si, Mn, Ga, Sn, and Be [19–27] and with the interstitial impurities carbon and nitrogen [28–32]. We focus our attention on the latter – the interstitials.

Carbon enters b.c.c. α-Fe and f.c.c. γ-Fe in interstitial lattice sites with octahedral symmetry. While the distortion around the interstitial carbon atom has cubic symmetry in the face centered cubic (f.c.c.) lattice, for the body centered cubic (b.c.c.) lattice the octahedron has only one four fold symmetry axis. In fig. 2 the iron sites in the b.c.c. structure around an interstitial carbon atom are shown. The numbers indicate the neighboring shells in ascending order of distance to the carbon atom at the origin. The presence of carbon atoms has mainly the effect of pushing apart the two iron atoms closest to the carbon atoms. The oriented localized octahedral distortion was called by Cohen [33] "distortion dipole".

Carbon austenite (f.c.c.) quenched from high temperature transforms by a martensitic transformation to martensite. The martensite structure is body centered tetragonal (b.c.t.) with the distortion dipoles aligned along one expanded axis, the tetragonal $c$ axis. The spectrum of a quenched 4.2 at % carbon alloy obtained by Moriya, Ino, Fujita and Maeda [29] is shown in fig. 3. This spectrum can be inter-

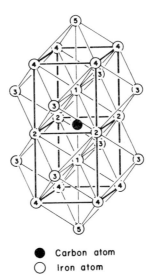

● Carbon atom
○ Iron atom

Fig. 2. Crystal structure of b.c.t. iron-carbon martensite around a carbon atom. Numbers indicate near neighbor shells.

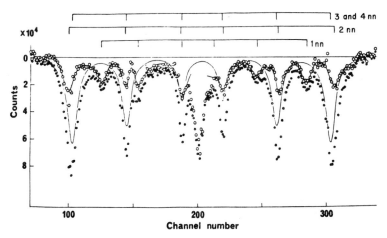

Fig. 3. Mössbauer transmission spectrum of a quenched 4.2 at % carbon alloy. The decomposition of the spectrum to the corresponding near neighbor shells (nn) is indicated at the top. The central line is due to retained austenite (after Moriya, Ino, Fujita and Maeda [29]).

preted in terms of two simultaneously present phases – (a) ferromagnetic martensite exhibiting a hyperfine spectrum at room temperature and (b) paramagnetic retained austenite exhibiting a broad single line in the center of the spectrum. The martensite phase can be analyzed further by considering the various possible nearest neighbor environments, first nn, second nn, third nn, etc., near neighbor shells. If we assume a random distribution of the carbon atoms, one can calculate the occupation probability of the various configurations. The probabilities have to match the intensities in the analysis of the Mössbauer spectrum. The decomposition of the Zeeman components to the corresponding nearest neighbor configurations (1 nn, 2 nn, 3 nn, etc.) is indicated on the top of the spectrum by the stick diagram. The analysis of the spectrum reveals that the hyperfine fields are appreciably effected by the proximity of the carbon atoms. The first four near neighbor shells can be distinguished. Actually, the spectrum in fig. 3 is simplified by subtracting an appropriate intensity (39%) of an $\alpha$-Fe component corresponding to nn $\geqslant 5$ which is considered undistinguishable from the $\alpha$-Fe spectrum. The recently developed stripping technique is helpful in the analysis of complex Mössbauer spectra [34]. The presence of carbon changes the isomer shift only slightly and creates a small electric field gradient. In fig. 4 the internal fields of the measured various nn iron sites are plotted as a function of the iron-carbon distance. It is interesting to note that the first and second nearest neighbor, having nearly the same distance to the carbon atom, show an appreciable difference in the internal field. The iron of the first nn exhibits an internal field smaller than $\alpha$-Fe and second and higher nn's have fields larger than $\alpha$-Fe. Very similar results have been obtained with interstitial nitrogen in b.c.t. iron.

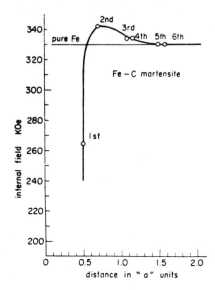

Fig. 4. The internal magnetic field of the different nn sites as a function of the carbon-iron distance (after Moriya, Ino, Fujita and Maeda [29]).

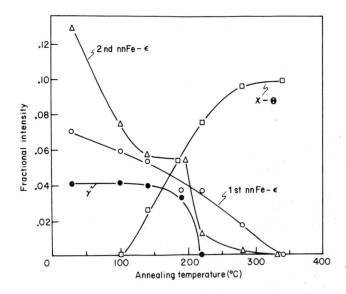

Fig. 5. Changes of the fractional absorption intensities for iron atoms in various phases and environments as a function of annealing temperature (after Ino, Moriya, Fujita, Maeda, Ono and Inokuti [30]).

The high concentration carbon martensite phase is metastable. Annealing causes aggregation of the carbon atoms. Transient carbides and finally $\theta$ carbide (cementite) are formed. The various processes can be followed by observing the appearance and disappearance of characteristic spectra due to various local perturbations and separation of phases [30]. In fig. 5 the fractional intensity of the first nn Fe and second nn Fe, the $\gamma$ phase and $\chi$, $\epsilon$, and $\theta$ phases are plotted as functions of annealing temperature. As the 1 nn Fe, 2 nn Fe and the retained austenite ($\gamma$-Fe) are removed in the material, the $\chi$ and $\theta$ phases precipitate.

In the Mössbauer spectra of carbon and nitrogen in retained f.c.c. austenite which is paramagnetic, one can distinguish a single peak and a quadrupole split doublet [28,31]. The former corresponds to iron without nearest carbon neighbor, while the quadrupole splitting is caused by the local perturbation of a next nearest neighbor carbon atom removing the local cubic symmetry. Attempts have been made to determine the diffusion parameter of the interstitial C atoms in f.c.c. iron [32]. The quadrupole interaction is expected to disappear when the species producing the interaction are jumping so fast that the electric field gradient averages to zero during the lifetime of the excited state.

## 3.2. Defect-impurity association in electron irradiated gold

Some preliminary results of an electron irradiation damage study of gold are presented [35]. $^{57}$Co – the parent isotope of $^{57}$Fe – was used as a probe. The experiment was based on the idea that the stress around the Co impurities can trap free migrating interstitials or vacancies. In cubic matrices the local cubic symmetry will be removed by the proximity of the defect giving rise to a quadrupole interaction and changes in the isomer shift. Thus, the Mössbauer parameters can detect the presence of the defects. In the experiment Au-$^{57}$Co foils were irradiated with 2 MeV electrons at liquid nitrogen temperature. We have chosen an integrated radiation which produces roughly as many Frankel pairs as there were $^{57}$Co impurities in the sample ($\approx$ 1 part in $10^5$). The Mössbauer spectrum was repeatedly measured at 80°K after subsequent anneal at various higher temperatures. On reaching 160°K a broadening of the Mössbauer resonance line occurred which we attributed to the perturbation in the immediate environment of the resonance atom. An annealing stage centered at 155°K was also found by measuring the resistivity change; see fig. 6. It seems most reasonable to associate this stage and the change in the Mössbauer spectrum (probably unresolved quadrupole splitting as main contribution) to gold interstitials trapped at the Co impurities. It is not intended at this time to speculate further on the nature and origin of the various stages, rather the goal is to demonstrate the potentialities of the Mössbauer effect, especially the ability to see a localized defect.

## 3.3. Resonance atom-vacancy complexes

In a number of experiments complexes of vacancies and resonance atoms have been investigated and certain lattice arrangements of the vacancy with the resonance

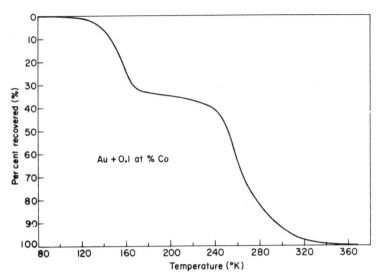

Fig. 6. Relative resistivity recovery of a 2 MeV electron irradiated Au-0.1 at % Co sample as a function of annealing temperature.

atom have been found [36–41]. Up to now the observations were all made in non-metal matrices. However, it seems certain that resonance atom-vacancy complexes in metals will be studied in the future.

### 3.4. *Diffusion broadening of iron and cobalt in gold and copper*

The inherent time scale in Mössbauer spectroscopy (lifetime of the excited state or Larmor precession frequency) can be used to study relaxation phenomena and jump frequencies of atoms. These phenomena and the well-known motional narrowing in NMR are closely related.

At high temperatures the presence of vacancies in metals can be observed by the broadening of the Mössbauer line due to vacancy diffusion [42]. More specifically, the line broadening $\Delta\epsilon$ one expects is related to the mean lifetime the resonance atom stays on a given lattice site, namely

$$\tau = \frac{2\hbar}{\Delta\epsilon[1 - \int \exp(i\mathbf{k}\cdot\mathbf{r})\,h(r)\,dr]}$$

$h(r)$ gives the probability of finding the atom at the position $r$ after a single jump. This relation can be equated to the well-known diffusion equation for f.c.c. metals:

$$\tau = r_0^2 f_{BH}/6D$$

$f_{BH}$ is the Bardeen-Herring correlation factor, $D$ the diffusion constant, and $r_0$ the nearest neighbor distance.

The possibility of measuring diffusion by Mössbauer spectroscopy was already recognized 8 years ago [42]. However, only just recently Knauer and Mullen [43] succeeded in measuring the diffusion broadening of $^{57}$Fe in copper and gold in the
vicinity of 1000°C. The temperature dependence of the Mössbauer line broadening
was found to be proportional to the temperature dependence of the diffusivity as
obtained by the tracer-sectioning technique. The absolute value of the diffusion constant determined by the Mössbauer technique was approximately a factor of two
smaller than predicted theoretically by the jump model of vacancy diffusion. This
discrepancy is still an unresolved question.

### 3.5. Cobalt interstitials in indium

The magnitude of the recoil-free fraction $f$, that is, the intensity of the Mössbauer line, can − in certain cases − give evidence that the resonance atom resides in
interstitial sites [44]. Fig. 7 shows the Mössbauer spectrum of a $^{57}$Co in indium
source and a sodium nitroprusside $(Na_2Fe(CN)_5NO \cdot 2H_2O)$ absorber. The small
quadrupole splitting originates from $^{57}$Co in indium. Indium has tetragonal structure and therefore a quadrupole splitting can be expected. The sodium nitroprusside
produces the large quadrupole interaction; therefore, the spectrum is essentially
duplicated. The spectral lines are rather resolved and narrow indicating that the
$^{57}$Co atoms in indium are located in *unique* lattice sites. The temperature dependence of the Debye-Waller factor is shown in fig. 8. The shape of the curve deviates
not much from a curve one expects from the Debye model. However, the magnitude of the corrected resonance intensity is unexpected. A simple model in which
the iron is substituted for indium, without change of force constants, would predict a room temperature value of about 0.15 to 0.2, much lower than observed.
Since the iron atom is much smaller than the indium atom, it would be expected to
be less strongly held in place than an indium atom. Thus, $f$ should even be lower.

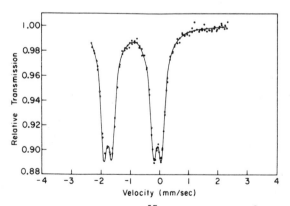

Fig. 7. Mössbauer transmission spectrum of a $^{57}$Co in In source at 80°K and an absorber of
$Na_2Fe(CN)_5NO \cdot 2H_2O$ at room temperature.

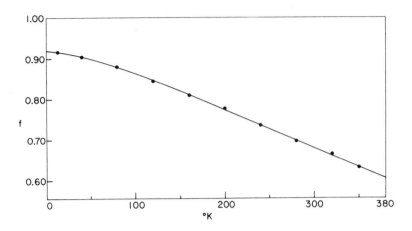

Fig. 8. Debye-Waller factor $f$ of $^{57}$Fe in indium as a function of temperature in $^{\circ}$K.

The large recoil-free fraction and small mean square displacement lead us to the interpretation that Co (and the daughter Fe) is in interstitial rather than substitutional sites. The possibility that a large fraction of the interstitials are close to dislocations and grain boundaries — as discussed by Dr. Anthony at this conference — can be ruled out in this case because a considerable broadening (unresolved mono- and quadrupole hyperfine interactions) as would result from the various sites in respect to the defect was not observed.

Already in 1933 Seith and Keil [45] deduced an interstitial diffusion mechanism in similar metallic systems (gold and silver in lead). For decades the suggestion of an interstitial mechanism in these systems was considered unrealistic. In the last years, the Harvard group [46—48] confirmed their earlier results and extended the investigation to a large number of systems.

So far the cases reported here represent effects which are primarily caused by a perturbation in the proximity of the resonating nucleus. Now two experiments involving defects will be mentioned where the bulk property is affected and detected by Mössbauer spectroscopy.

### 3.6. Nickel-hydride

The effect of hydrogen interstitials in nickel, stainless steel, and palladium have been studied by Mössbauer spectroscopy [49, 50]. Particularly the investigation in nickel by Wertheim and Buchanan [50] revealed some interesting information. $^{57}$Fe was used as a probe. The spectra of nickel containing various amounts

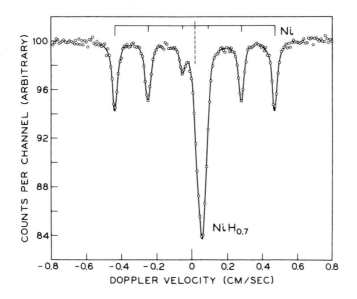

Fig. 9. Mössbauer transmission spectrum of $^{57}$Fe in partially hydrogen saturated nickel at
4.2°K (after Wertheim and Buchanan [50]).

of hydrogen show the presence of two phases: a nonmagnetic hydride phase and a
magnetic phase containing essentially no hydrogen. The Mössbauer spectrum in partially hydrogen saturated nickel at 4.2°K is shown in fig. 9. The line intensities are
roughly proportional to the fraction of the two phases present. The observed
isomer shift in the hydride phase indicates that electrons of the hydrogen go into
the d band of the iron increasing the effective d electron concentration by at least
0.35 d electrons.

### 3.7. *Neutron radiation damage in platinum*

In an experiment by Weiser and Wenzl [51] the 77 keV transition of $^{197}$Au was
used. The resonance isotope $^{197}$Au was produced in a platinum matrix in a reactor
and simultaneously lattice defects were produced by neutron radiation damage. The
observation made was a reduction in the recoil-free fraction. The effect was neutron
dose dependent indicating that this has to be a bulk and not a proximity effect by
the nuclear reaction creating the $^{197}$Au excited state. The real puzzle of this experiment seems to be the relatively large effect in the change of the vibrational modes
of the solid considering the low integrated neutron dose. Wenzl [52] has discussed
the experiment and possible interpretation of the results in more detail.

### 3.8. *Radiation effects in ordered Fe-Al alloys: Mössbauer experiments following neutron capture*

The nuclear excited state of an isotope in the source can be populated by radioactive decay, Coulomb excitation and nuclear reaction. The nuclear transitions in source and absorber are schematically shown in fig. 10. The bold arrows indicate the actual resonance transitions. Nuclear reaction and Coulomb excitation in conjunction with Coulomb-recoil implantation Mössbauer experiments (CRIME) gave Mössbauer spectroscopy a considerable boost over the last two or three years [53–66]. A number of isotopes where the excited state is not populated by radioactive decay, for example $^{40}K$, became accessible to Mössbauer spectroscopy. The recoil preceding the recoil-free resonance effect can be large. In most of the cases it exceeds by far the energy necessary to displace an atom from its lattice site (threshold displacement energy). The effects associated with the recoil are usually considered a nuisance. However, one might also see it as a new way to study lattice defects. The resonance signal is used to probe the environment of the primary recoiling atom during the lifetime of the excited state, so to speak, *in status nascendi*. When the resonance atom is incorporated in ionic crystals, in addition to the recoil effects, electronic effects may play an important role in determining where the atom comes to rest [67]. However, in metals we expect only effects from lattice disturbances.

Nuclear-angular correlation experiments are complimentary in nature [68,69]. Changes in the internal fields measured in implantation experiments can be attributed to lattice defects around the radiating nuclei [70,71].

The contributed paper by Berger and Czjzek [72] can be considered as the first systematic study of a nuclear reaction experiment where not the Mössbauer parameters but the lattice defects associated with the recoil were the primary goal. The neutron capture reaction of $^{56}Fe$ was used. The recoil energy involved from the

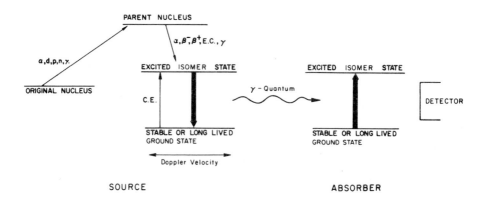

Fig. 10. Schematic representation of the nuclear transitions in source and absorber. The bold arrows indicate the resonance transitions.

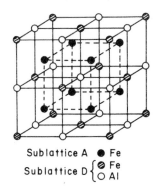

Sublattice A  ● Fe
Sublattice D {⊘ Fe
             {○ Al

Fig. 11. Structure of Fe₃Al.

prompt γ-radiation of the 7.64 MeV level is in the range of several hundred eV. The experiments were performed at the Karlsruhe FR2 reactor.

In the investigation the ordered alloy $Fe_3Al$ was used. The structure is shown in fig. 11 consisting of 2 interpenetrating simple cubic lattices, sublattice A containing iron atoms only and sublattice D containing alternatingly iron and aluminum atoms. At elevated temperature disorder takes place, however, in two steps. First, a pseudo-order occurs where the D sublattice disorders. A number of Mössbauer investigations on the magnetic and crystallographic ordering parameter in the Fe-Al system have been carried out [73–77]. Neutron scattering experiments in the ordered state have shown different magnetic moments for the iron at the A and D sites [78]. The Mössbauer spectrum of $Fe_3Al$ at room temperature seen in fig. 12a taken in the absorber mode can be decomposed into two nearly resolved Zeeman patterns having internal fields of 210 and 294 kOe for the A and D sites, respectively.

Now if the same material is used in the source mode where the excited state is populated by a (n,γ) reaction, the lower spectrum (fig. 12b) is obtained. This spectrum is quite different from the above. Only one Zeeman pattern can be distinguished with an internal field which is roughly an average of the field observed above. The difference between the two spectra has to be attributed to the foregoing recoil. For the interpretation of this result, Berger and Czjzek have considered the following three possibilities: 1) a disturbed order in the neighborhood, 2) defect clusters, that is, interstitials and vacancies in the environment, and 3) the recoiling atom comes to rest in an interstitial position. It is generally believed that the probability of finding the primary recoil atoms at an interstitial site is rather small, thus the interstitial model seems not to be the predominant cause of the effect.

In order to obtain additional information, samples in the concentration range from 32 to 52 at % Al were studied. These alloys are paramagnetic at room temper-

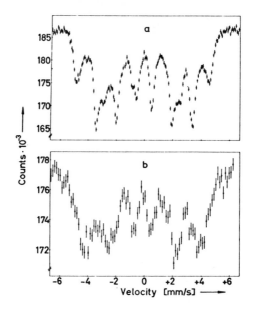

Fig. 12. Mössbauer transmission spectra of Fe₃Al in the absorber (a) and in the source (b) mode at room temperature. (a) was taken with a room temperature $^{57}$Co-Cu source, (b) was obtained with a $^{56}$Fe₃ Al-(n,γ) source and a single line absorber (after Berger and Czjzek [72].

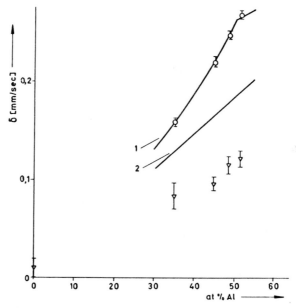

Fig. 13. Isomer shift δ in Fe-Al alloys relative to α-Fe. The points on the top (○) are taken in the absorber mode, the points at the bottom (△) in the (n,γ) source mode (after Berger and Czjzek [72]).

ature and the Mössbauer spectra consist of one, relatively broad line. In fig. 13 the isomer shift is plotted as a function of iron concentration. The points on the top correspond to the isomer shift in the absorber mode and the points at the bottom correspond to the isomer shift in the source mode, that is, after a $(n,\gamma)$ reaction. Also here significant differences for the absorber and source modes are observed. Assuming disorder around the resonance atom, curve 2 in fig. 13 was estimated. The discrepancy to the observed $(n,\gamma)$ reaction data indicate that lattice defects have to be taken into account. It might well be that lattice defects and disorder are both contributing factors in the experimental results.

## 4. Prospects of Mössbauer spectroscopy in regard to lattice defects

One can distinguish three areas in regard to lattice defects where Mössbauer spectroscopy might play an important role in the future and the information gained will not be easily obtainable by other techniques: (1) specific associations of lattice defects and resonance atoms, (2) radiation damage associated with nuclear reaction and Coulomb excitation and (3) the use of polarized recoil free $\gamma$-rays.

In Mössbauer spectroscopy the energy of source and absorber have to be matched by an appropriate Doppler velocity. Dealing with polarized (circularly or linearly) $\gamma$-rays, the intensity of the line is strongly dependent on the relative polarization of the corresponding transitions. On this basis linearly polarized recoil-free $\gamma$-rays have been utilized in determining spin orientations and axes of the electric field gradient [79–81]. As it was shown in various cases the local perturbation due to a defect can be determined by non-polarized $\gamma$-rays, the orientation of the distortion is best obtainable by polarized $\gamma$-rays. The relative line intensities indicate if any alignment of the localized distortions (texture on an atomistic scale) is present or, in some cases, where the alignment or preferred orientation can be imposed by mechanical, magnetic, or other means.

Mössbauer spectroscopy is still a young tool. I believe that new and unique information — similar to the cases discussed here — will elucidate our understanding of defects in metals.

## References

[1] R.L.Mössbauer, Z. Physik 151 (1958) 124.
[2] R.L.Mössbauer, Naturwissensch. 45 (1958) 538.
[3] A.H.Muir Jr., K.J.Ando and H.M.Coogan, Mössbauer effect data index 1958–1965 (Interscience, New York, 1966).
[4] H.Frauenfelder, The Mössbauer Effect (Benjamin, Inc., New York, 1962).
[5] A.J.F.Boyle and H.E.Hall, Rept. Progr. Phys. 25 (1962) 441.
[6] A.Abragam, L'Effet Mössbauer (Gordon and Breach, New York, 1964).
[7] G.K.Wertheim, Mössbauer Effect (Principles and Applications, Academic Press, New York, 1964).

[8] H.Wegener, Der Mössbauer-Effekt und seine Anwendungen in Physik und Chemie (Biblio-graphisches Institut AG, Mannheim, 1965).

[9] I.J.Gruverman, ed., Mössbauer Effect Methodology, Vols. 1–4 (Plenum Press, New York, 1965, 1966, 1967, 1968).

[10] U.Gonser and H.Wiedersich, J. Phys. Soc. Japan 18, Suppl. II (1963) 47.

[11] U.Gonser, Materials Science and Eng. 3 (1968) 1.

[12] C.Froidevaux and D.Rossier, J. Phys. Chem. Solids 28 (1967) 1197.

[13] C.P.Slichter and D.C.Ailion, Phys. Rev. 135 (1964) A1099.

[14] D.C.Ailion and C.P.Slichter, Phys. Rev. 137 (1965) A235.

[15] D.C.Ailion and Pei-Pin Ho, Phys. Rev. 168 (1968) 662.

[16] F.Y.Fradin and T.J.Rowland, Appl. Phys. Letters 11 (1967) 207.

[17] J.Kalus and J.Neuhauser, Z. Naturforschung 22a (1967) 792.

[18] A.G.Redfield, Phys. Rev. 130 (1963) 589.

[19] P.A.Flinn and S.L.Ruby, Phys. Rev. 124 (1961) 34.

[20] C.E.Johnson, M.S.Ridout and T.E.Cranshaw, Proc. Phys. Soc. (London) 81 (1963) 1079.

[21] G.Shirane, C.W.Chen, P.A.Flinn and R.Nathans, J. Appl. Phys. 34 (1963) 1044.

[22] G.K.Wertheim, V.Jaccarino, J.H.Wernick and D.N.E.Buchanan, Phys. Rev. Letters 12 (1964) 24.

[23] M.B.Stearns, J. Appl. Phys. 35 (1964) 1095.

[24] M.B.Stearns, J. Appl. Phys. 36 (1965) 913.

[25] M.B.Stearns, Phys. Rev. 147 (1966) 439.

[26] T.E.Cranshaw, C.E.Johnson, M.S.Ridout and G.A.Murray, Phys. Letters 21 (1966) 481.

[27] H.L.Marcus, M.E.Fine and L.H.Schwartz, J. Appl. Phys. 38 (1967) 4750.

[28] P.M.Gielen and R.Kaplow, Acta Met. 15 (1967) 49.

[29] T.Moriya, H.Ino, F.E.Fujita and Y.Maeda, J. Phys. Soc. Japan 24 (1968) 60.

[30] H.Ino, T.Moriya, F.E.Fujita, Y.Maeda, Y.Ono and Y.Inokuti, J. Phys. Soc. Japan 25 (1968) 88.

[31] J.M.Genin and P.A.Flinn, Trans. AIME 242 (1968) 1419.

[32] S.J.Lewis and P.A.Flinn, Phys. State Sol. 26 (1968) K51.

[33] Morris Cohen, Trans. AIME 224 (1962) 638.

[34] A.H.Muir, Mössbauer Effect Methodology, Vol. 4, ed. I.J.Gruverman, (Plenum Press, New York, 1968).

[35] U.Gonser, A.Sosin, R.W.Grant and K.Garr, to be published.

[36] M.De Coster and S.Amelinckx, Phys. Letters 1 (1962) 245.

[37] J.G.Mullen, Phys. Rev. 131 (1963) 1410.

[38] J.G.Mullen, Phys. Rev. 131 (1963) 1415.

[39] D.H.Lindley and P.G.Debrunner, Phys. Rev. 146 (1966) 199.

[40] K.Hennig, W.Meisel and H.Schnorr, Phys. Stat. Sol. 15 (1966) 199.

[41] A.N.Murin, B.G.Lur'e and P.P.Seregin, Sov. Phys.–Solid State 8 (1967) 3291; 9 (1967) 1100; 9 (1967) 1901; 10 (1968) 728.

[42] K.S.Singwi and A.Sjolander, Phys. Rev. 120 (1960) 1093.

[43] R.C.Knauer and J.G.Mullen, Phys. Rev. 174 (1968) 711, Appl. Phys. Letters 13 (1968) 150.

[44] P.A.Flinn, U.Gonser, R.W.Grant and R.M.Housley, Phys. Rev. 157 (1967) 538.

[45] W.Seith and A.Keil, Phys. Chem. B22 (1933) 350.

[46] T.R.Anthony and D.Turnbull, Phys. Rev. 151 (1966) 495.

[47] B.F.Dyson, T.R.Anthony and D.Turnbull, J. Appl. Phys. 37 (1966) 2370.

[48] T.R.Anthony, this volume.

[49] G.Bemski, J.Danon, A.M.De Graaf and X.A.Da Silva, Phys. Letters 18 (1965) 213.

[50] G.K.Wertheim and D.N.E.Buchanan, J. Phys. Chem. Solids 28 (1967) 225.

[51] J.Weiser and H.Wenzl, to be published.

[52] H.Wenzl, this volume.

[53] S.L.Ruby and R.E.Holland, Phys. Rev. Letters 14 (1965) 591.
[54] D.W.Hafemeister and E.B.Shera, Phys. Rev. Letters 14 (1965) 593.
[55] J.Fink and P.Kienle, Phys. Letters 17 (1965) 326.
[56] Y.K.Lee, P.W.Keaton, E.T.Ritter and J.C.Walker, Phys. Rev. Letters 14 (1965) 957.
[57] D.A.Goldberg, P.W.Keaton Jr., Y.K.Lee, L.Madansky and J.C.Walker, Phys. Rev. Letters 15 (1965) 418.
[58] D.Seyboth, F.E.Obenshain and G.Czjzek, Phys. Rev. Letters 14 (1965) 954.
[59] J.Chistiansen, E.Recknagel and G.Weyer, Phys. Letters 20 (1966) 46.
[60] G.Czjzek, J.L.C.Ford Jr., F.E.Obenshain and D.Seyboth, Phys. Letters 19 (1966) 673.
[61] E.T.Ritter, P.W.Keaton Jr., Y.K.Lee, R.R.Stevens Jr. and J.C.Walker, Phys. Rev. 154 (1967) 287.
[62] R.R.Stevens Jr., J.S.Eck, E.T.Ritter, Y.K.Lee and J.C.Walker, Phys. Rev. 158 (1967) 1118.
[63] G.Czjzek, J.L.C.Ford Jr., J.C.Love, F.E.Obenshain and H.H.F.Wegener, Phys. Rev. Letters 18 (1967) 529.
[64] G.D.Spouse, G.M.Kalvius and S.S.Hanna, Phys. Rev. Letters 18 (1967) 1041.
[65] F.E.Obenshain, Hyperfine Structure and Nuclear Reactions, ed. E.Matthias and D.A.Shirley (North-Holland Publishing Co., Amsterdam, 1968) p. 655.
[66] G.Czjzek, J.L.C.Ford Jr., J.C.Love, F.E.Obenshain and H.H.F.Wegener, Phys. Rev. 174 (1968) 173.
[67] P.Hannaford, C.J.Howard and J.W.G.Wignall, Phys. Letters 19 (1965) 257.
[68] L.Grodzins, R.Borchers and G.B.Hagemann, Phys. Letters 21 (1966) 214.
[69] F.Boehm, G.B.Hagemann and A.Winther, Phys. Letters 21 (1966) 217.
[70] M.Schmorak and E.Bøgh, Hyperfine Structure and Nuclear Reactions, ed. E.Matthias and D.A.Shirley (North-Holland Publishing Co., Amsterdam, 1968) p. 712.
[71] P.G.E.Reid, M.Sott and N.J.Stone, Hyperfine Structure and Nuclear Reactions, ed. E. Matthias and D.A.Shirley (North-Holland Publishing Co., Amsterdam, 1968) p. 719.
[72] W.G.Berger and G.Czjzek, Jül. Conf. 2, Vol. 2 (1968) p. 504.
[73] K.Ono, Y.Ishikawa and A.Ito, J. Phys. Soc. Japan 17 (1962) 1747.
[74] G.P.Huffman and R.M.Fisher, J. Appl. Phys. 38 (1967) 735.
[75] L.Cser, J.Ostanevich and L.Pal, Phys. Stat. Sol. 20 (1967) 581; 20 (1967) 591.
[76] G.K.Wertheim and J.H.Wernick, Acta Met. 15 (1967) 297.
[77] M.B.Stearns, Phys. Rev. 168 (1968) 588.
[78] R.Nathans, M.T.Pigott and C.G.Shull, J. Phys. Chem. Solids 6 (1958) 38.
[79] H.Frauenfelder, D.E.Nagle, R.D.Taylor, D.R.F.Cochran and W.M.Visscher, Phys. Rev. 126 (1962) 1065.
[80] C.E.Johnson, W.Marshall and G.J.Perlow, Phys. Rev. 126 (1962) 1503.
[81] U.Gonser, Hyperfine Structure and Nuclear Reactions, edited by E.Matthias and D.A.Shirley (North-Holland Publishing Co., Amsterdam, 1968) p. 343.

## Discussion

*G.Czjzek:* With the excellent representation Dr. Gonser has given to our work, I have nothing to add to the main part of it. But I want to introduce some new data taken with a sample containing 48 at % Al at various temperatures between 80°K and 770°K. Whereas the shifts of the absorber spectra relative to iron are independent of temperature within experimental error, the data obtained by neutron capture indicate a difference between the shifts observed at and below room tempera-

ture and those measured at higher temperatures (570 and 770°K), the high temperature value being somewhat closer to the absorber shift than the low-temperature
value. At these high temperatures the second-order Doppler shift should have the
classical, material independent temperature dependence, and no differences should
be observed. Therefore, we believe that the cause for this temperature dependence
of the relative shifts is a change in the vicinity of the final position of some primary
recoils due to the motion of a defect whose jump frequency becomes larger than
$1/\tau_{exc} \approx 10^7$ sec$^{-1}$ at a temperature between 300°K and 570°K.

*A.D.LeClaire:* With regard to your first example, the effect of C atoms in solution in $\alpha$ or $\delta$-Fe, is it possible to analyze the results so as to be able to say that the
C atoms *must* be situated on the octahedral interstitial sites, as you assumed, and
*not* on the rhombohedral sites? Are the measurements sufficiently precise to discriminate between these two possibilities?

*U.Gonser:* Up to now the measurements are not sufficiently precise to solve the
interesting problem you raise. In the paramagnetic $\delta$-Fe phase, the carbon diffusivity
is so large in respect to the relevant Mössbauer time scale ($\approx 10^{-7}$ sec) that information on the interstitial carbon configuration cannot be expected. However, it seems
possible to me that an accurate data analysis of the electric field gradient tensor in
conjunction with the nuclear Zeeman effect and spin orientations might distinguish
between the two carbon sites in $\alpha$-Fe.

*J.W.Corbett:* Following up Dr. LeClaire's question, this would seem to be a
good candidate for your polarized $\gamma$-rays since, by stress, you can align the carbon
stress dipoles.

*U.Gonser:* In collaboration with Professor F.E.Fujita and coworkers (Osaka University), we are in the process of making some investigations on the carbon-iron
system utilizing polarized recoil-free $\gamma$-rays.

*H.Wollenberger:* Do you get information about the number of gold interstitials
arriving at cobalt traps?

*U.Gonser:* I am afraid the answer is no. The reason might be phrased as follows:
The resonance atom-interstitial atom association determines the hyperfine interaction parameters. Although the various arriving gold interstitials at the $^{57}$Co impurity
trap will change the interaction parameters slightly, however, in practice the limited
resolution of the Mössbauer spectra will not allow a determination of the kind you
have in mind.

# STUDIES OF POINT DEFECTS IN METALS
# BY MEANS OF MECHANICAL AND MAGNETIC RELAXATION

## H. KRONMÜLLER

*Institut für Physik am Max-Planck-Institut für Metallforschung, Stuttgart, Germany*

## 1. Introduction

Investigations of point defects by electrical resistivity, stored energy or other conventional techniques give, in general, information only on the annealing processes of the defects. The characteristic property which is obtained from such studies is the migration energy of the defects. Such experiments, however, provide no information concerning the symmetry properties of the defects; furthermore, defect movements which are not related to long-range migration cannot be detected. A further disadvantage is the fact that, during the course of the experiment, the defects are annealed out. Such disadvantages present serious obstacles in an attempt to give a unique interpretation of the recovery stages in metals.

This article gives a review of the theoretical background and the experimental techniques which are necessary for an investigation of the symmetry of defects. The symmetry properties of point defects are briefly reviewed in section 2.

In sections 3 and 4 the theoretical background of elastic and magnetic relaxation due to point defects is developed with a view to the experimental techniques available for determining the symmetry of the defects.

As a well-known example the anelastic and magnetic relaxation processes of interstitial atoms and small vacancy clusters are discussed in section 5. In section 6 some of the experimental results published recently on nickel are reviewed.

The investigation of self-defects in metals by anelastic and magnetic relaxation phenomena begun in 1960 with an investigation of interstitial atoms in nickel [1–3]. These studies and numerous other investigations [4–15] have shown that relaxation techniques are powerful tools for the interpretation of the recovery stages as observed after irradiation, plastic deformation or quenching from high temperatures.

Reviews dealing with the magnetic after effect were published by Seeger et al. [3,16–18], Dautreppe [19], and Kronmüller [20]. The theoretical background of anelastic relaxation was discussed extensively in the articles of Nowick and Heller [21] and Nowick [22].

## 2. Symmetry and movements of point defects

### 2.1. *Symmetry*

The introduction of point defects in an ideal crystal lattice destroys the translational symmetry, and will in general reduce the point symmetry of the crystal. In order to determine the symmetry of the "macromolecule" which is created by introducing a defect in an "ideal" crystal one has to consider the atomic configurations produced by adding or removing the atoms necessary to generate the defect. All the other atoms are kept fixed in their normal positions. Applying the usual symmetry operation to the macromolecule allows the crystal class (point symmetry) of the defect to be determined. A new situation can occur if the atoms are allowed to relax. In this case it may be possible for the defect to lower its energy of formation by splitting into two "half defects" and thereby reducing its symmetry.

Group theory was applied extensively to the investigation of defect symmetries by Nowick and Heller [21,22]. From group theory it follows that point defects may possess any symmetry which is compatible with the symmetry of the ideal crystal. Such symmetries are all subgroups of the crystal class of the ideal crystal. According to this rule in cubic crystals the point defects may have all symmetries with the exception of the hexagonal ones. In hexagonal crystals on the other hand no cubic or tetragonal defects are allowed.

For the case of a single vacancy in a bcc crystal the possible appearance of the same defect in different configurations is shown in fig. 1. A single vacancy of cubic symmetry is produced by taking away an atom from its lattice site. The other three configurations shown are so-called split configurations, consisting of two half-vacancies and an atom in the middle between the two half-vacancies. The trigonal and the tetragonal configurations possess a preferred axis which is called the symmetry axis of the defect. The orthorhombic configurations possess three two-fold axes. The axis which is parallel to the main perturbation introduced by the defect is in general distinguished from the other two. Those defects with the symmetry of the ideal crystal are called "isotropic". Defects with a lower symmetry than the ideal crystal are called "anisotropic" defects. A characteristic feature of the anisotropic configurations is their possibility of reorienting their symmetry axis. In cubic crystals trigonal defects possess $n_E = 4$ different orientations corresponding to the four $\langle 111 \rangle$ axes. Tetragonal defects have $n_E = 3$ different orientations, which correspond to the three $\langle 100 \rangle$ axes. Orthorhombic defects have $n_E = 6$ different orientations, which may be assigned to the six $\langle 100 \rangle$ directions.

The energy of formation of a defect depends on its symmetry. Since the differences between the formation energies of different configurations of a particular class of defects will in general be larger than the thermal energy, in thermal equilibrium only the configuration with the lowest energy of formation will be present. This configuration is called the stable configuration. If the defects are produced by non-equilibrium processes, e.g., by irradiation with fast particles, metastable configurations may be generated in addition to the stable configuration. Such meta-

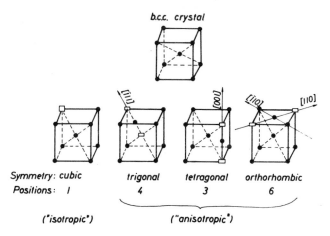

Fig. 1. "Isotropic and anisotropic" configurations of the single vacancy in bcc crystals. The numbers correspond to the energetically distinguishable positions.

stable configurations may be converted into the stable configuration with the help of thermal activation. A well-known example is the metastable crowdion which corresponds to one of the configurations of the interstitial atoms in fcc crystals.

In a crystal which is not subjected to a magnetic, electric, or elastic field the energy of formation of an anisotropic defect will be independent of the orientation of the symmetry axes of the defect. This means that the energy level of the energy of formation for "anisotropic" defects is degenerate. The degree of degeneracy corresponds to the number of possible crystallographically different orientations. In cubic crystals these numbers are, for defects with trigonal, tetragonal, and orthorhombic symmetry $n_E = 4, 3$, and 6. In the presence of an applied field (magnetic, electric or elastic) the degeneracy of the energy levels will in general be reduced. The degree of reduction of the degeneracy depends on the symmetry of the applied field with respect to the crystal axes. In the general case the energy levels of trigonal, tetragonal, and orthorhombic defects will be split into four, three, or six energy levels respectively. As we shall see in sections 3 and 4, this energy splitting is an essential feature of microscopic models of anelastic and magnetic relaxation.

## 2.2. Geometry of point defect jumps

A defect can change the orientation of its preferred axis by thermally activated jumps. The reorientation can take place either without any shift of the centre of gravity of the defect or may be combined with a local displacement into neighbouring positions. In general mechanical relaxation measurements are sensible to reorientations as well as to a diffusion of the defects. For this type of measurement is necessary to determine the number of defects with the $i$th orientation of the preferred defect axis. The defect changes its orientation by a jump over one of the saddle points of the surrounding potential wall. The number of jumps per second which occur between the orientations $i$ and $j$ over the saddle point $m$, $v_{ij}^m$, is given by an Arrhenius equation:

$$v_{ij}^m = v_0^{ij,m} \exp(S_{ij}^m/k) \exp(-E_{ij}^m/kT) . \tag{2.1}$$

Here $v_0^{ij,m}$ corresponds to a frequency factor of the order of the Debye frequency, and $S_{ij}^m$ to the activation entropy of the $m$th saddle point. The activation energy $E_{ij}^m$ corresponds to the value of the potential barrier at the $m$th saddle point. From eq. (2.1) it follows that in general only those saddle points with the lowest energy barrier are of importance as long as the thermal energy $kT$ is much smaller than $E_{ij}^m$. The total number of jumps undergone by the defect in unit time to neighbouring positions is equal to

$$v_i = \sum_m v_{ij}^m . \tag{2.2a}$$

The average time a defect stays in position $i$ between two jumps is given by

$$\bar{\tau}_i = \frac{1}{v_i} = \frac{1}{\displaystyle\sum_m v_0^{ij,m} \exp(S_{ij}^m/k) \exp(-E_{ij}^m/kT)} . \tag{2.2b}$$

Eq. (2.2b) may be much simplified if we consider situations in which all saddle points are equivalent. We may then set

$$v_0^{ij,m} = v_0 ; \quad S_{ij}^m = S ; \quad E_{ij}^m = E . \tag{2.3}$$

The total jump frequency is now equal to

$$v_i = n_S v_0 \exp(S/k) \exp(-E/kT) , \tag{2.4}$$

where $n_S$ corresponds to the number of neighbouring saddle points. Besides the numbers $n_E$ and $n_S$ which characterize symmetry and movement of a defect it is useful to introduce a further quantity, the number $n_0$ of crystallographically distinguishable orientations which can be reached by *one jump* starting from the original orientation. The number $n_0$ is given by

$$n_0 = n_E - 1$$

if from an orientation $i$ the remaining crystallographically distinguishable orientations can all be reached by one jump. If $n_0'$ of the crystallographically distinguish-

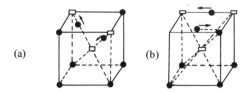

Fig. 2. Saddle point configurations of the trigonal single vacancy in bcc crystals.
(a) $\langle 111 \rangle$ saddle point, (b) $\langle 100 \rangle$ saddle point.

able orientations can only be reached by two successive jumps we have

$$n_o = n_E - n'_o - 1 .$$

The relation between $n_o$ and $n_S$ can be written as

$$n_S = \alpha n_o , \tag{2.5}$$

where $\alpha$ corresponds to the number of saddle points which lead from one orientation to another. In the following we shall consider only cases with $n'_o = 0$ or $n'_o = 1$.

The relation between crystallographically distinguishable orientations, saddle points and the symmetry of the defect in general is rather complicated. We shall discuss the interrelations between these properties for the case of the single vacancy in bcc crystals.

A single vacancy of cubic symmetry, as is shown in fig. 1, moves through the lattice by means of a jump of one of the neighbouring atoms into the position of the vacancy. The natural saddle points of this displacement lie on the cubic diagonals. Altogether there exist $n_S = 8$ saddle points, and $n_E = 1$ position. The situation is more complicated in the case of the trigonal split configuration (see fig. 1). In fig. 2a it is assumed that the displacement of the split configuration occurs over a saddle point on the $\langle 111 \rangle$ axis whereas in fig. 2b it is assumed that the saddle points lie on the $\langle 100 \rangle$ axes. In the first case there are $n_S = 12$ saddle points, and $n_o = 3$ crystallographically different orientations which can be reached by one jump. In the second case only $n_o = 2$ crystallographically different orientations can be reached by one jump. For these reorientations $n_S = 8$ saddle points exist. In order to arrive at the third orientation two successive jumps are necessary. For the latter movement there exist 4 saddle points.

The tetragonal configuration of the split vacancy (see fig. 1) possesses $n_o = 2$ crystallographically distinguishable orientations which can be reached over $n_S = 4$ saddle points on the $\langle 100 \rangle$ axes. The orthorhombic configuration has $n_S = 8$ saddle points which lead to $n_o = 4$ crystallographically distinguishable orientations. The remaining fifth crystallographically distinguishable orientation can only be reached by two successive jumps. The geometry of orthorhombic defects in fcc, bcc and hcp crystals has been discussed by the author in detail previously [20].

## 3. The anelastic relaxation

### 3.1. *General remarks*

Amongst the many physical properties which in principle enable the symmetry of crystal defects to be studied, the techniques of magnetic and mechanical relaxation have proved to be the most powerful. In this section the technique of mechanical relaxation as applied to the determination of defect properties will be discussed in some detail. A phenomenological theory of anelastic relaxation is presented in the book of Zener [23] and a more atomistic point of view is given in the review articles by Nowick and Heller [21] and Nowick [22]. We may call the latter type of treatment of anelastic relaxation the "micro-elastic" point of view. The aim of the microelastic theory of anelastic relaxation is to relate the phenomenological properties of relaxation to atomistic processes. The phenomenological quantities which can be determined by experiment will be discussed in the following subsection.

### 3.2. *Phenomenological theory*

If a constant external stress is applied to a crystal, the material is strained by an amount $\epsilon$. This induced strain $\epsilon$ is composed of an instantaneous part $\epsilon_0$, measured immediately after application of the stress, say at $t = 0$, and a time dependent contribution called the anelastic relaxation (see fig. 3). If the relaxation process is due to

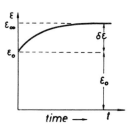

Fig. 3. Anelastic relaxation under a constant applied stress field.

point defects, the time dependent part can in general be described by a series of exponential functions such that

$$\epsilon = \epsilon_0 + \delta\epsilon_1 [1 - \exp(-t/\tau_\sigma^{(1)})] + \delta\epsilon_2 [1 - \exp(-t/\tau_\sigma^{(2)})] + \dots . \qquad (3.1a)$$

In the following we denote the time dependent part of $\epsilon$ as the anelastic strain

$$\epsilon^{an} = \epsilon - \epsilon_0 = \sum_i \delta\epsilon_i [1 - \exp(-t/\tau_\sigma^{(i)})] . \qquad (3.1b)$$

The characteristic quantities which describe the anelastic relaxation are the *relaxation strengths* $\delta\epsilon_i$ and the *relaxation times* $\tau_\sigma^{(i)}$, where the index $\sigma$ refers to the fact that the stress tensor $\boldsymbol{\sigma}$ is held constant during the experiment. The $\delta\epsilon_i$ are

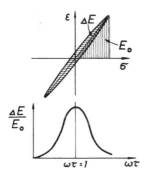

Fig. 4. Mechanical hysteresis loop and energy loss.

related to the thermal equilibrium, whereas the $\tau^{(i)}_{\sigma}$ describe the kinetics of the relaxation process. The appearance of several $\delta\epsilon_i$ and $\tau^{(i)}_{\sigma}$ may be due to either the presence of different kinds of defects or the existence of different reorientation modes of one and the same defect. The latter case for example is fulfilled for the split trigonal configuration of the single vacancy in bcc crystals if the saddle poinys lie on the $\langle100\rangle$ axes (see section 2.2). Under these conditions two relaxation times and two relaxation strengths exist due to the presence of two nearest and one next nearest neighbour.

The relaxation is also apparent in the response of a crystal to a periodic mechanical stress. In a perfect crystal stress and strain are in phase with each other. If, however, a relaxation takes place there will be a response which is out of phase. This results in a mechanical hysteresis loop as shown in fig. 4. According to Zener [23], in a linear approximation where $\sigma$ is a function of time, a simple relaxation process is described by the following first order differential equation:

$$\epsilon + \tau_\sigma \dot{\epsilon} = S^\infty(\sigma + \tau_\epsilon \dot{\sigma}) . \tag{3.2}$$

The meaning of the two relaxation times $\tau_\epsilon$ and $\tau_\sigma$ becomes clear if we consider relaxation processes under constant $\epsilon$ or $\sigma$. It then follows from eq. (3.2) that $\tau_\epsilon$ describes the kinetics at constant strain and $\tau_\sigma$ at constant stress. The meaning of $S^\infty$ becomes clear if we consider eq. (3.2) for large times, where $\dot{\epsilon}$ and $\dot{\sigma}$ may be equated to zero. Eq. (3.2) then gives:

$$\epsilon^\infty = S^\infty \sigma . \tag{3.3}$$

Eq. (3.3) corresponds to Hooke's law in the relaxed state with $S^\infty$ being a relaxed elastic coefficient. In the case of a tension or flexure experiment, $S$ corresponds to $E^{-1}$ ($E$ = Young's modulus), and in a torsion experiment we have to set $S = G^{-1}$ ($G$ = rigidity modulus) for an elastically isotropic material.

For small times $\epsilon$ and $\sigma$ can be neglected in comparison with $\tau_\sigma \dot{\epsilon}$ and $\tau_\epsilon \dot{\sigma}$ and eq. (3.2) may be written as:

$$\frac{d\sigma^0}{d\epsilon^0} = S^0 = S^\infty \frac{\tau_\epsilon}{\tau_\sigma} . \tag{3.4}$$

($\sigma^0$, $\epsilon^0$ = stress and strain at $t = 0$.)

Here $S^0$ corresponds to the compliance coefficient of Hooke's law in the unrelaxed state at $t = 0$. From eqs. (3.3) and (3.4) we derive the relations

$$S^\infty / S^0 = \tau_\sigma / \tau_\epsilon \tag{3.5}$$

and

$$\delta S = -S^\infty + S^0 = +S^0(1 - \tau_\sigma / \tau_\epsilon) . \tag{3.6}$$

$\delta S$ is called the relaxation strength of the corresponding elastic compliance coefficient. The relation between the relaxation strength $\delta\epsilon$ introduced in eq. (3.1) and $\delta S$ follows from eqs. (3.1), (3.2) and (3.6) (assuming for the moment one relaxation process)

$$\epsilon^0 + \delta\epsilon = \epsilon^\infty = S^\infty \sigma = (S^0 - \delta S)\sigma ,$$

$$\delta\epsilon = -\delta S \, \sigma . \tag{3.7}$$

Eq. (3.7) shows that the information we obtain concerning the relaxation process is the same whether we measure $\delta\epsilon$ or $\delta S$.

For a periodic stress $\sigma = \hat\sigma_0 \exp(i\omega t)$ the solution of eq. (3.2) is given by

$$\epsilon(t) = \hat\epsilon_0 \exp\left[i(\omega t + \delta)\right] \tag{3.8}$$

with

$$\hat\epsilon_0 = \frac{\epsilon^\infty}{1 + \omega^2 \tau_\sigma^2} \left[(1 + \omega^2 \tau_\sigma \tau_\epsilon)^2 + \omega^2(\tau_\epsilon - \tau_\sigma)^2\right]^{\frac{1}{2}} \tag{3.9}$$

and

$$\text{tg } \delta = \frac{(\tau_\epsilon - \tau_\sigma)}{1 + \omega^2 \tau_0 \tau_\epsilon} = \frac{\delta S}{S^0} \frac{\omega \tau_\sigma}{1 + \omega^2 \tau_\sigma \tau_\epsilon} .$$

The phase shift $\delta$ results in an energy loss

$$\Delta W = \int_0^{2\pi/\omega} \sigma \, d\epsilon = \pi \, \delta S \, (\hat\sigma_0)^2 \frac{\omega \tau_\sigma}{1 + \omega^2 \sigma_\sigma^2} . \tag{3.10}$$

For the relative energy loss $\Delta W / W_0$, where $W_0 = \frac{1}{2} S^0 (\hat\sigma_0)^2$ corresponds to the energy stored in the unrelaxed crystal per unit volume, one obtains

$$\frac{\Delta W}{W_0} = 2\pi \frac{\delta S}{S^0} \frac{\omega \tau_\sigma}{1 + \omega^2 \tau_\sigma^2}. \tag{3.11}$$

$\Delta W / W_0$ corresponds to the logarithmic decrement of the relaxation process. In the case $\delta S \ll S^\infty$ it follows from eq. (3.6) that $\tau_\sigma \approx \tau_\epsilon \approx \tau$. Then the following relation holds:

$$\frac{\Delta W}{W_0} = 2\pi \, \mathrm{tg} \, \delta = 2\pi \frac{\delta S}{S^0} \frac{\omega \tau}{1 + \omega^2 \tau^2}. \tag{3.12}$$

If several independent relaxation processes are present the total energy loss is given by the sum over expressions of the type (3.12).

The equations derived so far are valid for elastically isotropic materials. In order to extend eq. (3.2) to elastic anisotropic cubic crystals we consider Hooke's law for cubic crystals. The deformation of a cubic crystal can be described by the following three stress strain relations

$$\epsilon_{ii} = S \, \sigma_{ij}, \qquad\qquad i \neq j \, ;$$

$$\epsilon_{ii} - \epsilon_{jj} = \tfrac{1}{2} S'(\sigma_{ii} - \sigma_{jj}), \qquad i \neq j \, ; \tag{3.13}$$

$$\epsilon_{\mathrm{I}} = S'' \, \sigma_{\mathrm{I}} \, ,$$

with $\epsilon_{\mathrm{I}}$ and $\sigma_{\mathrm{I}}$ denoting the traces of the strains and the stress tensor, respectively. The elastic compliance coefficients $S$, $S'$ and $S''$ introduced in eq. (3.13) are related to the elastic compliance coefficients in the Voigt notation according to

$$S \ = s_{44} \, ,$$

$$S' = 2(s_{11} - s_{12}) \, , \tag{3.14}$$

$$S'' = s_{11} + 2s_{12} \, .$$

In analogy to eq. (3.2) we may now write down a set of three differential equations for the relaxation of the three deformation modes defined by eq. (3.13). These differential equations are

$$\epsilon_{ij} + \tau_\sigma^{(1)} \dot{\epsilon}_{ij} = S^\infty (\sigma_{ij} + \tau_\epsilon^{(1)} \dot{\sigma}_{ij}) \, ,$$

$$\epsilon_{ii} - \epsilon_{jj} + \tau_\sigma^{(2)} (\dot{\epsilon}_{ii} - \dot{\epsilon}_{jj}) = \tfrac{1}{2} S'^\infty [\sigma_{ii} - \sigma_{jj} + \tau_\epsilon^{(2)} (\dot{\sigma}_{ii} - \dot{\sigma}_{jj})] \, , \tag{3.15}$$

$$\epsilon_{\mathrm{I}} + \tau_\sigma^{(3)} \dot{\epsilon}_{\mathrm{I}} = S''^\infty (\sigma_{\mathrm{I}} + \tau_\epsilon^{(3)} \dot{\epsilon}_{\mathrm{I}}) \, .$$

Here $S^\infty$, $S'^\infty$ and $S''^\infty$ correspond to the elastic coefficients in the relaxed crystal, and $\tau_{\sigma,\epsilon}^{(1,2,3)}$ are the relaxation times of the corresponding deformations. The energy stored in a periodically deformed crystal may be written as ($\hat\sigma_{ij}$ = amplitudes of the applied periodical stress components)

$$W_o = \tfrac{1}{6} S'' \hat\sigma_I^2 + \tfrac{1}{12} S' \hat\sigma_{II} + \tfrac{1}{2} S \hat\sigma_{III} \tag{3.16}$$

with

$$\hat\sigma_I = \sum_i \hat\sigma_{ii},$$

$$\hat\sigma_{II} = \sum_{i \neq j} (\hat\sigma_{ii} - \hat\sigma_{jj})^2, \tag{3.17}$$

$$\hat\sigma_{III} = \sum_{i \neq j} \hat\sigma_{ij}^2.$$

In analogy to eqs. (3.11) and (3.12) the logarithmic decrement of a relaxation process in a cubic crystal is given by

$$\frac{\Delta W}{W_o} = \pi\,\delta S\, \frac{\hat\sigma_{III}}{W_o}\, \frac{\omega\tau_\sigma^{(1)}}{1+(\omega\tau_\sigma^{(1)})^2}\, \tfrac{1}{6} + \pi\,\delta S'\, \frac{\hat\sigma_{II}}{W_o}\, \frac{\omega\tau_\sigma^{(2)}}{1+(\omega\tau_\sigma^{(2)})^2}$$

$$+ \tfrac{1}{3}\pi\,\delta S''\, \frac{(\hat\sigma_I)^2}{W_o}\, \frac{\omega\tau_\sigma^{(3)}}{1+(\omega\tau_\sigma^{(3)})^2}, \tag{3.18}$$

where the relaxation strengths $\delta S$, $\delta S'$ and $\delta S''$ are defined as follows

$$\delta S = S^o - S^\infty = S^o\,(1 - \tau_\sigma^{(1)}/\tau_\epsilon^{(1)}),$$

$$\delta S' = S'^o - S'^\infty = S'^o\,(1 - \tau_\sigma^{(2)}/\tau_\epsilon^{(2)}),$$

$$\delta S'' = S''^o - S''^\infty = S''^o(1 - \tau_\sigma^{(3)}/\tau_\epsilon^{(3)}).$$

Eq. (3.18) shows that the logarithmic decrement depends in general on $\delta S$, $\delta S'$ and $\delta S''$ as well as on the expressions $\hat\sigma_{I,II,III}$ defined by eq. (3.17). In fact, $\delta S''$ vanishes in cubic crystals as will be shown in the following section. Therefore $\Delta W/W_o$ depends only on $\delta S$, $\delta S'$, $\hat\sigma_{II}$ and $\hat\sigma_{III}$. In order to study the dependence of $\Delta W$ on $\hat\sigma_{II}$ and $\hat\sigma_{III}$ we determine $\Delta W$ for tension and torsion experiments on rod-shaped single crystals along the $\langle 100 \rangle$ and the $\langle 111 \rangle$ axes.

(i) Tension
Tensile axis $\langle 100 \rangle$:

$$\frac{\Delta W}{W_0} = 2\pi \frac{\delta S'}{S_0' + S_0''} \frac{\tau_\sigma^{(2)}}{1 + (\omega \tau_\sigma^{(2)})^2}.$$ (3.19)

Tensile axis $\langle 111 \rangle$:

$$\frac{\Delta W}{W_0} = 2\pi \frac{\delta S}{S_0 + S_0''} \frac{\omega \tau_\sigma^{(1)}}{1 + (\omega \tau_\sigma^{(1)})^2}.$$ (3.20)

(ii) Torsion
Twist axis $\langle 100 \rangle$:

$$\frac{\Delta W}{W_0} = 2\pi \frac{\delta S}{S_0} \frac{\omega \tau_\sigma^{(1)}}{1 + (\omega \tau_\sigma^{(1)})^2}.$$ (3.21)

Twist axis $\langle 111 \rangle$:

$$\frac{\Delta W}{W_0} = 4\pi \frac{\delta S'}{S_0 + 2S_0'} \frac{\omega \tau_\sigma^{(2)}}{1 + (\omega \tau_\sigma^{(2)})^2} + 2\pi \frac{\delta S}{S_0 + 2S_0'} \frac{\omega \tau_\sigma^{(1)}}{1 + (\omega \tau_\sigma^{(1)})^2}.$$ (3.22)

The results derived here for the logarithmic decrement are in agreement with the results obtained previously by Seraphim and Nowick [24] for the relaxation strength of the Young's modulus and of the rigidity modulus.

### 3.3. *Microelastic model of anelastic relaxation*

#### 3.3.1. Criterion for relaxation

The relaxation strength $\delta \varepsilon$ depends on the symmetry of the applied stress tensor as well as on the symmetry of the crystal defect. In order to clarify this rather complicated interaction we consider the well-known example of C-atoms dissolved as interstitials in $\alpha$-Fe. The C-atoms, which lie in the middle of the cube edges, possess tetragonal symmetry and distort the lattice mainly along the tetragonal $\langle 100 \rangle$ axis. As indicated in fig. 5, the C-atoms may appear in three different positions corresponding to the three $\langle 100 \rangle$ axes (labelled as 1, 2 and 3). The distortions due to a point defect are described by the so-called dipole tensor $\mathbf{Q}$ which is defined as [25]

$$\mathbf{Q} = \lim_{\varepsilon^P \to \infty, \Delta V \to 0} \varepsilon^P \Delta V,$$ (3.23)

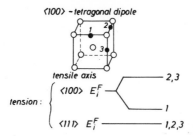

Fig. 5. Effect of stress and defect symmetry on the energy splitting in the case of tetragonal C-interstitials. In the present case the number of defects in orientation 1 increases.

where $\Delta V$ is a small volume element on which a plastic deformation $\boldsymbol{\varepsilon}^P$ is imposed. As a consequence of the plastic deformation, $\boldsymbol{\varepsilon}^P$, internal stresses are produced. Anisotropic defects possess an anisotropic dipole tensor. As a consequence these defects are orientable under the influence of an applied stress. Therefore these defects are called paraelastic. For the description of $\mathbf{Q}$ we choose a coordinate system with its axes parallel to the principal axes of the $\mathbf{Q}$-tensor. If we take the $x$-axis as parallel to the tetragonal axis of defect (1) the $\mathbf{Q}$-tensors for the positions 1, 2 and 3 may be written as

$$\mathbf{Q}^{(1)} = \begin{vmatrix} A & & \\ & B & \\ & & B \end{vmatrix},$$

(3.24)

$$\mathbf{Q}^{(2)} = \begin{vmatrix} B & & \\ & A & \\ & & B \end{vmatrix},$$

(3.25)

$$\mathbf{Q}^{(3)} = \begin{vmatrix} B & & \\ & B & \\ & & A \end{vmatrix}.$$

(3.26)

The principal values of $\mathbf{Q}$ for the axes perpendicular to the tetragonal axis have equal values $B$, whereas the tetragonal axes have the principal value $A$.

If no external stress acts on the crystal the energy of formation is equal for all three positions of the C-atoms. (This result is valid on the condition that the elastic interaction between the defects can be neglected.) One may say that the three positions form a three-fold degenerate energy level. If an external stress is now applied the degeneracy is destroyed giving in general three separated energy levels. This energy splitting is caused by the elastic interaction between the C-atoms and the applied stress. In terms of the dipole tensor $\mathbf{Q}$ the interaction energy is given by

$$E^{(i)} = -\mathbf{Q}^{(i)} \cdot \boldsymbol{\sigma}.$$

(3.27)

The elastic interaction energy $E^{(i)}$ may be considered as the cause of anelastic relaxation. If an energy splitting is generated by an applied stress the elastic dipoles will try to decrease their interaction energy by changing from energetically unfavourable to energetically more favourable orientations as is indicated in fig. 5. The rearrangement of the defects in general will result in a change of the dimensions of the crystal which is observed as an anelastic relaxation.

So far our discussion shows that a relaxation process will take place only if the applied field produces a splitting of the degenerate energy levels and a necessary condition for this is that the defects possess a lower symmetry than the ideal crystal. However, not all stress tensors induce an energy splitting. This is demonstrated in fig. 5 for the C-interstitials. If a uniaxial stress is applied parallel to the [100] axis of the crystal the three-fold degenerate level is split into a one-fold energy level and a two-fold degenerate energy level. The interstitials lying on the [100] axis are energetically favoured as compared with those lying on the [010] and the [001] axes which remain energetically equivalent. If the uniaxial stress is applied parallel to a ⟨111⟩ axis none of the interstitial sites are energetically different from one another and the energy level remains three-fold degenerate. For intermediate orientations of the crystal axis energy level splitting will always occur. If a torsion experiment is performed, energy splitting is induced for a ⟨111⟩ torsion axis. No energy splitting exists for a ⟨100⟩ torsion axis. According to these results it becomes clear that tetragonal defects show a relaxation effect for tension along a ⟨100⟩ axis or torsion around a ⟨111⟩ axis. No relaxation is found for a ⟨111⟩ tension axis or a ⟨100⟩ torsion axis.

3.3.2. Relaxation times

The kinetics of a relaxation process can in general be described by exponential time laws according to eq. (3.1a,b). The relaxation times $\tau$ are characteristic for the time necessary to establish thermal equilibrium. In thermal equilibrium at $t \rightarrow \infty$ the concentration of defects in the $i$th crystallographically distinguishable orientation is given by a generalized Boltzmann distribution

$$C_i^\infty = C \exp(-E^{(i)}/kT) \Big/ \sum_{i=1}^{n_E} \exp(-E^{(i)}/kT) , \qquad (3.28)$$

where $C$ corresponds to the total concentration of the defects. If the interaction energy $E^{(i)}$ is small in comparison to the thermal energy one finds from eq. (3.28) by expansion into a Taylor series:

$$C_i^\infty = C_0 \left( 1 - \frac{E^{(i)} - \bar{E}}{kT} \right) , \qquad (3.29)$$

where we have introduced the average concentration

$$C_o = C/n_E \qquad (3.30)$$

on each of the crystallographically distinguishable orientations, and the average interaction energy

$$\bar{E} = \frac{1}{n_E} \sum_{i=1}^{n_E} E^{(i)} . \qquad (3.31)$$

During the relaxation process the concentration $C_i$ in orientation $i$ changes due to jumps into other energetically distinguishable orientations, and due to jumps from these other orientations into orientation $i$. The jump frequency of a defect from orientation $i$ to orientation $j$ over the $m$th saddle point is given by an Arrhenius equation

$$\nu_{ij}^m = \nu_{o,ij}^m \exp(S_{ij}^m/k) \exp(-Q_{ij}^m/kT) . \qquad (3.32)$$

In general the parameters $\nu_{o,ij}^m$, $S_{ij}^m$ and $Q_{ij}^m$ will depend on the applied elastic stress field. If, however, the interaction energies $E^{(i)}$ are smaller than $kT$ we may apply the same approximation as in section 2.3 with

$$\nu_{o,ij}^m = \nu_o , \qquad S_{ij} = S \quad \text{and} \quad Q_{ij} = E .$$

From this it follows that

$$\nu_{ij} = \nu_{ji} = \nu = \nu_o \exp(S/k) \exp(-E/kT) . \qquad (3.33)$$

The number of jumps undergone by a defect in orientation $i$ in order to arrive at orientation $j$ and vice versa is

$$p_{ij} = p_{ji} = \alpha \nu_{ij} = \alpha \nu , \qquad (3.34a)$$

where $\alpha$ as defined in section 2.3 corresponds to the number of saddle points leading from orientation $i$ into orientation $j$. Experimentally it is not the individual jump from orientation $i$ to $j$ which is observed but the total number of jumps which lead to a reorientation. If the concentrations of the defects in orientations $i$ and $j$ are $C_i$ and $C_j$ the total number of jumps taking place from $i$ into $j$ is

$$P_{ij} = C_i \alpha \nu_{ij} = C_i \alpha \nu \qquad (3.34b)$$

and from $j$ into $i$

$$P_{ji} = C_j \alpha \nu_{ij} = C_j \alpha \nu . \qquad (3.34c)$$

For the rate $dC_i/dt$ at which the concentration of defects in the orientation $i$ changes the following rate equation holds

$$\frac{dC_i}{dt} = -\alpha \sum_j^{n_0} (\nu_{ij} C_i - \nu_{ji} C_j) , \tag{3.35}$$

where the summation runs over all crystallographically distinguishable orientations which can be reached by one jump. With the approximation (3.33) we can write for eq. (3.35)

$$\frac{dC_i}{dt} = -\alpha n_0 \nu C_i + \alpha \sum_j \nu C_j . \tag{3.36}$$

The general solution of eq. (3.36) can be represented in the form

$$C_i(t) = C_i^{\infty} + \sum_m d_i^{(m)} \exp[-t/\tau^{(m)}] \tag{3.37}$$

where the "eigenmodes" $d_i^{(m)}$ are determined by the symmetry of the problem and the initial distribution $C_i(0)$. The relaxation times $\tau^{(m)}$ are obtained as the eigenvalues of the secular determinant of eq. (3.36) [26,27].

Important solutions of eq. (3.36) are those for defects with only nearest neighbours, as for example C-interstitials in $\alpha$-Fe or self-interstitials in the interstitialcy configuration in fcc crystals [28,29]. Both defects possess tetragonal symmetry. For defects of this kind the solution of eq. (3.36) can be written as

$$C_i(t) = C_i^{\infty} + (C_i(0) - C_i^{\infty}) \exp(-t/\tau) \tag{3.38a}$$

or

$$C_i(t) = C_i(0) - (C_i(0) - C_i^{\infty})(1 - \exp(-t/\tau)) . \tag{3.38b}$$

If we introduce the deviations

$$d_i(t) = C_i(t) - C_i(0) \tag{3.39}$$

from the concentration $C_i(0)$ at $t = 0$, eq. (3.38) may be written

$$d_i(t) = d_i(\infty)(1 - \exp(-t/\tau)) . \tag{3.40}$$

The relaxation time $\tau$ is given by

$$\tau = \frac{1}{\alpha n_0} \frac{n_E - 1}{n_E} = \frac{1}{\nu} \frac{n_E - 1}{n_E} \bar{\tau} . \tag{3.41}$$

Compared with the time $1/\nu$ for one atomic jump the relaxation time is smaller by a factor $(n_E - 1)/\alpha n_o n_E$.

In the case of C-interstitials with $n_o = 4$, $\alpha = 2$, $n_E = 3$ we obtain

$$\tau = \frac{1}{6\nu} . \tag{3.42}$$

The same result also holds for the rotation process of self-interstitials in the interstitialcy configuration in fcc crystals (see fig. 9d).

Another important solution of eq. (3.36) is that for defects of *orthorhombic* symmetry. Defects of this kind are the divacancy in fcc metals [30] and the interstitial atom in the split configuration in bcc metals [31]. The principal axes of these defects are the [110], [$\bar{1}$10], and the [001] axes. The geometry of orthorhombic defects has been described in detail previously [20]. Both defects have $n_E = 6$ crystallographically different orientations. From a certain orientation only 4 of the $n_o = 5$ other orientations can be reached by one jump. In order to arrive at the fifth orientation two jumps are necessary. As a whole there are $n_o = 4$ nearest neighbours and $n_o' = 1$ next nearest neighbours. Each orientation can be reached over two saddle points ($\alpha = 2$). If we denote the concentration of the defects in the next-nearest neighbour orientation with respect to orientation $i$ by $C_i'$ the solution of eq. (3.36) is given by [30]

$$C_i(t) - C_i(0) = d_i(t) = \tfrac{1}{2}\{(C_i^\infty - C_i(0)) + (C_i'(0) - C_i'^\infty)\} \exp(-t/\tau_1) +$$

$$+ \tfrac{1}{2}\{C_i(0) - C_i^\infty) - (C_i'(0) - C_i'^\infty)\} \exp(-t/\tau_2) , \tag{3.43}$$

where

$$\tau_1 = \frac{1}{n_o\alpha} \frac{n_E - 2}{n_E} \frac{1}{\nu} \tag{3.44}$$

and

$$\tau_2 = \frac{1}{n_o\alpha} \frac{1}{\nu} .$$

With $n_o\alpha = 8$ and $n_E = 6$ it follows from eq. (3.44)

$$\tau_1 = \frac{1}{12} \frac{1}{\nu} ; \qquad \tau_2 = \frac{1}{8} \frac{1}{\nu} . \tag{3.45}$$

3.3.3. Relaxation strength

The rearrangement of the defects during the relaxation process results in a change of the dimensions of the crystal denoted by the anelastic strain $\varepsilon^{an}$. In terms of the elastic dipole tensor $\mathbf{Q}$ the anelastic strain is determined by

$$\varepsilon^{an}(t) = \sum_{i=1}^{n_E} \{ \mathbf{Q}^{(i)} \, C_i(t) - \mathbf{Q}^{(i)} \, C_i(0) \}$$

$$= \sum_{i=1}^{n_E} \mathbf{Q}^{(i)} \, d_i(t) , \tag{3.46}$$

where the $C_i$'s have to be calculated from the rate equation (3.36). The last term in the brackets of eq. (3.46) ensures that $\varepsilon^{an}$ vanishes at $t = 0$ where the relaxation process starts. From the anelastic strain the relaxation strength of the elastic compliance coefficients can be determined according to

$$\delta s_{mnkl} = \frac{d\epsilon_{mn}^{an}}{d\sigma_{kl}}\bigg|_{t \to \infty} , \tag{3.47}$$

where the differential quotient has to be taken for large times $t \to \infty$. Inserting eq. (3.46) into eq. (3.47) leads to

$$\delta s_{mnkl} = \sum_{i=1}^{n_E} Q_{mn}^{(i)} \frac{d(d_i(\infty))}{d\sigma_{kl}} . \tag{3.48}$$

Eqs. (3.46) and (3.48) combined with the results for $d_i$ derived in the preceding section from eq. (3.36) give $\varepsilon^{an}$ and $s_{mnkl}$ implicitly. This enables us to determine the relaxation strengths $\delta \varepsilon_i$ and the logarithmic decrements $\Delta W/W_0$ for special point defects. The following results for the modul effects have been derived by Nowick and Heller [21] and Nowick [22].

(i) Tetragonal defects
    Inserting eq. (3.40) into eq. (3.46) and taking into account eq. (3.27) and eq. (3.29) gives

$$\varepsilon^{an}(t) = C_0 \sum_{i=1}^{n_E} \mathbf{Q}^{(i)} \frac{\mathbf{Q}^{(i)} \cdot \boldsymbol{\sigma} + \overline{E}}{kT} (1 - \exp(-t/\tau)) . \tag{3.49}$$

With the dipole tensors (3.20) for tetragonal defects we find for the relaxation strength

$$\varepsilon^{an}(t) = \frac{C_0(A-B)^2}{3kT} \begin{vmatrix} 3\sigma_{xx} - \sigma_I & & \\ & 3\sigma_{yy} - \sigma_I & \\ & & 3\sigma_{zz} - \sigma_I \end{vmatrix}. \qquad (3.50)$$

From eq. (3.48) we now obtain by inserting eq. (3.50) and using Voigt's notation

$$2\delta(s_{11} - s_{12}) = \delta S' = \frac{C_0(A-B)^2}{kT}, \qquad (3.51)$$

$$\delta s_{44} = \delta S = 0,$$

$$\delta(s_{11} + 2s_{12}) = \delta S'' = 0.$$

(ii) Trigonal defects

In the case of trigonal defects with only nearest neighbour positions $\varepsilon^{an}$ is given by eq. (3.49) where the dipole tensor of the trigonal defect must be inserted. The relaxation strengths of the $S$-matrix follow from eq. (3.47) and are given by

$$\delta S = \frac{4}{9} \frac{c}{kT} (A-B)^2,$$

$$\delta S' = 0, \qquad (3.52)$$

$$\delta S'' = 0.$$

Here the component $A$ of the dipole tensor corresponds to the principal value of the $\langle 111 \rangle$ axis, and the component $B$ to that of the other two principal axes.

(iii) Orthorhombic defects

Orthorhombic defects possess three mutually perpendicular two-fold symmetry axes parallel to directions of the type $[110]$, $[\bar{1}10]$ and $[001]$. In this set of directions for the principal axes the dipole tensor $\mathbf{Q}^{(1)}$ is given by

$$\mathbf{Q}^{(1)} = \begin{vmatrix} A & 0 & 0 \\ 0 & B & 0 \\ 0 & 0 & C \end{vmatrix}. \qquad (3.53)$$

The dipole tensor taken with respect to the cubic axes $\langle 100 \rangle$ takes the form

$$\mathbf{Q}^{(1)} = \begin{vmatrix} \frac{1}{2}(A+B) & \frac{1}{2}(A-B) & 0 \\ \frac{1}{2}(A-B) & \frac{1}{2}(A+B) & 0 \\ 0 & 0 & C \end{vmatrix}. \qquad (3.54)$$

If eq. (3.43) for the $d_i$'s of orthorhombic defects is inserted into eq. (3.46) we find for the anelastic strain

$$\varepsilon^{an} = \delta\,\varepsilon_1\,[1-\exp(-t/\tau_1)] + \delta\,\varepsilon_2\,[1-\exp(-t/\tau_2)] . \tag{3.55}$$

The relaxation strengths $\delta\,\varepsilon_1$ and $\delta\,\varepsilon_2$ are given by

$$\delta\,\varepsilon_1 = \frac{C_o}{2kT} \sum_{i=1}^{n_E} \mathbf{Q}^{(i)}(\mathbf{Q}^{(i)}\cdot\boldsymbol{\sigma} + \mathbf{Q}^{(i')}\cdot\boldsymbol{\sigma} + 2\bar{\bar{E}}) \tag{3.56}$$

and

$$\delta\,\varepsilon_2 = \frac{C_o}{2kT} \sum_{i=1}^{n_E} \mathbf{Q}^{(i)}(\mathbf{Q}^{(i)}\cdot\boldsymbol{\sigma} - \mathbf{Q}^{(i')}\cdot\boldsymbol{\sigma}) . \tag{3.57}$$

Using our results for the dipole tensor $\mathbf{Q}^{(i)}$ we obtain from eq. (3.56)

$$\delta\,\varepsilon_1 = \begin{pmatrix} \delta\epsilon_{1,11} & 0 & 0 \\ & \delta\epsilon_{1,22} & 0 \\ & & \delta\epsilon_{1,33} \end{pmatrix} \tag{3.58}$$

with

$$\delta\epsilon_{1,ii} = \frac{C_o}{2kT} [(A+B)^2(\sigma_I + \sigma_{ii}) + 4C(A+B)(\sigma_I - \sigma_{ii})$$

$$+ 4C^2\sigma_{ii} - \tfrac{4}{3}(A+B+C)^2\sigma_I] , \tag{3.59}$$

and

$$\delta\epsilon_2 = \begin{pmatrix} 0 & \delta\epsilon_{2,12} & \delta\epsilon_{2,13} \\ & 0 & \delta\epsilon_{2,23} \\ & & 0 \end{pmatrix} \tag{3.60}$$

with

$$\delta\epsilon_{2,ij} = \frac{2C_o}{kT} (A-B)^2\sigma_{ij} , \qquad i\neq j. \tag{3.61}$$

The relaxation strengths of the elastic compliance coefficients may now be derived from eq. (3.48) giving

$$\delta S = \frac{\partial(\delta\epsilon_{2,12})}{\partial\sigma_{12}} = \frac{2C_o}{kT}(A-B)^2, \tag{3.62}$$

$$\delta S' = 2(\delta s_{11} - \delta s_{12}) = \frac{\partial(\delta\epsilon_{1,11})}{\partial\sigma_{11}} - \frac{\partial(\delta\epsilon_{1,11})}{\partial\sigma_{22}}$$

$$= \frac{2C_o}{kT}(\frac{A+B}{2} - C)^2. \tag{3.63}$$

$$\delta S'' = 0.$$

In all three cases so far treated, we have seen that $\delta S''$ vanishes. This is not a special result of the defects considered here but is valid quite general for all types of defects. It is due to the fact that in a linear approximation the total volume dilatation due to the defects

$$\epsilon_I^{an} = \sum_{j,i}^{n_E} Q_{ii}^{(j)} C_j$$

is independent of the orientation of the defects.


## 4. Magnetic relaxation

### 4.1. General remarks

It has been well-known since the end of the last century that the magnetization curve of a ferromagnet is not a static property but is time dependent [32,33]. The first systematic measurements were due to Richter [34], who studied systematically the time and temperature dependence of the relaxation in carbonyl-iron. It was shown later by Snoek [35,36] that it is the C-atom dissolved interstitially in $\alpha$-Fe that gives rise to this magnetic after effect, which is today called the "Richter-nachwirkung". This name is applied also to relaxation processes caused by other defects which show the same properties as the relaxation phenomena of C-atoms.

The experiments of Richter were interpreted by Snoek [35–37] as being due to the reorientation of the tetragonal axes of the C-atoms. A quantitative theory of the magnetic after effects was given by Néel [38,39]. The experiments of Fahlen-brach et al. [40,41] on FeSi suggested that "eigendefects" might give rise to magnetic after effects. Dietze [42] interpreted the after effect found by Fahlenbrach et al. [40,41] as being due to the long-range diffusion of vacancies. However, the interpretation in terms of a Zener-type relaxation appears now to be preferred [43]. Seeger et al. [1–3] were the first to apply the after-effect measurements to the

determination of the properties of self-defects; these initial measurements were
made on nickel in order to investigate the so-called dumbbell configuration of the
interstitial atoms. Since these early experiments a considerable number of papers
concerned with the study of point defects by the magnetic relaxation phenomena
have been published, in particular by the Grenoble group [4,8,9]. We shall discuss
in section 6 some of the recent results of Peretto on the magnetic after effect in Ni
at low temperatures together with some experimental results of the Stuttgart group
for the temperature range above 90°K.

## 4.2. *Basic experimental results*

The investigation of Richter and Snoek showed that C-atoms in $\alpha$-Fe give rise to
anelastic as well as to magnetic relaxation effects. However, due to the presence of
Bloch walls the magnetic relaxation shows some features which are different from
those of the anelastic relaxation. In order to demonstrate these differences we consider here some characteristic experiments.

### (i) Isothermal relaxation

If a ferromagnet is rapidly magnetized by the application of a magnetic field, the
final value of the magnetization is not obtained immediately after applying the field
but only after a finite time; this time is strongly temperature dependent. This
experimental result corresponds completely to the anelastic relaxation represented
in fig. 3. In particular, if we are dealing with a Richternachwirkung, the time dependence of the magnetization may be described by exponential terms, as in eq. (3.1)
for the anelastic relaxation.

### (ii) Isothermal ballistic experiment

Let us consider a ferromagnet which has been demagnetized at $t = 0$. After a time
$t_0$ a magnetic field is applied which produces a certain magnetization $\mathbf{J}(t_0)$. As
shown in fig. 6 this magnetization $\mathbf{J}(t_0)$ decreases with increasing time and after
very large times $\mathbf{J}(t_0)$ approaches asymptotically a value $\mathbf{J}_\infty$. The time dependence
of $\mathbf{J}(t_0)$ obeys the following equation

$$\mathbf{J}(t_0) = \mathbf{J}_0 - \sum_i \delta\mathbf{J}_i \left(1 - \exp(-t_0/\tau_i)\right) , \tag{4.1}$$

where $\mathbf{J}_0$ corresponds to the magnetization at $t_0 = 0$ and the $\delta\mathbf{J}_i$ are the relaxation
strengths of different relaxation processes contributing to the total relaxation. In
the present case, in contrast to the anelastic relaxation described by eq. (3.1), the
relaxation effect decreases the relaxing quantity.

### (iii) Isothermal disaccommodation

In this type of experiment the reversible susceptibility is measured continuously
as a function of time. The AC technique applied for the measurement of $\chi$ is de-

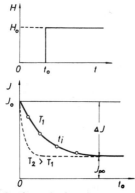

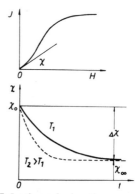

Fig. 6. Isothermal relaxation curves of the magnetization for ballistic experiments for two different temperatures. The magnetization is measured immediately after applying a magnetic field at $t_0$.

Fig. 7. Isothermal relaxation curves of the initial susceptibility for two different temperatures.

scribed elsewhere [6,7]. As is shown in fig. 7, the reversible susceptibility decreases with increasing time and approaches an asymptotic value at $t \to \infty$. The time dependence of $\chi$ is strongly temperature dependent and has, as in the case of the Richternachwirkung, an exponential time dependence

$$\chi(t) = \chi_0 - \sum_i \delta\chi_i \left(1 - \exp(-t/\tau_i)\right) , \qquad (4.2)$$

where we have assumed that several relaxation processes of relaxation strength $\delta\chi_i$ contribute to $\chi$. Equations of the form (4.1) and (4.2) are characteristic of Richtertype after effects. As will be shown later, there may also be other relaxation processes present which have different time dependences.

(iv) Isochronal relaxation curves

Isochronal relaxation curves may be constructed from the isothermal relaxation curves by a method described by Kronmüller et al. [10]. Whereas isothermal relaxation curves are convenient for a study of the time dependence of the relaxation process, isochronal relaxation curves are of particular value for the study of the temperature dependence of the relaxation phenomena and for the separation of different overlapping after effects. In particular, these curves allow a separation of rapidly varying thermally activated processes from a "background process" which varies slowly with temperature. The method of construction of isochronal relaxation is shown in fig. 8. The relaxation amplitudes of the susceptibility

$$\Delta\chi(t_1, t_2, T) = \chi(t_1) - \chi(t_2) \qquad (4.3a)$$

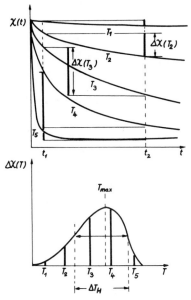

Fig. 8. Method of construction of isochronal relaxation curves from isothermal relaxation curves.

or of the inverse susceptibility, the reluctivity

$$\Delta r(t_1, t_2, T) = r(t_2) - r(t_1) , \tag{4.3b}$$

are determined as a function of temperature for fixed measuring times $t_1$ and $t_2$. If a relaxation process exists in the temperature range investigated, the isochronal relaxation curves have shapes similar to that of an error function. This can be explained as follows: At low temperatures the relaxation process proceeds so slowly that within the time interval $t_2 - t_1$ nearly no relaxation takes place. At high temperatures on the other hand the relaxation process proceeds so quickly that thermal equilibrium is established before the measurement starts at $t_1$. Between the low- and high-temperature ranges a maximum of the relaxation amplitude exists. The characteristic parameters of the relaxation peak are the temperature of the maximum $T_{max}$, the half-width $\Delta T$, and the relaxation amplitude $\delta \chi$ at $T_{max}$. It should be noted that the first two parameters are independent of the concentration of defects whereas the maximum relaxation amplitude is proportional to the concentration of the defects.

   In this case, when we are dealing with an exponential time variation of the form (4.2), the relaxation time $\tau$ at the maximum temperature is given by

$$\tau(T_{max}) = \frac{t_2 - t_1}{\ln t_2/t_1} . \tag{4.3c}$$

According to eq. (4.3c) the temperature dependence of $\tau$ can be determined either by a variation of $t_2$ or $t_1$.

### 4.3. Phenomenological theory of the Richternachwirkung

As long as we are concerned only with a Richter-type relaxation, the time dependence is controlled by the linear first order differential equation

$$\mathbf{J} + \tau_H \dot{\mathbf{J}} = \chi_\infty(\mathbf{H} + \tau_J \dot{\mathbf{H}}) , \qquad (4.4)$$

where $\chi_\infty$ is the susceptibility of the relaxed magnetization curve and $\tau_H$ and $\tau_J$ correspond to the relaxation times at constant $H$ and at constant magnetization, respectively. From eq. (4.4) we can derive analogous results as in the case of anelastic relaxation. The response of a ferromagnet to a periodic field is described by a complex susceptibility

$$\chi = \chi' - i\chi''$$

with

$$\chi' = \chi_0 + \sum_i \frac{\delta\chi_i}{1 + (\omega\tau_i)^2} \qquad (4.5)$$

and

$$\chi'' = \sum_i \frac{\delta\chi_i \omega\tau_i}{1 + (\omega\tau_i)^2} . \qquad (4.6)$$

In eq. (4.5) we have neglected the difference between $\tau_H$ and $\tau_J$ assuming only small relaxation strengths. The imaginary part of the susceptibility results in a relative energy loss $\Delta W/W_0$ or a phase shift $\delta$ of the magnetization given by

$$2\pi \operatorname{tg}\delta = \frac{\Delta W}{W_0} = 2\pi \sum_i \frac{\delta\chi_i}{\chi_0} \frac{\omega\tau_i}{1 + (\omega\tau_i)^2} . \qquad (4.7)$$

As in the case of anelastic relaxation, information on point defects may be obtained from the relaxation strengths $\delta\chi_i$ and the relaxation times $\tau$. Therefore we have to consider in the following the micromagnetic principles required for a determination of $\delta\chi_i$. The theory of relaxation times has been treated in section 3 and will not be considered further here.

### 4.4. Micromagnetic model of magnetic relaxation

#### 4.4.1. Domain theory

The experimental results described in section 4.2 may be explained quite simply by means of the Weiss model of ferromagnetism. As postulated by Weiss [44] a ferromagnet is divided into many homogeneously magnetized domains. Inside each domain the spontaneous magnetization is oriented parallel to the direction of easy magnetization. These directions in Ni are the $\langle 111 \rangle$ directions and in Fe the $\langle 100 \rangle$ directions. The transition regions between neighbouring domains are Bloch walls with a thickness between 500 to 2000 Å. In the demagnetized state the Bloch walls lie at the bottom of potential wells. According to this model relaxation phenomena may be explained by a time dependent potential $\phi_r$ which is superimposed on the static potential $\phi_0$. The potential $\phi_0$ corresponds to the interaction energy of the domain walls with all lattice defects which may be considered to be immobile, whereas $\phi_r$ is due to those defects which are mobile. For a quantitative calculation, we consider a domain wall which separates two domains with magnetization vectors $\mathbf{J}_1$ and $\mathbf{J}_2$. If a magnetic field is applied a magnetostatic force $\mathbf{P}_H$ will be exerted on the domain wall which thereby displaces it to a position $A'$. In the equilibrium position $A'$ the magnetostatic force $\mathbf{P}_H$ is balanced by the restoring forces due to the potentials $\phi_0$ and $\phi_r$. The increase of magnetization parallel to the applied field, which is due to a dusplacement $U$ of the domain wall, is given by:

$$\Delta J = 2 J_s \frac{U}{L_3} \cos\varphi \cos\theta_0 , \tag{4.8a}$$

where $L_3$ is the linear extension of the domain, $\theta_0$ the angle between $\mathbf{J}_1$ and the domain wall normal and $\varphi$ the angle between the applied field and the domain wall normal. In the following we introduce the abbreviations

$$p = 2 \cos\varphi \cos\theta_0$$

and $\hspace{6cm}$ (4.9)

$$S = 1/L_3 .$$

Eq. (4.9) inserted into eq. (4.8a) now gives

$$\dot{\Delta J} = p J_s S U . \tag{4.8b}$$

$S$ corresponds to the domain wall surface per unit volume. The magnetostatic force due to the applied field is given by

$$P_H = p J_s H . \tag{4.10}$$

The forces due to $\phi_0$ and $\phi_r$ are defined by

$$P_0 = -d\phi_0/dU ;$$

$$P_r = -d\phi_r/dU . \tag{4.11a}$$

For small relative displacements $U/L_3 \ll 1$, $\phi_0$ and $\phi_r$ may be expanded in terms of a Taylor series giving for the forces per unit surface of the domain wall

$$P_0 = -R_0 U, \qquad P_r = -R_r(t) U. \tag{4.11b}$$

At equilibrium we have

$$P_H + P_0 + P_r = 0, \tag{4.12}$$

which gives if eqs. (4.9) and (4.11) are introduced into eq. (4.12)

$$U = \frac{p J_s H}{R_0 + R_r(t)}. \tag{4.13}$$

Substituting eq. (4.13) into eq. (4.7b) gives

$$\Delta J = \frac{p^2 J_s^2 S H}{R_0 + R_r(t)}. \tag{4.14}$$

From eq. (4.14) we obtain finally for the reversible susceptibility

$$\chi_{rev}(t) = \frac{\Delta J}{H} = \frac{p^2 J_s^2 S}{R_0 + R_r(t)} \tag{4.15}$$

or for the inverse susceptibility, the reluctivity,

$$r(t) = \frac{R_0 + R_r(t)}{p^2 J_s^2 S}. \tag{4.16}$$

For $R_r(t) = 0$, eq. (4.16) gives the initial susceptibility $\chi_0$ of the unrelaxed magnetization curve. For small relaxations the condition $r(t) \ll R_0$ is valid. In this case the following relation between the susceptibility and the reluctivity may be derived

$$\chi_{rev}(t) = \frac{\chi_0^2}{p^2 J_s^2 S} R_r(t) = \chi_0^2 (r(t) - \frac{1}{\chi_0})$$

$$= \chi_0(\chi_0 r(t) - 1). \tag{4.17}$$

From eq. (4.16) we find that the relaxation amplitude of the reluctivity between the times $t_1$ and $t_2$ is given by

$$\Delta r(t_1, t_2) = r(t_1) - r(t_2) = \frac{R_r(t_1) - R_r(t_2)}{p^2 J_s^2 S}$$

$$= \frac{1}{p^2 J_s^2 S} \left( \frac{d^2\phi_r(t_2)}{dU^2} - \frac{d^2\phi_r(t_1)}{dU^2} \right)\Bigg|_{U=0} . \qquad (4.18)$$

Similarly we obtain for the relaxation amplitude of the susceptibility in the case of a small relaxation strength

$$\Delta\chi(t_1, t_2) = \chi(t_1) - \chi(t_2)$$

$$= \frac{1}{p^2 J_s^2 S} \chi_0^2 \{ R_r(t_2) - R_r(t_1) \}. \qquad (4.19)$$

4.4.2. The interaction energy

In the preceding subsection we have described the magnetic relaxation by means of a time dependent potential $\phi_r$. This potential may be attributed to a rearrangement of the defects by thermal activation. The rearrangement of the defects is caused by the interaction energy between the defects and the spontaneous magnetization. The interaction energy depends on the direction of the spontaneous magnetization and on the orientation of the defect. We may therefore write for the interaction energy:

$$E_i = E_i(\mathbf{J}(\mathbf{r}, t)) , \qquad (4.20)$$

where the index $i$ denotes the $i$th orientation of the defect. In contrast to the anelastic relaxation, where the applied stress is assumed to be constant, in a ferromagnet it must be taken into account that $\mathbf{J}$ is not only time dependent but depends also on the coordinates $\mathbf{r}$, since inside the domain walls the spontaneous magnetization changes its orientation. Since the magnetization $\mathbf{J}$ is an intrinsic property of ferromagnetic materials the splitting of energy levels takes place without application of an external field. The interaction energy is composed of two contributions, one term, $E_i^M$, is due to the magnetostrictive coupling energy between the internal stresses of the defects and the elastic magnetostrictive stresses of the domain walls, the other term $E_i^K$ is due to the disturbance of the electronic structure in the immediate neighbourhood of the defects. This energy may be considered to be an additional contribution to the crystal anisotropy of the ideal crystal. The latter energy term was introduced by Néel [39] in order to describe quantitatively the Richternachwirkung of the C-atoms in $\alpha$-Fe. A quantitative determination of the *magnetostrictive* and *magnetocrystalline* contributions to the total interaction energy is due to Rathenau [45] and Rathenau et al. [46, 47].

The dependence of the magnetic interaction energy on the direction cosines $\gamma_i$ of the spontaneous magnetization can be determined from group theoretical considerations; explicit expressions for $E_i$ have been given by the author elsewhere [20]. In the particular case when we are dealing with trigonal, tetragonal or orthorhombic defects in cubic crystals the magnetocrystalline energy depends on the direction cosines $\beta_i^k$ of the symmetry axis of the defects in the $k$'s position (trigonal defects: $\langle 111 \rangle$-axis, tetragonal defects: $\langle 100 \rangle$-axis; orthorhombic defects: $\langle 110 \rangle$-axis) with respect to the cube axes, and the direction cosines $\gamma_i$ of the spontaneous magnetization with respect to the cube axes. In terms of the functions

$$X_1(\gamma_i, \beta_i^k) = \sum_i \gamma_i^2 (\beta_i^k)^2$$

and

$$X_2(\gamma_i, \beta_i^k) = \sum_{i \neq j} \gamma_i \gamma_j \, \beta_i^k \, \beta_j^k \,. \tag{4.21}$$

The magnetocrystalline interaction energies may be written as follows *

(i) trigonal defects

$$E_k^K = \epsilon X_2(\gamma_i, \beta_i^k) \,; \tag{4.22a}$$

(ii) tetragonal defects

$$E_k^K = \epsilon X_1(\gamma_i, \beta_i^k) \,; \tag{4.22b}$$

(iii) orthorhombic defects

$$E_k^K = \epsilon_1 X_1(\gamma_i, \beta_i^k) + \epsilon_2 X_2(\gamma_i, \beta_i^k) \,. \tag{4.22c}$$

The average interaction energy

$$\overline{E^K} = \frac{1}{n_E} \sum_i E_i^K \,, \tag{4.23}$$

if determined with the expressions (4.21)–(4.22) gives $\overline{E}$ = const. In order to obtain an expression which depends on the direction of the magnetization we must take into account fourth order terms in $E_i^K$. The average energy then gives for the above

---

* The interaction constants $\epsilon$ introduced here should not be confused with the strain tensor $\boldsymbol{\varepsilon}$.

discussed symmetries of defects

$$\overline{E^K} = \overline{\epsilon} \sum_{i \neq j} \gamma_i^2 \gamma_j^2 \ .$$

(4.24)

The magnetostrictive coupling energy of the defects may be calculated according to eq. (3.27) which was derived for the interaction energy of an elastic dipole with an external stress field. In order to apply eq. (3.27) to the calculation of $E_i^M$ it is necessary to replace the stress tensor $\sigma$ by the elastic stresses of a domain wall. These stresses were calculated previously by Rieder [48, 49].

### 4.4.3. Definition of three relaxation types

In section 4.4.1 we have seen that the magnetic relaxation phenomena can be explained by means of a time dependent domain wall potential. With the help of the interaction energy $E_i$ of the defects with the magnetization this potential can be determined as follows: Suppose the crystal to be demagnetized at $t = 0$ by an a.c. field. After the demagnetization all possible orientations of the defects are occupied by the same defect density $C_0$. Due to the interaction energy $E_i$ the number of defects in the energetically favourable positions will increase. After a time $t$ the concentration in the $i$th orientation will be

$$C_i = C_i(z, t) \ .$$

Here we have assumed that we are dealing with plane domain walls with the normal to the domain wall parallel to the $z$-axis. $C_i$ has become inhomogeneous after a time $t$ because the interaction energy depends on the local direction of the spontaneous magnetization. If at time $t$ the domain wall is displaced from its original position at $z = 0$ to $z = U$ the total interaction energy is given by

$$\phi_r(U, t) = \int_{-\infty}^{\infty} \sum_i^{n_E} \{ C_i(z, t) E_i(z - U, t) - C_0 \overline{E} \} \ dz \ .$$

(4.25)

From eq. (4.25) it is found that at $t = 0$ the stabilization energy is zero. An increase of the stabilization energy can take place by three different types of movements of the defects.

#### (i) Orientation after effect

The after effect is called an orientation after effect if the thermal equilibrium is approached by a local reorientation of the symmetry axis of anisotropic defects. This type of relaxation is characterized by an equation of reaction

$$i \rightleftharpoons j \ ,$$

where the processes $i \rightarrow j$ take place more frequently than the processes $j \rightarrow i$ if $E_j < E_i$.

The relaxation constant $R_r(t)$ may be determined by inserting the expressions for the $C_i$ derived in section 3.3 and the corresponding interaction energies given in section 4.4.2 into eq. (4.25). For small displacements of the domain walls from their equilibrium positions ($U < \delta_0$, $\delta_0$ = parameter characterizing the domain wall thickness) the integration of eq. (4.25) over the $z$-coordinate gives, for trigonal and tetragonal defects, the following expression

$$R_r(t) = R_\infty \{1 - \exp(-t/\tau)\},\qquad(4.26)$$

whereas, in the case of orthorhombic defects one has:

$$R_r(t) = R_\infty^{(1)} \{1 - \exp(-t/\tau_1)\} + R_\infty^{(2)} \{1 - \exp(-t/\tau_2)\}.\qquad(4.27)$$

The value of the relaxation constant for $t \to \infty$, $R_\infty$ depends on the type of the domain wall. If only the magnetocrystalline interaction energy is taken into account, $R_\infty$ can be written as:

$$R_\infty = \text{const.}\,\frac{C_0}{kT}\frac{\epsilon^2}{\delta_0}.\qquad(4.28)$$

The relaxation constant $R_\infty$ was determined by the author for a number of defects in Ni taking into account both the magnetoelastic and the magnetocrystalline interaction energies [20]. In general, however, the magnetoelastic interaction energy will play a minor role. In particular this will be true for vacancy-type defects because these defects possess only a small elastic dipole tensor.

Eqs. (4.18)–(4.19) combined with eq. (4.26) give a simple explanation of the experimental results reviewed in section 4.2. The relaxation amplitude between the times $t_1$ and $t_2$ is found by inserting eq. (4.26) into eq. (4.18), and eq. (4.19). This gives:

$$\Delta r(t_1, t_2) = \frac{R_\infty}{p^2 J_s^2 S} \{\exp(-t_2/\tau) - \exp(-t_1/\tau)\}$$

and

$$\Delta\chi(t_1, t_2) = \frac{\chi_0^2 R_\infty}{p^2 J_s^2 S} \{\exp(-t_1/\tau) - \exp(-t_2/\tau)\}.\qquad(4.29)$$

Here $\Delta r$ and $\Delta\chi$ for fixed $t_1$ and $t_2$ are functions of the temperature and therefore correspond to isochronal relaxation curves as discussed in section 4.2.

(ii) Diffusion after effect

If the thermal equilibrium is approached by a long range migration of the defects the relaxation due to this process according to Dietze [42] is called a diffusion after effect. The migration of the defects takes place under the action of a force **P** which is due to the average interaction energy $\bar{E}$. As we have seen in section 4.4.2 the average interaction energy $\bar{E}$ depends on the orientation of the spontaneous magnetization. Inside a domain wall the orientation of the spontaneous magnetization changes continuously from one easy direction to another. Therefore domain walls exert a force $P$ on the defects, where $P$ is given by

$$P = - \frac{\mathrm{d}E}{\mathrm{d}z} . \tag{4.30}$$

Over a period of time the defects tend to leave regions with a high interaction energy in favour of regions with a small interaction energy and this leads to a rearrangement of the defects inside the domain wall. The migration of the defects is controlled by the diffusion equation for diffusion in a field:

$$\frac{\partial C}{\partial t} = \frac{\partial}{\partial z} \left[ D_z \left( \frac{\partial C}{\partial z} + \frac{C}{kT} \frac{\partial \bar{E}}{\partial z} \right) \right] , \tag{4.31}$$

where the linear diffusion coefficient parallel to the domain wall normal is given by

$$D_z = a^2 v \Gamma \tag{4.32}$$

with

$$\Gamma = \frac{1}{n_E \, a^2} \sum_i^{n_E} \sum_j^{n_0} s_{ij,z}^2 .$$

($a$ = edge length of the unit cell, $v$ = atomic jump frequency, $s_{ij,z}$ = $z$-component of the displacement vector for a jump from $i$ into $j$.) When thermal equilibrium is attained the concentration $C(z)$ of the defects obeys a Boltzmann distribution

$$C(z) = \bar{C} \exp(-\bar{E}(z)/kT) \approx \bar{C} \left( 1 - \frac{\bar{E}}{kT} \right) , \tag{4.33}$$

where $\bar{C}$ is the average concentration of the defects.

The time scale for the diffusion after effect is governed by a time constant $\tau_D$ which corresponds to the time required to migrate through a domain wall of thickness $\delta_0$. In terms of the diffusion coefficient $D_z$ the time constant $\tau_D$ is given by

$$\tau_D = \frac{\delta_0^2}{D_z} = \frac{1}{\Gamma} \frac{\delta_0^2}{a^2} \frac{1}{v} . \tag{4.34}$$

According to eq. (4.34) the time which is characteristic for the diffusion after effect is increased by a factor $(1/\Gamma)(\delta_0^2/a^2)$ in comparison to the relaxation times of the orientation after effect. In Ni this factor is of the order of $10^6$ at room temperature and at $50°K$ of the order of $10^4$. The temperature dependence of the factor $(1/\Gamma)(\delta_o^2/a^2)$ is due to the domain wall thickness.

The time dependence of the relaxation constant $R_r(t)$ does not obey a simple exponential law as in the case of the orientation after effect. At small times $t < \tau_D$, $R_r(t)$ is linear in $t$, whereas at large times $R_r(t)$ can be represented by the following series

$$R_r(t) = \sum_{n=0}^{\infty} \frac{a_n}{t_o^{\frac{3}{2}+n}} \ ,$$

with

$$t_o = \frac{t}{\tau_D} \ . \tag{4.35}$$

The parameter $a_n$ depends on the special domain wall under consideration, and may be written

$$a_n \approx \frac{\bar{C}\,\epsilon^2}{kT\delta_o} \ . \tag{4.36}$$

It follows from eq. (4.35) that for large times $R_r(t)$ tends to zero as $1/t_o^{\frac{3}{2}}$.

(iii) Combined after effect

In general the defects will be able to undergo both a reorientation of their symmetry axis and a long range migration. In this case an orientation after effect as well as a diffusion after effect will be observed. A relaxation phenomenon of this type is called a *combined after effect* [50]. Since the total density of the defects inside the domain walls becomes inhomogeneous due to a migration of the defects the relaxation strength of the orientation after effect will be changed by a certain amount. This modification of the orientation after effect results in a contribution to the relaxation constant $R_r$ which at large times varies as $1/t_o^{\frac{1}{2}}$. The relaxation constant for a combined after effect with one relaxation time $\tau$ can be represented as a sum of three terms

$$R_r(t) = R_\infty(1 - \exp(-t/\tau)) + \sum_{n=0}^{\infty} \frac{a_n}{t_o^{\frac{3}{2}+n}} + \sum_{n=0}^{\infty} \frac{b_n}{t_o^{\frac{1}{2}+n}} \ , \tag{4.37}$$

where $R_\infty$ is given by eq. (4.28), $a_n$ by eq. (4.36) and the $b_n$'s may be written as

$$b_n \approx \frac{\bar{\epsilon}\epsilon^2}{(kT)^2} \frac{1}{\delta_o} \ . \tag{4.38}$$

If the $a_n$'s are compared with the $b_n$'s it is found that they are larger by a factor

$(\epsilon^2/\bar{\epsilon})(1/kT)$ than the $b_n$'s. Since $\epsilon^2/\bar{\epsilon}$ is certainly smaller than $kT$ at not too low temperatures, the third term in eq. (4.37) in general will be smaller than the two other terms.

## 5. Application to special defects

### 5.1. *General remarks*

The anelastic and magnetic relaxation effects which were discussed in the pre-ceding sections may be used for the study of self defects in metals. The character-istic properties of the defects which may be determined by such experiments are the activation energies for the displacement modes of the defects and the symmetry of the defects; the latter is especially important for an interpretation of the recovery stages in metals. Point defects which are of special interest are Frenkel pairs, inter-stitial atoms, vacancies and vacancy clusters (especially di- and tri-vacancies).

The measurement of anelastic and magnetic relaxation is only possible in the case of ferromagnetic metals. It is, however, only a slight disadvantage that such combined measurements may only be performed in Ni, Fe, Co, and Gd because these metals may be considered to be representative of f.c.c., b.c.c., and h.c.p. metals in general.

In this section we shall discuss the relaxation properties of the above mentioned defects. This requires a study of the possible configurations of these defects and also their modes of displacement. The anelastic relaxation is characterized by the relaxation strengths $\delta S$ and $\delta S'$, and the corresponding relaxation times. For the study of the magnetic relaxation we shall determine isochronal relaxation curves as defined by eq. (4.2). The isochronal relaxation curves obtained for the orientation, diffusion, and combined after effect show characteristic differences which may afford useful information concerning the symmetry of the defects.

### 5.2. *Interstitial atoms in nickel*

A problem of great interest in the investigation of the recovery stages in f.c.c. metals is the interpretation of stages $I_E$ and III. At the present time all the theories which have been discussed in the literature are based on the assumption that stage $I_E$ corresponds to the annealing of a freely migrating interstitial atom. The differ-ences between the theories lie in the assumptions made concerning the configura-tion of the interstitial atom migrating in stage $I_E$. Seeger [51, 52] and Seeger et al. [53, 54] interpret this stage as being due to the free migration of metastable crowd-ions with orthorhombic symmetry. Other authors [55, 56, 19] assume that stage $I_E$ is due to the free migration of the tetragonal configuration of the interstitial atom, whereas Seeger [51] and Seeger et al. [53, 54, 57, 58] attribute stage III to just this tetragonal configuration of the interstitial atoms. In the other theories, stage III is mostly interpreted as the migration of vacancies or divacancies.

It is evident that the above mentioned problems cannot be solved by measure-

Table 1
Mechanical and magnetic relaxation of different interstitial configurations.

| Interstitial configuration | Mechanical relaxation | | | | Magnetic relaxation | | |
|---|---|---|---|---|---|---|---|
| | torsion | | tension | | Orientation | Diffusion | Combined |
| | $\langle 100 \rangle$-axis | $\langle 111 \rangle$-axis | $\langle 100 \rangle$-axis | $\langle 111 \rangle$-axis | | | |
| Cubic | − | − | − | − | − | + | − |
| Crowdion | − | − | − | − | − | + | − |
| Tetragonal | − | + | + | − | + | + | + |
| $E_I^R < E_I^M$ | | | | | $(E_I^R)$ | $(E_I^M)$ | |
| tetragonal | − | + | + | − | + | + | + |
| $E_I^R > E_I^M$ | | (annealing) | (annealing) | | $E_I^M$ | $E_I^M$ | $(E_I^M)$ |

−: no relaxation
+ : relaxation takes place
annealing: The relaxation anneals out during the measurement.
$E_I^{R,M}$: Activation energy which controls the relaxation effect.

ments of the recovery of the residual resistivity alone. It is hoped, however, that the techniques of anelastic and magnetic relaxation may afford conclusive experimental evidence in favour of one or the other model. In order to make a quantitative comparison between the theoretical results of this subsection and the experimental results of the following section we determine here the isochronal relaxation curves of the different interstitial configurations for an activation energy $E_I^M = 0.14$ eV and a pre-exponential factor $\nu_0 \exp(S/K) = 1.67 \times 10^{14}$ s. The activation energy of the order of 0.14 eV has been determined by Peretto [59] from relaxation experiments and by Oddou [62] from electrical resistivity measurements and the pre-exponential factor was chosen in such a way that optimum agreement between theory and experiment is achieved if the after effect in stage $I_E$ is interpreted as a diffusion after effect (see section 6.1). For the measuring times we choose, in accordance with Peretto's measurements, $t_1 = 3$ s and $t_2 = 162$ s.

The anelastic relaxation effects which are expected for the different configurations of the interstitial atom are summarized in table 1. The results represented here can easily be derived from eqs. (3.21)–(3.24).

The discussion of the magnetic after effect will be restricted to the isochronal relaxation curves and the method of calculation will not be discussed in detail here. The integration of eq. (4.25), which is required for a determination of the isochronal curves, has been performed for a number of defects by the author [20]. In this paper the numerical results of a computer calculation will be represented; these calculations were performed for a (112)–180°-Bloch wall in nickel. Other domain walls show only minor deviations from these results, and therefore will not be considered here.

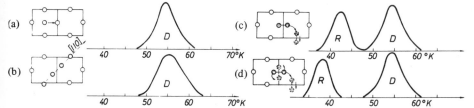

Fig. 9. Theoretically determined isochronal relaxation curves of different configurations of the interstitial atom for $t_1 = 3$ s and $t_2 = 162$ s; all numerical calculations were done with $\nu_0 \exp(S/k) = 1.67 \times 10^{14}$ s$^{-1}$, $E_{\mathrm{I}}^{\mathrm{M}} = 0.14$ eV. (a) Cubic symmetry. (b) Orthorhombic symmetry (crowdion). (c) Tetragonal symmetry (dumbbell configuration $E_{\mathrm{I}}^{\mathrm{R}} \geqslant E_{\mathrm{I}}^{\mathrm{M}}$). (d) Tetragonal dumbbell configuration $E_{\mathrm{I}}^{\mathrm{R}} = 0.9\, E_{\mathrm{I}}^{\mathrm{M}}$).

## 5.2.1. Cubic symmetry

The interstitial atom of cubic symmetry, as shown in fig. 9a, is isotropic and can give rise only to a diffusion after effect. No anelastic relaxation or magnetic orientation after effect can be observed. The time constant $\tau_D$ of the diffusion after effect follows from eq. (4.34) with $\Gamma = \frac{1}{3}$. The isochronal relaxation curve connected with the diffusion of the cubic symmetric interstitial atom is represented in fig. 9a.

## 5.2.2. Orthorhombic symmetry (crowdion)

The atomic arrangement of the atoms of an interstitial atom in the crowdion configuration is represented in fig. 9b. This configuration is, according to Seeger [51, 52], metastable and therefore can only be produced by non-equilibrium processes (irradiation by electrons or neutrons). Above a certain critical temperature the crowdion becomes unstable and is converted into the more stable tetragonal configuration. The crowdion can only move along the $\langle 110 \rangle$-direction in which the additional atom is introduced. Therefore the crowdions can only give rise to a diffusion after effect. Crowdions appear in the six different $\langle 110 \rangle$-orientations each of which can be treated as an individual defect and therefore in principle there exist six different time constants which are given by

$$\tau_D^{(i)} = \frac{1}{\Gamma_i} \left(\frac{\delta_0}{a}\right)^2 \frac{1}{\nu} , \tag{5.1}$$

with

$$\Gamma_i = \tfrac{1}{2} \cos^2 \theta_i \tag{5.2}$$

and

$$\nu^{-1} = \nu_0^{-1} \exp(-S^{\mathrm{M}}/k) \exp(E_{\mathrm{I}}^{\mathrm{M}}/kT) , \tag{5.3}$$

where $\theta_i$ corresponds to the angle between the Bloch wall normal and the $\langle 110 \rangle$-

directions of the crowdions. In the special case where we consider a $(110)-180°$-Bloch wall we have

$$\Gamma_1 = 0, \quad \Gamma_2 = \tfrac{1}{2}, \quad \Gamma_3 = \Gamma_4 = \Gamma_5 = \Gamma_6 = \tfrac{1}{8}.$$

The crowdion with $\Gamma_1 = 0$ has a time constant $\tau_D^{(1)} = \infty$, because its $\langle 110 \rangle$-direction is parallel to the domain wall. This crowdion therefore cannot lower its interaction energy with the domain wall and will not contribute to the diffusion after effect. From the remaining five other directions the one which has its $\langle 110 \rangle$-direction perpendicular to the domain wall has the time constant

$$\tau_D^{(2)} = 2 \left(\frac{\delta_o}{a}\right)^2 \frac{1}{\nu} = 2.8 \times 10^3 \, \nu_o^{-1} \, \exp(-S^M/K) \, \exp(E_I^M/kT) \qquad (5.4)$$

and the four other directions have a time constant

$$\tau_D^{(3)} = 8 \left(\frac{\delta_o}{a}\right)^2 \frac{1}{\nu} = 1.12 \times 10^4 \, \nu_o^{-1} \, \exp(-S^M/K) \, \exp(E_I^M/kT). \qquad (5.5)$$

In fig. 9b is shown the isochronal relaxation curve for a $(110)-180°$-Bloch wall. In comparison to the relaxation peak of the cubic configuration, the half width of the relaxation peak of the crowdion is broader and the temperature $T_{max}$ lies at $57°K$. This is due to the superposition of the relaxation curves with two time constants.

### 5.2.3. Tetragonal configuration (interstitialcy, dumbbell)

The split configuration of the interstitial atom is represented in fig. 9c. This configuration is also called the interstitialcy configuration or dumbbell interstitial. A characteristic feature of the split configuration is the two possible displacements which may lead to a reorientation of the tetragonal axis. One mode of displacement corresponds to a simple rotation of the 4-fold axis without any shift of the centre of gravity (fig. 9c). On the other hand the migration of the dumbbell is also connected with a reorientation of the tetragonal axis as indicated in fig. 9d. These displacements which lead to a rotation of the tetragonal axis give rise to an orientation after effect whereas the migration of the interstitials lead to a diffusion after effect. If the simple rotation process occurs with the atomic frequency $\nu^R = \nu_o^R \exp(S^R/K)$ $\times \exp(-E_I^R/kT)$ and the migration with the atomic frequency $\nu^M = \nu_o^M \exp(S^M/K)$ $\times \exp(-E_I^M/kT)$ the relaxation time for the orientation after effect is given by

$$\tau = (6\nu^R + 12\nu^M)^{-1} \qquad (5.6)$$

($\nu_o^{R, M}$ = atomic jump frequency for rotation and migration, $E_I^{R,M}$ = activation energy for rotation and migration). The time constant for the diffusion after effect follows from eq. (4.34) with $\Gamma = \tfrac{1}{3}$, which gives

$$\tau_D = 3 \left(\frac{\delta_o}{a}\right)^2 \frac{1}{\nu^M} = 4.2 \times 10^3 \, \nu_o^{-1} \, \exp(-S^M/K) \, \exp(E_I^M/kT). \qquad (5.7)$$

From eqs. (5.6) and (5.7) it follows that the orientation after effect depends in
general on the activation energy $E_I^R$ for rotation and the activation energy $E_I^M$ for
migration, whereas the time constant $\tau_D$ depends only on the activation energy for
migration. In fig. 9c and fig. 9d the isochronal relaxation curves are represented for
two combinations of values for $E_I^R$ and $E_I^M$. In the first case it is assumed $E_I^R \geqslant E_I^M$.
If this condition holds the orientation after effect and the diffusion after effect are
characterized by the activation energy $E_I^M$. If, however, the condition $E_I^R < E_I^M$ is
fulfilled the orientation after effect will be determined by $E_I^R$ whereas the diffusion
after effect is still described by the activation energy for migration $E_I^M$. In the latter
case the relaxation peak for the orientation after effect appears at lower temperatures. In fig. 9d it was assumed that $E_I^R = 0.9\,E_I^M$, this results in an orientation maximum which lies 4°C below the orientation maximum if $E_I^R \geqslant E_I^M$. It should be noted
that the relaxation maxima in fig. 9c for the orientation and the diffusion after effect
are separated by 12°K even for $E_I^R = E_I^M$. Furthermore it must be borne in mind
that the half width of the orientation peak corresponds to 4.7°K whereas the diffusion peak has a half width of about 6°K. The relaxation peak of the crowdion diffusion has a half width of 7.2°K.

### 5.3. Interstitial atom in α-Fe

Several configurations of the interstitial atom in b.c.c. crystals have been discussed by Johnson [31] and his investigations have led to the conclusion that the
most stable interstitial atom configuration is a split configuration of orthorhombic
symmetry as shown in fig. 10a. The split interstitial consists of two half interstitials
which are connected in the ⟨110⟩-direction; this direction is called the dumbbell
axis. A reorientation of the dumbbell axis occurs in the (111)-planes, which are
parallel to the dumbbell axis, by means of a rotation of 60°. In order to arrive at
the orientation with the dumbbell axis perpendicular to the original orientation two
successive rotations in different (111)-planes are required. As outlined in sect. 3.3
defects of orthorhombic symmetry with nearest and next nearest neighbours possess two relaxation times which are given by eq. (3.44). With $n_E = 6, n_o = 4$,

(a)
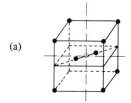

(b)
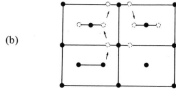

Fig. 10a. Orthorhombic configuration of the
split interstitial atom in b.c.c. metals.

Fig. 10b. Migration of the split interstitial in
the (110)-plane for $E_I^R > E_I^M$.

$n'_o = 1$ and $\alpha_s = 2$, we obtain for the relaxation times:

$$\tau_1 = \frac{1}{12} \frac{1}{\nu}, \quad \tau_2 = \frac{1}{8} \frac{1}{\nu}.$$

The reorientation for the dumbbell axis is not connected with a migration of the defect. This process therefore corresponds to an orientation after effect.

The migration of the interstitial atom may occur by means of a jump of one of the half interstitials to one of the two atoms lying nearest to it (see fig. 10b) *. The other half interstitial is shifted to the regular lattice site. Since it is most probable that the migrating half interstitial is displaced in the (110)-plane, which is parallel to the dumbbell axis, the new dumbbell formed has the same orientation as the original interstitial. Under these conditions the migration of an interstitial atom with dumbbell axis ⟨110⟩, takes place in the plane (1$\bar{1}$0) along the ⟨111⟩-directions lying in this (1$\bar{1}$0)-plane. Therefore a situation similar to the case of the crowdions exists. Each of the six dumbbell orientations can be treated as an individual defect with its own time constant for a diffusion after effect. The migration in the (110)-planes corresponds to a planar analogy of the linear migration of the crowdions. The observation of this planar migration, however, is only possible if the energy of reorientations $E_I^R$ is larger than the energy of migration $E_I^M$. In this case the orientation after effect is not observable because the interstitials have annealed out in a temperature interval where the reorientation processes do not take place. In the case, $E_I^R < E_I^M$, the relaxation process of the interstitial atoms correspond to a combined after effect and the migration now takes place in three dimensions.

The isochronal relaxation curves which can be observed in the case of split interstitial atoms in b.c.c. crystals depend according our statements on the relative values of $E_I^R$ and $E_I^M$. A diffusion after effect will be observed for $E_I^M < E_I^R$, and an orientation after effect together with a diffusion after effect for $E_I^M > E_I^R$. In the latter case the orientation after effect is described by the activation energy $E_I^R$ and the two relaxation times $\tau_1$ and $\tau_2$. The time constant of the diffusion after effect is characterized by the activation energy for migration.

## 5.4. Divacancy in nickel

In f.c.c. crystals it is expected that the most stable configuration of the divacancy consists of two vacancies on neighbouring lattice sites. These two vacancies are connected by a ⟨110⟩-direction. As we have seen, defects of this type possess orthorhombic symmetry. There are six different ⟨110⟩-orientations of the defects which form the edges of a regular tetrahedron as shown in fig. 11. The corners of the tetrahedron correspond to four regular nearest neighbour lattice sites. The centres of the divacancies are characterized in fig. 11 by the open circles in the middle of the edges. A reorientation of the divacancies can be described by jumps of the open circles to

---

* Another saddle point configuration leading to a more distant atom has been considered by Johnson [31].

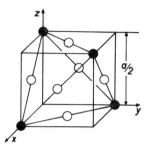

Fig. 11. Divacancy in a f.c.c. crystal. The full circles correspond to regular lattice sites. The open circles denote the centre of possible divacancies. The six edges of the tetrahydron shown are identical with the six crystallographically distinguishable $\langle 110 \rangle$-directions. Jumps of the divacancy correspond to jumps of one of the open circles to one of the neighbouring open circles.

the middle of the neighbouring edges. Such a jump corresponds to a rotation of the $\langle 110 \rangle$-axis of the divacancy in the $(111)$-plane by an angle of $60°$. In so far the displacement modes of the divacancies correspond to those of the split interstitial in b.c.c. metals. The atomic configuration of the divacancy in f.c.c. crystals, however, allows a random migration in contrast to the split interstitial in b.c.c. crystals which may be assumed to migrate in $\{110\}$-planes. Any reorientation of the $\langle 110 \rangle$-axis of the divacancy is connected with a shift of the centre of gravity. Therefore the relaxation process of the divacancies corresponds to a combined after effect and consequently the isochronal relaxation curve shows two relaxation peaks, one peak corresponds to the orientation after effect which is described by the two relaxation times $(n_0 = 4;\ n_0' = 1;\ \alpha = 2;\ n_E = 6)$:

$$\tau_1 = \frac{1}{12\nu}, \quad \tau_2 = \frac{1}{8\nu}\ ,$$

and the other corresponds to the diffusion after effect with a time constant:

$$\tau_D = 6 \left(\frac{\delta_0}{a}\right)^2 \nu_0^{-1} \exp(-S/k) \exp(E_{2V}^M/kT)$$

$$= 1.5 \times 10^5 \nu_0^{-1} \exp(-S/k) \exp(E_{2V}^M/kT)\ .$$

The results of a numerical calculation of the isochronal relaxation curve for a $(112)$–$180°$ domain wall are shown in fig. 12. The experimental values to be used for the calculation of the time constant $\tau_D$ of the diffusion after effect were

$$E_{2V}^M = 0.83\ \text{eV};\quad \nu_0 \exp(S/k) = 2.18 \times 10^{13}\ \text{s}^{-1}\ .$$

These values were determined previously from an analysis of magnetic after effect measurements [13, 14].

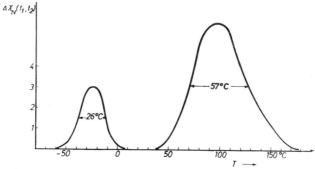

Fig. 12. The isochronal relaxation curve of the combined after effect of divacancies in nickel. The numerical calculations were performed for a $(112)-180°$ domain-wall and $E_{2V}^M = 0.83$ eV, $\nu_o \exp(S/k) = 2.18 \times 10^{14}$ s$^{-1}$.

## 5.5. *Trivacancy in nickel*

In principle the trivacancy can appear in several configurations. At low temperatures, according to Schottky [60], the $60°$-configuration is the most stable one and has the lowest energy of formation. This configuration is composed of three nearest neighbour vacancies which form a regular triangle as shown in fig. 13. A fourth atom (in fig. 13 number 1) lies nearest to the three vacancies, and atom 1 and the centre of gravity of the vacancy triangle determine the trigonal axis of the trivacancy. A reorientation of the trigonal axis occurs by means of a jump of atom 1 into the position of one of the three vacancies. As long as the energies of formation of other possible configurations of the trivacancy are larger than that for the $60°$-configuration no migration of the trivacancy takes place. In this case the trivacancy produces only an orientation after effect. The geometry of the trivacancy is characterized by $n_E = 4$ energetically different positions and $n_o = 3$ nearest neighbours. From eq. (3.41) it then follows for the relaxation time of the orientation after effect ($n_o = 3$; $n_E = 4$)

$$\tau = \frac{1}{4} \frac{1}{\nu} .$$

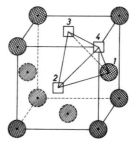

Fig. 13. Trivacancy in the $60°$-configuration in an f.c.c. crystal. The reorientation of the trigonal axis takes place by a jump of atom 1 to one of the neighbouring vacancies (2, 3, 4).

If the atom denoted in fig. 13 by the number 1 is replaced by an impurity atom, the relaxation time of this vacancy-impurity cluster still obeys eq. (3.41). However, the atomic jump frequency $\nu$ depends upon the nature of the impurity atoms. Therefore if different impurity atoms form clusters with trivacancies a discrete spectrum of relaxation times will be present.

## 5.6. Frenkel pairs in nickel

A Frenkel pair is composed of an interstitial atom and the vacancy which was generated by the formation of the interstitial atom. Since the vacancy must be considered to be immobile, relaxation processes must be due to a displacement of the interstitial atoms. Furthermore, since the interstitial atom cannot leave its vacancy, Frenkel pairs cannot establish a thermodynamic equilibrium inside the domain walls by diffusion. Therefore, Frenkel pairs do not give rise to a diffusion after effect. The interstitial atom of a Frenkel pair, however, can produce different kinds of orientation after effects. The most simple process of this kind will be a reorientation of the dumbbell axis of the interstitial atom without any shift of the interstitial atom. This orientation after effect is only possible if all orientations of the dumbbell axis correspond to stable configurations of the Frenkel pair. Another type of Frenkel pair orientation after effect is the diffusion of the interstitial atom between sites which are equidistant from the vacancy. In order that no annihilation of the Frenkel pair takes place these equidistant sites must correspond to nearest neighbour sites of the ideal lattice. The orientation after effect for this type of interstitial displacement arises due to a reorientation of the vacancy-interstitial axis as well as by a reorientation of the dumbbell axis. In the following we characterize the Frenkel pair by the vacancy-interstitial axis. Groups of Frenkel pair configurations in which the different orientations correspond to nearest neighbour sites are of special interest. As was shown by Peretto [59] and Peretto et al. [9] and also by the author [20] these conditions are fulfilled for groups lying in {111}- and {100}-planes. In the {111}-planes one can distinguish between two types of groups. One type of groups (A-type) consists of three lattice sites forming a regular triangle around the ⟨111⟩-direction. The axes vacancy-interstitial atoms are parallel to ⟨$2n + 1, 2n + 1, 2n$⟩- or to ⟨$2n, 2n - 1, 2n - 1$⟩-directions. Another type of groups (A′-type) in the {111}-planes consists of six lattice sites which form a regular hexagon around the ⟨111⟩-axis. The axes vacancy-interstitial atoms are parallel to ⟨$2n + 1, 2n + 2, 2n + 3$⟩-directions. Also in the {100}-planes two types of groups can be distinguished. One type of groups (B-type) consists of four lattice sites forming a square around a ⟨100⟩-direction. The axes vacancy-interstitial atoms are parallel to ⟨$1, 0, 2n + 1$⟩-directions. The groups of B′-type consists of two nearest neighbour lattice sites lying symmetrical to the {110}-plane in which the vacancy is situated. The axes vacancy-interstitial atoms are ⟨$n, n, m$⟩-directions.

Some typical Frenkel pair groups discussed here are represented in fig. 14. Those Frenkel pair configurations which are composed of interstitial atoms on second, fourth and sixth nearest neighbour sites have no nearest neighbours of their own group and therefore are not compatible with an orientation after effect.

## 6. Experimental results and discussion

### 6.1. *Magnetic and anelastic relaxation in stage I of nickel*
#### 6.1.1. Experimental results

Experimental investigations of the magnetic relaxation spectrum after neutron and electron irradiation at low temperatures ($<30°$K) have been carried out by Balthesen et al. [5], Peretto [59] and Peretto et al [8, 9]. Internal friction measurements after electron irradiation have been reported at this conference by Keating-Hart et al. [61]. The results of these authors will now be reviewed briefly.

The temperature dependence of the permeability $\mu(T) = 1 + 4\pi\chi(T)$ after electron irradiation is represented in fig. 15. The permeability $\mu(T)$ was measured at a frequency of $\omega = 2\pi f = 200$ s$^{-1}$. The upper curve in fig. 15 was measured 3 sec after demagnetization and the lower curve 166 sec after demagnetization. The $\mu(T)$ curves were constructed from relaxation curves which had been measured during a uniform temperature rise ($4°$K/10 min). On account of the small rate of change of temperature the two curves may be considered approximately as isochronal relaxation curves. In fig. 15 two characteristic features of the $\mu(T)$-curves can be observed; in certain temperature ranges the permeability decrease with increasing temperature whereas in other regions the permeability increases. The decreasing parts of the $\mu(T)$-curves are due to relaxation processes which produce a stabilization of the domain walls. If the point defects responsible for the relaxation process did not anneal out the $\mu(T)$-curve would remain at the lower level up to high temperatures. However, due to the increased mobility at higher temperatures the defects anneal out. This results in a decrease of the stabilization energy and consequently in an increase of the permeability. Those parts of the $\mu(T)$-curves where $\mu(T)$ increases with increasing temperature are therefore associated with the annealing of the point defects. From fig. 15 the relaxation amplitude

$$\Delta\mu(t_1, t_2, T) = 4\pi \, \Delta\chi(t_1, t_2, T) = \mu(t_1, T) - \mu(t_2, T) \qquad (6.1)$$

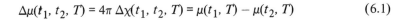

(a)                                      (b)                                      (c)

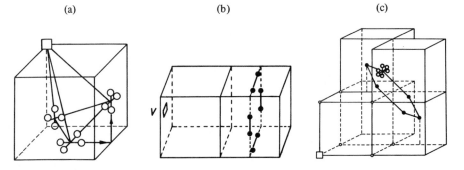

Fig. 14. Different configurations of Frenkel pair groups. (a) $\langle112\rangle$-configuration, (b) $\langle103\rangle$-configuration, (c) $\langle123\rangle$-configuration.

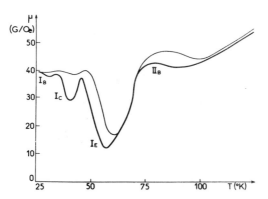

Fig. 15. The permeability $\mu(T)$ of electron irradiated nickel for $t_1 = 3$ s and $t_2 = 166$ s after de-magnetization [59]. Electron dose $\phi = 0.8 \times 10^{18}$ e⁻/cm². Irradiation temperature 30°K. $\mu(T)$ was measured during a linear increase of temperature (4°K/10 min).

can be determined by subtracting both curves from each other. In order to decide to which of the recovery stages the relaxation peaks must be attributed we compare in fig. 16 the derivative $d\mu(T)/dT$ of the increasing parts of the $\mu(T)$-curve with the derivative $d\rho(T)/dT$ of the annealing stages of the residual resistivity. A comparison of both curves in fig. 16 shows that the resistivity annealing stages $I_B$, $I_C$ and $I_E$ have analogous annealing peaks in the magnetic relaxation. It should be noted that the annealing stage $I_E$ may be observed even more clearly in the annealing curve of the magnetic relaxation than in the resistivity annealing curve where $I_E$ is observed only

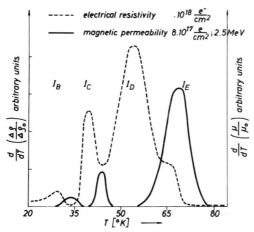

Fig. 16. The annealing rate $d\rho/dT$ of the electrical resistivity and the annealing rate $d\mu/dT$ of the permeability after Oddou [62] and Peretto [59]. The derivative $d\mu/dT$ was determined from the increasing branches of the permeability.

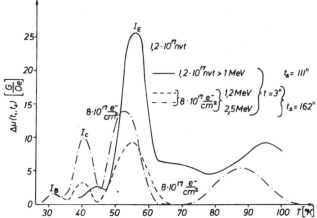

Fig. 17. Isochronal relaxation curves $\Delta\mu(t_1, t_2, T)$, for electron and neutron irradiated Ni samples.
—— neutron irradiated; $1.2 \times 10^{17}$ nvt; 1 MeV; $t_1 = 3$ s; $t_2 = 111$ s. – – – electron irradiated; $8 \times 10^{17}$ e⁻/cm²; 1.2 MeV; $t_1 = 3$ s; $t_2 = 162$ s. –·–·– electron irradiated; $8 \times 10^{17}$ e⁻/cm²; 2.5 MeV; $t_1 = 3$ s; $t_2 = 162$ s.

as a shoulder superimposed on stage $I_D$. The substage $I_D$, which is rather large in the resistivity curve, is not found in the magnetic annealing curve.

In fig. 17 three isochronal relaxation curves of electron and neutron irradiated Ni-samples are presented. The relaxation curves show maxima at about 30°K, 40°K, 54°K and 90°K.

In fig. 18 internal friction measurements in stage I after electron irradiation [61]

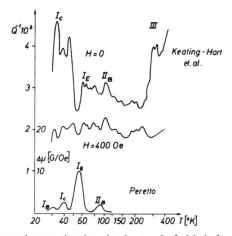

Fig. 18. Internal friction and magnetic relaxation in stage I of nickel after neutron irradiation at 28°K [61]. The internal friction was measured in a field $H = 0$ and $H = 400$ Oe (lower curve).

are compared with the magnetic relaxation peaks. According to Keating-Hart et al. [61] only stage $I_C$ shows three significant internal friction peaks, whereas in stage $I_E$ no internal friction peak can be observed (stage $I_B$ could not be studied by the authors [61] since their measurements did not extend below temperatures of about 30°K). The internal friction peaks depend sensitively on the state of magnetization; as is shown in fig. 18 the internal friction peaks in stage $I_C$ disappear completely in a field of 400 Oe.

### 6.1.2. Interpretation of experimental results

An analysis of the magnetic relaxation curves represented in fig. 17 shows that the positions of the $I_B$- and the $I_C$-peaks are nearly independent of the irradiation dose, whereas the peak $I_E$ is shifted to lower temperatures with increasing dose. These results are in accordance with the assumption that the relaxation peaks $I_B$ and $I_C$ are due to Frenkel pairs whereas $I_E$ is caused by freely migrating interstitial atoms.

As is discussed in section 5.6, only certain configurations of the Frenkel pairs can give rise to an orientation after effect. Such configurations are the $\langle 112 \rangle$-, $\langle 103 \rangle$-, and the $\langle 123 \rangle$-configurations (see fig. 14). Which of these configurations must be attributed to stages $I_B$ and $I_C$ is not yet clear. Possible interpretations are that $I_B$ corresponds to the A-type $\langle 112 \rangle$- and $I_C$ to the B-type $\langle 103 \rangle$-Frenkel pairs. Another model would be that $I_B$ corresponds to the $\langle 103 \rangle$-configuration and $I_C$ to the A'-type $\langle 123 \rangle$-configuration. The absence of any significant magnetic after effect corresponding to stage $I_D$ can only be explained by assuming that the Frenkel pairs of this stage cannot reorient the dumbbell axis or the axis between the vacancy and the interstitial atom. Therefore any movement of the interstitial atoms of the Frenkel pairs in stage $I_E$ must be accompanied by an annihilation of the Frenkel pairs. Frenkel pairs with this property do not belong to one of the groups of A-, A'- and B-type as defined in section 5.6. Frenkel pairs which may be attributed to stage $I_D$ are those with an axis between the vacancy and the interstitial atom parallel to a $\langle 100 \rangle$-direction. Another explanation of the missing $I_D$-relaxation may be that the interstitial atoms of the $I_D$ Frenkel defects are not in the interstitialcy but in the crowdion configuration as is assumed by Seeger et al. [53] in the case of copper.

For an interpretation of the magnetic after effect measured in stage $I_E$ two models have been proposed in the literature. The Grenoble group [9, 59] interprets the relaxation peak measured at 52°K as the *orientation after effect* of the *dumbbell* configuration of the interstitial atom. The Stuttgart group has proposed [16, 20] an interpretation of this relaxation peak as being due to the *diffusion after effect* of the interstitial atoms in the *crowdion* configuration. In particular, these two models, according to our discussion in section 5.2, predict the following properties for the $I_E$-relaxation effects:

I. Grenoble model

1. The defect gives rise to a combined after effect.
2. The relaxation peaks of orientation and diffusion after effect are separated by $\approx 12°K$.

3. The defect anneals out with an activation energy $E^M \geqslant E^R$.
4. The defect gives rise to a mechanical relaxation.
    II. Stuttgart model
1. The defect gives rise to a diffusion after effect.
2. The defect possesses *no* orientation after effect.
3. The diffusion after effect is controlled by the same activation energy as the annealing process in stage $I_E$.
4. The defect does *not* give rise to a mechanical relaxation effect.
The main experimental results which are available in order to discuss the two models by means of relaxation experiments are the following ones:
1. Mechanical relaxation
    The internal friction measurements of Keating-Hart et al. [61] have shown that in stage $I_E$ no significant internal friction takes place.
2. Isothermal relaxation curves
    In fig. 19 Peretto's results for the function

$$G(t) = \{(1/\mu(t) - 1/\mu(0)\}/\{1/\mu(\infty) - 1/\mu(0)\} \tag{6.2}$$

are represented as a function of $\ln(t/\tau)$. The time constants $\tau$ were determined from isothermal relaxation curves using $\ln \mu(0)/\mu(\tau) = 1$. In the case of a simple orientation after effect with a single relaxation time $G(t)$ is given by

$$G(t) = 1 - \exp(-t/\tau). \tag{6.3}$$

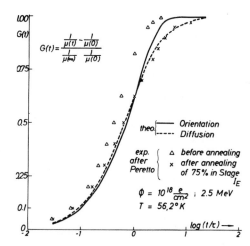

Fig. 19. The function $G(t)$ as calculated for the orientation after effect (full curve ——) and for the diffusion after effect (interrupted curve – – –) at 56°K. For the orientation after effect a relaxation time $\tau = 220$ s was used. The $G(t)$ function of the diffusion after effect was determined for crowdions and a (112)−180°-domain wall. The experimental points were taken from $G(t)$-functions as measured by Peretto [59] immediately after irradiation ($\vartriangle \vartriangle \vartriangle$) and after an anneal of 75% of stage $I_E$ (x x x). Theoretical and experimental $G(t)$-curves refer to 56°K.

The function $G(t)$ was determined by Peretto at $56.2°K$ immediately after irradiation and after an anneal of 75% of stage $I_E$. The two measured $G(t)$-curves are compared in fig. 19 with the $G(t)$-curves derived theoretically for an orientation and a diffusion after effect. The $G(t)$-curve measured immediately after irradiation corresponds to a good approximation to the $G(t)$-curve of the orientation after effect whereas the $G(t)$-curve measured after 75% annealing is compatible with a diffusion after effect *. In addition to these results Peretto finds furthermore that the time constant increases by the annealing process. It should be noticed that the $G(t)$-curves for the orientation and the diffusion after effect differentiates between the two types of after effects only at large times $t > \tau$. At small times $t < \tau$ both relaxation effects are linear in $t$ and therefore in this case both $G(t)$-curves coincide.

3. Isochronal relaxation curves

The isochronal relaxation peak measured at about $52°K$ (see fig. 17) must be compared theoretically with the relaxation peaks derived in section 5.2 for the orientation and the diffusion after effect of the dumbbell-interstitial and the crowdion configuration. The isochronal relaxation peak of the crowdion diffusion, which is represented in fig. 9b, is compared in fig. 20 with the relaxation peak measured after irradiation with 1.2 MeV electrons. As outlined in section 5.2 the activation energy $E_I^M$ and the atomic jump frequency used for the numerical calculation were

$$E_I^M = 0.14 \text{ eV} \quad \text{and} \quad \nu_0 \exp(S/k) = 1.67 \times 10^{14} \text{ s}^{-1}.$$

If the measured relaxation peak at $52°K$ is interpreted as an orientation after effect with the same activation energy as before the required atomic jump frequency is $\nu_0 \exp(S/k) = 2.5 \times 10^{10} \text{ s}^{-1}$. Here it was assumed that $\nu_0^R \exp(S/k) = \nu_0^M \exp(S/k)$. According to eq. (5.6) we have then $\nu = 18 \nu^M$. The half width of the relaxation peak for the orientation after effect is found to be $\Delta T_H \approx 5°K$ and for the diffusion after effect $7.2°K$.

4. The activation energy of the $I_E$-relaxation

Peretto [59] determined for the relaxation process in stage $I_E$ and for the migration energy of the $I_E$-defect approximately the same activation energy of $\approx 0.14$ eV.

Comparing the experimental and theoretical results of the preceding discussion with the two models developed for stage $I_E$ it is found that some of the experimental results are compatible with the orientation after effect, and some are in agreement with the diffusion after effect.

The time dependence of the relaxation process measured immediately after electron irradiation supports the *dumbbell model* for stage $I_E$, whereas after an anneal of 75% of stage $I_E$ the measured isothermal relaxation curve corresponds to a *diffusion after effect*. It is difficult to explain this change of the time dependence by a

---

* Peretto's [59] discussion of the diffusion after effect is based on Dietze's [42] results for the diffusion after effect of vacancies in Fe. These results cannot be applied, however, to the discussion of the diffusion after effect of crowdions in nickel.

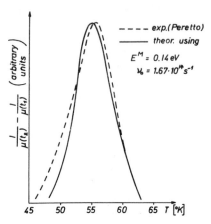

Fig. 20. Comparison between the calculated relaxation peak for crowdion diffusion (——) and the measured relaxation peak in stage $I_E$ (- - - -). The measured relaxation peak was taken from Peretto's [59] measurements on a nickel sample irradiated by $8 \times 10^{17}$ e/cm$^2$ with an energy of 1.2 MeV (see fig. 17).

spectrum of activation energies built up during the annealing process as was done by Peretto [59] because no convincing physical model that could account for this fact has been proposed. On the other hand, adopting the Stuttgart point of view the exponential time dependence measured immediately after irradiation may be explained as follows: If the measured relaxation is due to a diffusion after effect the time dependence of $\chi$ may be due, to some extent, to the annealing of the defects. Therefore the time dependence of $\chi$ actually corresponds to a superposition of the annealing and the relaxation process. Thus the resulting time dependence might simulate an orientation after effect. This model would also explain qualitatively the measured increase of the relaxation times with increasing annealing. The effect of the annealing on the time dependence is much reduced if 75% of the defects have annealed out. Under these conditions it is expected that the measured time dependence corresponds to the intrinsic relaxation process. An interpretation of the stage $I_E$ relaxation peak as a diffusion after effect also could account for the small frequency factor of $\nu_o^{exp} \exp(S/k) = 2.5 \times 10^{10}$ s$^{-1}$ as determined from Peretto's results. As discussed in section 5.2 the diffusion after effect is characterized by a frequency factor $\nu_o(\delta_o/a)^{-2}$. The factor $(\delta_o/a)^2$ at low temperatures in Ni is of the order of $10^{-4}$ and therefore would give a plausible explanation for the measured small frequency factor.

Finally the internal friction measurements of Keating-Hart et al. [61] do not show any significant relaxation peak in stage $I_E$, a fact which supports strongly the crowdion model for stage $I_E$. The Grenoble group has explained the absence of an internal friction peak in stage $I_E$ by the assumption that the elastic dipole tensor of the dumbbell interstitial is very small. This assumption, however, leads to difficulties because now it must be explained why in stage $I_C$ where internal friction is found the dumbbells possess a much larger elastic dipole tensor.

### 6.2. Magnetic and anelastic relaxation in stage III of nickel
#### 6.2.1. Experimental results

In nickel, stage III of the recovery curve of the electrical resistivity lies above room temperature at about 90°C. The precise position of stage III depends on the concentration of defects which were introduced by irradiation or plastic deformation. The technique of combining magnetic and anelastic relaxation experiments to investigate stage III in Ni was originally applied by Seeger et al. [1–3]. These early experiments have shown that, after irradiation with neutrons in the temperature range between 0°C and 20°C, a magnetic relaxation process is introduced. Further experiments have shown that this magnetic after effect anneals out in stage III at about 95°C with a reaction of second order and an activation energy for migration of the order of 1.0 eV. This value for the migration energy in stage III has also been found by numerous other authors [63–67].

Internal friction and magnetic measurements performed simultaneously have shown that, in plastically deformed Ni, an internal friction peak appears at about 50°C which corresponds to the anelastic analogy of the magnetic relaxation.

Magnetic relaxation experiments on electron irradiated Ni-crystals were published later by Kronmüller et al. [10]. Some isochronal relaxation curves of these authors for different measuring times $t_2$ are given in fig. 21. (The method whereby the isochronal relaxation curves can be determined is described in section 4.2.) The relaxation peak observed at $\approx 10°C$ anneals out in stage III [2, 10]. An analysis of the extrapolated relaxation peaks shows that these may be represented by the isochronal relaxation curve of a simple exponential relaxation process (see eq. (4.29)).

The mechanical relaxation in stage III of Ni-single crystals after plastic deformation has been investigated in detail by Seeger and Wagner [11]. For the measurements an inverted torsion pendulum was used.

The main results of Seeger and Wagner [11] are represented in fig. 22 and fig. 23. Fig. 22 represents the temperature dependence of the logarithmic decrement for a ⟨111⟩-single crystal. The different curves shown were measured after different annealing treatments with decreasing temperature. By this technique the simulation of internal friction peaks by a dislocation pinning effect due to the annealing of point defects is prevented. In fig. 22 the dotted line indicates how the internal friction peaks were extrapolated from a background damping.

In fig. 23 the isochronal annealing curves of the relaxation strength of the internal friction peaks of crystals with different orientations are compared with each other. At annealing temperatures below 80°C the logarithmic decrement decreases continuously for all three orientations shown, i.e., (⟨100⟩, ⟨111⟩, ⟨112⟩). For annealing temperatures above 80°C the ⟨111⟩- and the ⟨112⟩-crystals exhibit a shoulder in the annealing curve. Whereas in the case of the ⟨100⟩-crystals the internal friction peak has

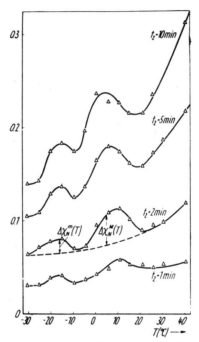

Fig. 21. Isochronal relaxation curves $\Delta\chi(t_1, t_2, T)$ in electron irradiated nickel for different measuring times $t_2$ and $t_1 = 30$ s. Electron irradiation took place at 41°C. Electron dose $\phi = 5.3 \times 10^{17}$ e⁻/cm². The relaxation curve was measured after 30 min annealing at 80°C. The method of extrapolation of the relaxation maxima is shown.

annealed out at 90°C, in the ⟨111⟩- and ⟨112⟩-crystals complete annealing has taken place at 100°C. Furthermore it should be noted that the relaxation strength is amplitude dependent below 80°C whereas above this temperature the relaxation strength becomes amplitude independent.

The magnetic relaxation peaks of the type shown in fig. 21 and the anelastic internal friction peaks as shown in fig. 22 can be used to determine the temperature dependence of the relaxation time $\tau$. From the magnetic relaxation peaks the relaxation time at $T_{max}$ can be determined according to eq. (4.3). By varying the measuring time $t_2$, $\tau$ can be determined for different temperatures. In the case of the internal friction peaks the relaxation time at the temperature of the maximum follows from the condition $\omega\tau = 1$.

By the combination of anelastic and magnetic experiments it is possible to determine the temperature dependence over a large range of temperatures. Therefore the activation energy and the pre-exponential factor of the relaxation process can be determined quite accurately. In particular if the relaxation time follows an Arrhenius

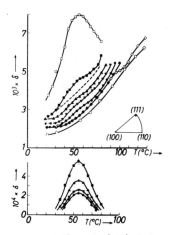

Fig. 22. The logarithmic decrement $\delta = \Delta W/W_0$ of a $\langle 111 \rangle$-single crystal according to Seeger and Wagner [11]. Plastic strain at room temperature $\epsilon = 13\%$. Measuring frequency $f = 0.305$ Hz. Measuring time at any measuring point $\Delta t = 9$ min. Temperature of the maximum $T_{max} = 55^{\circ}$C. Annealing treatment of the crystal after deformation:

| | | |
|---|---|---|
| 1. 24 h 20°C ($\square$) | 4. 30 min 90°C ($\blacktriangledown$) | 7. measured from 90°C with |
| 2. 30 min 80°C ($\blacksquare$) | 5. 30 min 95°C ($\bullet$) | increasing temperature ($\lozenge$) |
| 3. 30 min 85°C ($\blacktriangle$) | 6. 30 min 100°C ($\blacklozenge$) | 8. 10 min 120°C ($\circ$) |

In the lower part of the figure the extrapolated relaxation maxima are represented.

equation

$$\tau = \tau_0 \exp(E^R/kT) \qquad (6.4)$$

the activation energy for rotation, $E^R$, and the pre-exponential factor $\tau_0$ may be deduced from the so-called Arrhenius plot

$$\ln \tau = \ln \tau_0 + \frac{E^R}{kT} . \qquad (6.5)$$

In fig. 24 $\ln \tau$ is represented as a function of $1/T_{max}$. The experimental points determined by magnetic relaxation as well as by the internal friction lie on the same straight line; thus showing that the anelastic and magnetic relaxation belong to the same relaxation process. The Arrhenius plot gives an activation energy:

$$E^R = 0.87 + 0.03 \text{ eV}$$

and a pre-exponential factor:

$$\tau_0 = 10^{-13.8} \text{ s.}$$

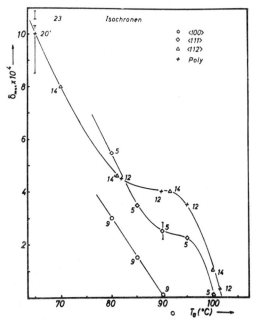

Fig. 23. Isochronal annealing curves of the relaxation maxima for different single crystals. Annealing time at any point 30 min for single crystals and 15 min for the polycrystal [11, 18]. ○ ⟨100⟩-single crystal, $\epsilon$ = 15%. △ ⟨112⟩-single crystal, $\epsilon$ = 15%. ◇ ⟨111⟩-single crystal, $\epsilon$ = 13%. + polycrystal, $\epsilon$ = 15%.

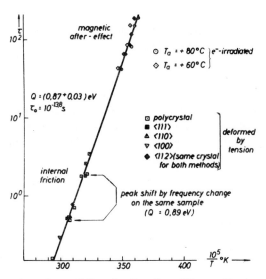

Fig. 24. Temperature dependence of the relaxation time $\tau(T)$ according to measurements of the magnetic after effect (points at the upper part of the straight line) and of the internal friction (points at the lower part of the straight line) [57].

## 6.2.2. Interpretation of experimental results

The magnetic relaxation measurements have shown clearly that the isochronal relaxation peak, which is observed at 10°C after electron or neutron irradiation, must be attributed to an orientation after effect. Seeger et al. [1–3, 57] have proposed that this relaxation may be interpreted as the reorientation of the tetragonal interstitial atoms shown in fig. 9d. The relaxation process of this defect was described in subsection 5.2.

Let us now consider whether or not the internal friction measurements, shown in fig. 22 and fig. 23, are compatible with the interpretation given for the magnetic relaxation measurements. From the annealing curves of the relaxation amplitude, which are represented in fig. 23, we may conclude that at least two types of relaxation processes contribute to the internal friction. One of these processes shows no significant dependence on the crystal orientation and has annealed out at 90°C. The other relaxation process corresponds to the shoulders of the annealing curves shown in fig. 23. This process is strongly dependent on the crystal orientation and has annealed out at 100°C. This second relaxation process is not observed in a crystal with ⟨100⟩-orientation. This latter relaxation process can be considered as the analogue to the magnetic relaxation [10]. The large internal friction peak observed below the annealing temperature of 90°C must, according to Seeger and Wagner [11], be interpreted as an induced Snoek effect [68, 69] which results from an interaction of the dislocations with the reorientable interstitial atoms. As shown by Schoeck [68] and Seeger and Schoeck [69] the dislocations which oscillate under the influence of the applied stress field, induce by their own stress field additional reorientations of the interstitial atoms. This process involves mainly the interstitial atoms in the neighbourhood of dislocations. Since the annealing of these interstitial atoms requires only a few atomic jumps, the induced Snoek effect will anneal out at lower temperatures than the relaxation process of the free interstitials. This model explains qualitatively the appearance of two types of relaxation processes as well as the different orientation dependences. The relaxation process remaining after an annealing treatment at 90°C is due to free interstitial atoms which anneal out at 100°C. The latter relaxation process is amplitude independent in accordance with the predictions of section 3.2 [11]. The measured orientation dependence corresponds to that of a defect with tetragonal symmetry. According to eq. (3.24) and eq. (3.51) the logarithmic decrement of tetragonal defects of ⟨100⟩-crystals is given by

$$2\pi \, \text{tg} \, \delta = \frac{\Delta W}{W_0} = \pi \frac{C_0}{kT} \frac{(A-B)^2}{2S'+S} \frac{\omega\tau}{1+(\omega\tau)^2} . \tag{6.6}$$

Eq. (6.6) may be used to determine either the dipole strength $A - B$ or the concentration of the defects depending upon whether $C$ or $A - B$ are known. The dimensionless expression $\{(A-B)^2/6S'kT\} \, 1/\Omega$ ($\Omega$ = atomic volume) was calculated for copper by Seeger et al. [29]. The calculated value of 24 may also be used for Ni.

Eq. (6.6) may then be written as

$$\frac{\Delta W}{W_o} \approx 60 \, C_A \, \frac{\omega\tau}{1 + \omega\tau^2} \tag{6.7}$$

where $C_A = 6C_o\Omega$ corresponds to the atomic concentration of defects. The experimental results discussed so far cannot be interpreted as a relaxation due to divacancies or vacancy-impurity clusters. These interstitial-impurity defects are expected to have orthorhombic symmetry and therefore cannot account for the orientation dependence of the anelastic relaxation. For divacancies reorientation and migration energies have to be equal.

The experimental facts which support the interpretation of the measured relaxation phenomena as a dumbbell reorientation may be summarized as follows:
1. The defect has a lower symmetry than cubic since it gives rise to magnetic as well as anelastic after effects.
2. The symmetry of the defect is compatible with a tetragonal configuration;
3. The magnetic and the internal friction peak correspond to a reorientation of the symmetry axes without a shift of the centre of gravity of the defect.
4. The activation energy for rotation is $E^R = 0.87 \pm 0.03$ eV and the activation energy of migration is given by $E^M = 1.0$ eV.
5. The same activation energy $E^R$ is measured after electron and neutron irradiation by magnetic relaxation experiments as well as after plastic deformation by internal friction measurements.
6. The relaxation strength of the internal friction after an annealing treatment at $90°C$ is amplitude independent.

## 6.3. Relaxation spectrum in nickel above $90°K$
### 6.3.1. Experimental results
   i) Neutron irradiation in stage III
Vacancies and vacancy clusters in general are produced by quenching from high temperatures. If the quenching rate is of the order of $10^4 °K/s$ the vacancies present in thermal equilibrium at high temperatures are almost completely retained at the lower temperature. Another method for the production of vacancies consists in the irradiation of the crystal by neutrons in the temperature range of stage III.

In this temperature range the interstitial atoms anneal out during the irradiation. Since not all interstitial atoms annihilate with vacancies − a certain percentage will anneal out at dislocations, impurity atoms, or will form interstitial clusters − some of the vacancies will be stored in the crystal. The advantage of this technique for the production of vacancies is the possibility of investigating vacancies below stage IV without the disturbing effects due to migrating interstitial atoms.

Fig. 25 gives the relaxation amplitude $\Delta\chi(t_1, t_2, T)$ as measured after neutron irradiation at $\approx 90°C$ ($t_1 = 0.5$ min, and $t_2 = 15$ min). Narrow relaxation maxima are observed at $-25°C$, $-79°C$, $-98°C$ and $-118°C$. Above $0°C$ a broad relaxation maximum appears which shows some substructure at $\approx 40°C$ and $\approx 90°C$. Annealing

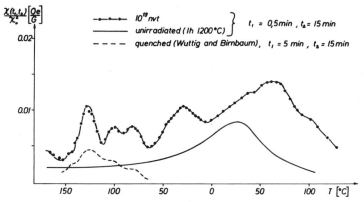

Fig. 25. Relaxation amplitudes of nickel after different treatments. —·—·— ⟨111⟩-Ni single crystal, neutron irradiated. Neutron dose $10^{19}$ n/cm$^2$. Irradiation temperature ≈90°C. The relaxation amplitude was determined for $t_1$ = 0.5 min and $t_2$ = 15 min. (After Seeger et al. [13] and Walz [14].) —— Middle oriented Ni single crystal. Unirradiated. Annealed for 1 h at 1200°C; $t_1$ = 0.5 min, $t_2$ = 15 min. (After Cantelli and Kronmüller [71].) - - - - - Polycrystalline quenched nickel sample. Quenched from 1000°C in CO–CO$_2$ atmosphere; $t_1$ = 5 min, $t_2$ = 15 min. (After Wutting and Birnbaum [12].)

experiments due to Beller [70] and Walz [14] have furthermore shown that the relaxation maxima anneal out in a wide temperature range between 100°C and 300°C. The activation energy measured for the annealing process increases continually from 0.5 eV below 200°C to 1.5 eV above 200°C.

ii) Magnetic relaxation in quenched nickel

Wuttig and Birnbaum [12] have measured the magnetic after effect in nickel after quenching from high temperatures. The quenched samples were annealed at 1000°C in a CO$_2$–CO atmosphere. After this treatment the residual resistivity ratio $R_{273°K}/R_{4.2°K}$ was of the order of 1000. This large ratio shows that the concentration of dissolved impurities was rather small. Under these conditions it must be expected that the quenched in vacancy concentration is rather large because the vacancies find only few annealing centres. The isochronal relaxation curves as measured by Wuttig and Birnbaum after quenching is represented in fig. 25 for $t_1$ = 5 min and $t_2$ = 15 min. A comparison of the relaxation curves in the irradiated and the quenched samples shows that in the quenched sample the relaxation curve reveals a significant substructure at the temperatures −80°C, −100°C and −120°C where we observe also maxima in the irradiated sample. It is not clear from the measurements of Wuttig and Birnbaum [12] whether the maxima found at −25°C and 90°C in the irradiated sample are present in the quenched samples or not. The magnetic after effect as measured by Wuttig and Birnbaum anneals out in a temperature range between 30°C and 170°C.

iii) Magnetic relaxation in as-grown Ni-single crystals

The magnetic after effect in as-grown single crystals of purity 99.8% (annealed 1 h at 1200°C) was measured by Cantelli and Kronmüller [71] in the temperature range between 90°K and 100°C. The results represented in fig. 25 reveal a relatively broad relaxation maximum at ≈40°C. At lower temperatures the relaxation amplitude decreases smoothly with decreasing temperature.

6.3.2. Analysis and interpretation of experimental results

The isochronal relaxation curve of the irradiated crystal suggests that the maxima observed below 0°C are due to simple relaxation processes which are superimposed on a background after effect. It must be expected that this background after effect corresponds to the relaxation curve measured in the as-grown crystal. This is supported by the fact that in the neutron irradiated crystal at ≈40°C appears a shoulder in the relaxation peak which may correspond to the 40°C maximum found in the as-grown crystal. The background after effect can be eliminated from the relaxation curve of the neutron irradiated crystal by subtracting both relaxation curves from each other. The relaxation curve resulting from this procedure can be analysed considering orientation, diffusion, and combined after effects. The result of such an analysis is shown in fig. 26. It is found that the relaxation maxima below 0°C may be attributed to orientation after effects, whereas the half-width of the relaxation maximum at 80°C is compatible with a diffusion after effect. Every relaxation peak can be described by a unique activation energy and one atomic jump frequency. In the case of the orientation after effect peaks the activation energy for reorientation was determined from the shift of $T_{max}$ with decreasing $t_2$ according to the method described in section 4.2. The activation energy of the diffusion after effect was determined from isothermal relaxation curves according to a method proposed by Seeger et al. [16]. In particular the analysis shows that the relaxation peak at −25°C decomposes into two orientation after effect peaks at −40°C and −20°C. Furthermore it is found that the activation energies for the relaxation peak at −20°C and +80°C are nearly the same thus suggesting that they are due to a combined after effect.

The interpretation of the observed relaxation peaks has to start from the fact that in the neutron irradiated crystal no free interstitial atoms are present. In fact, the isochronal annealing curves as measured by Walz [14] reveal no stage III, as must be expected in this case. The defects we are dealing with therefore are vacancies, vacancy clusters, clusters of interstitials or clusters of interstitials and vacancies with impurity atoms. The measurements of Wuttig and Birnbaum [12] on the magnetic relaxation in quenched nickel show that vacancy-type defects are involved in the relaxation peaks at −79°C, −98°C and −118°C (see fig. 25). Since the relaxation peaks observed below 0°C do not anneal out below 120°C they presumably are due to the reorientation of vacancy clusters with no long range migration. Vacancy clusters which are able to give rise to an orientation after effect without annealing out are trivacancies in the 60°-configuration and their compounds with impurity atoms. The latter defect is found by replacing atom number 1 in fig. 13 by an impurity

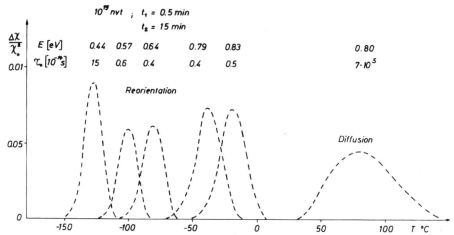

Fig. 26. Theoretical analysis of the isochronal relaxation curve of the neutron irradiated Ni single crystal. The time constant of the diffusion peak at $T_{max}$ is given by $\tau_D = 7 \times 10^5$ s.

atom. Therefore we ascribe the peaks at $-118°C$, $-98°C$ and $-79°C$ to trivacancies and their clusters with impurity atoms.

Since according to the experimental results the orientation peak at $-20°C$ and the diffusion peak at $\approx 80°C$ possess the same activation energy they presumably can be ascribed to a combined after effect. The most simple vacancy cluster which can account for such an after effect is the divacancy. The relaxation spectrum of this defect has been discussed in section 5.4. For the activation energy of the orientation after effect $E_{2V}^M = 0.83$ eV is found whereas the diffusion after effect is described at best by $E_{2V}^M = 0.80$ eV. In both cases the frequency factor $v_o^{-1} \exp(-S/k)$ $= 0.5 \times 10^{-14}$ s was used. The difference between the two activation energies may be due to the fact that different types of domain walls contribute to the diffusion after effect while the present calculation was performed only for the $(112)-180°$-wall.

In the discussion so far given we have not considered the physical reasons why divacancies and trivacancies are present together with single vacancies. This question has been investigated by Schottky [60], De Jong and Koehler [72] as well as by Seeger et al. [73–76]. According to these authors the formation of vacancy clusters is due to the binding energy between the vacancies. In thermal equilibrium the concentration $C_n$ of the vacancy cluster consisting of $n$ vacancies is given by

$$C_n = \gamma_n C_{1V}^n \exp(\Delta S_n/kT) \exp(E_{nV}^B/kT) , \qquad (6.8)$$

where the total concentration of defects, $C$, is given by

$$C = \sum_n nC_{nV} .$$

In eq. (6.8) the following quantities were introduced:

$C_{1V}$ = concentration of single vacancies

$E_{nV}^B$ = binding energy of the $n$th vacancy cluster

$\gamma_n$ = constant depending on the defect configuration with $\gamma_2 = 6$ and $\gamma_3 = 8$.

$\Delta S_{nV}$ = binding entropy of the $n$th vacancy cluster.

Eq. (6.8) shows that the concentration of trivacancies must be expected to be smaller than the concentration of divacancies since $C_{nV}$ is proportional to $C_{nV}^n$. The fact that trivacancies in spite of their small concentration give rise to an observable orientation after effect may be due to a large interaction constant $\epsilon$.

Due to the presence of vacancy clusters the annealing process is not controlled by a unique activation energy. A detailed investigation shows [73, 74, 76] that at small concentrations of vacancies the annealing process is controlled by the migration energy of single vacancies whereas at large densities of vacancies the annealing process is controlled by the migration energy of divacancies. The latter result is due to the fact that on the one hand the divacancies possess a smaller migration energy than single vacancies and on the other hand the concentration of divacancies according to eq. (6.8) increases proportional to $C_{1V}^2$. At an average density of vacancies the effective migration energy is given by [73, 74]

$$E^M = E_2^M - E_{2V}^B . \qquad (6.9)$$

The migration energy defined by eq. (6.9) in any case is smaller than $E_{2V}^M = 0.83$ eV. In order to understand the measured activation energy of 0.5 eV at 120°C we must put $E_{2V}^B = 0.33$ eV. A value of this order of magnitude for $E_{2V}^B$ was also determined by Mehrer et al. [67] from annealing measurements of the initial susceptibility in neutron irradiated Ni crystals and by Mughrabi and Seeger [77] from annealing experiments of the electrical resistivity in quenched Ni foils.

These experiments have shown that the recovery process in the temperature range between 120°C and 300°C after neutron-irradiation and quenching can fully be explained by a divacancy mechanism.

The experimental facts supporting the interpretation of the maxima at −25°C and 80°C as the combined after effect of divacancies according to Seeger et al. [13] can be summarized as follows:

1. The relaxation maxima at −20°C and 80°C are only found if by the sample treatment the production of vacancies is favoured.

2. The orientation after effect at −20°C and the diffusion after effect at 80°C have the same activation energy (0.80−0.83 eV).

3. Recovery experiments have shown that the orientation after effect and the diffusion after effect anneal out simultaneously [14, 70].

4. The kinetics and the effective activation energy ($> 0.5$ eV, $< 1.5$ eV) of the annealing of orientation and diffusion after effect can be explained by a divacancy mechanism [77, 70, 14].

5. The electrical resistivity of quenched Ni foils anneals out similarly to the orientation after effect at −25°C [77].

## Acknowledgements

The author is indebted to Prof. A. Seeger for helpful discussions and much valuable advice. He also would like to thank Dr.H.Mehrer for the numerical calculation of the diffusion after effect. He is further indebted to Dr. H.Blythe for supervising the English version of the paper.

## References

[1] A.Seeger, P.Schiller and H.Kronmüller, Phil. Mag. 5 (1960) 853.

[2] H.Kronmüller, A Seeger and P.Schiller, Z. Naturforsch. 15a (1961) 740.

[3] A.Seeger, H.Kronmüller, P.Schiller and H.Jäger, Radiation Damage in Solids (Rend. Scuola Intern. Fis. "Enrico Fermi" XVIII Corso) (Academic Press, New York–London, 1962) p. 809.

[4] P.Moser, D.Dautreppe and P.Brissonneau, Compt. Rend. Acad. Sci. Paris 250 (1960) 3963.

[5] E.Balthesen, K.Isebeck and H.Wenzl, Phys. Stat. Sol. 8 (1965) 593, 603.

[6] H.Rieger, Z. Metallk. 54 (1963) 229.

[7] H.Jäger, Z.Metallk. 55 (1964) 17.

[8] P.Peretto, P.Moser and D.Dautreppe, Compt. Rend. Acad. Sci. Paris 258 (1964) 499.

[9] P.Peretto, P.Moser and D.Dautreppe, Phys. Stat. Sol. 13 (1966) 325;
P.Peretto, J.L.Oddou, C.Minier-Cassayre, D.Dautreppe and P.Moser, Phys. Stat. Sol. 16 (1966) 281.

[10] H.Kronmüller, H.-E.Schaefer and H.Rieger, Phys. Stat. Sol. 9 (1965) 863.

[11] A.Seeger and F.J.Wagner, Phys. Stat. Sol. 9 (1965) 583.

[12] M.Wuttig and H.K.Birnbaum, J. Phys. Chem. Solids 27 (1966) 225.

[13] A.Seeger, F.Walz and H.Kronmüller, J. Appl. Phys. 38 (1967) 1312.

[14] F.Walz, Phys. Stat. Sol. 29 (1968) 245.

[15] J.Völkl and W.Schilling, Phys. Kondens. Materie 1 (1963) 296.

[16] A.Seeger, H.Kronmüller.and H.Rieger, Z. angew. Phys. 18 (1965) 377.

[17] A.Seeger, in: Magnetismus, Struktur und Eigenschaften magnetischer Festkörper (Intern. Conf. Magnetismus, held in Dresden, VEB Deutscher Verlag für Grundstoffindustrie, Leipzig, 1967) p. 160.

[18] A.Seeger and H.Kronmüller, in: Relaxation in Solids (in Russian), ed. W.S.Postnikov (Metallurgia, Moscow, 1968).

[19] D.Dautreppe, in: Studies in Radiation Effects, ed. G.J.Dienes, Ser. A, Physical and Chemical (Gordon and Breach, New York, London, 1968).

[20] H.Kronmüller, Nachwirkung in Ferromagnetika (Springer-Verlag, Berlin-Heidelberg-New York, 1968).

[21] A.S.Nowick and W.R.Heller, Advan. in Phys. 12 (1963) 251; 14 (1965) 101.

[22] A.S.Nowick, Advan. in Phys. 16 (1967) 1.

[23] C.Zener. Elasticity and anelasticity in metals (University of Chicago Press, Chicago, 1948).

[24] D.P.Seraphim and A.S.Nowick, Acta Met. 9 (1961) 85.

[25] E.Kröner: Kontinuumstheorie der Versetzungen und Eigenspannungen (Springer-Verlag, Berlin-Göttingen-Heidelberg, 1958).

[26] J.B.Wachtman, Jr. and H.S.Peiser, J. Phys. Chem. Solids 27 (1966) 975.

[27] J.B.Wachtman, Jr. and L.R.Doyle, Phys. Res. 135A (1964) 276.

[28] J.B.Gibson, A.N.Goland, M.Milgram and G.H.Vineyard, Phys. Rev. 120 (1960) 1229.

[29] A.Seeger, E.Mann and R.von Jan, J. Phys. Chem. Solids 23 (1962) 639.

[30] M.V.Klein and H.Kronmüller, J. Appl. Phys. 33 (1962) 2191.

[31] R.A.Johnson, Phys. Rev. 134A (1964) 1329.

[32] Lord Rayleigh, Phil. Mag. 23 (1887) 225.

[33] J.A.Ewing, Proc. Roy. Soc. 46 (1889) 269.

[34] G.Richter, Ann. Physik 29 (1937) 605; 32 (1938) 683.

[35] J.L.Snoek, Physica 6 (1939) 161.

[36] J.L.Snoek, Physica 6 (1939) 591.

[37] J.L.Snoek, Physica 8 (1941) 711.

[38] L.Néel, J. Phys. Rad. 12 (1951) 339.

[39] L.Néel, J. Phys. Rad. 13 (1952) 249.

[40] H.Fahlenbrach, Naturwissenschaften 32 (1944) 302.

[41] H.Fahlenbrach and G.Sommerkorn, Techn. Mitt. Krupp 15 (1957) 161.

[42] H.D.Dietze, Techn. Mitt. Krupp 17 (1959) 67.

[43] T.Boesono, G.J.Ernst, M.C.Lemmens, M.J.Van Langen and G.De Vries, Phys. Stat. Sol. 19 (1967) 107.

[44] P.Weiss, J. Phys. 6 (1907) 661.

[45] G.Rathenau, in: Magentic Properties of Metals and Alloys, ed. Am. Soc. Metals (Cleveland, Ohio, 1959) p. 168.

[46] G. De Vries, P.W. Van Geest, R.Van Gersdorf and G.W.Rathenau, Physica 25 (1959) 1131.

[47] G. De Vries, Physica 25 (1959) 1211.

[48] G.Rieder, Z. angew. Physik 9 (1957) 187.

[49] G.Rieder, Abhandl. Braunschweig. Wiss. Ges. 11 (1959) 20.

[50] M.V.Klein, Phys. Stat. Sol. 2 (1962) 881.

[51] A.Seeger, in: Handbuch der Physik, Band VII/1 (Springer-Verlang, Berlin-Göttingen-Heidelberg, 1955) p. 383.

[52] A.Seeger, in: Proc. 2nd Intern. Conf. on Peaceful Uses of Atomic Energy, vol. 6, Genèva (United Nations, New York, 1958) p. 250.

[53] W.Frank, A.Seeger and G.Schottky, Phys. Stat. Sol. 8 (1965) 345.

[54] W.Bauer, A.Seeger and A.Sosin, Phys. Letters 24A (1967) 195.

[55] D.K.Holmes, J.W.Corbett, R.M.Walker, J.S.Koehler and F.Seitz, in: Proc. 2nd Intern. Conf. on Peaceful Uses of Atomic Energy, Geneva, vol. 6 (United Nations, New York, 1958) p. 274.

[56] R.W.Balluffi, J.S.Koehler and R.O.Simmons, in: Recovery and Recrystallization of Metals, ed. L.Himmel (Internscience Publishers, Inc., New York, 1963) p. 1.

[57] A.Seeger, H.Kronmüller, H.-E.Schaefer and F.J.Wagner, Phys. Letters 16 (1965) 110.

[58] D.Schumacher, W.Schüle and A.Seeger, Z.Naturforsch. 17a (1962) 228.

[59] P.Peretto, Thesis, University of Grenoble, 1967.

[60] G.Schottky, Z.Physik 159 (1960) 584; 160 (1960) 16.

[61] G.De Keating-Hart, R.Cope, C.Minier and P.Moser, Jül. Conf. 2 (Vol. 1) 1968, p. 327.

[62] J.L.Oddou, Thesis, University of Grenoble, 1967.

[63] A.Sosin and J.A.Brinkman, Acta Met. 7 (1959) 478.

[64] P.Simson and R.Sizman, Z.Naturforsch. 17a (1962) 596.

[65] F.Bell and O.Krisement, Z.Metallk. 53 (1962) 115.

[66] F.Bell and O.Krisement, Acta Met. 10 (1962) 81.

[67] H.Mehrer, H.Kronmüller and A.Seeger, Phys. Stat. Sol. 10 (1965) 725.

[68] G.Schoeck, Phys. Rev. 102 (1956) 1458.

[69] G.Schoeck, and A.Seeger, Acta Met. 7 (1959) 469.

[70] M.Beller, Diplomarbeit, Universität Stuttgart (unveröffentlicht), 1965.

[71] R.Cantelli and H.Kronmüller, unpublished results.

[72] M.De Jong and J.S.Koehler, Phys. Rev. 129 (1963) 40.

[73] A.Seeger, V.Gerold and M.Rühle, Z. Metallk. 54 (1963) 493.

[74] A.Seeger, V.Gerold, K.P.Chik and M.Rühle, Phys. Letters 5 (1963) 107.
[75] A.Seeger, Phys. Letters 9 (1964) 311.
[76] A.Seeger and D.Schumacher, in: Lattice Defects in Quenched Metals (Academic Press, New York, 1965) p. 15.
[77] H.Mughrabi and A.Seeger, Phys. Stat. Sol. 19 (1967) 251.

## Discussion

*H.I.Dawson:* 1. If there is random interstitial diffusion in $I_E$ and close pair recombination in $I_C$, stage $I_D$ could involve a process somewhere in between these two, such as correlated diffusion, or could also be due to close pair recombinations. If one therefore observes magnetic permeability effects in $I_C$ and $I_E$, does one not also expect to find this in $I_D$? Also in view of the closeness of what you call $I_E$, with respect to $I_C$, is it not possible that $I_E$ should be labelled $I_D$?

2. From your experiments on Ni you conclude that stage III is due to dumbbell migration in agreement with the Stuttgart interpretation. How about stage III of Au, Ag, and Cu? I think there is strong evidence that there are more complex stages.

*H.Kronmüller:* 1. The analysis of the magnetic after effect spectrum as discussed here is based on experimental results due to Peretto et al. [9]. These authors conclude from their measurements that the recovery stage $I_D$ found in the recovery of the residual resistivity has no analogue in the recovery of the magnetic after effect. According to Peretto et al. [9] the maximum recovery rate of the residual resistivity in $I_D$ takes place at 53°K whereas the maximum recovery rate of the magnetic after effect is found in $I_E$ at about 68°K. As outlined in the review article, however, it is doubtful whether there is in fact no magnetic annealing at about 55°K, say in stage $I_D$. Further experiments must be undertaken in order to clarify definitively whether in $I_D$ a magentic after effect takes place or not.

Assuming for the present discussion the conclusions of Peretto to be correct the missing $I_D$ − magnetic after effect can be interpreted if the following points are taken into account:
(i) Point defects give rise to a magnetic after effect only if they are establishing a thermodynamic equilibrium with respect to the magnetic interaction energy.
(ii) Close pairs are expected to produce an after effect if their interstitial atom possesses nearest neighbour positions with the same distance from the vacancy. Frenkel pairs of this type are the configurations ⟨112⟩, ⟨103⟩ and ⟨123⟩. (For details see review article.)
According to the statements (i) and (ii) we therefore must interpret $I_D$ to be due to close pairs with interstitial atoms being not able to reorient their dumbbell axis by a jump to an equivalent nearest neighbour site. Close pairs of this kind are the ⟨100⟩-configurations.

2. The Stuttgart model for stage III also is assumed to hold for Au, Ag, and Cu.

In particular for copper a number of experimental facts represented on the conference by Frank support this interpretation strongly. Also for Au and Ag the interstitial model for stage III is a reliable model. As long as no direct evidences for a
freely migrating defect in stage I of Au are given we must allow for free interstitial
migration in stage III. This model does not exlude the fact that in the temperature
range of stage III also vacancy clusters are mobile. As discussed in may paper also
in Ni the annealing of divacancies takes place in the temperature range of stage III.

*M.Wuttig:* Would you care to present your interpretation of the disaccommodation
maxima found in quenched Ni by Wuttig and Birnbaum?
   Please state the irradiation temperature of your neutron irradiated nickel.

*H.Kronmüller:* The relaxation maxima found by Wuttig and Birnbaum in quenched
Ni at about $-100°C$ also were detected by Seeger et al. [13] and Walz [14] in Ni
single crystals after neutron irradiated at $+90°C$. It is suggested that this relaxation is
due to trivacancies (in the $60°$-configuration) and their agglomerates with impurity
atoms (see fig. 13). This is supported by the fact that the observed orientation after
effect anneals out at rather high temperatures $(50°C-250°C)$. If the relaxation maxima at about $-100°C$ are interpreted as a divacancy reorientation one would expect
a diffusion after effect and recovery of this after effect at about $-60°C$. The activation energies measured for the after effect and for the recovery should be equal. In
the temperature range in question, however, this is not observed.

*D.Dautreppe:* Just a comment on the close pairs. In Ni we found magnetic after-
effect zones associated with $I_B$ and $I_C$, but in the iron case no such zones are found.
This difference can be explained only by symmetry considerations. To get a magnetic
after effect one needs equivalent sites around the vacancy, and these sites must be
first neighbours between them if we want a second neighbour jump which can lead
to annihilation. In iron the equivalent sites are not first neighbours between them,
but in nickel such sites can be found.

# STUDY OF POINT DEFECTS BY MEANS OF
# DISLOCATION PINNING EFFECTS

A.SOSIN

*Department of Physics and Division of Materials Science and Engineering,
University of Utah, Salt Lake City, Utah, USA*

## 1. Introduction

In a conference on vacancies and interstitials in metals, it is reasonable to assume that the emphasis in a discussion of dislocation pinning effects should be on the pinners, interstitials and vacancies, rather than the pinned defect, the dislocations. I shall attempt to give precedence to point defects but any attempt to relegate dislocations to purely passive counters is doomed to failure. In fact, some of the most fascinating problems lie in the study of the nature of the point defect-dislocation interaction itself, with no regard to how the point defects may have originated or how they may have found their way to dislocation lines. Accordingly, an appreciable portion of this discussion will be directed to these problems, as well.

Two review articles [1,2] have appeared in rather recent times which present many of the detailed features of this subject. In addition, a conference was held just this summer in Harwell [3] devoted to this subject. Thus, the investigator who would care to acquaint himself with the literature is directed to these sources for fuller references. The purpose here is to highlight the problems, those problems which we believe are most appropriate and propitious for early study.

## 2. The basic model

The bulk of the observations in the field of dislocation pinning are profitably, if not precisely, described by the Granato-Lücke [4] theory, based on the original Koehler [5] vibrating string model. In this formulation, the dislocation is given all the attributes of a string — line tension, mass per unit length, etc. — and the atomic details are largely ignored. The dislocations are assumed to lie in reasonably straight lines, in the absence of stresses. The length of the individual segments of dislocation strings is determined by the presence of pinning points. In ordinary, well-annealed samples, such pinning points are best typified by impurities, dislocation jogs, and

729

nodal points in the dislocation network. Lattice defects produced by quenching, irradiation, or deformation may serve as additional pinning points. We shall be most concerned with the effects of these additional pinning points here, although the case of pinning by select impurity atoms is in evident parallel.

In terms of the vibrating-string model, the physical basis for the modulus and internal friction effects resides in the fact that dislocation motion constitutes a strain within the material and vibratory motion involves energy dissipation. The strain due to dislocation motion adds to the normal elastic strain, making the apparent modulus of the material appear lower. The energy loss contributing to the internal friction is typical of oscillatory motions in which a phase difference exists between stress and strain. Clearly, the contribution to internal friction should depend on frequency of the applied stress-one expects that the modulus contribution should be independent of frequency but should depend on line tension.

Within this framework, the development of the model depends on the solution of the damped oscillator equation

$$m \frac{d^2x}{dt^2} + B \frac{dx}{dt} + Kx = \sigma_0 \exp(i\omega t) , \qquad (1)$$

where $m$ is the mass per unit length of dislocation, $B$ is the damping constant which gives rise to energy losses and, therefore, to internal friction effects, and $K$ is the line tension of the dislocation. The applied stress is $\sigma$, a periodic stress with angular frequency $\omega$.

The boundary conditions on this equation are that displacements at the end are zero: $x = 0$ when $y = 0$ and $y = l$, where $l$ is the loop length between pinning points. The solution of eq. (1) shows that the dislocation motion has a resonance character with a natural frequency. The position of the natural frequency is a function of line tension, loop length, and damping constant. Since the loop length is shortened by irradiation (and it is fair to assume that the damping constant and line tension are relatively unaffected), irradiation is an excellent technique for shifting the natural frequency. This method has been used by Alers and Thompson [6] and by Stern and Granato [7] to obtain a very controlled test of the theoretical basis.

Experimental studies designed for the investigation of point defects are frequently performed at frequencies well below the natural dislocation frequency. In the lower frequency range, Granato and Lücke give the following expressions for the logarithmic decrement and modulus defect, valid in the amplitude-independent range:

$$\delta_{\mathrm{I}} = (120 \ \omega\Omega B/\pi^3 K) N l^4 \qquad (2)$$

and

$$\frac{\Delta Y}{Y} = \left( \frac{6\Omega}{\pi^2} \right) N l^2 \approx \tfrac{1}{5} N l^2 . \qquad (3)$$

In eqs. (2) and (3), $\Omega$ is an orientation factor which takes into account the fact that the force on a dislocation is determined by the resolved shear stress on the glide plane, a quantity which is less than the applied stress. Averaging over all the possible glide planes yields the approximate factor of $\frac{1}{5}$ in eq. (3).

In the amplitude-dependent range, Granato and Lücke propose that dislocations break away from weaker pinning points such as impurity atoms, vacancies, etc., but not from strong pinning points such as dislocation nodes. In the case of a single pinning species, with each pinner isolated (no clustering), breakaway from one weak pinning point is catastrophic in that breakaway occures along an entire line of dislocation between nodal points, unzipping the dislocation from all the weak pinning points. A hysteric energy loss arises, and the corresponding damping is

$$\delta_H = (\alpha_1 \, N l_N^3 / T D_W^2) \exp\left[-(\alpha_2/T l_W)\right] \,, \tag{4}$$

where $\alpha_1$ and $\alpha_2$, constants entailing dislocation parameters, are not of great significance here. The dislocation length between nodal points is $l_N$; $l_W$ is the dislocation length between weak pinning points. The important feature of eq. (4) is the exponential dependence.

## 3. Dislocation pinning

The use of dislocation pinning experiments in damage production studies has been most rewarding, indeed. Nevertheless, more remains for study than has been examined to date.

Considering irradiation studies primarily, the following observations have been made, mainly in copper:

1. Dislocation pinning rates, interpreted in terms of the number of pinners on dislocations at any particular irradiation fluence, parallel bulk defect production rates (as measured, most generally by residual electrical resistivity measurements). However, the ratio of interstitials and vacancies created in the lattice (removed from dislocations) to those created at dislocations plus those transported dynamically (presumable through focusing processes) reflects the importance of focusing, particularly in gold, compared with copper. Furthermore, "subthreshold" displacements are apparent in pinning studies as in resistivity measurements.

2. A fit between observed damage rates and the Granato-Lücke theory is found only when two independent types of dislocations are hypothesized. The original discovery of distinct dislocation types was made by Thompson and Holmes [8] and has been verified by Alers and Thompson [6], by Stern and Granato [7], and by Keefer et al. [9] observing amplitude-independent internal friction changes. Gruzin and Zharov [10] have also suggested the existence of two types, based on amplitude-dependent internal friction studies. The nature of these dislocations remains obscure although it is tempting to make the obvious assignment of edge and screw types. The mark of distinction between these two types is the rate at which

they are pinned – their pinning cross-sections. A difference in pinning rate can be rationalized by referring to the strength of the strains in the near-core regions and the relationship to defocusing; this rationalization remains purely conjectural at present. Obviously, it would be desirable to irradiate samples with purely screw or edge components. An important feature of the two-dislocation observation is that the pinning rates of "hard" and "soft" dislocations are in a common ratio for copper and gold. A second feature which is less well fitted into the above speculation is the observation that the relative pinning rates are essentially unchanged even if the irradiation is carried out above stage I where the absolute rates are much higher, reflecting diffusion of interstitials also.

In the absence of a detailed model, it is surprising that the ability of dislocations to "snare" point defects is not quite different depending on whether these defects are dynamically projected past dislocations or thermally migrate into the dislocation vicinity.

3. In general, low temperature recovery stages (i.e., stages in which resistivity decreases are rather inevitably observed) correspond to pinning. From a purely phenomenological point of view, this is a rather intriguing set of circumstances; most properties exhibit true recovery in that the properties tend to pre-irradiation values. But internal friction and elastic moduli actually anti-recover, i.e. they proceed to values further removed from pre-irradiation values. Of course, there is nothing mystic about this. Even an elementary picture of defects predicts this behavior.

4. However, the recovery of pinning phenomena, even at nominally low temperatures, is uneven. Internal friction and moduli measurements do show some "depinning" effect – small in copper, but readily apparent in aluminum and gold. The issues raised by these sequential pinning and depinning stages poses difficulty in interpretation. Assume, as it appears obvious, that interstitials are accumulated on dislocations in stage I and that these interstitials are unable at this temperature to diffuse along dislocations after arrival. (Even this may appear somewhat surprising in that one normally expects "pipe" diffusion to proceed more easily than bulk diffusion). However, observations of pipe diffusion have always involved diffusion of impurity atoms, quite different than interstitials diffusion when one considers that diffusion of self interstitials really proceeds by an interstitialcy mechanism which should be easier in the bulk than along the dislocation core. Subsequent depinning is then most logically related to release of interstitials from dislocations, with eventual annihilation or trapping in the bulk, or diffusion along dislocations to nodes, to regions of interstitial segregation, etc. The question then arises: what is the mechanism responsible for the further pinning stages? One obvious answer is vacancy pinning. This then gives rise to still another question: why don't interstitials and vacancies interact more frequently on dislocations? Still another related question is: how does one account for the *four* pinning stages observed in copper? Let us turn to the first of these.

5. The arrival of vacancies at dislocations has been demonstrated in a more direct way by quenching experiments. Keefer et al. [9] have observed dislocation pinning in quenched gold and copper, although the quenching rates in these experiments are very much slower than in typical quenching experiments designed for resistivity measurements. The importance of these measurements is that they readily identify which pinning stages following irradiation are due to vacancies. The answer is that the highest temperature pinning stages are due to vacancy pinning.

6. Limited to only the observations mentioned thus far, the presence of a multiplicity of pinning stages in copper can be easily accommodated. One need merely to attribute the second and third pinning stages to interstitials released from impurity traps. This explanation runs afoul of the stage III dilemma, so well known to the attendees at this conference. Thus, it is important to examine more closely how pinning experiments shed light on this dilemma.

The first report concerning the characteristics of stage III using pinning measurements was made by Keefer et al. [9]. The observations consisted of showing that the third of the four peaks, centered at about $225°K$, was governed by an activation energy of approximately 0.6 eV. The measurements were made at a reduced reference temperature, using a pulsing technique. The number of defects involved in this pinning stage were large relative to related experiments discussed shortly. Furthermore, in these same experiments, pinning at lower temperatures was also observed. And still further, the quenching experiments mentioned earlier revealed a pinning stage higher in temperature than this stage III process. Finally, the activation energy agrees, within the accuracy of the measurement, to the energy reported from resistivity measurements.

This apparently clear picture is complicated by the subsequent measurements of Thompson et al. [11]. In these experiments (using gamma irradiation), measurements were made *at* temperature of bombardment (333 to $393°K$) and the instantaneous and total defect concentrations were extremely low. Analyzing the earlier, simpler data, Thompson et al. reported an activation energy of 0.64 eV, in reasonable agreement with stage III values. However, the fascinating facet of this work is the absence of any indication of pinning by a defect which would migrate at an energy characteristic of stage I, namely about 0.12 eV. Thompson et al. make a most convincing case that migration by such a defect cannot be a factor in their results and that the diffusion of this defect occurs from the point of creation to the dislocation line with no sensible intermediate trapping. They agree that migration of a vacancy defect is ruled out by considerations of energy; a vacancy migration energy below 0.85 eV simply cannot be consistent with all other pertinent measurements. The conclusion which follows is that stage III represents a primordial interstitial defect.

But, again, what has happened to the "stage I defect" — the interstitial which migrates with an energy of 0.12 eV? Here, Thompson et al. agree with the suggestion of Bauer et al. [12] that there are indeed two types of interstitial defects and that the stage I interstitial is thermally unstable, converting to the stage III interstitial form with greater frequency at higher temperatures. The inescapable prediction which follows from this model is that irradiation at temperatures intermediate to stage I and stage III should produce a significantly higher concentration of persisting defects than irradiating below stage I, then warming to the intermediate range. Clearly, an experimental demonstration of this would constitute a critical experiment — in a field where critical experiments are infrequent.

The investigators at Atomics International have elaborated the model of thermal interstitial conversion. Bauer (unpublished) made appropriate resistivity measurements but was unable to discern a resolvable difference, perhaps due to the overlapping effects of stage II (release from impurities). Keefer [13] used dislocation pinning techniques and has uncovered a significant set of thermally-effected phenomena. In fact, it is the complexity of the phenomena which has forced Keefer to limit his interpretation to the level of speculation. Without going into the fine points of Keefer's observations, the succinct results are that the number of pinning points added to dislocations in the range from $75°K$ to $150°K$ depend on the temperature of irradiation and subsequent heating schedule. Some portion of these results appear to be most closely connected with dislocation characteristics. However, Keefer was also able to separate out effects which could be ascribed to an interstitial-conversion mechanism. The observation was that the magnitude of stage III was about 12% larger when the sample was irradiated at $150°K$ as compared to $77°K$. With this observation, one may estimate the energy for conversion: 0.15 eV, approximately. The fact that this energy is greater than the 0.12 eV is an important test on consistency. It would appear, therefore, that the conversion model is supported, if not confirmed, by pinning measurements.

Unfortunately, the hope that firm evidence in favor of one model is being achieved is rather diminished by the recent work of Winterhager and Lücke [3]. They irradiated copper samples with gamma rays at $220°K$, then annealed to $390°K$. Two pinning stages were found in these measurements: at $260°K$ and at $350°K$. The lower temperature stage was found to be governed by activation energy of 0.69 eV; the upper, by 1.45 eV. In supporting evidence, not yet published, Winterhager and Lücke suggest that these two stages are due to defects which "do not annihilate each other but interact in such a way as if they were of the same type". The implication, and the conclusion reached by these investigators, is that the two stages are both due to vacancy migration. They do not offer any comments on the apparently lower energy of vacancy migration (0.69 eV) and do conclude that the 1.45 eV activation energy cannot be interpreted as indicating a vacancy-impurity binding energy of $1.45-0.69 = 0.76$ eV, based on considerations of the number of jumps this defect would be expected to make.

It is clear then, that the pinning data related to stage III is of great importance to a final resolution of this problem, but has not thus far offered the key.

## 4. On the nature of dislocation pinning

To a large extent, the previous discussion has been based on accepting disloca-tions as passive point defect counters, even though in the introduction we cautioned against this procedure. There are a number of experimental observations which indi-cate the complexity of the dislocation-point defect interaction, to which we shall re-fer now. With few exceptions, the information on this problem consists of experi-mental implications; in the discussions of these data, the investigators rather inevi-tably have been forced to avoid interpretation except in the vaguest of terms.

The conclusion, which we state before citing the observations, is that there exists a dearth of theoretical structure to aid in the interpretation of available data, let alone to guide further investigation.

We have already cited evidence for two dislocation types. This evidence is derived from examination of dislocation pinning rates in radiation experiments. Less direct evidence is available in copper and gold from the inverse effect, dislocation depin-ning − the process by which point defects are removed from dislocations at suffi-ciently elevated temperatures. The indirect nature of this evidence stems from the un-fortunate fact that, in these metals (particularly copper), depinning extends in a rather structureless manner over a rather long temperature range. Most recently, Lenz and Lücke [3] have reported parallel observations in lead. As is to be expected, depinning occurs at lower temperatures in lead so that Lenz and Lücke were able to examine the details of depinning working in the convenient temperature range from $260°K$ to $350°K$. As a very valuable experimental technique, they simultaneously measured pinning rates as a function of gamma dose rate, and depinning rates as a function of temperature. It is gratifying that they find that a decomposition of their data is achieved when two dislocation types are introduced into the analysis. Furthermore, the activation energy of the slower process (i.e., the higher tempera-ture process) is governed by an activation energy ($1.22$ eV) which is sufficiently high to exclude a simple release mechanism. Instead, a more complex, as yet unde-fined process must be invoked. This is in full agreement with the less detailed ob-servations in copper.

Apparently there is truly a parallel in dislocation-point defect interactions in f.c.c. metals. It is not too much to hope that eventual clarification should be aided by this "gift of the Gods".

The identification of the two dislocation types is yet to be made, as stated ear-lier. In itself, this is of casual interest. The implications are of greater interest. Is it sensible to assume that dislocations are indeed truly edge or screw over a distance of $\approx 10^4$ atom sites? What is the role of dislocation jogs and kinks? And a very tantal-izing question apropos this conference: what about interstitial-vacancy annihilation along dislocations?

The final answers to these questions are matters for future study. I would merely like to offer some conjecture which, I believe, is supported by available data.

In my opinion, the following situation is most likely to be true. If dislocation pinning occurs at sufficiently low temperatures, the pinners consist of interstitials which arrive at dislocations by an interstitialcy diffusion mechanism. These interstitials certainly relax somewhat in the neighborhood of the dislocation, whether in the region of an extended partial dislocation as in copper, or in the core region as in aluminum. The interstitial-dislocation binding energy may typically be of the order of 1 eV in copper, as predicted by Friedel [14] and by Bullough and Newman [15] and implied by the data of Thompson et al. [11], but may be somewhat less in gold. The intrinsic diffusional energy along a dislocation line is about 0.4 eV, where we are again guided by the data of Thompson et al. In addition, there exists a binding between dislocation jogs and interstitials with an energy (for emission back along the dislocation line) of 0.2 to 0.5 eV.

If these conjectures are correct, those interstitials which arrive at dislocations at low temperatures provide pinning points in situ. At somewhat higher temperatures, diffusion down dislocation lines occur. In this diffusion, a small fraction of pinners are "lost" (i.e., interstitials reach dislocation nodes), a small fraction of interstitials collide to form immobile dimers, and the largest number move to jogs. In this model, the contribution of jogs to dislocation pinning is minimal at ordinary stress levels so that the join between an interstitial and a jog does not imply the loss of pinning points.

If interstitials arrive at more elevated temperatures (i.e., in stage III), we envision a relaxation occurring immediately such that there is no need to invoke two interstitial defect types on dislocations. It is implied that interstitials arriving at dislocations at such temperatures would diffuse readily to jog sites.

The studies of Thompson et al. in copper which show, among other things, defect clustering, are accommodated by this model. Furthermore, by adjusting the values of the pertinent energies, it is possible to understand the relative absence of depinning in copper until elevated temperatures, as well as the presence of depinning at low temperatures in gold and aluminum.

The list of pertinent data and unanswered questions has hardly been exhausted in this discussion. No reference has been made to deformation studies and the accompanying data both on dislocation pinning and relaxation peak (i.e., Bordoni and Hasiguti peaks). Indeed, it is the abundance of such processes that complicate interpretation.

## Acknowledgement

The author would like to acknowledge the valuable years of collaboration with D.W.Keefer in this area of defect studies. This work was supported by the U.S. Atomic Energy Committee under Contract No. AT(11−1)1800.

# References

[1] D.O.Thompson and V.K.Paré, in: Physical Accoustics, Ed. W.P.Mason (Academic Press, New York, 1966).

[2] A.Sosin and D.W.Keefer, in: Microplasticity, Ed. C.J.McMahon Jr. (Interscience Publishers, New York, 1968).

[3] Proceedings of the Conference "On the Interactions between Dislocations and Point Defects", Harwell, United Kingdom, July 1968.

[4] A.Granato and K.Lücke, J. Appl. Phys. 27 (1956) 583, 789.

[5] J.S.Koehler, in: Imperfections in Nearly Perfect Crystals, Ed. W.Shockley (J.Wiley and Co., 1952) p. 297.

[6] G.A.Alers and D.O.Thompson, J. Appl. Phys. 32 (1961) 283.

[7] R.Stern and A.Granato, Acta Met. 10 (1962) 92, 358; J. Appl. Phys. 33 (1962) 458.

[8] D.O.Thompson and D.K.Holmes, J. Appl. Phys. 27 (1956) 713.

[9] D.W.Keefer, J.C.Robinson and A.Sosin, Acta Met. 13 (1965) 1135; 14 (1966) 1409.

[10] P.L.Gruzin and Yu.D.Zharov, Dokl. Akad. Nauk. SSSR 164 (1965) 1280.

[11] D.O.Thompson, O.Buck, R.S.Barnes and H.B.Huntington, J. Appl. Phys. 38 (1967) 3051; and succeeding articles.

[12] W.Bauer, A.Seeger and A.Sosin, Phys. Letters 24A (1967) 195.

[13] D.W.Keefer, Acta Met., in press.

[14] J.Friedel, Dislocations (Addison Wesley, New York, 1964).

[15] R.Bullough and R.C.Newman, Phil. Mag. 7 (1962) 529.

# QUENCH HARDENING AND IRRADIATION HARDENING
# OF FACE CENTRED CUBIC METALS

J. DIEHL

*Max-Planck-Institut für Metallforschung, Institut für Sondermetalle,*
*Stuttgart, Germany*

## 1. Introduction

The common feature of quenching and particle irradiation of metals is the introduction of point defects. These point defects can interact with dislocations and in
this way influence the mechanical behaviour of a metal. One of the consequences
of such point-defect-dislocation interactions is the hardening which is observed after
quenching or after fast particle irradiation. The main objective of basic point defect
hardening studies is to identify the type of defects that are responsible for the hardening, and the nature of the defect—dislocation interaction causing the hardening
in different metals and after various treatments. In many cases such an identification
requires the knowledge of the types and the properties of the defects present in the
metal. In other cases hardening studies can contribute to a more general analysis of
the distribution and the behaviour of the defects introduced in a certain type of
experiment. Examples for both cases are contained in the present review.

"Hardening" quite generally means an increase of the resistance against a macroscopic plastic deformation. A first and commonly used measure of such hardening
is the change of the yield stress, or, if single crystals are investigated, the change of
the critical resolved shear stress (CSS). Although the presence of point defects in
most cases not only influences the stress necessary to initiate a plastic deformation
but also the deformation processes and the work hardening behaviour during an
extensive deformation, we will confine the present discussion of point defect hardening to the changes of the yield stress or the critical shear stress.

Since we understand hardening as the increase of the resistance against a *macroscopic* deformation, we will use, whenever possible, definitions of the yield stress or
the CSS that describe the stress necessary for initiating extensive plastic deformation,
i.e., motions of dislocations over relatively large distances. In samples with a smooth
transition between the elastic and the plastic region a frequently used definition of
the mentioned kind is the extrapolation of the first (linear) part of the plastic region

of the stress-strain curve to zero plastic strain. For samples which show a yield phenomenon the lower yield stress or in some cases the upper yield stress is used. It has
to be mentioned that hardening experiments in which these definitions of the yield
stress or of the CSS are applied may give informations different from experimental
techniques, in which only small strains and small dislocation motions are involved,
as, e.g., micro-yield stress or internal friction measurements.

Since the early observations on quench hardening by Li, Washburn and Parker [1]
and Maddin and Cottrell [2] and the first systematic studies of irradiation hardening
by McReynolds et al. [3] a great number of papers has been published on these topics.
It cannot be the task of the present paper to give a review which includes the complete historical development of the field. The paper will be selective in the sense that
examples are discussed which according to the author's judgment help to elucidate
to what extent the fundamental mechanisms of quench hardening and irradiation
hardening in pure fcc metals are understood at present, and to indicate the most
important unsolved problems. This selective procedure can be justified most easily
in the field of quench hardening, for which excellent and comprehensive review
articles were published only a few years ago [4,5].

## 2. Hardening mechanisms

Quite a number of possible mechanisms of hardening in quenched and irradiated
metals have been proposed by various workers. Most of them can be classified in
three groups. These three groups of hardening mechanisms will be described briefly
in the following. Only the main characteristics of the hardening mechanisms will be
summarised in this section, which is intended to give the basis for the discussions of
the hardening in the more specialized cases which are treated in the later sections
of the paper in some detail.

### 2.1. Dispersed barrier hardening

This type of hardening is a very frequent one in quench and irradiation hardening.
The hardening is caused by localised dislocation obstacles, which are mostly assumed
to be randomly distributed in the lattice. The obstacles can be either individual point
defects or small point defect agglomerates in different configurations. Dislocations
moving under an applied stress in their glide plane are hindered in their motion by
these obstacles. Because of the interaction between obstacle and dislocation the dislocations will be held up at the obstacles and (under the applied stress) bow out in
between them, as indicated schematically in fig. 1a, in which the dislocation is
assumed to be forced to move downwards under an effective shear stress $\tau^*$.

The interaction between a dislocation and an obstacle is represented in fig. 1b
by the relation between the interaction force $f$ and the (shortest) distance between
the obstacle and the dislocation $x - x_0$ ($x_0$ location of the centre of the obstacle).
Due to the applied shear stress the dislocation is pressed against the obstacle with a

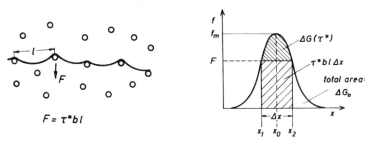

Fig. 1. Dispersed barrier hardening. (a) Geometrical arrangement in the slip plane; dislocation line is bowing out in between the obstacles (circles) under an applied stress. (b) Force-distance relation.

force $F$, which is, according to elementary dislocation theory,

$$F = \tau^* bl \tag{1}$$

($b$ is the modulus of the Burgers vector of the dislocation, $l$ means distance between neighbouring obstacles along the dislocation line — see fig. 1a).

Small obstacles can be overcome by the dislocation under the assistance of thermal activation. Without thermal activation the dislocation will approach the obstacle up to equilibrium position $x_1$, for which $f = F$. The narrowly hatched area in fig. 1b represents, according to Schoeck [6] (see also Frank [7]), the Gibbs free energy of activation $\Delta G$ for the overcoming of the obsctale *. This free energy of activation (which will be called simply activation energy in the following) determines the (shear) strain rate $\dot{a}$ of the sample

$$\dot{a} = \dot{a}_0 \exp(-\Delta G/kT) . \tag{2}$$

Equivalent to this equation is

$$\Delta G(\tau^*) = kT \log(\dot{a}_0/\dot{a}) . \tag{2b}$$

If all obstacles give rise to the same force-distance relation in the glide plane and are randomly distributed **, $\dot{a}_0$ should be a constant which contains the attempt frequency of the dislocations and geometrical factors, such as the number of dislocation segments pressed simultaneously against obstacles and the area swept out by a dislocation segment after passing the obstacle.

As can be seen from fig. 1b, the value of $\Delta G$ depends on $F$ and therefore on the effective shear stress $\tau^*$. The activation energy for zero stress, which is represented

---

* In earlier papers mostly $\Delta H$ instead of $\Delta G$ is used for the integral represented by this area.
** Deviations, which come in more complicated cases, will be discussed later.

by the total area under the force distance curve in fig. 1b, is called $\Delta G_0$ and can be taken as a characteristic value for the obstacle.

If the force distance relation $f(x)$ or the stress dependence of the activation energy $\Delta G(\tau^*)$ are known, the dependence of the shear stress $\tau^*$ on the deformation temperature $T$, the strain rate $\dot{a}$ and the obstacle density (represented by $l$) can be derived from eq. (2) by solving this equation for $\tau^*$. Some more qualitative conclusions can be obtained without a detailed knowledge of the functions $f(x)$ or $\Delta G(\tau^*)$:

(1) Since $\tau^*$ enters eq. (2) only through the term $\tau^*bl$, for constant temperature and strain rate, $\tau^*$ should be proportional to $1/l$ (at least to a first approximation, in which it can be assumed that a variation of $l$ influences $\log \dot{a}_0$ only little). In a random distribution $1/l$ will be proportional to the square root of the area density of the obstacles in the slip plane $N_A$, which is proportional to the volume density of the obstacles $c$. Therefore, the effective shear stress is expected to vary linearly with the square root of the obstacle concentration.

$$\tau^* \propto \sqrt{c} \qquad\qquad\qquad (3)$$

at constant strain rate and constant deformation temperature.

(2) If the assumption of a random distribution of obstacles of equal "size" is justified, the activation energy $\Delta G$ involved in the obstacle passing process varies, according to eq. (2b), linearly with the deformation temperature $T$. This relation is frequently used for checking whether the above mentioned assumptions are valid. For carrying out such a check the activation energy has to be determined at different deformation temperatures (and constant strain rate) by methods, which will be mentioned later.

(3) The variation of $\Delta G$ with the deformation temperature is, of course, not a direct temperature dependence of the activation energy, it rather reflects the temperature dependence of the shear stress $\tau^*$. By means of this correlation qualitative conclusions on the temperature dependence of $\tau^*$ can be deduced from eq. (2b) and fig. 1b. For very narrow obstacles (narrow force-distance curve) the $F$-level and consequently $\tau^*$ has to vary strongly with the temperature to account for the variation of the activation energy according to eq. (2b). For wide obstacles the contrary is true. Therefore, from differences in the temperature dependence of the CSS qualitative conslusions on differences in the sizes of obstacles can be obtained. Corresponding correlations exist between obstacle size and strength of the strain rate dependence of the shear stress (at constant temperature), as can be seen from the right-hand side of eq. (2b).

(4) Two extreme cases of dispersed barrier hardening, in which thermal activation does become unimportant have to be mentioned: As shown in the preceding paragraph, with increasing obstacle size, the temperature and strain rate dependence of the CSS becomes smaller. This already indicates that for the overcoming of very extended obstacles thermal activation can not contribute very much. In this case the dislocation can move over the obstacle only, if $F = f_m$ or if the effective shear

stress reaches the value $\tau_m$ with

$$\tau_m = f_m/bl .  \tag{4}$$

The second case of an athermal process occurs, if the maximum interaction force $f_m$ is rather high. Then it can happen that the shear stress $\tau_c$ necessary to bow out the dislocation in between two neighbouring obstacles far enough that it reaches the mechanically unstable configuration from which it can bow out further and surround the obstacle without a further increase in stress becomes smaller than the shear stress to overcome the obstacle and to break loose from it. The critical stress for this process, which is essentially the mechanism proposed by Orowan [8] for precipitation hardening, is the same as that for operating a Frank-Read source

$$\tau_c \approx \mu b/l .  \tag{5}$$

Thereby it is assumed that the line tension of a dislocation is independent of its orientation and its shape. Foreman [9] in a recent computer calculation took into account the variation of the line tension with the anlge between dislocation and Burgers vector as well as with the curvature of the dislocation and found, in agreement with earlier analytic calculations of De Witt and Koehler [10], that the dependence of the critical stress on the obstacle distance $l$ can be described very well by the formula

$$\tau_c = A \frac{\mu b}{2\pi} \frac{1}{l} [\log(l/r_0) + B] .  \tag{6}$$

$A$ and $B$ are constants, which are different for different orientations of the bowing out dislocation and different configurations of the side arms of the dislocation.

### 2.2. Hardening by defects attached to dislocations (source hardening)

If point defects are mobile in the lattice, some of them will be attracted by dislocations and can interact with these dislocations in such a way that they cause an impedance to dislocation motion and therefore hardening. So far mainly two cases were considered: (1) The point defects are bound to the dislocation without losing their identity in the form of strings or clouds along the dislocation line. If the mobility of these point defects attached to the dislocations is small, slip can be initiated only if the stress is high enough to pull the dislocation away from these attached point defects. The possibility that the attached point defects move together with the dislocation could play a role only if the strain rate is small and the thermal mobility of the defects rather high. (2) The point defects attracted to the dislocations are incorporated in them and give rise to jogs or superjogs [11] (jogs composed of several elementary jogs of the same sign) in these dislocations. Quite generally the jogs hinder the motion of these dislocations. The mechanisms by which a jog can be moved together with the dislocation, and the stress necessary for this motion depend on the kind of jogs, the number of jogs and the orientation of the dislocation.

It should be noted that in all cases mentioned in this paragraph the point defects have to migrate to the stationary dislocations before the beginning of deformation. Therefore, in general the temperature will have to be high enough to allow this migration of the point defects responsible for the hardening. Otherwise these mechanisms will not be operative.

### 2.3. *Defect collection and jog formation on moving dislocations*

This mechanism was first proposed by Cottrell [12] in order to discuss some features of quench hardening in aluminium and later on in more detail by Kuhl-mann-Wilsdorf et al. [13,14]. The basic idea is the following: When moving dis-locations meet dispersed point defects, it may occur that the dislocations drag the point defects along instead of passing over them. The point defects may be either dragged along as individual defects or they will be incorporated in the dislocations to form jogs or superjogs. For the formation of superjogs the point defects would have to move along the dislocations by means of pipe diffusion.

These processes require a certain mobility of the point defects, which enables them to follow the dislocation. For the conversion of point defects into jogs addi-tional thermal activation seems to be necessary. Therefore, the defect collection of dislocations during their motion seems to be favoured in a temperature range, which is not too low and which is also not so high, that the point defect will be annihilated or precipitated before the deformation begins. It is obvious that the dragging of point defects or the jogging of the dislocations occurring in the de-scribed way will impede the dislocation motion, but so far no detailed quantitative predictions about the influence of these processes on the critical shear stress exist.

## 3. Evaluation of experimental observations

### 3.1. *Quenched metals*

The overwhelming majority of all fundamental quench hardening studies have been carried out on fcc metals. In view of the already mentioned very compre-hensive review papers of Kimura and Maddin [4] and of Meshii [5], we will confine the present review on questions of a more general nature and concentrate on a dis-cussion of more recent results.

### 3.1.1. Hardening by single or multiple vacancies

The first question which arises is, inasmuch dispersed single vacancies or multi-ple vacancies like divacancies or trivacancies as they are expected to be present in quenched samples after fast quenching, can cause hardening. In most observations the yield stress or the CSS is higher in as-quenched samples than in well annealed ones. This "initial hardening" is, however, not necessarily caused by dispersed single or multiple vacancies. Mainly two effects can overshadow the hardening due to single vacancies: Quenching strains, which would cause a hardening due to the introduction of dislocations and internal stresses during quenching, and the formation of vacancy agglomerates, which might be formed during an incomplete quenching. Therefore, the lowest observed values for the initial hardening may be most indicative for the hardening due to individual vacancies.

Two examples are known, in which no observable initial hardening was obtained. The first is a careful study of Kimura et al. [14]. Using copper wires of 0.25 mm diameter and rapid quenches into water from various temperatures these authors observed initial hardening only for quenching from temperatures higher than 850°C and no initial hardening if the samples were quenched from 850 or 880°C. The second example refers to gold. Meshii and Kauffman [15] in an investigation of the influence of the quenching rate on the hardening of Au wires with 0.4 mm diameter quenched from 1030°C found no initial hardening for maximum quenching rates below 30 000 deg/sec, whereas for higher cooling rates initial hardening was observed. In both mentioned cases of no observable initial hardening appreciable hardening was observed upon subsequent annealing of the samples. This indicates that vacancies were present in these samples in the as-quenched condition, and it justifies the conclusion, that in fcc metals dispersed single vacancies (and possibly multiple vacancies) are very ineffective with respect to hardening. This conclusion was also reached from later experiments (see e.g. [16]). From a theoretical point of view this result seems to be quite reasonable, since various theoretical estimates about the interaction energy between a dislocation and a vacancy in fcc metals indicate that this energy is rather small and not higher than a few tenths of an eV (comp. ref. [4]).

### 3.1.2. Hardening by secondary defects

From the arguments in the last paragraph it is evident that in most cases quench hardening originates from processes occurring during incomplete quenching or during annealing, which involve the migration and precipitation of vacancies (if we neglect hardening due to quenching stresses). In such processes frequently larger vacancy agglomerates are formed, which can be observed more or less directly by special techniques as, e.g., electron transmission microscopy or small angle X-ray scattering. Therefore, the most informative studies of quench hardening seem to be those, which allow a direct correlation between mechanical measurements and independent observations on the formation, the sizes and the configurations of such agglomerates. In recent years a number of such "correlated" investigations was published, and we will discuss in the following the results of these studies preferentially.

### a) Copper

For polycrystalline copper wires, quenched into water from different temperatures, Kimura et al. [14] detected that the age hardening behaviour is qualitatively different for samples quenched from above 850°C and for those quenched from temperatures $\leqslant 850$°C. As shown in fig. 2, quenching from the lower temperature range causes during isothermal annealing at 100°C a slow increase of the yield stress

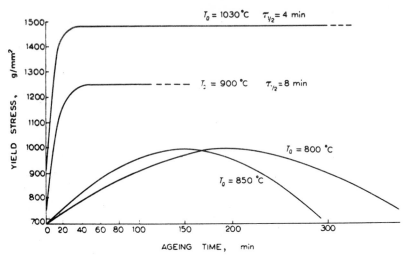

Fig. 2. Yield stress of copper wires quenched from the indicated temperatures $T_Q$ into water in dependence on ageing time. Aging temperature 100°C. After ref. [14].

and overaging for annealing times of more than 200 min. After quenching from the higher temperature range, the yield stress increase occurs much faster and no over-aging was detected. The slow hardening and overaging after low temperature quenches was attributed by the authors (comp. ref. [4]), to the formation of super-jogs on pre-existing dislocations due to an absorption of vacancies on these disloca-tions. (Maximum hardening is expected in this case for a certain ratio between the height of the superjogs and their average distance.) Kimura and Maddin [4] consid-ered as an alternative explanation the formation of small vacancy agglomerates, which are observed in transmission electron microscopy as so-called black dots [17,18]. Larger vacancy precipitates (Frank dislocation loops or stacking fault tetrahedra), the formation of which would be favoured by higher vacancy concen-trations, were thought to be responsible for the fast hardening after high temper-ature quenching.

More recently Davidson and Galligan [19] studied the age hardening phenomena after high temperature quenches (quenching temperature 1030°C) in more detail. These authors used single crystals and carried out mechanical measurements and transmission electron microscope observations in parallel. The change of the CSS at 78°K due to isochronal annealing (annealing time one hour at each temperature), shown in fig. 3, indicates clearly that also after high temperature quenching two different stages of hardening can be observed, the first of which is characterised by a gradual increase with aging temperature, up to about 200°C. The second one leads to a sharp increase of the CSS between 200°C and 300°C, whereas resoftening occurs only above 600°C.

In electron transmission microscopy Frank dislocation loops were observed and identified to be vacancy precipitates.

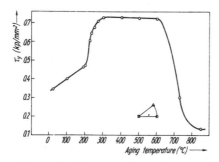

Fig. 3. CSS of copper crystals quenched from 1030°C in dependence on the aging temperature (aging time 1 hr, deformation temperature 78°K). After ref. [19].

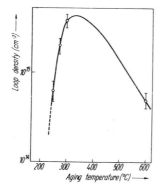

Fig. 4. Variation of the density of Frank dislocation loops in copper, quenched from 1030°C, with the aging temperature (aging time 1 hr). After ref. [19].

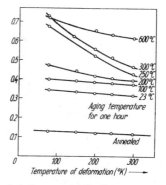

Fig. 5. Influence of the testing temperature on the CSS (in kp/mm$^2$) of quenched copper crystals after various quenching treatments. After ref. [19].

According to fig. 4, in which the volume density of the observed dislocation loops is plotted versus the annealing temperature, the first loops can be seen at 250°C. Obviously the formation of visible loops coincides with the steep rise of the CSS in the second hardening stage during isochronal annealing. It was observed that the decrease of the total loop density between 300°C and 600°C is accompanied by an increase of the average loop size. The dependence of the CSS on the deformation temperature after aging at different temperatures, shown in fig. 5, reflects this decrease in number and change·in size. The smaller temperature dependence after aging at 600°C in comparison to that of samples aged at 250 or 300°C is indicative for the presence of larger dislocation obstacles, and the fact that besides this smaller temperature dependence the (extrapolated) CSS at 0°K is smaller than after aging at lower temperatures is in accordance with a smaller density of obstacles. At a deformation temperature of 78°K the two influences just cancel out. Therefore, the observation in fig. 3 that the CSS remains the same for aging temperatures between 300 and 600°C is somewhat fortuitous.

For the second stage of hardening (aging temperatures > 200°C) the mechanical measurements and the electron microscope observations seem to be well correlated and the conclusion seems to be justified, that the observed Frank dislocation loops act as dispersed barriers to the dislocation motion.

The hardening after aging at temperatures below 200°C (first stage of hardening) is almost temperature independent (fig. 5) and also in this respect different from the second hardening stage. It can not be assigned to a defect observed directly with transmission electron microscopy. Davidson and Galligan conclude in an indirect way that little voids are responsible for this hardening. The hardening due to dispersed voids was treated theoretically by Coulomb [20] and by Kroupa and Hirsch [21]. The Kroupa and Hirsch formula, which takes into account the relaxation of the stress field of a dislocation and the decrease of the core energy, if the dislocation cuts through a cavity, seems to be able to account for the observed hardening in the present case quantitatively [19]. This makes it likely that the increase of the CSS after low temperature aging is caused by dispersed barrier hardening due to voids, too small to be observed in the electron microscope. Corroborating evidence for the existence and the hardening action of such voids comes from small angle X-ray scattering experiments carried out by Galligan and Washburn [16] and by Seeger, Gerold and Rühle [22]. Galligan and Washburn observed that in copper, quenched from 1070°C and aged at 25°C the yield stress and the radius of the X-ray scattering centres vary in a very similar way. Seeger et al. could identify the scattering centres in similarly treated copper to be three-dimensional voids.

It is tempting to correlate the two types of hardening observed by Kimura et al. [14] after quenching from different temperatures and annealing at a constant temperature to the two stages of hardening identified by Davidson and Galligan [19] after quenching from a constant (high) temperature and aging at different temperatures. Due to the different experimental techniques involved in these two studies and due to the use of polycrystals in ref. [14] and single crystals in ref. [19] a conclusive comparison seems to be impossible. Therefore, it cannot be excluded that besides the hardening due to dispersed voids and Frank dislocation loops after quenching from high temperatures, after quenching from lower temperatures and subsequent annealing the formation of jogs plays the role attributed to this process by Kimura et al. in ref. [14].

b) Gold

The main phenomena of quench hardening in gold after rapid quenching from temperatures ≳ 750°C are similar to those of copper, quenched from high temperatures. As already mentioned in section 3.1.1, the initial hardening is negligible, if quenching strains are avoided. Annealing at or above room temperature leads to age-hardening. No overaging is observed. The main part of the yield stress increase anneals out only at rather high temperatures (500–700°C) [15,23,24]. Therefore, at a first glance, the situation seems to be not very complicated. Quench hardening apparently is caused by a thermally rather stable defect, which is formed during aging at temperatures at which the vacancies are mobile. From electron microscope observations on quenched gold, the first of which were carried out by Silcox and Hirsch [25], it is known that the most prominent vacancy precipitates in fully aged gold are stacking fault tetrahedra. These tetrahedra anneal out in the temperature region, in which resoftening occurs [26]. Therefore, the hardening phenomena in quenched gold seemed to be caused by the interaction of dislocations with stacking fault tetrahedra.

The cutting of a dislocation through a stacking fault tetrahedron is geometrically and energetically a rather complicated process. Kimura and Maddin [4] considered several possibilities in some detail and came to the conclusion that up to a critical temperature (which depends on the number of tetrahedra, the strain rate and the migration energy of vacancies) thermal activation cannot help much in the cutting process, so that the yield stress should be independent of the deformation temperature. Above the critical temperature the migration of vacancies was considered to assist in the formation of the ledges produced at the tetrahedra during cutting. This critical temperature, above which a decrease of the yield stress with the deformation temperature is expected, was estimated to be in realistic cases in the order of a few hundred °C. This result was in agreement with observations of Meshii and Kauffman [15] according to which in samples quenched from 1030°C and fully aged, the yield stress varies with the deformation temperature from −196°C up to about 200°C as little as that of a slowly cooled sample and decreases rapidly above 200°C (fig. 6).

More detailed studies on the temperature and strain rate dependence of the yield stress of quenched gold, carried out more recently by Yoshida et al. [27] and

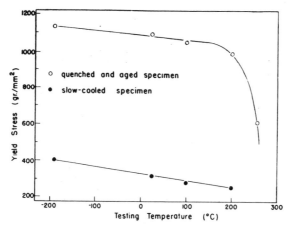

Fig. 6. Influence of the testing temperature on the yield stress of gold wires quenched from 1030°C and fully aged or slowly cooled. After ref. [15].

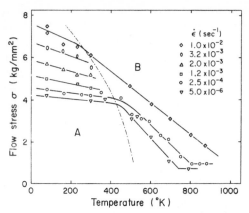

Fig. 7. Variation of the yield stress with testing temperature and strain rate of gold quenched from 1000°C and fully aged. After ref. [27].

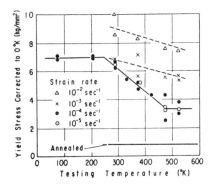

Fig. 8. Variation of the yield stress with testing temperature and strain rate of gold quenched from 900°C and fully aged at 100°C. After ref. [28].

Imashimizu and Kimura [28] revealed a more complicated behaviour (figs. 7 and 8). In both investigations polycrystalline gold samples were quenched from 900°C and fully aged at a final aging temperature of 100°C, after holding the samples on a lower temperature (20°C in ref. [27], 0°C in ref. [28]) for some time. Qualitatively the results of these two studies are in agreement: Small temperature dependence (proportional to the shear modulus) up to about room temperature (called region A in ref. [27]) a stronger linear decrease above this temperature (region B) and negligible temperature dependence at high temperatures. (The quantitative differences in the transition temperatures might be due to small differences in the materials and the heat treatments used.) It should be noted that the absolute values of the yield stress in Meshii's and Kauffman's measurements, in spite of the higher quenching temperature, are much lower than in the measurements of Yoshida et al. and of Imashimizu and Kimura, suggesting that in refs. [27,28] sharper quenching was used than in Meshii's and Kauffman's work.

Different interpretations are presented by Yoshida et al. and Imashimizu and Kimura for the dislocation defect interaction mechanisms in the three temperature regions. Imashimizu and Kimura argue that in their samples in addition to tetrahedra little voids or faulted dislocation loops might be present * and that the thermally activated cutting of dislocations through such faulted loops is responsible for the strong temperature dependence of the yield stress in region B. The high temperature region, in which the dislocation obstacles responsible for region B are apparently transparent for the dislocations, is tentatively interpreted by these authors by the interaction of the dislocations with the stacking fault tetrahedra, which is, in agreement with ref. [4], assumed to be temperature independent. The region A is attributed to the bowing out of the dislocations between the loops and the tetrahedra by means of the Orowan mechanism.

Yoshida et al. [27] combined their mechanical measurements with electron microscope studies on the formation of tetrahedra during aging and on the influence of deformation on the defect structure. The observation (see fig. 9) that

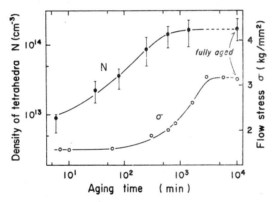

Fig. 9. Relation between the yield stress at 20°C and the nucleation of stacking fault tetrahedra during aging at 20°C. After ref. [27].

during aging the number of tetrahedra increases in a similar way as the yield stress (measured at 20°C with $\dot{e} = 2.5 \times 10^{-4}$ sec$^{-1}$) seems to confirm that in region A the hardening is caused by the presence of the tetrahedra. The pronounced strain rate dependence, observed by these authors in region A (see fig. 7) can hardly be brought into agreement with the Orowan mechanism suggested by Imashimizu and Kimura for this temperature range. To account for the experimental observations Yoshida et al. postulate, that a frictional stress impedes a dislocation while it moves across a tetrahedron. This friction-like counter stress is assumed to depend on the

* The authors conclude this from the observation that part of the hardening anneals out below 500°C, at temperatures which are regarded to be too small to be assigned to the dissolution of stacking fault tetrahedra.

speed of the dislocation but not on the deformation temperature. So far no atomistic process is known which meets these two characteristics.

Based on the observation that a deformation in the temperature region B produces channels along the paths of dislocations in which the tetrahedra are eliminated or transformed to dislocation loops, Yoshida et al. attribute the strong temperature dependence of the yield stress in region B to the stress-aided thermally activated elimination of the tetrahedra due to an interaction with moving dislocations.

For a decision between the controversial interpretations of Yoshida et al. and Imashimizu and Kimura for the regions A and B further experimental and theoretical work seems to be necessary.

### c) Aluminium

Since the first systematic experiments of Maddin and Cottrell [2] quench hardening in aluminium has been studied more extensively than in any other metal. Nevertheless there are still controversial views regarding the phenomena and their interpretation. Some of the difficulties in quench hardening studies of aluminium are due to the fact that even after very careful quenching in all experiments a relatively high initial hardening is observed. Maddin and Cottrell already could exclude that this initial hardening is caused only by quenching strains. So it has to be concluded that some vacancy precipitation occurs already during quenching. As a consequence thereof the initial hardening and also the vacancy precipitation during aging depends quite strongly on the quenching conditions. This makes it sometimes difficult to compare results from different investigations. Therefore, in the case of aluminium closely correlated investigations of the defect structure and of the mechanical behaviour are even more needed than for some other metals. This is the reason why we will pay special attention to investigations of Westmacott [29,30] who took the specimens for transmission electron microscope examination from undeformed sections of the samples which were used for mechanical testing.

Some of the characteristics of the initial hardening can be seen in fig. 10, which shows results of Shiotani et al. [31]. These authors measured the dependence of the yield stress on the deformation temperature of polycrystalline sheet specimens. The specimens were quenched from the temperature indicated in the figure into iced brine of $-2°C$. The as-quenched samples (AQ) were transferred rapidly from the quenching bath into liquid nitrogen, the fully annealed ones (FA) were kept at room temperature for 36 hr. It can be recognized that at all testing temperatures the initial hardening is not much smaller than the hardening after aging, in strong contrast to copper and gold. The difference in the initial hardening behaviour between aluminium and the noble metals is attributed to the lower activation energy for the migration of vacancies in aluminium or/and to the higher stacking fault energy of aluminium, which makes it easier for vacancies to become absorbed at dislocations. Shiotani et al. interpret the initial hardening observed in their experiments on the basis of such an absorption, which results in the formation of jogs at the dislocation lines. This jog formation is considered to be responsible for the increased yield stress of the as-quenched samples.

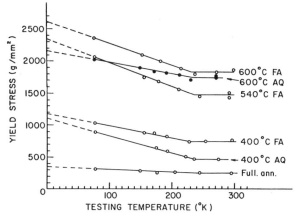

Fig. 10. Dependence of the yield stress on the testing temperatures of aluminium quenched from the indicated temperatures in the as-quenched (AQ) and the fully aged (FA) state. The yield stress is corrected to 0°C by taking into account the variation of the elastic moduli. After ref. [31].

According to earlier electron microscope observations [32] large dislocation loops and jogs in dislocations seemed to be the main structural defects caused by quenching in aluminium and, therefore, for a number of years these two defect types were regarded to be responsible for all phenomena of quench hardening. In agreement therewith Shiotani et al. [31] came to the conclusion that the results in fig. 10 can be interpreted best in terms of jog hardening for the as-quenched samples and of interactions of the moving dislocations with dislocation loops for the annealed specimens. Two types of interactions between dislocations and loops are taken into account in this interpretation: Long range elastic interaction according to theories of Kroupa and Hirsch [21] and of Friedel [33] is assumed to account for the almost temperature independent branch of the yield stress-temperature curve above $\sim 220°$K. The increase of the yield stress at lower temperatures is attributed to short range interactions, which occur if a dislocation cuts through a loop and jogs are formed in the loop dislocation and/or the moving dislocation.

Kiritani, Yoshida et al. [34–37] found that under certain quenching conditions in addition to the larger dislocation loops little voids, $< 100$ Å in diameter, can be observed in regions of the samples which are almost free of loops. According to Shiotani et al. [31] such voids do not seem to contribute to quench hardening in their experiments. Westmacott [29], however, did find a close correlation between the appearance of the little voids and the hardening phenomena.

Fig. 11 shows Westmacott's result on the temperature dependence of the yield stress of polycrystalline samples, which were quenched carefully from various temperatures into brine solution at 0°C and aged at this temperature for more than 24 hr. For quenching temperatures up to 607°C the yield stress at all testing tem-

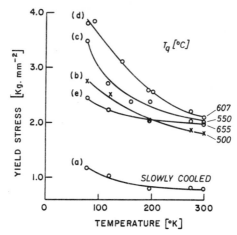

Fig. 11. Dependence of the yield stress of aluminium, quenched from various temperatures or
slowly cooled, on the testing temperature. After ref. [29].

peratures increases with increasing quenching temperature. A pronounced temperature dependence of the yield stress is observed, which is similar in strength to the
temperature dependence in the results of Shiotani et al. (fig. 10) *.

Dislocation loops were observed in electron micrographs for these quenching
temperatures with average loop diameters ranging from 1000 Å (500° quench) to
230 Å (607° quench). If the quenching temperature is raised to 655°C ** the absolute values of the yield stress are smaller than for the 607° quench, and the temperature dependence of the yield stress becomes almost negligible. Electron microscopy
revealed that after quenching from 655°C again dislocation loops are present but
with a much smaller concentration than after quenching from 607°C. The loops are
mostly arranged in colonies with loop free regions in between these groups. In the
loop free regions small vacancy clusters or voids of the type reported by Kiritani,
Yoshida et al. [34–37] could be detected. According to these observations the
changed hardening characteristics for quenching from above 607°C seem to be
correlated to the appearance of small voids. Qualitative agreement is stated by
Westmacott with the void hardening theories of Coulomb [20] and of Kroupa and
Hirsch [21] according to which hardening due to voids of the observed sizes should
show a negligible dependence on the deformation temperature.

It seemed to be feasible to explain the stronger temperature dependence of the
yield stress after quenching from lower temperatures in Westmacott's results [29]
in the same way as in the paper by Shiotani et al. [31] by the interaction of moving
dislocations with dislocation loops. Some serious doubts on the validity of this
interpretation were raised by more recent studies of Westmacott [30], in which

* In comparing figs. 10 and 11 it has to be noticed that in fig. 11 no corrections of the yield
  stress for the temperature dependence of the elastic moduli were made.
** Curve e in fig. 11.

refined electron microscope techniques were employed. For quenching conditions, under which in the previous work [29] only dislocation loops were seen, with the improved techniques in between the loops numerous small contrast spots with sizes close to the limit of resolution could be observed. They are believed to indicate the presence of small vacancy precipitates similar to those which are observed in neutron irradiated copper (see section 3.3.1 and ref. [38]). The interaction of dislocations with such small vacancy precipitates could easily account for a strong temperature dependence of the yield stress as can be seen from a comparison with the analysis of neutron irradiation hardening of copper. Westmacott [30] shows that indeed the temperature dependence of the yield stress follows a similar law as the yield stress of copper after neutron irradiation. For a final decision whether the large dislocation loops or small vacancy precipitates determine the yield stress in aluminium quenched from temperatures < 600°C further investigations are needed. Westmacott's investigations make it likely, however, that for quenches from lower temperatures as well as for those from rather high temperature small defects might be more important in quench hardening than the easily visible large dislocation loops, which for a long time were believed to be the predominant dislocation obstacle in aged aluminium samples.

### 3.2. Electron irradiated metals

Among irradiation experiments, those in which electrons of about 1 MeV are used are the simplest with regard to the defect structure introduced into the samples. Mainly close Frenkel pairs and individual dispersed vacancies and interstitials are produced. We, therefore, will discuss irradiation hardening due to electrons before we pass on to neutron irradiation hardening in section 3.3. The basic mechanisms of irradiation hardening have been most thoroughly investigated on pure fcc metals, and among those mainly on copper and aluminium.

### 3.2.1. Copper

Early measurements on the influence of electron irradiation on the mechanical properties of copper were performed by Meechan and Dixon [39,40]. They irradiated with 1 or 1.25 MeV electrons at −20°C or 77°K and employed hardness tests. These studies indicated clearly that there is a definite hardening action of electron irradiation, but because of the complicated deformation process involved in hardness tests a detailed evaluation of these experiments seems to be impossible. Better defined deformation experiments on single crystals irradiated with 4 MeV electrons and subsequently deformed in tension were reported by Makin and Blewitt [41]. These authors studied the dose dependence of the CSS (measured at 77°K) for irradiations between 77°K and 293°K. In this temperature range a great fraction of the produced defects anneal out already during irradiation. It is to be expected that experiments with irradiation temperatures low enough to avoid strong annealing during irradiation can be interpreted in a more straightforward way. Such experiments were carried out more recently by Ono, Mifune and Meshii [42]. They

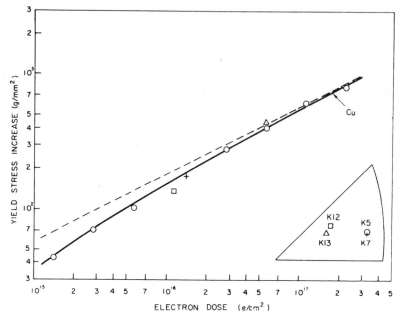

Fig. 12. Yield stress increase versus electron dose in copper crystals irradiated with 2 MeV electrons below 31°K and tested at 25°K. After ref. [42].

irradiated very thin copper single crystals with 2 MeV electrons at or below 31°K. The increase of the CSS $\Delta\tau$ in dependence of the electron dose $\varphi$ observed by these authors is shown in fig. 12 in a log-log plot. At doses exceeding $6 \times 10^{16}$ e/cm$^2$ $\Delta\tau$ is proportional to the square root of the dose (dashed straight line). All data can according to these authors be described by the empirical relation

$$\Delta\tau + \tau_c = K\varphi^{\frac{1}{2}}[1 + (\varphi_c/\varphi)]^{\frac{1}{2}}, \tag{7}$$

where $\varphi_c$, $\tau_c$ and $K$ are constants. The CSS can be related to the Frenkel pair concentration $c$ by comparing the data with the increase of the electrical resistivity under similar irradiation conditions and by using the resistivity per unit concentration of Frenkel pairs of 250 $\mu\Omega\cdot$cm (comp. Wenzl [43]).

Since according to Ono et al. [42] for most of the data in fig. 12, $[1 + (\varphi_c/\varphi)] \approx 1$ holds, eq. (7) can be rewritten into the form

$$\Delta\tau + \tau_c = \tau_i - (\tau_{ui} - \tau_c) = 0.075\mu c^{\frac{1}{2}}, \tag{8}$$

where $\mu$ is the shear modulus, $\tau_i$ is the CSS after irradiation, and $\tau_{ui}$ is the CSS before irradiation. Eq. (8) follows very closely the relation expected for dispersed barrier hardening, according to eq. (3) in section 2.1. Randomly dispersed Frenkel pairs are expected to be the predominant defects produced and since from the quench hardening experiments described in section 3.1.1. it is known that individual vacancies are very inefficient in hardening copper, it is concluded that the observed increase of the CSS originates from dispersed barrier hardening with the interstitial atoms being the barriers. The deviations at small doses described by the correction term $\tau_c$ indicate that the increase of the CSS caused by the interstitials (right-hand side of eq. (8)) is superimposed additively not to the total CSS of the unirradiated crystal $\tau_{ui}$ but only to $\tau_{ui} - \tau_c$ (see eq. (8)). This is not unexpected (comp. section 3.3.1), if $\tau_c$ is due to dislocation obstacles present in the unirradiated crystal, which can also be overcome by thermal activation (most likely forest dislocations) and which are in competition with the radiation induced obstacles.

In fcc metals dumb-bells with $\langle 100 \rangle$ orientation are the stable configurations of interstitials. The dumb-bells have a tetragonal symmetry and cause tetragonal distortions in the lattice which can be described as an elastic dipole. The interaction of such tetragonal distortions with dislocations was treated theoretically first by Fleischer [44,45] and later on in more detail by Frank [7]. In both theories the interstitial is substituted by a volume $v$ and it is assumed that the tensor of plastic deformation is approximately zero outside this volume and constant inside. The difference between the two components of the deformation tensor (parallel and perpendicular to the tetragonal axis) times the volume $v$ (measured in atomic volumes) is taken as a characteristic value for the distorsion of the tetragonal defect and (following ref. [7]) is called $\Delta\lambda^*$ (dipole strength). Using the above mentioned deformation tensor, the elastic interaction of a dislocation with the tetragonal defect is calculated and the force-distance relation (see section 2.1) for a dislocation moving on a glide plane, which is near to the defect, is derived. By means of eq. (2), Frank [46] obtains in this way for screw dislocations interacting with $\langle 100 \rangle$ interstitials in an fcc lattice the following dependence of the CSS on the defect concentration and the deformation temperature

$$\tau_{int} = 2\sqrt{2}\,\frac{\Delta G_0}{b^2}\,\sqrt{c}\,[1 - (T/T_0)^{\frac{1}{2}}]^2 \tag{9}$$

with

$$T_0 = \Delta G_0/k\,\log(\dot{a}_0/\dot{a}) . \tag{9a}$$

The activation energy at zero stress is related to the dipole strength $\Delta\lambda^*$ of the defects by

$$\Delta G_0 = \alpha\mu b^2 \Delta\lambda^* \tag{10}$$

with $\alpha \approx 0.25$. It should be noted that eqs. (9), (9a) and (10) differ from Fleischer's [44] results only by numerical factors.

By comparing the right-hand sides of eqs. (8) and (9) numerical values for the activation energy $\Delta G_0$ and the dipole strength $\Delta\lambda^*$ of interstitials in copper can be derived from the experimental results of Ono et al., if a reasonable assumption about $\log \dot{a}_0 / \dot{a}$ is made. With a value of 20 for this logarithm we obtain

$$\Delta G_0 = 0.39 \text{ eV} , \tag{11a}$$

$$\Delta \lambda^* = 0.33 . \tag{11b}$$

The dipole strength $\Delta \lambda^*$ is rather close to the theoretical values calculated for interstitials in copper by Seeger, Mann and von Jan [47], who obtained, depending on the constants in the Born-Mayer potential, values between 0.22 and 0.33. The values (11a) and (11b) are smaller by about 20% than those determined by Frank [46] from the measurements of Makin and Blewitt [41] on single crystals irradiated and deformed at 77°K, for which at small electron doses the CSS increases also proportional to the square root of the defect concentration (see ref. [48]). The small difference between the values (11a) and (11b) and those derived from Makin's and Blewitt's data is possibly caused by the rather indirect way in which the point defect concentrations corresponding to the CSS values had to be determined in refs. [46,48]. So in spite of this difference the conclusion seems to be justified that dispersed interstitial atoms are the dominant dislocation obstacles after 77°K irradiation as well as after the 31°K irradiation in Ono's, Meshii's and Mifune's experiments.

The annealing behaviour of the CSS of electron irradiated copper has not been studied in much detail. According to Makin and Blewitt [41] a gradual annealing takes place between room temperature and 575°K. Some comments on the difference between this observation and the annealing of the CSS of aluminium (see next section) are given in ref. [48].

### 3.2.2. Aluminium

Electron irradiation hardening of aluminium single crystals has been studied rather extensively by two groups of workers during recent years. The first investigations were carried out with irradiations at liquid nitrogen temperature by Ono, Meshii and Kauffman [50] and by Keefer and Sosin [48]. The two studies, in which 1.0 MeV (ref. [50]) and 1.4 MeV (ref. [48]) electrons were used, agreed in the basic observations that a strong hardening occurs and that this hardening anneals out upon annealing below room temperature (stage III). The two groups of authors disagreed in the interpretation of the hardening mechanism. While Ono et al., under the assumption that interstitial atoms are mobile at the irradiation temperature, assigned the hardening to condensation of interstitials and jog formation at the dislocations, Keefer and Sosin interpreted their results in terms of dispersed barrier hardening due to randomly distributed dumb-bell interstitials, which are regarded by these authors to be thermally stable up to the annealing stage III, in which radiation hardening recovers completely.

Less controversial are the interpretations of measurements of the two groups

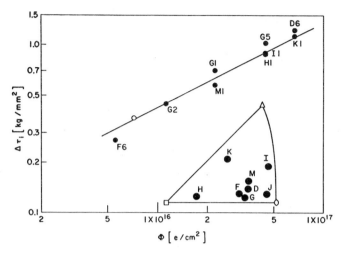

Fig. 13. Increase of the CSS of aluminium single crystals as a function of the electron dose. After ref. [54]. Straight line from ref. [53].

carried out later with 1.0 MeV irradiations at liquid hydrogen temperature (Ono and Meshii [51–53]; Buck, Keefer, Robinson, Sosin and Wiedersich [54]). In both investigations it was found that the increase of the CSS measured at or below the irradiation temperature is proportional to the square root of the electron dose. The log-log diagram in fig. 13 demonstrates this and shows that the data of Buck et al. [54] are in good agreement with the straight line with slope $\frac{1}{2}$, which was fitted by Ono and Meshii to their measurements. The authors of both investigations agree that this increase is due to dispersed interstitial hardening. The increase with the electron dose can be described by the equation

$$\Delta\tau = A\varphi^{\frac{1}{2}}, \quad A = 4.19 \times 10^{-9} \, (\text{kg/mm}^2)(\text{e/cm}^2)^{-\frac{1}{2}}. \tag{12}$$

For obtaining the corresponding relation between the CSS and the concentration of the radiation induced defects different effective displacement cross sections were used by Ono and Meshii and by Buck et al., so that for $\beta$ in the equation

$$\Delta\tau = \beta\mu\sqrt{c}. \tag{13}$$

Ono and Meshii find $\frac{1}{3}$ and Buck et al. 1/5.5. Numerical values for the activation energy and the dipole strength can be determined by applying eqs. (9) and (10). Frank [46] carried out the corresponding evaluation with Ono's and Meshii's data. The results are

$$\Delta G_o = 0.72 \text{ eV}, \quad \Delta\lambda^* = 0.67. \tag{14}$$

It should be noted that with the value of $\beta$ given by Buck et al. the values (14) would become somewhat smaller. Nevertheless, a comparison of eq. (14) with eqs. (11a) and (11b) indicates that tetragonality and hardening efficiency of interstitials are stronger in aluminium than in copper.

Keefer and Sosin [48] found that for irradiation and deformation at 77°K the CSS follows also eq. (13) with $\beta = 0.13$. Frank's [46] evaluation of these data in terms of $\Delta G_o$ and $\Delta\lambda^*$ gave numerical values of 0.69 eV and 0.64, respectively. The relatively good agreement of these numbers with (14) indicates that the same defects act as dislocation obstacles after a low temperature irradiation and after irradiation at 77°K. This would mean in the present case that at this higher temperature dispersed interstitial atoms are still present in the lattice.

Buck et al. [54] investigated this question more closely by correlating the recovery of the CSS during annealing between 20°K and 80°K with the corresponding change of the electrical resistivity. Fig. 14 shows rather good agreement between the relative changes of the resistivity increment and of the squared increase of the CSS. Since the resistivity, to a good approximation, is proportional to the defect concentration, the agreement in fig. 14 apparently means that $\Delta\tau \propto \sqrt{c}$ holds all through the annealing stage I, proving that only the number of dislocation obstacles decreases, but the type of obstacle does not change up to 80°K.

This conclusion is in contradiction to Ono's and Meshii's interpretation of the

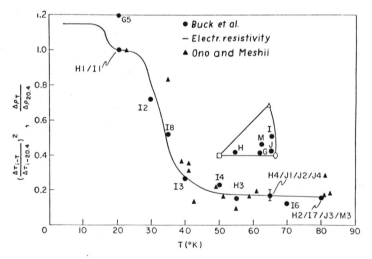

Fig. 14. Annealing of irradiation-produced CSS and resistivity increase of aluminium ($4.5 \times 10^{16}$ e/cm$^2$, deformation temperature 20.4°K). Both sets of data have been normalised at 20.4°K. $\Delta\tau_{i-T}$ is the increase of the CSS, remaining after annealing at temperature $T$, $\Delta\tau_{i-20.4}$ is the increase of the CSS immediately after irradiation at 20.4°K. The ratios plotted should be proportional to the defect concentration. After ref. [54]. Triangles show the corresponding CSS data of Ono and Meshii [53].

change of hardening during annealing in stage I. This interpretation is based, at least partly, on the observation that the CSS with isochronal annealing (compare Ono and Meshii's data in fig. 14) goes through a minimum at about 50°K and rises then slightly up to 80°K. The dip in the isochronal annealing curve was observed to be accompanied by the appearance of a yield point. These phenomena are explained by Ono and Meshii in the following way: In stage I a great fraction of the interstitials, causing the hardening before annealing, recombine with vacancies. A smaller fraction of them, however, form dilute atmospheres around the dislocations and cause a yield drop upon testing at 20°K. During annealing at higher temperatures the atmospheres collapse to form jogs at the dislocations. These jogs are considered to be responsible for the hardening remaining at 80°K, in agreement with the interpretation given by the same authors for their 77° irradiations, which was mentioned in the beginning of this section.

Buck et al. [54] presented evidence that the dip in the isochronal annealing curve observed by Ono and Meshii results from the experimental technique applied by these authors (successive measurements of the CSS at the same crystal after several annealing treatments). For this reason the annealing data of Buck et al. and the interpretations given by these authors seem to be the more convincing ones at present.

### 3.3. Neutron irradiation hardening

Already in 1955, McReynolds, Augustiniak, McKewon and Rosenblatt [3] detected a remarkable difference between hardening introduced by reactor irradiation in copper and aluminium. They observed that in copper the main portion of the radiation induced increase of the CSS (measured in torsion) anneals out after an 80°K irradiation only at temperatures between 300°C and 400°C with an activation energy close to that of self-diffusion (annealing stage V), whereas the increase of the CSS of aluminium was found to anneal out already in a temperature range centred at −60°C (stage III) with a much lower activation energy of about 0.55 eV.

Later on, neutron irradiation hardening of copper became the object of investigations of quite a number of workers with the result that it is at present the most thoroughly studied topic in the field of point defect hardening. We will discuss it in section 3.3.1. Because of the great number of papers published on this subject we can only briefly outline the main lines of development in the past and comment on the present state of knowledge.

Less intensive studies on other heavy fcc metals like Au [55–57], Ni [58,59], Ag [57] and Pt [60] have shown that qualitatively these behave with respect to neutron irradiation hardening very similarly to copper. Copper may, therefore, be taken as a typical example for this whole group of metals and in the following we will refer only occasionally to one of the other heavy fcc metals.

The above mentioned difference between copper (and other heavy metals) and aluminium has been confirmed by later investigations. We will devote to this metal a separate section (3.3.2).

### 3.3.1. Copper (and other heavy fcc metals)

#### a) Annealing of the CSS and correlation with the radiation induced defects

The first systematic study of radiation hardening due to reactor irradiation, in which single crystals and tensile deformation were used, was carried out by Blewitt, Coltman, Jamison and Redman [61]. In this work the result of McReynolds et al. [3] on the main annealing stage of hardening was proved to be correct. In addition Blewitt et al. observed that also during irradiation at very low temperature (14°K) strong hardening occurs and that only a small percentage of it (ca. 20%) anneals out upon annealing up to room temperature. This low temperature annealing was measured later on in some more detail by Diehl, Leitz and Schilling [62]. The results of these authors (fig. 15) are in good agreement with the findings of Blewitt et al. [61]. So it has to be concluded that radiation hardening in copper is caused by a thermally rather stable type of defect, which is produced in situ and only little affected by the single or small multiple point defects produced simultaneously, the majority of which anneal out below room temperature (compare resistivity data in fig. 15).

Based on such considerations, Seeger [63] suggested the defects responsible for

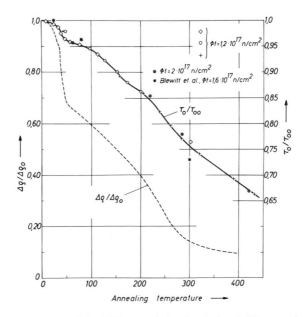

Fig. 15. Isochronal annealing of the CSS ($\tau_0$) and the electrical resistivity $\Delta\rho$ of neutron irradiated copper after low temperature irradiation; $\tau_{00}$ and $\Delta\rho_0$ are the values measured immediately after irradiation. All measurements are carried out at 4.5°K. After ref. [62]. Data of Blewitt et al. after ref. [61].

radiation hardening to be so-called depleted zones (vacancy rich regions originating at the end of the path of fast knock on atoms), which can be dissolved only by self-diffusion. Seeger proposed that these zones, which might be transformed in one of the usual configurations of small vacancy agglomerates, act as dispersed dislocation barriers. In the meantime agreement seems to be achieved quite generally on the basic concept of Seeger's interpretation (dispersed barrier hardening, the barriers being point defect agglomerates) among the workers in the field.

After small radiation induced defect clusters were made visible by means of transmission electron microscopy [64,65], it was tempting to identify these with the depleted zones. A rather conclusive correlation between these visible defects and radiation hardening was found by Makin, Minter and Manthorpe [66]. They studied the change in the density of the visible clusters during annealing for various times at temperatures between 275 and 336°C, and observed that the CSS measured at 4.2°K, which decreases appreciably during these annealing treatments, is proportional to the square root of the density of the defect clusters with diameters smaller than 50 Å. This relation, which corresponds to eq. (3) for dispersed barrier hardening, was found to be valid through almost all of the annealing treatments applied by Makin et al. An even closer but less direct correlation between CSS and visible defects was established recently by Frank, Rühle and Saxlová [67]. This work will be outlined in paragraph c. Furthermore, it should be mentioned that Galligan and Attardo [60] identified depleted zones with field ion microscopy in n-irradiated platinum and also observed a proportionality between the CSS and the square root of the number of these zones.

## b) Dose dependence of the CSS

If radiation hardening is caused by dispersed barriers and these barriers are produced in situ, as it would correspond to Seeger's [63] suggestion, the barrier concentration should be proportional to the neutron dose $\phi t$ and the CSS according to eq. (3) should then be proportional to the square root of the dose. Blewitt et al. [61] in their pioneering work did, however, find a different dose relation. By plotting the data for three deformation temperatures in a log-log diagram they established an empirical law according to which the absolute value of the CSS varies linearly with the cube root of the neutron dose over a large dose range (fig. 16). Afterwards, Diehl and coworkers [62,68–70], who used single crystals of identical orientation and concentrated their studies mainly on the range of small neutron doses, came to the conclusion that the $(\phi t)^{1/3}$ law of Blewitt et al. is only a useful approximation for describing the data over a large dose range, but that systematic deviations from this law exist at small and at high doses (see ref. [70] and fig. 17b). These authors preferred to account for their data by a proportionality of the radiation induced increase of the CSS with the square root of the neutron dose * at very

---

* Due to different calibrations of the neutron flux the dose scales in figs. 16 and 17 do not agree. For correlating data from different laboratories it is recommended to compare the CSS data rather than the dose values.

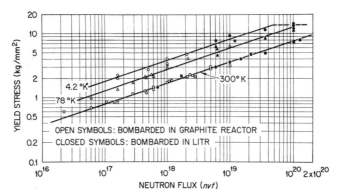

Fig. 16. Dose dependence of the CSS, measured at different deformation temperatures, after
Blewitt et al. [61].

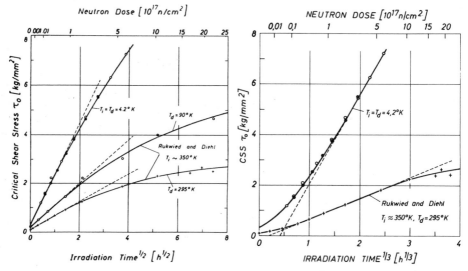

Fig. 17. Dependence of the CSS of copper single crystals on the $\frac{1}{2}$ power (a) and the $\frac{1}{3}$ power (b)
of the irradiation time or the neutron dose. Measurements for different irradiation temperatures
$(T_i)$ and deformation temperatures $(T_d)$, after refs. [62,69].

small neutron doses ($< 10^{17}$ n/cm$^2$) and a gradual decrease of $d\tau_0/d\sqrt{\phi t}$ with increasing dose due to a saturation tendency, which becomes noticeable at higher
doses. Some of the data of Diehl et al., which demonstrate their interpretations, are
shown in figs. 17a and b in which the CSS is plotted linearly versus $(\phi t)^{1/2}$ (fig. 17a)
and $(\phi t)^{1/3}$ (fig. 17b).

Starting from the different views on the basic law of the dose dependence of the
CSS in ref. [61] and ref. [68] a rather long lasting controversy on this question

developed between Blewitt and coworkers and Diehl and coworkers (see e.g. refs. [70–73]), which cannot be reviewed in all details here. From a theoretical point of view there are weak points in both interpretations. Whereas the linear increase of the CSS with the square root of the dose at small doses, as it is postulated by Diehl et al., agrees with a dispersed barrier hardening mechanism, so far no reasonable theoretical picture is known which could account for Blewitt's $(\phi t)^{1/3}$ law. On the other side, there is no simple theoretical treatment of the saturation effects in the CSS, as they are assumed to occur by Diehl et al. As outlined in ref. [68] these saturation effects are thought to be caused by interactions between newly formed depleted zones and already existing ones. These interactions affect the sizes of the zones (and at high enough doses possibly also the number of the dislocation obstacles due to a direct overlap between the zones). A theory of the dose dependence of the CSS, which would take into account such changes in the average size and of the size distribution of the dislocation obstacles with the neutron dose, will have to be rather complicated by nature. Therefore, it is not very astonishing that Blewitt and Koppenaal [71] did not succeed in applying simple radiation annealing laws derived from electrical resistivity measurements (which are sensitive to the total number of point defects and not only to the predominant dislocation obstacles) to the CSS.

From a more phenomenological point of view the above mentioned controversy focussed for some time on the question (see ref. [71]) whether the *total* CSS $\tau_0^i$ or only the radiation induced *increase* of the CSS $\tau_0^i - \tau_0^{ui} (\tau_0^i =$ CSS after irradiation, $\tau_0^{ui} =$ CSS of the unirradiated crystal before irradiation) follows one of the proposed power laws in the dose dependency. If radiation hardening is caused by dispersed dislocation obstacles, which can be overcome with the help of thermal activation only, the "effective" shear stress enters the equations derived in section 2. This effective shear stress is equal to the difference between the applied shear stress and the athermal long-range interaction stress between the dislocations $\tau_\mu$ (comp. e.g. Seeger [74]). Since in as-grown pure copper single crystals the CSS is not much higher than $\tau_\mu$, Diehl et al. put forward the opinion that only the radiation induced increase of the CSS should follow eq. (3). The results in fig. 17a seemed to confirm this view, as the initial slopes of the curves extrapolate to shear stress values for $\phi t = 0$, which are very close to the values of the CSS of unirradiated crystals. In contrast herewith Blewitt et al. [61,72] in their log-log plots used the total CSS and, therefore, according to the straight lines observed in these plots the total CSS would have to be proportional to $(\phi t)^{1/3}$.

In recent experiments the question whether radiation hardening is superimposed additively to $\tau_\mu$ was investigated in more detail by Diehl et al. [75]. In these experiments the flow stress of the unirradiated crystals was increased by predeforming the crystals prior to an irradiation at 20°K. For small prestresses (0.2 and 0.4 kg/mm$^2$) the additivity between the prestress and the radiation induced increase of the CSS is well proved as shown in fig. 18 by the parallelity of the respective curves and the agreement between the extrapolations of the curves to zero dose with the prestress values. Systematic deviations between this extrapolated shear stress and the prestress

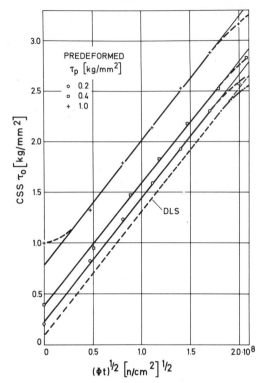

Fig. 18. Dose dependence of the CSS of copper crystals, predeformed to various flow stress values $\tau_p$. Irradiation temperature and deformation temperature 20°K. DLS: dose dependence of as-grown crystals, after ref. [62].

is observed for higher prestress values (in fig. 18: $\tau_p = 1$ kp/mm$^2$). These deviations can be accounted for by the fact that at higher predeformations the flow stress contains a thermally activated shear stress component (due to the cutting of forest dislocations), which is not negligible and to which the radiation induced increase of the CSS does not superimpose additively (compare section 3.2.1). So the data in fig. 18 confirm the view that the increase of the CSS is initially proportional to the square root of the dose and additively superimposed to the athermal component of the CSS before irradiation. It should be noticed that these conclusions are in full agreement with the observations on electron irradiated copper and aluminium, which are discussed in section 3.2.

The latest contribution to the discussion on the dose dependence of copper is contained in the paper of Blewitt, Arenberg, Clanck and Scott [76] submitted to this conference. In this paper measurements of the CSS at 4.2°K after irradiation at this temperature were fitted by a computer calculation to Foreman's formula (eq. (6)) for the athermal stress necessary to move a dislocation through an array of dispersed barriers of high strength. It is assumed that the average obstacle distance $l$ follows the equation

$$\frac{1}{l} = D_2 + k\phi t , \qquad (15)$$

where $D_2$ accounts for the fact that the total CSS is not zero at zero dose. Introduction of eq. (15) into eq. (6) gives a modified $\sqrt{\phi t}$-dependence for the CSS. Blewitt et al. [76] report that an excellent fit could be obtained by a proper adjustment of the constants in eqs. (6) and (15).

According to these results it may be noted that in at least two essential points agreement appears now to be achieved between the two groups with controversial views on the dose dependence: (1) The basic mechanism of hardening is of the dispersed barrier type. (2) The dose dependence follows a modified $(\phi t)^{1/2}$-dependence.

The justification for applying Foreman's formula, eq. (6), seems, however, to be questionable. This relation is derived for a strictly athermal hardening process. It is, however, well known that the CSS of n-irradiated copper depends in a large temperature range strongly on the deformation temperature (see next section). So, at least for all deformation temperatures in this range, it would seem to be fortuituous if Foreman's formula fitted the data. The 4.2°K deformations used by Blewitt et al. for the fitting may possibly be an exception to this statement. At very low temperatures the temperature coefficient of the CSS becomes relatively small * and Makin [77] recently proposed that an Orowan-type mechanism is responsible for this small temperature coefficient. If this interpretation is correct, Foreman's formula could be applied. This would, however, mean that the hardening mechanism is different at very low and at elevated deformation temperatures and it would become difficult to explain the close similarity in the dose dependence of the CSS at different deformation temperatures, revealed by the data in figs. 16 and 17. Therefore, according to the opinion of the author, in spite of the good fit obtained by Blewitt et al. [76] for their data by using Foreman's equation (which does not take into account any saturation) genuine saturation effects due to a decrease in the average size and/or the production rate of the dislocation obstacles with increasing dose cannot be excluded as an explanation for the deviation of the CSS from a proportionality to $(\phi t)^{1/2}$ at high neutron doses.

c) Temperature- and strain rate-dependence of the CSS

One of the characteristic features of neutron irradiation hardening of copper and other heavy fcc metals is a pronounced dependence of the CSS on the deformation temperature and the strain rate. If it is accepted (see above) that dispersed barrier

---

* This holds primarily for samples which were annealed at temperatures $\gtrsim 300°C$. But also with unannealed samples a slight decrease of the temperature coefficient of the CSS towards very low deformation temperatures is observed.

hardening is the predominant mechanism, these dependencies indicate that thermal activation contributes to the overcoming of the barriers. In recent years mainly two theories were applied in evaluating the temperature and strain rate dependence of the CSS. The one was proposed by Seeger [63], the other one by Fleischer [44,45]. Both are based on the principles of dispersed barrier hardening as they are outlined in section 2.1. Formally, they differ mainly in the force-distance relation used in deriving the temperature and strain rate dependence of the CSS *. Seeger introduced a $f(x)$ relation, which is approximated in the neighbourhood of $x = x_0$ (see fig. 1) by a parabola. With this approximation for high stresses (or low deformation temperatures) the CSS should follow the equation

$$\tau_0^{2/3} = \tau_0(T=0)^{2/3} \left[1 - (T/T_0)^{2/3}\right] \tag{16}$$

with

$$T_0 = \tfrac{2}{3}\Delta G_0/k \, \log(\dot{a}_0/\dot{a}) \,. \tag{16a}$$

Fleischer [45], in assuming that the dislocation barriers are small dislocation loops which interact with the dislocations like elastic dipoles, uses the $f(x)$ relation of such an interaction and obtains

$$\tau_0^{1/2} = \tau_0(T=0)^{1/2} \left[1 - (T/T_0)^{1/2}\right] \tag{17}$$

with $T_0$ having a numerical constant which is different from that in eq. (16a). We will return to Fleischer's relations later.

Seeger could show that the data of Blewitt et al. [61] on the $T$-dependence of the CSS of Cu single crystals can be fitted quite well to the linear relation between $\tau_0^{2/3}$ and $T^{2/3}$ of eq. (16). Experimental results of Makin and Minter [58] on the lattice friction component of the yield stress of polycrystalline copper and nickel also follow eq. (16) to a good approximation.

Deviations from eq. (16) at higher temperatures as they were revealed by more detailed measurements of Rukwied and Diehl [68,69] on Cu single crystals could be accounted for by using the complete force-distance relation proposed by Seeger [63] and the corresponding formula for the temperature dependence of the CSS (instead of the approximation for low temperatures).

Serious difficulties in applying Seeger's original relations arose whenever measurements on the temperature dependence and on the strain rate sensitivity of the CSS were combined for determining activation energies. If methods such as the one given in ref. [68] were used to determine $\Delta G_0$, different values were obtained for different deformation temperatures (and also for different neutron doses) [55,68–

---

* A further difference is that Seeger takes into account the shortening of the mean obstacle distance along a dislocation line $l$ with increasing shear stress, which is caused by the bowing out of the dislocation and follows according to Friedel [76a], the formula $l^3 = \mu b/\tau N_A$.

70,78]. This was interpreted (see e.g. [70]) in terms of the presence of an obstacle size spectrum instead of obstacles of uniform size, as they are assumed to be present in Seeger's original treatment. Roughly speaking, such on obstacle size spectrum would effect the temperature dependence of the CSS in such a way that in different temperature regions different sections of the size distribution would be predominant in determining the "effective" activation energy of slip. The reason for this is that at high temperatures the small obstacles are "transparent" for the moving dislocations * in comparison to the big ones, which then solely are rate determining for the dislocation motion, whereas at lower temperatures also smaller obstacles contribute effectively in impeding the dislocation motion (for more details see refs. [80,81]). Another indication for the presence of obstacles of different sizes was the observation that the activation energy $\Delta G(\tau)$ does not vary linearly with the deformation temperature [70,79] as it should be the case for dislocation obstacles of uniform size (see conclusion (2) in section 2.1).

Makin et al. [58,66], see also ref. [77], were led to conclude that obstacles of different size are present in n-irradiated Cu by the observation that upon "mild" annealing at temperatures around 300°C the CSS at low deformation temperatures decreases much faster than the CSS at high deformation temperatures (compare fig. 19). Cases were observed in which an annealing treatment decreased the CSS at 4.2°K as much as 50% without altering the CSS at room temperature appreciably. This can be accounted for easily with the view that at room temperature mainly big obstacles determine the CSS, which anneal out with an higher activation energy than the smaller ones contributing strongly to the low temperature CSS. Corresponding differences in the activation energy of annealing were observed by Makin, Whapam and Minter [65] **.

A second difficulty in analysing the temperature and strain rate dependence of the CSS was pointed out by Schwink and coworkers [82–84]. In most investigations it is assumed that the shear strain rate $\dot{a}$ within the regions of the crystal participating in the deformation process is proportional to the elongation rate $\dot{l}$ or to the (average) tensile strain rate $l^{-1}\dot{l} = \dot{\epsilon}$ for all strain rates and deformation temperatures. By microkinematography of the development of slip bands Schwink and Neuhäuser [83] found that the ratio between the actual shear strain rate within the slip bands and the elongation rate varies appreciably with the speed of deformation. For strain rates which are not to small empirically the following relation was observed

$$(\dot{a}/\dot{a}_1) - 1 = \beta(\dot{\epsilon}/\dot{\epsilon}_1 - 1) \ . \tag{18}$$

---

\* This means that the waiting times of the dislocations at small obstacles are very short in comparison to those at big obstacles.

\*\* It should be noted that annealing studies of Ast and Diehl [59] on nickel single crystals revealed that the annealing behaviour follows simpler laws in this metal, indicating that the size distribution of the dislocation obstacles in nickel after irradiation at ambient reactor temperatures is much narrower than in copper or (with respect to the analysis of the annealing of radiation hardening) negligible.

Thereby $\dot{a}_1$ and $\dot{\epsilon}_1$ correspond to a reference speed. If $\dot{a}$ and $\dot{\epsilon}$ would be proportional to each other, $\beta$ would be one. The actual $\beta$-values observed are much smaller. This effect obviously has to be correlated with the inhomogeneity of the deformation of neutron irradiated copper. Due to the formation of Luders bands, as they were observed first under these conditions by Blewitt et al. [61], slip is concentrated on a small portion of the crystal ("active crystal length" [84]) and not distributed homogeneously over the crystal in the beginning of deformation. The phenomenon observed by Schwink et al. indicates that the portion of the crystal participating in the deformation increases with increasing strain rate, leading to a decrease of the ratio $\dot{a}/\dot{l}$. This effect, which depends on the deformation temperature [79,85] has to be taken into account, if the CSS is evaluated quantitatively and especially if the strain rate sensitivity of the CSS $(\partial\tau/\partial \log \dot{a})_T$ is determined from tests in which the elongation rate is changed *.

The first analysis of the CSS of n-irradiated copper in which both the variation of the deformation inhomogeneity and the presence of an obstacle size spectrum were taken into account, was carried out by Diehl, Seidel and Niemann [79,80]. These authors assumed for all obstacles the force-distance relations of the Seeger type to hold and the "strengths" of the dislocation barriers to depend on one single parameter. On this basis semi-quantitative conclusions on the obstacle spectrum could be derived from experimental results on the temperature and strain rate dependence of the CSS.

A much more detailed treatment of the problem was given recently in a series of papers by Frank [81], Rühle [56], and Frank, Rühle and Saxlová [67]. In this treatment it is assumed that the defect agglomerates visible in transmission electron microscopy are the origin of the radiation induced increase of the CSS. According to earlier investigations by Rühle [88] these agglomerates are Frank dislocation loops and nearly all of them were determined to be of the vacancy type. The first step towards an analysis of the CSS was to determine the density and the size distribution of the observable defects and to measure, for the same neutron dose, the temperature dependence of the CSS. In qualitative agreement with Scheidler et al. [89], Rühle [56] observed that the volume density of defects with radii between $r - \frac{1}{2}\Delta r$ and $r + \frac{1}{2}\Delta r$ varies with the radius as

$$V(r)\Delta r = V(0) \exp(-r/r_0)\Delta r \tag{19}$$

with $V(0) = 1.2 \times 10^{11}$ $(\text{cm}^3 \times 25$ Å$)^{-1}$ and $2r_0 = 55$ Å. The corresponding results on the temperature dependence of the CSS are shown in fig. 19 **.

---

* Further studies on the variation of the microscopic shear strain rate with the test conditions were carried out by Makin and Sharp [86] and more recently in a very thorough way by Neuhäuser [85,87].

** Fig. 19 also contains the temperature dependence of the CSS of crystals annealed at 325°C for various annealing times. These results demonstrate the above mentioned observation of Makin et al. [58,66] and others that the CSS at low temperatures anneals out faster than the CSS at elevated temperature.

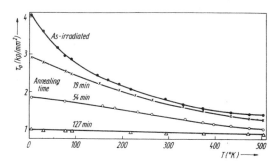

Fig. 19. Temperature dependence of the CSS of as-irradiated (irradiation temperature 80°C) and annealed copper crystals ($\phi t = 4 \times 10^{17}$ n/cm$^2$; annealing temperature 325°C). After Rühle [56].

The second step was to calculate by means of elasticity theory the force-distance relation and the corresponding activation energy for a dislocation moving on a slip plane close to a Frank dislocation loop in dependence of the three parameters: distance between slip plane and dislocation loop, diameter of the loop and relative orientation between slip plane and loop [90].

As a third step Frank [81] developed a theory for the thermally activated motion of dislocations in the presence of an obstacle spectrum, in which the strength of the obstacles is allowed to depend on an arbitrary number of characteristic parameters. According to this theory the shear strain rate $\dot{a}$ follows, even in the presence of a multiple spectrum of dislocation obstacles, an Arrhenius equation (see eq. (2)) with a constant pre-exponential factor and an average activation energy $\overline{\Delta G}$, which can be determined experimentally in the usual way (see below). This result will be used in the following.

The final step in the analysis of Frank et al. [67] was to calculate from the observed density and size distribution of the dislocation loops by means of the theoretical results in ref. [90] the distribution of the individual activation energies (in dependence on the effective shear stress and the deformation temperature) on a given slip plane and to feed these results and the measured temperature dependence of the CSS into the multiple spectrum theory. By means of rather laborious computer calculations the temperature dependence of the actual strain rate and of the average activation energy $\overline{\Delta G}$ shown in figs. 20 and 21 could be determined in this way. It should be mentioned that no adjustable parameters were introduced in this analysis.

The theoretical results in figs. 20 and 21 can be compared with experimental observations. Frank et al. determined the mean enthalpy of activation $\overline{\Delta H}$ from the temperature and the strain rate sensitivity of the CSS according to the frequently used formula

$$\overline{\Delta H} = -kT^2 (\partial \log(\dot{a}/\dot{a}_0)/\partial \tau_0)_T \, (\partial \tau_0/\partial T)_{\dot{a}/\dot{a}_0} \tag{20}$$

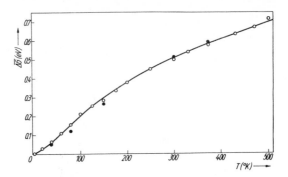

Fig. 20. Variation of the effective activation energy $\overline{\Delta G}$ of neutron irradiated copper with the temperature. Solid curve through the open circles calculated with the "spectrum theory", full circles: $\Delta H$-values determined from combined measurements of the strain rate and the temperature sensitivities of the CSS ($\phi t = 4 \times 10^{17}$ n/cm$^2$). After Frank et al. [67].

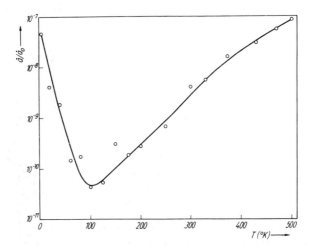

Fig. 21. Variation of the actual shear strain rate $\dot{a}$ with the deformation temperature evaluated by means of the "spectrum theory" ($\phi t = 4 \times 10^{17}$ n/cm$^2$). After Frank et al. [67].

(taking into account the variation of the inhomogeneity of the deformation) and presented arguments according to which in the present case $\overline{\Delta H}$ and $\overline{\Delta G}$ should differ only little. Fig. 20 shows that the experimental results on $\overline{\Delta H}$ (full circles) are in good agreement with the theoretically calculated variation of $\overline{\Delta G}$ (open circles).

The rather strong variations of the actual strain rate (for constant $\dot{\varepsilon}$) obtained from the spectrum theory (fig. 21) have to be compared with recent results of microkinematographical studies of Neuhäuser [85,87]. For a somewhat different neutron dose ($2 \times 10^{18}$ cm$^{-2}$) and a number of deformation rates he obtained the variation of the actual strain rate $\dot{a}$ with the deformation temperature, shown in

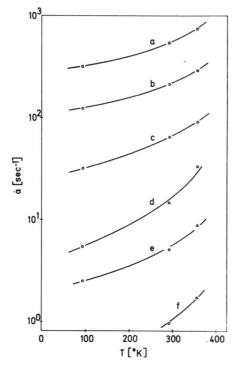

Fig. 22. Variation of the actual shear strain rate as determined by means of microkinematography with the deformation temperature ($\phi t = 2 \times 10^{18}$ n/cm$^2$) for various deformation speeds $l$ (mm/sec): (a) $3.75 \times 10^{-2}$, (b) $1.25 \times 10^{-2}$, (c) $1.78 \times 10^{-3}$, (d) $1.08 \times 10^{-4}$, (e) $1.88 \times 10^{-5}$, (f) $2.08 \times 10^{-6}$. After Neuhäusler [87].

fig. 22. The general tendency of these direct measurements agrees with the results of the theory in fig. 21. Since only for three deformation temperatures such direct measurements are available, it cannot be decided whether the minimum of $\dot{a}/\dot{a}_0$ at about 100°K and the strong increase towards lower temperatures in fig. 21 occurs in reality. According to Frank et al. [67] it seems to be not unlikely that $\dot{a}$ increases if the deformation temperature approaches 0°K, since at this temperature the strain rate dependence of the CSS vanishes and without a strain rate dependence of the CSS, there remains no energetic reason for spreading out the deformation over a larger volume of the crystal (which would reduce the actual strain rate).

The analysis of Frank, Rühle and Saxlová gives a rather consistent description of the temperature dependence of the CSS. What remains open for a complete understanding is the question for the physical reasons of the strong variations of the actual strain rate with deformation temperature and deformation rate. An attempt to interpret this originally rather unexpected behaviour is due to Schwink [84].

Another approach to a consistent interpretation of the temperature and the strain

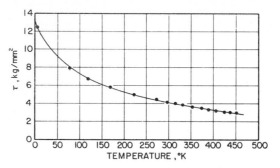

Fig. 23. Temperature dependence of the CSS of copper single crystals irradiated with $8 \times 10^{18}$ n/cm$^2$. After Koppenaal and Arsenault [91].

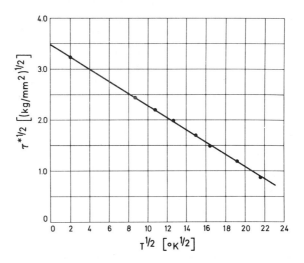

Fig. 24. Fleischer plot of the thermal component $\tau^*$ of the CSS with data from fig. 23, according to Koppenaal and Arsenault [91].

rate dependence of the CSS of heavy fcc metals is due to Koppenaal and Arsenault [91–96]. This interpretation is also based on the assumption that small dislocation loops formed during the neutron irradiation impede the dislocation motion by a dispersed barrier hardening mechanism. The force-distance relation which these authors prefer is that derived by Fleischer [44,45] for the interaction between a dislocation and a defect with tetragonal stress field, which leads to the temperature and strain rate dependence of eq. (17). Koppenaal and Arsenault reach good agreement with the predictions of Fleischer's theory on the temperature dependence of the CSS, the strain rate dependence of the CSS, and the stress dependence of the activation energy. As an example, the temperature dependence of the CSS of copper after irradiation with $8 \times 10^{18}$ n/cm$^2$ measured by Koppenaal and Arsenault [91] is shown in fig. 23. Fig. 24 gives the corresponding plot of the square root of the thermal component of the CSS versus the square root of the deformation temperature.

Although at a first glance the agreement between theory and experiment is very impressive in Koppenaal's and Arsenault's work, it has nevertheless to be considered with some precautions. The agreement seems to be enforced by rather arbitrary assumptions (see refs. [56,97,98]). One of them is the assumption that besides the thermal component of the CSS $\tau^*$ also the athermal component $\tau_\mu$ is increased appreciably by neutron irradiation. In the example given in figs. 23 and 24 $\tau_\mu$ was assumed to be as high as 2.0 kg/mm$^2$ (about 50% of the CSS at room temperature). Furthermore, the variation of the deformation inhomogeneity as well as the presence of an obstacle size spectrum is neglected in Koppenaal's and Arsenault's analysis. Neglecting the size spectrum involves the necessity to assume a second type of dislocation obstacles in a recent attempt [96] to interpret the above mentioned difference in the annealing of the "low temperature" and the "high temperature" CSS (compare ref. [77]). Although Koppenaal's and Arsenault's analysis of neutron irradiation hardening is the simpler one, the interpretations taking into account an obstacle size spectrum (as it will exist in all cases in which extended dislocation obstacles are present) and the experimentally observed deformation inhomogeneities seem to be the more realistic ones.

### 3.3.2. Aluminium

a) Annealing of the CSS after low temperature irradiation

The already mentioned observation of McReynolds et al. [3] that in pure aluminium the increase of the CSS due to a reactor irradiation at 80°K anneals out completely below room temperature was later on confirmed by Diehl et al. [99]. The isochronal annealing curve of aluminium single crystals irradiated with $2 \times 10^{17}$ n/cm$^2$ at a temperature $< 20°K$, measured by these authors, is shown in fig. 25. In addition, fig. 25 shows an annealing curve of the change in electrical resistivity, measured by Burger et al. [100] after irradiation with a similar neutron dose. A comparison of fig. 25 with fig. 15 indicates clearly the basic difference between neutron irradiation hardening of aluminium and of a heavy fcc metals like copper. Whereas the CSS of Cu is little affected by the annealing out of the defects, which cause most of the change in the electrical resistivity, in aluminium electrical resistivity and CSS show a very similar annealing behaviour and both anneal out completely in the annealing stage III between 200°K and 300°K. From the results in fig. 25 and the comparison with copper (fig. 15) the following conclusions can be drawn [70,99]: (1) Similarly as in copper, hardening originates from defects produced in situ and not by an agglomeration of defects, which involves thermally activated migration of the constituents of the agglomerates. (2) In aluminium the defect cascades, produced by energetic knock-on atoms, are less compact than in copper and, therefore, no depleted zones are formed within these cascades in

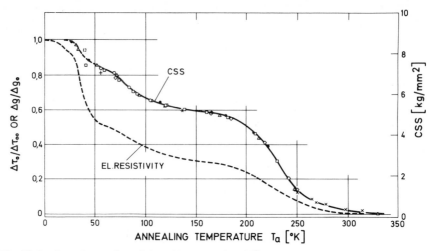

Fig. 25. Isochronal annealing of the CSS measured at 20°K and the electrical resistivity of neutron irradiated aluminium after low temperature irradiation ($\phi t = 2 \times 10^{17}$ n/cm$^2$). $\Delta \tau_{oo}$ and $\Delta \rho_0$ are the values measured immediately after irradiation. After refs. [99,100].

aluminium. (3) Hardening in aluminium must be caused by such simple point defects or defect configurations, which anneal out in the stages I to III. (4) Since the hardening is too strong to be caused by individual vacancies or small multiple vacancies, it originates most likely from interstitial atoms.

The conclusion that hardening in this case is caused by individual point defects rather than by bigger defect agglomerates (as e.g. in copper) was checked by a more quantitative comparison between the variations of the CSS and the electrical resistivity in stage III, in which vacancies and interstitials are believed to disappear by mutual annihilation. It was found [70,99] that within this annealing stage the remaining increase of the CSS is approximately proportional to the square root of the remaining change in electrical resistivity, as it would be expected for dispersed barrier hardening if during annealing only the number of the barriers decreases (without a change in the size or the configuration of the barriers) and if the electrical resistivity is proportional to the number of the barriers. So, the dispersed barrier hardening mechanism seemed to be applicable also in the case of neutron irradiated aluminium, although it has to be expected that deviations in the randomness of the barrier distribution exist if the barriers are point defects produced within displacement cascades.

b) Temperature- and strain rate-dependence of the CSS

For a further analysis of the hardening mechanism the dependence of the CSS on the deformation temperature was measured in refs. [99,101] after annealing the samples at 140°K. After this treatment only the "stage III defects" remain in the sample. If the above mentioned conclusions are correct and more or less randomly

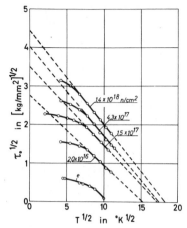

Fig. 26. Temperature dependence of the CSS of aluminium single crystals irradiated at $\leqslant 20°$K with various neutron doses and annealed at 140°K. After Leitz et al. [101]. Curve for e-irradiation after Buck et al. [54].

distributed interstitial atoms cause the hardening, Fleischer's [44] and Frank's [7] theories for dispersed barrier hardening due to defects with tetragonal symmetry, which were discussed in connection with electron irradiation hardening in section 3.2.2, should apply. Since these theories predict linearity between $\tau_0^{1/2}$ and $T^{1/2}$ (see eq. (9)), the results of Leitz et al. [101] presented in fig. 26 are plotted correspondingly.

Fig. 26 shows that the CSS depends strongly on temperature and follows eq. (9) at temperatures above 60°K. At lower temperatures the temperature dependence is much smaller. This behaviour will be discussed later.

In the temperature range in which $\tau_0^{1/2}$ varies linearly with $T^{1/2}$ the thermally activated motion of the dislocations was analysed further by Leitz et al. [101]. The main results are the following: (1) The influence of the deformation inhomogeneities on the strain rate sensitivity, determined by a method proposed by Diehl et al. [79], is relatively small. Neglecting it in determining the activation energy for slip leads to errors not larger than a few percent. (2) The activation energy $\Delta G$ determined from measurements of the strain rate sensitivity and the temperature dependence of the CSS by means of Schoeck's [6] formula (see also ref. [79]) varies within experimental errors linearly with the temperature of the measurements for three neutron doses investigated in this way. This indicates that eq. (2) holds. (3) An average value of the activation energy $\Delta G_0$ for measurements at $4 \times 10^{18}$ n/cm$^2$ is 0.69 eV. (This value was determined by means of eq. (9a); $\log(\dot{a}_0/\dot{a})$ was obtained from the slopes of the $\Delta G - T$ curves.)

All these results are consistent with the assumption that the CSS is determined by the interaction of the dislocations with dispersed interstitial atoms. The activation energy $\Delta G_0$ is close to the value (14) obtained from the dose dependence of the hardening after electron irradiation, indicating the similarity in the hardening mechanism for both types of irradiation. In the light of current interpretations of the annealing stages (see ref. [102]) the question arises whether the interstitials acting as dislocation obstacles in the samples, which were annealed at 140°K are trapped at impurities. On the basis of the present results such a trapping seems not to be very likely since for $4 \times 10^{17}$ and $1.4 \times 10^{18}$ n/cm$^2$ the obstacle concentration derived from eq. (9) is by more than a factor of 10 higher than the nominal impurity content of the samples.

The deviations in the temperature dependence of the CSS from the straight lines in fig. 26 at low temperatures has not yet been explained satisfactorily. This low temperature behaviour occurs at all neutron doses investigated. Since according to the measurements of Buck et al. [54], which are also shown in fig. 26, electron irradiated aluminium with a much lower obstacle concentration shows qualitatively the same behaviour at low temperatures, these deviations seem to be characteristic for the dislocation interstitial interaction. Among different possibilities to interpret this behaviour, Leitz [101] regards the stress induced rotation of interstitials in the dumb-bell configuration to be the most likely one. In this configuration the interstitials are split up in a ⟨100⟩ direction and, therefore, have three possible orientations in the lattice. If a dislocation is pressed against an interstitial with a high stress (small distance between dislocation and interstitial) it might be that the interstitial rotates under the action of the stress field into another orientation before the dislocation can pass the interstitial in the original orientation by means of thermal activation. If furthermore, in the course of this rotation, the interstitial reaches a configuration in which the interaction with the dislocation is smaller than in its original orientation, the stress induced reorientation will be rate determining for the dislocation motion. Leitz et al. [101] argue that at high stresses (low temperatures) this process becomes more likely in comparison to the normal thermally activated overcoming of the interstitials without a rotation and that, therefore, the stress induced reorientation of interstitials can possibly explain the deviations of the CSS at very low temperatures from the behaviour at higher temperatures.

c) Dose dependence

A linear increase of the CSS with the square root of the neutron dose, as it is expected for dispersed barrier hardening was observed only for very small doses. The slope $\mathrm{d}\tau_0/\mathrm{d}\sqrt{\phi t}$ of the dose curve decreases appreciably with increasing dose. This decrease could at least partly be due to radiation annealing. This influence can be suppressed by plotting the CSS versus the square root of the resistivity change, which is a measure of the actual defect concentration. Fig. 27 shows that also in such a diagram strong deviations from a linear relation occur. This is true for the crystals irradiated at < 20°K and annealed at 20°K, as well as for those annealed at 55°K or 140°K after irradiation with different doses.

Before these deviations from linearity will be discussed, it should be noted that

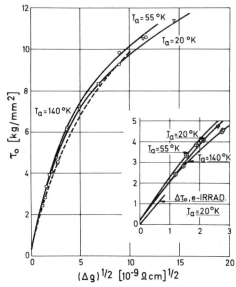

Fig. 27. Variation of the CSS of aluminium with the square root of the resistivity increase. $T_a$ annealing temperature; dashed curve; $T_a = 140°K$. After Leitz et al. [101]. Initial slope for e-irradiation corresponds to the values given in section 3.2.2.

the initial slopes of all three curves shown in fig. 27 are almost the same and that this initial slope agrees quite well with the corresponding slope of electron irradiated samples (compare section 3.2.2). This apparently confirms that the same type of dislocation obstacles is responsible for the CSS after neutron and after electron irradiation and it furthermore indicates that the type of obstacle does not change basicly upon annealing. This supports the conclusion drawn in the last paragraph, according to which also after annealing at 140°K interstitial atoms are the predominant dislocation obstacles.

It has been shown that the behaviour at very small defect concentrations (see last paragraph, agreement with electron irradiation) and at rather high concentrations (temperature dependence after neutron irradiation up to $1.4 \times 10^{18}$ n/cm$^2$) can consistently be interpreted by the same hardening mechanism. If this is accepted, the curvature of the dose curves in fig. 27 has to be accounted for by a decrease of the production rate of effective dislocation obstacles with increasing total defect concentration. A possible mechanism for this decrease is the athermal agglomeration (taking place already at $\leqslant 20°K$) of interstitials. The formation of such agglomerates would reduce the production rate of single interstitials, it would increase the average distance between the dislocation obstacles and consequently decrease the CSS (in comparison to the same number of interstitials being randomly distributed in the lattice). Such an athermal agglomeration will become more effective with increasing concentration of the defects and could, therefore, explain the general trend of the dose dependence of the CSS.

## 4. Concluding remarks

Most of the hardening mechanisms observed in quenched and irradiated fcc metals involve the thermally activated motion of dislocations. For a conclusive interpretation of such a hardening mechanism the thermally activated process has to be analysed by means of evaluating the temperature and the strain rate dependence of the CSS in terms of activation energies (in its dependence on stress and temperature). As outlined in section 3.3.1 in the case of neutron irradiated copper the methods for evaluating the thermally activated dislocation motion have been refined very much during recent years from an experimental as well as from a theoretical point of view. These improvements take into account deformation inhomogeneities and the presence of obstacles of different sizes. It could be learned from the experiences made in the past on the example of neutron irradiated copper that evaluations of the thermally activated processes can sometimes be quite misleading if deformation inhomogeneities and obstacle size distributions are disregarded.

In quenched metals investigations of the thermally activated processes of comparable thoroughness have not yet been carried out. Since, however, in most cases rather extended vacancy precipitates were found to be responsible for quench hardening and since furthermore in quite a number of cases a yield phenomenon (which is mostly combined with inhomogeneous deformation) is observed, it seems to be not unlikely that more detailed studies of quench-hardened metals would lead to similar complications as they have been found in neutron irradiated copper. To investigate this may be a task for further research. These considerations led the author to report quantitative results on activation energies only in cases where deformation inhomogeneities and obstacle size spectrum were taken into account or proved to be not of importance.

## References

[1] C.H.Li, J.Washburn and E.R.Parker, Trans. AIME 197 (1953) 1223.
[2] R.Maddin and A.H.Cottrell, Phil. Mag. 46 (1955) 735.
[3] A.W.McReynolds, W.Augustiniak, M.McKewon and D.B.Rosenblatt, Phys. Rev. 98 (1955) 418.
[4] H.Kimura and R.Maddin, Lattice Defects in Quenched Metals (Academic Press, New York, London, 1965) p. 319.
[5] M.Meshii, Lattice Defects in Quenched Metals (Academic Press, New York, London, 1965) p. 387.
[6] G.Schoeck, Phys. Stat. Sol. 8 (1965) 499.
[7] W.Frank, Z. Naturforsch. 22a (1967) 365, 377.
[8] E.Orowan, Symp. Internal Stresses in Metals and Alloys (Institute of Metals, London, 1948) p. 451.
[9] A.J.E.Foreman, Phil. Mag. 15 (1967) 1011.
[10] R.De Wit and J.S.Koehler, Phys. Rev. 116 (1959) 1113.
[11] D.Kuhlmann-Wilsdorf, R.Maddin and H.G.F.Wilsdorf, Strengthening Mechanisms in Solids (ASM, 1962) p. 137.

[12] A.H.Cottrell, Vacancies and Other Point Defects in Metals and Alloys (Institute of Metals London, 1958) p. 1.
[13] D.Kuhlmann-Wilsdorf and H.G.F.Wilsdorf, Electron Microscopy and Strength of Crystals (Wiley, New York, 1962) p. 575.
[14] H.Kimura, R.Maddin and D.Kuhlmann-Wilsdorf, Acta Met. 7 (1959) 154.
[15] M.Meshii and J.W.Kauffman, Acta Met. 7 (1959) 180.
[16] J.Galligan and J.Washburn, Phil. Mag. 8 (1963) 1455.
[17] R.M.J.Cotterill, Ph.D. Thesis, Cambridge University (1962).
[18] A.Eikum and G.Thomas, J. Appl. Phys. 34 (1963) 3363.
[19] J.L.Davidson and J.M.Galligan, Phys. Stat. Sol. 26 (1968) 345.
[20] D.Coulomb, Acta Met. 7 (1959) 556.
[21] F.Kroupa and P.B.Hirsch, Disc. Faraday Soc. 38 (1964) 49.
[22] A.Seeger, V.Gerold and M.Rühle, Z. Metallkunde 54 (1963) 493.
[23] M.Meshii and J.W.Kauffman, Phil. Mag. 5 (1960) 939.
[24] T.Mori, M.Meshii and J.W.Kauffman, Acta Met. 9 (1961) 71.
[25] J.Silcox and P.B.Hirsch, Phil. Mag. 4 (1959) 72.
[26] R.M.J.Cotterill, Phil. Mag. 6 (1961) 1351.
[27] S.Yoshida, M.Kiritani, Y.Deguchi and N.Kamigaki, Intern. Conf. on the Strength of Metals and Alloys; Trans. Japan Inst. Met. 9 (1968) 83.
[28] Y.Imashimizu and H.Kimura, Intern. Conf. on the Strength of Metals and Alloys; Trans. Japan Inst. Met. 9 (1968) 89.
[29] K.H.Westmacott, Phil. Mag. 14 (1966) 239.
[30] K.H.Westmacott, The Nature of Small Defect Clusters (AERE-R5269, H.M. Stationery Office, London, 1966) p. 521.
[31] N.Shiotani, H.Kimura, R.R.Hasiguti and R.Maddin, Acta Met. 15 (1967) 287.
[32] P.B.Hirsch, J.Silcox, R.E.Smallman and K.H.Westmacott, Phil. Mag. 3 (1958) 397.
[33] J.Friedel, Electron Microscopy and Strength of Crystals (Wiley, New York, 1962) p. 605.
[34] S.Yoshida, M.Kiritani and Y.Shimomura, J. Electronmicroscopy 12 (1963) 146.
[35] M.Kiritani, J. Phys. Soc. Japan 19 (1964) 618.
[36] M.Kiritani, Y.Shimomura and S.Yoshida, J. Phys. Soc. Japan 19 (1964) 1624.
[37] S.Yoshida, M.Kiritani and Y.Shimomura, Lattice Defects in Quenched Metals (Academic Press, New York, London, 1965) p. 713.
[38] M.Wilkens, this volume.
[39] C.H.Meechan and C.E.Dixon, NAA-SR-268 (1953).
[40] C.E.Dixon and C.H.Meechan, Phys. Rev. 91 (1955) 237.
[41] M.J.Makin and T.H.Blewitt, Acta Met. 10 (1962) 241.
[42] K.Ono, T.Mifune and M.Meshii. Phil. Mag. 17 (1968) 235.
[43] H.Wenzl, this volume.
[44] R.L.Fleischer, Acta Met. 10 (1962) 835.
[45] R.L.Fleischer, J. Appl. Phys. 33 (1962) 3504.
[46] W.Frank, Phys. Stat. Sol. 18 (1966) 459.
[47] A.Seeger, E.Mann and R.v.Jan, J. Phys. Chem. Solids 23 (1962) 639.
[48] D.Keefer and A.Sosin, Acta Met. 12 (1964) 696.
[49] M.Meshi, T.Mifune and K.Ono, Intern. Conf. on the Strength of Metals and Alloys; Trans. Japan Inst. Met. 9 (1968) 193.
[50] K.Ono, M.Meshii and J.W.Kauffman, Acta Met. 12 (1964) 361.
[51] K.Ono and M.Meshii, Acta Met. 13 (1965) 1123.
[52] K.Ono and M.Meshii, Appl. Phys. Letters 7 (1965) 191.
[53] K.Ono and M.Meshii, Lattice Defects and their Interactions (Gordon and Breach, New York, London, Paris, 1967) p. 713.
[54] O.Buck, D.Keefer, J.Robinson, A.Sosin and H.Wiedersich, Acta Met. 16 (1968) 195.

[55] J.Fischer, Z. Naturforsch. 17a (1962) 603.

[56] M.Rühle, Phys. Stat. Sol. 26 (1968) 661.

[57] T.J.Koppenaal, Intern. Conf. on the Strength of Metals and Alloys; Trans. Japan Inst. Met. 9 (1968) 205.

[58] M.J.Makin and F.J.Minter, Acta Met. 8 (1960) 691.

[59] D.Ast and J.Diehl, Phys. Stat. Sol. 17 (1966) 269.

[60] J.M.Galligan and M.J.Attardo, Phys. Stat. Sol. 27 (1968) 383.

[61] T.H.Blewitt, R.R.Coltman, R.E.Jamison and J.K.Redman, J. Nucl. Mat. 2 (1960) 277.

[62] J.Diehl, C.Leitz and W.Schilling, Phys. Letters 4 (1963) 236.

[63] A.Seeger, Proc. 2nd UN Intern. Conf. PUAE 6 (1958) 250.

[64] J.Silcox and P.B.Hirsch, Phil. Mag. 4 (1959) 1356.

[65] M.J.Makin, A.D.Whapam and F.J.Minter, Phil. Mag. 6 (1961) 465.

[66] M.J.Makin, F.J.Minter and S.A.Manthorpe, Phil. Mag. 13 (1966) 729.

[67] W.Frank, M.Rühle and M.Saxlová, Phys. Stat. Sol. 26 (1968) 671.

[68] J.Diehl, Radiation Damage in Solids, vol. I (IAEA, Vienna, 1962) p. 129.

[69] A.Rukwied and J.Diehl, Z. Metallkunde 55 (1964) 266.

[70] J.Diehl and W.Schilling, Proc. 3rd UN Intern. Conf. PUAE 9 (1965) 72.

[71] T.H.Blewitt and T.J.Koppenaal, Radiation Effects (Gordon and Breach, New York, London, Paris, 1967) p. 561.

[72] T.H.Blewitt and C.A.Arenberg, Intern. Conf. on the Strength of Metals and Alloys; Trans. Japan Inst. Met. 9 (1968) 226.

[73] J.Diehl, Intern. Conf. on the Strength of Metals and Alloys; Trans. Japan Inst. Met. 9 (1968) 231.

[74] A.Seeger, Encyclopaedia of Physics, vol. 7/II (Springer-Verlag, Berlin, Heidelberg, Göttingen, 1958) p. 1.

[75] J.Diehl, D.Brunner, W.Decker, C.Leitz and W.Mensch, unpublished (see ref. [73]).

[76] T.H.Blewitt, C.A.Arenberg, A.C.Clank and T.Scott, Jül. Conf. 2 (1968) p. 547.

[76a] J.Friedel, Les Dislocations (Gauthier-Villars, 1956).

[77] M.J.Makin, Phil. Mag. 18 (1968) 1245.

[78] T.J.Koppenaal, Phil. Mag. 8 (1963) 1725.

[79] J.Diehl, G.P.Seidel and L.Niemann, Phys. Stat. Sol. 11 (1965) 339.

[80] J.Diehl, G.P.Seidel and L.Niemann, Phys. Stat. Sol. 12 (1965) 405.

[81] W.Frank, Phys. Stat. Sol. 26 (1968) 197.

[82] C.Schwink and G.Grieshammer, Phys. Stat. Sol. 6 (1964) 665.

[83] C.Schwink and H.Neuhäuser, Phys. Stat. Sol. 6 (1964) 679.

[84] C.Schwink, Phys. Stat. Sol. 7 (1964) 481.

[85] H.Neuhäuser, Phys. Stat. Sol. 25 (1968) 593.

[86] M.J.Makin and J.V.Sharp, Phys. Stat. Sol. 9 (1965) 109.

[87] H.Neuhäuser, Phys. Stat. Sol. 27 (1968) 281.

[88] M.Rühle, Phys. Stat. Sol. 19 (1967) 263.

[89] P.G.Scheidler, M.J.Makin, F.J.Minter and W.Schilling, The Nature of Small Defect Clusters (AERE-R 5269, H.M. Stationery Office, London, 1966) p. 405.

[90] M.Saxlová, Czech. J. Phys. B19 (1969) 610.

[91] T.J.Koppenaal and R.J.Arsenault, Phil. Mag. 12 (1965) 951.

[92] R.J.Arsenault and T.J.Koppenaal, Appl. Phys. Letters 6 (1965) 159.

[93] T.J.Koppenaal, Phil. Mag. 11 (1965) 1257.

[94] T.J.Koppenaal and R.J.Arsenault, Phys. Stat. Sol. 17 (1966) 27.

[95] T.J.Koppenaal, Acta Met. 15 (1967) 681.

[96] T.J.Koppenaal, Intern. Conf. on the Strength of Metals and Alloys, Trans. Japan Inst. Met. 9 (1968) 200; Acta Met. 16 (1968) 89.

[97] J.Diehl and G.P.Seidel, Phys. Stat. Sol. 17 (1966) 43.

[98] C.Schwink and H.Neuhäuser, Phys. Stat. Sol. 17 (1966) 35.
[99] J.Diehl, C.Leitz, W.Meissner, W.Schilling and H.Wenzl, unpublished, see ref. [70].
[100] G.Burger, H.Meissner and W.Schilling, Phys. Stat. Sol. 4 (1964) 267.
[101] C.Leitz, W.Decker, J.Diehl and W.Mensch, to be published.
[102] W.Schilling, G.Burger, K.Isebeck and H.Wenzl, this volume.

# PART 6

# THEORETICAL STUDIES

# THEORY OF POINT DEFECTS IN METALS

## J.FRIEDEL

*Service de Physique des Solides \*, Faculté des Sciences, Orsay, France*

## 1. Introduction

When asked, as I am today, to review the theory of point defects in metals, one is struck by the multiplicity of apparently competitive models that have been used in this field, more than by the results obtained. These are by no means negligible; but one is often left wondering about the validity of some of their details at least.

My aim today will therefore be to analyze and compare the main assumptions of these various models; I will not describe in detail the results obtained.

When looking at a vacancy (fig. 1) or at an interstitial (fig. 2) in motion through a crystal, one might focus the attention on the *nuclei,* and try and compute the atomic configurations and the energies involved, assuming simple phenomenological but reasonable interatomic forces and potentials. In fact these forces are related to the electronic structure of the metal, which is locally perturbed, owing to the scattering of the *electrons* by the defects. Thus, as often in solid state physics, simple-minded mechanistic models have been developed in parallel with models which try to go deeper into the electronic structure of the metal. These two types of models will be analyzed in succession.

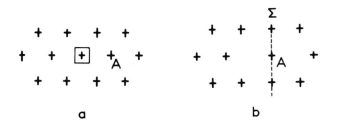

Fig. 1. Vacancy: a— full; b— split.

\* Laboratoire associé au CNRS.

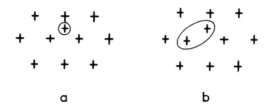

Fig. 2. Interstitial: a— full; b— split.

My main conclusion will be that these models are often complementary rather than competitive; and also that, at least in some simple cases such as light "normal" metals, there is now some hope of combining the two kinds of approaches into a more self-consistent description.

## 2. Continuous elasticity

### 2.1. *Description*

The simplest "mechanistic" model treats the defect $V'$ as a piece of elastic continuous medium, with its own size, form and elastic constants, stuck to the wall of a cavity $V$, with possibly different size and form, dug into the metal treated also as a classical elastic continuous medium [1—4] (fig. 3).

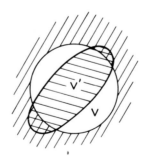

Fig. 3. Continuous elasticity model.

For a vacancy, the simplest assumption is that the cavity $V$ has atomic size and the defect itself has zero elastic constants (i.e. vacuum); an interstitial could be treated as an atomic volume $V'$ with the same elastic constants as the matrix, introduced into a very small cavity $V$ of the metal. For reasonably compact lattice structures, the cavity $V$ for the vacancy and the volume $V'$ for the interstitial can be assumed spherical for *full* defects (fig. 4a for fig. 1a, fig. 4c for fig. 2a), while elongated ellipsoids are more reasonable to picture *split* defects (fig. 4b for fig. 1b, fig. 4d for fig. 2b). With such rough schematization of the form of these defects, it would be rather senseless to use anything but the simplest *isotropic* elasticity.

## 2.2. Results

Let me recall the main results of this simple model:

*Atomic configuration:* The presence of *vacancies* should not produce any strain. Thus no change in lattice parameter should be observed; the only change in total volume, when a vacancy is created, should come from the atom extracted from the vacant site and added at the surface. Thus the relative decrease in density should be equal to the atomic concentration of vacancies. If anharmonic terms are neglected, the activation volume for vacancy creation should just equal the atomic volume; the activation volume for vacancy motion should be zero.

*Interstitials,* on the contrary, should produce large local lattice strains, decreasing in $r^{-3}$ with distance $r$. Because they are assumed to have the same elastic constants as the matrix, they should produce a total volume expansion which should just compensate for the loss of atoms at the surface when they are created. Thus the

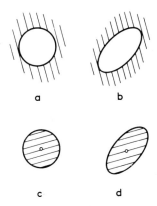

Fig. 4. Point defects in continuous elasticity: a– full vacancy; b– split vacancy; c– full interstitial; d– split interstitial.

relative increase in lattice parameter should just equal the atomic concentration of defects; there should thus be no change of density when interstitials are created, a general result for linear strains in a uniform medium [5] ; their activation volumes of formation and displacement should be zero.

*Stored elastic energy.* For a vacancy, it is zero in this model; for interstitials, it is of the order of

$$U \approx \tfrac{1}{2} E \epsilon^2 V' ,\qquad\qquad(1)$$

where $\epsilon$ is the shear necessary to adapt the defect to its cavity and $E$ the corresponding elastic constant. Here $\epsilon \approx 1$, leading to formation energies of the order of 5 eV. Furthermore, for the same volume $V'$, it is clear that the energy stored for an ellipsoidal defect is smaller than for a spherical one. This suggests the split interstitial to be a little more stable than the full one, but with a fairly small displacement energy.

*Coupling with external stresses.* Various effects can play a role here. *Vacancies* are soft spots, where the elastic energy stored by the external stress $\tau$ is locally relaxed. This "modulus" factor gives a coupling energy

$$w \approx -\frac{1}{2E} \tau^2 V ,\qquad\qquad(2)$$

where $E$ is again a suitable elastic constant. *Interstitials* can have on the other hand a "size" factor and, if split, a "shape" factor, leading to a coupling energy

$$w \approx \tau \epsilon V .\qquad\qquad(3)$$

$\tau$ is the hydrostatic component of the external stress for the size factor, and the shear stress for the shape factor; $\epsilon$ should be of the order of 1 in the first case, and is related to the elongation of the ellipsoid in the second.

Besides the diffusion effects already mentioned, these various factors should lead to the following effects:

a) For full defects or immobile split defects, no change of elastic constants for interstitials [6] ; a relative decrease of elastic constants of the order of the atomic concentration of vacancies.

b) For mobile split defects, a possible further lowering of the shear elastic constants, corresponding to an alignment of the defects with respect to the stress tensor. This effect disappears at a frequency equal to the free rotation frequency of the defect, where an internal friction Snoek peak is observed *.

c) Long-range interactions with dislocations *drag* interstitials towards the expanded side of the core of edge dislocations [7] with a force varying as $r^{-2}$ with the

---

* This alignment, if large enough, should reduce the X-ray line broadening due to the interstitials and produce anisotropic line shifts.

distance $r$. For vacancies, the dragging force exists for both types of dislocations (edge or screw) [8] and varies as $r^{-3}$. Furthermore, for split defects, a *torque* couples the direction of the defect with that of the local shear stress tensor [9].

*Couplings between point defects:* In this simple model, vacancies have clearly no elastic interactions; full interstitials have also no interaction force; full vacancies and interstitials attract each other with a force varying as $r^{-7}$, owing to the elastic relaxation, by the modulus factor of the vacancy, of the strains due to the size factor of the interstitial. Split interstitials attract [1].

## 2.3. Refinements

Two types of refinements have been proposed, each one for a different type of defect.

*Anharmonic terms.* The strains computed in the elastic model for the *interstitial* atom and the part of the matrix close to it are very large, of the order of 100%. The elastic approximation is not expected to hold in this range; anharmonic corrective terms can be included [2,10]. Because the interstitial atom is strongly compressed, the anharmonic terms make it definitely harder than the matrix. With a local compression of the order of 100%, a local increase in hardness of the order of 100% should result. This should lead to an increase in the elastic constants of the metal of the order of the atomic concentration of interstitials; this local hardness should also produce a local repulsion between interstitials, and a slight increase in the stored energy. Finally these anharmonic terms increase the local dilatation produced by the interstitials. The total increase in volume $\delta V$ due to the anharmonic terms is proportional to the elastic energy stored:

$$\delta V \approx \frac{\gamma U}{E} . \tag{4}$$

Gruneisen's constant $\gamma$ is of the order of two. $\delta V$ is of the order of an atomic volume. The activation volume for interstitial formation should be equal to $\delta V$, thus positive and proportional to the formation energy. The ratio of the volumes for motion and for creation should be small, as the ratio of the corresponding energies.

*Surface tension.* The elastic model neglects the strong scattering of the electrons of the metal by the cavity of the vacancy (fig. 1). This term can be taken roughly into account by treating the surface of the cavity as if it were a macroscopic free surface [11] with the same surface tension $\gamma$.

The energy of formation of the vacancies now contains a term $\gamma s$, where $s$ is the area of the cavity (fig. 4a or b). With $\gamma s \approx \mu b/10$ ($\mu$ shear modulus, $b$ interatomic distance), this is of the order of $\mu V/3 \approx 1$ to 2 eV. One can be tempted to refine this model, by allowing the surface $S$ of the cavity to shrink so as to minimize the total (elastic + surface) energy. Such a procedure always produces an appreciable shrinkage, by a notable fraction of the atomic volume in rather hard metals such as copper. It thus leads to very small voids in soft metals such as the alkalis. The same hypothesis of a constant surface tension would lead to split vacancy to be less stable than a full vacancy because of its larger area, whatever the exact model used (fig. 1b or 4b). The size factor of vacancies associated with this shrinkage leads to a long range interaction energy in $r^{-1}$ with edge dislocations and a small long range interaction between vacancies, due to the relaxation by one vacancy of the stresses due to the size effect of the other *.

### 2.4. Conclusions

This "prehistoric" model is admittedly very rough. Its main advantage is to give easily orders of magnitudes of many physical quantities. However, it cannot give a detailed description of the atomic structure and indeed some of its characteristic features, such as the ellipsicity of the split defects (figs. 4b and d) are hard to fix a priori. More refined atomistic models must be developed to answer these questions. Electronic structure studies are then necessary to test the validity of the whole "mechanistic" approach; they will also show the limitations of the concept of surface tension.

## 3. Model interatomic potentials

### 3.1. The assumptions

These models usually assume that the cohesive energy can be split into a sum of *pair potentials* [12] that are (fig. 5a and b)

a) independent, thus only a function of the interatomic distance,

b) short range, with a long-range exponential decrease which affects only very few neighbours.

Some early computations [13] used purely repulsive short range pair interactions. The cohesion of the crystal was maintained by applying an external pressure on its surface (fig. 5c).

This leads us to the problem of the boundary conditions. The main interest of these computations is to give a detailed description of the atomic distribution in the immediate neighbourhood of the defect. With this aim in view, most recent computations treat a microcrystal of typically 2000 to 3000 atoms. They introduce the defect near its center and only push the self-consistency of the computed displacements far enough from the defect to be within their limits of accuracy. In most cases, the size of the computed relaxed zone is definitely smaller than the size of the crystal. It is then clear that the exact nature of the boundary conditions is of no importance. The surface atoms can be free to move or be blocked on their lattice

---

* At nearest neighbour distance, the spheres of fig. 4a overlap, and the model breaks down. In that case, one can reasonably assume a total reduction of free surface of the order of $\frac{1}{6}$ of the total area, thus a binding energy of a divacancy of the order of $\frac{1}{3}$ of the formation energy of a single vacancy.

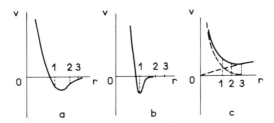

Fig. 5. Pair interaction potentials $v(r)$ (schematic): a. form in common use; b. very short range form; c. purely repulsive form compensated by an external pressure.

positions. But it is also clear that such computations cannot give any results on the long-range distortions, thus on the activation volumes of the defects. To describe more correctly these long-range strains, intermediary models have sometimes been used [14], where a very few atoms at the core of the defect have been treated by pair potentials. This core interacts elastically with the surrounding matrix, which is treated as in section 2.1 as an elastic continuum.

## 3.2. Vacancies

As emphasized in section 2, the lattice strains produced by a vacancy are at most fairly small. Tjus one can hope to construct reasonable pair potentials by fitting simple parametric formulae to physical properties of the pure metal which, besides the cohesive energy and the lattice parameter, only involve small atomic strains (elastic constants, phonon dispersion curves). Such a widely used pair interaction is deduced, for instance, from Morse potentials:

$$v(r) = D|\exp\{-2\alpha(r-r_0)\}- 2\exp\{-\alpha(r-r_0)\}|. \tag{5}$$

Numerical values of the constants $(D, \alpha, r_0$ in this case) have been given for a great number of metals [15].

The following remarks can be made on the results of such machine computations:

When a vacancy is created, the corresponding pair potentials of the removed atom with its neighbours is suppressed. As at these distances, $v(r)$ is usually assumed negative (fig. 5a, b), each "broken bond" contributes a positive term to the *energy of formation* of the vacancy. The main contribution usually comes from the nearest neighbours. With fairly long-range potentials such as (5), however, other neighbours also contribute significantly. Except in the extreme case of very short-range interactions (fig. 5b), the suppression of these pair potentials produces on the neighbours of the vacancy non-vanishing forces, i.e. $dv/dr \neq 0$ (fig. 5a). The condition of equilibrium of the perfect lattice requires this force to pull the first neighbours towards the vacancy, and further neighbours away from the vacancy. The elastic *relaxation* of these "external" forces lowers somewhat the energy of formation of the vacancy;

it also produces a local displacement of the atoms corresponding always to a contraction of the shell of nearest neighbours. It is clear, however, that the total displacement will be fairly complex, and that it depends critically on the exact form of $v(r)$. From that point of view, potentials of the form (5) have an unreasonably long-range tail. Therefore, results obtained with them must be looked at critically. Also, as emphasized earlier, the self-consistency of these computations has not been pushed far enough to obtain the long range behaviour of the strains. It is worth noting that the cruder model of fig. 5c leads to a strong lattice contraction around the vacancy, but does not allow for a computation of its energy of formation.

Besides a better atomic description of the core of the defect, these computations allow a reasonable estimate of the change in the phonon spectrum induced by the defect; the *vibrational enetropy of formation* $S_{1V}^F$ of a vacancy can be deduced. Although computations can, in principle, be made for any lattice structure and any form of pair potential $v(r)$, actual computations have been done so far in the extreme case where only nearest neighbour interactions are of importance [16] (fig. 5b). If we analyze the phonon modes in terms of the symmetry of the lattice site involved, it is clear that, for a cubic crystal for instance, both breathing (hydrostatic) modes and some shear modes will be affected (fig. 6). The suppression of the central atom changes the boundary condition at the origin. This is similar, for the breathing mode, to the change for a vibrating string from fixed to free ends. This effect both increases the amplitude of vibration of the neighbours to the vacancy and produces a spatial phase shift in the vibration mode which alters their energy. The change of vibrational entropy when an atom is extracted from a vacancy and put back on the surface of a crystal can then be computed for all temperatures. It takes an especially simple form at temperatures well above the Debye temperature. It is then near to that obtained with an Einstein model [2,17], where each atom would vibrate separately, with elastic forces proportional to their number of first neighbours. Thus, with $p$ first neighbours and $p \gg 1$,

$$S_{1V}^F \approx \frac{3pk_B}{2} \ln \frac{p}{p-1} \approx \frac{3k_B}{2} \text{ per vacancy .} \tag{6}$$

Similar computations show that the entropy of vibration $S_{2V}^F$ for a divacancy should be nearly equal to that for two isolated vacancies:

$$S_{2V}^F - 2S_{1V}^F \approx -\frac{3k_B}{2p}$$

Finally, a few words should be given to the problem of relaxation in vacancy motion. The usual assumption made [18] is that the atom A (fig. 1a, b) moves slowly enough for the atoms of the lattice to relax adiabatically to its motion; or, what is equivalent, A is assumed to stay at its excited state (fig. 1b) long enough for thermal equilibrium to be achieved. With such a hypothesis, the relaxation of the lattice around the moving atom A should be total and thus extend to the surface of the crystal. The (relaxed) energy of motion $E_{1V}^{MI}$ of the vacancy would be the difference

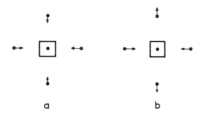

Fig. 6. Phonon modes around a vacancy: a— breathing mode; b— shear mode.

of energy of the fully relaxed states of fig. 1a and b. There should be an activation volume for vacancy motion corresponding to the supplementary long range dilatation produced when going from the states of fig. 1a to fig. 1b. Finally, the average frequency of vacancy jump should be given by a rate process formula

$$\bar{\nu} = \frac{\prod\limits_{i=1}^{N} \nu_i}{\prod\limits_{i=1}^{N-1} \nu_i'} \exp\left(-\frac{E_{1V}^{Mr}}{k_B T}\right), \tag{7}$$

where $\nu_i$ are the frequencies of vibration in the state of fig. 1a, and $\nu_i'$ the frequencies of vibration around its relaxed configuration of the state of fig. 1b, when A is bound to vibrate on an excited configuration along a surface such as $\Sigma$.

As emphasized by many authors, the hypothesis of adiabatic relaxation or of thermal equilibrium is not realistic for the excited state, because the actual jump of atom A occurs within a time comparable with the Debye period. Another extreme hypothesis is then that the jumping time of atom A is much shorter than the relaxation time of the lattice [19]. The average jump frequency should then be given by

$$\bar{\nu} = \frac{\nu_\perp \nu_\parallel}{\nu_\perp'} \exp\left(-\frac{E_{1V}^{Mu}}{k_B T}\right), \tag{8}$$

where $\nu_\perp$ and $\nu_\parallel$ are the frequencies of vibration of A perpendicular and parallel to its jumping motion, and $E_{1V}^{Mu}$ $(> E_{1V}^{Mr})$ is its unrelaxed motion energy. Eq. (8) could also be rewritten by projecting the unrelaxed excited state over the various contents of phonons.

It is clear that the real situation should be intermediary between these two extremes [20]. Thus the lattice relaxation should follow atom A in its motion quasi-adiabatically only at a few interatomic distances at most. The most effective excited states should thus correspond to an energy $E_{1V}^M$ somewhat intermediary between $E_{1V}^{Mr}$ and $E_{1V}^{Mu}$. As most of the relaxation in energy occurs at very short range, it is probable that $E_{1V}^M$ is much nearer to $E_{1V}^{Mr}$ than $E_{1V}^{Mu}$. On the other hand, the activation volume for vacancy motion should be very small. No convincing and systematic study of this point has been given so far. Approaches pointing out the similarity of the core structure (fig. 1b) to that of a liquid [21] do not seem very convincing.

### 3.3. *Interstitials*

The close-range interactions between the interstitial atoms and their neighbours play here a leading role. Approximations such as (5) are then insufficient. Reasonable close-range approximate forms can, however, be constructed and checked with analysis of radiation damage.

It is therefore probable that the atomic configurations computed for the core of these defects are reasonable, as well as their energies of formation. As, however, full and split interstitials have very similar energies, their difference is probably known with much less certainty and even the computation of their relative stability is not very convincing. The same remark applies for the uncertainties for the activation volumes and motion energy as for vacancies.

## 4. Electronic structure

One would now like to put to the theoreticians three successive questions concerning the underlying electronic structure:

1) What is the validity of the pair interactions used to describe the cohesion of perfect metals?

2) How does the local scattering of the electrons by the point defects alter locally these pair interactions?

3) What role does this electron scattering play in electric or mass transport phenomena?

Historically, these questions have been answered in the reverse order. "Normal" metals have been mostly considered, and little has been done so far for transitional metals.

### 4.1. *Free electron scattering*

The first efforts centred on the scattering by the point defects, treating the valence electrons of the metal as free, thus neglecting the details of its atomic structure.

As for impurities in general, one can distinguish three factors — valence, period, size — and assume the first one to predominate [22].

Thus the scattering by a vacancy should be similar to that by a substitutional rare gas atom. The difference arises from the introduction, in the wave functions on the impurity site, of supplementary nodes. These correspond to phase shifts near to multiples of $\pi$, thus there is no large scattering. The perturbing potential introduced in the lattice by such a rare gas atom can then be treated as scattering fairly weakly the conduction electrons.

It is usually sufficient to treat this scattering within *first order perturbation.* Owing to this "valence" effect, the scattering by a vacancy is roughly equivalent to that by a negative point charge of amount equal to the valence of the metal. In a similar way, the scattering by an interstitial atom is roughly equivalent to that by a positive point charge equal to the valence of the metal. In both cases, the local unbalance of ionic charge is screened out by the conduction electrons.

The lattice *distortions* around these defects alter this scattering in two ways:

1) The local contraction or dilatation alters the local density of ionic charge, thus the effective valency of the defect (so-called Harrison-Blatt correction [23]).

2) The local variations in strain around the defects can scatter the electrons by terms similar to phonon scattering.

It seems that both terms are small for vacancies; the second term has, however, rarely been treated very seriously, especially not for interstitials [24].

The results obtained with such a model are well known.

Thus the *residual resistivity* of both vacancies and interstitials should be comparable, and correspond to scattering cross sections of atomic dimensions.

The *electrolysis* of interstitials, when an electric current is flowing under an applied electric field, should merely be due to the effect of the "wind of carriers" blowing past the defect and transmitting to it part of their momentum by collisions [25,26]. In the case of vacancies, one must probably take also into account the work done by the force due to the external field on the inner ions of the metal; but no convincing analysis of this case has been made so far.

The *formation energy* for vacancies should be directly related to the Fermi energy, a result which gives reasonable values only for monovalent metals [27].

Finally, as for any local imperfection, the self-consistent perturbing potential $V(r)$ around a point defect should die out at long range with oscillations which are related to the Fermi wavelength (fig. 7). Within the first order perturbation scheme recalled here [28],

1) the value of $V$ at the neighbours distance $b$ gives the electronic part of the energy of interaction with substitutional impurities;

2) the slope $(dV/dr)_b$ at that distance gives the force acting on the neighbours due to the presence of the defects, and

3) the curvature $(d^2V/dr^2)_b$ gives the change of elastic constants due to the defects.

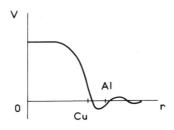

Fig. 7. Perturbing potential due to a vacancy in a free electron model.

It seems that the binding force due to this electronic term is often smaller than the elastic terms discussed in sect. 2. The curvature $(d^2V/dr^2)$ is too poorly known for reliable predictions to be made on changes of elastic constants. Only the slope $(dV/dr)_b$ has given so far results of interest. Thus for monovalent metals, where the nearest neighbour distance falls before the first node of $V(r)$, $(dV/dr)_b$ is fairly strongly negative, producing a strong contraction of the lattice around a vacancy and a strong repulsion of the lattice around an interstitial. The computed effects are of an order of magnitude which seems to agree with experiments [29]. The model also predicts smaller effects for metals of higher valencies, thus nearest neighbour distance larger compared with the oscillations of $V(r)$. In particular, for trivalent metals such as aluminium, the model predicts a slight dilatation around a vacancy, a result which seems to agree with the activation volume larger than the atomic volume observed for diffusion in this metal [30].

Some improvements of this simple free-electron model have been attempted [32]:

1) One can try to solve the problem self-consistently but taking higher than first-order perturbation terms.

2) For interstitials, one can orthogonalize the wave functions in the central cell to the inner shells of the interstitial atom, while keeping a free electron approximation for the remaining matrix.

It is not clear whether such partial improvements are worth the considerable numerical effort. It is not clear, in particular, whether the self-consistency is kept to the same accuracy as in the simpler Born approximation. One can note, however, that Keating and Lee's recent computations along these lines [32] give a fair agreement for the size and compressibility effects of **Cu Zn** : $da/a\,dc = 0.06$ (exp. 0.08); $d\chi/\chi\,dc = 0.4$ (exp. 0.8).

## 4.2. Pseudopotentials

It is tempting to try and take into account the atomic structure of the metal by going from a free to a nearly free approximation. One knows that in normal metals the energies of the valence electrons deviate only slightly from a free electron gas; and these deviations can be treated as if the valence electrons were slightly scattered by weak atomic pseudopotentials. In the usual OPW approximation [33], these potentials are the sum of three terms.

1) The strong attractive potentials of the inner ions.

2) Strongly repulsive and localized terms due to the orthogonalization to the inner shells.

3) The potential of the valence electrons, which screens out the two first terms.

As long as the total self-consistent pseudopotentials are weak, the whole scattering can be treated by perturbation up to second order only. The total energy of a perfect lattice can then formally be written as [34]

$$E = E_0 + \sum_i E_i + \sum_{i \neq j} E_{ij}, \qquad (9)$$

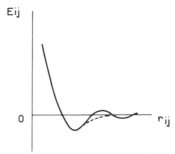

Fig. 8. Pair interaction potential $V(r)$ in a metal.

where $E_0$ is the energy of the free electron gas; $E_i$ is the self-energy of one atomic
pseudopotential dissolved into the free electron gas; $E_{ij}$ is the energy of interaction
of two atomic pseudopotentials scattering as two impurities in an otherwise free
electron gas.

In a (uniform) straining of the lattice, only the terms $E_{ij}$ are altered. They play
therefore the role of interatomic interactions $v(r)$ of section 3. In most normal
metals, the pseudopotentials are weak enough for higher order (many-body) interactions to be negligible. The interatomic interactions are then additive radial functions, as assumed in section 3.

However, general results on the energy of interaction between impurities tell us
that $E_{ij}$ is at long range an oscillating function of the distance [33], with a wavelength equal to twice the Fermi wavelength (fig. 8). The long-range interactions
have a different nature from the exponential decrease assumed in section 3 (cf. fig.
5a, b). Some details of these computations are therefore not reliable, although the
general outlook and order of magnitude of energies will usually be dominated by
the short-range interactions, which can be similar (fig. 8).

Furthermore, eq. (8) is still valid when the atoms are displaced from their positions in a perfect lattice. It can therefore give the interatomic forces involved in
some defects. But strictly speaking, this is only true if the atomic displacements
preserve the atomic volume, i.e. they involve *pure shears* (shear wave, stacking
fault, twin boundary. . .) only. This comes from the fact that the terms of eq. (8)
all depend on the Fermi wavelength, itself a function of the atomic volume.

It is therefore clear that the same interatomic forces and eq. (8) are not sufficient to compute the energies involved in point defects, which obviously alter the
local atomic density. This can also be seen from the fact that each atomic pseudopotential contains a contribution from the valence electrons contained in the
atomic cell. If, for instance, a vacancy is created, the external perturbation which
scatters the electrons and needs be screened by them is the removal of the corresponding atomic pseudopotential *minus the uniform density of valence electrons in
the atomic shell*. The corresponding total negative charge $-pe$ (if $p$ is the valency
of the metal) usually scatters the valence electrons much more strongly than the
mere atomic pseudopotential. It provides the local repulsion of $p$ electronic charge

which empties the vacancy of electrons. It is this repulsion which insures that, outside the vacancy, the Fermi gas has exactly the same electronic density as in a perfect metal. Formula (9), strictly applied, would assume on the contrary that when a vacancy has been created, the (uniform) Fermi gas has its density decreased, owing to the reduction in the average electron density. This effect seems to have been neglected in recent works on vacancies [32,35]. Thus, Torrens and Gerl's computation of vacancy motion energy in normal metals must be more fully justified before their results can be discussed in detail.

In conclusion, the use of pseudopotentials presents some fundamental difficulties that have not yet been completely clarified. There is, however, some hope to do some reasonable studies along these lines, at least in the light normal metals where the pseudopotentials can be computed with a fair degree of accuracy.

### 4.3. Transitional metals

Very little has been done on metals other than "normal".

In transitional metals, only vacancies have been considered so far. In a simple tight binding approximation, one has to remove the d wave functions on the vacant site, and thus their overlap integrals with the neighbouring sites.

In a very crude approximation [36], which completely neglects the scattering of the d Bloch states by the vacancy, the large formation energy of vacancies and divacancies can then be simply related to the cohesive energy, and thus, approximately, to the number of broken d interatomic bonds. This can in principle be easily improved [37].

A more detailed study of d scattering is a priori possible. It poses some problems of self-consistency. For Ni and Co, size effects and binding energies with impurities have been related tentatively to the long-range oscillations produced by this scattering in the d band of the surrounding matrix [38]. More work is certainly needed in this field.

### References

[1] J.D.Eshelby, Solid State Phys. 3 (1956) 79.
[2] J.Friedel, Phil. Mag. 43 (1952) 153; Ispra Conference on radiation damage (Gordon and Breach, New York, 1962).
[3] J.Friedel, Phil. Mag. 44 (1953) 444.
[4] Y.Quéré, Les défauts ponctuels dans les métaux (Masson, Paris, 1967).
[5] J.Friedel, Dislocations (Pergamon Press, London, 1964).
[6] G.Leibfried, Z. Physik 126 (1949) 781.
[7] A.H.Cottrell and B.A.Bilby, Proc. Phys. Soc. (London) A62 (1949) 49.
[8] C.Crussard, Métaux et Corrosion 25 (1950) 203.
[9] G.Schoeck and A.Seeger, Acta Met. 7 (1959) 469.
[10] A.Stehle and A.Seeger, Z. Physik 146 (1956) 217.
[11] H.Brooks, Impurities and imperfections (A.S.M., 1955) p. 1.
[12] For a fairly recent review, cf. ref. [4], Chapter III.

[13] J.B.Gibson et al., Phys. Rev. 120 (1960) 1229.
[14] L.Tewordt, Phys. Rev. 109 (1958) 61;
R.A.Johnson and E.Brown, Phys. Rev. 127 (1962) 446.
[15] L.A.Girifalco and V.G.Weiger, Phys. Rev. 114 (1959) 687; J. Phys. Chem. Solids 12 (1960) 260.
[16] L.Dobrjinski, Thèse Orsay, 1968 (to be published);
J.Friedel and L.Dobrjinski, Surface Science (in press).
[17] R.Fricke, Z. Physik. Chem. B52 (1942) 284;
H.Karge, H.Heyer and G.M.Pound, Phys. Chem. 53 (1961/2) 294.
[18] G.Vineyard, J. Phys. Chem. Solids 3 (1957) 121.
[19] A.C.Damask, G.L.Dienes and V.G.Weizer, Phys. Rev. 113 (1959) 871;
R.A.Johnson, Phys. Rev. 134A (1964) 1329.
[20] P.Wynblatt, Acta Met. 15 (1967) 1453; J. Phys. Chem. Solids 29 (1968) 215.
[21] J.J.Paltenghi, Jül. Conf. 2 (Vol. II) 1968, p. 634.
[22] J.Friedel, Advan. Phys. 3 (1954) 446.
[23] F.J.Blatt, Phys. Rev. 108 (1957) 285.
[24] M.T.Béal-Monod and W.Kohn, J. Phys. Chem. Solids 29 (1968) 1877.
[25] V.B.Fiks, Soviet Phys. Solid State 1 (1959) 14;
H.B.Huntington and A.R.Grone, J. Phys. Chem. Solids 20 (1961) 76, 88.
[26] C.Bosvieux and J.Friedel, J. Phys. Chem Solids 23 (1962) 123.
[27] F.G.Fumi, Phil. Mag. 46 (1955) 1007.
[28] A.Blandin and J.L.Déplanté, J. Phys. 23 (1962) 609;
J.L.Déplanté, Thèse Orsay (1963);
J.L.Déplanté and A.Blandin, J. Phys. Chem. Solids 26 (1965) 381.
[29] C.T.Tomizuka et al., Bull. Am. Phys. Soc. 5 (1960) 181; Phys. Rev. 137 (1965) 618;
A 1264 cf. (30);
B.M.Butcher, H.Hutto and A.L.Ruoff, Appl. Phys. Letters 7 (1965) 34.
[30] M.Beyeler, Thèse Paris, 1968; J. Phys. 29 (1968) 345.
[31] R.Bullough and J.R.Hardy, Phil. Mag. 17 (1968) 833.
[32] B.A.Keating and P.M.Lee, Jül. Conf. 2 (Vol. II) 1968, p. 553;
I.Torrens and M.Gerl, Jül. Conf. 2 (Vol. II) 1968, p. 619.
[33] W.A.Harrison, Pseudopotentials in the theory of metals (Benjamin, New York, 1966);
R.Pick, J. Phys. 28 (1967) 539.
[34] R.Pick and A.Blandin, J. Cond. Matter 3 (1964) 1.
[35] J.L.Beeby, Proc. Roy. Soc. (London) A302 (1967) 113.
[36] J.Friedel, in: The Interaction of Radiation with Solids (North-Holland Publishing Co., Amsterdam, 1964) p. 114.
[37] P.Lenglart and M.Lannoo, to be published.
[38] F.Gautier, Thèse Orsay.

## Discussion

*I.M.Torrens:* With reference to your remarks regarding the influence of a vacancy in the lattice on the pseudopotential pair interaction through local electron scattering by the defect, I should like to ask to what extent these criticisms of the pseudopotential apply to the situation of vacancy *migration* as distinct from *formation*. Dr. Gerl and I at Saclay have assumed a constant volume condition during migration

which enabled us to use pure metal pseudopotentials to calculate energies of migration of vacancies. We should be interested to know whether, in your opinion, significant further errors are introduced by modifications of the electron scattering by
the migrating vacancy.

*J.Friedel:* The criticism applies to both migration formation and migration. However, in the latter case, one makes errors in the energies of the stable and excited
states that are certainly similar and, we can hope, roughly compensate.

*G.Leibfried:* What about the Cauchy relations for the elastic modulus if the pair
potential of the pseudopotential theory is used?

*J.Friedel:* The use of pair potentials is, strictly speaking, only valid for computing shear module, not the compressibility. When a change of volume is involved,
corrections must be added, due to the change in electronic density; these are at
best very rough approximations. As a result, elastic constants seem on the whole to
be computed with a better accuracy for shears than for compression.

*R.Huebener:* You indicated that recent experiments have shown that the activation volume of aluminium is somewhat larger than one atomic volume, as expected
from theory. Which experiments had you in mind?

*J.Friedel:* Beyeler's recent measurements of *diffusion* volumes in aluminium (J.
Phys. 29 (1968) 345).

*Wilkes:* Could you extend your remarks to the problem of impurity atoms and
alloys in the pseudopotential formulation.

*J.Friedel:* Strictly speaking, the potential to use in the impurity cell is the sum
of

    a) the ionic potential (nuclear charge + inner shells),

    b) the orthogonalization potential to the inner shells,

    c) the potential of a uniform charge equal to that of the valence electrons in the
matrix,

    d) the screening potential, due to the excess nuclear charge of the impurity.

It is neither the "bare" nor the "clothed" pseudopotential of the impurity atom,
as computed for the pure solute metal.

# HIGH ENERGY FRENKEL PAIR CASCADES

## G.LEIBFRIED

*Institut für Theoretische Physik der Technischen Hochschule, Aachen, Germany*

## 1. Introduction

In recent years the slowing down of energetic particles in crystals has found considerable interest. A typical situation is shown in fig. 1, where a beam of energetic "primary" particles, P, with velocity v incides on a crystal surface. After the primaries have slowed down to rest by collisions, the distribution of their final positions can be measured if the primaries are marked, e.g., radioactive. This distribution gives information about the interaction between primary and lattice. The most striking effect here is the drastic increase in penetration if the incident velocity is parallel to a low index crystallographic direction (channeling [1]). However, off those directions the crystal structure becomes less important, so that, approximately, the crystal can be considered as an amorphous substance with the same atomic density. Another typical situation is illustrated in fig. 2. Here the primary starts from a lattice site; it can be produced by a nuclear process, such as a nuclear reaction or an $\alpha$ decay, or by wide angle scattering of an external beam (Coulomb scattering). Again the primary is a distinguishable particle and on leaving the surface its velocity distribution or its escape rate can be measured. The most pronounced effect here is the decrease in intensity along low-indexed directions (blocking [1]).

In radiation damage the primary (primary knock-on) is produced by interaction with external radiation such as neutrons. The primary starts from a lattice site inside the crystal and slows down to rest either at an interstitial site (as in fig. 3) or at an atomic site, replacing a lattice atom. By collisions with other atoms of the lattice

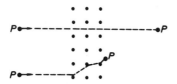

Fig. 1. Channeling situation; the primary is incident on a crystal surface.

Fig. 2. Blocking situation; the primary starts from a lattice site.

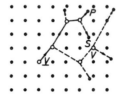

Fig. 3. Cascade containing primary, secondaries and vacancies.

the primary can produce secondary particles (indicated by dashed lines in fig. 3) with enough energy to escape their lattice sites and leave a vacancy (V) behind. The secondaries also slow down and come to rest, either interstitially or substitutionally. In this way a cascade is produced which eventually consists of $\mu$ Frenkel pairs, i.e., $\mu$ interstitials at positions $\mathbf{r}_1 \ldots \mathbf{r}_\mu$ and an equal number of vacancies at $\mathbf{r}'_1 \ldots \mathbf{r}'_\mu$. The number and the positions of the defects depend on magnitude and direction of the primary velocity $\mathbf{v}$, the distribution of which is given by the irradiation conditions. In reactor irradiation, for instance, the distribution of $\mathbf{v}$ would be nearly isotropic. The numbers $\mu$ and the positions $\mathbf{r},\mathbf{r}'$ are subject to fluctuations depending on the $\mathbf{v}$ distribution and one usually discusses averages such as the average numbers of Frenkel pairs $\nu = \bar{\mu}$ and the average density of interstitials or vacancies, because one hopes that these quantities already give sufficient information about the cascade. This, however, is only a first, relatively fast, step in the cascade production. After this, one has to consider the interaction between vacancies and interstitials present in the cascade which might lead to annihilation of Frenkel pairs if interstitial and vacancy are close enough-for instance, the pair S-V in fig. 3. Theoretical [2] and experimental [3] evidence shows that the annihilation volume for a Frenkel pair can be of the order of 100 atomic volumes. Consequently, if the density of Frenkel pairs is of the order of larger than 1 at % one must expect a reduction of the numbers and the density due to this effect of "self-annealing". If, at higher temperatures, interstitials and/or vacancies are mobile, one has to consider further thermal annealing due to diffusive motion.

So far the experimental evidence on cascades has only been very indirect. It has not been possible to observe the defect cascade directly *in statu nascendi*. But the whole picture of radiation damage for high energy primaries is based on this concept, which is certainly qualitatively correct. In contrast to the first methods where the primary distribution can be measured, in radiation damage only the distribution of defects where the primary is not distinguished matters. The cascade and the primary distributions are, of course, connected. Consequently, at this stage theoretical investigations about primary and cascade distributions and their connections are important to obtain a more rounded picture of radiation damage cascades. Experimental evidence about primary distributions can then help to obtain more detailed information about cascades.

In this paper it will be attempted to give a review of the development of cascade theory. The emphasis will be on high energy cascades where the number of Frenkel pairs is large, and on the analytical treatment rather than on machine calculations, which will be treated only briefly.

One has to distinguish between three basically different approaches to the problem.

*Dynamical computer models* [4]. Here a small crystal model (typically containing 1000 atoms) is investigated on a computer. The crystal atoms interact through a two-body potential (central forces); further, surface forces are introduced. The potential is chosen such that at small interatomic distance it goes over into the potential of Thomas-Fermi theory and that for distances near equilibrium the potential together with the surface forces yields the experimental elastic data * and equilibrium distance. Due to the necessarily small size of the crystal, these investigations are confined to the production of one or a small number of Frenkel pairs. They are extremely useful for problems such as the threshold for production of pairs, replacement and focusing sequences, channeling and the annihilation volume where the lattice structure plays an important role. For high energy cascades the crystal size is too small.

Another model has been used by Harrison [5]. Only repulsive forces are taken into account, and initially the atoms occupy the ideal lattice sites. The crystal starts to explode but the explosion time is large as compared with the slowing down time and should, therefore, not appreciably change the essential collision events of a primary.

*Static computer models* [6–8]. In these calculations also an appropriate two-body potential is selected. It is further assumed that only two atoms interact at one time (binary collision model). This model is illustrated in fig. 4. The lattice is divided into nonoverlapping spheres of radius $R_1$ **. If the primary enters one sphere, for instance the sphere around atom number 1, it interacts with the corresponding

---

* Deviations from the Cauchy relations between the elastic moduli (valid for central forces) are represented by properly chosen surface forces. Consequently, the model is not quite correct atomistically. But since in the simulation of a radiation damage event the repulsive part of the interatomic potential plays the most important role, this microscopic inaccuracy is probably not important.

** $R_1$ is half the distance between nearest neighbors.

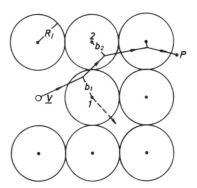

Fig. 4. Static computer model.

atom. The final path and velocity are calculated from the potential and the impact parameter $b_1$, and the procedure is repeated when the primary enters the interaction sphere of another stationary atom of the lattice (in fig. 4 the sphere around lattice atom number 2 with impact parameter $b_2$). The collisions always occur between the primary and a lattice atom at rest. The binary collision itself is calculated dynamically. The interaction cut-off $R_l$ can be effected either by truncating the potential or by assuming a maximum impact parameter $R_l$ with the full interaction potential. For the secondaries, such as atom number 1 in fig. 4, the final path and velocity can also be calculated and subsequently the same procedure can be applied. In the calculations of ref. [8], interstitial and vacancy formation and their annealing are included and also taken into account for the cascade collisions. So at least part of the effect of prior collisions on subsequent collisions is included.

The requirement for the validity of the binary collision model is that the interaction for impact parameters of the order $R_l$ is small. Otherwise, the interaction with several atoms at the same time would play an essential role. If $T(b)$ is the energy transfer to a stationary atom by an incident atom of energy $E$, a simple condition for the validity of the binary collision approach would be $T(R_l) = T_l \ll E$, which implies that the scattering angle, $\theta'$, of the incident particle is small $(\theta'_l \cong \sqrt{T_l/E})$.

Another simple, more or less equivalent, condition may be expressed in terms of a hard core approximation where the hard core radius $R(E)$ equals the distance of closest approach, i.e., with a potential $V(r)$, the hard core radius is defined by $V(R) = E/2$. Then the condition would be $R(E) \ll R_l$, or approximately, for repulsive potentials, $E_l = 2V(R_l) \ll E$. The energy limit, $E_l$, for binary collision approach is typically of the order of 100 eV. Consequently, for initial energies much larger than $E_l$ one can use the binary collision model for primary and cascade calculations because the error introduced by the low energy part will be small.

*Random model.* In analytical calculations it is very difficult to include the lattice structure. Only special lattice effects have been treated analytically, such as channeling and focusing, but to include those effects in the primary motion or cascade production has not yet been possible in a consistent way. In the random model the lattice is replaced by a random arrangement (gas) of equal density. The errors in this approach are difficult to assess. For high initial energies where the primary during slowing down suffers several collisions with major changes in its direction (large angle scattering), the lattice influence may be smeared out. A comparison [7,9] of lattice and random models shows that indeed the differences between the two models are not very large, at least if the primary starts from a lattice site with an isotropic distribution.

In the following the basic theory of the random model in the binary collision approach will be reviewed briefly. Although inelastic energy losses (electronic excitation) for high energy primaries are certainly important, they will be left out. It is hoped that the connection between primary and cascade distributions is not very sensitive to electronic stopping, so that only the scale is slightly reduced by inelastic events. Furthermore, only the equal mass case, referring to damage in elemental crystals, is treated. The generalization to different masses is not difficult.

## 2. Binary collisions [10]

The collision between an incident particle of velocity **v** and a stationary target atom is defined by the atomic potential $V(r)$, where $r$ is the interatomic distance, and by the impact parameter $b$. Figure 5a shows the situation qualitatively. After the collision the incident particle, the "primary", possesses the velocity $\mathbf{v}'$ and the target particle, the "secondary", the velocity $\mathbf{v}''$. The final velocities are connected through energy and momentum conservation. This connection is shown in fig. 5b. The most important quantity we need for further consideration is the differential cross section,

$$d\sigma = K(\mathbf{v};\mathbf{v}',\mathbf{v}'') \, d\mathbf{v}' \, d\mathbf{v}'', \qquad \frac{d\sigma}{d\mathbf{v}' \, d\mathbf{v}''} = K, \tag{1}$$

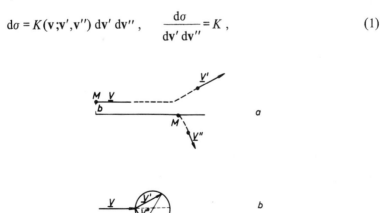

Fig. 5. Binary collision. a) Paths of the two particles; b) energy momentum conservation.

which is the cross section for processes leading to final velocities in the intervals $dv'$ and $dv''$ and which refers to an incident beam with homogeneous distribution of impact parameters. The total cross section is given by integrating over all $v'$ and $v''$ ($E = Mv^2/2$ = initial energy),

$$\sigma(v) = \sigma(E) = \int K(v;v',v'')\, dv'\, dv'' \ . \tag{2}$$

The total cross section in a classical theory is finite only if the potential or the impact parameter distribution is cut off. In the model discussed in the Introduction, $\sigma(E)$ would be independent of energy and equal to $\pi R_I^2$.

Starting from the most general cross section (1), one can define reduced differential cross sections; for instance, for the primary alone

$$d\sigma/dv' = K_P(v;v') = \int K\, dv'' \ , \tag{3a}$$

or for the secondary alone

$$d\sigma/dv'' = K_S(v;v'') = \int K\, dv' \ . \tag{3b}$$

If one is only interested in the energies of the primary or the target atoms, one can reduce further and define a differential cross section of the final energy, $E'$,

$$d\sigma/dE' = K_P(E;E') = \int K_P(v;v')\, \delta(E' - \tfrac{1}{2}Mv'^2)\, dv'$$

$$= \int K\, \delta(E' - \tfrac{1}{2}Mv'^2)\, dv'\, dv'' \tag{4a}$$

or for the energy, $E''$, transferred to the target particle,

$$d\sigma/dE'' = K_S(E;E'') = \int K_S(v;v'')\, \delta(E'' - \tfrac{1}{2}Mv''^2)\, dv'' \ . \tag{4b}$$

Further integration over the remaining variables always gives the total cross section,

$$\sigma(E) = \int K_P(v;v')\, dv' = \int K_P(E;E')\, dE'$$

$$= \int K_S(v;v'')\, dv'' = \int K_S(E;E'')\, dE'' \ . \tag{5}$$

The ratio $d\sigma/\sigma$ is a normalized probability distribution for the corresponding final quantities,

$$G(v;v'') = K/\sigma \ , \qquad\qquad G_P(v;v') = K_P(v;v')/\sigma \ ,$$

$$G_P(E;E') = K_P(E;E')/\sigma, \text{ etc.} \tag{6}$$

$$\int G\, dv'\, dv'' = \int G_P(v;v')\, dv' = 1 \ .$$

$G_P(v;v')\, dv'$, for instance, is the probability for finding the primary velocity in $(v', dv')$ after one collision.

Because of energy momentum conservation, $K$ must vanish for values of $v', v''$ for which energy and momentum are not conserved. For this reason $K$ must contain $\delta$-functions which express the conservation laws and only one genuine variable remains, e.g.,

$$K(\mathbf{v};\mathbf{v}',\mathbf{v}'') = K_P(E;E') \frac{M^2 v}{2\pi} \, \delta(E - E' - E'') \, \delta(\mathbf{v} - \mathbf{v}' - \mathbf{v}'') , \qquad (7)$$

where $K$ is expressed by $K_P(E;E')$ alone. In eq. (7) instead of $K_P(E;E')$ one can as well write $K_S(E;E'') = K_P(E;E-E'')$. If one divides eq. (7) by $\sigma(E)$, one obtains the corresponding relation for the $G$ functions.

Another useful differential cross section is that for the primary using the variables energy, $E'$, and solid angle, $\Omega'$,

$$\frac{d\sigma}{dE' \, d\Omega'} = K_P(E;E') \frac{\delta(\hat{\mathbf{v}} \cdot \hat{\mathbf{v}}' - \sqrt{E'/E})}{2\pi} , \qquad (8a)$$

where $\hat{\mathbf{v}} = \mathbf{v}/v$ and $\hat{\mathbf{v}}' = \mathbf{v}'/v'$ are the initial and final directions. The $\delta$-function indicates that the angle, $\theta'$, between $\mathbf{v}'$ and $\mathbf{v}$ is given by $\cos \theta' = \sqrt{E'/E}$, which can be seen immediately from fig. 5b. Correspondingly, one has

$$\frac{d\sigma}{dE'' \, d\Omega''} = K_S(E;E'') \frac{\delta(\hat{\mathbf{v}} \cdot \hat{\mathbf{v}}'' - \sqrt{E''/E})}{2\pi} \qquad (8b)$$

for the target particle.

According to (7), only the calculation of the partial cross section $K_S(E;E'')$ is needed. If one knows the dependence of the transferred energy, $E'' = T$, on the impact parameter, $T(b^2)$, then

$$K_S(E'T) = \left| \frac{\pi \, db^2}{dT} \right| = \frac{\pi}{|dT(b^2)/db^2|} . \qquad (9)$$

If the potential, $V(r)$, is given, one most conveniently calculates first the scattering angle in the center of mass system,

$$\bar{\theta} = \pi - \int_{r_c}^{\infty} \frac{2b \, dr}{r^2 \left\{ 1 - \dfrac{V(r)}{E/2} - \dfrac{b^2}{r^2} \right\}^{\frac{1}{2}}} . \qquad (10)$$

Here $r_c(b,E)$ is the distance of closest approach for given $b$ where the square root in (10) vanishes. Then $T$ is given by

$$T = E \sin^2 \bar{\theta}/2 . \qquad (11)$$

Only for few potentials, such as $V(r) \propto r^{-1}, r^{-2}$, can analytical solutions of (10) be given. In machine calculations $\bar{\theta}$ and related quantities are calculated by numerical integration. For a further analytical treatment one must employ approximations with simple analytical properties, which then can partly be checked by comparison with the exact solution for special values of $b$.

For monotonically decreasing potentials the energy transfer $T$ will decrease with increasing $b$, which is shown qualitatively in fig. 6a. The differential cross section, $K_S(E,T)$, for head-on collisions, $b = 0$, is given by the tangent in $b = 0$,

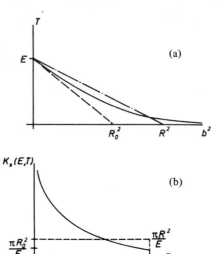

Fig. 6. a) Energy transfer $T$ versus $b^2$. b) Differential cross section for energy transfer. ---- hard core approximation.

$$K_S(E,E) = \pi R_0^2/E .\tag{12}$$

Here $R_0$ can be determined from

$$R_0 \int_R^\infty \frac{dr}{r^2 \left\{ 1 - \frac{V(r)}{V(R)} \right\}^{\frac{1}{2}}} = 1\tag{13}$$

where

$$R(E) = r_c(E, b = 0) , \qquad V(R) = E/2\tag{14}$$

is the distance of closest approach for head-on collisions. For power potentials

$$V(r) = \frac{C_s}{r^s} , \qquad \frac{V(r)}{V(R)} = \left(\frac{r}{R}\right)^s ,\tag{15}$$

one has *

$$\frac{R}{R_0} = \frac{1}{s} B\left(\frac{1}{2}, \frac{1}{s}\right) = \frac{1}{s} \beta\left(\frac{1}{s}\right) = 2, \pi/2, \; 1.32, \; 1 + \ln 4/s\tag{16}$$

for $s = 1, 2, 4, \gg 1$, where

$$B(\alpha,\beta) = \Gamma(\alpha) \, \Gamma(\beta)/\Gamma(\alpha + \beta)\tag{17}$$

* $\beta(\zeta) = B\left(\frac{1}{2}, \zeta\right).$

is the beta function. In fig. 6b the quantity $K_S(E, T)$ is drawn qualitatively. The high energy value is given by (12,13) and for $T \lesssim E$ one can use corresponding methods to obtain the behavior of $K_S$. But the results are only simple for power potentials which can serve as a good example resembling the interatomic repulsion. For low energy transfers one can employ the impulse approximation, in which the potential is treated as a small perturbation and which holds for small $\bar{\theta}$ and small $T/E$. Here one has

$$\bar{\theta} \simeq 2\sqrt{T/E} \simeq -\int_b^\infty \frac{2b \, dr}{E\sqrt{r^2 - b^2}} \, \partial_r V(r) \tag{18}$$

which for power potentials results in

$$\frac{T}{E} = \left(\frac{C_s D_s}{Eb^s}\right)^2 \quad \text{with} \quad D_s = \frac{s}{2} B\left(\frac{1}{2}, \frac{1}{2} + \frac{s}{2}\right) = \frac{s}{2} \beta\left(\frac{1}{2} + \frac{s}{2}\right) \tag{19}$$

and gives

$$K_S(E;T) = \frac{\pi}{s} \{C_s D_s\}^{2/s} \frac{1}{E^{1/s} T^{1 + 1/s}} = \frac{c_s}{E^{1/s} T^{1 + 1/s}}, \tag{20}$$

which is a simple power law in $T$ and $E$.


## 3. Approximate cross sections

Unless the differential cross section $K_S(E;T)$ is sufficiently simple, analytical treatments are impossible. Because even for simple potentials the differential cross sections are relatively complicated, one has to look for crude approximations with simple analytical properties.

One simple method is to replace the potential $V(r)$ by an approximate potential $V_A(r)$ which can be handled more easily and which matches $V(r)$ near $R(E)$ relatively well. This procedure aims at a representation of $K_S$ at $T \lesssim E$. For monotonically decreasing potentials, which will be considered exclusively in the following, a good $V_A$ would be a power potential * matched in magnitude and derivative in $r = R$,

$$V_A(r) = V(R)\left(\frac{R}{r}\right)^s, \qquad s = -R\partial_R \ln V(R). \tag{21}$$

Because simple analytical solutions are available only for $s = 1, 2$, one must look for even simpler and necessarily cruder approximations. The simplest approximation is the hard core approximation (hca), where for every energy the potential is replaced

---

* Other matching potentials and comparison with numerical cross sections can be found in ref. [10].

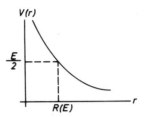

Fig. 7. Distance of closest approach, $R(E)$, in a binary collision.

by a hard sphere of radius $R(E)$, fig. 7. This approximation can only give reliable results for rapidly decreasing potentials, i.e., for corresponding matching powers $s \gg 1$,
and for large energy transfers. In the hca one has

$$\sigma_{hc}(E) = \pi R^2(E) , \qquad G_S(E,\epsilon) = G_P(E,\epsilon) = \frac{1}{E} \theta(E - \epsilon) \qquad (22)$$

with

$$\theta(E - \epsilon) = \frac{1}{0} \quad \text{for} \ \epsilon \begin{matrix} \leqslant E \\ > E \end{matrix} .$$

The distributions $G_S$ and $G_P$ are extremely simple, which facilitates the analytical
procedure a great deal. In the hca one obtains

$$K_S(E,E) = \pi R^2/E . \qquad (23)$$

One sees by comparison with eqs. (12,16) that indeed for large $s$ the hca agrees with
the exact value of power potentials. The hca overestimates $K_S(E,E)$ and for $s = 10$
the error is still 20 percent. For low energy transfers the hca underestimates $K_S$.
This is qualitatively shown in fig. 6b. Figure 6a shows the dependence $T(b^2)$ in the
hca.

Another version [9] of the hca uses a different determination of the hard core
cross section. An important quantity in slowing down theory is the stopping power,

$$S(E) = \int dT K_S(E,T)T , \qquad (24)$$

which in the hca becomes

$$S_{hc}(E) = \sigma_{hc}(E) E/2 . \qquad (25)$$

If one defines $\sigma_{hc}$ by equating $S(E)$ and $S_{hc}(E)$, one obtains another definition of
the hard core radius,

$$\pi R_1^2(E) E/2 = S(E) = \sigma_{hc}^{(1)} E/2 . \qquad (26)$$

Comparisons with computer calculations on primary distributions show a substantial improvement over the simple hca. By the definition (26) the low energy transfers are somewhat better taken into account, though it is difficult to find a criterion
for the reliability of the approximation.

In the hca, however, the radius may be defined, one has a very simple picture of the slowing down process. A separation into interaction spheres $R_I$ is no longer necessary; the hca gives a natural separation if $R < R_I$. If $R$ becomes of the order of $R_I$, that is, at low energies, the lattice effects come in and the binary collision model breaks down anyway. Coming from high energies, one can cut off the motion of any particle if its energy is such that $R(E) \leqslant R_I$. The additive motion at lower energies will give only a small contribution.

Another approximation to $K_S$ has been worked out by Lindhard [11] and co-workers. Here the impulse approximation (IA) (20) is used also for large $T$ values up to $T = E$. The reliability of this approximation for power potentials is checked by comparing the value of $K_S(E,E)$ with the exact result of (12) and (13), because the head-on collision presumably gives the largest error. The ratio of the values $K_S(E,E)$ is given by

$$\frac{K_S(E,E)|_{\text{exact}}}{K_S(E,E)|_{\text{IA}}} = \frac{\pi R_0^2}{E} \frac{E^{1 + 2/s}}{c_s}$$

$$= \frac{s^3}{\beta^2 \left(\frac{1}{s}\right)} \left(\frac{4}{s\beta \left(\frac{1+s}{2}\right)}\right)^{2/s} \quad \begin{array}{l} \text{for } s = 1,\ \tfrac{3}{2},\quad 2,\quad \tfrac{5}{2},\quad 3,\quad 4,\quad \gg 1, \\[4pt] = 1,\ 0.88,\ 1.03,\ 1.25,\ 1.52,\ 2.13,\ \sim s. \end{array} \qquad (27)$$

For $s = 1$ (Coulomb scattering) Lindhard's approximation gives the exact Coulomb cross section. In the range $1 \leqslant s \leqslant \tfrac{5}{2}$, the error for $T \cong E$ is less than 25 percent, which seems good enough for qualitative purposes if the potential can be approximated by a power law in these limits *.

Lindhard's procedure is illustrated in fig. 8, which shows qualitatively the exact dependence of $T$ on $b^2$ and the corresponding impulse approximation. At $b^2 = b_0^2$ in the impulse approximation one has $T_{\text{IA}}(b_0^2) = E$. The above approximation consists then in replacing $T(b^2)$ by $T_{\text{IA}}(b^2 + b_0^2)$, which results in (20) for power potentials and which also can be used for general potentials as long as corresponding power is in the neighborhood of 2.


## 4. Potentials

Many different forms and approximations for the interatomic potential $V(r)$ have been used. The following contains only a few remarks about the potentials which have been in use.

---

* If the cross section (20) were exact it would correspond to a potential $V_s(r,E)$ which in general depends on energy. M.T.Robinson (private communication) has carried out the calculations for $s = 2$ where to a good approximation

$$V_2(r,E) \cong \frac{C_2}{r^2} \left\{ 1 - 0.02\, \frac{2C_2}{Er^2} + 0.003 \left(\frac{2C_2}{Er^2}\right)^2 \dots \right\} .$$

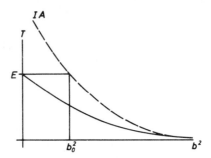

Fig. 8. Transferred energy $T$ versus $b^2$ in the impulse approximation (IA).

For small separations (high energies) the potentials have been taken from statistical models (Thomas-Fermi, Thomas-Fermi-Dirac) and approximations thereof. The potential is a screened Coulomb potential

$$V(r) = \frac{Z^2 e^2}{r} \phi\left(\frac{r}{a}\right) , \tag{28}$$

where $\phi$ is a screening function containing a screening distance $a$. To obtain simple, manageable expressions the screening function has been approximated by various methods. According to Firsov [12] in the Thomas-Fermi model a good approximation of $a$ is *

$$a = a_{\text{H}} \frac{0.88}{(2Z^{\frac{1}{2}})^{\frac{2}{3}}}$$

and $\phi$ is the Thomas-Fermi screening function. For this screening function itself, several approximations have been employed; for instance, the Sommerfeld approximation [13]

$$\phi(x) \cong \frac{1}{\left[1 + \left(\frac{x}{\alpha_1}\right)^{\alpha_2}\right]^{\alpha_3}} , \quad \alpha_{1,2,3} = 5.2, \ 0.8, \ 3.7 ; \tag{29a}$$

an approximation by Lindhard [11],

$$\phi(x) \cong \frac{x}{(3 + x^2)^{\frac{1}{2}}} ; \tag{29b}$$

the $1/x$ approximation [11], approximately valid for $x \gtrsim 1$,

$$\phi(x) \cong 1/2x ; \tag{29c}$$

---

* For unlike atomic numbers $Z_{1,2}$ one has to replace $2Z^{\frac{1}{2}}$ by $Z_1^{\frac{1}{2}} + Z_2^{\frac{1}{2}}$.

the Molière approximation [14],

$$\phi(x) \cong 0.35\ e^{-0.3x} + 0.55\ e^{-1.2x} + 0.1\ e^{-6x}\ ; \qquad (29d)$$

and the Bohr approximation [15],

$$\phi(x) \cong e^{-x}\ . \qquad (29e)$$

The representations (29a, b, d) give a relatively good fit, whereas (29c) overestimates and (29e) underestimates the potential for $x > 1$. Figure 9 shows a comparison of (29a, b, d, e).

For distances of about, and smaller than, the equilibrium distance, other potentials, well known from lattice theory of crystals, have been employed. Here the properties of the outer shell electrons are more important and the statistical model is inappropriate. Typical forms are: the Born-Mayer potential,

$$V(r) = A\ e^{-r/a}\ ; \qquad (30a)$$

the Morse potential,

$$V(r) = A\ e^{-r/a} - A\ e^{-r/a'}\ ; \qquad (30b)$$

power potentials,

$$V(r) = C_s/r_s\ , \qquad (30c)$$

where $s$ is the order of 10. The potentials (30a, c) represent only the repulsive part of the interatomic potential. It has to be completed by an attractive part, and the data are usually determined by fitting to equilibrium values such as lattice distance, cohesive energy and elastic moduli. Potentials of this kind are used in dynamical models where the potential has to be approximately correct up to distances of the order of the equilibrium distance. Figure 10 shows as a typical example [4] the

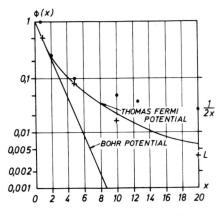

Fig. 9. Several approximations to the Thomas-Fermi screening function $\phi(x)$. The points $+$ (L) correspond to (29b).

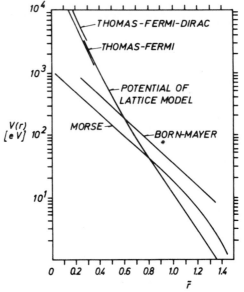

Fig. 10. Potentials used in dynamical computer model, $\tilde{r} = \sqrt{3}\,r/2R_l$.

potential for a lattice model of Fe. The potential eventually chosen contains three parts, namely: for small $r$, $\tilde{r} \leqslant 0.7$, a Bohr potential fitting the potential of statistical theory (Thomas-Fermi and Thomas-Fermi-Dirac) for intermediate $r$, $0.7 \leqslant \tilde{r} \leqslant 1.35$, a Born-Mayer potential which interpolates between small distances and separations near equilibrium ($\tilde{r} = \sqrt{3}$), where a Morse potential is used which fits the equilibrium data.

These few remarks should only show what problems arise in the choice of the potential. These questions are difficult, and the choice of a general Thomas-Fermi potential (28) is certainly a well educated guess--but no more.

## 5. Random model

In the random model one works as in gas theory with the concept of a mean free path $\lambda(E)$ which is defined by

$$\lambda(E) = 1/n_{at}\,\sigma(E) \tag{31}$$

where $n_{at}$ is the atomic density. A particle of energy $E$ will move freely over a distance $\xi$ until it collides. The free flight distance $\xi$ is distributed according to

$$\omega(\xi)\,d\xi = \frac{e^{-\xi/\lambda(E)}}{\lambda(E)}\,d\xi\,, \qquad 0 \leqslant \xi \leqslant \infty\,, \qquad \int_{0}^{\infty} \omega\,d\xi = 1\,, \tag{32}$$

and the mean free path is

$$\bar{\xi} = \int_0^\infty d\xi \, \xi \omega(\xi) = \lambda(E) \, . \tag{33}$$

## 6. Equations for the primary distribution $w(\mathbf{r},\mathbf{v})$

The above introduced concept of the free flight distance, $\xi$, and its probability distribution makes it possible to derive an equation for the distribution, $w(\mathbf{r},\mathbf{v})$, of the primary which is supposed to start at $\mathbf{r} = 0$ with the velocity $\mathbf{v}$. Here $w(\mathbf{r},\mathbf{v})\,d\mathbf{r}$ is the probability of finding the primary in $(\mathbf{r},d\mathbf{r})$ after it has come to rest. In the lattice the end position is uniquely determined by $\mathbf{v}$. One obtains a distribution only if one has an angular variation of the initial direction of $\mathbf{v}$. Hopefully, the random model and the lattice distributuon already agree approximately if only small variations of the initial directions are taken into account.

For the following it is convenient to introduce an escape probability, $p(E)$, and a sticking probability, $q(E)$, of a primary, with $p + q = 1$. These quantities are sort of remainders of the underlying lattice theory. This means that, e.g., $p(E)$ is the probability for an atom of energy $E$ to leave its lattice site. We will further use a symmetrical model which does not distinguish between primary and secondaries. For the sake of simplicity, it is assumed that $p$ and $q$ do not depend on direction, only on energy. For low energies $p \to 0$, $q \to 1$, and the slowing down history of a particle is finished if its energy becomes so low that $q = 1$.

Now, we can follow the primary until it suffers its first collision at a point $\xi\hat{\mathbf{v}}$. After the collision its velocity distribution is $G_P(\mathbf{v};\mathbf{v}')$, and for every $\mathbf{v}'$ we obtain the contribution $w(\mathbf{r} - \xi\hat{\mathbf{v}},\mathbf{v}')$ to $w(\mathbf{r},\mathbf{v})$. These contributions have to be averaged over $\mathbf{v}'$ and over $\xi$, employing the respective distributions of those quantities, which results in

$$w(\mathbf{r},\mathbf{v}) = q\delta(\mathbf{r}) + p \int_0^\infty d\xi \, \frac{e^{-\xi/\lambda}}{\lambda} \, d\mathbf{v}' \, G_P(\mathbf{v};\mathbf{v}') \, w(\mathbf{r} - \xi\hat{\mathbf{v}},\mathbf{v}') \, , \tag{34}$$

where $q = q(E)$ and $p = p(E)$ are escape and sticking probabilities for the initial energy $E = Mv^2/2$. Eq. (34) corresponds to

$$w(\mathbf{r},\mathbf{v}) = q \, \delta(r) + p \, \tilde{w}(\mathbf{r},\mathbf{v}) \, , \tag{34a}$$

where $\tilde{w}$ is the primary distribution in case the primary can escape. Consequently, one obtains for $\tilde{w}$

$$\tilde{w}(\mathbf{r},\mathbf{v}) = \int_0^\infty d\xi \, \frac{e^{\xi/\lambda}}{\lambda} \, d\mathbf{v}' \, G_P(\mathbf{v};\mathbf{v}') \, \{q'\delta(\mathbf{r} - \xi\hat{\mathbf{v}}) + p'\tilde{w}(\mathbf{r} - \xi\hat{\mathbf{v}},\mathbf{v}')\} \tag{35}$$

$$q' = q(E') \, , \qquad p' = p(E') \, .$$

By direct manipulation it is now easy to verify that $\widetilde{w}$ obeys

$$(1 + \hat{v}\partial_r)\,\widetilde{w}(\mathbf{r},\mathbf{v}) = G_P(p\widetilde{w} + q\,\delta(\mathbf{r})) \tag{36}$$

which is an integro-differential equation for $\widetilde{w}$. In (36) $G_P$ stands for an integral operation with respect to $\mathbf{v}$, i.e., for any function $h(\mathbf{v})$,

$$G_P\,h(\mathbf{v}) = \int d\mathbf{v}'\,G_P(\mathbf{v};\mathbf{v}')\,h(\mathbf{v}')\,, \tag{37}$$

and if $h$ depends only on energy,

$$G_P\,h(E) = \int dE'\,G_P(E;E')\,h(E')\,. \tag{37a}$$

For high energies where $p, q = 1, 0$ and $\widetilde{w} = w$, one also can replace $p', q'$ in (35) by $1, 0$, and obtains

$$(1 + \hat{v}\partial_r)\,w(\mathbf{r},\mathbf{v}) = G_P\,w(\mathbf{r},\mathbf{v})\,. \tag{38}$$

In (38) the mean free path must tend to zero sufficiently fast as $E$ goes to zero in order to define the final positions. In case of a sharp threshold $E_d$ below which $q$ becomes 1, one can require $\lambda(E \leqslant E_d) = 0$ to include the lattice effect represented by $p$ and $q$. However, for $E \gg E_d$ and for fast decreasing $\lambda(E)$, the contributions of energies $E < E_d$ do not matter. The solution of (38) for $\mathbf{v} = 0$ would then be $w(\mathbf{r},0) = \delta(\mathbf{r})$. From the above equations one can also see that the normalization of $w$ and $\widetilde{w}$, e.g., $\int d\mathbf{r}\,w\widetilde{w} = 1$, is guaranteed.

Equation (38) can be written in an alternative form $\lambda(E) = 1/n_{at}\,\sigma(E)$, $\sigma(E)\,G_P = K_P$,

$$\hat{v}\partial_r\,w(\mathbf{r},\mathbf{v}) = \frac{1}{\lambda}\,(G_P - 1)\,w(\mathbf{r},\mathbf{v}) = n_{at}\,(K_P - \sigma(E))\,w(\mathbf{r},\mathbf{v})$$

or

$$\hat{v}\partial_r\,w(\mathbf{r},\mathbf{v}) = n_{at}\int d\mathbf{v}'\,K_P(\mathbf{v},\mathbf{v}')\,\{w(\mathbf{r},\mathbf{v}') - w(\mathbf{r},\mathbf{v})\}. \tag{38a}$$

This notation corresponds to Lindhard's formulation [16], in which only the differential cross section $K_P$ enters. If the restriction to impact parameters smaller than $R_l$ is unimportant, one can use in (38a) the full differential cross section, including $\mathbf{v}' = \mathbf{v}$, corresponding to $b = \infty$. Here $K_P(\mathbf{v},\mathbf{v}')$ diverges for $\mathbf{v}' = \mathbf{v}$, but the factor $w(\mathbf{v}') - w(\mathbf{v})$ vanishes and the integral remains finite.

Another quantity of interest is the distribution of the total path $L$, traveled by the primary $w(L,v) = w(L,E)$, which obeys for high energies

$$(1 + \lambda\partial_L)\,w(L,E) = G_P\,w(L,E) = \int dE'\,G_P(E;E')\,w(L,E') \tag{39}$$

or

$$\partial_L\,w(L,E) = n_{at}\int dE'\,K_P(E;E')\,\{w(L,E') - w(L,E)\}. \tag{39a}$$

So far analytical solutions for the distribution functions have not been obtained *. However, it is relatively easy to calculate certain averages over the distribution function from (38). This will be demonstrated only for the quantity $\mathbf{r} \cdot \hat{\mathbf{v}} = x$, the projection of $\mathbf{r}$ in direction $\hat{\mathbf{v}}$ of the initial velocity, which locates the center of the primary distribution. If one multiplies (38) by $x_i$ ($i = 1, 2, 3$) and integrates over $\mathbf{r}$, the first term on the left gives by definition the average of the $x_i$ component

$$\bar{x}_i(\mathbf{v}) = \int d\mathbf{r} \, x_i \, w(\mathbf{r}, \mathbf{v}) \,. \tag{40}$$

In the second term one can integrate once by parts, and has

$$\bar{x}_i(\mathbf{v}) - \lambda \hat{v}_i = G_P \, \bar{x}_i(\mathbf{v}) \,. \tag{41}$$

Because the problem is isotropic,

$$\bar{x}_i(\mathbf{v}) = \bar{x}(E) \hat{v}_i \,. \tag{40a}$$

In $G_P \, \bar{x}_i(\mathbf{v}) = G_P \, \bar{x}(E) \hat{v}_i$ one uses (8a)

$$G_P \, \bar{x}(E) \hat{v}_i = \int d\mathbf{v}' \, G_P(E;E') \, \frac{\delta(\hat{\mathbf{v}} \cdot \hat{\mathbf{v}}' - \sqrt{E'/E})}{2\pi} \, \bar{x}(E') \hat{v}_i'$$

$$= \int dE' \, G_P(E;E') \sqrt{E'/E} \, \bar{x}(E') \hat{v}_i \,,$$

and after multiplying (41) by $\hat{v}_i$ and summing over $i$ ( $\sum_i \hat{v}_i^2 = \hat{\mathbf{v}} \cdot \hat{\mathbf{v}} = 1$), one has

$$\lambda(E) = \left(1 - \frac{1}{\sqrt{E}} \, G_P \sqrt{E}\right) \bar{x}(E) \,, \tag{42}$$

or in Lindhard's formulation

$$1 = n_{at} \frac{1}{\sqrt{E}} \int dE' \, K_P(E;E') \, \{\sqrt{E} \, \bar{x}(E) - \sqrt{E'} \, \bar{x}(E')\} \,. \tag{42a}$$

In the hca, eq. (42) can be solved easily by establishing a differential equation of first order for $\bar{x}(E)$, with the result

$$\bar{x}(E) = \lambda(E) + \frac{1}{\sqrt{E}} \int_0^E dE' \, \frac{\lambda(E')}{\sqrt{E'}} = \left(1 + \sqrt{E} \, G_P^{hc} \, \frac{1}{\sqrt{E}}\right) \lambda(E) \,, \tag{43}$$

---

* An exception [10] being $w(L,E)$ for power potentials in the hca, where

$$w(L,E) = \frac{L^{s/2} \, e^{-L/\lambda(E)}}{\Gamma(1 + \frac{1}{2}s) \, \lambda^{1+s/2}} \,.$$

which for power potentials becomes $(\lambda(E) \propto E^{2/s})$

$$\ddot{x}(E) = \lambda(E) \frac{4 + 3s}{4 + s} . \tag{44}$$

However, the solution (43) is general and does not depend on the assumption of a power law.

If in (42a) the full cross section is used and the approximation (20) for power potentials is employed,

$$K_P(E;E') = \frac{c_s}{E^{1/s} (E-E')^{1 + 1/s}} ,$$

one can solve [17,18] for $\ddot{x}(E)$, which also must be proportional to $E^{2/s}$ as in (44),

$$\ddot{x}(E) = cE^{2/s} .$$

Then * one obtains $c$ from (42a)

$$1 = n_{at}\, c_s\, c \int_0^1 dt\, \frac{1 - t^{\frac{1}{2} + 2/s}}{(1 - t)^{1 + 1/s}} =$$

$$= n_{at}\, c_s\, c\, s \left\{ \left( \frac{1}{2} + \frac{2}{s} \right) B \left( \frac{1}{2} + \frac{2}{s}, 1 - \frac{1}{s} \right) - 1 \right\} . \tag{44a}$$

Other averages can be calculated analogously, [18,19] e.g., $\overline{y^2}$ where $y$ is perpendicular to $\hat{v}$ and where $\sqrt{\overline{y^2}}$ gives information about the extension of the cascade perpendicular to $\hat{v}$, $\overline{x^2}$ where $\sqrt{\overline{x^2} - \bar{x}^2} = \sqrt{\overline{\Delta^2 x}}$ gives an idea about the extension of the cascade in $\hat{v}$ direction about the center $\bar{x}$, and higher orders such as $\overline{xy^2}$ and $\overline{(x-\bar{x})^3} = \overline{\Delta x^3}$ which give some more information about the form of $w(\mathbf{r},\mathbf{v})$ and can be used to fit parameters in approximately chosen distributions functions.

Table 1 gives the calculated values for several averages according to ref. [19] **. Figs. 11 and 12 illustrate the form of the primary distribution for $s = 2$ and 4, if one assumes rotationally symmetric elliptical distribution given by $\bar{x}$ and widths $\propto \sqrt{\overline{\Delta x^2}}$ and $\sqrt{\overline{y^2}}$. They show ellipsoids with $\bar{x}$ as center and values of the two principal distances of $\sqrt{\overline{y^2}}$ and $\sqrt{\overline{\Delta x^2}}$. If one assumes a Gaussian distribution, the ellipsoid corresponds to a line of equal density which is smaller by $e^{\frac{1}{2}}$ than the density in the center, $\bar{x}$.

A comparison with the hard core approximation has also been given in ref. [19]. The hard core cross section was determined by the $\int T\, d\sigma$ fit, eq. (26), using the Lindhard approximation for power potentials which gives

$$\sigma_{hc}^{(1)}(E) = \frac{2}{E} \int T\, d\sigma = \frac{2s\, c_s}{s - 1} E^{-2/s} = \frac{2s}{s - 1} \frac{\pi}{s} C_s^{2/s} D_s^{2/s} E^{-2/s} \tag{45}$$

---

* In the hca where $K_P(E;E') = \sigma(E)/E \propto 1/E^{1 + 2/s}$ one can solve for $\bar{x}$ in the same way.
** Values for the unequal mass case are also given there.

Table 1

Averages for primary distributions.

| $s$ | $\dfrac{\dot{x}}{E^{2/s}/n_{at}C_s}$ | $\dfrac{\overline{\Delta x^2}}{\dot{x}^2}$ | $\dfrac{\overline{y^2}}{\dot{x}^2}$ | $\dfrac{\overline{x\,y^2}}{\dot{x}\,y^2}$ | $\dfrac{\overline{\Delta x^3}}{\dot{x}^3}$ |
|---|---|---|---|---|---|
| $\frac{3}{2}$ | 0.204 (0.258) | 0.204 (0.652) | 0.145 (0.064) | 1.14 (1.72) | 0.023 (0.843) |
| 2 | 0.369 (0.417) | 0.276 (0.611) | 0.176 (0.095) | 1.20 (1.62) | 0.078 (0.735) |
| 3 | 0.597 (0.619) | 0.341 (0.568) | 0.241 (0.159) | 1.20 (1.48) | 0.138 (0.610) |
| 4 | 0.750 (0.750) | 0.385 (0.556) | 0.308 (0.222) | 1.17 (1.39) | 0.162 (0.547) |

instead of the normal hc cross section

$$\sigma_{hc}(E) = \pi(2C_s)^{2/s}\,E^{-2/s}\ .$$

The ratio

$$\frac{\sigma_{hc}^{(1)}}{\sigma_{hc}} = \frac{2}{s-1}\left(\frac{D_s}{2}\right)^{2/s} = \frac{\pi/2 \cong 1.52}{1.085} \quad \text{for } s = \frac{2}{4}$$

is $> 1$ for $s$ values around 2. The hca, which is not particularly good for $s$ values near 2 in any case, gives generally too large values of $\lambda$ and therefore too large values of $\dot{x}$. This is somewhat compensated by the $\int T\,d\sigma$ fit which tends to smaller $\lambda$. With the fit (45) the averages for $\dot{x}$ are given in table 1 in brackets. They are still somewhat too large, but they agree much better. The values for the higher order averages are also given in brackets. The corresponding values are relative and do not depend on how one defines $\sigma_{hc}$. Only the scale is set by selecting a procedure to obtain $\sigma_{hc}(E)$. One recognizes that the hca gives more elliptically shaped distributions whereas the distributions of the power potentials are more spherical *.

So far no justification has been given for the use of the $\int T\,d\sigma$ fit except for demonstrating some improvement in the calculated low order averages. A crude and simple try to justify this fit can be obtained as follows. One can try to obtain the simplest approximation for $\bar{x}(E)$ by using a continuous slowing down theory, where eq. (42) is replaced by a differential equation of first order. This can be done by considering the quantity $\sqrt{E'}\,\bar{x}(E')$ as varying slowly with $E'$ and expanding it about $E' = E$, only keeping first order terms. One obtains

$$1 = n_{at}\frac{1}{\sqrt{E}}\,\partial_E\sqrt{E}\,\bar{x}(E)\ \int T\,d\sigma$$

---

* This has also been found in computer calculations [7].

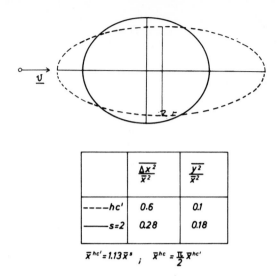

|        | $\dfrac{\overline{\Delta x^2}}{\overline{x^2}}$ | $\dfrac{\overline{y^2}}{\overline{x^2}}$ |
|--------|------|------|
| ----hc' | 0.6 | 0.1 |
| ——s=2  | 0.28 | 0.18 |

$$\overline{x}^{hc'} = 1.13\,\overline{x}^s \quad ; \quad \overline{x}^{hc} = \frac{\pi}{2}\,\overline{x}^{hc'}$$

Fig. 11. Primary distribution for power potential and hca ($s = 1$).

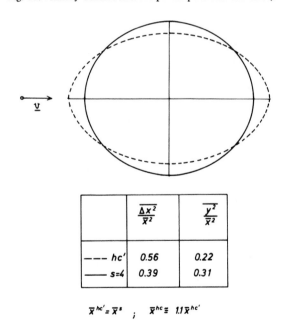

|        | $\dfrac{\overline{\Delta x^2}}{\overline{x^2}}$ | $\dfrac{\overline{y^2}}{\overline{x^2}}$ |
|--------|------|------|
| --- hc' | 0.56 | 0.22 |
| —— s=4  | 0.39 | 0.31 |

$$\overline{x}^{hc'} = \overline{x}^s \quad ; \quad \overline{x}^{hc} \cong 1.1\,\overline{x}^{hc'}$$

Fig. 12. Primary distribution for power potential and hca ($s = 4$).

because

$$\int K_P(E,E')\,(E-E')\,dE' = \int K_S(E,E'')\,E''\,dE'' = \int T\,d\sigma = S(E)\,.$$

In order to obtain the same equation in the hca, where $K_P(E,E') = \sigma_{hc}(E)\,G_{hc}(E;E')$, one must obviously use the $\int T\,d\sigma$ fit. This can serve as a justification * and it will give a crude picture of the $w$ distribution shown in the low-order averages but not the details contained in the higher-order averages.

Another remark must be made with respect to comparing (42) and (42a) or (38) and (38a), where one uses the full cross section in (42a, 38a). For the sake of simplicity let us consider power potentials and assume the Lindhard approximation. As was pointed out in the Introduction, in a numerical model one would use a constant cross section $\pi R_l^2$ with a maximum impact parameter $R_l$ which corresponds to a transferred energy $T_l$,

$$\frac{T_l}{E} = \frac{T(R_l^2)}{E} = \frac{1}{E^2}\frac{C_s^2 D_s^2}{R_l^{2s}} = \left(\frac{D_s}{2}\right)^2 \left(\frac{R}{R_l}\right)^{2s} \rightarrow \left(\frac{\pi}{2}\right)^2 \frac{R^4}{R_l^4} \quad \text{for } s = 2$$

or a maximum primary energy

$$E'_{max} = E - T_l\,.$$

If one wants to use the full cross section, $T_l/E$ must be small as compared with 1 or $R \ll R_l$, corresponding to high energies, which condition must be fulfilled anyhow in the binary collision model; i.e., the conditions of the binary collision approximation and Lindhard's treatment are the same, and require "high energy". For very high energies the corresponding power approaches $s = 1$, where $\int T\,d\sigma$ diverges because of the contribution by large impact parameters. This means that the power potential approximation breaks down at very high energies and one must take into account that the power changes appreciably with interatomic distance. If one uses $\int T\,d\sigma$ as criterion, the condition for the validity of the power approach would be

$$\frac{\displaystyle\int_0^{T_l} T\,d\sigma}{\displaystyle\int_0^{E} T\,d\sigma} = \left(\frac{T_l}{E}\right)^{1 - 1/s} \ll 1\,,$$

showing that values near $s = 1$ have to be excluded. On the other hand, for initial

---

* Expanding $\dot{x}(E')$ around $E$ also gives an equation of first order, but the above procedure is simplest. If one applies the same method in the equation for $w(L,E)$, its solution is

$$w(L,E) = \delta\left(L - \int_0^E dE'/n_{at}\,S(E')\right)\,,$$

where $\int dE'/n_{at}\,S(E')$ is an approximation to the correct average $\overline{L}$.

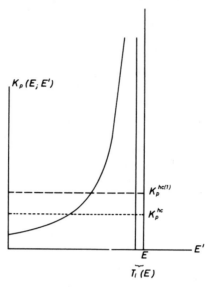

Fig. 13. Differential cross section for power potential ($s = 2$), hard core approximations and cut-off $T_l(E)$ in computer models.

energies where $s \gtrsim 1$, inelastic losses are important and have to be included in the slowing down theory.

Fig. 13 shows qualitatively the differential cross section $K_p(E;E')$ for $s = 2$, the simple hca and the hca with $\int T \, d\sigma$ fit, together with the cut-off $E - T_l(E)$.

## 7. Cascades

### 7.1. Interstitials

The average number of interstitials produced in $(\mathbf{r}, d\mathbf{r})$ by a primary starting at $\mathbf{r} = 0$ with $\mathbf{v}$ will be denoted by $F(\mathbf{r}, \mathbf{v}) \, d\mathbf{r}$. The average interstitial density *, $F$, can be written as

$$F(\mathbf{r},\mathbf{v}) = p \, \widetilde{F}(\mathbf{r},\mathbf{v}) \tag{46}$$

---

* Instead of defect densities, Sanders [18] has considered recoil densities representing collisions where one atom within the cascade first obtains an energy in the interval $(\epsilon, d\epsilon)$ where $\epsilon$ is smaller than a certain limit $\epsilon_l$ below which the lattice effects become important. The energy $\epsilon$ can be obtained either during the slowing down or by a first collision leading into $d\epsilon$. The number of recoils per unit energy

$$\nu(E;\epsilon) = \frac{s-1}{s} \frac{E}{\epsilon_l^{1-1/s} \, \epsilon^{1+1/s}}$$

for $E \gg \epsilon_l$ and shows a strong tendency toward small $\epsilon$, whereas in the hca $\nu(E;\epsilon) = 2E/\epsilon_l^2$. The equations and averages for the recoil density are for $E \gg \epsilon_l$ identical with those for $F$.

where $\widetilde{F}$ is the density produced by a primary which escaped its lattice site. The average number, $\nu$, of interstitials is given by

$$\nu(E) = \int d\mathbf{r}\, F(\mathbf{r},\mathbf{v}) = p \int d\mathbf{r}\, \widetilde{F}(\mathbf{r},\mathbf{v}) = p\widetilde{\nu} \tag{47}$$

where $\widetilde{\nu} \geqslant 1$ because at least one interstitial is formed once the primary leaves its lattice site.

Equations for $F, \widetilde{F}$ can be derived [20,21] as in the case of the primary distribution. Again one has to consider what happens in the first collision after the primary has escaped. Four cases have to be considered:

1) primary and secondary which have velocity $\mathbf{v}'$ and $\mathbf{v}''$ after the collision cannot leave the collision site $\xi\hat{\mathbf{v}}$; an interstitial is formed there with the probability $q'q'' = q(E')q(E'')$; the contribution to $\widetilde{F}(\mathbf{r},\mathbf{v})$ is $q'q''\,\delta(\mathbf{r}-\xi\hat{\mathbf{v}})$;

2) the primary moves on and the secondary remains; probability $p'q''$; contribution $p'q''\widetilde{F}(\mathbf{r}-\xi\hat{\mathbf{v}},\mathbf{v}')$;

3) as in 2) but secondary and primary permuted; contribution $q'p''\widetilde{F}(\mathbf{r}-\xi\hat{\mathbf{v}},\mathbf{v}'')$;

4) both primary and secondary move on; contribution $p'p''(\widetilde{F}(\mathbf{r}-\xi\hat{\mathbf{v}},\mathbf{v}') + \widetilde{F}(\mathbf{r}-\xi\hat{\mathbf{v}},\mathbf{v}''))$.

If one sums over these four possibilities and averages over $\xi,\mathbf{v}',\mathbf{v}''$ with the corresponding contributions, one has

$$\widetilde{F}(\mathbf{r},\mathbf{v}) = \int_0^\infty d\xi\, \frac{e^{-\xi/\lambda}}{\lambda} \int d\mathbf{v}'\, d\mathbf{v}''\, G(\mathbf{v};\mathbf{v}',\mathbf{v}'')\, \{p'\widetilde{F}(\mathbf{r}-\xi\hat{\mathbf{v}},\mathbf{v}')$$

$$+ p''\widetilde{F}(\mathbf{r}-\xi\hat{\mathbf{v}},\mathbf{v}'') + q'q''\,\delta(\mathbf{r}-\xi\hat{\mathbf{v}})\}. \tag{48}$$

The corresponding integro-differential equation becomes

$$(1 + \lambda\hat{\mathbf{v}}\partial_{\mathbf{r}})\,\widetilde{F}(\mathbf{r},\mathbf{v}) = G_{PS}\, p\widetilde{F}(\mathbf{r},\mathbf{v}) + I\delta(\mathbf{r}) \tag{49}$$

where $G_{PS}$ stands for $G_P + G_S$,

$$G_{PS}\, h(\mathbf{v}) = \int d\mathbf{v}'\, \{G_P(\mathbf{v};\mathbf{v}') + G_S(\mathbf{v};\mathbf{v}')\}\, h(\mathbf{v}')$$

$$= \int d\mathbf{v}'\, \{G_P(\mathbf{v};\mathbf{v}') + G_P(\mathbf{v};\mathbf{v}-\mathbf{v}')\}\, h(\mathbf{v}')$$

$$= \int d\mathbf{v}'\, G_P(\mathbf{v};\mathbf{v}')\, \{h(\mathbf{v}') + h(\mathbf{v}-\mathbf{v}')\},$$

$$G_{PS}\, h(E) = \int dE'\, G_P(E;E')\, \{h(E') + h(E-E')\}$$

$$= \int dE''\, G_S(E;E'')\, \{h(E'') + h(E-E'')\}$$

and

$$I = \int dE' \, G_P(E;E') \, q(E') \, q(E-E')$$

$$= \int dE'' \, G_S(E;E'') \, q(E'') \, q(E-E'') \,.$$

If (49) is integrated over $\mathbf{r}$, the $\partial_{\mathbf{r}}$ term drops out and one obtains

$$\widetilde{\nu}(E) = G_{PS} \, p\widetilde{\nu} + I = G_{PS} \, \nu(E) + I \,, \qquad (50)$$

which determines $\widetilde{\nu}$ and $\nu = p\widetilde{\nu}$ as a function of $E$. For simplicity we use a sharp threshold $E_d$ above which $p = 1$, $q = 0$, $\nu = \widetilde{\nu}$. Also one has in this model of Kinchin and Pease [22]

$$0 \leqslant E \leqslant E_d: \quad \nu = 0, \quad \widetilde{\nu} = 1; \quad E_d \leqslant E \leqslant 2E_d: \quad \nu = \widetilde{\nu} = 1;$$

$$2E_d \leqslant E: \quad I = 0 \,.$$

Consequently,

$$\nu(E) = G_{PS} \, \nu(E) = \int dT \, G_S(E;T) \, \{\nu(T) + \nu(E-T)\},$$

$$\text{for} \quad E \geqslant 2E_d \,, \qquad (51)$$

which can also be written

$$\int dT \, G_S(E;T) \, \{\nu(T) + \nu(E-T) - \nu(E)\} = 0 \qquad (51a)$$

or in Lindhard's notation

$$\int dT \, K_S(E;T) \, \{\nu(T) + \nu(E-T) - \nu(E)\} = 0 \qquad (51b)$$

If one multiplies (51a) with $\sigma(E)$. The required solution of (51) must obey $\nu(2E_d) = 1$.

From eq. (51) one can see that for high energies the solution will be

$$\nu(E) = \alpha E \qquad (52)$$

where $\alpha$ has yet to be determined. In the hca where $G_{PS} = 2G_P^{hc}$ one obtains easily

$$\nu(E) = E/2E_d \,. \qquad (53)$$

For power potentials in the Lindhard approximation where $K_S \propto 1/T^{1 + 1/s}$, the value of $\alpha$ has been calculated by Robinson [23]. Fig. 14 shows, as a function of $s$, the quantity $\alpha 2E_d$ which is the reduction of the hard core value due to the abundance of low energy transfers in the power scattering law. This reduction * is about

---

* In the calculations of Beeler [8], channeling of primaries and secondaries has only a small effect on $\nu(E)$, whereas the most important effects is self-annealing within the cascade.

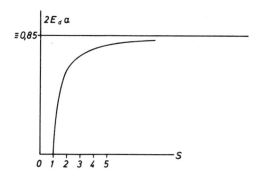

Fig 14. Number of Frenkel pairs for power potentials.

40% for $s = 2$ and 25% for $s = 4$. For larger values of $s$, the Lindhard approximation breaks down; for large $s$ the hard core value ($\alpha 2E_d = 1$) should be reached.

The value of $\alpha$ is mainly determined by the low-energy behavior of $\nu(E)$ and $K_S$. Therefore, the $\alpha$ values are not very reliable even for a pure power potential because of the lattice cut-off represented by $T_l(E)$ which should increase $\alpha$ to some extent. For the following we require only that $\nu \propto E$ at high energies; the value is not important and does not influence the form and extent of the cascade very much. In a cascade, as in the primary distribution, the low energy contribution is small if one starts at high energy. This is in contrast to the behavior of $\nu(E)$, for which the low energy part is essential for the value at high $E$.

The kernel of the integral operator $G_{PS}(E;\epsilon)$ in (50),

$$G_{PS} \, h\,(E) = \int d\epsilon \; \{G_P(E;\epsilon) + G_S(E,\epsilon)\} \, h(\epsilon)$$

$$= \int d\epsilon \; \{G_P(E;\epsilon) + G_P(E;E-\epsilon)\} \, h(\epsilon) \,,$$

is symmetrical in $\epsilon$ with respect to $E/2$. Fig. 15 shows the kernel $K_{PS}(E;\epsilon)$ $= \sigma(E) G_{PS}(E;\epsilon)$ qualitatively for $s = 2$. If one uses instead of the hca for $G_P(E;\epsilon)$ a kernel which contains preferred forward scattering, such as $G_P \propto$ const. + const. $\cdot \epsilon$, the forward scattering part cancels in $G_{PS}$, and though a forward scattering tendency is contained in $G_P$ the quantity $G_{PS}$ equals the hard core operator $2G_P^{hc}$. Therefore, it has been argued that the hca is more reliable for cascade calculations than for primary distributions, because only the symmetrical operator $G_{PS}$ enters the cascade equations. We will come back to this point later.

7.2. *Averages over the interstitial cascade*

We will only treat the averages of $x_i$ in detail, which are

$$\bar{x}_i = \frac{\int dr \, x_i F(\mathbf{r},\mathbf{v})}{\int dr F(\mathbf{r},\mathbf{v})} = \frac{\int dr \, x_i F}{\nu} = \frac{\int dr \, x_i \widetilde{F}}{\widetilde{\nu}} \,. \tag{54}$$

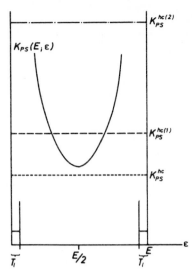

Fig. 15. The function $K_{PS}(E; \epsilon)$ with three hard core approximations and cut-off $T_l(E)$.

This is an average over the normalized distribution

$$f(\mathbf{r},\mathbf{v}) = F(\mathbf{r},\mathbf{v})/\nu = \widetilde{F}(\mathbf{r},\mathbf{v})/\widetilde{\nu}$$

which represents the form and the extent of the cascade. For high energies eq. (49) becomes

$$(1 + \lambda \hat{v}\partial_{\mathbf{r}})\, F(\mathbf{r},\mathbf{v}) = G_{PS}\, F(\mathbf{r},\mathbf{v}) , \tag{55}$$

or in Lindhard's notation

$$\hat{v}\partial_{\mathbf{r}}\, F(\mathbf{r},\mathbf{v}) = n_{at} \int d\mathbf{v}'\, K_P(\mathbf{v};\mathbf{v}')\, \{F(\mathbf{r},\mathbf{v}') + F(\mathbf{r};\mathbf{v}-\mathbf{v}') - F(\mathbf{r},\mathbf{v})\}. \tag{55a}$$

In eq. (55, 55a) the interstitial density $F$ can be replaced by $\alpha E f$ or by $E f$ because $\alpha$ drops out.

If one multiplies (55) with $x_i$ and integrates over $\mathbf{r}$, one obtains

$$\nu\lambda\hat{v}_i = \nu \bar{x}_i - G_{PS}\, \nu \bar{x}_i$$

and with $\bar{x}_i = \bar{x}(E)\,\hat{v}_i$ analogous to the derivation of (42)

$$\nu\lambda = \nu\bar{x} - \frac{1}{\sqrt{E}}\, G_{PS}\, \sqrt{E}\, \nu(E)\, \bar{x}(E) , \tag{56}$$

or with $\nu = \alpha E$

$$\lambda(E) = \bar{x}(E) - \frac{1}{E^{\frac{3}{2}}}\, G_{PS}\, E^{\frac{3}{2}}\, \bar{x}(E) . \tag{57}$$

In Lindhard's notation eq. (57) reads

$$1 = n_{at} \left\{ \sigma \bar{x} - \frac{1}{E^{\frac{3}{2}}} \int d\epsilon \, K_{PS}(E;\epsilon) \, \epsilon \sqrt{\epsilon} \bar{x}(\epsilon) \right\}$$

$$= n_{at} \frac{1}{E^{\frac{3}{2}}} \int d\epsilon \, K_P(E;\epsilon) \, \{ E^{\frac{3}{2}} \bar{x}(E) - \epsilon^{\frac{3}{2}} \bar{x}(\epsilon) - (E-\epsilon)^{\frac{3}{2}} \bar{x}(E-\epsilon) \}. \quad (57a)$$

In the hca, where $G_{PS} = 2G_P^{hc}$, again the solution of (57) is simple *:

$$\bar{x} = \lambda(E) + 2\sqrt{E} \, G_P^{hc} \frac{\lambda(E)}{\sqrt{E}} = \left( 1 + 2\sqrt{E} \, G_P^{hc} \frac{1}{\sqrt{E}} \right) \lambda(E). \quad (58)$$

For Lindhard's power approximation one can solve (57a) by $\bar{x}(\epsilon) = c\epsilon^{2/s}$ and obtains $c$ with $K_P = c_s/E^{1/s} (E-\epsilon)^{1 + 1/s}$ from

$$1 = n_{at} c_s c \int_0^1 dt \frac{1}{(1-t)^{1+1/s}} \{ 1 - t^{\frac{3}{2}+2/s} - (1-t)^{\frac{3}{2}+2/s} \}$$

$$= n_{at} c_s c \left\{ s\left( \frac{3}{2} + \frac{2}{s} \right) B\left( \frac{3}{2} + \frac{2}{s}, 1 - \frac{1}{s} \right) - s - \frac{1}{\frac{3}{2}+2/s} \right\}. \quad (58a)$$

As for the primary distribution, higher order averages can be calculated. The results [18,19] are given in table 2. The hard core values are given in round brackets. As in table 1, the hard core value for $\bar{x}$ depends on the choice of $\sigma_{hc}$, which here is given by matching $\int T \, d\sigma$. The other values are independent of the choice of $\sigma_{hc}$. By comparison with table 1, one recognizes that the fluctuation, i.e., the form of the distribution, for power potentials and hca agrees much better in the cascade than in the primary distribution. On the other hand, the average $\bar{x}$ in the cascade is off by a fac-

* For the primary distribution

$$\bar{x} = \frac{1}{\sqrt{E}} \frac{1}{1-G_P^{hc}} \sqrt{E}\lambda \,,$$

and for the cascade

$$\bar{x} = \frac{1}{E^{\frac{3}{2}}} \frac{1}{1 - 2G_P^{hc}} E^{\frac{3}{2}} \lambda \,.$$

If $C$ is a constant, one has

$$\frac{1}{1 - CG_P^{hc}} = 1 + C E^C \, G_P^{hc} \frac{1}{E^C}$$

which leads to (43) and (58).

Table 2
Averages for cascade distributions.

| $s$ | $\dfrac{\bar{x}(E)}{E^{2/s}/n_{\mathrm{at}}C_s}$ | $\dfrac{\overline{\Delta x^2}}{\bar{x}^2}$ | $\dfrac{\overline{y^2}}{\bar{x}^2}$ | $\dfrac{\overline{xy^2}}{\bar{x}\,\overline{y^2}}$ | $\dfrac{\overline{\Delta x^3}}{\bar{x}^3}$ |
|---|---|---|---|---|---|
| $\frac{3}{2}$ | 0.156 (0.348) [0.155] | 0.337 (0.489) | 0.130 (0.092) | 1.40 (1.50) | 0.096 (0.469) |
| 2 | 0.295 (0.583) [0.292] | 0.380 (0.451) | 0.157 (0.132) | 1.41 (1.40) | 0.172 (0.387) |
| 3 | 0.505 (0.905) [0.503] | 0.407 (0.423) | 0.220 (0.210) | 1.33 (1.28) | 0.222 (0.305) |
| 4 | 0.656 (1.125) [0.656] | 0.429 (0.429) | 0.286 (0.286) | 1.26 (1.20) | 0.232 (0.263) |

tor of roughly 2. Further, $\bar{x}$ for the cascade is smaller than that of the primary, whereas the hca shows the reverse behavior (compare eqs. (58) and (43)). Fig. 16 shows the elliptical form of the cascade given by lowest-order averages for $s = 2$. One sees that the form is approximately similar but that the scale disagrees about a factor of 2. The disagreement in the scale would become worse if one used the simple hca without fitting $\int T\,d\sigma$. This is contrary to the expectation that the hca should give relatively better results in the cascade than in the primary distribution.

But if one uses a fitting method to improve the hca, the question is whether to use the same fitting in the primary and the cascade equations. If we now use in (57a) the same method to fit $\sigma_{\mathrm{hc}}(E)$ as was applied in (42a), namely, expansion of the quantity $\sqrt{E'}\,\bar{x}(E')$, and which led to the simplest differential equation for $\bar{x}(E)$ with the $\int T\,d\sigma$ fit, then the quantity $\sqrt{\epsilon}\,\bar{x}(\epsilon)$ will be expanded and replaced by $\sqrt{E}\,\bar{x}(E) + (\epsilon-E)\,\partial_E\,\sqrt{E}\,\bar{x}(E)$. This leads to *

$$1 = n_{\mathrm{at}}\,\frac{1}{E^{\frac{3}{2}}}\;\{\int K_{\mathrm{PS}}(E;\epsilon)\,\epsilon(E-\epsilon)\,d\epsilon\}\,\partial_E\,\sqrt{E}\,\bar{x}\,.$$

The same equation in the hca ($K_{\mathrm{PS}}^{\mathrm{hc}} = 2\sigma_{\mathrm{hc}}(E)\,G_{\mathrm{P}}^{\mathrm{hc}}(E;\epsilon)$) is

$$1 = n_{\mathrm{at}}\,\frac{1}{E^{\frac{3}{2}}}\,2\sigma_{\mathrm{hc}}(E)\,\frac{E^2}{6}\,\partial_E\,\sqrt{E}\,\bar{x}(E)\,,$$

---

* $\dfrac{1}{E}\,G_{\mathrm{PS}}\,E$ const. = const.

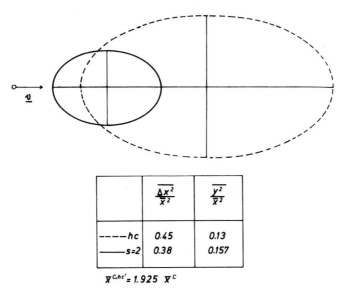

| | $\dfrac{\overline{\Delta x^2}}{\overline{x^2}}$ | $\dfrac{\overline{y^2}}{\overline{x^2}}$ |
|---|---|---|
| ----$hc$ | 0.45 | 0.13 |
| ——$s=2$ | 0.38 | 0.157 |

$$\overline{x}^{C,hc'} = 1.925 \ \overline{x}^{\,C}$$

Fig. 16. Cascade for power potential and hca ($s = 2$).

or by comparison

$$\sigma_{hc}^{(2)}(E) = \frac{3}{E^2} \int K_{PS}(E;\epsilon)\, \epsilon(E-\epsilon)\, d\epsilon = \frac{6}{E^2} \int K_S(E;T)\, T(E-T)\, dT , \quad (59)$$

in contrast to the $\int T\, d\sigma$ fit (45),

$$\sigma_{hc}^{(1)}(E) = \frac{2}{E} \int T\, d\sigma = \frac{2}{E} \int K_S(E;T)\, T\, dT . \tag{59a}$$

For power potentials where

$$K_S(E;T) = \frac{c_s}{E^{1/s}\, T^{1\,+\,1/s}} ,$$

it is

$$\sigma_{hc}^{(2)} = \frac{6c_s}{E^{2/s}} \left\{ \frac{1}{1 - 1/s} - \frac{1}{2 - 1/s} \right\} = \frac{6c_s}{E^{2/s}} \frac{1}{1 - 2/s} \frac{s}{2s - 1} , \tag{60}$$

$$\sigma_{hc}^{(1)} = \frac{2c_s}{E^{2/s}} \frac{1}{1 - 1/s} , \tag{60a}$$

and

$$\frac{\sigma_{hc}^{(2)}}{\sigma_{hc}^{(1)}} = \frac{3s}{2s - 1} .$$

The hard core cross section for the fit (59) is by $3s/(2s-1)$ larger than that of the $\int T\,d\sigma$ fit, the mean free path and $\bar{x}$ correspondingly smaller. The values of this hca are the values in square brackets of table 2; they are ridiculously close to the power potential values. Using this kind of fit, the cascade values of the hca agree much more closely than before. Consequently, by using the appropriate fit the hca can still serve as a rough approximation, though one has to employ different fits for different quantities.

## 7.3. Vacancies

For the average vacancy density we use the same notation $F(\mathbf{r},\mathbf{v})$ as for the interstitials. The equations for vacancies are different but they agree with the interstitial equations for high energies. In

$$F(\mathbf{r},\mathbf{v}) = p\{\delta(\mathbf{r}) + \widetilde{F}(\mathbf{r},\mathbf{v})\}, \tag{61}$$

$\widetilde{F}$ is the average vacancy density produced by an escaping primary. The first term on the right in (61) represents the production of the vacancy at the origin. The equations for $\widetilde{F}$ are obtained analogously to those of the interstitials:

$$\widetilde{F}(\mathbf{r},\mathbf{v}) = \int\limits_{0}^{\infty} d\xi \, \frac{e^{-\xi/\lambda}}{\lambda} d\mathbf{v}' \, d\mathbf{v}'' \, G(\mathbf{v};\mathbf{v}',\mathbf{v}'') \, \{p'p''\,\delta(\mathbf{r}-\xi\hat{\mathbf{v}})$$

$$+ p'\widetilde{F}(\mathbf{r}-\xi\hat{\mathbf{v}},\mathbf{v}') + p''\widetilde{F}(\mathbf{r}-\xi\hat{\mathbf{v}},\mathbf{v}'')\} \tag{62}$$

and

$$(1 + \lambda\hat{\mathbf{v}}\partial_{\mathbf{r}})\,\widetilde{F}(\mathbf{r},\mathbf{v}) = G_{PS}\,p\widetilde{F} + I\delta(\mathbf{r}) \tag{63}$$

where

$$I = \int G_P(E;E')\,p(E')\,p(E-E') \, .$$

It can be shown easily that the average number of vacancies

$$\nu = \int d\mathbf{r} F = p(1 + \int d\mathbf{r}\widetilde{F})$$

obeys the same equation as the number of interstitials (50), as it must. For high energies one has $F \cong \widetilde{F}$; one can neglect $I \cong 1$ in (63) and obtains the same equation as for interstitials, eq. (55). Vacancies and interstitials are equally distributed in high energy cascades and all that has been said in the foregoing applies as well to vacancies.

## 7.4. Pair densities

Of particular interest are the average pair densities, $P(\mathbf{r},\mathbf{r}',\mathbf{v})$, where, e.g., $P\,d\mathbf{r}\,d\mathbf{r}'$ is the average of interstitial-vacancy pairs in $d\mathbf{r}\,d\mathbf{r}'$, the interstitial being in $(\mathbf{r},d\mathbf{r})$ and the vacancy in $(\mathbf{r}',d\mathbf{r}')$. For high energy cascades the pair densities for interstitial-vacancy, interstitial-interstitial, and vacancy-vacancy pairs all agree. The equation determining the pair density for high energies is [20]

$$(1 + \lambda \hat{v}(\partial_{\mathbf{r}} + \partial_{\mathbf{r}'})) P(\mathbf{r}, \mathbf{r}', v) = G_{PS} P(\mathbf{r}, \mathbf{r}', v)$$

$$+ \int dv'\, G_{PS}(v, v')\, F(\mathbf{r}, v)\, F(\mathbf{r}', v - v'),\quad (64)$$

and

$$\int d\mathbf{r}\, d\mathbf{r}'\, P(\mathbf{r}, \mathbf{r}', 0) = v^2(E) \propto E^2 . \tag{65}$$

Equations for averages over the pair density distribution, such as

$$\overline{(\mathbf{r} - \mathbf{r}')^2} = \frac{\int (\mathbf{r} - \mathbf{r}')^2\, P\, d\mathbf{r}\, d\mathbf{r}'}{v^2} \tag{66a}$$

$$\overline{(x - x')^2} = \frac{\int (x - x')^2\, P\, d\mathbf{r}\, d\mathbf{r}'}{v^2}, \qquad x = \mathbf{r}\hat{v}, \tag{66b}$$

$$\overline{(y - y')^2} = \frac{\int (y - y')^2\, P\, d\mathbf{r}\, d\mathbf{r}'}{v^2},$$

$y$-component perpendicular to $\hat{v}$,          (66c)

can be obtained as before. They have been calculated in the hca [20] for (66a) and for the power approximation [24] for (66a–c). They contain also averages over the cascade distributions because (64) contains the simple densities $F$. Table 3 shows the ratios of the averages (66) to the averages substituting $F(\mathbf{r}) F(\mathbf{r}')$ for $P(\mathbf{r}, \mathbf{r}')$, which assumes uncorrelated pairs. The values in brackets are hca values, which do not depend on the kind of fitting.

Essentially, it is the pair density which gives information about the actual density in a cascade and decides the magnitude of possible subsequent self-anneal. The densities $F$ are averages over many single cascades with different forms, densities, and locations. Consequently, one obtains a wrong picture if one uses the normal cascade averages to picture the extent of a cascade. The pair densities will always give smaller extents. A simple example can illustrate this point. Let us assume for the moment that a single cascade is spherical, radius $R_0$, and has constant density $\rho_0$. If now the single cascade centers are distributed also spherically, radius $R_1$, around $\bar{x}$ as center, then the average density $F$ is smaller than $\rho_0$ by a factor $R_0^3/R_1^3$ if $R_0/R_1 \gg 1$. The cascade volume of a single cascade is therefore smaller than that of $F$ by about the $\frac{3}{2}$ power of the ratios in table 3. For power potentials the cascade volume is proportional to $E^{2/s}$, and since $v \propto E$ the density in a cascade falls with increasing energy. Therefore, in neutron damage the pair density will decrease with in-

Table 3
Averages for pair distributions.

| $s$ | $\dfrac{\overline{(\mathbf{r}-\mathbf{r}')^2}^P}{\overline{(\mathbf{r}-\mathbf{r}')^2}}$ uncorr | $\dfrac{\overline{(x-x')^2}^P}{\overline{(x-x')^2}}$ uncorr | $\dfrac{\overline{(y-y')^2}^P}{\overline{(y-y')^2}}$ uncorr |
|---|---|---|---|
| $\frac{3}{2}$ | 0.47 (0.29) | 0.52 | 0.37 |
| 2 | 0.50 (0.40) | 0.52 | 0.47 |
| 3 | 0.59 (0.56) | 0.55 | 0.63 |
| 4 | 0.67 (0.67) | 0.60 | 0.72 |

creasing energy. Sigmund has discussed this more quantitatively in ref. 24 and concluded that the cascade densities in light materials such as Al, where the primary energies are high, will be so small that substantial self-annealing will not occur, whereas for heavy materials such as Au the concentrations are so large that one has to expect a good deal of annihilation between Frenkel pairs.

The pair densities also decide the extent of the vacancy and interstitial cascade. Recent work [25] has shown that the vacancy cascade has smaller extent than the interstitial cascade (vacancy clustering). Since for high energies the pair density is the same for all kinds of pairs, one has here to treat more complicated equations including the threshold effect. Vacancy clustering is therefore essentially an effect more pronounced at lower energies. Clustering of vacancies has also been found in computer calculations [4,8].

## Acknowledgements

I would like to thank Drs. P.H.Dederichs and M.T.Robinson for various discussions and helpful suggestions.

## References

[1]  For a review compare S.Datz et al., Ann. Rev. Nucl. Sci. 17 (1967) 129.
[2]  J.B.Gibson, A.N.Goland, M.Milgram and G.H.Vineyard, Phys. Rev. 120 (1960) 1229.
[3]  G.Burger, M.Meissner and W.Schilling, Phys. Stat. Sol. 4 (1964) 281.
[4]  Compare: C.Erginsoy, G.H.Vineyard and E.Englert, Phys. Rev. 133 (1963) 595;
      C.Erginsoy, G.H.Vineyard and A.Shimitu, Phys. Rev. 139 (1965) 118; and the references quoted there;
      L.T.Chadderton and I.McC.Torrens, Proc. Roy. Soc. A294 (1966) 93; planar model.

[5] D.E.Harrison Jr. and D.S.Greiling, J. Appl. Phys. 38 (1967) 3200.

[6] P.V.Pavlov, P.I.Tetelbaum, E.I.Zorin and V.I.Alekseev, Soviet Phys.—Solid State 8 (1967) 2141.

[7] M.T.Robinson and O.S.Oen, Phys. Rev. 132 (1963) 2385 and references quoted there (motion of primaries starting from a lattice site and under channeling conditions).

[8] J.R.Beeler Jr., Phys. Rev. 150 (1966) 470 and references quoted there (cascades including self and thermal annealing).

[9] O.S.Oen, M.T.Robinson and D.K.Holmes, Oak Ridge Nat. Lab. Solid State Div. Ann. Progr. Rept. (1962) p. 3, ORNL-3364.

[10] Compare: G.Leibfried, Bestrahlungseffekte in Festkörpern (B.G.Teubner, Stuttgart, 1965).

[11] J.Lindhard, V.Nielsen and M.Scharff, Mat. Fys. Medd. Dan. Vid. Selsk. 36 (1968) Nr. 10.

[12] O.B.Firsov, JETP 6 (1958) 534.

[13] A.Sommerfeld, Z. Phys. 18 (1932) 283;
     N.H.March, Proc. Cambridge Phil. Soc. 46 (1950) 356.

[14] G.Molière, Z. Naturforsch. 2a (1947) 133.

[15] N.Bohr, Mat. Fys. Medd. Dan. Vid. Selskab. 18, Nr. 8 (1948).

[16] J.Lindhard, V.Nielsen, M.Scharff and P.V.Thomsen, Mat. Fys. Medd. Dan. Vid. Selskab. 33, Nr. 10 (1963).

[17] J.Lindhard, M.Scharff and H.Schitt, Mat. Fys. Medd. Dan. Vid. Selskab. 33, Nr. 14 (1963).

[18] J.B.Sanders, Thesis, Amsterdam (1968).

[19] P.Sigmund and J.B.Sanders, in: Proceedings of Grenoble (1967) Conference on Application of Ion Beams to Semiconductor Technology, p. 215 (1967) (edition Ophrys).

[20] P.H.Dederichs, Phys. Stat. Sol. 10 (1965) 303 and references quoted there.

[21] A.Corciovei and M.Croitoru, Rev. J. Phys. 11 (1966) 317 and references quoted there.

[22] G.H.Kinchin and R.S.Pease, Rep. Progr. Phys. 18 (1955) 1.

[23] M.T.Robinson, Phil. Mag. 17 (1968) 639; 12 (1965) 74.

[24] P.Sigmund, G.P.Scheidler and G.Roth, Proceedings of Conference on Solid State Research with Accelerators (Brookhaven, 1967; BNL 50083, p. 374).

[25] P.Sigmund, Bull. Am. Phys. Soc. 13 (1968) 464.

## Discussion

*H.Wenzl:* Is it correct, that an average over the different cascades present in a sample, corresponding to the theoretical average, could be found by small angle neutron scattering experiments?

Another physical property which depends on a certain average of the cascade "size" is the pinning force of magnetic flux lines in superconductors of 2nd kind. (c.f. niobium-measurements Munich).

*G.Leibfried:* The "size" of a cascade is essentially given by the pair distribution function, e.g. the pair density determines directly the scattering cross section.

*J.R.Beeler:* Concerning Professor Leibfried's remarks on self-annealing during the evolution of a collision cascade, the following schematic diagram deduced from our computer experiments is informative (fig. 17). As the primary knock-on energy $E$ increases, the displacement efficiency $K(E)$ decreases from the Kinchin-Pease levels given by curve (1) to curve (2) given by computer experiments for elastic collision

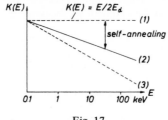

Fig. 17

cascades. This decrease is due to self-annealing which proceeds from overlap among the sub-branches of the cascade as it evolves. When a correction is made for inelastic collision energy dissipation on the basis of Lindhard's theory, curve (3) is obtained from curve (2).

The latter correction was made by Dr. Sheely and gives a good correlation between neutron irradiation-induced changes in the lower yield point of metals and irradiation exposure.

PART 7


VACANCIES AND INTERSTITIALS
IN BCC AND HCP METALS

# VACANCIES AND INTERSTITIALS
# IN BODY-CENTRED CUBIC TRANSITION METALS

## J. NIHOUL
*S.C.K.–C.E.N. Mol, Belgium* *

## 1. Introduction

The study of defects and, more particularly, of vacancies and interstitials in bcc transition metals has always been strongly influenced by the corresponding work on fcc metals. This can be explained not only by the fact that the former work started some five years earlier than the latter but especially by the preponderance of the efforts paid to the research on fcc metals, as compared to the bcc metals. A first reason of this preference for fcc metals is to be found in the better theoretical knowledge of the structural and physical properties of the noble metals in comparison with the transition metals. The second reason has a more experimental character; the close-packed noble metals were more easily available with a high purity degree and they are less exposed to contamination by the surrounding atmosphere than the more open bcc metals.

On the other hand the motives guiding the research on bcc metals can be summarized as follows: (i) Most of these metals have high melting points and the technological interest in refractory metals was ever growing during the last decade; (ii) Most of the recovery stages of high melting point metals could be expected to occur at higher temperatures. Recovery stages at and above room temperature not only have more direct technological importance but they are also more convenient to be investigated from an experimental point of view: significant irradiation and plastic deformatioin experiments can be performed at room temperature; (iii) There is a steadily increasing availability of very pure specimens of bcc metals and, furthermore, improved vacuum techniques allow thermal treatments to be performed without appreciable contamination.

With this historical background in mind it is easy to understand how the interpretation of formation and recovery of point defects in the bcc metals has often been given in the light of the experience with fcc metals. General similarities were found between "corresponding" recovery stages and it did not last very long before, following the example of the investigations on fcc metals [1–3], the interpretations

---

* Work performed in association with R.U.C. Antwerpen and K.U. Leuven.

diverged into two different directions: stage III recovery corresponding either to free vacancy migration or to free interstitial migration. The situation is even more difficult than for the fcc metals since, in spite of important progress, specific evidence for vacancy migration remains very scarce. Quenching experiments are in general very difficult to perform on these metals indeed. As a consequence, only very few recovery experiments following successful quenching have been reported until now.

An additional difficulty arising for bcc metals as compared to fcc metals is to be found in the fact that interstitial impurities are known to play an important part in many recovery processes. As a result, a third line of interpretation is often advanced, according to which "stage III" recovery in bcc metals does not correspond at all to migration of any intrinsic defect, but to interstitial impurity migration.

This very controversial recovery stage has thus been explained in terms not only of the three types of defects: self-interstitials, vacancies, and interstitial impurities, but also of some combinations of these elementary defects, such as divacancies, interstitial clusters, impurity-trapped self-interstitials and so on. This confusion is mainly a result of the indirect character of the experimental methods which are based on measurements of a defect-sensitive physical property.

A promising bright spot for the case of point defects in bcc metals could be available in the technique of field ion microscopy, for which we refer to the contributions of Müller [4] and Galligan [5] in this volume. Notwithstanding the extreme precautions required for this method, it seems reasonable to expect that it will increasingly yield decisive arguments for the identification of the various recovery processes.

It should also be mentioned that the specific experimental difficulties dealt with in the study of bcc metals have resulted in the development of new techniques, e.g., quenching in clean conditions, based on the use of liquid helium II, which method has been applied successfully to tungsten and has shown to be of great interest also for other metals.

This review will mainly be restricted to vacancies and interstitials in the bcc transition metals of the Vth and the VIth subgroup (especially niobium, tantalum, molybdenum and tungsten) and to alpha-iron of the VIIIth subgroup. For the production mechanisms of these defects by irradiation, plastic deformation or quenching, rather little specific results are known and we may refer to the general data about the corresponding mechanisms described elsewhere in this volume for the fcc metals. The case of neutron irradiation of $\alpha$-iron has been studied with computer simulations by Beeler [6,7]. As another limitation of our subject the discussion will chiefly be confined to the main recovery data reported for these metals.

It should also be mentioned, from the start on, that significant differences in many physical properties exist between the metals of the Vth and those of the VIth subgroup. These differences are related to the electronic structure and seem also to be reflected in the annealing behaviour of these metals. The most important characteristics of these elements will be summarized in the next section.

## 2. General properties of body-centred cubic transition metals

A number of physical properties of the bcc transition metals are directly related
to their electronic structure, which is mainly determined, according to the rigid
band model, by the number of valence electrons per atom. Rather pronounced differences are observed in the electronic properties between group V and group VI
transition metals. These differences are reflected not only in such properties as the
electrical resistivity, the transition temperature to superconductivity, the magnetic
susceptibility and the electronic specific heat, but also in the heat of solution of
interstitial impurities and in the elastic constants. Table 1 summarizes a few relevant
data. For more details and references we refer to the recent review paper by
Schultz [8].

Table 1
Comparison of some physical properties of Nb, Ta, Mo and W.

| Physical property | Nb | Ta | Mo | W |
|---|---|---|---|---|
| Electrical resistivity at 0°C ($10^{-6}$ $\Omega$cm) | 13.5 | 12.6 | 5.0 | 4.9 |
| Superconductivity transition temper- ature (°K) | 9.1 | 4.48 | 0.92 | 0.01 |
| Magnetic suceptibility (e.m.u. $\times 10^6$) | 209 | 153 | 90 | 55 |
| Electronic specific heat at 300°K (cal mol$^{-1}$ °K$^{-1}$) | 0.63 | 0.5 | 0.15 | 0.11 |
| Heat of solution of nitrogen (eV) | $-1.85$ | $-1.90$ | $+1.96$ | $+1.60$ |
| Young's modulus (psi $\times 10^{-6}$) | 14 | 26 | 47 | 68 |

The low solubility of impurity interstitials in the group VI metals involves that
only little diffusion data of these impurities are known for these metals. Some mean
values are summarized in table 2. For references see Schultz [8] and Köthe and
Schlät [9—11].

Table 2
Mean experimental values for activation energies in bcc metals (eV).

| | H | C | O | N | "Stage III" $(0.15-0.20T_m)$ | Q | $E^F_{1V}$ |
|---|---|---|---|---|---|---|---|
| Nb | 0.2 | 1.5 | 1.2 | 1.5 | 1.2 | 4.3 | (2.0) |
| Ta | 0.2 | 1.8 | 1.1 | 1.6 | 1.2 | 4.1 | (2.9) |
| Mo | 0.6 | 1.4 | (1.1) | 1.2 | 1.3 | 4.4 | (2.2) |
| W | | 2.0 | | (2.1) | 1.7 | 6.0 | (3.1) |
| Fe | 0.1 | 0.9 | 1.0 | 0.8 | 0.8 | 2.7 | (1.1) |

Apart from the activation energies for migration of interstitial impurities, this table also shows some other typical activation energies, i.e., the activation energies as measured for "stage III" recovery (see section 3.3). $Q$ is the self-diffusion activation energy and $E_{1V}^F$ the formation energy of single vacancies. The numbers quoted here represent an average of values reported in the literature. More details and references can be found in the review paper of Schultz [8]. For the particular problem of hydrogen diffusion and of nitrogen diffusion we refer tom the contribution in this conference respectively by Alefeld [12] and by Evans and Eyre [13]. The interstitial migration of oxygen in α-iron has been investigated both experimentally, e.g., by Swisher and Turkdogan [14], and theoretically by Frank et al. [15,16]. More data about the determination of the formation energy and entropy of vacancies are reviewed in Hoch's and Kraftmakher's contributions to this volume.

Since the electrical resistivity is a frequently used property for studying point defects in metals it would be interesting to know the quantitative relation between the resistivity increment and the concentration of the particular defects. Unfortunately the available data on transition bcc metals are very scarce. From electron irradiation experiments, Lucasson and Walker [17] estimated a fractional residual resistivity increase of 1.4 $\rho_0$/at % Frenkel pairs (F.P.) for α-iron ($\rho_0$ is the electrical resistivity at 0°C) and 1.0 $\rho_0$/at % F.P. for molybdenum, $\rho_0$ being the electrical resistivity at 273°K. Hörz et al. [18] reported values of about 0.3 $\rho_0$/at % nitrogen or oxygen in vanadium and niobium and of about 0.4 $\rho_0$/at % for these interstitials in tantalum. The resistivity increase due to interstitial carbon was estimated by Krautz et al. [19] for tungsten to be 0.77 $\rho_0$/at % and by Köster [20] for α-iron to be 0.55 $\rho_0$/at %.

Recently, Szkopiak and Pouzet [21] systematically investigated the effect of oxygen and nitrogen content on resistivity of annealed niobium as measured at 77°K. A linear relationship was found of the form:

$$\rho = \rho_0 + \alpha_O C_O + \alpha_N C_N , \tag{1}$$

where $\rho_0$ represents the resistivity of the oxygen- and nitrogen-free niobium, $C_O$ and $C_N$ the concentrations of oxygen and nitrogen, $\alpha_O$ and $\alpha_N$ the oxygen and nitrogen dependence coefficients, which were found to be $2.2 \times 10^{-9}$ $\Omega$cm/wt.ppm, or about 0.3 $\rho_0$/at %, in agreement with the above mentioned value of Hörz et al. [18]. For a literature survey on this subject we refer to Szkopiak and Pouzet [21], Köthe [10] and Schultz [8].

## 3. Recovery of point defects in bcc metals

### 3.1. General considerations

More than it is the case for fcc metals, the interpretation of the various recovery stages in bcc metals is still moving considerably. In this subsection we shall try to

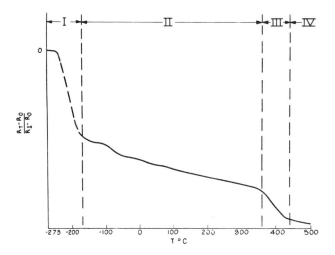

Fig. 1. Schematic recovery curve for neutron-irradiated tungsten, indicating main recovery stages
I, II, III and IV' (After Thompson [23].)

sketch briefly the historical background of this evolution up to a couple of years
ago.

In the late fifty's the labelling introduced by Van Bueren [22] for indicating the
five main recovery stages of fcc metals, was applied to the bcc metals by Thompson
[23], as it seemed that a rather similar sequence of stages occurred at comparable
homologous temperatures (fig. 1).

This straightforward way of labelling the recovery stages was based on the assumption that the characteristic temperatures of the annealing stages above stage I
are a well-determined fraction of the absolute melting point. Since, e.g., a pronounced "stage III" recovery in fcc metals occurred around $0.20\,T_m$ * ($T_m$ being
the melting point) it was quite natural to label a similar process occurring around
$0.16\,T_m$ in the VIa metals tungsten [23,24] and molybdenum [25,26] in the same
way. This was also done for the Va metals niobium [27,28] and tantalum [27]
and for $\alpha$-iron [29]. This general nomenclature has sometimes contributed to the
confusion about the interpretation of the various recovery stages in different metals.
Arguments supporting one recovery model which were based on experiments on a
given metal were too easily generalized for explaining the "corresponding" recovery
behaviour of other metals. Although this confusion also occurs with fcc metals, it
must be pointed out that it is more pronounced for bcc transition metals, owing to
the role played by interstitial impurities, especially in niobium, tantalum and iron.

---

* It has become quite common to indicate recovery stages in terms of fractions of the absolute
  melting point. It should be kept in mind that such "homologous" temperatures can only serve
  for a rough indication, since even for identical processes they depend on the heating program,
  the concentration of defects involved, etc.

A tentative definition of the recovery stages, which should be reserved to intrinsic processes, could be for the bcc metals:

a) Stage I: important recovery stage after electron or neutron irradiation, occurring usually below 100°K, composed of a number of substages.

b) Stage II: rather steady recovery range, involving a spectrum of activation energies, between stage I and stage III.

c) Stage III: prominent and essentially singly-activated recovery stage, showing approximately second order kinetics (for molybdenum and tungsten: about $0.16\,T_m$).

General definitions are difficult for the higher recovery stages. For molybdenum and tungsten, we may distinguish three further stages: stage IV (about $0.22\,T_m$), stage V (about $0.30\,T_m$) and stage VI (about $0.35\,T_m$ or higher).

Since it would lead us too far if we discussed all these stages for all considered metals separately, we have grouped the experimental results as follows: (i) low temperature recovery stages (subsection 3.2); (ii) interstitial impurities and "stage III" recovery (3.3); (iii) stage III recovery in molybdenum and tungsten (3.4); (iv) higher recovery stages (3.5). In section 4 some special topics dealing with recent developments will be treated.

### 3.2. Low temperature recovery stages

Blewitt [30] was the first to show that about 50% of the electrical resistivity induced by neutron irradiation in tungsten annealed out at liquid nitrogen temperature and this result was confirmed by Thompson [23], a few years later.

During the last 2 or 3 years a number of more detailed investigations of low temperature recovery in bcc metals have been reported. Fig. 2 shows recovery spectra by Burger et al. [31] after neutron irradiation on tantalum, niobium, α-iron and tungsten, indicating a great number of small and large recovery peaks below 200°C, but very different for each metal. Even for the two Va metals tantalum and niobium, an important difference is to be noted in that tantalum shows two important peaks between 100 and 200°K, whereas niobium does not.

Mainly in analogy with fcc metal results (see, e.g., Holmes [3] and the review papers on fcc metals in this volume) it is generally assumed that some of the substages are to be associated with close pair recombination, whereas at least one recovery peak should be related to free migration of a defect. We will come back to the low temperature recovery in tantalum when discussing the more recent results of Hemmerich et al. [33] on electron irradiated tantalum (see section 4.1). Previously it has been found out also by Bürger et al. [31] that doping with oxygen impurities induced drastic changes in the low temperature recovery of neutron-irradiated tantalum (fig. 3) and, as we shall see further, this effect has been observed for electron-irradiated tantalum as well. Fig. 4 shows isochronal annealing results of electron-irradiated niobium by the group of Grenoble [34], in fair agreement with the previously mentioned work, except for the peak above room temperature which is felt to be impurity-induced. Annealing spectra between 13 and 300°K of electron-

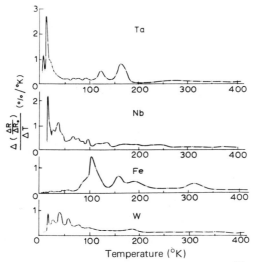

Fig. 2. Recovery spectra of neutron-irradiated bcc metals (7.2 × 10$^{17}$ nvt, $E > 0.1$ MeV. (After Burger et al. [31].)

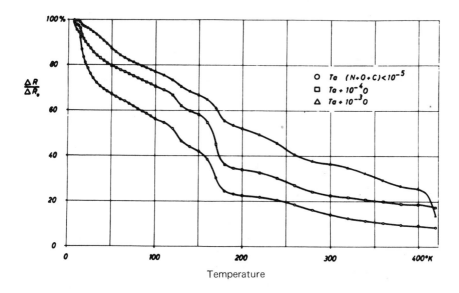

Fig. 3. Isochronal recovery of the electrical resistivity of neutron-irradiated tantalum with different oxygen content. $\Delta t = 10$ min. Dose 7.2 × 10$^{17}$ nvt, $E > 0.1$ MeV. (After Burger et al. [31].)

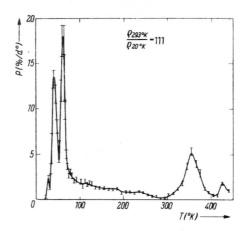

Fig. 4. Recovery spectrum of the electrical resistivity of niobium electron-irradiated at 20°K.
Dose $5 \times 10^{17}$ electrons $cm^{-2}$. $E$ = 3 MeV. (After Pichon et al. [34].)

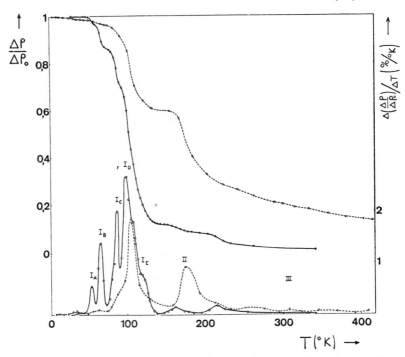

Fig. 5. Recovery of the electrical resistivity and the derivative curves of pure iron irradiated at
low temperature. (1) (full curves) Electron irradiation at 20°K (3 MeV – $1.2 \times 10^{18}$ el/cm² isochrones, $\Delta t$ = 10 min, $\Delta T$ = 3°K (20–150°K), 5°K (180–250°K) and 10°K (250–350°K) (after
Bilger et al. [36]). (2) (dashed curves) Neutron irradiation at 4°K (after Burger et al. [31])
$(4.8 \times 10^{18}$ nvt, $E > 0.1$ MeV), isochrones $\Delta t$ = 10 min.

irradiated niobium and tantalum have also been reported by Abd El-Salam and De Ford [35]. They found peaks at $25°K$, $99°K$ and $136°K$ in niobium and at $27°K$, $34°K$, $41°K$, $125°K$ and $157°K$ in tantalum.

Very detailed investigations on the kinetics in this temperature range were performed on $\alpha$-iron, as described in the review article of this volume by Kronmüller and in the contribution by Bilger et al. [36], summarizing the point of view of the Grenoble group, who found evidence for long range migration in stage $I_E$ ($\approx 120°K$) of a defect having $\langle 110 \rangle$ symmetry. This conclusion was based on measurements of resistivity, magnetic aftereffect, stored energy and internal friction. It seems to confirm machine calculations by Johnson [37], who found the most stable interstitial in $\alpha$-iron to be a $\langle 110 \rangle$-orientated split interstitial migrating with an activation energy of 0.33 eV. A typical recovery spectrum is shown in fig. 5 where it is compared with the results of Burger et al. [31]. For more details we refer to the original papers by Dautreppe et al. [38], Minier-Cassayre [29], Moser [39], and Bilger et al. [36].

A rather extended number of results are now available for low temperature irradiation experiments on tungsten. First of all the results of field ion microscopy by Muller [40,41] and by Sinha and Muller [42] who were able to observe in atomic resolution the damage resulting from fast helium bombardment, consisting of vacancies, interstitials, and their clusters. These authors established migration of interstitials in a temperature range beginning at $50°K$ and proceeding fast at 85 to $95°K$. This result is in fact the first direct establishment of the nature of the migrating defect in this stage.

More indirect evidence for interstitial migration at low temperatures in tungsten has been reported later on. So Di Carlo and coworkers [43,44] studied irradiation damage in tungsten single crystals and polycrystalline tungsten wires following irradiation at $20°K$ with 2.5 MeV electrons. The electrical resistivity recovery spectrum showed at least 6 peaks between 20 and $45°K$, the predominant one lying about $31°K$. They are schematically represented in the upper part of fig. 6. Simultaneous internal friction experiments resulted in a prominent peak about $30°K$ being most probably due to stress-induced ordering of close-pair interstitials. From the directional dependence of this peak the authors conclude that these interstitials are probably orthorhombic defects in general and $\langle 110 \rangle$ split interstitials in particular [44], so that the crowdion seems to be excluded as a possible configuration. The symmetry found here is the same as the one reported by Bilger et al. [36], for bcc iron, as mentioned above. Radiation doping experiments at $100°K$ further suggest that all peaks below $45°K$ are caused by close pair mechanisms and that free interstitial migration occurs above this temperature.

This is in agreement with the observations of Neely and Keefer [45], who performed electrical resistivity measurements on polycrystalline tungsten following 2.1 MeV electron bombardment (fig. 6, second curve from top). They found that the $70°K$ peak in electron irradiation tungsten corresponds to second order kinetics and ascribed it to interstitial-vacancy recombination effected through interstitial diffusion. This process would be accompanied with trapping of interstitials at impuri-

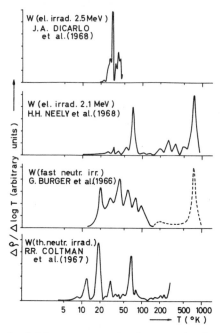

Fig. 6. Schematic plot of resistivity recovery peaks of tungsten irradiated at low temperatures in different experiments as indicated.

ties and some suggestions are made as to how the second order kinetics can be preserved with such a complex mechanism. Although one may question some details of this analysis, the conclusion that free migration of a defect takes place in this stage seems to be rather well justified.

Apart from electron irradiation experiments also the recovery at low temperatures following fast neutron irradiation (Burger et al. [31]) and thermal neutron irradiation (Coltman et al. [46]) has been reported for tungsten. Fig. 6 schematically compares four recovery spectra for this metal.

This comparison indicates that even results that are obtained on the same metal, show rather important differences. It appears that the various substages can be "populated" very differently. Consequently many systematic investigations have still to be done before the situation will be cleared up.

For the other bcc metals under consideration the data of low temperature recovery are even scarcer. Lucasson and Walker [17] found after electron irradiation of molybdenum two recovery peaks centred about 28°K, 35°K and 42°K.

Similar peaks have recently been reported by Takamura et al. [47] for neutron irradiated molybdenum. They found that the 28°K is influenced by pre-irradiation cold work, pointing to an alteration of the production of close pairs by the presence of a high density of dislocations. Very recently, Lomer and Taylor [48] found by internal friction experiment on electron-irradiated molybdenum dislocation pinning to occur between 50 and 70°K, whence they conclude that interstitials are migrating in this temperature range. Depinning was found to occur in a broad range (90–330°K).

A general establishment to be made with respect to low temperature recovery in bcc metals is that one needs more systematic data about the dose dependence and the energy dependence of the various substages. Moreover, isothermal annealing experiments are lacking almost entirely. As long as these data are not available, the interpretation remains very speculative. This remark is even more true for the stage II range where usually a steady recovery is being observed, associated with gradually increasing activation energies up to stage III [25,26].

The most detailed research on stage II recovery in bcc metals after neutron irradiation was performed on tungsten by Thompson [23] who showed that second stage recovery was enhanced by the presence of cold work and affected by impurities. A similar conclusion resulted from recent neutron irradiation experiments by Takamura et al. [47]. Thompson [23] was able to establish a quantitative theory being concistent with the experimental observations about stage II. This theory was based on the thermal activation of interstitials from impurities and dislocations. For α-iron stage II recovery has been subdivided by some authors as IIa and IIb (see, e.g., Minier-Cassayre [29]). The latter substage will be discussed in the next subsection.

## 3.3. Interstitial impurities and "stage III" recovery in transition bcc metals

In table 2 it has already been shown that for the transition bcc metals considered, one or more interstitial impurities exist, the activation energy for migration of which corresponds to the activation energy found for the recovery stage about $0.16 T_m$ ($0.20 T_m$ for α-iron) being known as "stage III". Rosenfield [49] has been the first to draw the attention upon this fact. In this respect it follows from the data of table 2 that one has to consider oxygen interstitials for niobium and tantalum; carbon and nitrogen interstitials for molybdenum, tungsten and α-iron. For more data concerning the heat of solution and diffusivity, more particularly with respect to nitrogen in molybdenum, we refer to the contribution of Evans and Eyre [13], for hydrogen diffusion to the paper by Alefeld and coworkers [12], for the diffusion and solubility of oxygen in α-iron we refer to Frank et al. [16].

It is already known for a long time that after plastic deformation these impurities may migrate to dislocations according to a Cottrell-Bilby mechanism of strain ageing. Apart from this strain aging, Damask and coworkers have reported on the role of carbon in neutron-irradiated α-iron: in the temperature range that was normally being associated with "stage III" of this metal, they measured an important stored energy release (Arndt and Damask [50]), a rapid decrease in Snoek damping (Wagenblast and Damask [51]) and of the electrical resistivity (Fujita and Damask [52]). All these phenomena could be described in terms of an interaction of quenched-interstitial carbon atoms with the vacancies created by neutron irradiation. This also explains the "undershoot" effect shown in fig. 7. This phenomenon is often revealed in electrical resistivity measurements on pure metals. Measurements performed by Nihoul [25,26] on commercial neutron-irradiated molybdenum also showed a slight undershoot effect from which it could be concluded, as Kothe and Schlat [9] have done, that also there mobile carbon impurities were captured by radiation-induced defects. Although it cannot be excluded that this phenomenon has partially influenced these measurements, more recent experiments on purer molybdenum did not show any undershoot effect as will be shown later on (see section 3.5, fig. 21).

Very systematic investigations on the behaviour of interstitial oxygen and nitrogen in niobium and tantalum, both after plastic deformation and after irradiation have been performed during the last years. Gregory [53] observed that "stage III" recovery in cold worked niobium increases with increasing interstitial impurity concentration. Formby and Owen [54] followed quench-ageing and strain-ageing of tantalum containing oxygen, nitrogen and carbon by measurements of the Petch parameters over a range from 100 to 200°C.

Combined impurity-doping and plastic deformation experiments have been carried out at Dresden on niobium, tantalum and, to a smaller extent, vanadium. These investigations were based on measurements of electrical resistivity (Kothe [10[) and of internal friction, modulus defect, and anelastic after-effect (Schlat [11]). A few conclusions of this work will be summarized here: (i) for a given deformation degree of about 50% reduction in thickness the resistivity increment of wires is found to be linear with interstitial impurity concentration (carbon, nitrogen); (ii) for small and mean deformation degrees the resistivity increment is larger in gas containing specimens than in degassed specimens. This difference, however, decreases with increasing deformation degree; (iii) the results of the above-mentioned mechanical property measurements confirm earlier work by Powers and Doyle [55], for non-deformed specimens and by De Lamotte and Wert [56], for deformed specimens. More particularly it is found that the height of the oxygen Snoek peak decreases in the "stage III" range, pointing to oxygen migration to the dislocation lines; (iv) resistometric isochronal annealing experiments show that a pronounced "stage III" is only produced in oxygen doped niobium (fig. 8) and tantalum (fig. 9). In the latter case also a nitrogen stage is found at higher temperature and a pronounced "undershoot" effect can be observed; (v) the isothermal annealing kinetics are only partially in agreement with a $t^{2/3}$ law of Cottrell and Bilby [57], and with the theory of Bullough and Newman [58,59], for the formation of equilibrium atmospheres. The deviations are mainly ascribed to an inhomogeneous distribution of dislocations, which would also be the cause of the observed deviation of Matthiessen's rule.

The recent work on niobium by Szkopiak and Pouzet [21], already mentioned in section 2, is in good agreement with these findings of the group of Dresden. These authors also find that the increase of resistivity due to plastic deformation is proportional to the oxygen content and they show that it is directly proportional to the deformation energy calculated from the area under the stress-strain curves, the proportionality constant being oxygen content independent. This is in agreement

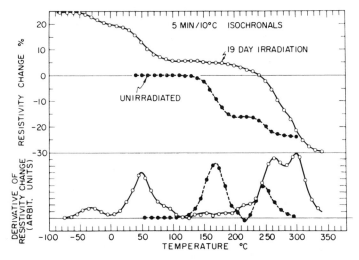

Fig. 7. Isochronal recovery of electrical resistivity of α-iron containing 115 wt ppm quenched in carbon after neutron-irradiation (open circles) and as quenched (black circles). (After Fujita and Damask [52].)

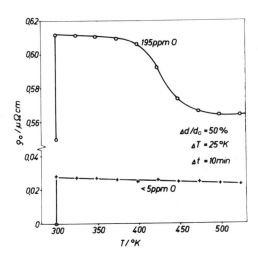

Fig. 8. Electrical resistivity increment and recovery following plastic deformation of niobium containing different amounts of oxygen. (After Rexer et al. [32].)

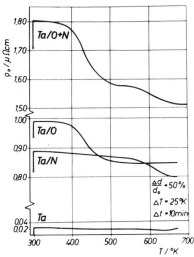

Fig. 9. Electrical resistivity increment and recovery following plastic deformation of tantalum containing different amounts of oxygen and/or nitrogen. The lower curve refers to a degassed specimen. (After Kothe and Schlat [9].)

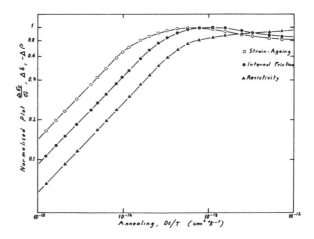

Fig. 10. Comparison of yield point return, internal friction and resistivity annealing curves within the stage III range. Pre-strain 4%, annealing temperature 155°C, 400 wt ppm oxygen content. (After Szkopiak and Pouzet [21].)

with results obtained for cold-worked fcc metals by Kovacs [60] and with the model proposed by Saada [61]. Also Szkopiak and Pouzet reported that the amount of "stage III" resistivity recovery is proportional to the oxygen content for a given deformation degree. In fig. 10 isothermal annealing curves of yield point return, internal friction and electrical resistivity are shown for prestrained niobium containing 400 wt ppm oxygen. It should be remarked that the straight line portion of the three curves have the same slope of 2/3, in agreement with a Cottrell-Bilby [57] mechanism. In the same work it was found that for very low oxygen content (about 5 wt ppm) there was no change in resistivity on annealing cold-worked specimens, which confirms that "stage III" recovery in niobium is primarily due to the formation of Cottrell atmospheres at dislocations.

Apart from strain ageing effects it has also been found out that neutron irradiation of transition bcc metals may induce a stage III recovery which is caused by the migration of interstitial impurities to radiation produced defects. Substantial evidence in this respect has been presented by a group of research workers of Oak Ridge (see e.g. Tucker and Ohr [62], Williams et al. [63], and Stanley et al. [64]) indicating that stage III recovery in irradiated niobium arises from the segregation of oxygen impurity atoms. The latter authors were able to show a clear connection between the oxygen Snoek peak decrease and the resistivity decrease in stage III as illustrated in fig. 11. In oxygen free samples that were either heavily cold-worked or neutron-irradiated no significant resistivity decrease in the "stage III" range has been observed. Fig. 12 shows some isochronal annealing curves for irradiated and non-irradiated niobium, both for pure (i.e. oxygen-free) and impure specimens. It can be remarked that only the impure and irradiated specimen shows a "stage III" re-

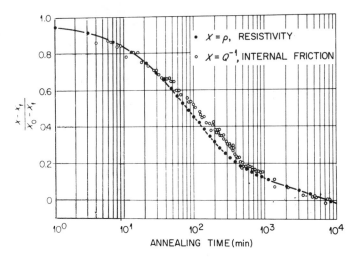

Fig. 11. Normalized resistivity and internal friction decrease as a function of time at 150°C of niobium containing 50 wt ppm of oxygen (following neutron irradiation $2 \times 10^{18}$ nvt, $E >$ 1 MeV). $X_0$ and $X_f$ refer to the property immediately after irradiation and after annealing for 8000 min, respectively. (After Stanley et al. [64].)

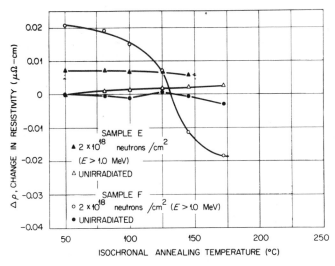

Fig. 12. Isochronal annealing of irradiated and unirradiated pure and impure niobium samples. Sample E contained less than 4 wt ppm oxygen, whereas in sample F the oxygen content amounted to 260 wt ppm. (After Williams et al. [63].)

covery and that the peak is associated with a decrease of the resistivity well below the pre-irradiation value. This "undershoot" phenomenon can again be understood as a natural consequence of removal of oxygen from random solid solution. The same figure shows for the pure sample a very slight resistivity decrease (about $1.5 \times 10^{-9}$ $\Omega$cm), but the non-irradiated pure specimen increases by about $2.5 \times 10^{-9}$ $\Omega$cm, which could suggest some competitive processes going as in the temperature range investigated, although they are probably not very significant.

These results clearly show that oxygen can give rise in niobium to a recovery stage in the so-called stage III range. A few years ago Stals et al. [65,66] reported on such a recovery in very heavily cold-worked niobium associated with essentially the same activation energy (1.20 eV). This recovery was explained as a bimolecular intrinsic process on account of internal friction results that pointed to a very low oxygen concentration. In the light of recent investigations, however, such as reported above it can be presumed that oxygen nevertheless influenced these results, so that these experiments should be repeated in better controlled conditions. In an attempt to do so, Kothe [10] only found a continuous recovery in this temperature range for degassed and heavily deformed niobium.

As to the recovery experiments on neutron irradiated niobium by Peacock and Johnson [27] it can now be considered as established that these results were at least strongly influenced by the presence of oxygen, since the specimens were reported to contain 500 ppm of oxygen. So the question arises as to the existence and the position of an intrinsic stage III in the bcc metals niobium, tantalum and $\alpha$-iron.

Whereas for $\alpha$-iron the labelling "stage III" has often been given to the recovery stage occurring in a temperature range about $340°K$ ($T/T_m = 0.20$) (see e.g. Minier-Cassayre [29], Cuddy and Raley [67,68], Neely and Keefer [45]), in other investigations by Oi and Sato [69], and by Cuddy [70], the recovery stage about $0.12 T_m$ is called stage III. In the latter work, Cuddy shows that the $0.20 T_m$ stage is related to carbon precipitation and that it only disappears from the recovery spectrum when the total carbon content is not higher than a few wt ppm. In carefully decarbonized $\alpha$-iron, however, an intrinsic recovery stage could be produced at $0.12 T_m$, which only showed up clearly for relatively severe deformation degrees (i.e. for elongations between about 20% and 100%). It is worthwhile to compare this with the results of Oi and Sato [69] showing a recovery stage after low deformation degrees already, e.g. 2 to 5%. It is hard to judge whether this qualitative difference is important enough to exclude that both observed stages correspond to the same process. Impurities could possibly have played a role in the investigations of Oi and Sato, who used iron containing 500 wt ppm impurities (mainly C, N and O) as contrasted with the specimens of Cuddy, where the corresponding impurity content was only of the order of 10 wt ppm. Nevertheless there is a remarkable correspondence in the activation energies as illustrated in table 3. In this table also a few data of the Grenoble group have been included. There are a number of indications that the three results deal with a same annealing process and, although the mechanisms proposed are

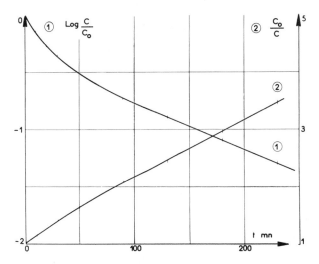

Fig. 13. Test for pure first or second order kinetics in electron irradiated $\alpha$-iron about $0.12\,T_m$.
(After Minier-Cassayre [29].)

rather different, they seem to present a common basis also if one looks more closely
to some details of the annealing kinetics. Minier-Cassayre [29] reported that the
annealing kinetics of the $0.12\,T_m$ peak are complex even after electron bombardment. A test for simple first or second order kinetics (see fig. 13) shows that none
of both is completely satisfactory. It can be remarked, however, that the curvature
of the initial part of the second order plot points to a reaction order higher than 2,
which fact seems to imply a changing reaction order. Cuddy [70] has shown that
the isothermal recovery of cold-worked iron in the same temperature range occurs
according to a model of stress-assisted vacancy migration to dislocation, as proposed
by Bullough and Newman [58,59]. This interpretation is contradicted by the results
of Glaeser and Wever [71] pointing to vacancy migration in iron around $0.25\,T_m$
(see section 3.5). Moreover, the physical basis for the applicability of this model in
the given conditions has been criticized by Balluffi and Seidman [72]. Nevertheless
it is worthwhile to note that the isothermal stage III recovery curves not only of
$\alpha$-iron, but also of other bcc metals appear to satisfy rather well the annealing law:

$$C = C_0 \exp(-\alpha t)^n \qquad\qquad (2)$$

with $n$ approximately equal to 2, as required in the Bullough-Newman model.
Cuddy's analysis is illustrated in fig. 14.

Stals and Nihoul [75] have shown that this type of analysis does not allow to
decide whether Bullough-Newman kinetics or bimolecular diffusion controlled
kinetics are involved (see subsection 3.4). In a reanalysis of Cuddy's results they
showed that these results are also consistent with a bimolecular diffusion controlled
process. In such cases a changing reaction order, starting from values above 2, may

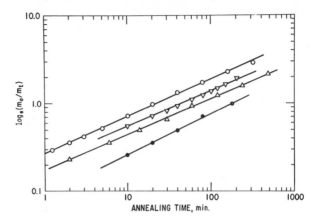

Fig. 14. Analysis of recovery stages observed in plastically deformed bcc metals, according to
equation (2).

○ α-iron, 210°K, $n$ = 0.43 (Cuddy [70])
△ niobium, 433°K, $n$ = 0.40 (Stals and Nihoul [65])
△ molybdenum, 455°K, $n$ = 0.40 (Stals and Nihoul [65])
● tungsten, 623°K, $n$ = 0.46 (Schultz [91])
(After Cuddy [70].)

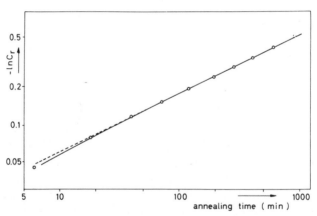

Fig. 15. Same type of diagram as fig. 14 for cold-worked molybdenum (white circles). The full
line represents a theoretical curve according to Waite [103] kinetics, the dashed straight line
corresponds to equation (2). (After Stals and Nihoul [73].)

normally be expected (Nihoul and Stals [74]). A similar analysis of stage III recovery of cold worked molybdenum (fig. 15) resulted in the same impossibility to decide on this basis between the two types of kinetics. This is a consequence of the
fact that the first terms of the series expansion of the annealing equation in both

Table 3
Comparison of recovery stages around 210°K in α-iron.

| Type of damage | Peak temperature (°K) | Labelling | $E$ (eV) | Initial reaction order (see text) | Migrating defect proposed | Ref. |
|---|---|---|---|---|---|---|
| fast neutrons | 190 | "II b" | 0.5 ± 0.1 | > 2 | di-interstitials | [29] |
| 2.9 MeV electrons | 220 | "II b" | 0.5 ± 0.1 | > 2 | di-interstitials | [29] |
| 1.3 MeV electrons | 225 | "II b" | | − | − | [45] |
| cold work (78°K) | 210 | "III" | 0.53 ± 0.06 | > 2 | di-vacancies to dislocations | [69] |
| cold work (78°K) | 210 | "III" | 0.55 ± 0.01 | > 2 | vacancies to dislocations | [70] |
| mean result and interpretation of present paper) | 210 | "III" | 0.5 | > 2 [74] | interstitials to vacancies | this paper |

cases shows the same time dependence, namely

$$C/C_0 - 1 = At^{1/2} + Bt + \dots \, . \tag{3}$$

As can be observed from fig. 14 the experimentally found value of $n$ from eq. (2) is often closer to 0.4 than to 0.5. By analysing theoretical curves for diffusion controlled bimolecular reactions, Goedemé et al. [75] have shown that the apparent value of $n$ varies from $n \approx 0.4$ at high defect concentrations to $n \approx 0.7$ at very low defect concentrations. A careful investigation of this concentration dependence could be used for deciding between the two types of kinetics as pointed out also by Van den Beukel [76].

For the sake of completeness we should mention here that Oi and Sato [69] suggest still another model for stage III recovery in α-iron originally proposed by Lement and Cohen [77], in which the recovery obeys the law:

$$1 - C/C_0 = \exp(-Kt^{1/3}) \tag{4}$$

which in the initial stage of recovery is more or less equivalent with eq. (2) with $n = \frac{1}{3}$ instead of $\frac{1}{2}$. An analysis of such a type of kinetics according to the method of Nihoul and Stals [74] again yields a decreasing reaction order from high to low values, but with a mean value close to 2. In all cases summarized in table 3 the kinetics thus appear to be more complex than simple first or second order, starting with higher reaction orders. More examples of such cases will be discussed in the next section.

As a conclusion we may state that α-iron seems to present an intrinsic recovery stage that is consistent with the definition of stage III we have premised in subsection 3.1. In subsection 3.4 we will review the more abundant evidence for the existence of such a stage about $0.16 T_m$ in molybdenum and tungsten. It is tentatively proposed here that the $0.12 T_m$ stage in α-iron and the $0.16 T_m$ stages in molybdenum and tungsten are basically to be ascribed to the same process, i.e., migration of self-interstitials to vacancies.

Now the question arises why no cprresponding recovery stage has been observed for niobium or tantalum. As pointed out by Schultz [8] the reason for it is probably not to be found in a difference of the electrical resistivity per defect as compared to other metals. This author rather suggests as possible reasons: (i) a different mechanism of defect production or (ii) a higher mobility of point defects. The first suggestion seems to be supported — as far as the production of point defects by plastic deformation is concerned — by differences in the individual dislocation properties between group Va and group VIa metals. But when it is taken into account that also following irradiation experiments this stage III does not occur at normally expected temperatures, the second possibility, i.e., higher mobility of point defects, looks more plausible. Recent measurements by Hemmerich et al. [33] on electron irradiated tantalum seem to support the latter assumption. The discussion of these experiments will be given in subsection 4.1.

### 3.4. Stage III recovery in molybdenum and tungsten

Whereas for niobium, tantalum and α-iron the position and even the existence of an intrinsic stage III remain somewhat uncertain, for molybdenum and especially for tungsten a number of converging data point to such a stage at about $\frac{1}{6}$ of the melting point. This stage has been found in molybdenum following neutron irradiation by means of electrical resistivity measurements (Kinchin and Thompson [24], Nihoul [25,26,78], Peacock and Johnson [27,79], Ibragimov et al. [80], Stals et al. [73,75], Takamura et al. [47]) and also by means of other methods, e.g., stored energy (Kinchin and Thompson [27]) yield stress (Wronski and Johnson [81]), lattice parameter (Gray [82]) and linear expansion (Adam and Martin [83]). In plastically deformed molybdenum a similar stage III recovery has been found, e.g., by Martin [84] and by Stals et al. [73,75]. In electron-irradiated molybdenum by De Jong [94].

In neutron-irradiated tungsten a stage III recovery around $0.16 T_m$ has been reported by Kinchin and Thompson [23,24], Blons et al. [86], Nihoul [78], Kuhlmann and Schultz [87], Moteff and Smith [88], in electron-irradiated tungsten by Burger et al. [31] and Neely et al. [89] and finally in plastically deformed tungsten by Schultz [90,91]. A more detailed discussioin of these various experiments will be given in a forthcoming monograph by Nihoul and Stals [92]. For the present purpose it is important to note the general agreement on the activation energies of stage III: 1.3 eV in molybdenum, 1.7 eV in tungsten.

It may be remarked that until 1962 there was general agreement to describe stage III in molybdenum and tungsten in terms of vacancy migration. The observation, however, that the kinetics showed a tendency towards second order made Nihoul [25,26], Schultz [91] and Moteff [88,93] suggest that this stage could be explained as a bimolecular annealing process involving free migrating interstitials to relatively more stable vacancies. This model was strongly supported (i) by electron irradiation experiments on molybdenum above room temperature by De Jong and Afman [94], giving rise to a pronounced and complete recovery in one singly activated recovery stage III; (ii) by the field ion microscopic observations of Galligan and coworkers [5,95,96] who observed the presence of interstitials, also in very pure irradiated tungsten [97], being annihilated in the course of stage III, and of vacancies surviving up to stage IV.

Unfortunately the same type of bimolecular diffusion controlled kinetics could successfully be applied to describe both the probably extrinsic recovery "stage III" in e.g. niobium (Stals et al. [65,66]) and the intrinsic stage III recovery in e.g. molybdenum (De Jong and Afman [94], Stals et al. [73]). This could support the idea that in none of the transition bcc metals an intrinsic point defect recovery stage occurs above room temperature. However, as already illustrated in subsection 3.3 for the kinetics of the $0.12\,T_m$ stage in $\alpha$-iron, we are confronted with the somewhat disappointing situation that different diffusion type kinetics, involving a few parameters that can be adapted for optimal fitting, may successfully describe the same experimental data. As a consequence, the above-mentioned double use of bimolecular kinetics for both "stage III" in niobium and stage III in molybdenum and tungsten does not imply that the latter stages would be impurity induced as well. In contrast with the Va metals, the solubility of interstitial impurities in the VIa metals molybdenum and tungsten is very low at intermediate temperatures. The solubility limit e.g. of carbon in molybdenum has been studied by Rudman [98].

More particularly, no observations have been reported of an absence of stage III in these metals after cold work or irradiation. Kuhlmann and Schultz [87] have shown that even in very carefully decarbonized tungsten annealing after neutron irradiation gave rise to the normal recovery stage about $700°K$ which cannot have been induced by carbon impurities. In previous experiments it had already been shown that this stage in tungsten is rather insensitive to various impurities (Schultz [91]).

In view of the extremely low solubility of carbon in tungsten and molybdenum it seems also very hard to explain the frequently observed stage III recovery after electron irradiation in another way than by an intrinsic mechanism. Where it is still conceivable that a large amount of carbon is put interstitially into non-equilibrium

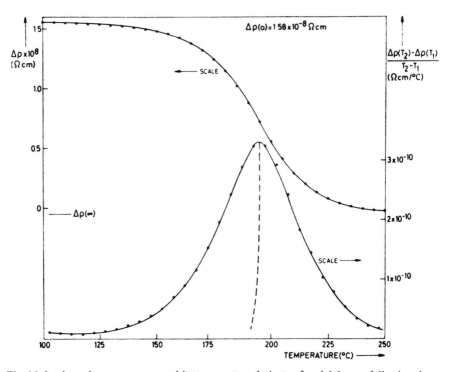

Fig. 16. Isochronal recovery curve and its temperature derivate of molybdenum following electron irradiation. (After De Jong and Afman [94].)

solution by drastic methods such as plastic deformation, irradiation with fast heavy particles (and, of course, quenching from high temperatures), it would be surprising that bombarding with electrons, not far above displacement threshold energy, would produce large amount of carbon-vacancy pairs annealing out completely in stage III, without any undershoot effect. Fig. 16 shows results obtained by De Jong [94] for electron irradiated molybdenum, illustrating such a case.

Similar stage III recovery has been observed for electron irradiated tungsten as e.g. shown in the recent results of Neely et al. [89]. A weak point with respect to the latter results of Neely et al. is to be found in the fact that they determined an activation energy for stage III recovery in tungsten of only 1.1 eV, whereas normally 1.7 eV or more has been reported for corresponding investigations by other authors. This determination, however, has been performed on the assumption of constant second order kinetics in stage III. From the contribution by Rosch et al. [99] and by Bauer [100] in this conference, it follows that this second order method can easily give rise to wrong activation energies and this could also be the reason for the abnormally low activation energy found here. Therefore it is preferable to use methods which are independent of the reaction order, e.g., the method of

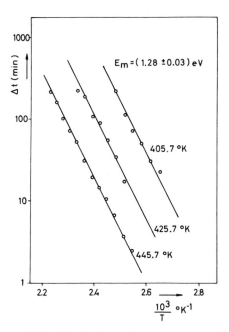

Fig. 17. Meechan-Brinkman [101] plot of isothermal recovery curves of molybdenum following plastic deformation. (After Stals and Nihoul [73].)

Meechan and Brinkman [101], as illustrated in fig. 17 for cold worked molybdenum.

A changing reaction order from high values in the beginning of the process to approximately 2 has often been observed in stage III recovery data as already mentioned in subsection 3.3 (see also Stals et al. [73–75], Bauer [100], Kulcinski et al. [102] and subsection 4.3). One of the recovery models that comes up to a decreasing reaction order with increasing concentration is that of a diffusion controlled bimolecular reaction involving an appreciable interaction volume, the equations of which have been established by Waite [103]. From the previous discussion it is clear that the fact that one is able to fit annealing data to a theoretical curve, or in this case, to Waite kinetics, does not prove that the corresponding model is the right one. But it does prove that the recovery mechanism involved is more complex than a simple first order or second order chemical reaction, and this implies that analytical methods, based on the assumption of constant reaction order, must not be used.

These qualifications being made, we show an example of such "theoretical" curves (fig 18) fitting isothermal recovery data for cold worked molybdenum. If this correspondence is taken serious, effective capture radii between 5 and 10 lattice distances have to be accepted, the lower value resulting from annealing data after neutron irradiation, the higher one from results on deformed molybdenum. We may remember that De Jong and Afman [94] found an effective capture radius of about 8 lattice distances for electron irradiated molybdenum.

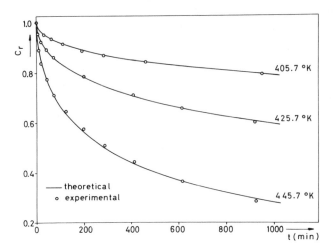

Fig. 18. Isothermal recovery of plastically deformed molybdenum (white circles). The full lines correspond to Waite [103] kinetics. (After Stals and Nihoul [73].)

It must be pointed out that the conditions for this Waite kinetics to be vigorously valid, are certainly not fulfilled. Among these conditions we mention: (i) the whole recovery stage has to be singly-activated; (ii) the initial concentrations of the reacting defects should be equal, or at least their values should be known, otherwise one has to introduce a supplementary parameter describing the difference in both concentrations; (iii) the defects are homogeneously distributed, either in a correlated, or in an uncorrelated way; (iv) the role of impurities and dislocations can be neglected.

It has to be remarked also that Waite's theory is based on the assumption of the existence of a sharply confined capture volume for spontaneous recombination, outside of which the migration of the mobile defect occurs with a constant activation energy. As pointed out, however, by Von Jan [104] and by Stals et al. [66] the volume to be considered for stage III recovery problems is a larger "bound pair" volume, inside which migration is not spotaneous although associated with a lower activation energy than that of free migration outside of this volume.

Taking into account moreover that the theory itself is based on a number of approximations, it is clear that quantitative conclusions about the various parameters can only serve for a rough guidance to arrive at a satisfactory picture of the recovery mechanism. Therefore, either theory should be refined or detailed comparisons of experimental and theoretical curves should be performed with computer simulations as described by Mehrer [105].

At this moment the main conclusions with respect to stage III recovery in molybdenum and tungsten are:
a) it is intrinsic and essentially singly-activated stage;

b) it involves migration of interstitials;

c) in its temperature range vacancies are relatively stable;

d) its kinetics are in good qualitative agreement with bimolecular kinetics.

These points are all in favour of a model based on interstitial migration to vacancies. Divacancy migration seems less probable in view of the results after electron irradiation. Vacancy migration seems to be excluded, at least for tungsten, on account of field ion microscope observations. Hardening effects observed in the course of stage III [81,106,107] usually explained on the basis of a vacancy mechanims, could also be explained by an interaction of interstitial clusters with dislocations.

Since free interstitial migration probably occurs also in stage I (see subsection 3.2), the model proposed above for stage III in molybdenum and tungsten requires two types of interstitial configurations. However, as will be pointed out in subsection 4.1, the same configuration has been proposed for both interstitials, so that this question cannot be resolved as yet.

### 3.5. Higher recovery stages

There is some confusion about the labelling of the three recovery stages above stage III, occurring in tungsten and molybdenum about 0.22, 0.30 and o.35 $T_m$. These stages are sometimes called IVa, IVb and V, sometimes IV, Va and Vb and sometimes IV, V, VI. As they are rather distinct both in temperature range and in activation energy, we will use the latter nomenclature.

Stage IV is usually not very pronounced in electrical resistivity measurements after cold work on fast particle irradiation. In analogy with fcc metals this stage can quite naturally be ascribed to migration of vacancies surviving after stage III. As a consequence, one would normally expect this stage to show up most clearly after quenching from high temperatures. However, resistometric recovery results after quenching experiments performed in good conditions are practically not available for bcc metals as yet. Measurements by Nihoul [26] on water-quenched commercially pure molybdenum were consistent with vacancy migration in stage IV but could not be reproduced on pure molybdenum, so that probably an impurity effect had been observed [108]. Direct evidence for vacancy migration has been given by Galligan and coworkers [5,95,96], on the basis of field ion microscope observations of neutron-irradiated tungsten and quenched tungsten. Thanks to careful determination of vacancy concentrations, after annealing treatments outside the microscope, these authors were able to establish quantitative recovery curves. In this way the annealing of vacancies has been found to occur well above stage III with an activation energy $E_{1V}^M$ = 3.3 eV, being about half the self-diffusion activation energy for tungsten [109].

Fig. 19 shows the isochronal decay of the vacancy concentration. Although this logarithmic plot would suggest recovery to occur mainly in the range 800–900°C ($\approx$ 1100°K or $\approx$ 0.30 $T_m$), it should be remarked that a 50% decrease in vacancy concentration is already attained at 650°C. This would point to a recovery stage about 0.25 $T_m$. So the question arises whether this recovery has to be associated

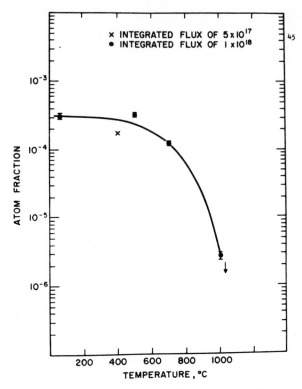

Fig. 19. Isochronal decay of vacancy concentration as determined by field ion microscopy.
(After Attardo and Galligan [95]).

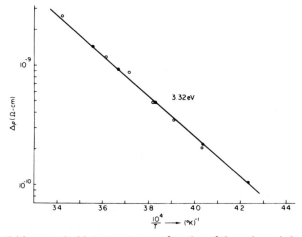

Fig. 20. The resistivities quenched into tungsten as a function of the reciprocal absolute temperature. (After Schultz [110].)

with the recovery stage being called in this paper "stage V" ($0.30\,T_m$), as done by Jeannotte et al. [95] and by Schultz and coworkers [8,33] or with stage IV ($0.22\,T_m$). It should be remarked that these observations were made on tungsten of commercial purity. In later experiments on ultrapure tungsten vacancy migration was observed to occur around 600°C (as compared to 900°C) which is certainly consistent with stage IV corresponding to single vacancies being removed (Galligan [97]). A comparison of this result with the results in the less pure material would point to some vacancy-impurity interaction in the latter case. Consequently the above-mentioned activation energy $E_{1V}^M = 3.3$ eV could include some binding energy and may thus be too high.

The formation energy of vacancies in tungsten could be determined from resistivity measurements after quenching from different temperatures into liquid helium II by Schultz [110]. He derived an activation energy $E_{1V}^F = 3.32$ eV (fig. 20). This sum $E_{1V}^M + E_{1V}^F = 6.6$ eV is equal to the activation energy for self diffusion as determined by Andelin et al. [109], which gives some confidence with respect to the individual values of $E_{1V}^M$ and $E_{1V}^F$.

Quenching experiments on molybdenum have been followed by electron microscopic observations by Meakin et al. [112]. Assuming that all vacancies are found back as observable loops, the authors derived from the density and the average diameter of loops (100 Å after 1 hour annealing at 400°C) an energy of formation $E_{1V}^F \approx 2.5$ eV. Using Askill and Tomlin's [113] value of the self-diffusion energy $Q = 4.0$ eV in molybdenum, they derived $E_{1V}^M \approx 1.5$ eV. These results at least show the possibility to quench in an appreciable number of vacancies in molybdenum, unlike Gregory's assumption [114].

Successful quenching experiments on iron have been reported by Glaeser and Wever [71]. The resulting recovery spectrum showed a "stage III" ($0.20\,T_m$) attributed to carbon migration and a stage IV ($0.25\,T_m$) being ascribed to vacancy migration. A recovery stage in the $0.12\,T_m$ range could not be found, in contrast with Cuddy's interpretation that this stage should correspond to vacancy migration [70]. The following activation energies are proposed [71]: $E_{1V}^M \approx 1.1$ eV, $E_{1V}^F \approx 1.5$ eV, the sum of which is consistent with the activation energy for self-diffusion in iron.

Thus far positive quenching experiments have not been reported for niobium nor tantalum. On the latter metal negative results have been reported by Schultz [110]: unlike for tungsten, the technique of quenching in liquid helium II did not give rise to appreciable resistivity increments for tantalum. This can be attributed to a high formation energy and/or low migration energy of vacancies in this metal (see also section 4.1).

Stage V ($\approx 0.30\,T_m$) is usually very pronounced after plastic deformation in resistivity measurements, e.g., for tungsten (Schultz [91], fig. 21) and for molybdenum (Stals and Nihoul [73,85], fig. 22). This suggests that dislocations are involved in this recovery stage. In fig. 22 the isochronal recovery of pure molybdenum is shown following heavy plastic deformation at room temperature (curve c) and following fast neutron irradiation (curve d). A typical pre-irradiation value of

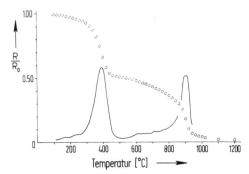

Fig. 21. Isochronal recovery curve and its derivate of plastically deformed tungsten.
$\Delta t$ = 15 min. (After Schultz [91].)

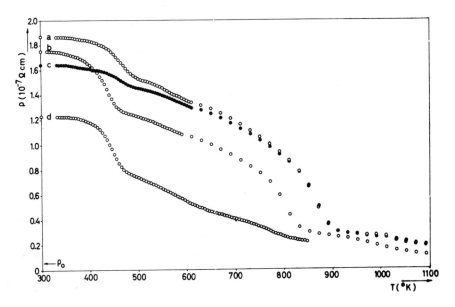

Fig. 22. Isochronal recovery curves of the electrical resistivity of molybdenum:
a. cold worked at 300°K, annealed 1 h at 520°K + n-irradiated at 330°K for 20 h,
b. idem but irradiated for 7 h,
c. cold worked at 300°K,
d. annealed + n-irradiated at 330°K for 70 h.
(After Stals and Nihoul [73].)

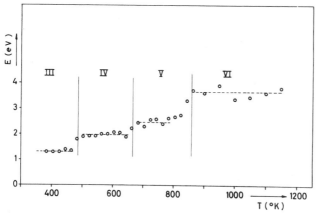

Fig. 23. Activation energies as experimentally determined by the change-in-slope method on
plastically deformed molybdenum in a wide range of temperatures.
(After Stals and Nihoul [73].)

the resistivity is indicated. It can be remarked that no undershoot effect is observed, as discussed in subsection 3.3. Curves a and b correspond to lower dose irradiations on deformation doped specimens, before irradiation annealed only at 520°K (i.e., just above stage III) after heavy plastic deformation. If one compares a and b with curve c it follows that, although irradiations to low doses have only little influence on the amount of stage V recovery, they do influence the annealing temperature, which is increased by some 60°K. This effect might indicate that the dislocations are pinned by radiation induced defects, e.g., depleted zones (Seeger [1]) or dislocation loops.

Fig. 23 shows a number of activation energies as determined by the method of Overhauser [115] for plastically deformed pure molybdenum, with increasing temperatures. Not only stages III, but also stages IV, V and VI seem to be fairly well characterized by the activation energies respectively 1.3, 2.0, 2.5 and 3.7 eV.

Although stages V and VI after fast particle irradiation are rather small, as far as e.g. electrical resistivity measurements are concerned, they are associated with important changes in the mechanical properties (see e.g. Moteff and Smith [88]). Since these stages are no longer related to single point defect annihilation, they do not belong as such to the subject of this paper and will therefore not be discussed into further details. Very important work on bcc metals in this temperature range has been performed by the technique of transmission electron microscopy. We refer e.g. to the work of Eyre et al. [107,116,117], Higgins and Roberts [118], Tucker and Ohr [62], Moteff [93], Rao and Thomas [119], Meakin and Greenfield [120]. The general trend of these observations after irradiation seems to point to vacancy cluster break-up in stage V and interstitial cluster annealing in stage VI. Also recrystallization (V, VI) and self-diffusion (VI) are taking place in this temperature range.

## 4. Recent developments

In this section we shall review a few important topics dealing with recent results or interpretations on recovery transition bcc metals, but still having a preliminary character. Although this can perhaps be said also about a number of topics treated above, we have preferred to pay special attention to the following investigations, also because most of them formed the subject of contributed papers to this conference.

### 4.1. *Recovery stages of irradiated tantalum*

In subsection 3.3 we have seen that there are reasons to change the use of labelling the $0.20\,T_m$ stage in $\alpha$-iron as stage "III", since it is related to impurity reactions, and instead reserve this name for the $0.12\,T_m$ stage, being most,probably an intrinsic higher order process. Hemmerich et al. [33] have tentatively proposed a similar though much more drastic change with respect to the situation of stage III recovery in tantalum. Where e.g. Peacock and Johnson [79] described a recovery peak associated with an activation energy of about 1.3 eV ($\approx 0.16\,T_m$) as "stage III", in analogy with other bcc and fcc metals, Hemmerich and coworkers found reasons to believe that stage III for tantalum is in fact to be found about $170°$K, i.e., at an

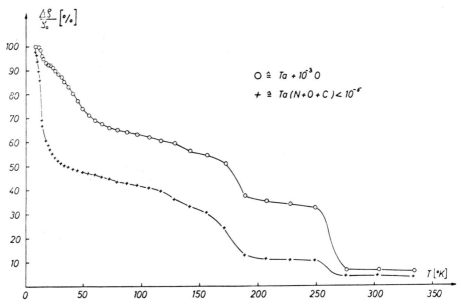

Fig. 24. Isochronal recovery of high purity and oxygen doped tantalum after irradiation with 3 MeV electrons at $4.5°$K, recovery time $\Delta t = 10$ min, fluence $7.8 \times 10^{18}$ electrons/cm$^2$. (After Hemmerich et al. [33].)

homologous temperature of not more than $0.05\ T_m$. Also the other main recovery
stages would correspondingly occur at lower temperatures than usually accepted
before. The experimental data will briefly be exposed now.

High purity tantalum wires have been irradiated with 3 MeV electrons at 4.5°K.
The isochronal recovery curves are given in figs. 24 and 25 (the corresponding
curves, after neutron irradiation, have been shown in fig. 3). The effect of doping
with 1000 at. ppm oxygen is also indicated. The most remarkable results to be
mentioned are: (i) the strong influence of oxygen on stage I; (ii) the fact that recovery is nearly complete at room temperature; (iii) the fact that oxygen doping has
little or no influence on the recovery at about 170°K but does influence stage IV.

A strikingly close correlation can be established with the recovery stages in tungsten, another bcc transition metal with comparable melting point, provided that a
scale factor of about 4 is applied to the temperature axis, as shown in table 4.

As a possible indication for rationalyzing this large scale factor the authors
invoke the fact that the shear modulus of tungsten is 2.5 times higher than that of
tantalum (see also table 2), and that in the elastic model the migration energy of a
point defect is proportional to the appropriate elastic constants. We may add here

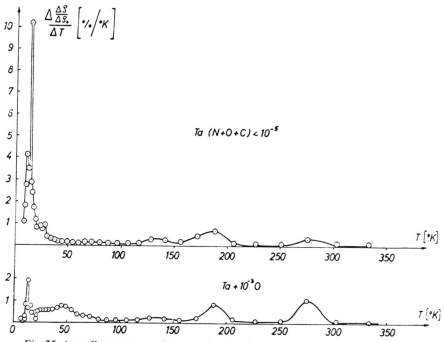

Fig. 25. Annealing spectrum of electron irradiated tantalum, resulting from fig. 24.
(After Hemmerich et al. [33].)

Table 4
Comparison of recovery stages in tungsten and tantalum
(after Hemmerich et al. [33]).

| Recovery stage | | Temperature (°K) | |
| --- | --- | --- | --- |
| | | W | Ta |
| I | | | |
| | close pairs | 30 | 9 |
| | free migration | 70 | 15 |
| II | | 80–600 | 20–120 |
| III | | | 125 |
| | | | (substage) |
| | | 700 | 170 |
| IV | | 1100 * | 250 |

* This recovery stage has been called stage V throughout this paper.

that some theoretical calculations, based on the elastic model, do in fact point to the same conclusion. As an example it may be referred here to the calculation of the migration energies of single vacancies in metals by Wynblatt [121]. For tungsten he found $E_{1V}^M$ = 2.26 eV, whereas the corresponding value for tantalum appeared to be only 0.66 eV.

On account of these results, the authors tentatively proposed a 2-interstitial model, involving free migration of one type of self-interstitial in stage I and of another type in stage III. The stage I interstitial was proposed to have a ⟨100⟩ symmetry, according to preliminary results reported by Di Carlo et al. [43], the stage III interstitial to have a ⟨110⟩ as observed in field ion microscopy experiments by Galligan and coworkers [95,96]. The basis of this suggestion has in the meantime somewhat been invalidated owing to further investigations by Di Carlo et al. [44] pointing to a ⟨110⟩ rather than to a ⟨100⟩ symmetry for the freely migrating stage I interstitial (see section 3.2). So if there are a number of data supporting a two-interstitial recovery model for the transition bcc metals, one is still in the dark as to what would be the configurational properties of the two types of interstitials.

Hemmerich and coworkers further pointed out that the 2-interstitial model allows one to explain the effect of doping on stage I by trapping reactions between the oxygen interstitials and — what we shall call here — the "stage I interstitials". Some of these trapped interstitials would be released between 20 and 40°K, whereas about 50% would remain trapped until the "stage IV" range sets on. A few possibilities are suggested for explaining this latter phenomenon: (i) the remaining stage I interstitials are trapped with a stronger binding energy or (ii) after being released they form more stable complexes. Also the remarkable result that stage III is not affected by the presence of oxygen impurities can be explained on this assumption.

If the $250°K$ "stage IV" of electron irradiated tantalum is ascribed to single vacancy migration, its increase with oxygen content can be explained by assuming a higher number of vacancies surviving stage III in the doped specimens, as a consequence of the fact that in this case more interstitials are trapped and thus unable to annihilate vacancies. Finally the unsuccessful attempts (mentioned in section 3.5) to quench in vacancies in tantalum could naturally be explained as due to the high mobility of the vacancies.

However fascinating and tempting this new vision on recovery stages in tantalum might be, it is clear that it needs many additional investigations, as pointed out also by the authors. One of the most difficult consequences to accept from this model seems to be the identification of the $250°K$ stage of tantalum with the $1100°K$ stage of tungsten (which we have called stage V, see subsection 3.5). As discussed in subsection 3.5, this recovery stage in tungsten is most probably related with more complex defects than point defects, e.g., dislocations or defect clusters and with recrystallization. It seems rather unlikely that this type of recovery in tantalum would occur at temperatures as low as $250°K$, i.e., at homologous temperatures below $0.1\,T_m$.

If this interpretation by Hemmerich et al. is to be confirmed in further investigations, it will strongly invalidate the general assumption that the higher recovery stages are more or less proportional to the melting point of the metal. It would be worthwhile to investigate whether differences in elastic properties can be correlated with the recovery stages in fcc metals as well.

### 4.2. *Comparison of annealing results in single crystal and polycrystalline molybdenum*

Thus far it has tacitly been assumed that recovery in the stage III range is basically the same for polycrystalline specimens as for single crystals. Recent experiments performed by Kissinger et al. [122] seem to throw a new light on this problem.

Combined measurements of changes in lattice parameters and in length (fig. 26) on neutron irradiated molybdenum showed significant differences for single crystals and for polycrystalline specimens. Although qualitatively similar curves are obtained, there are remarkable quantitative differences. The relative length changes are identical, but the sign of the difference $\Delta L/L - \Delta a/a$ is different for the two cases (at least for fluences up to about $10^{19}$ n/cm$^2$), suggesting that more interstitials than vacancies are present in the polycrystalline samples and that the contrary situation occurs for the single crystals. This work has been complemented with electron microscopic observations, when different cluster sizes were obtained for the two cases (fig. 27) following irradiation to $10^{19}$ n/cm$^2$ at $40°C$. The clusters, which are believed by the authors to be interstitial in nature, are considerably larger, about 100 Å, in the single crystals than in the polycrystalline specimens. The authors assume that an intrinsic interstitial is mobile at $40°C$ and although the overall impurity content is much the same in both cases, a different impurity distribution could cause more effective trapping of isolated interstitials in the polycrystalline material.

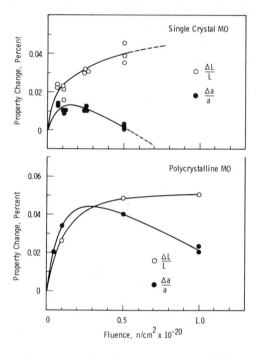

Fig. 26. Relative changes in length $\Delta L/L$ and lattice parameter $\Delta a/a$ for neutron-irradiated single crystal and polycrystalline molybdenum. (After Kissinger et al. [122].)

These differences were not only observed in the as-irradiated samples but also the annealing behaviour above room temperature was found to be considerably different. The stored energy release in the stage III range was more important with polycrystals than with single crystals (fig. 28). If the defect production (or resistivity) curves of fig. 26 would be disregarded, the stored energy curves of fig. 28 showing a peak shift to lower temperatures with higher energy release would simply suggest that this was due to a correspondingly higher concentration of the same type of defects annihilating in a higher order (e.g. bimolecular) recovery process.

Fig. 29 shows the isochronal recovery of $\Delta L$ and $\Delta a$. Whereas again for the length changes identical recovery curves are obtained, the recovery of the lattice parameter is quite different in stage III. For the single crystal the recovery of the lattice parameter below 400°C seems to be quite independent of the length change recovery. However, the interpretation of such type of annealing results is very difficult if the possibility is considered that point defects may occur both as single defects and as clusters, and contribute to the observed properties in an equal way or in different ways, depending on the geometrical properties of the clusters. Therefore additional systematic investigations seem to be required before one might take for sure the conclusion of the authors, according to which the interstitial defects and vacancies or

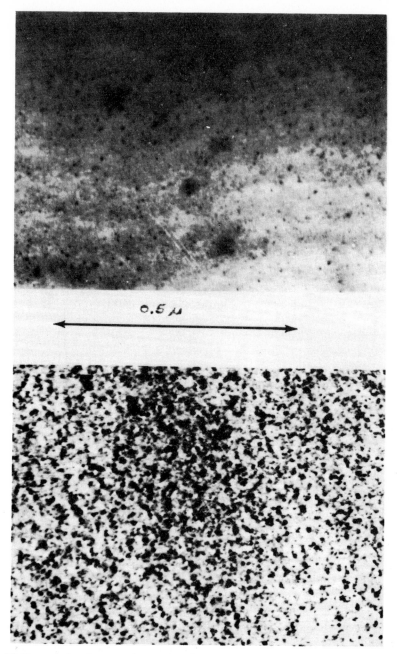

Fig. 27. Transmission electron micrographs of (a) single crystals and (b) polycrystalline molybdenum showing differences in defect cluster sizes after exposure to a fast neutron fluence of $1 \times 10^{19}$ n/cm$^2$. (After Kissinger et al. [122].)

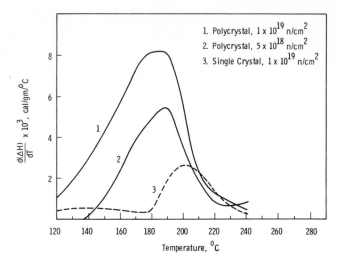

Fig. 28. Recovery of length and lattice parameter during isochronal annealing of neutron-irradiated single-crystals and polycrystalline molybdenum. Annealing time was two hours at each temperature. (After Kissinger et al. [122].)

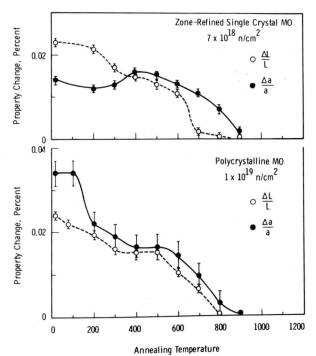

Fig. 29. Release of stored-energy from irradiated single-crystal and polycrystal molybdenum. (After Kissinger et al. [122].)

divacancies anneal independently without appreciable mutual annihilation.

It is also suggested [122] that the stage III recovery in irradiated molybdenum may consist of both reactions proceeding simultaneously. Hence it is postulated that in the polycrystalline samples a higher concentration of trapping sites is present, either from differences in impurity content or from a different distribution of impurities.

If the observed different behaviour is explained in terms of different impurity distribution it is hard to understand why such a difference has never been observed before in resistometric studies on polycrystalline material of various origins and purity degree (see section 3). On the other hand, if it is to be ascribed specifically to the fact that in this experiment single crystals have been studied, it would mean that stage III recovery in polycrystalline material strongly depends on the presence of grain boundaries or that these extended defects play a predominant role in the production mechanism of the defects which are stable in molybdenum above room temperature. A very speculative interpretation at this moment could perhaps be sought in the light of a 2-interstitial model, if it is assumed that the grain boundaries act as converters of "stage I interstitials" into "stage III interstitials".

Assuming that stage III recovery involves both interstitial and vacancy annihilation, occurring independently, Kissinger and coworkers arrive at the following quantitative results:

a) stored energy release per vacancy: 1.4 eV;
b) stored energy release per interstitial: 6 eV (if the interstitials are not absorbed at sinks but annihilate at vacancies, this latter value would correspond to the stored energy release for a vacancy and an interstitial);
c) volume change per vacancy: 0.37 atomic volume.

## 4.3. Pressure dependence of recovery in molybdenum

In the same laboratory the recovery of neutron irradiated molybdenum has been studied both at normal and at high pressures (20 kbar) by Kulcinski et al. [102]. In this work the attention was limited to polycrystalline molybdenum.

It is known that the temperature at which self-diffusion occurs, is increased with increasing hydrostatic pressure [123], pointing to a positive activation volume. In this contribution the influence on the recovery stages above room temperature was observed for irradiated molybdenum. At normal pressure, four recovery stages were detected (III–VI) with measurements of several physical properties. Stage III is characterized by an activation energy of 1.25 eV, and a reaction order varying from 3.4 to 1.7 in agreement with previous experiments (see section 3). Under 20 kbars, stages III and V are lowered by 60°K and 300°K (figs. 30 and 31).

Also electron microscopic observations were made. Fig. 32 illustrates how the defect cluster annealing temperature is lowered by about 200°K with the application of 20 kbar, and a similar effect occurs with stage VI as revealed by means of hardness measurements (fig. 33). A comparison of differential recovery curves for irradiated molybdenum annealed at low and at high pressures is presented in fig. 34 and in table 5.

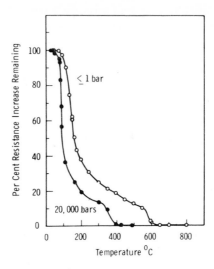

Fig. 30. Effect of hydrostatic pressure on the isochronal recovery of the irradiation induced electrical resistance increase in molybdenum. (After Kulcinski et al. [102].)

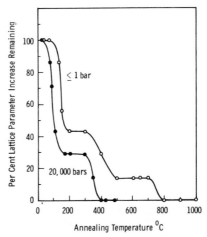

Fig. 31. Effect of hydrostatic pressure on the isochronal recovery of the irradiation induced lattice parameter increase in molybdenum. (After Kulcinski et al. [102].)

It should be remarked that the recovery of electrical resistance is completed when 30–50% of the observable defect clusters are still present, suggesting that these large defects contribute very little to the resistance increment. On the other hand, they seem to be related in some manner to the hardness.

The shift of the apparent peak temperature with pressure allows one to derive an

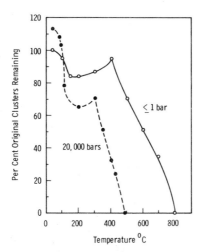

Fig. 32. Effect of hydrostatic pressure on the isochronal annealing of observable defect clusters in irradiated molybdenum. (After Kulcinski et al. [102].)

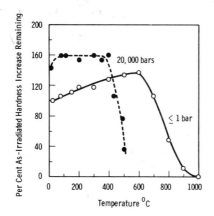

Fig. 33. Effect of hydrostatic pressure on the isochronal annealing of the irradiation induced hardness increase in molybdenum. (After Kulcinski et al. [102].)

activation volume on the basis of the annealing equation

$$dC/dt = F(C) K_o \exp(-H/kT) \tag{5}$$

with $C$ = concentration of defects considered and $H$ = the activation enthalpy of the process; $H = E + p\Delta V$, where $E$ is the activation energy and $\Delta V$ the activation volume of the process. At normal pressures $p\Delta V$ can usually be neglected with

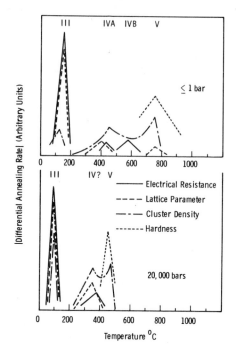

Fig. 34. Comparison of the differential recovery curves for irradiated molybdenum isochronally
annealed at (a) low (≤1 bar) and (b) high (20.000 bar) pressure.
(After Kulcinski et al. [102].)

Table 5
Summary of annealing stages for isobaric-isochronal annealing of irradiated molybdenum.
(After Kulcinski et al. [102].)

| Stage * | 1 bar | | | 20 kbar | | |
|---|---|---|---|---|---|---|
| | temp. range (°K) | $T/T_m$ ** | property *** measured | temp. range (°K) | $T/T_m$ ** | property *** measured |
| III | 430 | 0.15 | ER, LP, CD | 360 | 0.13 | ER, LP, CD |
| IV | 670–720 | 0.24 | ER, LP, CD | 620–650 | 0.22 | ER, LP, CD |
| V | 860 | 0.29 | ER | | | |
| VI | 1020 | 0.35 | LP, CO, H | 720–750 | 0.25 | CD, H |

   * In the nomenclature used throughout this article.
  ** $T_m$ = absolute temperature at normal pressure.
*** ER = electrical resistance, LP = lattice parameter, CD = cluster density, H = hardness.

respect to $E$. With increasing pressures, however, a positive activation energy involves an increasing activation enthalpy and consequently the considered process occurs at higher temperatures than normally. The fact that in the present case the recovery processes are shifted to lower temperatures with increasing pressure implies a negative activation volume, if the pre-exponential factor of equation (5) is assumed to be pressure independent. Under these assumptions Kulcinski and co-workers derived from the observed peak shift a large negative activation volume $\Delta V \approx -0.9$ atomic volume [122,124].

The possible physical significance of this result is not clear. The authors consider divacancy migration, untrapping of interstitials from substitutional impurities, due to negative pressure coefficient of the binding energy, or forced recombination of interstitials and vacancies, due to an increased capture radius with increased hydrostatic pressure.

The latter interpretation would support the model in which stage III is explained by free migration of interstitials. The peak shift in this case would probably not require a negative activation volume, but would be the result of an increase of the pre-exponential factor in equation (5), owing to a decreased number of "free" jumps the defect would have to make before annihilation. On the other hand, although a negative activation volume is not very frequently being observed, it has definitely been measured in a few cases, e.g., by Peart [125]. Moreover a negative, but much smaller activation volume, has been predicted by the machine calculations for interstitials in copper (Johnson [126]) and for vacancies in gamma-iron (Johnson [127]).

As stated by the authors, this series of experiments has not resolved the stage III—IV dilemma but it has placed more stringent requirements on the models to be proposed for explaining the recovery of point defects. It seems justified to pay both theoretical and experimental efforts to this phenomenon and to extend these investigations to other types of metals as well.

### 4.4. Concentration dependence of stage III annealing

As it is well known, a recovery process associated with an overall reaction order higher than one will show up in isochronal annealing experiments by a lowering of the peak temperature with increasing concentration of defects involved in that particular process. For a constant reaction order $\gamma$, the temperature of the inflection point $T_i$ in the isochronal curve (considered here as the result of a continuous and linear heating program, see Gevers et al. [128]) is given by

$$T_i = A \ C_i^{(1-\gamma)/2} \ \exp(E/2kT_i) , \tag{6}$$

where $A$ is constant if the reaction order $\gamma$, the activation energy $E$, and the heating rate are constant. If the activation energy is known, equation (6) allows one to calculate either the apparent reaction order from an observed peak shift with concentration, or vice versa. If we write "apparent" reaction order, this is to account for the frequently observed case that the recovery process is not of simple "chemical" nature, but has a diffusion-controlled character, involving a continuously changing reaction order. Since most of the methods for determining reaction orders are intrinsically based on the assumption of a constant reaction order, their application in these cases yield some "mean" or "apparent" reaction order. Fig. 35 shows an example of an application of the method of Meechan and Brinkman [101] to a theoretical curve, illustrating the possibility to draw wrong conclusions from such a type of analysis [74].

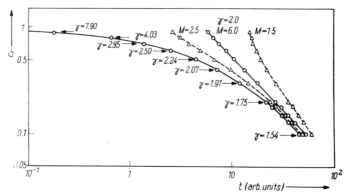

Fig. 35. Determination of reaction order of bimolecular diffusion controlled process, for slightly different initial concentrations (theoretical curve) using the method of Meechan and Brinkman [101]. An apparently constant reaction order $\gamma = 2$ is found. Some real values of the changing reaction order are indicated. (After Nihoul and Stals [74].)

Although a number of authors have reported second order or "bimolecular" kinetics for stage III in bcc metals, as discussed in section 3, only very few systematic experiments are known in which these kinetics have been tested systematically on the basis of the peak shift criterion. In those investigations where isochronal curves have been measured for different concentrations, this difference was not important enough to show a clear effect and no special attention was paid to it. In this respect the only experiments performed in suitable conditions are those of Moteff and coworkers [88,93] on neutron irradiated tungsten (fig. 36). A well-pronounced effect has been observed, as expected for a higher order process. However, Keys et al. [129,130] have recently attributed this effect mostly to a transmutation effect (formation of Re) caused by thermal neutron $(n, \gamma)$ reactions in tungsten. The temperature shift would then result primarily from the weakening of the lattice by rhenium. Moreover, it is mentioned that no corresponding peak shift occurred in molybdenum [129] in which transmutation effects are in fact less important. It is not commented in this paper how to reconcile this absence in peak

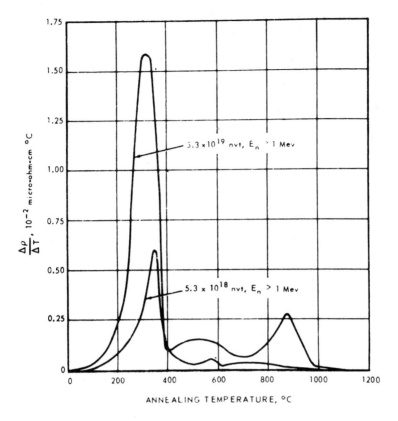

Fig. 36. Recovery spectrum of neutron-irradiated tungsten for two different fluences.
(After Moteff [93].)

shift for molybdenum with the otherwise assumed second order kinetics.

As a consequence, we may state that no clear demonstration of intrinsic higher order kinetics has been given for transition bcc metals thus far on the basis of isochronal peak shifts. In an attempt to do so, Goedemé et al. [75] have started a series of experiments with plastically deformed and neutron-irradiated molybdenum up to different concentrations of defects. A preliminary result obtained on specimens deformed to various degrees is shown in fig. 37. As can be observed, the peak temperature changes with concentration. This shift could correspond to a mean reaction order of about 2.5 in agreement with a previous analysis of isothermal recovery curves (see section 3).

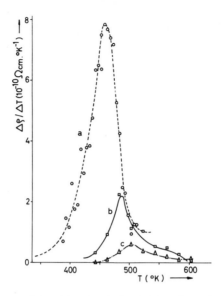

Fig. 37. Stage III recovery peaks of the electrical resistivity of molybdenum plastically deformed
to various degrees (heating rate 30°K/h):

a. $\Delta\rho = 16.4 \times 10^{-8}$ $\Omega$cm

b. $\Delta\rho = 4.8 \times 10^{-8}$ $\Omega$cm

c. $\Delta\rho = 2.4 \times 10^{-8}$ $\Omega$cm

(After Goedemé et al. [75].)

## 5. Concluding remarks

Many problems remain to be solved with respect to the behaviour of point defects in transition bcc metals. Additional systematic irradiation experiments, involving different energies and fluences, have still to be performed. The influence of
various doping treatments on the production and on the recovery of point defects
should be investigated into more detail.

The behaviour of interstitial impurities is relatively well known for bcc iron and
the Va metals, but much less for the VIa metals. On the other hand, for the latter
metals it seems possible to associate the recovery stages I, III and IV with intrinsic
point defects, in agreement with recovery in fcc metals.

In this paper it has been proposed that the most satisfactory model for interpreting these recovery stages in molybdenum and tungsten would be a 2-interstitial
model, involving "stage I" and "stage III interstitials". For niobium, tantalum and
bcc iron there are indications that the traditional labelling of the recovery stages
should be revised, in the light of results obtained on very pure specimens.

There is a general need for more data concerning the behaviour of single vacancies in bcc metals. Therefore, additional quenching experiments in clean conditions combined with annealing, would be of primordial importance. It would also suit very well if the uncertainty with respect to self diffusion data could be decreased in order to compare, e.g., the sum of the activation energies for formation and migration of vacancies with the self diffusion activation energy.

## Acknowledgements

Thanks are due to Professor S.Amelinckx and Professor R.Gevers for their continuous interest. I also thank Dr. L.Stals and Lic. Sc. G.Goedemé for many helpful discussions, bibliographic research and permission to refer to unpublished work.

## References

[1] A.Seeger, in: Proc. of a Symp. on Radiation Damage in Solids, Venice, Italy, vol. 1 (IAEA, Vienna, 1962) p. 101.
[2] J.W.Corbett, Electron radiation damage in semiconductors and metals, Series on Solid State Physics, eds. F.Seitz and D.Turnbull, Suppl. 7 (Academic Press, New York, 1966).
[3] D.K.Holmes, in: The Interaction of Radiation with Solids, eds. R.Strumane et al. (North-Holland, Amsterdam, 1964) p. 147.
[4] E.W.Müller, this volume.
[5] J.M.Galligan, this volume.
[6] J.R.Beeler Jr., J. Appl. Phys. 37 (1966) 3000.
[7] J.R.Beeler Jr., in: Lattice Defects and Their Interactions, ed. R.R.Hasiguti (Gordon and Breach, New York, 1967) p. 621.
[8] H.Schultz, Mater. Sci. Eng. 6 (1968) 189.
[9] A.Köthe and F.Schlät, Realstruktur und Eigenschaften von Reinststoffen (Akademie-Verlag, Berlin, 1967) Teil 3, p. 649.
[10] A.Köthe, Thesis, IMR nr. 33, Deutsche Akademie der Wissenschaften, Institut für Metallphysik und Reinstmetalle, Berlin (1968).
[11] F.Schlät, Thesis, Technische Universität Dresden (1968).
[12] G.Alefeld, this volume.
See also G.Schaumann, J.Völkl and G.Alefeld, Jül-Conf-2 (Vol. II) 1968, p. 881.
[13] J.H.Evans and B.L.Eyre, Jül-Conf.2 (vol. II) 1968, p. 858.
[14] J.H.Swisher and E.T.Turkdogan, Trans. Met. Soc. AIME 239 (1967) 426.
[15] W.Frank, H.J.Engell and A.Seeger, Z. Metallk. 58 (1967) 452.
[16] W.Frank, H.J.Engell and A.Seeger, Trans. Met. Soc. AIME 242 (1968) 749.
[17] P.G.Lucasson and R.M.Walker, Phys. Rev. 127 (1962) 485, 1130.
[18] G.Hörz, E.Gebhard and W.Dürrschnabel, Z. Metallkunde 56 (1965) 554.
[19] E.Krautz, H.H.Kühlmann and H.Schultz, Z. Metallkunde 59 (1968) 133.
[20] W.Köster, Arch. Eisenhüttenw. 2 (1928) 603.
[21] Z.C.Szkopiak and B.Pouzet, Jül-Conf-2 (vol. II) 1968, p. 709.

[22] H.G.Van Bueren, Z. Metallkunde 46 (1955) 272.

[23] M.W.Thompson, Phil. Mag. 5 (1960) 278.

[24] G.H.Kinchin and M.W.Thompson, J. Nucl. Energy 6 (1958) 275.

[25] J.Nihoul, Phys. Stat. Sol. 2 (1962) 308.

[26] J.Nihoul, in: Proc. of a Symp. on Radiation Damage in Solids, Venice, Italy, vol. I (IAEA, Vienna, 1962) p. 309.

[27] D.E.Peacock and A.A.Johnson, Phil. Mag. 8 (1963) 563.

[28] J.Nihoul, Phil. Mag. 9 (1964) 167.

[29] C.Minier-Cassayre, Thesis, Rapport CEA R.2905, Grenoble (1965).

[30] T.H.Blewitt, private communication (1957).

[31] G.Burger et al., Phys. Letters 20 (1966) 470, 472.

[32] E.Rexer, F.Schlät and A.Köthe, Second Intern. Conf. on Electron and Ion Beam Science and Technology, New York, IMR Report no. 24 (1966).

[33] H.Hemmerich, D.Meissner, H.Schultz and F.Walz, Jül-Conf-2 (vol. II) 1968, p. 724.

[34] R.Pichon, C.Minier-Cassayre, V.Hivert and P.Moser, Phys. Stat. Sol. 17 (1966) K33.

[35] E.M.Abd El-Salam and J.W.De Ford, Phys. Rev. 161 (1967) 600.

[36] H.Bilger, V.Hivert, J.Verdone, J.L.Leveque and J.C.Soulie, Jül-Conf-2 (vol. II) 1968, p. 751.

[37] R.A.Johnson, Phys. Rev. 134 (1964) A1329.

[38] D.Dautreppe et al., Compt. Rend. Acad. Sci. Paris 258 (1964) 4539.

[39] P.Moser, Mém. Sci. Rev. Mét. 63 (1966) 343, 431.

[40] E.W.Müller, Proc. IVth Intern. Conf. Reactivity of Solids (Elsevier, Amsterdam, 1960) p. 282.

[41] E.W.Müller, J. Phys. Soc. Japan 18, Suppl. II (1963) 1.

[42] M.K.Sinha and E.W.Müller, J. Appl. Phys. 35 (1964) 1256.

[43] J.A.Di Carlo, C.L.Snead and A.N.Goland, Bull. Am. Phys. Soc. 13 (1968) 381.

[44] J.A.Di Carlo, C.L.Snead and A.N.Goland, Internal Report, Brookhaven, Upton, New York, BNL 12807 (1968).

[45] H.H.Neely and D.W.Keefer, Phys. Stat. Sol. 24 (1967) 217.

[46] R.R.Coltman, C.E.Klabunde and J.K.Redman, Phys. Rev. 156 (1967) 715.

[47] S.Takamura, H.Maeta and S.Okuda, J. Phys. Soc. Japan 25 (1968) 418.

[48] J.N.Lomer and R.J.Taylor, to be published.

[49] A.R.Rosenfield, Acta Met. 12 (1964) 119.

[50] R.A.Arndt and A.C.Damask, Acta Met. 12 (1964) 341.

[51] H.Wagenblast and A.C.Damask, J. Phys. Chem. Solids 23 (1962) 221.

[52] F.E.Fujita and A.C.Damask, Acta Met. 12 (1964) 331.

[53] D.P.Gregory, Acta Met. 11 (1963) 455.

[54] C.L.Formby and W.S.Owen, J. Less Common Met. 9 (1965) 25.

[55] R.W.Powers and M.V.Doyle, J. Appl. Phys. 30 (1959) 514.

[56] E.De Lamotte and C.Wert, J. Phys. Soc. Japan 19 (1964) 1560.

[57] A.H.Cottrell and B.A. Bilby, Proc. Phys. Soc. 62A (1949) 49.

[58] R.Bullough and R.C.Newman, Proc. Roy. Soc. A266 (1962) 209.

[59] R.Bullough and R.C.Newman, J. Phys. Soc. Japan 18S (1963) 27.

[60] I.Kovacs, Acta Met. 15 (1967) 1731.

[61] G.Saada, Thesis, Paris (1960).

[62] R.P.Tucker and S.M.Ohr, Progress Report ORNL-4195 (1967).

[63] J.M.Williams, J.T.Stanley and W.E.Brundage, Progress Report ORNL-4097 (1967).

[64] J.T.Stanley, J.M.Williams and W.E.Brundage, Progress Report ORNL-4195 (1967).

[65] L.Stals and J.Nihoul, Phys. Stat. Sol. 8 (1965) 785.

[66] L.Stals, J.Nihoul and R.Gevers, Phys. Stat. Sol. 15 (1966) 717.

[67] L.J.Cuddy, Phil. Mag. 12 (1965) 855.

[68]  L.J.Cuddy and J.C.Raley, Acta Met. 14 (1966) 44o.
[69]  T.Oi and K.Sato, Trans. Japan Inst. Metals 7 (1966) 32.
[70]  L.J.Cuddy, Acta Met. 16 (1968) 23.
[71]  W.Glaeser and H.Wever, Jül-Conf-2 (vol. II) 1968, p. 733.
[72]  R.W.Balluffi and D.N.Seidman, Phil. Mag. 17 (1968) 843.
[73]  L.Stals and J.Nihoul, Physica 42 (1969) 165.
[74]  J.Nihoul and L.Stals, Phys. Stat. Sol. 17 (1966) 295.
[75]  G.Goedemé, L.Stals and J.Nihoul, to be published.
[76]  A.Van den Beukel, private communication (1968).
[77]  B.S.Lement and M.Cohen, Acta Met. 4 (1956) 469.
[78]  J.Nihoul, SCK-CEN (Mol, Belgium) Report R 1587 (1958).
[79]  D.E.Peacock and A.A.Johnson, Nature 195 (1962) 169.
[80]  S.S.Ibragimov, V.S.Lyaskenko and A.I.Zavyalov, Atomnaya Energy 8 (1960) 413;
      English translation: J. Nucl. Energy 16 (1962) 45.
[81]  A.S.Wronski and A.A.Johnson, Phil. Mag. 8 (1963) 1067.
[82]  D.L.Gray, Acta Met. 7 (1959) 431.
[83]  J.Adam and D.G.Martin, Phil. Mag. 3 (1958) 1329.
[84]  D.G.Martin, Acta Met. 5 (1957) 371.
[85]  J.Nihoul and L.Stals, SCK-CEN (Mol, Belgium) Report BLG 424 (1967).
[86]  J.Blons, P.Imbert, G.Perriot and G.Tourand, Faraday Colloquium, Saclay (1960).
[87]  H.H.Kuhlmann and H.Schultz, Acta Met. 14 (1966) 798.
[88]  J.Moteff and J.P.Smith, Flow and Fracture of Metals, Spec. Techn. Publ. no. 380,
      Am. Soc. for Testing and Materials (1965) p. 171.
[89]  H.H.Neely, D.W.Keefer and A.Sosin, Phys. Stat. Sol. 28 (1968) 675.
[90]  H.Schultz, Z. Naturforsch. 14a (1959) 361.
[91]  H.Schultz, Acta Met. 12 (1964) 761.
[92]  J.Nihoul and L.Stals, The Recovery of Structural Defects in Metals, Monograph in the
      Series Defects in Crystalline Solids, eds. S.Amelinckx et al. (North-Holland, Amsterdam,
      to be published).
[93]  J.Moteff, Report GE-TM-65-9-2 (1965).
[94]  M.De Jong and H.B.Afman, Acta Met. 15 (1967) 1.
[95]  M.Attardo and J.M.Galligan, Phys. Stat. Sol. 16 (1966) 449.
[96]  D.Jeannotte and J.M.Galligan, Phys. Rev. Letters 19 (1967) 232.
[97]  J.M.Galligan, private communication (1967).
[98]  P.S.Rudman, Trans. AIME 239 (1967) 1949.
[99]  K.Rösch, F.Bell and R.Sizmann, Jül-Conf-2 (vol. I) 1968, p. 444.
[100] W.Bauer, Jül-Conf-2 (vol. I) 1968, p. 275.
[101] C.J.Meechan and J.A.Brinkman, Phys. Rev. 103 (1956) 1193.
[102] G.L.Kulcinski, Jül-Conf-2 (vol. II) 1968, p. 693.
[103] T.R.Waite, Phys. Rev. 107 (1957) 463.
[104] R. von Jan, Phys. Stat. Sol. 17 (1966) 361.
[105] H.Mehrer, Jül-Conf-2 (vol. II) 1968, p. 643.
[106] M.J.Martin and E.Gillies, J. Inst. Met. 86 (1958) 108.
[107] M.E.Downey and B.L.Eyre, Phil. Mag. 11 (1965) 53.
[108] J.Nihoul, unpublished results, reported at the "Diskussionstagung über atomare Fehl-
      stellen", Schliersee, Germany, 21–24 September 1965.
[109] R.L.Andelin, J.D.Knight and M.Kahn, Trans. AIME 233 (1965) 19.
[110] H.Schultz, in: Lattice Defects in Quenched Metals, ed. R.M.J.Cotterill et al. (Academic
      Press, New York, 1965) p. 761.
[111] R.Gripshover, J.Zetts and J.Bass, Jül-Conf-2 (vol. I) 1968, p. 228.
[112] J.D.Meakin, A.Lawley and R.C.Koo, Appl. Phys. Letters 5 (1964) 133.

[113] J.Askill and D.M.Tomlin, Phil. Mag. 8 (1963) 997.

[114] D.P.Gregory, Acta Met. 11 (1963) 623.

[115] A.W.Overhauser, Phys. Rev. 90 (1953) 393.

[116] B.L.Eyre and M.E.Downey, Metal Sci. J. 1 (1967) 5.

[117] D.M.Maher and B.L.Eyre, Phil. Mag. 17 (1968) 1.

[118] P.R.B.Higgins and A.C.Roberts, J. Less Common Met. 6 (1964) 472.

[119] P.Rao and G.Thomas, Acta Met. 15 (1967) 1153.

[120] J.D.Meakin and I.G.Greenfield, Phil. Mag. 11 (1965) 277.

[121] P.Wynblatt, J. Phys. Chem. Solids 29 (1968) 215.

[122] H.E.Kissinger, J.L.Brimhall, B.Mastel and T.K.Bierlein, Jül-Conf-2 (vol. II) 1968, p. 681.

[123] A.W.Lawson, in: High Pressure Physics and Chemistry, vol. 1 (Academic Press, New York, 1963) p. 411.

[124] G.L.Kulcinski, BNWL-844 (1968), to be published in Phys. Rev. (1969).

[125] R.F.Peart, Phys. Stat. Sol. 20 (1967) 545.

[126] R.A.Johnson, Phys. Rev. 127 (1962) 446.

[127] R.A.Johnson, Phys. Rev. 145 (1966) 423.

[128] R.Gevers, J.Nihoul and L.Stals, Phys. Stat. Sol. 15 (1966) 701.

[129] L.K.Keys, J.P.Smith and J.Moteff, Scripta Metall. 1 (1967) 71.

[130] L.K.Keys, J.P.Smith and J.Moteff, Phys. Rev., to be published.

## Discussion

*A.Brenac:* What do you think about the vacancy concentration in tungsten near the melting point, some disagreement being apparent between Schultz's resistivity measurements and Kraftmakher's specific heat result?

*H.Schultz:* The vacancy concentration derived from Kraftmakher's specific heat data, appears to be too high. It was mentioned in the paper of M.Hoch and in the following discussion, that the specific heat results include a contribution of the anharmonicity of lattice vibrations, which is difficult to separate from the vacancy contribution. In my opinion, the He-II quenching results give the correct order of magnitude for the vacancy concentration in tungsten.

*A.Brenac:* Taking into account the high formation energy of vacancies in tungsten, do you think it is possible to have a sufficiently high equilibrium concentration of vacancies to freeze them in, in quenching experiments and make useful observations using electron microscopy techniques, after adequate annealing?

*H.Schultz:* There are quenching experiments on molybdenum combined with electron microscopy (Meakin et al. [112]). In this work a vacancy concentration of $5 \times 10^{-5}$ at the melting point was derived, which can be compared with the resistivity results on tungsten ($1 \times 10^{-4}$). Therefore, it appears possible to do useful observations using electron microscopy techniques.

*H.Bilger:* Why do you interpret the 250°K stage in tantalum (Hemmerich et al. [33], section 4.1) by vacancy migration? Is it not surprising firstly that this stage does not exist after neutron irradiation and secondly that about 10% of the resistivity increases are not annealed after this stage?

*H.Schultz:* We tried to correlate the annealing steps in tantalum to similar steps in tungsten as shown in table 4. Then the 250°K stage in tantalum should be called stage IV. The corresponding stage IV in tungsten can be interpreted by vacancy migration.

A weak indication of the 250°K stage in tantalum also exists after neutron irradiation.

The remaining resistivity in the high-purity electron irradiated tantalum is about 5% of the resistivity increase. It is higher in the impurity doped sample. We may suppose, that this is related to more stable defect clusters.

*J.L.Leveque:* I would like to bring some more experimental data in accordance with your explanation of stage III.
1) "Stage III" is not observed in very pure iron within experimental error.
2) The presence of carbon strongly increases the amplitude of stage III.

*J.Nihoul:* There seems to be quite general agreement indeed to explain the recovery in $\alpha$-iron near $0.20\,T_m$ ("stage III") in terms of carbon interstitial migration. As pointed out in section 3.2, it looks preferable to label rather the intrinsic recovery stage near $0.12\,T_m$ as stage III.

*J.Galligan* (presented by H.Schultz): I would like to report a strain-ageing effect in tantalum at 165°K. Tantalum wire samples have been deformed by tension at 78°K and isothermal ageing treatments above this temperature have been performed. In the range of 165°K a strain-ageing effect was observed, which suggests the migration of a point defect at this temperature. This agrees with the annealing data of Hemmerich et al. [33] where after electron irradiation a recovery step in this temperature region has been observed.

*P.Wilkes:* Glaeser and Wever [71] are to be congratulated on their success in using a very difficult technique. We have been working on quenching in iron containing Mo (8 and 12 at %). We find that, in contrast to the pure iron, one can quench in high concentrations of vacancies which form loops and helical dislocations after ageing at temperatures $\geqslant 500$°C. The loop formation is preceded by a resistivity decrease. A binding energy may be estimated from the loop density as $0.25-0.5$ eV (Mo–V). This work is continuing.

*M.Wuttig:* With respect to the paper of Glaeser and Wever [71] I should like to mention the results of the study by Wuttig, Stanley and Birmbaum (Phys. Stat. Sol. 27 (1968) 701). Here we found no carbon trapping after quenching of high purity iron while we detected it in impure iron. Furthermore, the carbon was detrapped at around 600°C. These results are very much in disagreement with the interpretation given by Glaeser and Wever.

*T.Anagnostopoulos:* A magnetic after-effect band attributed to the reorientation of carbon-vacancy pairs appears in iron at the same temperature where the electrical resistivity stage III starts to anneal. It is accompanied by a diminution of the vacancy-carbon concentration.

This band disappears at about 450°C followed by an increase of the free carbon concentration. At this temperature Dr. Glaeser remarks an increase of the resistivity which could be therefore explained by the dissociation of the carbon-vacancy pairs.

*J.Takamura:* I have a rather general remark with respect to the contribution of Bilger et al. [36]. It has been reported that the diffusion activation energy in iron changes at the Curie point. It seems that the formation energy of vacancies would be little affected by the magnetic contribution, and the migration energy might be influenced by the change in the magnetic properties such as magneto-striction.

*H.Wenzl:* (1) At the low temperature irradiation group in Munich electrical resistivity and stored energy on niobium have been measured after 4°K 4 MeV-$\alpha$ and fast neutron irradiation (F.Rau, Thesis, Physik-Department, Technische Hochschule München, 1968).

Several sharp resistivity annealing maxima were found between 4 and 280°K after $\alpha$-irradiation, whereas after neutron irradiation the annealing structure is smeared out, a behaviour also observed in fcc metals.

The ratio of stored energy release and residual resistivity change between 4°K and 300°K amounts to 14 eV/1000 $\mu\Omega$cm.at.

Resistivity saturation effects during $\alpha$- and n-irradiation at 4°K in a supercritical magnetic field or at 10°K were found. The extrapolated saturation value is approximately 3 $\mu\Omega$cm.

(2) For niobium a new exciting field is the study of interactions of magnetic flux lines and lattice defects in the superconducting state. Experiments have already been performed by the Munich group (H.Berndt, N.Kartascheff, H.Wenzl, Z. Angew. Physik 24 (1968) 305). The magnetic susceptibility behaviour in the superconducting mixed state is extremely sensitive to irradiation-induced defects, comparable with that of the electrical resistivity. The underlying elementary process, the pinning of flux lines, depends not only on the concentration, but also on the arrangement of the defects, so that new possibilities arise to study this arrangement.

(3) Ta is a Mössbauer effect candidate. The Mössbauer line width and the isomeric shift are very sensitive to plastic deformation and doping with foreign atoms, as was shown by Sauer (Physik-Department, Technische Hochschule München). One can highly recommend such measurements to study defect properties.

# VACANCIES AND INTERSTITIALS IN HEXAGONAL CLOSE-PACKED METALS

D. SCHUMACHER *

*Département de Métallurgie, Centre d'Etudes Nucléaires, Grenoble*

## 1. Introduction

In a recent review of electron radiation damage in solids, Corbett [1] has expressed that there are two instances when a particular field of study is easy to review: firstly, when the field is very young, and secondly, when it is old and moribund. Attempting to review point defect phenomena in hexagonal close-packed metals (see table 1) falls clearly into the *first* category. For none of these metals a complete set of experimental investigations is yet available, which would have to include quenching, cold work, irradiation and thermal equilibrium techniques, such as one has got used to for many of the fcc metals.

Table 1
Hcp metals [2]

| Metal | $c/a$ | Melting point (°K) | Debye temperature (°K) | Transformation temperature (°K) |
|---|---|---|---|---|
| Cadmium | 1.886 | 594 | 188 | – |
| Zinc | 1.856 | 693 | 310 | – |
| Magnesium | 1.622 | 923 | 400 | – |
| Beryllium | 1.568 | 1556 | 1160 | – |
| Gadolinium | 1.59 | 1585 | 320 | – |
| Cobalt | 1.623 | 1763 | 445 | 690 (fcc) |
| Titanium | 1.59 | 2085 | 420 | 1157 (bcc) |
| Zirconium | 1.59 | 2125 | 310 | 1135 (bcc) |
| Rhenium | 1.62 | 3420 | 430 | – |

* Present address: Dornier System GmbH, Friedrichshafen, Germany.

The present review is thus primarily a collection of studies in literature which are directly concerned with point defects in hcp metals or which at least seem to provide some information on them. They will be grouped according to the technique employed. In view of the purpose of this article we shall also mention experiments which *failed* to show particular effects expected; in some cases they may be equally informative as successful experiments. Where possible, we shall try to arrive at a more general picture of the observed phenomena. It will be seen that in many cases our advanced knowledge on point defect phenomena in fcc metals will be a useful guide.

While it would be by far too optimistic to expect a general understanding of point defect phenomena in hcp metals at this stage or a complete list of point defect properties, it is hoped that the present review will nevertheless serve as a basis for discussion and will thus stimulate further research in this field.

## 2. Thermal equilibrium studies

### 2.1. Self-diffusion

#### 2.1.1. Atomistic theory [3]

The atomistic description of self-diffusion in hcp metals must account for the anisotropy of the crystal, which leads in general to different jump frequencies in the directions parallel and perpendicular, respectively, to the basal plane.

A vacancy in a hcp lattice may reach by one jump six neighbours in the basal plane (jump frequency $\Gamma_1$) and six neighbours outside the basal plane (jump frequency $\Gamma_2$). We may expect $\Gamma_1 = \Gamma_2$ at best for the ideal hcp structure ($c/a = \sqrt{8/3}$). Since

$$D_x = \frac{1}{2} \sum_{1}^{n} \Gamma_i \, \Delta x^2 , \tag{1}$$

the diffusion coefficient in the basal plane ($D_x = D_y$) is given by

$$D_\perp \equiv D_x = \frac{1}{2} \left[ 2\Gamma_1 a^2 + 4\Gamma_1 \frac{a^2}{4} + 4\Gamma_2 \frac{a^2}{4} \right] = \frac{a^2}{2} (3\Gamma_1 + \Gamma_2) \tag{2}$$

(or $2\Gamma a^2$ for the ideal case $\Gamma_1 = \Gamma_2$), where $a$ is the lattice constant in the basal plane. The diffusion coefficient in $c$-direction follows by the same argument from (1) as

$$D_\parallel \equiv D_z = \frac{1}{2} 6\Gamma_2 \frac{c^2}{4} = \frac{3}{4} \Gamma_2 c^2 \tag{3}$$

(ideal structure: $D_z = 2\Gamma a^2$).

The general diffusion coefficient reads

$$D(\theta) = D_\parallel \cos^2\theta + D_\perp \sin^2\theta ,$$

where $\theta$ is the angle between the diffusion direction and the hexagonal axis.

If we take into account correlation factors $f_{ij}$ between individual jumps, the diffusion coefficients perpendicular $(D_\perp)$ and parallel $(D_\parallel)$ to the c-axis read

$$D_\perp = \tfrac{1}{2}a^2(3f_{1x}\Gamma_1 + f_{2x}\Gamma_2) ,$$

$$D_\parallel = \tfrac{3}{4}c^2 f_{2z}\Gamma_2 ,$$

(4)

respectively. The degree of diffusion anisotropy is consequently given by

$$\left(\frac{c}{a}\right)^2 \frac{D_\perp}{D_\parallel} = \frac{2}{3}\,\frac{3f_{1x}\Gamma_1/\Gamma_2 + f_{2x}}{f_{2z}} .$$

(5)

It was shown by Mullen [4] that (5) does not differ much from the case where correlation effects are neglected, i.e.

$$\left(\frac{c}{a}\right)^2 \frac{D_\perp}{D_\parallel} = 2\Gamma_1/\Gamma_2 + \tfrac{2}{3} .$$

(6)

Thus, if the ratio of $D_\perp$ and $D_\parallel$ is known from experiment, one can determine the ratio of the jump frequencies in the basal plane and in direction outside the basal plane. It is emphasized that according to eq. (6) equal diffusion coefficients $D_\perp$ and $D_\parallel$ do not necessarily indicate equality of the jump frequencies (and vice versa).

The correlation factors for single vacancy migration in hcp metals (with ideal $c/a$) were determined by Compaan and Haven [5]. The numerical values read

$$f_x = f_y = 0.78121 , \qquad f_z = 0.78146 .$$

(7)

The mechanism of self-diffusion and correlation effects were recently studied by Batra [6] and by Peterson and Rothman [7], employing isotope effect measurements on zinc single crystals. These experiments confirmed the *vacancy* mechanism of self-diffusion.

2.1.2. Experimental values and empirical relations

Numerical values for the pre-exponential factor $D_o$ and the activation energy $Q$ from self-diffusion experiments in hcp metals, as compiled in ref. [3], are listed in table 2. The data indicate that — except for cadmium at high temperatures — the diffusion is fastest in the direction of the most distant near neighbour, i.e.

$$\frac{D_\perp}{D_\parallel} > 1 \quad \text{for} \quad \frac{c}{a} < \sqrt{\tfrac{8}{3}} \quad \text{and} \quad < 1 \quad \text{for} \quad \frac{c}{a} > \sqrt{\tfrac{8}{3}} .$$

Table 2
Self-diffusion in hcp metals
(P polycrystal, S single crystal, $\perp$ perpendicular to $c$-axis, $\parallel$ parallel to $c$-axis)

| Metal | Crystal | $T$-range (°C) | $D_0$ (cm$^2$/sec) | $Q$ (eV) | Reference |
|-------|---------|----------------|---------------------|----------|-----------|
| Cd | S | 110–315 | $\perp$ 0.10 | 0.82 | } Wajda [8] |
|    |   |         | $\parallel$ 0.05 | 0.78 | |
|    | S | 200–280 | 0.14 | 0.85 | Mahmoud [9] |
|    | Foil | 20–250 | 0.05 | 0.76 | Masuda [10] |
|    | S, P | 180–305 | $\parallel$ 0.68 | 0.89 | Schrödter [11,12] |
|    | P | 200–280 | 0.08 | 0.81 | Apel [13] |
| Zn | S | 340–410 | $\perp$ 93 | 1.34 | } Miller [14] |
|    |   |         | $\parallel$ $4.6 \times 10^{-2}$ | 0.88 | |
|    | S | 300–419 | $\perp$ 1.3 | 1.09 | } Huntington [15] |
|    |   |         | $\parallel$ 0.1 | 0.94 | |
|    | S | 240–410 | $\perp$ 0.58 | 1.05 | } Shirn [16] |
|    |   |         | $\parallel$ 0.13 | 0.94 | |
|    | S | – | $\perp$ 1.6 | 1.12 | |
|    |   |   | $\parallel$ $2.15 \times 10^{-2}$ | 0.84 | Lin [17] |
|    | P | – | 0.42 | 1.03 | |
|    | S | 200–415 | $\perp$ 0.39 | 1.07 | |
|    |   |         | $\parallel$ 0.08 | 0.95 | |
|    | P | 200–415 | 0.19 (sect.) | 0.98 | Jaumot [18] |
|    |   |         | 0.11 (abs.) | 1.01 | |
|    | S | 267–367 | $\perp$ 2.79 | 1.15 | } Naskidashvili [19] |
|    |   |         | $\parallel$ $1.33 \times 10^{-2}$ | 0.82 | |
|    | P | 325–405 | $3.1 \times 10^{-2}$ | 0.88 | Hilliard [20] |
|    | S | 289–418 | $\perp$ $0.18 \pm 0.01$ | 1.00 | } Peterson [7] |
|    |   |         | $\parallel$ $0.18 \pm 0.01$ | 0.95 | |
| Mg | S | 468–635 | $\perp$ 1.5 | 1.4 | } Shewmon [21] |
|    |   |         | $\parallel$ 1.0 | 1.39 | |
|    | P | 468–551 | 1.0 | 1.38 | Shewmon [22] |
| Be | S | 553–1024 | $\perp$ 0.18 | 1.66 | Lee [23] |
|    | S | 560–1048 | $\perp$ 0.52 | 1.62 | } Dupouy [24] |
|    |   |          | $\parallel$ 0.62 | 1.7 | |
| Co (fcc) | P | 1015–1260 | 0.032 | 2.67 | Ruder [25] |
|    | P | 1050–1250 | 0.37 | 2.89 | Nix [26] |
|    | P | 1000–1300 | 0.2 | 2.67 | Gruzin [27] |
|    | P | 1104–1406 | 0.83 | 2.92 | Mead [28] |
|    | P | 772–1048 | 0.50 | 2.82 | Hirano [29] |
|    |   | 1192–1297 | 0.17 | 2.68 | |
|    | P | 1047–1311 | 1.66 | 2.96 | Hässner [30] |
| $\alpha$-Ti | P | 690–850 | $6.4 \times 10^{-8}$ | 1.26 | Libanati [31] |
| $\alpha$-Zr |   | 300–700 | $5 \times 10^{-8}$ | 0.95 | Gruzin [32] |
|    |   | 630–827 | $5.9 \times 10^{-2}$ | 2.24 | Lyashenko [33] |
|    |   | 700–800 | $10^{-7}$ | 0.95 | Borisow [34] |

It should be noted that in several cases a slight curvature of individual Arrhenius plots of the self-diffusion coefficients cannot be excluded, although the authors described their data by straight lines. Thus, similarly as in fcc metals, future self-diffusion studies on hcp metals should in principle account for possible temperature dependences of the activation parameters. In the case of fcc metals, this kind of careful analysis of self-diffusion data has turned out to be a powerful technique for deducing vacancy parameters (see ref. [35] for more details). This technique might be particularly useful in the case of hcp metals, since here quenching experiments are so far more difficult than for fcc metals (see below).

Empirical relations for the activation energy of self-diffusion in metals have been proposed by v. Liempt [36] and by Nachtrieb and Handler [37]. Taking into account also more recent self-diffusion data [3], these relations read

$$Q = 35\, T_M \qquad [36] \tag{8}$$

and

$$Q = 15.2\, L_M \qquad [37]\,,$$

where $T_M$ is the absolute melting temperature and $L_M$ is the latent heat of melting. The ratio of the numerical coefficients in (8) and (9) amounts to 2.3 cal/degree and corresponds to the melting entropy $L_M/T_M$ which is equal to this value for the majority of the metals [38]. The relations (8) and (9) hold remarkably well also for hcp metals. Other empirical and semi-empirical approaches were proposed by Sherby and Sinnad [39], Gibbs [40] and by Feisel and Armstrong [41].

## 2.2. Thermodiffusion and electrotransport [3]

Only few experiments have been reported for the diffusion phenomena in a temperature gradient. As in pure metals of other structures and in alloys, the experimental phenomena are not yet satisfactorily understood. It is now generally agreed upon that it is not justified to identify a priori the heat of transport — as deduced from thermodiffusion experiments — with the defect migration energy. It was shown by Lidiard [42] that the atomistic models proposed so far do not permit to calculate correctly the energy transport associated with the transport of atoms and thus the heat of transport. The difficulties are due to the fact that it is not possible to assign a physically meaningful definition of temperature to atomistic regions in the crystal.

More successful approaches appear to be those taking into account the forces exerted on the point defects by the heat carriers (electrons, electron holes, or phonons) in the thermal gradient and the interaction of electrons and point defects (see e.g. refs. [43,44,33]). It is nevertheless too early to draw quantitative conclusions as to a correlation of the thermal diffusion phenomena with individual point defect properties (see ref. [45] for details).

An earlier study of the thermodiffusion in *zinc* by Shewmon [46] had not shown any marker movement and yielded for the difference of the heat of transport

$Q^*$ and the single vacancy formation energy $E_{1V}^F$, $Q^* - E_{1V}^F \sim 0$. Later experiments by Swalin et al. [47] *did* show the occurrence of thermodiffusion. In the latter experiments the crystals were placed in a thermal gradient of 50 °C/cm at a mean temperature of 385°C. The quantity $Q^* - E_{1V}^F$ was found to be $-0.1 \pm 0.03$ eV. In other thermodiffusion work on zinc, Archbold and McCormick [48] found marker motion to the high temperature side and obtained $Q^* - E_{1V}^F \sim 0.15$ eV.

Wever and coworkers studied thermodiffusion (and electro transport) in the high temperature phases of titanium and zirconium [49,50]. Markers moved to the hot side in β-Ti and to the cold side in β-Zr.

Similar as in the case of thermodiffusion, only a few studies have been performed on the phenomena of mass diffusion in *electric fields*. Again the theory of electromigration and/or the experimental precision do not permit as yet a quantitative comparison with defect properties (see ref. [45]).

Kuzmenko [51] has studied electrotransport in *cadmium* at 250°C and in *zinc* at 350°C. He found for the effective valency $Z^*$ values of $-5$ and $-4$, respectively, i.e. markers moved towards the cathode and atoms to the anode. Similar results were obtained by Thernqvist [52] on zinc, but the effective valence was found to be $-3$ at $0.95T_M$. Routbort [53] studied in zinc the correlation of Hall constants and effective charges.

Ho [54] studied marker motion in *cobalt* under the influence of a direct current at temperatures from 1250–1360°C. The cobalt ions migrated to the cathode with an effective charge of $+1.6$. He also observed a Soret effect due to the presence of a thermal gradient in the electromigration experiment. The cobalt ions moved down the temperature gradient. Campbell [55] observed electrotransport in *zirconium* and found a small value of $Z^*/f = +0.3$ ($f = $ correlation factor) which was almost constant.

### 2.3. *Other thermal equilibrium techniques*

The numerical results of several experiments employing other thermal equilibrium techniques are compiled in table 3.

Gertsriken and Slyusar [56] determined the electrical resistance and the thermal expansion of 99.98% pure *zinc* in a wide temperature range (0–400°C). At temperatures near the melting point, deviations from linearity indicated the presence of thermal lattice defects. An analysis of the data in terms of vacancies according to

$$R(T) = A + BT + CT^2 + D \exp(-E^F/kT) \tag{10}$$

(where $A$, $B$, $C$, and $D$ are constants) yielded the following apparent vacancy parameters: $E_{1V}^F = 0.31$ eV (resistivity measurement) and $E_{1V}^F = 0.44$ eV (length measurement). Using the latter value for $E_{1V}^F$, the concentration of defects at the melting point is $3.3 \times 10^{-3}$ and the pre-exponential factor $\exp S_{1V}^F/k$ amounts to 5.18, i.e. $S_{1V}^F = 1.65\,k$. The electrical resistivity $\rho_V$ of vacancies in zinc is estimated to amount to $5.52 \times 10^{-6}$ Ωcm/at% vacancies. Taking these values for $E_{1V}^F$ and the self-diffusion

Table 3
Information on vacancies from other equilibrium techniques

| Metal | Technique | $E_{1V}^F$ (eV) | $C(T_M)$ | Reference |
|-------|-----------|-----------------|----------|-----------|
| Cd | $\rho(T)$ | 0.38 | 0.24 | Gertsriken [56] |
|  | $\rho(T)$ | 0.36–0.39 | $3 \times 10^{-3}$ | Hillairet [57] |
|  | $l(T)$ | 0.42 | 0.24 | Gertsriken [56] |
|  | $(\frac{\Delta l}{l} - \frac{\Delta a}{a})$ | $0.44 \pm 0.04$ | $6.2 \times 10^{-4}$ | Feder [58] |
| Zn | $\rho(T)$ | 0.31 $\Big\}$ | 0.33 | Gertsriken [56] |
|  | $l(T)$ | 0.44 |  |  |
| Mg | $\rho(T)$ | 0.81 | $4.5 \times 10^{-4}$ | Mairy [59] |
| Ti | $c_p(T)$ | 1.55 | $1.7 \times 10^{-2}$ | Shestopal [60] |
| Zr | $c_p(T)$ | 1.75 | $7 \times 10^{-3}$ | Kanel [61] |

Explanation:

$\rho$ = electrical resistivity
$l$ = length
$a$ = lattice parameter
$c_p$ = specific heat
$E_{1V}^F$ = formation energy of single vacancy
$C(T_M)$ = vacancy concentration at the melting point as given in the references

data of Shirn et al. [16], the migration energy of vacancies in zinc is expected to amount to about 0.6 eV [62] (see, however, below).

A similar analysis of experiments on *cadmium* [56] yielded $E_{1V}^F$ = 0.38–0.42 eV, $S_{1V}^F$ = 2.1 $k$ and $\rho_V$ = 3.67 × 10⁻⁶ $\Omega$cm/at% vacancies. Hillairet [57] found from electrical resistivity measurements $E_{1V}^F$ = 0.36–0.39 eV and $C(T_M)$ = 3 × 10⁻³. The latter authors discuss various extrapolation laws in detail.

High temperature electrical resistivity measurements on *magnesium* showed also faster than ideal increases of $\rho$ near the melting point [59]. In this case, the difference between the measured electrical resistivity and the extrapolated resistivity of a defect free crystal could be described in terms of equilibrium lattice defects when a *linear* extrapolation was chosen. The increment could then be described by (fig. 1)

$$\Delta\rho = 7.6 \times 10^{-3} \exp(-0.81 \text{ eV}/kT) \quad [\Omega\text{cm}]. \tag{11}$$

This formation energy is by 0.08 eV lower than that reported for quenching experiments [63] (see below).

Kanel [41] employed the temperature dependence of the heat capacity to detect in *zirconium* the presence of vacancies at elevated temperatures. The expression

$$C_V = 100 \exp(-1.75 \text{ eV}/kT) \tag{12}$$

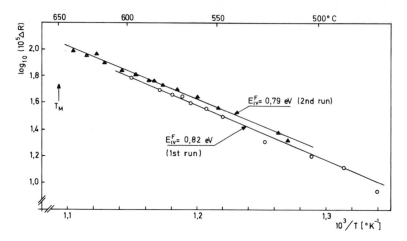

Fig. 1. Contribution of thermal vacancies to the electrical resistivity of magnesium at temperatures near the melting point. $E^F_{1V}$ = energy of formation of vacancies [59].

is given for the total vacancy concentration. The pre-exponential factor corresponds to a formation entropy $S^F_{1V}$ = 4.6 $k$. Similar experiments by Shestopal on *titanium* led to the expression

$$C_V = 170 \exp(-1.55 \text{ eV}/kT) \tag{13}$$

which corresponds to $S^F_{1V}$ = 5.1 $k$ and $E^F_{1V}$ = 1.55 ± 0.15 eV [60].

Small additions of cadmium and silver to zinc were found to lower the apparent formation energy of vacancies with respect to the pure metal by several hundredths of an eV. They led to an increase of the vacancy concentration and to an apparent decrease of the electrical resistivity of vacancies [56].

The preceding results should be seen in the light of similar experiments in fcc metals. For the latter, it is well known that the energies of formation as derived from $\rho(T)$ curves or $l(T)$ curves are usually lower than the "true" values obtained from quenching experiments, self-diffusion or Simmons-and-Balluffi-type equilibrium studies [64]. The difficulties are essentially due to the uncertainties connected with the extrapolation procedure for the property change of the ideal crystal. A low formation energy leads to an overestimate of the equilibrium vacancy concentration and an underestimate of the electrical resistivity of vacancies. The present conference has demonstrated that the degree of modification of physical properties by the presence of point defects in high temperature thermal equilibrium is still a matter of controversy, ranging from the view that the phenomena are associated with anharmonic vibrations [65] to the view that they are true vacancy effects [66].

The only direct determination of the equilibrium concentration of vacancies in hcp metals by the dilatometric/X-ray technique has so far been performed on *cad-*

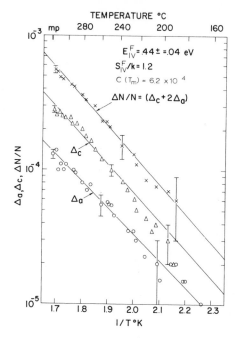

Fig. 2. $1/T$ plot of the change in lattice parameter and length, and of the total defect population $\Delta N/N$ in cadmium [58].

*mium* [58]. These experiments have demonstrated that the temperature dependence of $\Delta l$ (length) and $\Delta a$ (lattice parameter) are in agreement with the concept of thermal vacancies. According to these measurements, the equilibrium concentration at the melting point amounts to

$$C_V(T_M) \equiv \frac{\Delta N}{N} = 2 \left[ \frac{\Delta l_a}{l_a} - \frac{\Delta a}{a} \right] + \left[ \frac{\Delta l_c}{l_c} - \frac{\Delta c}{c} \right] = 6.2 \times 10^{-4} . \qquad (14)$$

$E_{1V}^F = 0.44$ eV, which is about half the activation energy of self-diffusion (see table 2), and $S_{1V}^F = 1.2\,k$ (fig. 2). The latter value is seen to be somewhat smaller than that obtained from the cruder extrapolation experiments in refs. [56] and [57].

Similar dilatometric/X-ray measurements on *magnesium* are in progress at the Ecole des Mines at Nancy, France.

Dilatation measurements on hcp metals such as cadmium are difficult because of the anisotropy of the thermal expansion, which may include even negative values of the expansion coefficient. For a recent redetermination of the low temperature thermal expansion of cadmium see ref. [67]. Thermal expansion data for zirconium between 4.2 and 1130°K were reported by Goldak et al. [68].

## 3. Quenching experiments

Quenching experiments on hcp metals are for several reasons generally more complicated than on the majority of the fcc metals. Experimental difficulties may arise from tendencies of hydride formation (Zr, Re, Ti), from complications due to phase transformations (Co) or from high vacancy mobilities at room temperature (Cd, Zn, Mg). The lack of unambiguous information on vacancy type defects is particularly serious in the interpretation of the recovery phenomena, as will be seen in the following sections. In this section we will give a survey of quenching experiments on hcp metals (irrespective of whether they were "successful" or not) and of what can be deduced from them.

### 3.1. Cadmium

Zen et al. [69] have quenched zone-refined cadmium wires from various temperatures $T_Q$ into a bath at $-5°C$ and measured increase and recovery of the specimen length. Similarly as in the work of Takamura on fcc metals [70], the data were sensitive to the specimen diameter. Upon extrapolation to zero diameter and to infinite quenching rate, the total vacancy concentration could be described as

$$C_V = \frac{\Delta V}{\alpha V} = \frac{A_o}{\alpha} \exp(-E_{1V}^F/kT_Q) \tag{15}$$

(where $\alpha$ is the volume relaxation of a vacancy) with $A_o = 0.026$ and $E_{1V}^F = 0.31$ eV. The latter value is considerably lower than those obtained by the equilibrium techniques (see section 2.3). The reason for this discrepancy is presumably the fact that a quenching bath temperature of $-5°C$ is too high to freeze in isolated vacancies, since the difference of the activation energies for self-diffusion (0.80 eV) (see table 2) and that for vacancy formation (0.44 eV [58]) indicate a migration energy of 0.36 eV. The quench-induced change in length is therefore more likely due to vacancy agglomerates than to individual vacancies. In fact, considerable recovery of the length change occurs only at temperatures above 440°K, i.e. in a temperature range where self-diffusion becomes appreciable.

Indirect evidence for a high vacancy mobility at room temperature is provided by the experiments of Savitskiy et al. [71] who observed on 99.95% Cd the formation of pores and hollows at grain boundaries after repeatedly quenching from 300°C into water. The microhardness of the specimens increased with the number of quenches, approaching a saturation value after approximately 15 consecutive quenches. The quench-hardening recovers at 300°C. Similarly the density of the specimens decreased on repeated quenching. These data indicate that in these experiments the precipitation of vacancies is essentially completed in the as-quenched state.

The authors deduce from these measurements a vacancy concentration of $1.5 \times 10^{-3}$ at the melting point and an apparent formation energy of $0.37 \pm 0.03$ eV for individual quenches. Naturally the physical meaning of these values is difficult to access, particularly in view of the fact that the authors were unable to detect similar effects in *zone-refined* (99.998%) Cd. The formation of pores in industrial grade Cd and their absence in the zone-refined material are taken to indicate that in the thermal cycling the nucleation of pores is the result of a combined migration of vacancies and impurities to the grain boundaries [72].

Sharp et al. [73] quenched cadmium from 300°C directly to 90°K. The recovery spectrum of the electrical resistivity was found to be similar to that of the cold-worked samples (see below), i.e., the same two recovery stages were observed. This was taken to indicate that lattice defects were introduced during the quench by plastic deformation caused by anisotropic thermal contraction. This conclusion should be considered with caution, since it is well known that in fcc metals, for example, a quenched specimen recovers generally also in two stages (except for very low quenching temperatures), the first one being associated with the migration of individual vacancy type defects (single vacancies, divacancies, etc.) and the second one being due to the annihilation of vacancy precipitates. The above mentioned experiments of Zen et al. [69] and Savitsky et al. [71,72] indicate that vacancy clustering may indeed be appreciable in cadmium quenched from near the melting point.

Preliminary quenching experiments by Sprusil et al. [74] seem to confirm these general conclusions. They quenched cadmium from 543°K (silicon oil bath) into liquid nitrogen and measured resistivity increases of $(1.14-1.39) \times 10^{-8}$ $\Omega$cm, corresponding to vacancy concentrations of several $10^{-5}$. Isochronal annealing exhibit-

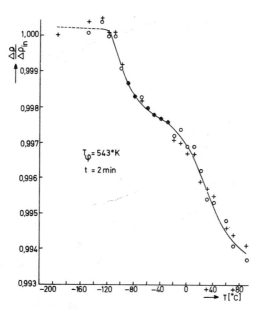

Fig. 3. Isochronal recovery of cadmium quenched from 543°K to 77°K. $\Delta t = 2$ min [74].

ed two recovery stages centered near 160°K and 300°K, respectively (fig. 3). Furthermore, they observed approximately 1st order annealing kinetics at 177°K and 195°K, and they deduced an activation energy of 0.23 ± 0.03 eV for the first stage. These authors suppose that in the first stage a simple vacancy type defect is migrating, while the second stage is felt to be associated with vacancy clusters. The value of 0.23 eV appears to be somewhat low to be associated with $E_{1V}^{M}$, when compared with the self-diffusion and $E_{1V}^{F}$-data in tables 2 and 3, respectively. On the other hand, $T_Q = 574°K$ is close to the melting point, so that multiple vacancies presumably have to be accounted for in the diffusion kinetics.

It appears that — except for the inconveniences of having to quench down to rather low temperatures — cadmium is a very suitable metal for quenching effects in hcp metals. Last but not least it is commercially available at very high purity, which is a problem for several other hcp metals.

### 3.2. Zinc

Rapid cooling from elevated temperatures leads to a considerable increase of the yield stress of zinc single crystals as was investigated quantitatively by Fegredo [75]. Quenching from near the melting point into water at 2°C increased the yield stress (measured at 77°K) by almost an order of magnitude. This increase recovered essentially in one stage centered at room temperature. Since single or other small multiple vacancies are not considered to cause considerable hardening, it is justified to assume that the frozen-in vacancies had agglomerated during the quench and/or during the pretest period. The agglomeration is favoured by the relatively low quenching rates obtainable with Fegredo's apparatus. The data indicate that the recovery stage at room temperature is likely to be due to the annihilation of vacancy agglomerates, and that single vacancies must be mobile below room temperature.

Similar results were obtained earlier also by Li et al. [76] who have shown that the room temperature flow stress of zinc crystals cooled rapidly from 400°C is greater by 20% than that of slowly cooled crystals. Okada and Koda [77] observed a quenching rate sensitivity of the twinning in zinc single crystals.

### 3.3. Magnesium

A rather detailed quenching study has been performed on magnesium by Beevers [63]. The specimens were allowed to fall freely from a vertical furnace (atmosphere of dry argon) into a bath of methyl alcohol at −80°C. A two hour anneal at 240°C recovered the quench-induced electrical resistivity completely in one stage centred at 180°C. The resistivity difference between the as-quenched state and the fully annealed state followed the relation

$$\Delta\rho = 3.8 \times 10^{-3} \exp\left[-0.89 \text{ eV}/kT\right] \quad [\Omega\text{cm}] \tag{16}$$

for quenching temperatures between 400 and 600°C. Beevers interpreted this activation energy in terms of the single vacancy formation energy $E_{1V}^{F} = 0.89$ eV.

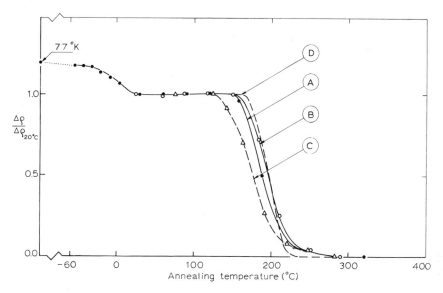

Fig. 4. Isochronal recovery of the electrical resistivity of quenched magnesium ($\Delta t$ = 15 min) [78].
A. zone-refined Mg – 498°C/77°K
B. zone-refined Mg – 520°C/20°C
C. 99.95% Mg       – 518°C/20°C
D. 99.97% Mg       – 516°C/–80°C.

This conclusion is, however, in conflict with Beevers' annealing experiments. The recovery of the electrical resistivity occurs above 140°C (fig. 5) with an activation energy of 1.54 ± 0.17 eV which is somewhat larger than that of self-diffusion [21,22]. We must conclude that Beever's specimens contained in the as-quenched state vacancy agglomerates rather than isolated vacancies. Hence either the temperature of the quenching bath was too high or the quenching rate was too low to freeze-in single vacancies in these experiments. This is why the above mentioned activation energy of 0.89 eV is likely to be associated with vacancy agglomerates rather than with single vacancies, although the order of magnitude appears reasonable.

Preliminary experiments in this laboratory [78] have shown that the recovery spectrum of quenched magnesium might be more complex than would be expected from Beever's results (see fig. 4). Two qualities of magnesium, namely Mg bisublimé (99.9%, $R_{300°K}/R_{20°K}$ = 120) and zone-refined magnesium (99.999%, $R_{300°K}/R_{20°K}$ = 660) were quenched either from an argon atmosphere into an oil bath at room temperature or directly to liquid nitrogen temperature in a metallic enclosure filled with pure helium gas and immerged in the refrigerant.

The recovery spectrum after quenching depends sensitively on the impurity content: After quenching to 77°K, the impure magnesium did not show any recovery between 77°K and room temperature. The zone-refined magnesium exhibits, however, a well-defined recovery stage between –50°C and +20°C (fig. 4). Above room temperature, the recovery for quenches to 77°K does not differ from that for quenches to room temperature. The resistivity increment of the zone-refined material recovers essentially in *one* stage situated near 190°C while *two* stages occur in the impure magnesium near 170 and 360°C. The latter stage appears to be due to the precipitation of iron.

The two recovery stages in the pure magnesium are analogous to the two-stage recovery spectrum normally observed in metals quenched from intermediate or elevated quenching temperatures. It must be emphasized, however, that in the case of magnesium the low temperature stage amounts to less than 20% of the total quench-induced resistivity increment, while in the fcc metals it amounts generally to more than 80%. In the case of quenched cadmium [74], the ratio of the two stages was seen to be roughly 40% : 60% (fig. 3).

The low temperature stage is felt to be associated with the migration of a simple vacancy type defect, presumably the monovacancy. The temperature range of the stage and the annealing kinetics are consistent with an activation energy $E_{1V}^M = 0.5-0.6$ eV as would be expected from self-diffusion data (table 2) and $E_{1V}^F$ measurements (table 3 and [63]). In some cases, however, this stage exhibited a complex nature.

With respect to the predominant second recovery stage, transmission electron microscope studies demonstrate clearly the correlation of the annealing of vacancy precipitates and electrical resistivity [78]. Again the defect nature and distribution depends strongly on the purity. The impure magnesium shows faulted loops (1000 Å – 1 $\mu$) in the basal plane and with a Burgers vector of the type $\frac{1}{6}$ [20$\bar{2}$3]. The high purity material shows an essentially homogeneous distribution of *perfect* loops in prismatic planes of second type (11$\bar{2}$0) and perpendicular to their Burgers vector $\frac{1}{2}$ [11$\bar{2}$0]. The latter loops are not present in specimens quenched to 77°K and thinned at −50°C, i.e., they are formed during the low temperature annealing stage.

Evidence for appreciable vacancy agglomeration in quenched magnesium was obtained earlier by Lally and Partridge [79] by transmission electron microscopy. Thin sheets were quenched using a vertical furnace with a flow of dry argon gas inside and an oil bath as quenching medium beneath. The micrographs exhibited large dislocation loops on the basal plane and rows of prismatic dislocation loops. The relative importance of the two defect types depend on the atmospheric conditions in the furnace. The minimum quenching temperature for which prismatic punching and vacancy loops are observed, is 500°C. The authors propose a mechanism which associates the production of rows of punched loops with the precipitation of hydrogen in small voids.

An alternative interpretation of the results of Lally and Partridge was suggested by Schwartzkopff [80] who proposed that the shape of the dislocation dipoles depends on the geometric shape of the specimen foil. In this model, the vacancy agglomerates are initially circular and are subsequently, upon further growth, flattened, since the line tension is not strong enough to push the dislocation through the oxide layer on the specimen. Vacancy agglomeration in each one of the prismatic planes is always associated with the formation of an $a$-dislocation loop without stacking fault, the most stable plane of which is the prismatic plane perpendicular to the $a$-dislocation.

In still earlier work, Thomas et al. [81] had failed to find dislocation loops resulting from vacancy condensation after quenching 99.98% pure magnesium foils from 620°C into brine at −15°C. The foils contained usually complex dislocation networks. Aluminium foils, however, quenched identically at the same time, did show loops.

Beevers [82] quenched magnesium foils from 620°C into methyl alcohol at −80°C. After aging for 1 hour at 100°C he observed large dislocation loops (density $< 10^8$ cm$^{-2}$) in the thicker part of the foil. When aged at room temperature, the foils contained some small vacancy platelets with densities again below $10^8$ cm$^{-2}$.

### 3.4. Cobalt

Quenching experiments on cobalt encounter the difficulty that when quenched from above the transformation temperature (415°C), i.e. from the fcc phase, considerable internal stresses may arise when the transformation point is passed. Thus the quench-induced property changes and their subsequent recovery may not be due to a super-saturation of thermal defects only.

In the light of these difficulties, the physical meaning of data deduced from quenching experiments on cobalt [83] is somewhat difficult to assess. The authors quenched cobalt wires of 0.5 mm diameter (metallic impurities $< 0.001$%) by turning off a direct heating current and simultaneously admitting a blast of cold air into the evacuated specimen chamber. The average cooling rate is reported to have been of the order of $10^4$ °C/s. The internal friction $Q^{-1}(0)$ of the as-quenched specimens appeared to be depending on the quenching temperature $T_Q$. While $\Delta Q^{-1}(0)$ could not be determined directly in the as-quenched state, this quantity was inferred from subsequent isothermal decay curves of the internal friction. For a range of $T_Q$ from 560°C to 1060°C, the initial internal friction could be described by

$$\Delta Q^{-1}(0) = A \exp(-E/kT_Q) \qquad (17)$$

with $E = 1.25$ eV. The latter value is ascribed to the formation energy of single vacancies in fcc cobalt, since the authors consider vacancies to be responsible for the internal friction phenomenon.

## 4. Irradiation experiments

### 4.1. Cadmium

Bauer et al. [84] irradiated 99.999% cadmium with 3 MeV electrons at low temperatures. The maximum temperature during irradiation was 8°K. The damage production curve of the electrical resistivity as a function of the flux was linear up to a flux of $7.5 \times 10^{17}$ el/cm$^2$. The damage rate was calculated to be $4.29 \times 10^{-27}$ Ωcm/(el/cm$^2$).

The fractional recovery of electron irradiated cadmium is rather small between

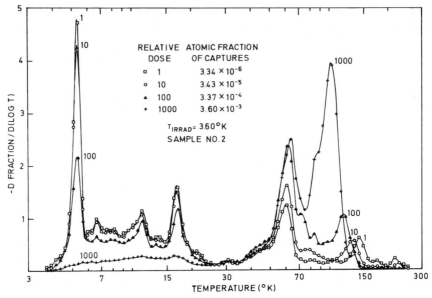

Fig. 5. Isochronal recovery rates of the electrical resistivity of cadmium after four thermal neutron irradiations at 3.6°K [87].

the irradiation temperature and 67°K, similar to the behaviour of electron irradiated gold [84]. It is, however, noteworthy that the recovery of gold exhibits the well known stage I fine structure (at least 8 annealing peaks) [84] while in the case of cadmium similar phenomena could not be detected by the applied procedure.

Pile irradiation experiments with thermal neutrons, as performed in detail by Coltman and coworkers [85–88], are of particular interest for several reasons: 1. The mean recoil energy of $^{133}$Cd from a neutron capture event is 130 eV, i.e., very simple damage in the form of 1 or 2 Frenkel pairs per event should be produced [85]. 2. Transmutation effects may be neglected. 3. It is possible to study radiation damage over a wide range of defect concentrations at a modest thermal neutron flux because of the high capture cross section of cadmium.

A constant damage rate was observed at 3.5°K for all irradiations performed [87]. Recovery studies were performed for 4 different initial defect concentrations (for relative doses of 1:4:34:107) (fig. 5). The peaks at 5.2, 11, 17, and 60°K are due to first order processes, while those occurring above 70°K are not first order. The authors report for increasing dose an almost uniform and increasing suppression of the recovery below 26°K and correspondingly an enhancement of recovery in the higher stages. This effect is not accompanied by a decrease in damage rate which would be expected for irradiation annealing. Complete recovery is achieved at 200°K.

Coltman et al. take the experiments to indicate that production and recovery mechanisms are closely associated with the anisotropic nature of the cadmium lattice. The ideas imply that during irradiation the interstitial member of a sub-threshold pair oriented in the easy direction could be blocked from spontaneous recovery with its vacancy by the presence of a nearby stable defect.

Seeger [89] proposed an annealing model for cadmium, according to which the last stage near 225°K is associated with monovacancy migration and the dose-dependent stage near 100°K corresponds to what is called "stage III" in fcc metals. For the latter stage, single vacancy migration can safely be ruled out on the grounds of the low mean jump number for vacancies at these low temperatures. A tentative assignment of free interstitial migration in this stage is shown to offer a rather natural interpretation for the low temperature recovery behaviour. The strong dose dependence of the stage heights is proposed to be due to two different pair configurations (*a*-pairs and *c*-pairs) with individual production rates and with the possibility of converting from *a* to *c* or vice-versa in the course of the annealing.

In cadmium ion-bombarded at −90°C, Price [90] observed vacancy type dislocation loops in transmission electron microscope studies.

### 4.2. *Zinc*

The energy dependence of damage production by electrons in *zinc* at 7—20°K was determined by Lucasson and Walker in preliminary experiments [91,92]. Considerable experimental difficulties arise apparently from specimen deformations during the thermal cycling between an annealing temperature and the base temperature for resistivity measurement. The electrical resistivity change per electron was found to rise slowly from $7 \times 10^{-28}$ to $2 \times 10^{-27}$ $\Omega$cm/(el/cm$^2$) in the range 1.0 MeV to 1.4 MeV. It increased rapidly for electron energies above 1.4 MeV. The production rate was not proportional to the electron flux; the curves had always a curvature directed towards the flux axis.

In more recent experiments, Maury et al. [93] extended the range of irradiation temperatures down to 4.9°K. At 7.6°K the defect production rate (resistivity over electron flux) was found to be linear. The authors deduce from their data a threshold energy for atomic displacement of 17.5 ± 1.5 eV. At least one other displacement mechanism is felt to begin at ≈ 65 eV and higher, which is interesting in view of the anisotropy of this material.

Isochronal recovery curves of the electrical resistivity of electron irradiated zinc were obtained between 10°K and 150°K [92]. Although the reproducibility was rather poor, the authors observed annealing stages at 14, 22 and 32°K in which 35, 12 and 18%, respectively, of the irradiation-induced resistivity increment recovered. These stages were followed by a continuous recovery between 40°K and 100°K (amounting to 10% of the $\Delta\rho$) while 20% recovered between 100 and 150°K, leaving 5% unrecovered.

The more recent electrical resistivity recovery experiments [93] show large stages near 5°K, 7°K, and 12°K. The first two of these stages seem to depend on the energy of the incident electrons: The first stage decreases with rising energy while the second stage was not seen at 0.8 MeV but seems to grow above 1.0 MeV.

The effect of low temperature *reactor* irradiation on the electrical resistivity of

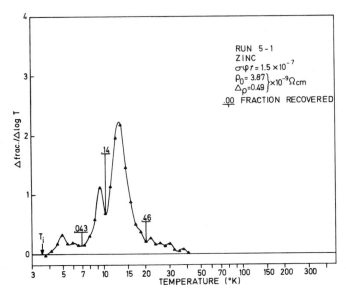

Fig. 6. Isochronal recovery (derivative) of the electrical resistivity of zinc after thermal neutron irradiation at 3.6°K [87].

zinc was first investigated by Blewitt et al. [94]. At 18°K the resistivity increased linearly with the time at a rate of $2.56 \times 10^{-2}$ Ωcm/hour during the first 150 hours. The effect was similar in magnitude as for iron and cobalt but considerably larger than for aluminium, copper and nickel.

A detailed investigation of the annealing kinetics of zinc after *neutron* irradiation at 77°K was performed by Nihoul [95]. He observed at 77°K a rate of resistivity increase of $3 \times 10^{-25}$ Ωcm/n/cm$^2$ which is by a factor 3 larger than the value of Blewitt et al. at 18°K [94]. The discrepancy may be due to an error in the fast flux determination [95]. The recovery spectrum exhibits two distinct stages centered at 105°K (second order kinetics, activation energy 0.21 eV, with a shoulder on the high temperature side) and at 155°K (0.50 eV) followed by a long tail of the recovery curve between 200 and 300°K (see fig. 6). A slight increase of the electrical resistivity was observed upon annealing above 300°K.

Nihoul compares the two major recovery stages with the stages III and IV, respectively, of irradiated copper. This correspondence is suggested by the following facts: 1. Qualitative agreement of the recovery spectrum — on a reduced temperature scale — up to 0.5 $T_M$. 2. Second order annealing kinetics in "stage III" of both metals. 3. "Stage III" is considerably larger than "stage IV" in both metals. In line with the recovery models for copper [96], the author suggests that in neutron irradiated zinc single interstitials are mobile near 105°K ($E_{1I}^M$ = 0.21 eV) and single vacancies near 155°K ($E_{1V}^M$ = 0.50 eV).

Coltman et al. [87] reported a recovery spectrum of thermal neutron damage in zinc, which showed annealing maxima at 5, 9 and 13°K. Above 40°K the recovery was obscured by intergranular cold work during pulse annealing (fig. 6).

Kunz and Holden [97] investigated the effect of neutron irradiation on the mechanical properties of zinc. Room temperature irradiation for one week caused considerable hardening as measured by tensile tests at room temperature. Recovery measurements were not reported. The fact that irradiation hardening does occur at room temperature (where individual point defects are believed to be annihilated) indicates, however, that in the case of zinc neutron irradiation introduces stable defect agglomerates (zones) which anneal at temperatures at which self-diffusion occurs. This hardening effect is in agreement with the fact that in Nihoul's experiments [95] several percent of the irradiation-introduced electrical resistivity increment are not recovered at room temperature.

Haager and Siebinger [98] studied the orientation dependence of the electrical resistivity increase of zinc crystals during α-bombardment. For irradiations of 75 hours, the change in resistivity at 78°K was 0.58% for α = 8° and 0.38% for α = 88°, where α is the angle between crystal axis and hexagonal axis.

### 4.3. Magnesium

Although only a few irradiation studies have been performed on this metal, the resulting data are apparently relatively easy to classify and to understand. After irradiation with low energy *electrons* (0.3–0.4 MeV) magnesium exhibits the following recovery phenomena of the electrical resistivity [99,100]: 1. thermal annealing at 4.2°K, 2. strong recovery stages near 6.8 and 11.4°K corresponding to 40% and 35% recovery, respectively, of the radiation induced resistivity increment $\Delta\rho$, 3. a gradual decrease of $\Delta\rho$ above 15°K. The predominance of the *low* temperature part of the recovery spectrum in these experiments is a natural consequence of the fact that — particularly at these low electron energies — the radiation damage will consist primarily of close pairs (see the experiments on zinc in the previous section). The above-mentioned strong recovery stages are therefore likely to be associated with close-pair recovery. Such an assignment is in agreement with the fact that these two stages are very small in the case of *neutron* irradiated magnesium (see below). If one of the stages were due to long range (interstitial) migration, one would expect such a stage in both electron and neutron irradiated magnesium.

In neutron irradiated magnesium [101], the electrical resistivity damage curve at 4.2°K shows a slight curvature from the very beginning, indicating thermal annealing at this low temperature. The resistivity recovery below 30°K amounts to less than 15% of $\Delta\rho$ only, in contrast to the case of electron irradiation (see above). The predominant recovery events occur above 30°K, with substages emerging at 50°K, 75°K and 140°K. At 340°K the pre-irradiation resistivity value is reattained within very narrow limits (fig. 7). These results are in general agreement with an isochronal recovery curve published earlier by Blewitt et al. [102].

The following additional experimental informations help to understand the recovery phenomena occurring above 30°K:
1. It was noted in section 3.3 that single vacancies are likely to become mobile

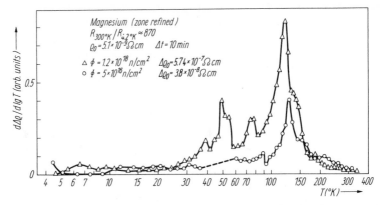

Fig. 7. Isochronal recovery (derivative) of the electrical resistivity of zone-refined magnesium for two different doses of neutron irradiation at 4.2°K. $\rho_0$ pre-irradiation residual resistivity. $\Delta\rho$ irradiation-induced resistivity increment [101].

near 240°K in quenched magnesium [78].

2. Preliminary studies of the annealing kinetics of magnesium neutron irradiated at 77°K yielded for the large 140°K stage an activation energy of 0.40–0.45 eV and second order kinetics in the high-temperature part of the stage [103].

3. Stored energy measurements on neutron irradiated magnesium show essentially the same recovery spectrum as the electrical resistivity [101,103]. In both cases the large 140°K stage shifts to lower temperatures with increasing dose.

4. Internal friction experiments on neutron irradiated magnesium show a pronounced relaxation peak near 150°K which increases with increasing neutron dose, shifts to lower temperatures with decreasing frequency and recovers near the peak temperature. This maximum is associated with a pronounced increase of the modulus defect by several percent [101,104].

5. After irradiation with high energy electrons (3 MeV) at 20°K, electrical resistivity measurements show above 77°K the end of a recovery stage near 90°K, a predominant stage centred near 150°K, and a long tail of the recovery extending up to room temperature [101,103]. We have thus above 77°K a similar recovery behaviour of magnesium after (high energy) electron irradiation and after neutron irradiation.

Although in principle vacancy type defects could be involved in the large 140°K stage, we are inclined to associate the stage primarily with interstitial migration. Single vacancies are rather immobile at this temperature. Furthermore, the above-mentioned internal friction peak and change-in-modulus appear to be easier to understand in terms of interstitial reorientation and migration than in terms of similar processes due to divacancies etc., since the observed mechanical effects seem to be too strong to be associated with individual vacancy type defects. We emphasize also the fact that for this strong dose dependent stage in the high temperature part of the recovery spectrum there seem to be equivalent stages in the recovery spectra of neutron irradiated cadmium (see section 4.1), zinc (section 4.2) and beryllium (section 4.4). Although the question of interstitial or vacancy is not yet decided for the latter metals either, the interstitial model is apparently not too bad to explain the experimental evidence (compare refs. [89,95]) *.

Two models are on hand to explain the *substructure* of the large stage: 1. It is possible that in neutron irradiated magnesium interstitial atoms are annihilated first by migration to vacant lattice sites within the cascade zones and subsequently by a true random walk. This would explain why second order kinetics are observed in the high temperature part of the stage only. Annealing kinetics of this type have been found, for example, in stage III in neutron irradiated aluminium [105]. 2. Alternatively, it is possible that defects other than single interstitials are mobile in addition, e.g., divacancies. It is, however, not clear to what extent divacancies are created by electron irradiation, for which the recovery phenomena are similar.

The available data do not permit as yet any conclusion as to the nature of the recovery stages near 50 and 75°K. They can be considered as "stage II phenomena" if — with reference to fcc metals — the large 140°K stage is considered to correspond to stage III.

There is still some uncertainty as to defect *clusters* in irradiated magnesium. In transmission electron microscope work, Beevers [82] failed to observe clusters or dislocation loops in magnesium irradiated at 80—100°C by $10^{18}$ n/cm$^2$ or by $10^{14}$ fission fragments/cm$^2$. On the other hand, Hillairet [104] observed in neutron irradiated material ($10^{18}$—$10^{19}$ n/cm$^2$) a large number of black spots, the analysis of which is in progress. Clearly, the complete recovery of the electrical resistivity at room temperature would favour the *former* results. Internal friction and modulus measurements, however, seem to be more compatible with the *latter* microscope observation, since they indicate even above room temperature continuing dislocation pinning. Mechanical recovery occurs only above 300°C [104].

## 4.4. Beryllium

The study of point defect phenomena in irradiated beryllium is difficult because of the limited purity of the available material. Furthermore, the majority of irradiation work on beryllium was performed *above* room temperature and was primarily focussed on the formation and precipitation of helium gas bubbles in this metal. Nevertherless, the experimental results of a few low temperature studies (electrical resistivity [102,106—109], stored energy [110,111]) permit to give a rough picture of the point defect phenomena involved.

During neutron irradiation at 4.2°K one observes a slight curvature of the damage curve (electrical resistivity) already at doses of the order of $10^{16}$ n/cm$^2$ [109]. Since thermal recovery was not observed at this low temperature, the saturation effect

* The available experimental data do of course not exclude interstitial migration *below* 4.2°K. In that event, however, one would have difficulties to understand the strong recovery stages just above 4.2°K in the (low energy) electron irradiation experiments of refs. [99,100].

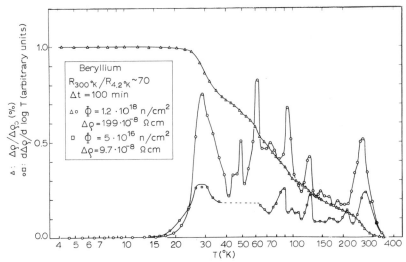

Fig. 8. Isochronal recovery (fractional recovery and derivative) of the electrical resistivity of beryllium for two different doses of neutron irradiation at 4.2°K. $\Delta\rho$ irradiation-induced resistivity increment [109].

must be due to non-thermal recovery. Theoretical considerations [112] and the annealing experiments (see below) suggest that in the light metal beryllium (even more than in aluminium) individual defect cascades are rather extended. It is therefore likely that the saturation effect is due to an overlapping of different cascades which leads to athermal recombination of close pairs.

The recovery spectrum of the electrical resistivity is shown for two neutron doses in fig. 8 [109]. No recovery was detected below 15°K, the recovery spectrum exhibits a rather continuous decrease of the electrical resistivity, with several annealing peaks clearly emerging from a strong background recovery. At 350°K, 99% of the initial resistivity increment are recovered, in agreement with the earlier data of Blewitt et al. [102]. The recovery stage between 20 and 40°K is particularly broad and might correspond in nature to the principal peak observed in other irradiated metals (stage $I_D$ in copper and aluminium) [88,113]. Such assignment would then suggest the onset of free defect migration on the high temperature side of this peak, but this assumption is highly speculative and cannot be checked yet by means of the available data.

The stages at 65°K, 90°K, and 130°K appear to be due to first order processes, and they might correspond to the stage II substructure in neutron irradiated aluminium which shows similar characteristics. However, not even in the case of aluminium is their nature yet well understood. Burger et al. [113] proposed that they might be due to the recombination of close pair configurations which are generated at high collision energies only. On the other hand, it is well known that these substages are very sensitive to the impurity contents [114].

The final stage between 200 and 340°K exhibits similar characteristics as stage III in irradiated aluminium: It is well separated from the above mentioned first order processes. Its relative height with respect to the low temperature fraction of recovery increases with increasing neutron dose, and at the same time its peak temperature shifts to lower temperatures, indicating a recovery process of order > 1. The activation energy in the high temperature part ($\approx$ 0.8 eV [106,108]) corresponds to roughly one half of the activation energy of self-diffusion [24].

The experimental data appear to be best accounted for by assuming that this stage sees the interaction of interstitial and vacancy type defects (leading to mutual annihilation), with one or both of these defects being mobile. This again corresponds to a large extent to the interpretational situation in aluminium [115]. It is, however, uncertain whether an interstitial atom and a vacancy could have approximately equal mobilities in hcp structures.

The recovery of the electrical resistivity after electron irradiation at 20°K [106, 108] follows approximately that of neutron irradiated beryllium, but the final recovery stage is smaller and less clearly resolved. Walters et al. [116] observed prismatic loops in beryllium irradiated to $2 \times 10^{20}$ n/cm$^2$ at 350°C. It is clear that under these experimental conditions the defect phenomena are somewhat different from the above mentioned experiments at low doses and at low temperatures.

### 4.5. Gadolinium

A detailed recovery study of gadolinium after electron and after neutron irradiation was presented at this conference [117]. This metal is of considerable interest since magnetic after-effect phenomena offer additional experimental evidence. The interpretation of the magnetic data is, however, somewhat difficult since the directions of easy magnetisation are tilted from the c-axis by an angle $\theta$ which is temperature dependent ($\approx$ 30° at 100°K) [118].

Fig. 9 shows the recovery of the electrical resistivity of gadolinium after electron irradiation at 20°K to three different fluxes. The high temperature shoulder (near 150°K) of the principal peak shifts to lower temperatures with increasing dose and is therefore called $I_E$ (in analogy to other metals). The neutron irradiated samples behave similarly as the electron irradiated ones.

Based on these resistivity data, the authors assign interstitial migration to this shoulder. They run, however, into the dilemma that — other than in nickel — they did *not* find a magnetic after-effect associated with this stage. This result (which is the same in cobalt — see below) is felt to suggest that the magnetic perturbation of a free interstitial is oriented along the axis, so that reorientation between two successive jumps is not detectable.

Neither did the authors find a magnetic afrer-effect in one of the stages below $I_E$, for example in $I_D$ where cobalt *does* show a strong effect (see below). Cope et al. believe that the reason for this discrepancy might be the different mobilities of interstitials in a- and c-directions which depend on the c/a ratio. According to this view, close pair magnetic after-effect do not occur in gadolinium because the inter-

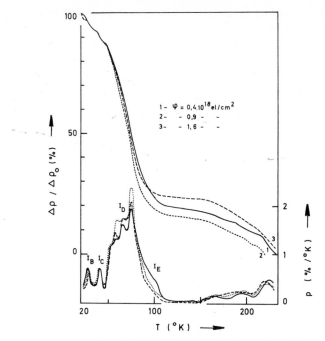

Fig. 9. Isochronal recovery of the electrical resistivity of 3 electron irradiation gadolinium samples [117].

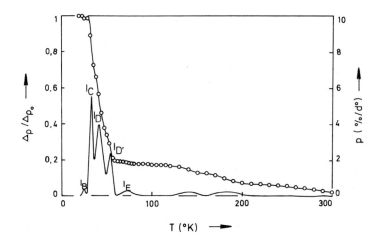

Fig. 10. Isochronal recovery of the electrical resistivity of electron irradiated cobalt [117].

stitial migration is such that it cannot perform jumps between equivalent crystallographic positions.

## 4.6. Cobalt

*Electron* irradiation experiments (1.4 MeV) on cobalt at 20°K [117,119] have shown that the electrical resistivity increase is linear in the applied dose range (up to $8.2 \times 10^{17}$ el/cm$^2$). The rate of resistivity increase is larger than that observed for nickel under the same conditions. The authors suggest a value of 5.5 $\Omega$cm for the electrical resistivity of 1% Frenkel pairs (deduced from a comparison with analogous experiments on nickel [91].

In annealing experiments, they observed essentially two recovery ranges (fig. 10). Stage I ($< 60°$K) amounts to 80% recovery of the initial increment $\Delta\rho$ and consists of several substages in the ranges 1) 22–28°K, 2) 28–37°K, 3) 37–49°K, and 4) 49–60°K. The reported activation energies amount to 0.05, 0.065, 0.08, and 0.12 eV, respectively. The second and the fourth substage exhibit first order annealing kinetics. Neither one of these four stages shifts its temperature position when the electron dose varies by a factor of 7. With increasing *dose,* the second and the third substage increase while the fourth stage decreases. With increasing *electron energy*, substage 2 decreases, substage 3 increases and substage 4 is not altered. The first substage occurs in the vicinity of the irradiation temperature and is therefore difficult to detect entirely.

A strong magnetic after-effect is observed in the temperature range of the fourth substage. After neutron irradiation, the following characteristics of this effect are reported [117,120]: 1. Temperature range of reorientation 42–55°K. 2. Temperature range of recovery 45–65°K. 3. The activation energies of reorientation and recovery are alike and of the order of 0.1 eV. A similar magnetic after-effect was also observed in electron irradiated cobalt [121].

After the large stage I, the electrical resistivity of the electron irradiated material decreases in a more or less continuous manner, with three weak peaks occurring near 70°K, 140°K, and 180°K. At room temperature more than 98% are recovered.

The absence of a magnetic after-effect in what is felt to be stage $I_E$ is ascribed to an orientation of the interstitial magnetic perturbation along the hexagonal axis, as in the case of gadolinium (previous section). The magnetic after-effect in "stage $I_D$" is interpreted in terms of interstitial reorientations around its correlated vacancy [117]. Additional experiments are in progress.

In other irradiation work on cobalt, Wruck and Wert [122] irradiated cobalt at $-150°$C with 12 MeV deuterons. The resistivity change of cobalt was similar to that of nickel but considerably smaller than in iron and titanium. Two recovery stages occur near 150°K and 270°K. After room temperature annealing, approximately 30% of the initial resistivity increment (at $-180°$C) remain.

The recovery spectrum of the electrical resistivity of cobalt irradiated by thermal neutrons was reported by Coltman et al. [88] and is shown in fig. 11.

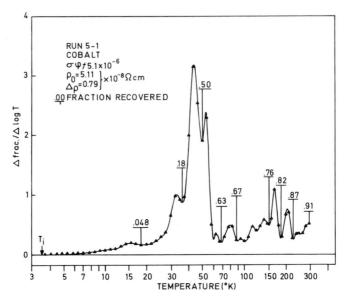

Fig. 11. Isochronal recovery (derivative) of the electrical resistivity of thermal-neutron-irradiated cobalt [87].

For a more detailed discussion of magnetic after-effect phenomena see the paper of Kronmüller in this volume [123].

### 4.7. Other hcp metals

The energy dependence of electron irradiation damage in *titanium* was determined at 20°K by Lucasson and Walker [91]. The resistance versus dose curves at constant beam energy were linear. An isochronal recovery curve of the electrical resistivity is given up to 80°K, but — as in the case of zinc — the authors experienced considerable experimental difficulties since the polycrystalline specimens were grossly affected by the temperature cycling.

In *zirconium,* deuteron bombarded at 170°K, 60% of the electrical resistivity increment is reported to recover at room temperature [124].

Neely (see ref. [125]) has observed a recovery stage of the electrical resistivity in electron irradiated zirconium at 35°K which amounted to 4% of the initial increment only. A similar, but more pronounced stage was observed in cold-worked zirconium (see below) [125].

In zirconium foils irradiated to $2.7 \times 10^{18}$ n/cm$^2$ at 40°C, Roy [126] observed black spots varying in size from $\approx 65$ to 4000 Å. Large interstitial loops were reported for irradiated zirconium after post-irradiation annealing at elevated temperatures [127].

Coltman et al. [88] determined the recovery of thermal neutron damage at 4.2°K in *rhenium* (fig. 12). The principal recovery peak occurs at 72°K and is preceded by

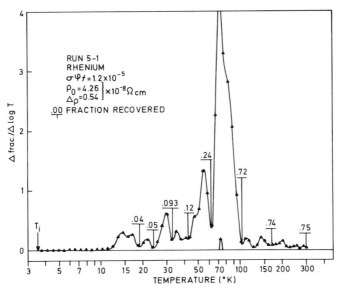

Fig. 12. Isochronal recovery (derivative) of the electrical resistivity of thermal-neutron-irradiated rhenium [87].

a more complex structure than in comparable fcc metals. The authors suspect that this might be due to a greater variety of stable close pairs in this metal, the mean recoil energy of 39 eV being relatively low. 75% of the resistivity increment are recovered at room temperature.

Brimball and Mastel performed transmission electron microscopy studies on rhenium foils irradiated at 60°C [128] and at 550°C [129]. In both experiments they observed small defect clusters. In the latter case they were identified by means of the stereo technique described by Rühle [130]. The clusters of 25—120 Å diameter were interpreted to be predominantly interstitial in nature. The authors feel that at 550°C interstitials are mobile enough to form clusters while vacancies are still rather immobile. A few of the images indicated, however, vacancy clusters.

For a more detailed discussion of the study of point defect agglomerates, see the paper of Wilkens at this conference [131].

### 4.8. Miscellaneous

A phenomenon which is indirectly connected with point defects is the crystal growth under neutron irradiation. This effect is observed not only in α-uranium, but also in a number of other metals with anisotropic structure [132]. Cadmium, zirconium, zinc and titanium exhibit pronounced growth effects when irradiated at −196°C, the growth rate decreasing in this order (i.e. with the atomic mass). At 75°C zirconium and titanium grow at a slightly decreased rate, but zinc and cadmium are dimensionally stable. In magnesium and beryllium, as in cubic metals, no growth was detected. For cadmium, zinc, zirconium and titanium, the growth direction corresponds to the crystallographic axis of minimum thermal expansion [11$\bar{2}$0].

Buckley [132] feels that the dependence of the growth rate on atomic mass, and the temperature dependence of the growth rate suggest a growth mechanism which is associated with the generation of depleted zones in neutron irradiated metals. He shows that the thermal spike stresses can overcome the anisotropy of dislocation loop energy and force vacancies and interstitials to aggregate into plates on different crystal planes, giving the anisotropic shape change. According to this model, elongation (due to interstitial aggregates) occurs in the direction of minimum thermal expansion, and contraction (due to collapsed vacancy clusters) in the direction of maximum expansion.

The fact that the growth rate vanished above self-diffusion temperatures, i.e. where both interstitial and vacancy aggregates are instable, favours a growth mechanism of this kind.

Bement [133] expects for the radiation induced defect clusters in hcp metals (at equivalent temperatures) differences among the subgroups cadmium and zinc ($c/a >$ ideal), magnesium ($c/a$ near ideal) and zirconium, titanium, beryllium ($c/a <$ ideal). Differences are expected for the crystallographic nature of the defects generated and for the interactions between these defects and the deformation modes of these subgroups. This $c/a$ criterium is in agreement with the fact that dislocation loops form predominantly along *basal* planes in cadmium [90] and on *prismatic* planes in beryllium [116].

## 5. Plastic deformation

### 5.1. *Cadmium*

Resistivity-elongation curves for cadmium were measured at liquid nitrogen temperature by Stevenson and Peiffer [134]. The resistivity of 99.999% cadmium increases linearly with the strain $\epsilon$ up to approximately 6% elongation, the total resistivity change at 77°K amounting to more than 20%. The linear increase of $\Delta\rho$ is similar in cadmium doped with up to 1000 ppm copper or magnesium; it is somewhat lower in lead-doped cadmium, in 99.99% cadmium, and in commercially pure material. In the latter case, a linear $\Delta\rho$ versus $\epsilon$ relation is reported up to 13% elongation only. The low-temperature deformation of cadmium appears therefore to offer no particular problem. It is apparently possible to introduce a large concentration of lattice defects this way. This is important in view of the difficulties encountered in the low temperature deformation in some other hcp metals.

The same authors attempted to identify the deformation induced lattice defects by means of recovery measurements [135,136]. In both 99.99% and 99.999% cadmium the electrical resistivity recovers in a rather continuous manner, starting already at the temperature of deformation (77°K). From the recovery rates of isothermal recovery segments, and from the variation of the activation energies with annealing temperature, it is apparent that a pronounced recovery stage occurs between 120 and 180°K. The major part of this stage is reported to be characterized by activation energies of 0.24 eV and 0.34 eV, respectively, for the high purity and the less pure cadmium. The authors attribute these energies to single vacancy migration and to a vacancy-impurity interaction effect, respectively.

Upon reviewing the analysis leading to the activation energies, it is felt that the experimental data presented do not permit such conclusions. The limitation of the change-of-slope methods in detecting a unique recovery process in an otherwise continuous recovery spectrum are well known. In the second technique employed by the authors, the initial resistances of several specimens were arbitrarily normalized at one constant value. Subsequently the activation energies were deduced from comparing equal amounts of recovery at various annealing temperatures in the different specimens. This technique is valid only if it is established that at the chosen annealing temperatures identical recovery processes occur indeed. Also, even numerically equal amounts of cold work on several specimens may involve a rather pronounced scatter in the electrical resistivity increase in certain temperature ranges [137] and, more important, dissimilar defect distributions. Recovery occurs already at the deformation temperature. Thus it is not advisable to make the initial resistivity values correspond to each other. The reported activation energy spectrum may therefore not be representative for the true annealing phenomena.

It is felt though that in spite of these constrictions the data can be taken to indicate an activation energy of roughly 0.30 eV (average value) for the main annealing peak in both the 99.999% and the 99.99% cadmium. (The peaks occur at the same annealing temperature.) Unfortunately, the concentration dependence of the stage position with respect to temperature was not investigated.

Sharp et al. [73] extended 99.9997% cadmium (single and polycrystals) by 12% at 90°K. Isochronal and isothermal recovery curves of the electrical resistivity exhibit the following phenomena: A well defined annealing stage occurs at 125–160°K (corresponding to the major recovery range in [136]). In the polycrystal it is twice as large as in the single crystal. A second, less important stage is found at 185–210°K, in which range also the yield stress recovers strongly. X-ray work demonstrates that the latter stage involves dislocation rearrangement. No change of the dislocation structure is observed below 195°K, suggesting that the 140°K stage is to be associated with point defect recovery. The activation energies (0.25 ± 0.2 eV and 0.72 ± 0.2 eV, respectively) as obtained from isothermal recovery curves are close to Peiffer's value [136] and to the activation energy for self-diffusion (table 2). In view of the method employed in their determination, they are, however, subject to the same restrictions as the above-mentioned work.

Isothermal internal friction and elasticity measurements were performed on cadmium uniformly twisted at room temperature [138]. Recovery occurs already at the deformation temperature, i.e. well below the onset of recrystallisation (150°C), while two other processes occur at more elevated temperatures. The phenomena are believed to be associated with dislocation rearrangements and recrystallisation.

Transmission electron microscope studies of cadmium foils cold-rolled in brine revealed contrast effects due to regular geometrical shapes and dislocation loops. They were attributed to the condensation of interstitials and vacancies, respectively, generated during cold-work [139].

## 5.2. Zinc

Only little information on point defects has been obtained on cold-worked zinc. Peiffer [140] elongated 99.999% pure polycrystalline zinc at room temperature up to 9% elongation and measured the increase in electrical resistivity. It increased linearly up to 1.5% and approached then a saturation value which was reached at 4% elongation. This increase recovered in the range 90–120°C which corresponds to the temperature range of self-diffusion in zinc. No recovery was observed at room temperature. These data indicate that any recovery stages due to point defects would be expected considerably *below* room temperature.

Attempts to deform 99.9997% zinc crystals at low temperatures did not yield any conclusive results [73]. Polycrystalline specimens failed before appreciable changes of the electrical resistivity had been induced. Single crystals deformed at 90°K showed no resistivity change during annealing, while a bicrystal exhibited very slight recovery at 170–230°K. Mechanical recovery (initial flow stress and reversible flow stress ratio) occurred in the range 140–260°C.

Zinc single crystals which were initially fatigued at −55°C were tested in unidirectional shear at −55°C and −196°C. Recovery experiments showed that a well defined activation energy of recovery does not exist in the range −14 to +15°C for crystals fatigued at −55°C for a number of cycles [141].

Anderson and Brown analysed transient rises in electrical resistivity which occur during discontinuous yielding of zinc single crystals [142]. More than half of the crystals did not show any jump deformation at all during deformation near room temperature. In 10% of the jump-deformed crystals the resistance changes were large enough to be analysed. The measured decay time of recovery of the jump-induced resistance increment amounted to between 0.3 ms and more than 10 ms at temperatures between 10 and 100°C. These decay times could be described by an activation energy of 0.32 ± 0.03 eV. The authors attribute the decay to the migration of point defects generated during the deformation jump and having a rather short lifetime at room temperature. Since the activation energy is appreciably lower than $E_{1V}^M$ estimates for single vacancies in zinc (see sections 3.2 and 4.2), the authors suggest that divacancy migration might be the rate determining recovery process. The vacancy concentration in the slip zone is considered high enough to have appreciable divacancy concentrations. The electrical resistivity of single vacancies is estimated at 10 $\mu\Omega$cm/at%.

Drouard et al. [143] studied the temperature dependence of the rate of recovery in zinc single crystals after simple shear deformation at −50°C. The yield stress of the crystals recovered in the range −30 to +20°C with an activation energy close to that found for self-diffusion in *c*-direction, namely 0.88 eV [14]. The data are interpreted in terms of recovery processes within the dislocation substructure. The same authors showed that the yield stress of zinc single crystals depend on the prior annealing temperature and the rate of cooling after annealing [76] (see section 3.2).

### 5.3. Magnesium

Beevers [63] supplemented his quenching experiments on magnesium by submitting the same material to cold work. The electrical resistivity increase of magnesium deformed by wire drawing at room temperature was measured up to 12% area reduction. The increase shows a saturation type behaviour. It recovers in one large stage between room temperature and 200°C, the activation energy of recovery increasing from 0.5 eV to 2.0 eV. Attempts to cold-work magnesium at −196°C were unsuccessful, since fracture occurred after very small extensions. At −79°C, wires could be deformed up to 2.5% elongation. Change of slope experiments in these specimens yielded activation energies of 0.52 ± 0.04 eV in the room temperature region. Beevers assigned single vacancy migration to this recovery range since the activation energy was independent of the annealing temperature and since the value reported agrees well with the difference of the activation energies of self-diffusion [21,22] and vacancy formation [59,63].

In tensile experiments on magnesium single and polycrystals, Sharp et al. [73] observed a strong recovery stage of the electrical resistivity between 80°C and 150°C in crystals deformed at room temperature (activation energy 1.2−1.8 eV, assuming that the annealing mechanisms are identical at different isothermal temperatures). A single crystal deformed at 90°K showed a first recovery stage below 120°K and a second one at 180−220°K. The main recovery stage of the flow stress corresponds to the high temperature resistivity stage. For complete recovery it was necessary to recrystallize specimens as in the case of cadmium.

In other deformation work, Nicoud [144] achieved a tensile deformation of 3−4% elongation at 77°K before mechanical failure. When the magnesium wires were deformed *with* potential leads spot-welded on the surface, failure occurred at smaller elongations (≈ 1.7%). The electrical resistivity increased linearly up to these degrees of deformation.

In resistivity recovery experiments after compression at 77°K, Nicoud [144] observed essentially three stages: 90−170°K, 170−400°K, and 400−550°K. The first one of these stages coincides with the large 140°K stage found after neutron and electron irradiation (see section 4.3) and might therefore be associated with an interstitial type defect. The third stage is likely to be due to recrystallisation according to the work of Montariol et al. [145]. Finally, the second, complex stage is that which had also been found partially by Beevers [63], Sharp et al. [73], and Montariol [145]. It might be associated partially with vacancy migration (cf. the quenching experiments) and furthermore with some more stable defect agglomerate or rearrangements in the dislocation substructure. It does not occur in a single crystal deformed at 90°K [73] and neither in zone-refined magnesium, where recrystallisation takes place near 0°C [145].

## 5.4. *Beryllium*

Preliminary experiments on defect production and recovery in cold-worked beryllium were performed by Nicoud [103], using similar techniques as in the experiments on magnesium [144]. The increase of the electrical resistivity during tensile deformation at 77°K was rather small before failure, so that no quantitative analysis was possible. The recovery followed a more or less continuous resistivity decrease without particular evidence for individual recovery stages. It is emphasized that the material used was rather impure (99.9%).

## 5.5. *Cobalt*

The recovery up to 550°K of the electrical resistivity of cobalt after cold work at 4.2°K was measured by Bilger and Kronmüller [146]. The recovery is more or less continuous, but several characteristic recovery ranges may nevertheless be recognized. The data are in qualitative agreement with the work of Zwetaew et al. [147] who cold-worked polycrystalline cobalt at 77°K by compression. The latter authors observed in the range 150—310°K a recovery law of the form $\Delta\rho(t) \approx \ln(t)$ for isothermal recovery. The recovery range between 150 and 365°K was studied by Gerward [148] by means of magnetic after-effect measurements on deformed single crystals. He observed below 305°K a weak after-effect phenomenon and above this temperature a strong increase. The latter after-effect recovered partially in two stages with activation energies of 0.7 eV (305—330°K) and 1.0 eV (> 330°K) and first order kinetics in both cases. The coincidence of these after-effect phenomena with those observed by Kamel and Botros [83] (see section 3.4) is pointed out.

A well defined recovery stage is observed also between 330 and 610°K. Zwetaew et al. [147] determined between 440 and 505°K a unique activation energy of 1.03 eV and second order annealing kinetics. A further stage occurred between 620°K and the transformation temperature.

The recovery of the electrical resistivity of polycrystalline cobalt extended at 90°K shows stages at approximately 110°K and at 200—250°K [73]. The initial flow stress did not recover below 400°C.

## 5.6. *Titanium*

At 20°K, the electrical resistivity of *titanium* wires (99.9% pure) strained by 6% increases by 30%, of which 20% recovery at 78°K. 6% strain at 78°K leads to an increment of 8% and to 50% recovery up to room temperature [149].

## 5.7. *Zirconium*

The electrical resistivity of zirconium rolled at room temperature shows prior to recrystallisation (> 250°) a more or less continuous recovery with a slight fine structure [150,151]. The pre-recrystallisation annealing shows some change with the purity of the material (99.5% and 99.95% Zr, respectively). It is felt, however, that apparent substages are not necessarily physically meaningful as to indicating a particular annealing process, since each "substage" is based on one or two points of the isochronal recovery curves only. Similarly, the "linear variation of activation energy with the resistivity increment" between 50 and 315°C and the logarithmic time law ($\Delta\rho \approx \ln t$) in the 99.5% Zr should not be considered to indicate one unique annealing process in this large temperature range. They are felt to be of an apparent nature only. Any typical recovery process would be expected in the purer material as well. The activation energy spectrum of the pure samples shows an approximately constant value of 1.35 ± 0.05 eV in the range 125−225°C which appears to be more likely associable with a unique recovery process, although it is difficult to check this in the isochronal recovery curve.

Polycrystalline zirconium wires (99.9% pure) were strained at 20°K and at 78°K [149]. At 20°K the residual electrical resistivity increased by 60% for a strain of 6%. 20% of this increment recovered at 78°K. Straining at 78°K by 6% resulted in a resistivity increment of 5% of the resistivity at 78°K. Here, 30% annealed up to room temperature.

The low temperature recovery of zirconium deformed at 4.2°K shows several interesting phenomena [125,152]. Samples of two different purities were extended by 0.5−1.5%, the chief difference being the amount of oxygen content (0.7 at% and 0.015 at%). The electrical resistivity increment $\Delta\rho$ for 0.7% strain was $3 \times 10^{-8}$ $\Omega$cm in the former and smaller for the purer zirconium.

A surprisingly strong recovery stage of the electrical resistivity occurred between 30 and 40°K. For equal $\Delta\rho$, the amount of recovery (up to 30% $\Delta\rho$) was strongly purity dependent. The relative magnitude of the stage was roughly proportional to the oxygen content of the specimens. The oxygen sensitivty of the recovery was corroborated by similar experiments on oxygen doped zirconium. The peak temperature is practically independent of the degree of deformation (34°K and 36°K, respectively).

Isothermal and isochronal recovery curves of the electrical resistivity indicate that the recovery process at 35°K is not a single uniquely activated process, but is rather of a complex nature. The activation energy is centred at 0.11 eV. According to this value and the characteristic times of annealing only the order of one atomic jump is required for the basic recovery event, i.e. the processes follow essentially first order annealing kinetics. This is corroborated by the fact that the peak temperature does not shift with the degree of deformation. A Primak type analysis [153] of the isothermal recovery curves suggests that the recovery stage might be described by a series of first order processes with discrete activation energies. Kinetics of this kind would be expected, for example, for rearrangements of point defect-oxygen complexes. According to this model, the oxygen atoms in the matrix are believed to favour the generation of point defects in their immediate vicinity during plastic deformation. At somewhat higher annealing temperatures the point defect would move towards the oxygen atom which was responsible for its generation. The fine structure of the stage would then correspond to different point defect-oxygen separations.

While the purer zirconium recovered gradually between 50 and 340°K, the less pure zirconium showed two substages at 190 and 310°K, each one amounting to ≈10% in a less deformed specimen and to less in a stronger deformed sample. 80% of the initial resistivity increment in the less pure zirconium recovered at 360°K. The nature of these substages is not yet clear.

Deviations from Matthiessen's rule were observed in zirconium at 20°K by Renucci et al. [154]. They propose a relation of the form $\rho = f(m) H(T) + G(T)$ to account for the temperature ($T$) and impurity ($m$) dependence of the electrical resistivity, in particular for oxygen-doped zirconium.

### 5.8. Rhenium

A study of the recovery of cold-worked rhenium was presented at this conference [155]. The essential result is a pronounced recovery stage near 0.18 $T_M$ (melting point) with an activation energy of 2.2 ± 0.1 eV. This stage exhibits similar phenomena as what is called stage III in fcc and in other hcp and cc metals.

## 6. Theoretical and semi-empirical approaches

Mukherjee [156] has proposed an empirical relation between the formation energy $E_{1V}^F$ of a single vacancy and the Debye temperature $\Theta_D$ for close packed metals. This relation reads

$$\Theta_D = 34.3 \, (E_{1V}^F / MV^{\frac{2}{3}})^{\frac{1}{2}} \quad [E_{1V}^F \text{ in cal/gatom}] \,, \tag{18}$$

where $M$ and $V$ are the mass and the volume, respectively, of one mole of the solid. Eq. (18) was later shown by March [157] to follow directly from a screening theory in metals. In the case of magnesium, Mukherjee proposed $E_{1V}^F = 0.86$ eV which is in rather good agreement with experimental determinations (see sections 2.3 and 3.3).

It was shown by Glyde [158] that in the Debye model the usual "dyamical" theories of diffusion lead directly to a relation between $E_{1V}^M$ and $\Theta_D^2$, where the Debye temperature appropriate to frequency spectrum averages appearing in the Debye-Waller factor is used for $\Theta_D^2$ rather than $\Theta_D^2(c_V)$ ($c_V$ = specific heat). This relation reads

$$E_{1V}^M = K_1(k/h)^2 m\Theta_D^2 a^2 \,, \tag{19}$$

where $K_1$ is a constant, $a$ is the interatomic spacing and $m$ the atomic mass. A similar relation between $E_{1V}^F$ and $\Theta_D$ reads

$$E_{1V}^F = K_2(k/h)^2 m\Theta_D^2 a^2 \tag{20}$$

(for the assumption see ref. [158]). Glyde estimates for magnesium $E_{1V}^F = 0.89$ ± 0.06 eV, which again is in good agreement with the experimental data in sections 2.3 and 3.3.

Osipov has reported an apparent relationship of diffusion phenomena and melting [159]. He calculated the formation energy for zones of limited thermodynamic stability (local melting zones). This energy $Q$ was determined as

$$Q = -T_M \left[ \frac{H_{T_M} - H_{298°K}}{T_M - 298°K} (6.7 - \ln T_M) - S_{298°C} \right]. \tag{21}$$

where $H$ and $S$ are the heat content and entropy (in g-atom) at the indicated temperatures, and $T_M$ is the melting point. For a number of fcc metals, the value $Q$ turned out to be in the same range as the single vacancy formation energy. The following $Q$-values were given for hexagonal metals: Cd 0.27 eV, Zn 0.26 eV, Mg 0.35 eV, $\alpha$-Co 1.05 eV and $\alpha$-Zr 1.58 eV. It is seen that these values appear to be somewhat low to be associated with $E_{1V}^F$, i.e. the above-mentioned relation appears less applicable in the case of hcp metals than in fcc metals.

The mechanical relaxation modes for paired point defects in hcp metals were determined by Povolo and Bisogni [160] using group theory methods. The symmetry groups are calculated for interstitial-interstitial-pairs, and for divacancies. In a subsequent paper [161], these authors investigated the possibility of relaxation phenomena due to isolated point defects (vacancies, substitutional and interstitial atoms) in hcp structures. They found that mechanical relaxation effects are not expected to arise from such isolated defects occupying either octahedral or tetrahedral sites. Relaxation effects are, however, predicted for defects which change their site with respect to symmetry, e.g. for an interstitial atom occupying an octahedral site and jumping into a tetrahedral position (and vice versa).

In earlier work, Bovarnik [162] had studied interstitial atoms in octahedral sites in $\beta$-titanium. In agreement with the work of Povolo et al. [161], he felt that one could not expect stress-induced ordering of the solute atoms.

Beshers [163] predicted for hcp metals with non-ideal $c/a$ ratios the occurrence of mechanical relaxation due to a reorientation of interstitial atoms on tetrahedral sites.

A more general criterion for the occurrence or nonoccurrence of mechanical relaxation was proposed by Nowick and Heller [164], who related the order of the point symmetry group of the crystal to the order of the defect tensor group. This criterion suggests the occurrence of mechanical relaxation for interstitial atoms on either octahedral or tetrahedral sites in hcp crystals, in disagreement with the conclusions of Povolo and Bisogni [161]. For vacancies and substitutional atoms (with hexagonal defect symmetry), however, both models predict zero mechanical relaxation.

A detailed and general theoretical treatment of relaxation phenomena in metals was recently published by Kronmüller [165].

## 7. Conclusion

The preceding review is hoped to give an up-to-date account of our present knowledge on point defect phenomena in hcp metals. We have seen that, although in some cases the amount of data is still rather poor and fragmentary, in other cases one can already classify the data to the extent that future experiments can be pinned down to very specific questions. It is expected that the next few years will see a considerably increasing research activity on metals other than fcc and bcc.

## Acknowledgments

The major part of this review has been prepared during a postdoctoral stay at the Centre d'Etudes Nucléaires, Départment de Métallurgie, Grenoble. The author wishes to express his gratitude to the Commissariat à l'Energie Atomique and in particular to Dr. Y.Adda for the hospitality and for the continuous interest in this work. Special thanks are due to Drs. Delaplace, Hillairet and co-workers for a stimulating cooperation and for numerous discussions. Fruitful contacts to the Solid State Division (Dr. D.Dautreppe) are appreciated.

The author is indebted to Dr. Sprusil, Prague, for communicating results before publication.

## References

[1] J.W.Corbett, Electron Radiation Damage in Semi-Conductors and Metals (Academic Pres, New York, London, 1966).
[2] American Institute of Physics Handbook (McGraw-Hill, New York, Toronto, London, 1957).
[3] Y.Adda and J.Philibert, La Diffusion dans les Solides (Presses Universitaires de France, Paris, 1966).
[4] J.G.Mullen, Phys. Rev. 124 (1961) 1723.
[5] K.Compaan and Y.Haven, Trans. Faraday Soc. 54 (1958) 1498.
[6] A.P.Batra, Phys. Rev. 159 (1957) 487.
[7] N.L.Peterson and S.J.Rothman, Phys. Rev. 163 (1967) 645.
[8] E.S.Wajda, G.A.Shirn and H.B.Huntington, Acta Met. 3 (1955) 39.
[9] K.A.Mahmoud and R.Kamel, Int. Conf. Radioisotopes in Scientific Research 1 (1958) 271; Acta Met. 5 (1957) 476.
[10] Y.Masuda, J. Phys. Soc. Japan 13 (1958) 597.
[11] W.Schrödter, Thesis, Techn. Universität Berlin (1966).
[12] W.Hirschwald and W.Schrödter, Z. Physik. Chem. Neue Folge 53 (1967) 392.
[13] K.Apel, S.Häntzsch and K.E.Brescher, Z. Metallk. 58 (1967) 6.
[14] P.H.Miller and F.R.Banks, Phys. Rev. 61 (1942) 648.
[15] H.B.Huntington, G.A.Shirn and E.S.Wajda, Phys. Rev. 87 (1952) 211.
[16] G.A.Shirn, E.S.Wajda and H.B.Huntington, Acta Met. 1 (1953) 513.
[17] T.Lin and H.G.Drickamer, J. Chem. Phys. 22 (1954) 312.

[18] F.E.Jaumot and R.L.Smith, Trans. AIME 206 (1956) 137.

[19] I.A.Naskidashvili and V.M.Dolidze, Soobshch. Akad. Nauk. Gruz. SSR 18 (1957) 671.

[20] J.E.Hilliard, B.L.Averbach and M.Cohen, Acta Met. 7 (1959) 86.

[21] P.G.Shewmon, Trans. AIME 206 (1956) 918.

[22] P.G.Shewmon and F.N.Rhines, Trans. AIME 200 (1954) 1021.

[23] C.H.Lee, G.E.Spangler, M.Herman and J.B.Drew, unpublished.

[24] J.M.Dupouy, J.Mathie and Y.Adda, Mém. Sci. Rev. Métall. 63 (1966) 481.

[25] R.C.Ruder and C.E.Birchenall, Trans. AIME 191 (1951) 142.

[26] F.C.Nix and F.E.Jaumot, Phys. Rev. 80 (1950) 119; 82 (1951) 72.

[27] P.L.Gruzin, Dokl. Akad. Nauk SSSR 86 (1952) 289.

[28] H.W.Mead and C.E.Birchenall, Trans. AIME 203 (1955) 994.

[29] K.Hirano, R.P.Agarwala, B.L.Averbach and M.Cohen, J. Appl. Phys. 33 (1961) 3049.

[30] A.Hässner and W.Lange, Phys. Stat. Sol. 8 (1965) 77.

[31] C.M.Libanati and S.F.Dyment, Acta Met. 11 (1963) 1263.

[32] P.L.Gruzin, V.S.Emelyanov, G.G.Ryabova and G.B.Fedorov, Proc. 2nd U.N. Conf. on the Peaceful Uses of Atomic Energy, vol. 19 (IAEA, Vienna, 1958), p. 187.

[33] V.S.Lyashenko, B.N.Bikov and L.V.Pavlinov, Phys. Met. Metall. 8 (1959) 362.

[34] E.V.Borisov, Y.G.Godin, P.L.Gruzin, A.I.Yevstyukhin and V.S.Emelyanov, Met. i Metalloved. Izd. Akad. Nauk SSSR (1958) 291.

[35] A.Seeger and H.Mehrer, this volume.

[36] J.v.Liempt, Z. Physik 96 (1935) 534.

[37] N.H.Nachtrieb and G.S.Handler, Acta Met. 2 (1954) 797.

[38] K.K.Kelley and E.G.King, Bulletin 592 (Bureau of Mines, Washington, 1961).

[39] O.Sherby and M.T.Simnad, ASTM Quart. Rep. 54 (1961) 227.

[40] G.B.Gibbs, Mém. Sci. Rev. Métall. 62 (1965) 841.

[41] D.H.Feisel and R.W.Armstrong, Trans. AIME 230 (1964) 867.

[42] A.B.Lidiard, Symp. Thermodynamics and Atomic Transport (IAEA, Vienna, 1965) SM-66/30.

[43] G.Schottky, Phys. Stat. Sol. 8 (1965) 357.

[44] M.Gerl, J. Phys. Chem. Solids 28 (1967) 725.

[45] Th.Hehenkamp, this volume.

[46] P.G.Shewmon, J. Chem. Phys. 29 (1958) 1032.

[47] R.A.Swalin, W.C.Olander and P.Lin, Acta Met. 13 (1965) 1063.

[48] T.F.Archbold and P.G.McCormick, Trans. AIME 236 (1966) 713.

[49] H.G.Feller and H.Wever, J. Phys. Chem. Solids 24 (1963) 969.

[50] H.Dübler and H.Wever, Phys. Stat. Sol. 25 (1968) 109.

[51] P.P.Kuzmenko and E.I.Kharkov, Ukr. Fiz. Zh. 4 (1959) 401, 537; 7 (1962) 117.

[52] P.Thernqvist and A.Lodding, Z. Naturforsch. 21a (1966) 1310.

[53] J.L.Routbort, Phys. Rev. 176 (1968) 796.

[54] P.S.Ho, J. Phys. Chem. Solids 27 (1966) 1331.

[55] D.R.Campbell and H.B.Huntington, Phys. Rev., to be published.

[56] S.D.Gertsriken and B.F.Slyusar, Ukr. Fiz. Zh. 2 (1957) 376; 4 (1959) 137.

[57] J.Hillairet, B.Martinet and D.Schumacher, Phys. Stat. Sol., in press.

[58] R.Feder, A.S.Nowick and H.Charbnau, Bull. Am. Phys. Soc. 12 (1967) 388, and private communication.

[59] C.Mairy, J.Hillairet and D.Schumacher, Acta Met. 15 (1967) 1258.

[60] V.O.Shestopal, Soviet Phys. Solid State 7 (1966) 2798.

[61] O.M.Kanel, Y.A.Kraftmakher, Soviet Phys. Solid State 8 (1966) 232.

[62] B.Sprusil, Phys. Stat. Sol. 3 (1963) K 86.

[63] C.J.Beevers, Acta Met. 11 (1963) 1029.

[64] A.Seeger and D.Schumacher, in: Lattice Defects in Quenched Metals (Academic Press, New York, London 1965) p. 15.

[65] M.Hoch, this volume.

[66] J.A.Kraftmakher and P.G.Strelkov, this volume.

[67] N.Madaiah and G.M.Graham, Can. J. Phys. 42 (1964) 221.

[68] J.Goldak, L.T.Lloyd and C.S.Barrett, Phys. Rev. 144 (1966) 478.

[69] K.R.Zen, S.S.Wang and Y.C.Wang, Acta Phys. Sinica 21 (1965) 2033.

[70] J.Takamura, in: Lattice Defects in Quenched Metals (Academic Press, New York, London, 1965) p. 521.

[71] A.P.Savitskiy and L.K.Savitskaya, Phys. Met. Metall. 17, No. 6 (1964) 86.

[72] A.P.Savitskiy and L.K.Savitskaya, Phys. Met. Metall. 18, No. 1 (1964) 52.

[73] J.V.Sharp, A.Mitchell and J.W.Christian, Acta Met. 13 (1965) 965.

[74] B.Sprusil, P.Vostry and R.Svobodová, private communication.

[75] D.M.Fegredo, J. Inst. Metals 93 (1965) 268.

[76] C.H.Li, J.Washburn and E.R.Parker, J. Metals 197 (1953) 1223.

[77] K.Okada and S.Koda, J. Inst. Metals 89 (1960–61) 479.

[78] V.Lévy, J.Hillairet, D.Schumacher, G.Revel and T.Chaudron, Jül. Conf. 2 (Vol. II) 1968, p. 782.

[79] J.S.Lally and P.G.Partridge, Phil. Mag. 13 (1966) 9.

[80] K.Schwartzkopff (Berlin), private communication.

[81] G.Thomas, R.B.Benson and J.Nadeau, Proc. European Regional Conf. Electron Microscopy, Delft, 1961, Vol. I, p. 447.

[82] C.J.Beevers, Proc. 3rd European Conf. Electron Microscopy, Prague, 1964, Vol. A, p. 215.

[83] R.Kamel and K.Z.Botros, Phys. Stat. Sol. 12 (1965) 399.

[84] W.Bauer, J.W.DeFord and J.S.Kochler, Phys. Rev. 128 (1962) 1497.

[85] R.R.Coltman, Jr., C.E.Klabunde, D.L.McDonald and J.K.Redman, J. Appl. Phys. 33 (1962) 3509; Solid State Div. Ann. Progr. Rept. ORNL-3364 (1962) p. 66.

[86] R.R.Coltman, Jr., C.E.Klabunde, J.K.Redman and G.F.Fielder, Solid State Div. Ann. Progr. Rept. ORNL-3676 (1964) p. 61.

[87] R.R.Coltman, Jr., C.E.Klabunde and J.K.Redman, Phys. Rev. 156 (1967) 715.

[88] R.R.Coltman, Jr., C.E.Klabunde, J.K.Redman and R.L.Southern, Jül. Conf. 2 (Vol. II) 1968, p. 770.

[89] A.Seeger, discussion of ref. [88], see discussion following this paper.

[90] P.B.Price, Phys. Rev. Letters 6 (1961) 615.

[91] P.G.Lucasson and R.M.Walker, Phys. Rev. 127 (1962) 485.

[92] A.Lucasson and P.Lucasson, J. Phys. Chem. Solids 27 (1966) 1423.

[93] F.Maury, A.Lucasson and P.Lucasson, Proc. Intern. Conf. Solid State Physics Research with Accelerators, ed. A.N.Goland, Brookhaven, 1967, p. 314.

[94] T.H.Blewitt, R.R.Coltman, D.K.Holmes and T.S.Noggle, in: Dislocation and Mechenical Properties of Crystals (Wiley, New York, 1957) p. 603.

[95] J.Nihoul, Phys. Stat. Sol. 3 (1963) 2061.

[96] C.J.Meechan and J.A.Brinkman, Phys. Rev. 103 (1956) 1193.

[97] F.W.Kunz and A.N.Holden, Acta Met. 2 (1954) 816.

[98] M.Haager and K.Siebinger, Berg-Hüttenmänn. Monatsh. 111 (1966) 112.

[99] T.N.O'Neal and R.L.Chaplin, Bull. Am. Phys. Soc. 13 (1968) 254.

[100] T.N.O'Neal and R.L.Chaplin, Phys. Letters 26A (1968) 453.

[101] J.Delaplace, J.Hillairet, J.C.Nicoud, D.Schumacher and G.Vogl, Phys. Stat. Sol. 30 (1968) 119.

[102] T.H.Blewitt, R.R.Coltman, C.E.Klabunde, D.K.Holmes and J.K.Redman, ORNL-Report No. 2614 (1958).

[103] J.C.Nicoud (Grenoble), to be published.

[104] J.Hillairet (Grenoble), to be published.

[105] K.Isebeck, R.Müller, W.Schilling and H.Wenzl, Phys. Stat. Sol. 18 (1966) 467.

[106] J.C.Nicoud, J.Delaplace and J.Hillairet, in: Fragilité et Effets de l'Irradiation (Presses Universitaires de France, Paris, 1967) p. 27.

[107] D.Schumacher, J.C.Nicoud, J.Delaplace and J.Hillairet, Phys. Letters 25A (1967) 610.

[108] J.C.Nicoud, J.Delaplace, J.Hillairet, D.Schumacher and Y.Adda, J. Nucl. Materials 27 (1968) 147.

[109] J.Delaplace, J.C.Nicoud, D.Schumacher and G.Vogl, Phys. Stat. Sol. 29 (1968) 819.

[110] E.Bonjour, J.C.Nicoud and J.Delaplace, Compt. Rend. Acad. Sci. Paris 264 C (1967) 2112.

[111] J.C.Nicoud, E.Bonjour, D.Schumacher and J.Delaplace, Phys. Letters 26A (1968) 228.

[112] P.Sigmund, G.P.Scheidler and G.Roth, Proc. Intern. Conf. on Solid State Physics Research with Accelerators, ed. A.N.Goland, Brookhaven, 1967, p. 374.

[113] G.Burger, K.Isebeck, J.Völkl, W.Schilling and H.Wenzl, Z. Angew. Physik 22 (1967) 452.

[114] C.Frois and O.Dimitrov, Compt. Rend. Acad. Sci. Paris 264 C (1967) 1923.

[115] K.R.Garr and A.Sosin, Phys. Rev. 162 (1967) 691.

[116] G.P.Walters, C.M.v.d.Walt and M.J.Makin, J. Nucl. Materials 11 (1964) 335.

[117] H.Cope, G.Sulpice, C.Minier, H.Bilger and P.Moser, Jül. Conf. 2 (Vol. II) 1968, p. 792.

[118] R.M.Bozorth and C.S.Graham, Jr., General Electric Metallurgy and Ceramics Laboratory Report No. 66 C 225, Schenectady, New York (1966).

[119] G.Sulpice, C.Minier, P.Moser and H.Bilger, J. Phys. 29 (1968) 253.

[120] P.Moser, P.Peretto, D.Dautreppe and P.Vigier, J. Appl. Phys. 36 (1965) 1227.

[121] J.Verdonne, P.Peretto, P.Moser, D.Dautreppe and J.Verdier, Compt. Rend. Acad. Sci. Paris 260 (1965) 5209.

[122] D.Wruck and C.Wert, Acta Met. 3 (1955) 115.

[123] H.Kronmüller, this volume.

[124] I.F.Zartman, Nucl. Eng. Sci. Congr., Cleveland, 1955, Preprint No. 89.

[125] M.L.Swansson, Can. J. Phys. 44 (1966) 3241.

[126] R.B.Roy, AE-130, Aktiebolaget Atomenergi, Stockholm (1963).

[127] I.M.Bernstein and T.Gulden, The Nature of Small Defect Clusters, AERE-R 5269, Vol. II, ed. M.J.Makin (London, 1966) p. 441.

[128] J.L.Brimhall and B.Mastel, Phil. Mag. 12 (1965) 419.

[129] J.L.Brimhall and B.Mastel, Phys. Stat. Sol. 27 (1968) K89.

[130] M.Rühle, Phys. Stat. Sol. 19 (1967) 263, 279.

[131] M.Wilkens, this volume.

[132] S.N.Buckley, in: Properties of Reactor Materials and the Effects of Radiation Damage, ed. D.J.Littler (Butterworth, London, Washington, 1962) p. 413.

[133] A.L.Bement, Report BNWL-SA 236 (1965).

[134] F.R.Stevenson and H.R.Peiffer, Nature 200 (1963) 771.

[135] H.R.Peiffer and F.R.Stevenson, J. Appl. Phys. 34 (1963) 2804.

[136] F.R.Stevenson and H.R.Peiffer, Phys. Stat. Sol. 4 (1964) 411.

[137] T.Broom, Proc. Phys. Soc. 65 B (1952) 871.

[138] R.Kamel and E.A.Attia, Phil. Mag. 4 (1959) 644.

[139] K.Bahadur, K.L.Chandhary and R.P.Aggarwala, Indian J. Pure Appl. Phys. 3 (1965) 453.

[140] H.R.Peiffer, Can. J. Phys. 36 (1958) 1245.

[141] D.M.Fegredo, J. Inst. Metals 93 (1964–65) 189.

[142] J.M.Anderson and A.F.Brown, Phys. Stat. Sol. 12 (1965) 309.

[143] R.Drouard, J.Washburn and E.R.Parker, J. Metals 197 (1953) 1226.

[144] J.C.Nicoud, J.Delaplace and D.Schumacher, Phys. Letters 28A (1968) 2.

[145] F.Montariol, J.P.Catteau, C.Boucheron and A.Vanderschaeghe, Compt. Rend. Acad. Sci. Paris 261 (1965) 3605.

[146] H.Bilger and H.Kronmüller, Phys. Stat. Sol. 22 (1967) 683.

[147] A.A.Zwetaew, R.K.Tschuschko and N.Golowanow, Phys. Stat. Sol. 4 (1964) 299.

[148] L.Gerward, Phys. Stat. Sol. 22 (1967) 659.
[149] E.Smith and M.S.Stagg, Nature 189 (1961) 300.
[150] A.Desalvo, P.Gondi, G.F.Missiroli and F.Zignani, Metall. Ital. 57 (1965) 177.
[151] A.Desalvo and F.Zignani, J. Nucl. Materials 20 (1966) 108.
[152] M.L.Swansson, A.F.Quenneville and H.Schultz, Appl. Phys. Letters 6 (1965) 49.
[153] W.Primak, J. Appl. Phys. 31 (1960) 1524.
[154] L.Renucci and J.P.Langeron, Compt. Rend. Acad. Sci. Paris 264 C (1967) 2012.
[155] H.Vandenborre, L.Stals and J.Nihoul, Jül. Conf. 2 (Vol. II) 1968, p. 802.
[156] K.Mukherjee, Phys. Letters 8 (1964) 18.
[157] N.H.March, Phys. Letters 20 (1966) 231.
[158] H.R.Glyde, J. Phys. Chem. Solids 28 (1967) 2061.
[159] K.A.Osipov, Soviet Phys. Doklady 3 (1958) 848, 862.
[160] F.Povolo and E.A.Bisogni, Acta Met. 14 (1966) 711.
[161] F.Povolo and E.A.Bisogni, Acta Met. 15 (1967) 701.
[162] E.Bovarnick, Rept. US Army WAL 401/122 (1952).
[163] D.N.Beshers, J. Appl. Phys. 36 (1965) 291.
[164] A.S.Nowick and W.R.Heller, Advan. Phys. 12 (1963) 251.
[165] H.Kronmüller, Nachwirkung in Ferromagnetika (Springer Verlag, Berlin, Heidelberg, New York, 1968).

## Discussion

*R.v.Jan:* I wish to comment on the magnesium data. Two low-temperature re-covery stages are found below $130°K$ after electron irradiation but are suppressed after neutron irradiation. Arguing that energy dissipation by focussing is not very efficient in this metal, this effect can be attributed to spontaneous recombination in the displacement spike. Such an interpretation supports your view that those recovery stages are close pair stages and are *not* due to free migration because spike effects cannot completely suppress a free migration stage.

*R. M. Mayer:* Is the data of Coltmann and the electron microscope evidence you mentioned consistent with migration of interstitials at room temperature or can the Coltmann data be interpreted by long range migration at some tempera-ture below room temperature?

*D. Schumacher:* Both the resistometric and the electron microscope work sug-gest that in cadmium the basic point defects (vacancies and interstitials) migrate at temperatures well below room temperature.

*A. Seeger* (partly contributed): The experiments of Coltman et al. [88] on ther-mal neutron damage in cadmium appear to me remarkable in several respects:
1) The damage pattern caused by the recoil events is among the simplest that we may envisage.
2) The experiments were carried out on high-purity single crystals with reasonable dimensions, so that size-effect corrections are necessary only at very small doses.
3) The annealing data extend over an unusually wide temperature range, from $3.6°K$ to complete annealing.

4) The annealing experiments cover a dose range of 1:1000 on *one* specimen.

5) A large number of individual annealing peaks has been resolved. Only one of them (at fairly high temperatures) has been found to shift with increasing concentration to lower temperatures.

6) The population of the peaks changes with dose much more than would be expected from radiation annealing effects.

Item 6 is a feature which appears to have no analogue in the fcc metals and is probably related to the hexagonal crystal structure. We shall therefore postpone the discussion of it to the end of this contribution.

The self-diffusion data of cadmium indicate no complication except for a small anisotropy in the activation energy of self-diffusion (activation energy for self-diffusion parallel to $c$-axis 0.78 eV ± 0.02 eV, for self-diffusion perpendicular to $c$-axis 0.82 eV ± 0.03 eV [8]). Feder and Nowick [58] have determined the concentration of vacant lattice sites as a function of temperature by thermal expansion and lattice parameter measurements. They observed a rather good Arrhenius-type relationship which they fit to a monovacancy formation energy $E_{1V}^F$ = 0.44 eV and a monovacancy formation entropy $S_{1V}^F$ = 1.2 $k$. It appears that the effects of multiple vacancies and of possible temperature dependences of the defect energies and entropies are small. A good average value for the monovacancy migration energy (which seems to be slightly higher for migration in the basal plane than for migration perpendicular to the basal plane) is thought to be $E_{1V}^M$ = 0.36 eV.

In the experiments by Coltman et al. [88] the last annealing peak before complete annealing of the irradiation-induced resistivity occurs at about 225°K. At this temperature the Boltzmann factor for monovacancy migration is $\exp(-0.36$ eV$/k \cdot 225°$K$) = 10^{-8}$. In the experiments 5-minutes pulses were employed; assuming a frequency factor of $10^{13}$ sec$^{-1}$ we estimate that the number of jumps of a monovacancy during one pulse at the peak temperature is between $10^7$ and $10^8$. This is indeed the order of magnitude that we would expect for the final annealing stage. We may therefore have some confidence in the assignment of monovacancy migration to this annealing stage.

Let us now consider the one peak that shows a clear dependence of its temperature on defect concentration. It resembles in this respect the annealing stage III of the fcc metals and will therefore be designated by stage III. After an atomic fraction of captures of $3.6 \times 10^{-3}$ this peak occurs at about 105°K. The monovacancy Arrhenius factor at this temperature is $10^{-17}$. Using the same frequency factor as before, we conclude that the number of jumps of a monovacancy during one pulse at the peak temperature lies between $10^{-2}$ and $10^{-1}$. This means that Cd is among the metals for which we may safely rule out monovacancy migration as a possible candidate for the explanation of stage III annealing.

In view of the simplicity of the irradiation conditions, the purity of the material, the wide dose range investigated, and the absence of a concentration dependent low-temperature stage, the only serious alternative for stage III in the Cd experiments of Coltman et al. is the free migration of interstitials. Such an interpretation would immediately account for the large number of annealing peaks with concentration-independent positions: They represent series due to recombination of close Frenkel pairs with increasing distance. The limits of these series correspond to free migration of the interstitial with an activation energy that is expected to be not very different for migration parallel or perpendicular to the basal plane. (If the configuration and migration of an interstitial in cadmium is analogous to that of a ⟨100⟩ dumbbell in an fcc crystal, the elementary step of interstitial migration is in an oblique direction to the basal plane (compare ref. [165]). The peak shift of stage III is not analyzed in the paper by Coltman et al. [88]. Qualitatively it appears compatible with the migration of interstitials to randomly distributed vacancies.

Let us finally discuss the change in the population of the substages with dose (item 6). As pointed out by Coltman et al. the suppression of the stages below 26°K and the enhancement of the stages above 26°K with increasing dose appears to be related to the bends in the damage curves at atomic capture fractions of about $5 \times 10^{-4}$. The authors are of the opinion that these two anomalies should be explained in terms of long-range defect migration in the 6–26°K temperature range. However, in the absence of an annealing peak in this temperature range that shifts to lower temperatures with increasing defect concentration we must consider the evidence for low-temperature long-range migration as rather weak. Furthermore, even if direct evidence for long-range migration were found at low temperatures, the peaks *above* the temperature of long-range migration would remain unexplained unless a two-interstitial model was invoked.

The hexagonal structure of Cd suggests that it may be expedient to describe the close pairs by two populations $C_a$ and $C_c$ with different production rates $\phi_a$ and $\phi_c$. If we denote the atomic fraction of capture events by $N$, the simplest set of rate equations for these populations is

$$\frac{dC_a}{dN} = \phi_a - \alpha_a C_a - \alpha_c C_c , \tag{1a}$$

$$\frac{dC_c}{dN} = \phi_c - \gamma_a C_a - \gamma_c C_c . \tag{1b}$$

If $\alpha_c$ and $\gamma_a$ were zero, we would have the usual equations describing radiation annealing, in which $\alpha_a$ and $\gamma_c$ have the meaning of twice the number of sites inside the volume of spontaneous interstitial-vacancy recombinations. The physical meaning of the cross coefficients $\alpha_c$ and $\gamma_a$ can be seen by visualizing the $a$- and $c$-populations as belonging to close pairs that lie approximately perpendicular or parallel to the $c$-axis. A displacement that in a perfect lattice would lead to the formation of a $c$-pair may not only lead to the elimination of an existing $c$-pair (described by $\gamma_c$), but also to the elimination or new formation of an $a$-pair. Thus the cross coefficients contain not only a positive contribution due to recombinations, but also a negative contribution from the transformations of $a$-pairs into $c$-pairs and vice versa.

The general solutions of (1) are well-known. For both $C_a$ and $C_c$ they consist of a constant term plus a linear combination of two exponential functions $\exp(-N/N_1)$ and $\exp(-N/N_2)$. The vanishing of the secular determinant of (1) gives

$$\frac{1}{N_{1,2}} = \tfrac{1}{2}(\alpha_a + \gamma_c) \pm \tfrac{1}{2}[(\alpha_a + \gamma_c)^2 - 4(\alpha_a \gamma_c - \gamma_a \alpha_c)]^{\frac{1}{2}}.$$

In a plot of the damage rate $d(C_a + C_c)/dN$ versus $N$, one expects from this simple model to obtain a sum of two exponential functions. If $N_1$ and $N_2$ are sufficiently different from each other, one exponential will dominate at small doses and the other at *large* doses. The physical meaning of such a representation is that at small doses we have predominantly the $c$-type pairs and at large doses predominantly the $a$-type pairs or vice versa. The plot of the damage rate against the atomic fraction of captures is not contained in the paper by Coltman et al., but it may be qualitatively seen from the plot against the radiation induced resistivity that a representation by two exponentials is presumably quite good. In order to account also for the change of the annealing stages with dose we have to make the assumption that the group dominating at small doses has rather small threshold energies for recombination, while the other group has threshold energies leading up to the above mentioned series limit of free interstitial migration. These ideas are in fact very similar to those discussed by Coltman et al. [88]; what I wish to emphasize in this context is that at the present stage to me it does not appear necessary to invoke long-range migration below 26°K in order to explain the experimental findings.

# PART 8

# INTERSTITIAL IMPURITIES

# INTERSTITIAL METAL IMPURITY DIFFUSION IN METALS

T.R.ANTHONY

*General Electric Research and Development Center, Schenectady, New York*

## 1. Introduction

An examination of the common metallic lattices shows that the size of the available interstices is restricted. If atoms behaved as hard spheres, only very small atoms with atomic radii less than one Ångstrom could squeeze into the interstitial sites in most metals.

By such size arguments, Hägg [1] explained the occurrence of carbon, nitrogen, hydrogen and boron in the interstitial sites in many of the polyvalent transition metals. He proposed that a solute atom could fit into the interstices of a solvent matrix if the ratio of the diameter of the solute atom, $R_s$, to that of the solvent, $R_m$, was less than 0.59. This diameter ratio corresponds to the largest sphere $s$, that will fit into the interstices of a close-packed lattice of spheres $m$.

The Hägg rule for the formation of interstitial solutions is reasonable provided that large repulsive forces between solute and solvent atoms become effective at an interatomic separation, $R_s + R_m$, defined by the atomic size. If the rule is modified for the diamond cubic structure of the semiconductors, it can also account for the interstitial character of solutions of copper, nickel, gold, hydrogen and helium in some of the semiconductors.

The success of Hägg's rule in these cases suggests that it has a general applicability in determining whether a solute can dissolve interstitially in a given solvent. According to Hägg's criterion, no system constituted entirely of metals with the exception of the alkalis should have any interstitial components. This conclusion is in agreement with the general experience that metallic alloys are substitutional solutions.

However, recent experimental evidence [2–8] shows that the noble metals (copper, silver and gold) diffuse interstitially and thus form at least partial interstitial solutions in lead, tin, thallium and indium. In addition, there is evidence that gold, silver and cobalt in praseodymium [9], gold in lanthanum [10] and cobalt in indium [11] form partially or wholly interstitial solutions. These findings are surprising in that:

a. They are the first metal-metal solutions found to exhibit an interstitial character.
b. They clearly violate Hägg's rule as shown in fig. 1.

An immediate conclusion that can be drawn from the interstitial character of
these solutions is that repulsive forces between impurity and solvent atoms in these
solutions are not significant at a separation defined by the atomic sizes of impurity
and solvent atoms. Rather the important size parameter appears to be the ion sizes
of impurity and solvent atoms, for if one redefines Hägg's rule in terms of ion size
instead of atom size, then the occurrence of these partial interstitial solutions does
not violate his geometric rules. As will be seen later, however, a small enough ion
size is only a necessary but not a sufficient condition for the formation of a partial
interstitial solution since there are many metallic ions as small or smaller than those
of gold, silver, copper and cobalt that do not form partial interstitial solutions in the
above-mentioned solvents.

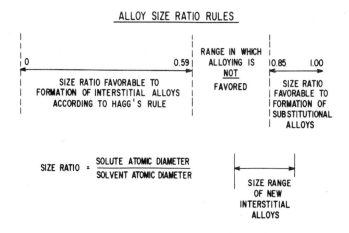

Fig. 1. Atom size rules for substitutional and interstitial alloys.

## 2. Interstitial impurities

### 2.1. *Interstitial impurities in lead solutions*

During the first investigation of solid state diffusion in 1896, Roberts-Austen established that gold diffuses rapidly in lead at moderate temperatures [12]. This work
was later confirmed by Orstrand and Dewey [13]. In contrast, Hevesy showed that
the self diffusion of lead atoms in solid lead is very small in the same temperature
range [14]. Noting this apparent contradiction, Seith and Keil in 1933 measured

and found no enhancement of the diffusivity of lead atoms in a dilute lead (gold) *
alloy by any mixing action [15–17] of the rapidly moving gold solute atoms [15].
This discovery implies that a gold atom can make a large number of diffusional
jumps in a lead (gold) alloy without any accompanying lead diffusion. Seith and
Keil concluded that the interchange, vacancy, or any type of multi-vacancy mechanism is not responsible for the diffusion of gold in lead and that the interstitial
mechanism is most likely. Following the investigations of Seith and his co-workers
[18–20] and a discussion of their work by Wagner [16], no more work was done
on the lead (gold) system for several decades.

   In the meantime, the high mobility of atoms in grain boundaries and dislocations had been demonstrated in a number of experiments. The possibility thus arose
that the rapid diffusion of gold in lead was due to one of these mechanisms. In
1960, Ascoli [21] showed that the fast diffusion of gold in lead was not caused by
grain boundary short circuiting by showing that the diffusivities of gold were identical in poly and single crystals of lead. These results were confirmed by Dyson et
al. in 1966 [3].

   With the elimination of the vacancy, interchange, interstitialcy and grain boundary mechanisms of diffusion, the search for the correct description of gold diffusion in lead was narrowed to two mechanisms: dislocation short circuiting and interstitial volume diffusion. In 1966, Kidson [2] showed that a dislocation diffusion
mechanism for gold in lead was inconsistent with the experimental gold-concentra-
tion penetration profiles and the magnitude of the dislocation density of his lead
crystals. In addition, he found that neither the diffusion coefficient nor the solubility of gold in lead was affected by increasing the dislocation density of his lead
crystals. Consequently, Kidson concluded that the observed diffusion of gold in
lead is due almost entirely to gold atoms moving as interstitials through the perfect
lead lattice.

   Although it appears that the migration of gold atoms through lead is accomplished almost entirely by interstitial volume diffusion, it is believed that gold dissolves in both interstitial and substitutional sites in lead [2, 4, 22]. In such a case,
the diffusion of gold in lead would be most accurately described by the dissociative diffusion mechanism proposed by Frank and Turnbull [23]. If $D_I$ and $D_S$
are the respective diffusivities of interstitial and substitutional gold and $C_I$ and $C_S$
are the respective concentrations of interstitial and substitutional gold, then the
diffusivity of gold $D$ may be expressed as:

$$D = \frac{C_I}{C_I + C_S} D_I + \frac{C_S}{C_I + C_S} D_S .$$  (1)

Because the experimentally observed diffusion constant of gold in lead is many orders of magnitude greater than its expected substitutional diffusivity in lead, the
second term in eq. (1) may be neglected and eq. (1) becomes:

* The following alloy notation is used: solvent (solute).

$$D = \frac{C_I}{C_I + C_S} D_I = \frac{K}{K + 1} D_I \tag{2}$$

where $K = C_I/C_S$. Anthony et al. [4] have calculated the pressure dependence of the diffusion constant in this type of dissociative solute solution and found that the second derivative of the logarithm of the diffusivity with respect to pressure could be expressed as:

$$\frac{\partial^2 \ln D}{\partial p^2} = -\frac{K}{(K + 1)^2} \left( \frac{\Delta V}{kT} \right)^2 \tag{3}$$

where $\Delta V$ is the change in volume accompanying the transfer of a solute atom from an interstitial to a substitutional position in the solvent. From the pressure dependence of the diffusivity of gold in lead measured by Ascoli et al. [22], Anthony and his co-workers concluded that the interstitial/substitutional ratio of gold solute is either very large or very small. Rossolimo and Turnbull, on the other hand, estimate from their quench and resistivity experiments that 10—15% of gold solute atoms dissolve interstitially at 300°C [24]. The difference in these results is probably mainly a result of the indirectness of both experiments and the consequent uncertainties inherent in their interpretation. The determination of the exact interstitial/ substitutional ratio awaits an equilibrium experiment like that performed on the aluminum (silver) system by Beaman et al. [25].

The early work of Seith and Keil [15] suggested that silver might also diffuse interstitially in lead. Dyson et al. [3] confirmed their work and found that the dissolution of silver in lead caused no enhancement of the lead diffusivity although a minimum increase of a factor of ten was dictated if diffusion occurred by an interchange, interstitialcy or vacancy mechanism. After ruling out the possibilities of grain boundary or dislocation short circuiting, Dyson et al. [3] concluded that silver also diffuses interstitially in lead. From the pressure dependence of the diffusivity of silver in lead determined by Curtain et al. [26], Anthony et al. [4] concluded that the interstitial/substitutional ratio of silver solute is, similar to the gold case, either very large or very small.

Despite the fact that gold and silver have the same atomic size and valence, the diffusivity of gold in lead is an order of magnitude greater than the diffusity of silver, as can be seen in fig. 2. It is believed [5, 6, 27] that this difference originates in a proportionately higher gold than silver interstitial solute population. This diffusion behavior of gold and silver in lead is opposite to that found in known substitutional solutions such as gold and silver in copper, gold, silver and zinc solvents, where the diffusivity of silver is consistently higher than that of gold.

The partial interstitial dissolution of gold and silver in lead is not only reflected in the diffusion behavior described previously but in the magnitude of the solution hardening in these alloys. Westbrook and Aust [28] observed that additions of silver and gold to lead cause solution hardening approximately fifty times larger per atomic per cent than that associated with known substitutional solutes

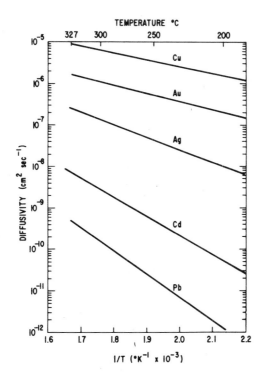

Fig. 2. The diffusivities of copper, silver, gold, cadmium and lead in lead.

in lead. The much larger amount of solution hardening is probably caused by a disproportionate increase in the local elastic modulus of the solution around interstitial impurity atoms.

For equal atomic fractions of gold and silver, gold causes two to three times as much hardening as silver in lead even though gold and silver have equal atomic diameters and the same valence. If the anomalously large solution hardening in these systems is a result of interstitial solution, the greater effect of gold again suggests that a higher proportion of gold solute atoms occupy interstitial sites than do silver.

Aust and Westbrook [29] on the basis of Seybolt et al.'s model [30] have suggested that the non-equilibrium grain boundary hardening observed after quenching and annealing lead (gold) and lead (silver) solutions may be a result of the partial interstitial nature of these solutions. Anthony [31], however, has pointed out some difficulties with this interpretation.

Dyson et al. [3] have also measured the diffusivity of copper in lead and found that it was another order of magnitude higher than that of gold in lead. This result was not unexpected since copper belongs to the family of noble metals and has a smaller atom size than silver and gold.

Miller has recently investigated the diffusion of cadmium in lead and has found that the diffusivity of cadmium is much smaller than the diffusivity of the noble metals in lead [33]. An acceleration of the lead diffusivity by cadmium additions was noted, implying that cadmium does not diffuse by a purely interstitial mechanism. However, the enhancement coefficient that was found by Miller is inconsistent with a vacancy mechanism of diffusion. He suggests that the diffusion of cadmium in lead can be accounted for in terms of an interchange mechanism in which a cadmium atom moves momentarily from a substitutional to an adjacent interstitial position leaving behind a vacancy. A lead atom in a neighboring site interchanges sites with the vacancy and the interstitial cadmium atom then falls into the new position of the vacancy, completing the interchange. Miller has proposed a similar mechanism to describe the diffusion of gold in germanium [34] and indium in silicon [35].

A summary of the diffusion data of copper, silver, gold, cadmium and lead in lead is given in table 1 and fig. 2.

Table 1
Diffusion constants of gold, silver, copper, cadmium and lead in lead.

| Element | $D = D_0 \exp(-Q/kT)$ | | Reference |
|---|---|---|---|
| | $D_0$ (cm$^2$/sec) | $Q$ (eV) | |
| gold | 0.103 | 0.641 | 15 |
| | $4.1 \times 10^{-3}$ | 0.407 | 21 |
| | $8.7 \times 10^{-3}$ | 0.436 | 2 |
| silver | $7.45 \times 10^{-2}$ | 0.663 | 15 |
| | $4.6 \times 10^{-2}$ | 0.630 | 3 |
| copper | $7.9 \times 10^{-3}$ | 0.349 | 3 |
| cadmium | 0.405 | 0.923 | 33 |
| lead | 0.281 | 1.055 | 49 |
| | 1.17 | 1.120 | 50 |
| | 1.37 | 1.137 | 51 |
| | 6.6 | 1.215 | 14,52 |

2.2. Interstitial impurities of tin solutions

White tin has a body-centered tetragonal structure that causes diffusion in tin to be anisotropic. Meakin and Klokholm [36] in interpreting their self diffusion data in tin, demonstrated that the faster tin diffusion in the a-direction than the c was consistent with a vacancy mechanism.

White tin's crystal structure is expected to have the opposite effect on the anisotropy of diffusion of an interstitial solute. Down the c-axis of white tin, there are large rectangular interstitial tunnels along which interstitials could migrate easily. In contrast, in the a-direction of tin, no comparable interstitial channels exist and a migrating interstitial atom is forced to follow a much more twisting path. Consequently, one would anticipate that the c-direction instead of the a-direction would be the fast diffusion axis for an interstitial.

This expectation is born out by the diffusion data of gold and silver in tin of Dyson [7] and the diffusion data of copper in tin reported by Dyson et al. [8]. It was found that both gold and silver diffuse ten times faster in the c-direction than in the "a", and that their diffusivities are several orders of magnitude greater than the self diffusivity of tin.

Copper's diffusivity along the a axis of tin is another three orders of magnitude greater than the diffusivity of gold and silver in this direction. The mobility of copper along the c axis of tin is so high that Dyson et al. [8] were forced to go down to room temperature to measure its mobility with the experimental technique that they were using. At this temperature, the diffusivity of copper in the c-direction is 12 orders of magnitude greater than the self-diffusivity of tin along the same axis.

The anisotropy of diffusion and the magnitudes of the diffusivities of copper, silver and gold in tin strongly suggest that the noble metals migrate interstitially and thus dissolve at least partially in the interstitial state in tin. The diffusivities of copper, silver, gold, zinc and tin in tin appear in fig. 3. A summary of the diffusion data is given in table 2.

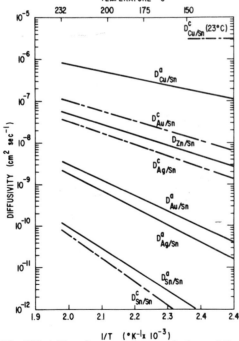

Fig. 3. The diffusivities of copper, silver, gold, zinc and tin in tin.

Table 2
Diffusion constants of gold, silver, copper, zinc and tin in tin.

| | | $D = D_0 \exp(-Q/kT)$ | | |
|---|---|---|---|---|
| Element | Axis | $D_0$ (cm$^2$/sec) | $Q$(eV) | Reference |
| gold | $c$ | $5.8 \times 10^{-3}$ | 0.478 | 7 |
| | $a$ | $1.6 \times 10^{-1}$ | 0.770 | 7 |
| silver | $c$ | $7.1 \times 10^{-3}$ | 0.536 | 7 |
| | $a$ | $1.8 \times 10^{-1}$ | 0.802 | 7 |
| copper | $c$ | $2 \times 10^{-6}$ cm$^2$/sec at 25°C | | 8 |
| | $a$ | $2.4 \times 10^{-3}$ | 0.344 | 8 |
| zinc | | $5.9 \times 10^{-3}$ | 0.513 | 37 |
| tin | | 8.2 | 1.115 | 36 |
| | | 1.4 | 1.015 | 36 |

Bergner and Lange [37] have measured diffusion coefficients of tin and zinc in pure tin and a homogeneous tin (zinc = 1 at %) alloy. They found that the diffusivity of zinc is much larger than the diffusivity of tin. If the zinc were diffusing by a vacancy mechanism, the diffusivity of tin in the homogeneous alloy should be increased by at least an order of magnitude because of the mixing action [15–17] of the rapidly moving zinc solute. Bergner and Lange, however, found little or no enhancement of the tin diffusivity in the homogeneous alloy. This lack of enhancement suggests that zinc may be diffusing interstitially in tin. From the data presented by Berger and Lange, however, neither grain boundary diffusion nor dislocation short circuiting can be ruled out as the possible diffusion mechanism.

### 2.3. Interstitial impurities in indium solutions

The diffusion of gold and silver in indium is qualitatively very similar to the diffusion of gold and silver in lead. Anthony and Turnbull [5] showed that gold's diffusivity is an order of magnitude greater than silver's diffusivity in indium which in turn is two orders of magnitude greater than the self diffusivity of indium [38]. A graph of the diffusivity of gold, silver and indium in indium versus reciprocal temperature is shown in fig. 4 and the diffusion constants are listed in table 3.

Indium possesses a slightly distorted face-centered cubic structure with a $c/a$ ratio of 1.07. For self diffusion, which is most probably by a vacancy mechanism, the diffusional anisotropy is small with the $a$ axis being the fastest axis. In contrast, silver diffuses faster in the $c$-direction but again the anisotropy is small. Unlike the case of impurity diffusion in tin [7,8], the small anisotropy of diffusion of silver in indium is difficult to interpret in terms of a particular diffusion mechanism.

In a solution of indium saturated with gold, Powell and Braun [38] detected no increase in the diffusivity of indium. The lack of mixing action of the rapidly moving gold solute indicates that gold is not diffusing by an interchange, interstiti-

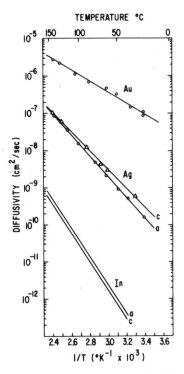

Fig. 4. The diffusivities of gold, silver and indium in indium.

Table 3
Diffusion constants of gold, silver and indium in indium.

| | | $D = D_0 \exp(-Q/kT)$ | | |
|---|---|---|---|---|
| Element | Axis | $D_0$ (cm$^2$/sec) | $Q$(eV) | Reference |
| silver | $c$ | $1.1 \times 10^{-1}$ | 0.501 | 5 |
| | $a$ | $5.2 \times 10^{-1}$ | 0.557 | 5 |
| gold | | $9 \times 10^{-3}$ | 0.292 | 5 |
| indium | $c$ | 2.7 | 0.815 | 38 |
| | $a$ | 3.7 | 0.815 | 38 |

alcy or vacancy mechanism. No similar data is available for silver. Dislocation short circuiting of gold and silver solutes in indium was also ruled out as a possible mechanism for essentially the same reasons that it had been excluded from consideration with lead as the solvent. Consequently, Anthony and Turnbull [5] concluded that gold and silver diffuse interstitially and thus form at least partial interstitial solutions in indium.

Other investigators using the Mössbauer effect have found indications that cobalt also dissolves interstitially in indium. In Mössbauer studies, the recoil free fraction $f$ of gamma rays is an important parameter. The recoil free fraction $f$ is related to the recoil displacement $x$ and the wavelength $\lambda$ of the radiation of the radioactive atom by

$$f = \exp(-4\pi^2 \langle x^2 \rangle / \lambda^2) . \tag{4}$$

The recoil displacement $x$ is dependent on the properties of the radioactive nucleus and its interaction with the host material in which it sits. If the radioactive atom is firmly wedged in the host lattice, the recoil displacement $x$ will tend to be small and the recoil free fraction $f$ will be large.

Gonser and his co-workers [11] have found that the recoil free fraction $f$ of gamma rays from radioactive $Co^{57}$ (actually from its daughter $Fe^{57}$) in indium is much larger than that expected if Co forms a substitutional solution with indium. They suggest that an explanation of the anomalously high $f$-value of $Fe^{57}$ in indium is that cobalt, its parent, occupies interstitial sites in indium and thus its radioactive daughter $Fe^{57}$ experiences larger restoring forces than if it occupied a substitutional site. Their suggestion of larger restoring forces with interstitial cobalt and iron is consistent with the unusually large amounts of solution hardening observed in other partial interstitial solutions [28]. The line width of the gamma radiation from $Co^{57}$ in indium, corrected for instrumental broadening, is the natural line width. This observation rules out the possibility that the cobalt is associated with dislocations in indium.

## 2.4. Interstitial impurities in thallium

Of the solvents in which gold and silver diffuse interstitially, thallium is one of the most interesting for two reasons. First, thallium transforms at 232°C from a low temperature h.c.p. form to a high temperature b.c.c. phase. In this transformation, the linear dimensions of the largest interstitial site decrease by 15%. Secondly, the low temperature h.c.p. phase of thallium is anisotropic and any resulting anisotropy of solute diffusion coefficients can help to identify their diffusion mechanisms.

When thallium transforms from a close-packed hexagonal structure to a body-centered cubic structure, a more open form results in which the volume per atom has increased by 2%. Consequently, from a hard sphere model of the crystal lattice, one would anticipate that the transformation would increase the atomic mobility. This is indeed the case for thallium self diffusion (which is undoubtedly by a vacancy mechanism) where the diffusivity increases by a factor of 25 on the change of phase from h.c.p. to b.c.c. [39] (fig. 5).

However, in a situation where solute atoms are distributed between substitutional and interstitial sites, the effect of the phase transformation on the solute diffusivity is less clear. For such a solute, the diffusion coefficient is given by eq. (1). It is expected that both the interstitial diffusivity $D_I$ and substitutional diffusivity

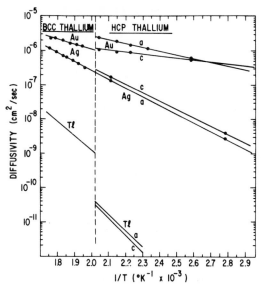

Fig. 5. The diffusivities of gold, silver and thallium in thallium.

Table 4

Diffusion constants of gold, silver and thallium in thallium.

| | | | $D = D_0 \exp(-Q/kT)$ | | |
|---|---|---|---|---|---|
| Element | Phase | Axis | $D_0$ (cm$^2$/sec) | $Q$(eV) | Reference |
| silver | T h.c.p. | $c$ | $2.7 \times 10^{-2}$ | 0.488 | 6 |
| | | $a$ | $3.8 \times 10^{-2}$ | 0.513 | 6 |
| | T b.c.c. | | $4.2 \times 10^{-2}$ | 0.518 | 6 |
| gold | T h.c.p. | $c$ | $2.0 \times 10^{-5}$ | 0.122 | 6 |
| | | $a$ | $5.3 \times 10^{-4}$ | 0.226 | 6 |
| | T b.c.c. | | $5.2 \times 10^{-4}$ | 0.261 | 6 |
| thallium | T h.c.p. | $c$ | 0.4 | 0.997 | 39 |
| | | $a$ | 0.4 | 0.984 | 39 |
| | T b.c.c. | | 0.7 | 0.870 | 39 |

$D_S$ will increase as thallium transforms to the more open b.c.c. structure. In contrast, the interstitial concentration $C_I$ will probably decrease because of the decrease in size of interstitial sites accompanying the h.c.p. to b.c.c. transformation. If the drop in $C_I$ is larger than the increase in $D_I$, the measured diffusivity will decrease during the transformation provided that $C_I D_I \gg C_S D_S$. This is apparently the case for gold solutions in thallium since the diffusivity of gold decreases on the phase transformation from h.c.p. to b.c.c. thallium in contrast to the twenty-five fold increase in thallium self diffusion in the same transformation.

The diffusivity of silver in thallium in unchanged by the h.c.p. to b.c.c. transformation. Apparently for this solute, variations in $C_I$, $C_S$, $D_I$, $D_S$ cancel out in the phase change, leaving the measured diffusivity unaltered.

Anthony et al. [6] have interpreted the difference in activation energies for gold and silver diffusion between the $c$- and $a$-directions in h.c.p. thallium in terms of an interstitial model. A h.c.p. crystal contains large octahedral and small tetrahedral interstitial sites. In the basal plane of a h.c.p. crystal, these types of sites alternate so that every other site that an interstitial atom migrating along the basal plane must pass through is a small tetrahedral interstitial site. Perpendicular to the basal plane, however, the large octahedral sites are piled in columns, one on top of another. Hence, an interstitial solute atom travelling along the $c$ axis can jump from one large octahedral site to another and need never pass through the small tetrahedral sites. Consequently, one would anticipate that the activation energy for interstitial migration would be less along the $c$ axis than along the $a$ axis as is observed for both gold and silver diffusion in thallium.

In view of the above characteristics of the diffusion constants of silver and gold in thallium and the striking similarity of these systems with other gold and silver interstitial solute systems, Anthony et al. [6] concluded that both gold and silver diffuse interstitially and thus form at least partial interstitial solutions in both the h.c.p. and b.c.c. phases of thallium.

## 2.5. Interstitial impurities in the rare earth metals

Dariel et al. [9] have measured the diffusivities of gold and cobalt in both the h.c.p. and b.c.c. phases of praseodymium. The diffusion behaviour of gold and praseodymium in praseodymium is qualitatively identical to the diffusion behavior of gold and thallium in thallium as seen in fig. 6 and table 5. In the phase transformation from the low temperature h.c.p. phase to the high temperature b.c.c. phase, the diffusivity of gold decreases by a factor of two whereas the self diffusivity of praseodymium increases by two orders of magnitude. The diffusivity of cobalt increases slightly in the same transformation. Dariel et al. calculate on the basis of ion core sizes that cobalt can be accommodated in interstitial sites in both the h.c.p. and b.c.c. phases of praseodymium with no ion core overlap. Gold on the other hand will only fit into the low temperature h.c.p. phase with no ion core overlap. Thus Dariel et al. argue that the interstitial concentration of gold should decrease during the h.c.p. to b.c.c. transformation whereas the interstitial concentration of cobalt should remain constant. Moreover, the interstitial diffusivity should increase slightly in the same transformation. Since the measured diffusivity is a product of the interstitial concentration times the interstitial diffusivity, Dariel et al. conclude that if these solutes dissolve at least partially interstitially that the diffusivity of gold should decrease while the diffusivity of cobalt should increase in the h.c.p. to b.c.c. transformation. This is exactly what is observed experimentally.

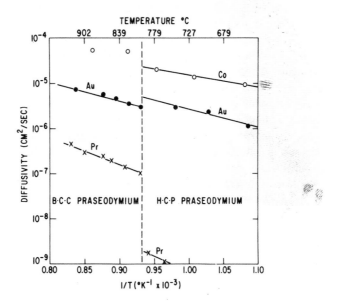

Fig. 6. The diffusivities of gold, cobalt and praseodymium in praseodymium.

Table 5
Diffusion constants of gold, cobalt and praseodymium in praseodymium.

| Element | Phase | $D_0$ (cm$^2$/sec) | $Q$(eV) | Reference |
|---------|-------|-----|-------|-----------|
| Au | Pr h.c.p. | $4.3 \times 10^{-2}$ | 0.85 | 9 |
|    | Pr b.c.c. | $3.3 \times 10^{-2}$ | 0.87 | 9 |
| Co | Pr h.c.p. | $4.7 \times 10^{-2}$ | 0.79 | 9 |
| Pr | Pr b.c.c. | $1.2 \times 10^{-1}$ | 1.31 | 9 |

In some recent unpublished work, Dariel [10] has found that silver also diffuses very rapidly in praseodymium and that its diffusivity is only slightly increased by the h.c.p. to b.c.c. phase transformation. This behavior is again very similar to that found in thallium. The diffusivity of indium in praseodymium [10] is very similar to the self diffusion of the praseodymium and increases two orders of magnitude in the h.c.p. to b.c.c. phase change. Thus indium in contrast to gold, silver, and cobalt appears to dissolve substitutionally rather than interstitially in praseodymium.

## 2.6. The alkali metals

Although the mechanism of solute diffusion in the alkali metals has not been established, a number of characteristics of the solute diffusion behavior are indicative

of an interstitial mechanism. While sodium self diffusion is believed to be by a
vacancy mechanism [40,41], the diffusion behavior of gold in sodium obtained by
Barr et al. [42] strikingly resembles the diffusion behaviour of gold in lead, tin, thallium, indium and praseodymium. The interstitial diffusion of gold in sodium would
not be too surprising since sodium has a very open lattice with a lattice spacing
larger than that of lead, tin, thallium, indium or praseodymium.

Recently Ott and Lodding [43] have measured the diffusivities of lithium, gold,
silver, sodium, gallium, mercury, cadmium, indium and tin in lithium as shown in
fig. 7. Several anomalies were noted by them. First, gold diffused five times faster
than silver did in lithium despite the fact that gold and silver have the same atomic
size and valence. As we shall see in the next section, gold is expected and does diffuse faster in interstitial solutions and slower in substitutional solutions than does
silver. Thus, the faster diffusivity of gold strongly suggests an interstitial mechanism.

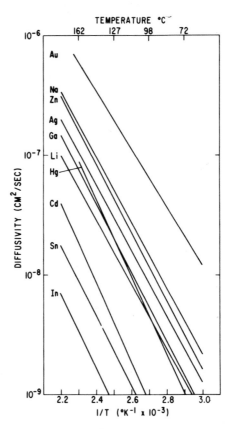

Fig. 7. The diffusivities of gold, silver, sodium, zinc, cadmium, mercury, gallium, indium, tin
and lithium in lithium.

Secondly, the diffusivity of gold was one order of magnitude greater than the self diffusivity of the lithium. This behavior is very similar to other interstitial systems previously described. Finally, it was found that the solute diffusivity in lithium decreases with increasing solute valence. This decrease is opposite to an expected increase in solute diffusivity with increasing solute valence, if a vacancy mechanism were operative [44]. As we shall see in the next section, a decrease in solute diffusivity with increasing solute valence is what one would predict in a dissociative solute solution where diffusion proceeds mainly by an interstitial mechanism.

## 3. Discussion

A solute atom in a solvent lattice can occupy two different types of lattice sites. The solute atom may replace a host atom becoming a substitutional solute or it can lodge in the intertices of the host lattice, becoming an interstitial solute. The most general type of solution that may form is the dissociative solute solution in which solute atoms occupy both interstitial and substitutional sites.

The distribution of solute between interstitial and substitutional sites is determined by the condition that the chemical potential of the solute must be equal on both sites. If $\mu_o$ is the standard state chemical potential of the solute, then $\mu_I$ and $\mu_S$, the respective chemical potentials of the interstitial and substitutional solute atoms, are given by

$$\mu_I = \mu_o + kT \ln \gamma_I X_I$$

$$\mu_S = \mu_o + kT \ln \gamma_S X_S$$

(5)

where $X_I$ and $X_S$ are the mole fractions of interstitial and substitutional solute, respectively, and $\gamma_I$ and $\gamma_S$ are their activity coefficients. Equilibrium demands that

$$\mu_I = \mu_S \quad \text{or} \quad \frac{X_I}{X_S} = \frac{\gamma_S}{\gamma_I} .$$

(6)

For dilute solutions, solution theory gives

$$\gamma = \exp\left(\Delta G/kT\right)$$

(7)

where $\Delta G$ is the change in free energy from the standard state. Thus,

$$\frac{X_I}{X_S} = \exp\left(-\frac{\Delta G_{IS}}{kT}\right) = K \exp\left(\frac{\Delta S_{IS}^T}{k}\right) \exp\left(-\frac{\Delta H_{IS}}{kT}\right) .$$

(8)

Here $\Delta H_{IS}$ represents the enthalpy difference between an interstitial and a substitutional solute atom, $\Delta S_{IS}^T$ is the difference in a solute atom's thermal entropy between the two types of lattice sites and $K$ is a geometric factor related to the relative numbers of interstitial and substitutional sites for the particular crystal structure being considered.

In order to determine the thermal entropy difference $\Delta S_{IS}^T$, a simple Einstein model of the solid will be considered. In this approximation, the thermal entropy of the solution is equivalent to the thermal entropy of a system of harmonic oscillators. Let the local force constants of the harmonic oscillators equal $f_S$ for the substitutional and $f_I$ for the interstitial dissolution of solute atoms. If the thermal energy is much larger than the vibrational energy of the oscillators, then it can be shown [45] that the change in thermal entropy between the substitutional and interstitial dissolution of a solute atom is

$$\Delta S_{IS}^T = -1.5\,k \ln{(f_I/f_S)}\,. \tag{9}$$

Because the interstitial site is considerably smaller than the substitutional site, $f_I > f_S$. Thus $\Delta S_{IS}^T$ is negative and will be more negative, the larger or more highly charged the interstitial ion is. Consequently, on the basis of thermal entropy alone, one would expect that those solute atoms with the smallest atomic size and valence would have the highest proportion of their atoms in interstitial positions in a solvent.

Weiser [46] and Millea [34] have considered the different energies that make up the total change of enthalpy of a solute atom between a substitutional and an interstitial position. For the heat of mixing of a substitutional impurity, Weiser envisioned the following process. First, the solute is evaporated from its own lattice ($H_L'$). Concurrently a solvent atom is evaporated from the interior of its own lattice and condensed back on its own surface ($H_L$). The solute atom in the gas phase is ionized ($I$), and the solute atom is placed in the vacancy created in the solvent lattice. Simultaneously, the solute's ionized electrons are placed in the solvent lattice and fall to an electronic energy $E_k^S$. On introduction of the substitutional solute ion, there is an increase in the electrostatic binding $E_B^S$ along with an increase in the strain energy $E_R^S$ caused by the difference in charge and size between solute and solvent atoms. Thus, the heat of mixing of a substitutional impurity is

$$H_S = H_L' + H_L - E_B^S + E_R^S - E_k^S + I\,. \tag{10}$$

Here $H_L$ is the heat of sublimation of the solvent, $H_L'$ is the heat of sublimation of the solute, $E_B^S$ is the electrostatic binding of the substitutional solute in the solvent, $I$ is the energy necessary to ionize the solute atom, $E_R^S$ is the strain energy produced by the substitutional solute and $E_k^S$ is the energy difference between free, ionized electrons and the substitutional solute's electrons in the solvent lattice.

A parallel process is considered for the interstitial solute. First, the solute atom is evaporated from its own lattice ($H_L'$) and ionized ($I$). Then the solute is introduced into an interstitial site in the solvent lattice. With the introduction of the interstitial solute ion, an increase in electrostatic cohesion results from the interaction of the positive ion core of the interstitial solute with the solvent's conduction electrons ($E_B^I$). In addition, there will be a repulsion between the interstitial solute ion and neighbouring solvent ions $E_R^I$. Finally, the solute's ionized electrons enter the solvent crystal and drop to the top of the solvent's Fermi surface $(E_k^I)$. Thus the heat of solution of an interstitial solute is:

$$H_I = H_L' + I - E_k^I + E_R^I - E_B^I \tag{11}$$

where $E_k^I$ is approximately equal to the work function of the solvent metal times the solute valence, $E_R^I$ is the repulsive energy between these same ions, and $E_B^I$ is the electrostatic interaction between the solvent's conduction electrons and the interstitial solute ion. The difference in enthalpy between a solute atom in an interstitial and substitutional site is then

$$\Delta H_{IS} = H_I - H_S = [(-H_L + E_B^S) - E_B^I] + [E_R^I - E_R^S] + [E_k^S - E_k^I] \tag{12}$$

The interstitial population will increase with a decreasing $\Delta H_{IS}$.

Although any quantitative calculation of these three terms is not yet feasible, some physical arguments can be made to obtain a rough estimation of how the interstitial and substitutional heats of solutions should vary with solute valence. As a simplification, only metal solute ions which are small enough to fit into both substitutional and interstitial sites in a solvent will be considered. Consequently, we may center our interest on the effect of valence on the substitutional and interstitial heats of solution of a solute.

Given the above conditions, if the valence of a solute is zero, then its substitutional heat of solution $H_S$ is expected to be approximately the heat of formation of a vacancy. As the solute valence increases, $H_S$ is expected to decrease to zero at the point where the solute valence equals the solvent valence and then to reverse direction and increase with a further increase in solute valence.

In contrast, the solute's interstitial heat of solution $H_I$ is expected to increase monotonically and rapidly with solute valence from a small value at a solute valence of zero. The anticipated variation of $H_I$ and $H_S$ and $H_I - H_S$ with solute valence is shown schematically in fig. 8. As can be seen in fig. 8, valence considerations indicate that *the tendency towards interstitial dissolution of a solute atom should increase with decreasing solute valence.*

A consideration of valence and size effects leads us to postulate the following three conditions for the interstitial dissolution of a solute:

1. a polyvalent or very electropositive solvent
2. a sufficiently small ion size
3. a low solute valence.

Let us then examine the experimental evidence. In all of the metal-metal interstitial solutions that have been verified or suspected, all of the solvents had either a valence of plus three or plus four [2–11] or were very electropositive [42–43]. Thus the first condition for interstitial dissolution is satisfied in these systems.

Secondly, it has been shown that in all metal-metal solutions exhibiting interstitial characteristics, the solute ion could be accommodated in the interstices of the solvent matrix with little or no ion core overlap.

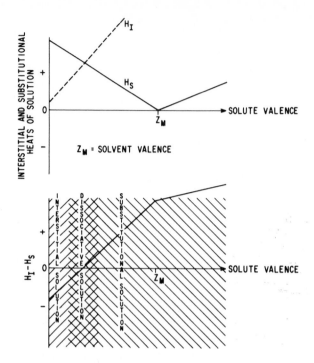

Fig. 8. The variation of the interstitial and substitutional heats of solution of a small metal solute ion with solute valence.

Once the necessary condition of a sufficiently small ion size is satisfied, valence effects will then determine whether a substitutional or interstitial solution will be formed. If one assumes that the valence of an atom in solution is the number of electrons in excess of the last completed shell, then one obtains the valencies shown in table 6 [47]. These valencies must be adjusted for screening effects in solution. For example, a very electropositive element may have an effectively higher valency and a very electronegative element may have an effectively lower valency than those values given in the table. From the table, one can see that the transition metals and the noble metals should have the greatest tendency to dissolve interstitially according to our criterion of low solute valence. This prediction is in agreement with experimental evidence since the only metal-metal interstitial solutions that have been identified involved either the noble metals or transition metals as solutes [2–11,42,43].

The diffusion mechanism in a dissociative solute solution was described by Frank and Turnbull [23]. If $X_I$ and $X_S$ are respectively the fractions of interstitial and substitutional solute and $D_I$ and $D_S$ are respectively the interstitial and substitutional diffusivities of the solute, then the measured diffusivity $D$ of the solute may be expressed as

Table 6
Valencies of selected elements.

| Valence | Elements |
| --- | --- |
| 0 | Fe, Co, Ni, Ru, Pd, Pt, Ir, Os |
| 1 | Cu, Ag, Au |
| 2 | Be, Mg, Zn, Cd, Hg |
| 3 | Ga, Al, In, Tl |
| 4 | Si, Ge, Sn, Pb |
| 5 | P, As, Sb, Bi |

$$D = X_I D_I + X_S D_S .  \tag{13}$$

Since the interstitial diffusivity $D_I$ is normally much larger than the substitutional diffusivity $D_S$, an increase in the interstitial/substitutional solute ratio will cause an increase in the measured diffusivity. From preceding discussion, it is anticipated that the tendency for the interstitial dissolution of a solute will increase with a decrease in solute valence. Moreover since the interstitial diffusivity $D_I$ should also increase with decreasing solute valence, we expect that *in systems which have some interstitial character, the measured solute diffusivity will increase with a decrease in solute valence.* This valence effect is opposite to the valence effect reported for diffusion in substitutional solutions where the diffusivity of a solute increases with increasing solute valence presumably because of an attraction between negatively charged vacancies and positively charged solute ions [44].

A possible example of valence effects on solute diffusivities in partial interstitial solutions is solute diffusion in lead. Here it is found that the diffusivity of a solute decreases with increasing solute valence. For example, in the fifth period of the periodic table, $D(Ag^{+1}) > D(Cd^{+2}) > D(In^{+3}) > D(Sn^{+4})$ and in the sixth period $D(Au^{+1}) > D(Hg^{+2}) > D(Tl^{+3}) > D(Pb^{+4})$ [18]. This decrease of solute diffusivities in lead from silver to tin and from gold to lead takes place despite an accompanying decrease in ionic size across both periods. The character of the solute diffusion also varies across the periods as might be expected. For example, silver diffuses by an interstitial [3,15] cadmium by an interchange [33] and tin by a vacancy mechanism.

In contrast to the decrease in ion size across both periods, the atomic size increases so one can reasonably argue that it is the increase in atomic size rather than the increase in solute valence that is causing the decrease in solute atom mobility. In order to eliminate the complication of different atomic sizes, it is necessary to examine the diffusion behavior of two different solute atoms with equal atomic diameters. Fortunately nature has provided us with such a pair, namely gold and silver.

Table 7

Comparison of the diffusivities of gold and silver in substitutional and partially or wholly interstitial solutions.

| $\alpha \equiv D_{Ag}/D_{Au}$ | | | | |
| --- | --- | --- | --- | --- |
| Substitutional solutions [53] | | | | |
| Solvent | Au | Ag | Cu | Zn |
| $a$ | $>1$ | $>1$ | $>1$ | $>1$ |
| Interstitial solutions [2–10] | | | | |
| Solvent | Pb | Sn | Tl | In | Pr |
| $a$ | $<1$ | $<1$ | $<1$ | $<1$ | $<1$ |

According to Muldawer [48], the screening of a monovalent solute ion is proportional to its first atomic ionization potential since the retention of electrons around an ion should be directly related to the energy necessary to remove them from the neutral atom. Because the first ionization potential of gold is 0.25 eV larger than the first ionization potential of silver, Muldawer argues that the screening around a gold ion will be greater than the screening around a silver ion in a metallic solution. Thus the effective solute valence of a gold atom will be less than the effective valence of a silver atom in a solid solution.

As a consequence, one would anticipate that silver would diffuse faster than gold in substitutional solutions and that gold would diffuse faster than silver in solutions with an interstitial character. In table 7, the relative diffusivities of silver and gold in four substitutional solutions and five partially or wholly interstitial systems are given. It is seen that the valence ideas correctly predict the relative diffusivities of gold and silver in both types of solutions. Other arguments involving either the difference in ion sizes of gold and silver or the difference in polarizabilities of their ion cores would incorrectly call for, respectively, a larger diffusivity of silver in both types of solutions or a larger diffusivity of gold in both types of solutions.

## 4. Conclusion

Experimental evidence indicates that the noble metals in tin, thallium, lead and indium, and gold, silver and cobalt in praseodymium diffuse interstitially and thus form at least partial interstitial solutions. In addition to these systems, there are strong indications that the noble metals in lithium and sodium, and zinc in tin also diffuse interstitially and hence form at least partial interstitial solutions. Finally, Mössbauer evidence shows that cobalt dissolves completely interstitially in indium. The occurrence of these partial or wholly interstitial systems has been explained qualitatively in terms of a model in which solute valence, solvent valence and solute ion size are important.

## Acknowledgements

I would like to acknowledge a number of stimulating and invaluable discussions with M.Dariel, B.Dyson, W.Miller, A.Lodding, A.Ott, A.Rossolimo, P.Thernquist and D.Turnbull. I would also like to thank R.Fullman and L.Johnson for a critical review of this manuscript.

## References

[1] G.Hägg, Z. Phys. Chem. 6B (1929) 221; 7B (1930) 339; 8B (1930) 445.
[2] G.V.Kidson, Phil. Mag. 13 (1966) 247.
[3] B.F.Dyson, T.R.Anthony and D.Turnbull, J. Appl. Phys. 37 (1966) 2370.
[4] T.R.Anthony, B.F.Dyson and D.Turnbull, J. Appl. Phys. 37 (1966) 2925.
[5] T.R.Anthony and D.Turnbull, Phys. Rev. 151 (1966) 495.
[6] T.R.Anthony, B.F.Dyson and D.Turnbull, J. Appl. Phys. 39 (1968) 1391.
[7] B.F.Dyson, J. Appl. Phys. 37 (1966) 2375.
[8] B.F.Dyson, T.R.Anthony and D.Turnbull, J. Appl. Phys. 38 (1967) 3408.
[9] M.P.Dariel, G.Erez and G.M.J.Schmidt, Jül. Conf. 2, Vol. 1 (1968) p. 91.
[10] M.P.Dariel, Personal communication.
[11] P.A.Flinn, U.Gonser, R.W.Grant and R.M.Housely, Phys. Rev. 157 (1967) 530.
[12] W.C.Roberts-Austen, Proc. Roy. Soc. 59 (1896) 281; Phil. Trans. Roy. Soc. 187 (1896) 404.
[13] C.E.Van Ostrand and F.P.Dewey, U.S.Geol. Survey, Prof. Paper 95 (1915) 83.
[14] G.V.Hevesy, Wien-Ber-II(A) 129 (1920) 549.
[15] W.Seith and A.Keil, Physik Chem. 22 (1933) 350.
[16] C.Wagner, Z. Phys. Chem. B38 (1938) 325.
[17] R.E.Hoffman, D.Turnbull and E.W.Hart, Acta Met. 3 (1955) 417.
[18] W.Seith, Z. Elektrochem. 41 (1935) 872.
[19] G.Von Hevesy and W.Seith, Z. Elektrochem. 37 (1931) 528.
[20] W.Seith and H.Etzold, Z. Elektrochem. 40 (1934) 829.
[21] A.Ascoli, J. Inst. Met. 89 (1960–1961) 218.
[22] A.Ascoli, B.Bollani, G.Guarini and D.Kustudic, Phys. Rev. 141 (1966) 732.
[23] F.C.Frank and D.Turnbull, Phys. Rev. 104 (1956) 617.
[24] A.Rossolimo and D.Turnbull, personal communication.
[25] D.R.Beaman, R.W.Balluffi and R.O.Simmons, Phys. Rev. 134 (1964) A532.
[26] H.Curtain, D.L.Decker and H.B.Van Fleet, Phys. Rev. 139 (1965) A1552.
[27] T.R.Anthony, Bull. Am. Phys. Soc. 11 (1966) 216.
[28] J.H.Westbrook and K.T.Aust. Acta Met. 11 (1963) 1151.
[29] K.T.Aust and J.H.Westbrook, in: Lattice Defects in Quenched Metals (Academic Press, New York, New York, 1964) p. 711.
[30] A.U.Seybolt, J.H.Westbrook and D.Turnbull, Acta Met. 12 (1964) 1456.
[31] T.R.Anthony, Scripta Met. 2 (1968) 509.
[32] D.Turnbull, Proceedings of the Memorial Lecture Meeting, National Research Instititute for Metals, Tokyo, Japan (1966).
[33] J.W.Miller, Bull. Am. Phys. Soc. 12 (1967) 1072; Phys. Rev. (1969) to be published.
[34] M.F.Millea, J. Phys. Chem. Solids 27 (1966) 309.
[35] M.F.Millea, J. Phys. Chem. Solids 27 (1966) 315.
[36] J.D.Meakin and E.Klokholm, Trans. AIME 218 (1960) 463.

[37] D.Bergner and W.Lange, Phys. Stat. Sol. 18 (1966) 67.
[38] G.W.Powell and J.D.Braun, Trans. AIME 230 (1960) 694.
[39] G.A.Shirn, Acta Met. 3 (1955) 87.
[40] J.N.Mundy, L.W.Barr and F.A.Smith, Phil. Mag. 14 (1966) 785.
[41] N.H.Nachtrieb, E.Catalano and J.A.Weil, J. Chem. Phys. 20 (1952) 1185.
[42] L.W.Barr, J.N.Mundy and F.A.Smith, Phil. Mag. 14 (1966) 1299.
[43] A.Ott and A.Lodding, Jül. Conf. 2, Vol. 1 (1968) p. 43.
[44] D.Lazarus, Solid State Physics 10 (1960) 71.
[45] A.J.Dekker, Solid State Physics (Prentice-Hall, Inc., Englewood Cliffs, N.J., 1961) 63.
[46] K.Weiser, J. Phys. Chem. Solids 17 (1960) 149.
[47] C.S.Barrett and T.B.Massalski, Structure of Metals (McGraw-Hill Co., New York, 1966) 249.
[48] L.Muldawer, personal communication to D.Turnbull.
[49] N.H.Nachtrieb and G.S.Handler, J. Chem. Phys. 23 (1955) 1569.
[50] B.Okkerse, Acta Met. 2 (1954) 551.
[51] H.A.Resing and N.H.Nachtrieb, J. Phys. Chem. Solids 21 (1961) 40.
[52] G.Von Hevesy, W.Seith and A.Keil, Z. Phys. 79 (1932) 197.
[53] C.J.Smithells, Metals Reference Book, 4th ed. (Plenum Press, New York, 1967) 467.

## Discussion

*J.Friedel:* 1. Are there residual resistivity measurements? If the valence effect predominates, which I would agree to, one should expect low values especially since the local repulsion expected for the surrounding matrix should reduce the "effective" valence of the interstitial (Blatt and Harrison correction).

2. Are there X-ray parameter measurements? This would distinguish *by itself* interstitials or substitutionals (lattice expansion in the first case, lattice contraction in the second). You don't need to measure also length changes in this simple case. These measurements would also help for 1.

3. Comparison Ag/Au: Ag has a more stable and thus less polarizable d-shell than Au. Thus one expects Ag to act as a harder point than Au. This "modulus" factor has to be considered in addition to the "size" factor you mentioned.

*T.R.Anthony:* There have been no residual resistivity measurements or accurate X-ray parameter measurements in these systems to my knowledge. I agree that they are critical experiments that should be done.

We have also considered the possibility that the greater ability of the gold ion core to distort may allow it to squeeze through the interstices of a solvent lattice faster than a silver ion. However, one would expect to see the same effect in substitutional diffusion to some degree but here silver seems to diffuse consistently faster than gold. Another possibility is that the relatively greater screening of gold increases its interstitial mobility rather than its interstitial population relative to silver. Experiments which may give some measure of the relative interstitial/substitutional populations of silver and gold in these solvents should settle this question.

*M.P.Dariel:* The diffusivity of silver in the d.h.c.p. and the b.c.c. phases of praseodymium have been recently measured. The results corroborate the conclusion of Anthony, namely, that the solute diffusivity of gold is higher than that of silver. Similar to cobalt and gold, the diffusivity of silver is affected only to a small extent by the phase transformation occurring in praseodymium.

Lanthanum self diffusion and gold solute diffusion have also been measured in f.c.c. lanthanum. The results indicate that the combined substitutional-interstitial mechanism presented by Anthony is quite common in rare-earth solvents. The solutes, which may diffuse by this mechanism include, in addition to the noble metals, also a number of transition metals and possibly zinc.

*A.D.LeClaire:* All of the results you have quoted refer to diffusion in polyvalent solvents. I would like to describe some measurements we have made at Harwell on Au diffusion in Na which show this to occur at a *very* fast rate indeed, probably again due to the gold being in interstitial solution. These measurements have been made by Barr and Mundy.

The general features of impurity diffusion in Na are quite similar to those of diffusion in Pb, Sn and other solvents mentioned. For many impurities, K., Rb, Cd, etc., the values of $D_0$ and $Q$ are not too far removed from those for Na self diffusion. But for Au diffusion in Na, the $D$ values are 2 to 3 orders of magntide larger than, and the $Q$-value ($\sim 0.1$ eV) less than a quarter that for self diffusion. $D$ is as large as $10^{-5}$ cm$^2$/sec and in fact the sectioning must be carefully timed and allowance made for the appropriate amount of diffusion that occurs while it is being done. We believe that the situation is just the same as those Dr. Anthony has described—that Au is diffusing by a mechanism different from that of other solutes and most probably by an interstitial process. However, in this case, size conditions are probably sufficient to account for gold being in interstitial solution and Dr. Anthony's arguments in terms of a valence difference favoring interstitial solution do not, of course, apply here.

*T.R.Anthony:* I believe that valence effects may also be important here and that size effects are only *a necessary but not a sufficient* condition to explain the high diffusivity of Au. First, Cd which has both an atomic and ionic size smaller than Au diffuses two to three orders of magnitude slower as you have mentioned. I think it's no coincidence that Cd has a higher valency and is more electropositive than Au. Secondly, although Au and Na have the same nominal valence, Au is the most electronegative of all metals and Na one of the most electropositive. Thus, the effective valency of Au dissolved in Na may be considerably less then effective valency of Na.

*A.R.E.Lodding:* Your systematics of dissociative, partially interstitial, solubility seems to fit strikingly well to our results of impurity diffusion measurements in lithium (Ott-Lodding, Jül. Conf. 2, Vol. 1 (1968) p. 43). Thus the diffusivity in Li is very great for univalent solutes, and decreases markedly with increasing valency. Just as in the systems you have been investigating, the diffusion of gold is particularly fast, that of silver slower by about an order of magnitude, but still considerably faster than self-diffusion. Atom size seems less important than ion core structure.

The parallel of our results in Li with yours in polyvalent metals is gratifying, as also from other evidence (see Jül. Conf. 2, Vol. 1 (1968) p. 55) we have had reason to suspect the presence of an interstitial-like mechanism in the alkali metals. In view of the open b.c.c. structure and the high ratio of atom to ion size, dissociative solubility does not seem paradoxical in lithium.

*A.D.Le Claire:* While we are discussing the solubilities of the very fast diffusers, may I say that Barr, Mundy and Smith have also measured the solubility of Au in Na. They find it to be very small and with a high enthalpy of solution (0.49 ± 0.06 eV). It may be drawing a red herring to report the results in this way, but it is rather remarkable that the entropy (5.8 ± 1.1 k) and enthalpy of solution are both the same, within experimental error, as the corresponding quantities describing the concentrations of thermal vacancies in Na, as measured by Feder and Charbrau.

# HYDROGEN DIFFUSION IN METALS

## G.ALEFELD

*Institut für Festkörper- und Neutronenphysik der Kernforschungsanlage Jülich, Germany*

## 1. Introduction

The diffusion of hydrogen interstitials in solids deserves special attention for several reasons:

1) The diffusivity of hydrogen atoms in metals is extremely high ($4 \times 10^{11}$ jumps/sec at room-temperature in niobium [1]) and exceeds that of e.g. oxygen or nitrogen interstitials by at least 10 orders of magnitude. Phenomenologically this high diffusivity can be attributed to the low activation energy for hydrogen diffusion (0.11 eV for hydrogen in niobium in the room-temperature region [1]).

2) Because of the small activation energy hydrogen diffusion can be observed at relatively low temperatures. One therefore expects quantum effects in the diffusion of hydrogen in metals. It is possible, that hydrogen atoms stay mobile even at zero temperature *. Yet for the very light hydrogen atom it is not really necessary to perform low temperature experiments in order to study quantum effects **. By inelastic neutron scattering [2] the energy difference between the ground-state and the first excited state of the hydrogen atom in niobium has been found as $\hbar\omega =$ 0.114 eV which corresponds to an Einstein temperature of 1370°K. So room temperature is far below the Einstein temperature of the hydrogen mode.

3) A third reason to use hydrogen for the study of isotope effects is the availability of three isotopes with the largest possible relative mass difference.

4) Hydrogen metal alloys can be prepared relatively easily by loading either electrolytically or from the gas phase.

For all these reasons one should have thought, that research in isotopes effects in solid state diffusion would have used hydrogen isotopes. Interestingly this has not been the case. The cause for this reluctance in activity in this field may be that special experimental techniques are required for hydrogen diffusion measurements.

---

\* Experiments are in preparation to check the mobility at very low temperatures.
\*\* Independent of the mass of the diffusing atom the rate of diffusion can be expected to deviate from the high temperatures relation for temperatures below the Debye-temperature of the host-lattice. For very light atoms different criteria apply.

The most common method has been the permeation method. The main experimental difficulty and chief source of error is the slowness of the surface reaction when compared to the rate of bulk diffusion. Hydrogen absorption is easily poisoned by many substances which are adsorbed at the surface of the metal. There have been many more or less successful attempts to avoid the problem of a surface barrier either by covering the surface by a catalyst or by loading electrochemically and using changes in the electro-chemical potential on the unloaded side as an indication that hydrogen has permeated the specimen [3,4].

Another source of error and reason for large scatter in diffusion data is the uncontrolled impurity content in many experiments. It is evident, that for activation energies of 0.1 eV binding energies to impurities or dislocations which are of the same order of magnitude can cause appreciable errors. The progress of the last years in purification techniques for metals and the availability of new experimental techniques for the measurements of extremely high diffusion constants, make the enterprise of measuring the diffusion of hydrogen and its isotopes more promising. We will confine our discussions to those experimental methods in which surface permeation is avoided. These methods are:

1) Nuclear magnetic resonance,
2) quasielastic neutron scattering,
3) internal friction and elastic relaxation.

Since the measurements have been performed on different phases of the hydrogen metal systems we will first briefly discuss the phase diagrams. We will concentrate the discussion on palladium and niobium.


## 2. The phase diagrams

The most characteristic feature for those hydrogen metal systems which show high solubility for hydrogen is a miscibility gap (fig. 1). At high temperatures hydrogen in interstitial solution can be considered as an example for a lattice gas because of the following reasons:

1) The hydrogen atoms do not occupy regular sites of the lattice (substitutional) but the interstitials sites.

2) The hydrogen atoms interchange their position with a rate of $10^{11} - 10^{12}$ jumps/sec (H in niobium).

This rate of diffusion is as high as that for water molecules in water. Consequently, hydrogen behaves less like a solid component of an alloy but more like a gas or liquid in a space which is provided by the host-lattice. The critical point of the miscibility gap can be interpreted as the critical point for the phase transition gas-liquid [5]. The only difference between the two phases $\alpha$ and $\alpha'$ (fig. 1) is the higher hydrogen concentration in the $\alpha'$-phase. For both phases the host-lattice is cubic but with a slightly larger lattice constant for the $\alpha'$-phase indicating the separation of the hydrogen into a more dense and a less dense phase which are in equili-

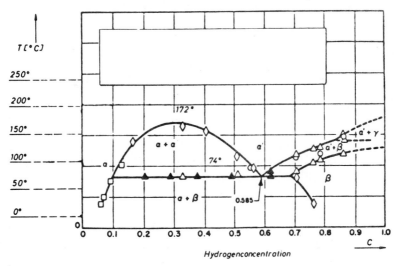

Fig. 1. Phase-diagramm for hydrogen in niobium (R.J.Walter and W.T.Chandler, Trans. AIME 233 (1965) 762.

brium with each other. In palladium this liquid like phase extends to approximately 50°K. At this temperature a peak in specific heat [6] as well as in electrical resistivity [7] has been observed. The critical point of the hydrogen palladium phase has been found at approximately 290°C, the room-temperature concentration in the α-phase amounts to approximately 2%. For niobium (fig. 1) a phase transition in the liquid phase occurs already at 90°C. The liquid changes into a new phase which is being called β-phase. The difference in phase-diagramm for H in Pd (fcc) and Nb (bcc) may be attributed to the different crystal structure of these metals. The elastic dipol-dipol interaction is small for hydrogen in the octahedral position [8] of the f.c.c. palladium (This interaction is zero for isotropic f.c.c. materials.) For hydrogen in a b.c.c. lattice like Nb the dipol-dipol interaction gives the leading term for elastic interaction, independent which position is occupied by the hydrogen atom.

## 3. Diffusion measurements

In tables 1 and 2 recent measurements with nuclear magnetic resonance, internal friction and quasielastic neutron scattering technique are being presented. Besides parameters like authors, temperature range of measurements, concentration, phase and experimental technique, a further important parameter is the purity. Since the purity was uncontrolled in all the experiments except for one, this parameter is omitted in tables 1 and 2.

Table 1
Diffusion measurements for hydrogen in niobium.

| Authors | $U$ (eV) | $\nu_0$ (sec$^{-1}$) | Temperature range (°K) | Phase and concentration | | Experimental technique |
|---|---|---|---|---|---|---|
| D.Zamir and R.M.Cotts (1964) [9] | 0.16 0.22 | $1.9 \times 10^{12}$ $5 \times 10^{11}$ | $450 < T < 390$ $220 < T < 330$ | $\alpha'$ $\beta$ | $C = 0.70$ $C = 0.70$ | NMR |
| G.Cannelli and L.Verdini (1966) [10] | 0.18 | $3.5 \times 10^{13}$ | $96 - 110$ | | $C = ?$ probably $\beta$ | Internal friction |
| P.Schiller and A.Schneiders (1968) [11] | $U_H = 0.12$ $U_D = 0.18$ | $1.9 \times 10^{10}$ $1.3 \times 10^{11}$ | $77 - 112$ $105 - 143$ | $\alpha + (\beta?)$ $\alpha + (\beta?)$ | $C < 0.002$ $C < 0.002$ | Internal friction |
| G.Schaumann et al. (1968) [1] | $U_H = 0.110$ $U_D = 0.135$ | $1.2 \times 10^{13}$ $1.2 \times 10^{13}$ | $250 < T < 550$ $250 < T < 550$ | $\alpha$ $\alpha$ | $C = 0.01$ $C = 0.025$ | Gorsky-effect |
| G.Verdan et al. (1968) [2] | $D = 2 \times 10^{-5}$ | | 523 | $\alpha$ | $C = 0.09$ | Quasielastic neutron scattering |

Table 2
Diffusion measurements for hydrogen in palladium.

| Authors | $U$ (eV) | $\nu_0$ (sec$^{-1}$) | Temperature range (°K) | Phase and concentration | | Experimental technique |
|---|---|---|---|---|---|---|
| R.E.Norberg (1952) [16] | 0.16 | $1 \times 10^{11}$ | 230 – 300 | $\alpha + \alpha'$ | $C = 0.52$ | NMR |
| H.C.Torrey (1958) [17] | 0.24 <br> 0.08 | $2 \times 10^{12}$ <br> $2 \times 10^{9}$ | $T > 220$ <br> $T < 220$ | $\alpha'$ <br> $\alpha'$ | $C = 0.64$ <br> $C = 0.64$ | NMR |
| W.Spalthoff (1961) [18] | 0.10 | $3.2 \times 10^{9}$ | 100 – 300 | $\alpha'$ | $C = 0.63$ | NMR |
| J.P.Burger et al. (1961) [19] | 0.21 <br> 0.06 | $5 \times 10^{12}$ <br> $5 \times 10^{9}$ | $T > 230$ <br> $T < 230$ | $\alpha'$ <br> $\alpha'$ | $C = 0.64$ <br> $C = 0.64$ | NMR |
| R.R.Arons et al. (1967) [27] | 0.16 <br> 0.21 | $6.6 \times 10^{10}$ <br> $1.3 \times 10^{13}$ | 90 – 125 <br> 95 – 125 | $\alpha$ <br> $\alpha'$ | $C = 0.73$ <br> $C = 0.73$ | Internal friction |
| R.R.Arons et al. (1968) [20] | 0.14 (H) <br> 0.14 (D) | $10^{8} - 10^{10}$ <br> $10^{8} - 10^{10}$ | 55 – 70 <br> 55 – 70 | | $C = 0.69$–0.76 <br> $C = 0.61$–0.73 | Elastic after-effect |
| K.Sköld and G.Nelin (1967) [15] | 0.16 | $1.1 \times 10^{13}$ | 570 – 700 | $\alpha$ | $C = 0.02$ | Quasielastic neutron scattering |

### 3.1. Niobium

We will first discuss the measurements on niobium. The values for the activation energy range from 0.1 eV to 0.2 eV depending on the phase and temperature range of measurement.

The first measurement with NMR [9] was performed on 70% loaded niobium and shows a change of activation energy at the transition from the $\alpha'$- to the $\beta$-phase. The number of jumps/sec is $10^{10}$ in the $\alpha$-phase and decreases by a factor of 40 when going from $\alpha'$ to $\beta$.

The next measurement in table 1 is an internal friction measurement by Cannelli and Verdini [10] who were expecting a Snoek-Peak due to hydrogen. For this measurement the concentration and the phase have not been specified by the authors. Unfortunately, the concentration of hydrogen in the $\alpha$-phase at 100°K is not known. Yet from the phase diagram fig. 1 one can conclude that only a small amount of hydrogen (e.g. $10^{-3} - 10^{-4}$) remains in solution. This concentration is small compared to the average interstitial impurity content of standard niobium metal. It is therefore possible that hydrogen was trapped on impurities at 100°K. Under these conditions the internal friction peak may be due to the change in orientation of impurity hydrogen pairs. The activation energy $U = 0.18$ eV, which is larger than that found for freely migrating hydrogen [1], is modified by the strain-field of the impurity trap.

The measurements by Schiller and Schneider [11] are subjected to the same problems. Nevertheless, these authors report a large isotope effect similarly to that found by Cannelli and Verdini [10] in Ta in the same temperature range.

The measurements by Schaumann et al. [1] as well as those by Verdan et al. [2] were performed in pure $\alpha$-phase. For the experiment by Schaumann et al. high purity niobium (outgassed at $10^{-10}$ Torr at 2300°C) was used. Since the Gorsky-effect has been discovered only very recently [1] it will be explained here very briefly:

Mobile point defects with strain fields of lower symmetrie than the lattice give rise to a relaxation process of the Snoek-type (orientation after-effect). Yet any point defect, asymmetric or symmetric, will be the source of another type of a relaxation process if the point defect causes lattice parameter changes and if the applied stress produces a gradient in lattice dilatation (diffusion after-effect). This condition is not very restrictive since it is hard to find point defects which do not cause lattice parameter changes. If e.g. a hydrogen-loaded specimen is bent elastically the hydrogen will diffuse through the specimen from the compression site to the dilatation site thus causing an extra amount of strain (fig. 2). After removal of the elastic stress the time-dependence strain disappears with a rate proportional to the diffusion coefficient. For a specimen with rectangular dimensions the relaxation time $\tau$ for this long-range diffusion process is connected with the diffusion constant $D$ and the diameter $d$ by the relation

$$\pi^2 D\tau = d^2 . \tag{1}$$

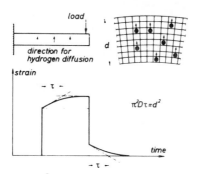

Fig. 2. Elastic after-effect due to long range diffusion of hydrogen (Gorsky effect).

For niobium at room-temperature the relaxation time for a 1 mm specimen has been found as 150 sec which is very convinient to measure. Further results for the diffusion after-effect for H in Nb are as follows [12]:

1) In spite of being diffusion controlled, the after-effect obeys a simple exponential law except for only approximately 1% of the time-dependence strain at the very beginning.

2) The relaxation time follows the $d^2$-dependence of eq. (1), thus confirming that the diffusion proceeds over the complete diameter of the specimen (The grain size was of the order of the specimen diameter.)

3) The relaxation strength is proportional to the hydrogen concentration (1 at % hydrogen gives 1.6% after-effect).

4) The relaxation strength for the diffusion after-effect is determined by the trace of the double-force tensor, as is the lattice parameter change caused by interstitial hydrogen. Within experimental error the above stated relaxation strength is consistent with the experimentally observed lattice parameter change: $\Delta a/a = 7 \times 10^{-4}$ at % H [13].

With help of eq. (1) the diffusion coefficient can be determined absolutely without any adjustable parameter. Fig. 3 shows the results for hydrogen and deuterium in Nb. The isotope dependence of the diffusion coefficients is much larger than predicted by classical rate theory [14].

The activation energies amount to $(0.110 \pm 0.005)$ eV for hydrogen and $(0.135 \pm 0.005)$ eV for deuterium, whereas $D_o = (5.4 \pm 0.6) \times 10^{-4}$ cm$^2$/sec is the same for both isotopes. Within experimental error the activation energy for hydrogen diffusion is equal to the energy difference $\hbar\omega$ between the ground-state and the first excited state of the hydrogen atom in solution.

In fig. 3 one more point for the diffusion coefficient is included which has been determined by Verdan et al. [7] by quasielastic neutron scattering technique. Again this is a very new technique [15] which should be explained briefly: A neutron beam with a well-defined energy is being scattered by the hydrogen atoms in

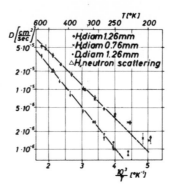

Fig. 3. Diffusion coefficient for hydrogen and deuterium in niobium [1].

solution. Due to the diffusive motion of the hydrogen atoms the energy of the scattered neutrons is broadened. The energetic width of the neutron line observed at small scattering angles gives directly the diffusion coefficient without any adjustable parameter. The point by Verdan et al. happens to fall on the deuterium line. There is only a discrepancy by a factor of two to our value. This discrepancy may be attributed either to the relatively high concentration of 9% hydrogen in the sample used for neutron scattering, or to different purity. Recent measurements by W.Gissler, et al. [28] of the quasielastic scattering at 100°C and 200°C of 3% hydrogen loaded samples, which were identical with the samples used for the Gorsky effect, fall within experimental scatter on the hydrogen line. This agreement of the results gained with two completely different techniques strengthens the confidence in the reliability of the data in fig. 3.

### 3.2. Palladium

Sköld and Nelin [15] were the first to apply the quasielastic neutron scattering technique to a solid system, namely to Pd-samples loaded with 2% hydrogen ($\alpha$-phase). The measurements were performed in the range of 570 to 700°K. The technique of quasielastic neutron scattering cannot only determine the diffusion coefficient but also independently the mean time of stay $\tau$ which is connected with the diffusion coefficient by the relation $D = a^2/12\tau$ for octahedral-octahedral jumps and $D = a^2/24\tau$ for tetrahedral-tetrahedral jumps in f.c.c. lattices. Sköld and Nelin found that $D$ and $\tau$ followed the relation with the numerical factor 12, thus confirming that hydrogen occupies octahedral positions in palladium. Furthermore, the authors could determine the activation energy $U = 0.16$ eV and the pre-exceptional factor $1/\tau_o = 1.1 \times 10^{13}$. Again we think that these data for the diffusion coefficient are quite reliable at least for the palladium-purity used by these authors. Most of the measurements in palladium have been performed in the high concentration $\alpha$-phase. Inspite of a fairly large scatter there is one common feature to the nuclear magnetic resonance measurements [16–19]. The activation energy is of the order

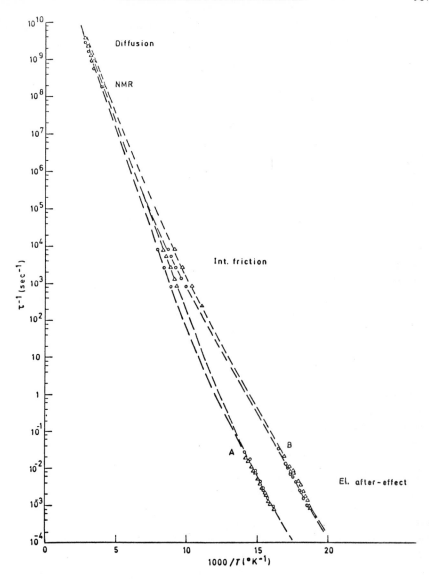

Fig. 4. The jump frequency of H and D in Pd versus temperature [20].
          A: o H/Pd = 0.76                    △ D/Pd = 0.73
          B: o H/Pd = 0.69                    △ D/Pd = 0.61

of 0.2 eV above 250°K and decreases below 250°K. The same tendency has been reported by Arons [20] for internal friction and elastic after-effect measurements
(fig. 4). The activation energy for these processes decreases with decreasing temperature. Simultaneously the pre-exponential factor $\nu_o$ becomes unusually small (e.g. $10^8$

compared to $10^{14}$ for nitrogen diffusion). Arons [20] suggested the following formula for the mean jump probability for D in palladium:

$$\tau^{-1}(C_D) = (1 - C_D) \times 10^{13} \cdot \exp(-0.19 \, \text{eV}/kT)$$

$$+ (10^{10} - 10^8) \cdot \exp(-0.13 \, \text{eV}/kT).$$

Unusual small pre-exponential factors have been reported previously by Cannelli and Verdini [10] for internal friction peaks in Ta loaded with hydrogen or deuterium. These authors report an activation energy of 0.12 eV for both isotopes but pre-exponentials of $1.2 \times 10^9$/sec for deuterium and $10^{11}$/sec for hydrogen. Besides Heller's [21] measurements for H and D in iron, Cannelli and Verdini were actually the first to discover such large isotope effects which have been confirmed by Arons et al. [27] for H and D in Pd, by Schiller and Schneider [11] for H and D in niobium and by Schaumann et al. [1] for H and D in niobium. Although it is by no means evident that the relaxation times of the internal friction measurements are those of the elementary steps for diffusion the following statements can be extracted from the combined data with some confidence:

1) Unusual large isotope dependence for the mobility of hydrogen and deuterium in metals is found at and below room-temperature.

2) For decreasing temperature the activation energy decreases as well as the pre-exponential factor.


## 4. Theory

How can these observations, especially for H and D in niobium, be explained? First we will consider the naive picture of particles performing Brownian motion in the lattice and thus moving statistically over a saddlepoint: Due to the large mass difference between H and Nb the hydrogen oscillations are nearly completely decoupled from the oscillation of the host-lattice.

The difference $\Delta U = 25 \pm 10$ meV in activation energy for H and D can be attributed to the lower zeropoint energy of deuterium [22]. If in a first order approximation the same lattice potential for both isotopes is assumed, the zero-point energies for the modes of oscillation towards the saddlepoint differ by $\Delta U = \hbar\omega(1 - \sqrt{m_H/m_D})$, which is 17 meV with $\hbar\omega = 114$ meV [2]. The absence of an isotope dependence for $D_0$ has been predicted by Ebisuzaki et al. [23] in a semiclassical extension of rate theory for low temperatures and indicates that $D_0$ is determined by the motion of the host-lattice only. The coincidence of the hydrogen activation energy with the energy difference between the groundstate and the first excited state of the hydrogen atom in solution is in this picture purely accidental but consistent with the concept that the saddlepoint exists only statistically. Nevertheless, this picture for diffusion is too naive for the following reason: The concept of a saddlepoint, over which an atom moves continuously is not applicable,

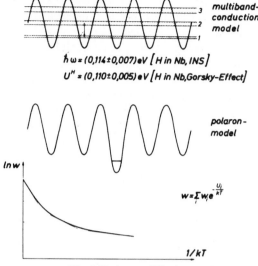

$$\hbar \omega = (0{,}114 \pm 0{,}007)\,eV\;[H\;in\;Nb,\;INS]$$
$$U^H = (0{,}110 \pm 0{,}005)\,eV\;[H\;in\;Nb,\;Gorsky\text{-}Effect]$$

$$w = \sum_i w_i e^{-\frac{U_i}{kT}}$$

Fig. 5. Hydrogen diffusion models.

once the energy levels of the system are comparable with the activation energy. In this case more refined quantum mechanical calculations have to be applied to determine the rate of transition between two equilibrium positions.

To this conference two papers have been submitted [20,24], both considering the possibility that hydrogen diffusion proceeds via tunnelling as has been suggested by Heller [21] H in iron and as it is commonly discussed for example for ice and organic substances [25]. Fig. 5 shows a simplified proton band scheme. The probability $w$ for transition from one side to another is given by probability $w_i$ for the transition in a certain band times the occupation $\exp(-U_i/kT)$ of this band. Therefore:

$$w = \sum_i w_i \, e^{-U_i/kT} \; .$$

The transition probability $w_i$ is small for the lowest band and increases from band to band. It depends on temperature which of the different bands gives the main contribution to the diffusion current. One has to optimise between the transition probability $w_i$ and the occupation of the bands. For decreasing temperature the higher bands are less occupied, therefore, a lower lying band will take over the transport inspite of the smaller transition probability. In this model the activation energy is the energy difference between the conduction band and the ground-state (for narrow bands this is a well-defined quantity). These band-gaps can be determined by inelastic neutron scattering. Yet for experimental reasons in most cases the distance between the ground-state and the first excited state can be measured only. For H and Pd one finds 0.056 eV [26] compared to 0.160 eV for the activation energy at $\approx 600°K$. For Pd therefore, it must be postulated that a higher band e.g. the third band gives the main contribution at 600°K. In contrast to Pd for niobium the activation energy for hydrogen diffusion agrees within experimental error with the energy difference between ground-state and first excited state of the H-atom.

Inspite of this remarkable agreement we think that this picture of proton conduction bands is too simple. We have so far ignored the lattice distortion in the neighbourhood of the hydrogen atom. Actually the periodic potential of the hydrogen atom is strongly disturbed right at the position of the hydrogen atom, as indicated in fig. 6 for the "polaron model". The hydrogen atom can lower its energy in the lattice by causing elastic distortions in the neighbourhood of the occupied site. This self-trapping destroys the simple band picture and suggests a model similar to the polaron with the thermally activated hopping process, yet with the modification of multiband conduction. Again in such a model the temperature dependence of diffusion is mainly determined by the energy states of the hydrogen atom. In the simple band model diffusive jumps over several atomic distances are possible in contrast to the polaron model, for which jumps over more than one atomic distance are very unlikely. From the experimental evidence existing up today there is no indication for diffusive jumps over several potentials.

## 5. Final conclusion

From the experimental point of view the physical problem of hydrogen diffusion in solids, especially at lower temperatures can be considered as a challenging and so far nearly unexplored area. The main problem will be the preparation of samples either with extreme purity or with controlled doping. The situation is very similar to that for semiconductors 20 years ago.

From the theoretical point of view the metal-hydrogen system may be the first one for which a diffusion theory can be formulated starting from first principles. Besides more reliable diffusion experiments, an increasing amount of information about the lattice dynamics of the host-lattice and about the energy states of the hydrogen atom is becoming available from inelastic neutron scattering experiments.

## References

[1] G.Schaumann, J.Völkl and G.Alefeld, Phys. Rev. Letters 21 (1968) 891.
[2] G.Verdan, R.Rubin and W.Kley, IAEA Inelastic Scattering of Neutrons Conf. Copenhagen (1968) (in the press).
[3] W.Jost, Diffusion in Solids, Liquids and Gases (Academic Press, New York, 1960).
[4] R.Wagner and R.Sizmann, Z. angew. Physik 18 (1964) 193.
[5] G.Alefeld, Phys. Stat. Sol. 32 (1969) 67.
[6] D.M.Nace and J.G.Aston, J. Am. Chem. Soc. 79 (1957) 3623.
[7] A.I.Schindler, R.J.Smith and E.W.Kammer, Proc. Tenth International Congress of Refrigeration, Copenhagen, Vol. 1 (Pergamon Press, New York, 1960) p. 74.

[8] J.E.Worsham, M.K.Wilkinson and C.G.Shull, Phys. Chem. Solid 3 (1957) 303 have shown by neutron diffraction, that H in Pd occupies the octahedral position.
[9] D.Zamir and R.M.Cotts, Phys. Rev. 143A (1964) 666.
[10] G.Cannelli and L.Verdini, Ric. Sci. 36 (1966) 246.
[11] P.Schiller and A.Schneiders, Jül. Conf. 2 (Vol. II) 1968, p. 881.
[12] G.Schaumann, J.Völkl and G.Alefeld, to be published.
[13] W.M.Albrecht, W.D.Goode and M.W.Mallet, J. Electrochem. Soc. 106 (1959) 981.
[14] G.H.Vineyard, J. Phys. Chem. Solids 3 (1957) 121.
[15] K.Sköld and G.Nelin, J. Phys. Chem. Solids 28 (1967) 2369.
[16] R.E.Norberg, Phys. Rev. 86 (1952) 745.
[17] H.C.Torrey, Nuovo Cimento Suppl. 9 (1958) 95.
[18] W.Spalthoff, Z. Phys. Chem. Neue Folge 29 (1961) 258.
[19] J.P.Burger, N.J.Poulis and W.A.Hass, Physica 27 (1961) 514.
[20] R.R.Arons, Jül. Conf. 2 (Vol. 2) 1968, p. 901.
[21] W.R.Heller, Acta Met. 9 (1961) 600.
[22] C.A.Wert and C.Zener, Phys. Rev. 76 (1949) 1169.
[23] Y.Ebisuzaki, W.J.Kass and M.O'Keeffe, Phil. Mag. 15 (1967) 1071.
[24] G.Blaesser and J.Peretti, Jül. Conf. 2 (Vol. II) p. 886.
[25] See e.g. International Symposium on Physics of Ice, Munich, 1968, Editor N.Riehl, to be published.
[26] J.Bergsma and J.A.Goedkoop, Physica 26 (1960) 744.
[27] R.R.Arons, J.Bouman, M.Wijzenbeek, P.T.A.Klaase, C.Tuyn, G.Leferink and G.de Vries, Acta Met. 15 (1967) 144.
[28] W.Gissler, G.Alefeld and T.Springer, to be published.

## Discussion

*R.R.Arons:* Measurements of NMR should be done at various $\omega$, because a spreading in relaxation times can give rise to the different activation energies observed on the right and left hand sides of the peak in $T_1$.

*G.Alefeld:* I agree with you that the NMR measurements on hydrogen metal systems are by no means complete; actually they can only be considered as a preliminary demonstration of the applicability of this experimental technique. Changes of activation energies as deduced from the tails of the peak in $T_1$ are not very reliable.

*H.Wenzl:* I can understand the band effect of hydrogen diffusion if all potentials are identical. But if the polaron effect is important, then generally there are no longer any bands for the hydrogen and one cannot see how the band model works then.

*G.Alefeld:* From the experimental evidence compiled so far, there is no real need for a band model for hydrogen diffusion. On the other hand quantum effects cannot be ignored in hydrogen diffusion. I personally think that a polaron-type model has the best chance to describe the hydrogen jump diffusion. The situation would change immediately if it were shown that the mean free path of a moving hydrogen atom is larger than the distance between two neighbouring equilibrium positions. To my knowledge the only method so far which can measure the mean jump distance is the method of quasielastic neutron scattering performed at different scattering angles. We therefore have planned to perform such experiments at Jülich.

# PART 9

# APPENDIX

# PANEL DISCUSSION ON
# THE INTERPRETATION OF RECOVERY STAGES IN FCC METALS

| | |
|---|---|
| Chairman: | R.S.BARNES |
| Panel members: | A.v.d.BEUKEL |
| | L.M.CLAREBROUGH |
| | J.W.CORBETT |
| | D.DAUTREPPE |
| | W.FRANK |
| | D.K.HOLMES |
| | J.S.KOEHLER |
| | Y.QUÉRÉ |
| | W.SCHILLING |
| | A.SEEGER |
| | J.TAKAMURA |
| Secretary: | D.SCHUMACHER |

The chairman opened the discussion by introducing the panel members and giving a short run-down of the historical development of this 15-year-old controversy. He urged the panel members and the audience to point out the areas where there *is* complete agreement, so that one could concentrate better on the controversial issues. Prior to the panel discussion, the review papers presented by W.Schilling (this volume, p. 427) and by A. van den Beukel (this volume, p. 255) had given a survey of the experimental data, so that the discussion speakers could restrict themselves to the actual interpretational problems. The chairman first turned the microphone over to three leading advocates of the different schools of thought who presented their personal ideas, namely J.W.Corbett, J.S.Koehler and A.Seeger. The written versions of their talks, as submitted shortly after the conference, are reproduced on the following pages. This will be followed by an extract of the discussions among the panel members and with the audience (as prepared from the tape recording).

# ON THE INTERPRETATION OF THE RECOVERY STAGES
# IN FCC METALS

J. W. CORBETT

*State University of New York at Albany, Albany, New York, 12203, USA*

In case the reader is not aware of it, it should be pointed out that there is, and has been, a long-standing controversy on the interpretation of the recovery stages in fcc metals. I suspect that after this conference there will still be a controversy! Hopefully, however, we can focus on the areas of disagreement and suggest potential experiments to clarify the issues. I find my own position very much in keeping with the modern trend in literature with its "anti-hero" and "anti-plot", since I am not so much "pro" a specific assignment of the recovery processes to the recovery stages as I am "anti" the two-interstitial model. Moreover, I am somewhat embarrassed and very much gratified by the masterful presentation made by Dr. Schilling. So much that I am tempted to simply say "Amen" and stop my presentation; I will resist that impulse. I am somewhat embarrassed because I find that most of the things that I would want to say, he has already said at some length; I am most gratified in that his presentation was made, and received so matter of factly as though the conclusions were beyond cavil — after all it was not very long ago that many of the features that he presented were subject to considerable controversy. In view of this I think the appropriate thing for me to do is to present a historical perspective which will encompass somewhat the areas of controversy but will more particularly emphasize the growing area of agreement.

From the early work of Koehler using deuteron irradiation, Blewitt, Coltman and Holmes with neutron irradiation, Meechan and Brinkman using electron irradiation, on pure metals and alloys, it was natural that a point of view would arise which assigned interstitial migration to what is now termed Stage III and vacancy migration to Stage IV. The natural presumption was that the lower temperature recovery stages would be assigned to close-pairs. Of course the work of Magnuson, Palmer and Koehler [1] and our own work [2] resolved recovery sub-stages in Stage I (see fig. 1), and we were able to show that some of these sub-stages were clearly close-pair recovery processes. I should comment here that we took the numerical derivative of this isocronal curve (see fig. 2), for the purpose of comparing our data to that of Magnuson et al. who had derived a recovery spectrum from their data. We were aware, as many who follow this practice apparently forget, that

such a derivative plot gives no information about activation energies or recovery
kinetics. For that reason we took extensive isothermal data (see fig. 3). From the
isothermal data we were able to show that sub-stage $I_D$ and $I_E$ had one activation
energy (see fig. 4). Moreover using the Waite theory [3] we found that the recovery

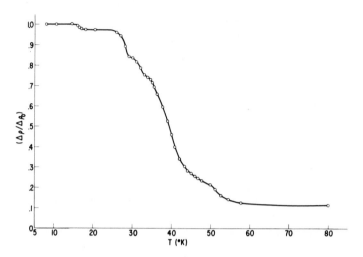

Fig. 1. Isochronal recovery curve of electron-irradiated copper.

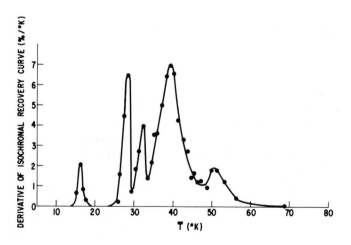

Fig. 2. Point-to-point "derivative" of the curve in fig. 1.

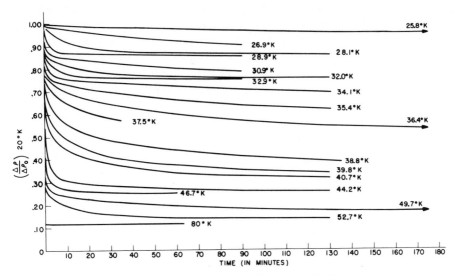

Fig. 3. Isothermal recovery curves of electron-irradiated copper.

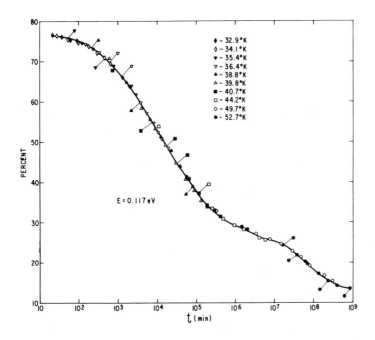

Fig. 4. Superposition of $I_D$ and $I_E$ isothermal data from fig. 3 using a single activation energy
— 0.117 eV.

kinetics could be described satisfactorily by attributing $I_D$ to correlated recovery and sub-stage $I_E$ to uncorrelated recovery of a freely migrating defect. As you may know there was at one time considerable controversy about this interpretation. There has been extensive experimentation which seemed to indicate a number of additional sub-stages in $I_D$ and $I_E$, and at one time all of this recovery was attributed to close-pair recovery with no long-range motion taking place. Dr. Schilling has already commented on the sub-sub-stages in $I_D$ and $I_E$. I will simply note that the progression of experiments with higher and higher "resolution" which have been performed with the view of resolving better the sub-sub-stages, have if anything found less and less of the sub-sub-stages. Moreover these experiments have suffered from what I consider a serious flaw, namely, the fact that they did not correct for the recovery which took place during the time which it took to reach the annealing temperature. This correction is straight forward and was in fact included in our early data; it can contribute very large uncertainties in such derivative plots. I think it is accurate to say that there is a growing consensus that sub-stages $I_D$ and $I_E$ do belong to a common migration energy which is due to a randomly migrating defect. A major contribution in clarifying this issue was made by Coltman and co-workers [4] who studied the recovery at very dilute defect concentrations. Let me emphasize, however, that I think there can be significant, and interesting, deviations from Waite's theory. I think that there is interesting physics for us here, as I have recently described [5].

Returning then to the question of long range motion in stage I, we did the concentration dependence of the isochronal and found the concentration dependence of uncorrelated recovery given by the Waite theory; we also did the concentration dependence of isothermal recovery. Moreover we reasoned if long-range motion was occurring this had implications for the damage production rate at high temperatures, and we made such measurements (see fig. 5). Specifically we showed that if a large concentration of impurities was present we would get a production rate which was linear in the fluence since all the liberated interstitials were trapped. In our high purity, zone-refined copper we found that the production rate quickly became proportional to the square root of the fluence; we showed that this whole production grate curve could be described in terms of unsaturable traps. Moreover we showed that the Meechan and Brinkman production rate, which eventually became linear in the fluence, could be described in terms of nucleation traps. We also found, that if you irradiated at low temperatures and annealed to $80°K$ that the percent of defects which remained after annealing was approximately constant. From this we deduced that agglomeration of defects was occurring. Of course earlier in this conference Dr. Scheidler showed that such agglomerates have now been observed in the electron microscope in electron-irradiated copper.

We also did radiation-doping experiments. We showed that prior irradiation at $80°K$ enhanced the subsequent recovery at $53°K$; similarly irradiation at $20°K$ and annealing to $80°K$ enhanced the recovery of a subsequent $20°K$ irradiation at $53°K$

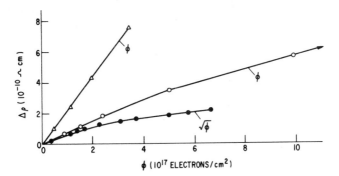

Fig. 5. Damage production rates for electron-irradiation of copper at 80°K. The top curve was obtained for impure copper in which all the mobile interstitials are trapped. The middle curve is for purer copper and exhibits a dependence characteristic of nucleation traps. The bottom curve is for zone-refined copper and exhibits a dependence characteristic of unsaturable traps.

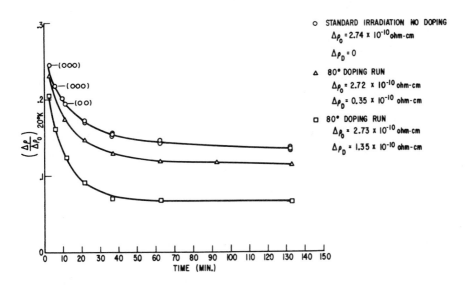

Fig. 6. Examples of how radiation doping can influence subsequent Stage I isothermal recovery.

(see fig. 6). Moreover we showed that the degree of enhancement was *quantitatively different for the two types of radiation doping* (see fig. 7), a fact to which I will return shortly.

From all of these experiments we concluded that long range motion was occuring and attributed it to the free migration of an interstitial. We found that the Stage

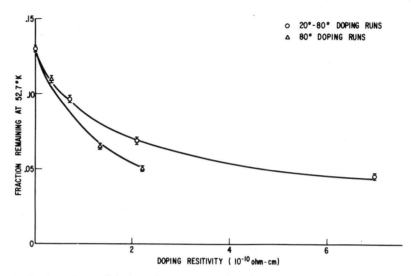

Fig. 7. The dependence of the long-time asymptote in radiation-doping experiments (see fig. 6) on the doping resistivity increment. Note that a resistivity increment introduced by irradiating at 80°K enhances the recovery more than the same increment introduced by irradiating at 20°K and annealing to 80°K.

III recovery was roughly the same in crude Stage III annealing experiments for irradiations in which we had agglomerates and for irradiations in which we had trapped interstitials. Consequently we tentatively concluded that the Stage III recovery was due to the common defect in both experiments — namely the vacancy. (I will return to this point shortly.)

Thus the stage was set for a confrontation between the two schools of thought: the one school that said that the interstitial migrated in Stage III and the other school which said that the interstitial migrated in Stage I. All of the data and arguments that I have presented were in fact available at that confrontation. The confrontation took place at the Canoga Park conference [6] almost 10 years ago to the day from this present conference. Out of that confrontation came a modified controversy in that the one school still held that the interstitial migrated in Stage I, but the other school now took the position that there were two interstitials [7], one which migrated in Stage I and one which migrated in Stage III. But the data which has been presented also bore on this particular point. Specifically the square-root of fluence dependence of the 80°K production rate placed an upper limit on the production rate of intrinsic interstitials that were said to migrate in Stage III. Specifically it showed that not enough interstitials were produced directly (that is with a linear production rate) to account for the Stage III recovery. After this issue was argued somewhat, there evolved the present model which as you know is called the "conversion" two-interstitial model [8]. Of course, as Dr. Schilling showed, in a

pre-quenched sample this production rate is even more drastically reduced and the
requirement for the conversion two-interstitial model is even more stringent.

There's also another area in which there is more or less an agreement, namely,
that in Stage II impurities can play a role in the recovery. Indeed it was the more or
less ill-defined character of the common Stage II recovery that caused it to receive
the early designation "garbage annealing". More recent workers have shown that
with sufficient impurities well-defined discrete recovery stages can be observed in
Stage II (see for example refs. [9,10]). In fact in some cases several discrete recovery
processes have been associated with a given kind of impurity. Specific recovery
models have been assigned to some of these recovery processes. Without comment-
ing on the validity of those recovery processes let me make some additional comments as well. First it should be remembered that when an alloy is prepared, even
when the solubility limit has not been exceeded, there will be a certain equilibrium
concentration of impurity agglomerates present in the sample; all the more so when
the solubility limit has been exceeded. This means that a given alloy may not necessarily have the impurity in one specific configuration. Moreover it should be
realized that the trapped interstitial itself can serve as a subsequent trap for an interstitial. This can be seen in the following way. Let us focus our attention on a
specific population of interstitials trapped at a specific impurity site. At low temperatures effectively all of the interstitials will be bound to this impurity. At a
higher temperature, however, a certain fraction of the interstitials will be free from
the impurity and a certain fraction will still be bound to the impurity, the ratio of
these fractions being given roughly by the Boltzmann factor for the binding energy.
If we go to high enough temperatures where the Boltzmann factor describing the
binding energy becomes unity, then essentially all of the interstitials are free of
that impurity trap. This is shown in fig. 8 where we have plotted the concentration
of the free interstitials as a function of temperature. This sort of curve can be used
in considering annealing experiments. The experiment starts at a low temperature
with the interstitials bound to the impurities. Then the sample is pulsed to a high
temperature during which time some of the interstitials are freed. There are two
regimes. You can pulse to the temperature where some of the interstitials are free
and some are bound. In that case the migrating free interstitial sees some of the
bound interstitials as potential trapping sites as well as the vacancies as annihilation
sites. The other regime is where you pulse to a very high temperature rapidly. Then
all of the interstitials are free, the impurities no longer appear as effective trapping
sites and in essence vanish from the problem; the annealing is then described by a
population of free interstitials migrating to their vacancies. Of course the experi-

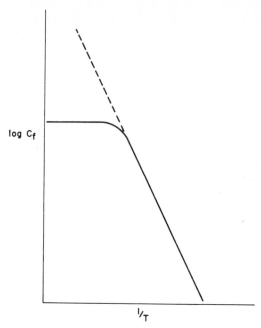

Fig. 8. Concentration of free interstitials in equilibrium with trapped interstitials. At high temperature the traps are exhausted, i.e., effectively all interstitials are free. The curve refers to the initial concentration prior to any significant migration and other recovery processes.

ments show that in that situation the interstitials can find each other and agglomerate. The point here is that regardless of how the experiment is conducted, there are other potential trapping sites available to the free interstitials — even though we have only one type of impurity in the lattice. We should note moreover that most of these experiments are done in the first regime where the pulse is effectively slow and each free interstitial really sees a population of vacancies and trapped interstitials in its migration. Thus a single kind of impurity can give rise to a variety, in fact a whole hierarchy of trapping configurations and (potentially discrete) recovery processes. The same considerations of course obtain if we consider starting with agglomerated interstitials. They too can account for a multiplicity of trapping and recovery processes. In fact the recent work of Dr. Schilling and his group in studying the recovery of high-dose electron-irradiated materials (his fig. 12 at this conference) shows that with increasing dose the Stage II recovery increases. From the character of the experiment we know that these are intrinsic processes occurring in the Stage II recovery; presumably these are the interstitial agglomerate processes that we have just been referring to. Moreover we note that in the aluminium data shown in that figure, at higher electron irradiation doses a discrete intrinsic Stage II process appears which apparently also occurs in the fast neutron irradiation damage experiments. Thus we can have in Stage II not only the impurity processes and the intrinsic continuum recovery processes, but also intrinsic discrete recovery processes.

This brings us to the abiding point of controversy, namely, what is going on in Stage III? Early work on Stage II, such as we have just been discussing, showed that impurity effects and cold-work effects would strongly modify Stage II and that these effects would persist and indeed impinge upon Stage III. Dawson [11] and I [12], independently, were led to question whether Stage III was in fact intrinsic. That question of course is central to the two-interstitial model since the whole motivation for that model is to ascribe an interstitial to an intrinsic process in Stage III. It is my own view that the increasing trend is that experiments in many cases find that Stage III is not unique but in fact is a composite of several processes. (See, for example, refs. [10,13,14 and 15]. The last is in my view the "coup de grace". Johnson emphasizes unambiguously the difficulty of extracting information from complicated kinetics such as occurs in the environment of Stage III.) To the two interstitial protagonists let me simply note that in the very paper which introduced the two-interstitial model, Meechan, Sosin and Brinkman [7] carried out an experimental study of the recovery in cold-work copper. They found that, whereas Meechan and Brinkman [16] had found an activation energy of 0.60 eV in annealed copper, in lightly cold-work copper the activation energy was 0.67 eV and in heavily cold-work material there was no unique activation energy. Moreover they observed: "We are inclined to believe that the 0.07 eV difference in the activation energy . . . is due to an actual shift in the energy brought about by cold work and not simply experimental error."! There is a tendency on the part of some to slight the 0.60 eV activation energy observed by Meechan and Brinkman and to pretend that the linear production rate at high fluence observed by them at 80°K was due to an experimental mistake (although we showed as I noted earlier that it could be described in terms of nucleation traps). I find my position delightfully ironic in that I am defending the experiments which gave rise to the two-interstitial model; nonetheless I feel I must maintain that these experimental differences observed by Meechan and Brinkman are probably very real and very significant. The fact that they are not observed presently I attribute simply to the fact that their copper was probably different from that which is in common use today. It must be realized that almost all experiments today use a copper from a single source. Moreover that early, classic paper by Meechan and Brinkman is the very paper where the "Meechan and Brinkman method" for analyzing energetics and kinetics was introduced — one of the better methods that is in current use.

The assignment of recovery processes to annealing stages that I presently favor is as follows:

I — close pairs and free migration of the interstitial, during which the interstitial can annihilate, undergo trapping at various impurity or physical trapping sites, or agglomerate.

II — the interstitial can be released from traps or undergo rearrangement type annealing (possible divacancy recovery also occurs in Stage II): the interstitial progresses to progressively deeper and deeper traps.

III — in this recovery stage the interstitial is released from the deepest trap in the lattice, and/or vacancy migration takes place which cleans up the lattice. It is now increasingly common to see vacancy migration assigned to at least the high temperature portion of Stage III. It is also clear that Stage II processes continue right up to Stage III and in fact may impinge upon Stage III, which is what I mean by the deepest trap.

IV — the release of trapped vacancies where these occur.

V — recrystallization.

In coming to this conference it was clear that the two major anomalies with respect to such an interpretations scheme were platinum and gold, and each deserves some comment here. Platinum has appeared commonly in the body of the conference, nonetheless it is worthwhile to point out that the work of Attardo and Galligan [17] showed that in Stage III of *neutron-irradiated* platinum they observed in the field-ion-microscope that interstitials migrated to the surface. The key point, as Dr. Galligan well appreciates, is that this was neutron-irradiated platinum; the point being that in neutron irradiation there is an appreciable probability of forming di-interstitials directly, since the damage is created in a localized site with a number of interstitials and vacancies simultaneously present. Thus while they have many more interstitials than impurities, and though they presumably observe the interstitials in isolation and not in clusters at impurity site, they still cannot rule out the release of interstitials from di-interstitials or indeed rule out the migration of di-interstitials as occurring in Stage III. Moreover in this conference Dr. Schilling has shown that what was formally called *Stage III is not an intrinsic process in platinum* but is variable from sample to sample. For that reason Dr. Schilling advocates relabeling the stages so that what was Stage IV now becomes Stage III. With the relabeling the platinum data become fully consistent with the interpreration presented here.

Gold is another matter! It has always been another matter! It was always such that the two-interstitial protagonists would say "Ah, but what about gold?" And with considerable justification. But then Swanson and Piercy [18] performed an experiment in which they quenched in vacancies and then irradiated at low temperatures. They found an enhanced recovery in gold which, I argued [12], indicated that long-range motion was indeed occurring in the low temperature Stage I recovery of gold. I gather that Dr. Swanson now [19] concurs in this interpretation. Moreover we have heard at this conference the exciting and provocative results of Dr. Gonser in which he studies the electrical resistivity and Mössbauer effect in a dilute alloy of cobalt 57 in gold. He irradiates at $80°K$ and introduces a certain resistivity increment but observes no change in the Mössbauer pattern. He then anneals in what we would call Stage II. He observes a discrete resistivity annealing process and correlated with it now a change in the Mössbauer pattern is observed. To me this indicates unambiguously that interstitial motion has occurred and has resulted in the trapping of an interstitial at the cobalt-57 site. Upon further annealing Dr. Gonser finds in Stage III an additional recovery in his electrical resistivity

and the modified Mössbauer pattern anneals as well, that is the original unmodified
Mössbauer pattern is obtained as though the interstitial which was trapped at the
cobalt-57 is now removed. That removal can of course occur by either the interstitial being removed from the cobalt-57 by untrapping or by a vacancy coming to the
interstitial and annihilating the interstitial. The experiment as presented is of course
preliminary but is provocative and exciting. The position I presently hold on gold
was originally derived from an experimentalist's intuition and little more. Specifically the recovery in gold looks very similar to the sort of recovery that would be
obtained in copper if it were impure copper. So I raise the question whether in fact
we are dealing with very high purity gold (or platinum for that matter). The point
being that in copper, aluminum, etc. one recognized that he had an impurity problem and worked very hard to solve it; on the other hand in the noble metals the
natural presumption is they are very pure. But this may not be so. In particular the
other semi-noble metals may be present as significant impurity concentrations.

Let me conclude with a few remarks concerning the radiation doping experiments. We have heard at this conference of the exciting experiments performed by
Dr. Wollenberger in using the high-temperature irradiations to elucidate the configuration of the interstitials retained in the lattice. This line of experimentation has already proven quite helpful and I am confident it will prove even more helpful as
the technique matures. I want to emphasize here that the radiation doping experiments are a related diagnostic tool which remains to be exploited more fully. As
shown in fig. 7, the radiation doping experiments can be sensitive and discriminat-
ing with respect to quantitative differences in interstitial configurations.

The analysis irradiations and the radiation-doping experiments are clearly very
similar. In both cases interstitials migrate through the lattice to vacancies and to
other interstitials or trapping sites in various configurations. In the case of the anal-
ysis-irradiations the interstitials are produced one at a time; in the case of the radiation-doping experiments a large concentration of interstitials is introduced before
the migration is permitted. This difference may warrant a program exploiting the
radiation-doping technique together with the analysis-radiation technique.

Finally let me conclude by noting that the radiation-doping experiments as already performed have something to say about the recovery in Stage III. As I noted
earlier the crude experiments which we performed on Stage III recovery in which
the irradiation had been carried out in such a way that agglomeration had occurred
or interstitial trapping had occurred showed that either way roughly the same recovery was observed. Subsequently of course Bauer and Sosin [20] have repeated
this kind of experiment somewhat more carefully. They too found that the recovery was largely the same, independent of how the interstitials were retained in
the lattice. (Since they only made isochronal measurements in these experiments,
there is still latitude for more extensive experimentation which will determine the
activation energies and kinetics in the two types of experiments. Superficially at
least however at present there seems no difference between the recovery in the two
types of experiments.) As I argued earlier this type of result suggested that the com-

mon defect, namely the vacancy, was responsible for the preponderant recovery in Stage III in copper. Let us return now to the question of radiation-doping with pre-doping of interstitials retained as trapped interstitials or interstitials retained as agglomerated interstitials. It is agreed now generally that the Stage I recovery where this radiation-doping was studied is in fact due to the long-range migration of some sort of interstitial. Fig. 7 shows that the recovery in the two cases is quantitatively different. This is to be contrasted to the Stage III recovery where there is *no* quantitative difference in the recovery. Thus *the Stage I recovery is generically different from the Stage III recovery*. This makes it very difficult for the Stage III recovery to be predominantly interstitial type recovery.

## References

[1] G.D.Magnuson, W.Palmer and J.S.Koehler, Phys. Rev. 109 (1958) 1990.
[2] J.W.Corbett and R.M.Walker, Phys. Rev. 110 (1958) 767;
    J.W.Corbett, R.B.Smith and R.M.Walker, Phys. Rev. 114 (1959) 1452, 1460;
    J.W.Corbett and R.M.Walker, Phys. Rev. 115 (1956) 67;
    J.W.Corbett, Phys. Rev. 137 (1965) A1806.
[3] T.R.Waite, Phys. Rev. 107 (1957) 463, 471.
[4] R.R.Coltman Jr., C.E.Klabunde and J.K.Redman, Phys. Rev. 159 (1967) 521.
[5] J.W.Corbett, Phys. Rev. Letters 21 (1968) 817.
[6] Proceedings of the Lattice Defects Conference, October 1958, eds. J.A.Brinkman, C.J. Meechan and A.Sosin (Atomics International, Canoga Park, 1960).
[7] C.J.Meechan, A.Sosin and J.A.Brinkman, Phys. Rev. 120 (1960) 411.
[8] W.Bauer, A.Seeger and A.Sosin, Phys. Letters 24A (1967) 195.
[9] A.Sosin and L.H.Rachal, Phys. Rev. 130 (1963) 2238.
[10] D.A.Grenning and J.S.Koehler, Phys. Rev. 144 (1966) 439.
[11] H.I.Dawson, Acta Met. 13 (1965) 463.
[12] J.W.Corbett, Electron Radiation Damage in Semiconductors and Metals (Academic Press, New York, 1966) Suppl. 7 to Solid State Physics, eds. F.Seitz and D.Turnbull.
[13] K.Herschbach and J.J.Jackson, Phys. Rev. 158 (1967) 661.
[14] P.B.Peters and P.E.Shearin, Phys. Rcv. 174 (1968) 691.
[15] R.A.Johnson, Phys. Rev. 174 (1968) 684.
[16] C.J.Meechan and J.A.Brinkman, Phys. Rev. 103 (1956) 1193.
[17] M.J.Attardo and J.M.Galligan, Phys. Rev. Letters 14 (1965) 641;
    J.M.Galligan and M.J.Attardo, Phys. Rev. Letters 17 (1966) 1173;
    M.J.Attardo and J.M.Galligan, Phys. Rev. 161 (1967) 558.
[18] M.L.Swanson and G.R.Piercy, Phys. Letters 7 (1963) 97.
[19] M.L.Swanson, Phys. Stat. Sol. 23 (1967) 649.
[20] W.Bauer and A.Sosin, Phys. Letters 24A (1967) 193.

# ATOMIC MECHANISMS DURING THE ANNEALING OF
# IRRADIATED METALS *

J.S.KOEHLER

*Department of Physics and Materials Research Laboratory,*
*University of Illinois, Urbana, Illinois, USA*

By now most research workers have agreed on the major outlines of what happens during stage I annealing. The small subpeaks in stage I, which obey first order annealing, are ascribed to close interstitial vacancy pair recombination. Then at a temperature near the upper end of stage I a second order peak is seen. This results from the long range three dimensional migration of an interstitial to vacancies, to impurity traps, to interstitial clusters, to surfaces, to grain boundaries, or to dislocations.

There are a few questions which remain. They are:

1) What is the geometrical structure of the interstitial in fcc and also in bcc crystals?

2) Why is the annealing peak structure so different in gold from its appearance in stage I from copper, silver, nickel, platinum, and aluminum?

3) Is stage $I_D$ in copper a collection of overlapping close pair peaks or is it correlated recovery of the free interstitial with its close vacancy?

Koehler and Leibfried [3] suggest that questions 1 and 2 have the following answers: The stable form of the interstitial in most fcc crystals is the cube centered interstitial. This gives the $I_A$, $I_B$, $I_C$, $I_D$ close pair recombination peak structure easily. In gold they propose that the split $\langle 100 \rangle$ interstitials are the stable interstitials which are easily seen to give a more complicated close pair recovery structure. Snead, Wiffen, and Kauffman [4] give stage I annealing data on gold irradiated to low dose with 2 MeV electrons which shows features resembling copper. They claim that $I_E$ occurs at 21°K in gold. It is clear that impurity interstitial interaction can give rise to discrete annealing peaks in stage II. However, in neutron-irradiated metals and in heavily damaged specimens prepared by electron, proton, or deuteron irradiation a large essentially continuous stage II annealing is observed. This might possibly arise as follows: During the stage $I_E$ annealing the freely migrating intersti-

* Research supported by the U.S. Atomic Energy Commision, Contract AT(11-1)1198.

tials form clusters which are interstitial platelets on the ⟨111⟩ planes. These clusters have been observed below stage III in gold [5]. The interstitial clusters have a large strain field and it is possible that the strains may lower the vacancy migration energy into the stage II region.

Let us next consider stage III annealing. First we make some general remarks. All metals if irradiated at 4°K show a prominent low temperature annealing which has in many metals been shown to be associated with long range defect migration. Long range migration has been demonstrated in aluminum, copper, silver, and gold mainly by showing that the damage production rate at 100°K is larger in impure samples [6].

Both experiment and theory [7] unite in saying that the migration energy associated with interstitials in fcc metals is small, of the order of 0.1 eV. Moreover, existing theory does not suggest that a metastable interstitial exists which under very special circumstances can be converted into the stable interstitial. M.Doyama and I tried to produce such a metastable interstitial. We used one of five-fold symmetry hoping that its unusual symmetry and complexity would prevent its relaxation into one of the simpler types of interstitial. However, it did relax into a split ⟨100⟩ interstitial with a continuous decrease in the energy of the system. The Morse potential appropriate for copper was used for atom atom interaction. This is not a proof, of course, but it does indicate that some new physical reason for metastability will be needed.

It is fairly evident also that vacancies and di-vacancies migrate at temperatures which are approximately the temperatures associated with stage III annealing. Thus it seems that the simplest model one could propose would be that interstitials migrate in stage I and vacancies migrate in stage III. In fact, this is what we shall contend happens in aluminium, gold and platinum. Schilling and v.d.Beukel will present the evidence for platinum. Let us consider the evidence for aluminum and gold.

The evidence for aluminum and gold is mainly based on the fact that the activation energy observed in stage III annealing is the same as that seen in the annealing of a specimen quenched from low temperature. In aluminum Federighi [8] and coworkers observed $E_{III}$ = 0.61 ± 0.03 eV after neutron irradiation and $E_v^M$ = 0.62 ± 0.04 eV in a specimen quenched from 600°C. For quenched specimens Zamboni and Federighi determined the activation energy by plotting log $t_f$ versus the reciprocal of the absolute temperature. $t_f$ is the time to anneal out a fraction f of the damage. The slope of the line gives the migration energy. For neutron-irradiated specimens they used slope change, Meechan-Brinkman and the above method. Doyama and Koehler [9] using the slope change method observed $E_v^M$ = 0.60 ± 0.04 eV in a pure aluminum specimen quenched from 300°C. Sosin and Garr [10] obtained a low migration energy in stage III for electron-irradiated aluminum. They use a second order method to determine the activation energy. W.Bauer [11] in this conference shows that the second order method leads to erroneous activation energies. Lwin, Doyama and Koehler [12] irradiated high purity aluminum at 100°K using 2 MeV electrons. They determined the stage III migration energy using slope change and also by using Primak (second order) analysis. They find that $E_{III} = 0.62 \pm 0.04$ eV. Their long isothermal runs at $223°$K are observed to follow second order annealing kinetics.

It is therefore clear that the same defect as revealed by activation energy migrates in quenched and in irradiated aluminum. If isochronals are done on quenched and on irradiated specimens one observes that the temperature associated with most rapid annealing is lower in an irradiated specimen than in a quenched specimen if both start with the same $\Delta\rho$ at $-150°$C. To say it in another way, the number of jumps that a defect makes before annihilation is anomalously small in an irradiated specimen. If a frequency factor is used which gives about the correct number of jumps $n_j$ in a quenched specimen (i.e. $n_j$ is approximately the reciprocal of the vacancy concentration) and the same frequency factor is then used for an irradiated specimen the calculated rate of annealing will agree with experiment only if the number of jumps made by a vacancy until its annihilation is too small by at least a factor of thirty. We believe that this results from the interaction between the vacancies and the interstitial clusters present in the irradiated aluminum below stage III. We shall discuss this discrepancy more quantitatively in gold where the interstitial clusters have been observed and measured below stage III.

In the case of gold Sharma, Lee and Koehler [13] have shown that the same defect (as distinguished by energy of migration) is observed during the annealing of very pure gold which has been (a) lightly deformed (b) fast quenched from $700°$C and (c) irradiated with 3 MeV electrons at $100°$K. The activation energy was determined by the slope change method. The activation energies observed by Lee and Koehler [14] were for 3 MeV electron irradiation at $100°$K

$$E_{III} = 0.85 \pm 0.02 \text{ eV},$$

$$\rho_{4.2°K} \approx 0.5 \times 10^{-9} \text{ ohm cm},$$

and for the fast quenched specimens (quenched from $700°$C with $dT/dt > 4 \times 10^4$°C/sec)

$$E_v^M = 0.86 \pm 0.02 \text{ eV},$$

$$\rho_{4.2°K} \approx 0.5 \times 10^{-9} \text{ ohm cm}$$

Kino and Koehler [15] got after a fast quench from $700°$C

$$E_v^M = 0.90 \pm 0.05 \text{ eV},$$

$$\rho_{4.2°K} < 0.56 \times 10^{-9} \text{ ohm cm}.$$

Sharma and Koehler [16] found on gold fast quenched from $700°$C
$$E_v^M = 0.87 \pm 0.04 \text{ eV}$$

$$\rho_{4.2°K} < 0.5 \times 10^{-9} \text{ ohm cm}.$$

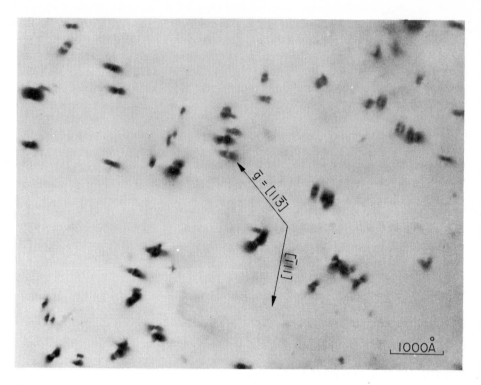

Fig. 1. High magnification picture of defects observed before stage III annealing in pure gold irradiated with 3 MeV electrons observed from [112] direction.

The $\rho_{4.2°K}$ was the residual resistivity of the 5 mil thick gold strip before quenching. It provides a measure of the purity. The above values of $\rho_{4.2°K}$ were not
corrected for size effect. Such a correction would give $\rho_{4.2°K\ corr} \approx 0.13 \times 10^{-9}$
ohm cm (for $\rho_{4.2} = 0.5 \times 10^{-9}$ ohm cm and assuming diffuse reflection of the conduction electrons at the specimen surface).

Shimomura [5] thinned electron irradiated gold at +2°C and in some cases at
−30°C and examined the specimens using a cold stage (100°K) in the electron
microscope. An example of his pictures is shown in fig. 1 obtained on 99.9999%
pure gold. The number per $cm^3$ and the size distributions associated with various
values of integrated flux are given in figs. 2 and 3. Examination of high magnification pictures taken with different diffraction vectors operating shows that the
clusters are platelets on the (111) planes. A gold specimen quenched from 900°C to
−20°C and thinned at 2°C shows no clusters. However, if the specimen is quenched
from 900°C, annealed at 20°C for ten days and then thinned one sees the usual
vacancy tetrahedra. Thus the clusters are interstitial clusters. Annealing in the stage
III region causes the interstitial clusters to shrink. Fig. 4 shows the size distribution

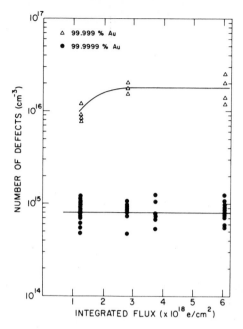

Fig. 2. Density of defects in irradiated samples versus total flux. This figure shows that number of defects are constant for electron dose between $1.2 \times 10^{18}$ and $6.0 \times 10^{18}$ e/cm$^2$.

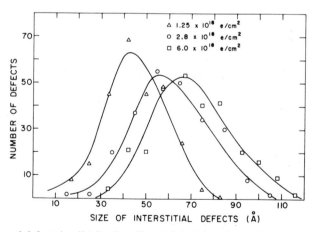

Fig. 3. Measured defect size distribution. Size of defects increases with increasing electron dose.

after irradiation and then after subsequent annealing. Thus in gold the vacancies migrate to interstitial clusters in stage III causing them to shrink. Note that in electron irradiated pure gold and pure aluminum essentially all of the damage anneals out during stage III. Lee and Koehler [14] found that the purer the gold the less

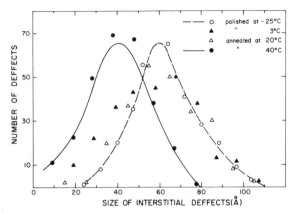

Fig. 4. Defect size distribution during stage III annealing.

remains after stage III. For a specimen having $\rho_{4.2°K} \approx 0.5 \times 10^{-9}$ ohm cm less than 3% of the resistance put in by irradiation at $100°K$ remains after stage III. A similar result was found in the case of aluminum [11] where 1% or less remains after stage III.

There is a difficulty in reconciling Shimomura's electron microscope data with the resistivity data. Consider 6N pure gold irradiated with $6.0 \times 10^{18}$ electrons/cm$^2$. If one uses the size distribution observed after irradiation and assumes that for each interstitial in a platelet there is a lattice vacancy present then one can calculate the resistivity increase expected. One uses the measured edge dislocation resistivity and the observed stacking fault resistivity and the observed resistivity of lattice vacancies. For the case in question one predicts $\Delta\rho = 2.58 \times 10^{-9}$ ohm cm. However, one observes $\Delta\rho = 13.9 \times 10^{-9}$ ohm cm which is five times larger. In this case, Shimomura's size distribution of loops drops to zero at 25 Å for small loops (see fig. 3). He believes that he does not miss very many of such loops. It is possible that there are a large number of very small interstitial clusters each containing only one or two interstitials trapped at some impurity. Further work is needed.

There is, however, another problem associated with stage III. If vacancies migrate to interstitial clusters how is it that one observes second order annealing kinetics? Let us examine this problem. Lee and Koehler [14] write the following rate equations during annealing:

$$\dot{C}_{1V} = -K_1 C_{1V}^2 - \sum_{n=1}^{\infty} K_{1n} C_{nI} C_{1V} , \tag{1}$$

$$\dot{C}_{2V} = +\tfrac{1}{2} K_1 C_{1V}^2 - \sum_{n=1}^{\infty} K_{2n} C_{nI} C_{2V} , \tag{2}$$

$$C_{1V} + 2C_{2V} = \sum_{n=1}^{\infty} nC_{nI} , \qquad (3)$$

$$\Delta\rho = f_V C_{1V} + (2f_V - \Delta f)C_{2V} + f_I' \sum_{n=1}^{\infty} nC_{nI} , \qquad (4)$$

or

$$\Delta\rho = (f_V + f_I')(C_{1V} + 2C_{2V}) - \Delta f C_{2V} , \qquad (5)$$

where $C_{1V}$ is the single vacancy concentration, $C_{2V}$ is the divacancy concentration, $\Delta\rho$ is the resistivity associated with defects, $C_{nI}$ is the concentration of interstitial clusters containing $n$ interstitials, $f_V/100$ is the resistivity of one percent vacancies, $f_I'/100$ is the resistivity of 1% interstitials in clusters, $(2f_V - \Delta f)/100$ is the resistivity of one percent divacancies. Let us assume that the rate of capture of vacancies by interstitial clusters is proportional to the cluster size. Thus

$$K_{1n} = K_{1\bar{n}} \, n , \qquad (6)$$

so that

$$\sum_{n=2}^{\infty} K_{1n} \, C_{nI} = K_{1\bar{n}} \sum_n n C_{nI} = K_{1\bar{n}} \, (C_{1V} + 2C_{2V}) . \qquad (7)$$

Similarly, we put

$$K_{2n} = K_{2\bar{n}} \, n , \qquad (8)$$

so that

$$\sum K_{2n} \, C_{nI} = K_{2\bar{n}} \sum_n n C_{nI} = K_{2\bar{n}} \, (C_{1V} + 2C_{2V}) . \qquad (9)$$

If we neglect $\Delta f$ in eq. (5) we get

$$\Delta\rho = (f_V + f_I')(\dot{C}_{1V} + 2\dot{C}_{2V}) ,$$

or

$$\Delta\rho = -(f_V + f_I')(C_{1V} + 2C_{2V})(C_V K_{1\bar{n}} + C_{2V} K_{2\bar{n}}) . \qquad (10)$$

The divacancy concentration is initially very small in comparison with the single vacancy concentration. If it remains small then (10) gives second order annealing and the rate constant $K_{1\bar{n}}$ is associated with vacancy migration. The rate eqs. (1) and (2) can be written:

$$\dot{C}_{1V} = -K_1 C_{1V}^2 - K_{1\bar{n}} C_{1V}(C_{1V} + 2C_{2V}) = -K_1 C_{1V}^2 - K_{1\bar{n}} C_{1V} z, \quad (11)$$

$$\dot{z} = -K_{1\bar{n}} C_{1V} z - K_{2\bar{n}} z(z - C_{1V}), \quad (12)$$

where

$$z = C_{1V} + 2C_{2V}.$$

Dividing eq. (12) by (11) and integrating the result one finds:

$$z = C_{1V} \left[ \frac{K_{2\bar{n}} + K_1 - K_{1\bar{n}}}{K_{2\bar{n}} - K_{1\bar{n}}} - \left( \frac{K_1}{K_{2\bar{n}} - K_{1\bar{n}}} \right) \left( \frac{C_{1V}}{C_V^o} \right)^{\frac{K_{2\bar{n}} - K_{1\bar{n}}}{K_{1\bar{n}}}} \right], \quad (13)$$

where $C_V^o$ is the initial vacancy concentration. Experiment shows that the number of jumps of a vacancy to annihilation in stage III in gold is 30 to 50 times smaller in an irradiated specimen than it is in a quenched specimen. We therefore expect $K_{1\bar{n}}$ and $K_{2\bar{n}}$ to be much larger than $K_1$. When $t = 0$ the square bracket in eq.(13) is unity. At $t = \infty$ it is very nearly unity since the second term is zero. Eq. (11) becomes therefore

$$\frac{\dot{C}_{1V}}{C_{1V}^2} = -(K_1 + K_{1\bar{n}}). \quad (14)$$

Thus the vacancy annealing obeys a second order annealing equation with a rate constant which is determined by vacancy migration to interstitial clusters. From eq. (13) one sees that $\Delta\rho$ will also obey second order annealing kinetics.

One can also get second order annealing kinetics if most of the interstitial clusters are small ones not seen in Shimomura's experiments. If so, the vacancy interaction with the cluster must still be large since the frequency factor observed in stage III annealing in gold is 40 times that found in quenched gold.

The main point of this discussion is that the interaction of the lattice vacancies with the interstitial clusters is important for both aluminum and gold. It is the fact that $K_{1\bar{n}} \approx 40K_1$ in eq. (14) which in isochronals causes the irradiation peak to occur at a lower temperature than the quench peak for similar defect concentrations.

The situation in copper and silver is not clear. The stage III annealing obeys second order annealing kinetics and is associated with an activation energy which is smaller than the vacancy migration energy (i.e. $E_{III} = 0.70 \pm 0.04$ eV [17], $E_v^M = 0.88 \pm 0.1$ eV [18] in copper; $E_{III} = 0.67 \pm 0.04$ eV [17], $E_v^M = 0.83 \pm 0.05$ eV [19] in silver). At present, it is not clear what these differences mean. It is possible that the strain field of the interstitial cluster reduces the vacancy migration energy by 0.1 to 0.2 eV. It could be that divacancies take part in the annealing. Grenning and Koehler [20] used small atomic core impurities to immobilize interstitials in copper, silver, and gold. In copper and in silver containing small amounts of beryllium they found the same activation energy and the same frequency factor as Dworschak, Herschbach, and Koehler [17] observed for the pure metals. The annealing kinetics was second order for both the pure and the alloyed metals. This raises questions concerning the reason for second order kinetics in gold. In these copper and silver experiments the fractional impurity concentrations were $10^{-4}$ or larger. Therefore, the probability of forming large clusters of interstitials is small since most of the migrating interstitials will encounter an impurity before they meet an impurity interstitial complex. Thus, in this case the second order annealing kinetics results from small-sized clusters.

In summary, we can say that Stage III annealing in aluminum, gold, and platinum results from vacancy migration. At present it is not clear whether the great majority of the interstitials present are in small clusters (containing one to three interstitials) or in large clusters (containing several hundred interstitials). It is clear that the interaction between the migrating vacancy and the interstitial clusters is important in aluminum, gold, and platinum.

The situation in copper and in silver is not clear. The activation energies seen in irradiated silver and copper are not the vacancy migration energy.

## References

[1] A.V.Granato and T.G.Nilan, Phys. Rev. 137A (1965) 1250.
[2] J.W.Corbett, Phys. Rev. 137A (1965) 1806.
[3] J.S.Koehler and G.Leibfried, J. Phys. Soc. Japan 18, Supp. III (1963) 266.
[4] C.L.Snead, F.W.Wiffen and J.W.Kauffman, in: Proceedings of the International Conference on Solid State Physics with Accelerators, ed. A.Goland (Brookhaven National Laboratory, 1968) p. 230.
[5] Y.Shimomura, Phil. Mag. 19 (1969) 773.
[6] D.A.Grenning and J.S.Koehler, Phys. Rev. 144 (1966) 439;
Y.A.Lwin, M.Doyama and J.S.Koehler, Phys. Rev. 165 (1968) 787;
C.Lee and J.S.Koehler, Phys. Rev. 176 (1968) 813.
[7] For theory see:
R.A.Johnson and E.Brown, Phys. Rev. 127 (1962) 446;
K.H.Benneman, Z. Physik 165 (1961) 445;
M.Doyama and R.M.J.Cotterill, Phys. Rev. 137 (1965) A994;
G.Schottky, A.Seeger and G.Schmid, Phys. Stat. Sol. 4 (1964) 419.
For experiment see:
Cu, Ag: G.D.Magnuson, W.Palmer and J.S.Koehler, Phys. Rev. 109 (1958) 1990;
Cu: J.W.Corbett, R.B.Smith and R.M.Walker, Phys. Rev. 114 (1959) 1460;
Al: K.Herschbach, Phys. Rev. 130 (1963) 554;
C.L.Snead and P.E.Shearin, Phys. Rev. 140 (1965) A1781.
[8] S.Ceresara, T.Federighi, D.Gelli and F.Pieragostini, Nuovo Cimento 29 (1963) 1244;
L.Zamboni and T.Federighi, see article by T.Federighi, in: Lattice Defects in Quenched Metals, eds. Cotterill, Doyama, Jackson and Meshii (Academic Press, New York, 1965) p. 217;
S.Ceresara, H.Elkholy, T.Federighi and F.Pieragostini, Phys. Letters 16 (1965) 9.

[9] M.Doyama and J.S.Koehler, Phys. Rev. 134 (1964) A522.

[10] A.Sosin and L.H.Rachel, Phys. Rev. 130 (1963) 2238;
K.R.Garr and A.Sosin, Phys. Rev. 162 (1967) 681.

[11] W.Bauer, Jul. Conf. 2 (Vol. I) 1968, p. 275.

[12] Y.N.Lwin, M.Doyama and J.S.Koehler, Phys. Rev. 165 (1968) 787.

[13] R.K.Sharma, C.Lee and J.S.Koehler, Phys. Rev. Letters 19 (1967) 1379.

[14] C.Lee and J.S.Koehler, Phys. Rev. 176 (1968) 813.

[15] T.Kino and J.S.Koehler, Phys. Rev. 162 (1967) 632.

[16] R.K.Sharma and J.S.Koehler, to be published.

[17] F.Dworschak, K.Herschbach and J.S.Koehler, Phys. Rev. 133 (1963) A293;
F.Dworschak and J.S.Koehler, Phys. Rev. 140 (1965) A941.

[18] A.Kuper, H.Letaw, L.Slifken and C.Tomizuka, Phys. Rev. 98 (1955) 1870;
R.O.Simmons and R.W.Balluffi, Phys. Rev. 129 (1963) 1533.

[19] M.Doyama and J.S.Koehler, Phys. Rev. 127 (1962) 21.

[20] D.A.Grenning and J.S.Koehler, Phys. Rev. 144 (1966) 439.

# INTRODUCTION TO THE PANEL DISCUSSION *

Alfred SEEGER

*Max-Planck-Institut für Metallforschung, Institut für Physik, Stuttgart, Germany*

The present conference has made it amply clear that the main remaining task in the interpretation of annealing stages in fcc metals is to decide between two principal views, namely (A) free migration of single interstitial atoms (in three dimensions) at very low temperatures (in the usual Cu-nomenclature : in the annealing stage $I_E$) or (B) free migration of interstitial atoms at fairly high temperatures (annealing stage III). In cases where there is evidence for thermally activated long-range migration at low temperatures this is attributed by (B) to the migration of a metastable interstitial configuration which may be converted into the "stage-III" interstitial, e.g., by "thermal conversion" at higher temperatures.

I) In my opinion the task of differentiating between the two view points (A) and (B) is somewhat akin to that of finding the small difference between two very large numbers. The reason for this is that the two models agree very closely in their predictions for many of the conventional experiments, or more precisely, can be made to agree by a suitable choice of the adjustable parameters. By "conventional experiments" I mean the investigation of recovery stages (isochronal annealing), annealing kinetics (isothermal annealing), apparent activation energies, damage curves etc. by means of electrical resistance measurements. We shall see presently that only if careful attention to fine details is paid and a high experimental accuracy is achieved can we hope to discriminate between the two models on the basis of such measurements. As I shall show later, less conventional experiments designed for testing *specific* predictions are much more helpful in answering those questions that are still open.

The approximate equivalence of the two models with respect to the usual resistance measurements may be most easily seen from the following table of corresponding processes or concepts in the two models:

---

* The author would like to express his appreciation and gratitude to Dr. W.Frank for numerous stimulating discussions and for his advice in preparing the present contribution.

| Model A | Model B |
|---|---|
| free interstitial migration | migration of metastable interstitial configuration |
| trapping at impurities | trapping at impurities |
| formation of di-interstitials (dimer formation) | athermal double conversion (formation of two stage-III interstitials from two encountering metastable interstitials) |
| no equivalent | thermal conversion of metastable interstitials to stage-III interstitials |
| no equivalent | conversion of metastable interstitial into stage-III interstitial at impurities, without effective trapping |
| breaking up of di-interstitials into two mono-interstitials | no equivalent |
| migration of monovacancies to trapped interstitials or di-interstitials *or* di-interstitial migration to mono-vacancies | free migration of stage-III interstitial configuration |

It has been known for quite some time that the rate equations for the two models (including their variants, see last entry in the A-column) have essentially the same form. I am nevertheless emphasizing this fact since I still see considerable efforts being made with the aim to exclude one of the models (usually B, but this is besides the point) on the basis of the analysis of resistance measurements in terms of rate equations. These workers usually find that they can fit their data by one of the models, and then hasten to conclude that the other one must be wrong. In my experience such conclusions must be considered with utmost suspicion, unless they are based on *specific* details, which, however, must be backed by correspondingly careful theoretical analysis and control of the experiments.

Having cautioned the reader sufficiently against an overemphasis on kinetic data I would like to give one example of conclusions that may be drawn from a special feature of the annealing kinetics, namely the reaction order towards the end of stage $I_E$. In principle, this may be used to distinguish between different models. If after low-temperature electron irradiation an appreciable recovery stage III is observed, one expects towards the end of the low-temperature long-range migration stage

in *model A* reaction order one,

in *model B* either reaction order one if the migrating interstitial performs a three-dimensional random walk (example: metastable tetrahedral interstitial) *or* reaction order two if the migrating interstitial performs a one-dimensional random walk (example: metastable crowdion) and may be either annihilated at a vacancy or converted into a stage-III interstitial.

Experimentally, the reaction orders two (for Cu [1]) and three (for Ni [2]) have been observed. The experiments of Corbett, Smith and Walker [1] on copper thus speak for model B with the additional information that the low-temperature interstitial migrates one-dimensionally, i.e., is in all likelihood a crowdion. This statement can be made since the necessary conditions for its validity are fulfilled:

a) An appreciable stage III (10% of the damage introduced by electron bombardment at $20°K$) has been found.

b) In $80°K$ electron irradiation no range of constant production rate at intermediate or high doses has been found, indicating that the stage-III interstitials are not generated directly but by conversion from the stage-$I_E$ interstitials.

Furthermore the absence of stage-II annealing in very pure copper after low-temperature electron irradiation shows that no distant Frenkel pairs involving the stage-III interstitial have been formed. It appears most likely that few *free* interstitials have been generated directly.

The theoretical explanation why in the low-temperature electron bombardment of copper free stage-III interstitials (presumably ⟨100⟩-dumbbells) are not or only rarely directly generated has been supplied by v.Jan [3]. v.Jan shows that in the usual electron irradiations the transferred energies are not large enough to separate ⟨100⟩-dumbbells sufficiently far from their vacancies for them to act as free interstitials. The ⟨100⟩-dumbbells that are created directly (e.g., by displacements in ⟨100⟩-directions) recombine with their vacancies in one of the low-temperature close pair stages. This explanation is not applicable to heavy particle (proton, deuteron, neutron) irradiation, in which the transferred energies are higher and in which the more distant Frenkel-pair stages are populated, giving rise to an appreciable stage-II annealing.

The reaction order three observed by Oddou [2] on nickel may be explained by one-dimensional migration, provided the migrating interstitials are mainly removed by annihilation with vacancies, and not by conversion to stage-III interstitials. This condition appears to be fairly well satisfied for nickel which shows an exceptionally small stage-III annealing (3% after electron bombardment at $20°K$). To account for reaction order three (in fact, for any order higher than two) would require extremely artificial assumptions for model A. To my knowledge, the literature contains no such proposal. I think that it is fair to say that one-dimensional migration of the interstitial involved is a necessary condition for (approximate) reaction order three in $I_E$. However, as we have seen above in the discussion on Cu, it is not a sufficient condition.

The preceding example was mainly meant to show how much detail one has to go into in order to draw definite conclusions from kinetic and radiation damage rate arguments. In the present example the conclusions are that in Cu and Ni the $I_E$-defect performs a *one-dimensional* and not a *three-dimensional* random walk, thus supporting the crowdion version of model B.

As a final word with regard to resistivity measurements I should like to say that I do not plead for these experiments to be abandoned. They are extremely useful for monitoring other, more specific, experiments, and they are capable, for a given model, of producing accurate values for the parameters of that model. However, if someone has the ambition of refute an otherwise well-founded model and to achieve more than ephemeral success, he should turn his principal attention to more specific effects, such as those to be discussed below.

II) From the table of correspondences given above it is evident that there are features in (B) with no counterparts in (A) and vice versa. Such features are particularly helpful in ruling out one of the models. I should like to discuss in some detail first two such features of the first category [absent in (A)], namely (i) thermal conversion and (ii) the possible absence of stage-$I_E$ annealing (i.e. of a low-temperature annealing peak that shifts appreciably to lower temperatures with increasing defect concentration) and then to turn to (iii) effects that would be explainable in (A) but not in (B).

(i) *Thermal conversion.* After low-temperature irradiation of Cu stage $I_E$ has been observed to be associated with strong dislocation pinning [4,5]. The accepted interpretation is that the defects migrating in stage $I_E$ reach and anchor the dislocations. During warm-up further dislocation pinning occurs, in particular in stage III [5,7]. This may be explained in (A) by the migration of either detrapped interstitials or di-interstitials to the dislocations, in (B) by the pinning of the dislocations by ⟨100⟩-dumbbells. So far both models are able to account equally well for the observations. Consider now measurements at the temperature of irradiation in the temperature range of stage III. In model A one would expect a fast pinning component due to the very mobile stage $I_E$ defects followed by a slow component. In model B this is not necessarily so, since the temperature may be high enough for the metastable interstitials to be converted by thermal fluctuations into ⟨100⟩ dumbbells before they can reach and pin the dislocations. This "thermal conversion" has, as far as I can see, no analogue in model A. Its experimental verification would provide very strong evidence against (A) and would at the same time support one of the most specific features of (B), the metastability of the $I_E$-defect.

The decisive experiment on Cu has been done by Thompson, Buck and co-workers [8–10] under — in my opinion — extremely clean conditions. Copper single crystals were irradiated between 333°K and 393°K with γ-rays from a $^{60}$Co source. From measurements of the dislocation internal friction and modulus defect the number of pinning defects arriving at the dislocations at the irradiation temperature was deduced. Using the cross sections for atomic displacements of Oen and Holmes [11] and a threshold energy for displacements of 20 eV, the authors [8] calculated a production rate of about $10^7$ Frenkel pairs/cm$^3$ or of a defect concentration of about $10^{-16}$ per second. In these experiments the instantaneous concentration of radiation-induced defects never exceeded $10^{-10}$ and was in most runs below the value $10^{-13}$. This means that there is no question of an appreciable formation of di-interstitials or di-vacancies or larger clusters, and that the defects migrating to the dislocations in the experiments of Thompson and Buck must be either single interstitials or single vacancies.

We shall return to the question of the final identification of these defects in connection with fig. 1. What we wish to emphasize now is

(a) that the experiments of Thompson and Buck show no evidence whatsoever

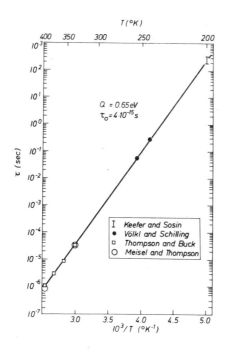

Fig. 1. Relaxation time $\tau$ for dumbbell migration in Cu as a function of temperature $T$, deduced
from different types of dislocation pinning studies on irradiated copper.

for a fast pinning component, i.e., that all pinners arrive at the dislocations with a
migration energy corresponding to the migration energy observed in stage III,

(b) that the number of pinners arriving at the dislocations agrees with the number
of displaced atoms as calculated from the dose and energy of the $\gamma$-irradiation [10],
showing that no substantial fraction of the displaced atoms migrates to sinks other
than the dislocations, or to traps, and

(c) that the activation energy observed by Thompson and Buck ($\approx 0.64$ eV) is the
migration energy of a well-defined defect, and that it is not to any appreciable
amount falsified by binding to impurities [10].

These observations indicate quite clearly that the defects that are responsible for
the low-temperature pinning of the dislocations are unable to migrate to the dislocations at the temperatures of the Thompson-Buck experiments. Since the observations exclude the possibility that these defects are pinned by impurities immediately
after their generation and are later slowly released, we have to conclude that in the
Thompson-Buck experiments the stage-$I_E$ defect has either not been generated at
all or that it has been converted to a much less mobile defect before it could come
close to the dislocations. The first alternative is very unlikely indeed, since one
would not expect such a profound influence of the irradiation temperature on the

defect production. It remains the second alternative, which means that the stage-$I_E$ defect is transformed on account of the increased temperature (and not on account of the action of impurities or dislocations), i.e., by thermal conversion. This means that the most important feature attributed to the stage-$I_E$ defect by model B has been confirmed rather directly. The question of the final identification of this defect is discussed in some detail by Thompson and Buck [10], and they come to the conclusion that a metastable crowdion would well account for their experiments and also for the available data on dislocation pinning in the $I_E$-temperature range. This is in line with the conclusions drawn above from the kinetics of the recovery of the electrical resistivity of electron-irradiated copper.

With regard to the identification of the defects acting as dislocation pinners in their experiments, Thompson and Buck point out that the observed energies of migration are incompatible with the existing information on mono-vacancy migration, and that this leaves as the only alternative the mono-interstitial. The configuration of this interstitial has to be different from that of the metastable configuration responsible for $I_E$-recovery. It seems reasonable to identify it with the ⟨100⟩-dumbbell configuration, which in almost all theoretical work on interstitial atoms in Cu has been found to be the most stable configuration.

In the early work [12,13] on the dumbbell interstitials it was pointed out that a ⟨100⟩-dumbbell in an fcc crystal is capable of two basic modes of motion, namely *rotation*, characterized by an activation energy $E^R$, and *migration,* characterized by an activation energy $E^M$. Both types of motion lead to a change of the direction of the dumbbell axis and may therefore give rise to a mechanical relaxation effect (Snoek effect). Calculations [13] on copper indicated that $E^R < E^M$, which would mean that different activation energies should be observed in relaxation and recovery experiments on dumbbell interstitials in Cu. However, from a comparison of the internal friction experiments of Völkl and Schilling [14] with the stage-III annealing data, Seeger and Wagner [15] deduced that in Cu mechanical relaxation and annealing give the same activation energy, and hence $E^R \geqslant E^M$. This allows us to draw the following conclusions and to test them experimentally:

(a) The relaxation time $\tau(T)$ at the temperature $T$ of a Snoek-type maximum in the internal friction is given by $\tau = \omega^{-1}$, where $\omega$ is the angular frequency employed in the internal friction measurement. Apart from small corrections, which need not be discussed here, $\tau(T)$ should show the same temperature dependence as the time constant $\tau_{LE}(T)$ for the migration of the interstitial atoms to the dislocations deduced by Thompson and Buck from their *steady state* experiments. The proportionality factor between $\tau(T)$ and $\tau_{LE}(T)$ is related to the dislocation density.

(b) If the relaxation strength of the dumbbells is large enough to lead to a measurable Snoek effect, the *transient* stage in the Thompson-Buck pinning experiment should be governed by the drift of the dumbbells in the strain field of the dislocations. Meisel and Thompson [16] have recently shown that this is indeed the case. Using the Cottrell-Bilby [17] approximation they were able to deduce from the transient of the Thompson-Buck experiments the product of the Cottrell-Bilby interaction parameter $A$ and the diffusion constant $D$ of the interstitials. The latter is related to the relaxation time $\tau$ by

$$D = \frac{a^2}{18} \cdot \frac{1}{\tau} \ ,$$

where $a$ is the lattice parameter (for Cu: $a = 3.6\,\text{Å}$).

(c) If the elementary step for the migration and the reorientation of a dumbbell interstitial is the same, the pinning of dislocations due to the migration of dumbbells to dislocations (obeying approximately the Cottrell-Bilby law) should be preceded by a "fast" process due to the formation of "Snoek" atmospheres in the environment of dislocations, i.e., a partial ordering [18,19] of the dumbbell axes in the stress-fields of the dislocations. The accompanying reduction in the dislocation mobility should follow an exponential time law characterized by the relaxation time $\tau(T)$ of the Snoek effect.

According to the preceding conclusions the relaxation times of four distinct experiments should be related to each other in a well defined manner. Fig. 1 shows the Arrhenius plots of these relaxation times. The full circles give the results of the Völkl-Schilling [14] experiments as analyzed by Seeger and Wagner [15]. The perpendicular bar gives the relaxation time as deduced from the Keefer-Sosin pinning experiment on electron-irradiated copper, which does indeed clearly indicate a "fast dislocation pinning" preceding the Cottrell-Bilby regime *. The squares in fig. 1 have been obtained from the Arrhenius plot of $\tau_{LE}$ as given by Thompson and Buck [10] by a displacement parallel to the $T^{-1}$ axis. As mentioned above, the amount of this displacement is related to the dislocation density; it is in quite good agreement with the estimated dislocation density of the specimen. The open circles are obtained from the Meisel-Thompson [16] values of the product $AD$ by assuming a suitable value for $A$. The chosen $A$ value lies within about a factor two of the theoretically predicted value. This is about as good an agreement between experiment and theory as one might expect in view of the approximate nature of the Cottrell-Bilby law employed by Meisel and Thompson.

We see that the relaxation times determined from four different experiments obey Arrhenius' law $\tau = \tau_0 \exp(Q/kT)$ over $8\frac{1}{2}$ powers of ten with

$$Q = 0.65 \text{ eV} , \qquad \tau_0 = 4 \times 10^{-15} \ s .$$

Essentially the same activation energy for pinning by long-range migration has recently been found in the megacycle experiment of Winterhager and Lücke [20]. (The Thompson-Buck experiments were performed in the kilocycle range.) The two

---

* The author is very indebted to Drs. Keefer and Sosin for making available their experimental data to shorter times than given in the publication [5], and for numerous discussions. The determination of $\tau(T)$ must be considered preliminary since the theory for the separation of the "fast" and "slow" pinning effects has not yet been completed.

high-temperature experiments (open symbols) of fig. 1 and the Winterhager-Lücke experiments measure the long-range migration of the stage-III defects, the other two experiments measure the reorientation of the preferred axes of the defects. The agreement between these two classes of experiments excludes immediately the possibility that the pinning might be due to a mono-vacancy with cubic symmetry, since this defect would not be able to reorient. (A pinning stage with an activation energy of about 1 eV, which is in good agreement with the monovacancy migration energy as deduced from other experiments, has been observed at higher temperatures [6,21–25].) In principle, di-vacancies could account for the identity of the elementary steps for migration and reorientation. However, apart from serious doubts whether the relaxation strengths of di-vacancies would be large enough to lead to an observable relaxation effect, the extremely low defect concentration in the Thompson-Buck experiments precludes such an explanation in the present case. We may thus conclude this discussion of the Thompson-Buck experiments by stating that they support model B in every detail.

(ii) *Absence of a $I_E$-annealing peak.* A second feature which is naturally accounted for by model B but has no analogue in model A is the possible absence of an annealing peak of $I_E$-type, i.e., of a low-temperature peak at or near the end of stage I that shifts appreciably to lower temperatures with increasing defect concentration. So far in two pure metals, Au and Cd, $I_E$-type peaks could not be found in spite of intense searches for them. It has been argued by some writers that in these metals long-range migration of point defects may nevertheless occur at low temperatures, possibly below the temperatures to which the present annealing experiments extend. Two points should be noted here, however. 1. From the view-point that the $I_E$-defect is a crowdion there is very little physical difference between the dynamic propagation of a crowdion and a migration at extremely low temperatures, say below 1°K. For many purposes we do not have to distinguish between these two possibilities, and we may leave the question open whether in a particular metal the crowdion exists only while propagating dynamically or whether it is metastable with very low temperatures of migration and conversion. 2. In both Au [26,27] and Cd [28] large numbers of low-temperature peaks have been resolved which appear all to be intrinsic (i.e., not seriously affected by impurities) and associated with first-order annealing processes. The natural explanation is that the majority of them is associated with the recombination of various close Frenkel pairs. Even if prolonged search should provide evidence for long-range migration in the lower part of stage I, the difficulties for model A would persist, since one would not expect a substantial number of close-pair annealing stages above the temperature of free migration of the interstitial. In contrast to this, in model B one may have two series of close-pair stages, of which that associated with the stage-III interstitial may extend well beyond the temperature of the migration of the stage-$I_E$ defect. We may thus state the present point more concisely by saying that model A is unable to account for close-pair stages at temperatures above the temperature of long-range migration, whereas model B accounts for them in a straightforward way.

(iii) *Effects predicted by model A but unexplainable by model B.* We shall restrict ourselves to the discussion of those effects in this category that have been specifically looked for. In view of the present writer's position he considers it as fortunate that to his best knowledge all efforts to find such effects have yielded negative results.

According to model A, no single interstitials can be present above stage-$I_E$ temperatures. They must either have formed di-interstitials, tri-interstitials, etc., or been trapped by impurities or dislocations. Irrespective of whether these complexes are assumed to be the migrating defects in stage III or the sinks for the stage-III defects, it should be possible to break them up by pulse annealing at temperatures above stage III and to get in this way radical deviations from the usual stage-III kinetics. This was attempted by Dworschak and Koehler [29] on Au, Ag and Cu after proton irradiation, with completely negative results. The usual stage-III activation energies of 0.80 eV, 0.67 eV and 0.71 eV were observed after the pulses. Incidentally, these experiments provide additional evidence against the proposal that in Cu and Ag the migration of di-vacancies might be important in stage III, since there is little doubt that di-vacancies were broken up completely during these experiments. Model B, however, predicts this negative result in a straightforward manner, since according to this model both the migrating defects (interstitials) and the main sinks (vacancies) are simple defects, which in no way may be broken up.

The second experiment in the present category with a negative result is that of Bauer and Sosin [30] on copper, which has repeatedly been referred to during this conference.

The basic idea of this experiment is as follows: It has been demonstrated that the residual resistivity increment in copper remaining after an 70°K-anneal following irradiation at or below 20°K is larger than the increment obtained by an equal irradiation dose at 70°K (fig. 2). Model A interprets this as meaning that interstitials are mobile at 70°K but not at or below 20°K. In an 70°K-annealing treatment the density of interstitials is high enough for them to encounter each other during the anneal and to form dimers or trimers that do not anneal out. During 70°K-irradiation, however, the instantaneous concentration of mobile interstitials should always be so low that dimer formation is unlikely. The difference of the resistivity increments obtained by the two treatments is, according to model A, related to the presence of dimers or larger interstitial clusters. The conversion-two-interstitial model B assumes that practically all stage-III interstitials surviving stage-I annealing are formed by conversion of stage-$I_E$ interstitials. After the 20°K-irradiation the concentration of stage-$I_E$ interstitials is large enough for some of the conversion to stage-III interstitials to occur by double conversion, i.e., during the encounter of two stage-$I_E$ interstitials. This process is unlikely during an 70°K-irradiation, during which the conversion must have taken place at traps such as impurities. In contrast to model A, model B does not have to make any special assumptions about the magnitude of the binding of interstitial atoms to other interstitial atoms or impurities. If we disregard for the time being the presumably small differences between intersti-

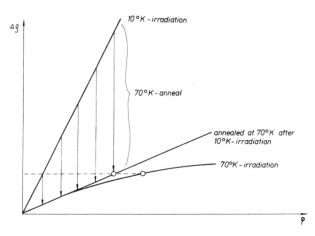

Fig. 2. Schematic representation of the Bauer-Sosin [30] experiment on the influence of the irradiation temperature on stage-III annealing in Cu ($\Delta\rho$ = radiation-induced resistivity, $\varphi$ = electron irradiation dose).

tials near impurities or near other interstitials (or, for that matter, interstitials in an otherwise perfect crystal) we may say that the damage pattern after the 70°K irradiation and after the 20°K irradiation plus an 70°K anneal is predicted by model B to be essentially the same. In specimens that have undergone the two different pretreatments discussed here with the same final increment of the residual resistivity (as indicated by the circles in fig. 2), one expects hence essentially the same annealing behaviour above 80°K. As we have seen, however, model A postulates quite a different damage structure after the two pre-treatments, the difference being mainly due to the presence or absence of di-interstitials. Unless very special assumptions are made, on the basis of model A the two specimens would be expected to show a a rather different annealing behaviour.

Bauer and Sosin [30] have carried out the experiment just described and have compared the annealing between 90°K and 340°K of copper specimens that have been irradiated at 10°K and annealed at 70°K or just irradiated at 70°K with the result that, apart from small differences in stage II that may have to do with the effects disregarded in our discussion of model B, there is no difference in the annealing characteristics. This is in particular true in stage III, where on the basis of model A the largest differences would have been expected. Thus the negative result of the Bauer-Sosin experiment is another example of an effect predicted by model A but not by model B that has not been found. For a further discussion of the implications the reader is referred to the note by Bauer, Seeger, and Sosin [31] accompanying the original paper.

Further experiments that might be mentioned here, although they are possibly less clear cut than the two preceding ones, are those on the suppression of stage-I annealing by the addition of impurities. In both models this may be explained by the trapping of the stage-$I_E$ defect by impurities. In both models one would expect that the trapped defects are freed by a temperature which is unrelated to that of stage III, and in a number of cases this is observed. (Sosin [32] makes the additional point that it is considerably easier in model B than in model A to explain the existence of more than one such detrapping stage associated with one impurity.) In other cases one observes that the suppression of stage $I_E$ simply increases stage III. To explain this, model A must make artificial assumptions, e.g., about the impurity-interstitial binding energy, whereas in model B the observed result comes out naturally as a consequence of the conversion of the stage-$I_E$ defect into the stage-III defect near an impurity site.

III) Let me now turn to the third group of experiments, namely those which indicate in a *specific* way the presence of certain defects. The four most important experiments that come to my mind in this category, which have all been touched upon in this conference, are

   (i) internal friction and modulus defect experiments,
   (ii) electron microscopy,
   (iii) field-ion microscopy,
   (iv) magnetic aftereffect.

(i) The *internal friction experiments* are capable of determining the symmetry of any defect in a cubic crystal with a point symmetry lower than cubic, provided the product of the concentration and the relaxation strength of the defects is large enough. This has been discussed in detail in Kronmüller's article presented at this conference. The most complete experiments in this category available to date are those of Wagner [15] on nickel. They indicate unambiguously that the stage-III defect in nickel has ⟨100⟩-symmetry and that its activation energy for rotation is lower than that for migration. They support further the view that this defect is not associated with impurities, a viewpoint amply demonstrated by other experiments on stage III, e.g., those by Duesing and Schilling [33] on electron-irradiated nickel. In view of the importance of these experiments it appears worthwhile to point out that Wagner's experiments were repeated after disassembling, modifying, and reassembling the measuring apparatus, with the same results as the published experiments. With the modified apparatus accurate measurements of the modulus defect were carried out, and these results supported in all respects the published interpretation of the internal friction experiments. Finally it should be mentioned that the most important result of Wagner's original experiments, namely the ⟨100⟩-symmetry of the stage-III defects, has rece..tly been verified by Wagner in the following independent way.

In a ferromagnetic material containing domain walls one expects a significant contribution to the loss of mechanical energy from the motion of domain walls which are displaced by the magnetostrictive interaction with the elastic strains. Such a contribution may be suppressed by the application of a sufficiently large magnetic field. In nickel, in which the magnetization inside the Weiss domains points in $\langle 111 \rangle$-directions, the only defects undergoing reorientation that do not give rise to a large domain wall contribution to the energy loss in internal friction experiments are those with $\langle 100 \rangle$-symmetry, since only in this special case remains the interaction between the defects and the magnetization unaffected by a redistribution of the defects over the different $\langle 100 \rangle$-directions. Wagner has recently found that, in contrast to the majority of internal friction peaks in nickel, the peak attributed to dumbbell rotation is indeed not changed by the application of a magnetic field. In the present writer's opinion the internal friction work on nickel constitutes the most direct proof that the stage-III defect in nickel has $\langle 100 \rangle$-symmetry.

(ii) The application of *transmission electron microscopy* to the study of radiation damage in metals has been reviewed by Wilkens at this meeting. Of particular interest in the present context are observations on electron-irradiated metals. During this conference, such observations have been reported on Cu (Scheidler and Roth [34]), Au (Koehler [35]), and Ni (Bourret [36]). We shall discuss here the latter observations, since fairly complete accounts are available (see also Bourret and Dautreppe [37]) and since the observations were made both below and above stage III, so that they are particularly relevant to the present discussion. Bourret interprets his results as either involving conservative climb of small loops or interstitial migration in stage III. We shall see that the latter interpretation is by far preferable to the former. In fact, we shall see that Bourret's results are in complete agreement with the predictions of model B.

In nickel foils irradiated with 2 MeV- or 3 MeV-electrons at temperatures between $-40°C$ and $+10°C$, Bourret finds a critical dose for the formation of visible interstitial clusters of about $2 \times 10^{19}$ e/cm$^2$. The existence of such a rather well-defined nucleation dose is most simply explained by the Lück-Sizmann [38] mechanism of cluster formation in heavily irradiated metals. The interstitial clusters formed in this way may or may not have grown further by the capture of the $I_E$-defects, depending on whether or not the irradiation temperature is above or below the conversion temperature (see II (i)) of these defects. In this context it should be noted that the fraction of the total interstitial concentration observed by Bourret in visible loops is very small (0.3%).

A most significant observation of Bourret is that annealing at $100°C$ (i.e., in stage III) leads to a substantial increase of both the density of visible loops and of the total number of interstitials in these loops. Bourret's and Dautreppe's interpretation of this in terms of conservative climb and coalescence of loops is not convincing for a number of reasons:

1. One would have to postulate an extraordinarily large density of invisible interstitial loops, many times larger than the extrapolation of the visible size distribution to small loop sizes would suggest.

2. One would have to assume that these small loops would have to migrate by conservative climb towards other interstitial loops and join them in spite of the fact

that each loop is surrounded by a high density of mono-vacancies and also some small vacancy clusters. Such a process is hard to envisage without the almost complete annihilation of the migrating loops.

3. The agreement of the temperature range of the cluster growth with stage III would be entirely coincidental.

In contrast to this, model B explains these experiments simply and without any additional hypotheses by the migration of single interstitials to the existing clusters, including those which are too small to have been visible before the annealing treatment.

(iii) The *field-ion* microscope observations so far available have been discussed fully by Galligan [39] and Müller [40]. It is clear that these observations will eventually be of great help in determining the properties of individual point defects. We may look forward to the extension of these experiments to fcc metals other than platinum.

(iv) It is my belief that an eventual *direct* proof of the nature of the stage-$I_E$ defect will come from *magnetic aftereffect* measurements at low temperatures. The crowdion model makes the following four specific predictions:

1. The stage-$I_E$ defect should give rise to a diffusion magnetic aftereffect.

2. It should not give rise to a reorientation magnetic aftereffect.

3. It should not give rise to a simple relaxation effect in the internal friction (or the elastic modulus).

4. Annealing should take place concurrently with the diffusion aftereffect.

As discussed in the paper by Kronmüller, in our opinion the recent experiments on Ni in Grenoble have verified all four of these predictions. This opinion has led to a controversy, particularly on the question of whether annealing takes place simultaneously with the observed aftereffect. However, this has recently been confirmed by the experiments of Lampert and Schaefer, who have been working with the 3 MeV-van-de-Graaff accelerator in Mülheim/Ruhr, and is also evident from the work of the Munich group on neutron-irradiated nickel. Lampert and Schaefer are expected to have available more complete results fairly soon, and we hope that these will help to answer the remaining questions. The Grenoble group denies the importance of annealing during the observed magnetic aftereffect and invokes instead a spectrum of relaxation times. In this interpretation an additional hypothesis is needed to explain the absence of the corresponding relaxation effects in internal friction.

IV) Let me make a few remarks on the comparison of the activation energies observed in stage-III annealing, $E_{III}$, with the migration energies of mono-vacancies, $E_{1V}^M$. In the majority of the fcc metals that have been thoroughly investigated, namely Cu, Ag, and Ni, $E_{1V}^M$ appears to be larger than $E_{III}$ by a margin which, in my opinion, clearly exceeds the experimental errors. Thus in these metals stage-III annealing cannot be associated with the migration of mono-vacancies. In gold the margin is much smaller ($E_{III} \approx 0.81$ eV, $E_{1V}^M = 0.89$ eV), but even in this case I think that the difference between these two values is outside the experimental error, although there may be individual experiments from which this is less evident than from a critical evaluation of all the relevant data available. An open situation appears to exist in aluminium. It is still true that the mono-vacancy migration energy as deduced from high-temperature and quenching experiments ($E_{1V}^M = 0.61-0.62$ eV) is higher than the migration energy obtained from measurements in the temperature range of stage III ($E_{III} = 0.58-0.59$ eV), but it is less clear than in other metals that this difference is outside the experimental errors. Let us now assume for the sake of the argument that in Al the activation energies $E_{III}$ and $E_{1V}^M$ do agree with each other within experimental error. Would this mean that stage III should be in general attributed to mono-vacancy migration? The answer is clearly no, since for the other fcc metals there is enough evidence to rule this out as a general explanation. Within the framework of model B the result $E_{III} \approx E_{1V}^M$ could be interpreted to mean one of two things: (i) By coincidence, the migration energies of interstitials and of mono-vacancies in Al are almost the same. (ii) The mobility of mono-vacancies in Al is higher than that of interstitials, so that the interstitials that persist up to stage-III temperatures are removed not by their migration to sinks but by annihilation with migrating mono-vacancies.

V) In this presentation I have gone through the discussion of four different classes of experiments, which allow different conclusions to be drawn and which may be summarized as follows:

i) *"Conventional" resistance experiments, e.g., on damage rates or annealing kinetics.* I have emphasized that in general such experiments do not permit a valid decision to be made between the two principal viewpoints mentioned in the introductory paragraph. I have given one example of a more detailed analysis of kinetic data. This analysis does support model B with the additional information that the defect migrating in stage $I_E$ in Cu and Ni performs a one-dimensional (in contrast to a three-dimensional) migration, i.e., that in all likelihood it is a crowdion.

ii) *Effects which may occur in one of the two principal models but have no counterpart in the other model.* If such effects are observed they provide strong evidence against that model in which they should not occur. Two effects ("thermal conversion" and "absence of $I_E$-annealing") have been found which are easily explained in model B but which, in the opinion of the present writer, are extremely difficult to accommodate within the framework of model A. Of these the observation of the phenomenon of "thermal conversion" is particularly significant, since it was this feature of model B which its opponents found particularly hard to accept. There are also effects for which the reverse should be true, i.e., they should be observed in model A but not in model B. Fortunately for the viewpoint held by the present writer, none of these effects appear to have been observed so far, a fact which lends at least "moral" support to model B and strengthens the expectation that within the framework of the ideas under discussion a consistent solution to the problem of annealing stages in fcc metals can be found.

iii) *"Specific" experiments. Electron microscopy* can be used to distinguish, through the observation of nucleation, growth, or shrinkage of point defect clusters and their analysis by the stereo technique of Diepers [41] and Rühle [42], between the migration of vacancies and interstitials. The most complete results of this kind so far available are those of Bourret on electron-irradiated nickel presented at this conference. As discussed above, they are clearly in favour of model B. In the writer's opinion the available data on the low-temperature *magnetic aftereffect* of nickel and the associated internal friction experiments of the Grenoble group are also in favour of model B, although some open questions remain to be resolved. The experiments in progress by Lampert and Schaefer, who use rather refined experimental techniques, are expected to resolve these questions fairly soon. With regard to the *internal friction and modulus defect experiments* of Wagner on nickel I should like to emphasize that all conceivable checks have been made to ensure the reproducibility and significance of these results. I have pointed out that the most important single result of this work, namely the $\langle 100 \rangle$-symmetry of the stage-III defect, has been obtained by two independent experiments, namely from the dependence of the internal friction on both the crystal orientation and the magnetic field. Taking this together with the demonstration of Thompson and Buck (admittedly on Cu, not on Ni) that the stage-III defect must be a mono-interstitial, we arrive at the conclusion that this defect is indeed the $\langle 100 \rangle$-dumbbell.

iv) *Stage III activation energies versus mono-vacancy migration energies.* It is true that in aluminium these two energies are fairly close, possibly within experimental error. It is, however, also true that from this one should not conclude that stage III in fcc metals may be explained by mono-vacancy migration, since in Cu, Ag, and Ni — and in the author's present opinion also in Au — the two energies are sufficiently far apart to rule out such an assignment for fcc metals in general. I think that enough reliable experimental evidence on these metals has been collected that it would be futile to wait for a revision of the experimental data that would let these two energies coincide.

The author's final conclusion is that not only is the so-called two-interstitial-conversion model (model B) clearly superior to model A, but also that our picture of the annealing processes in fcc metals is now fairly complete. He hopes that the few remaining "white spots" will be filled in by this and the next generation of Ph. D. students. On the other hand, the controversies which we have had on some of the subjects discussed here appear to me to be a firm guarantee for the Ph.D. students working on some of the open questions that they will not be suddenly put out of business by an agreement between the principal opponents.

## References

[1] J.W.Corbett, R.B.Smith and R.M.Walker, Phys. Rev. 114 (1959) 1460.
[2] J.–L.Oddou, Thesis, Grenoble 1967.
[3] R.von Jan, Phys. Stat. Sol. 17 (1966) 361.
[4] D.O.Thompson, T.H.Blewitt and D.K.Holmes, J. Appl. Phys. 28 (1957) 742.
[5] D.Keefer, J.C.Robinson and A.Sosin, Acta Met. 13 (1965) 1135.

[6] D.O.Thompson and V.K.Paré, J. Appl. Phys. 31 (1960) 528.
[7] A.Sosin and D.W.Keefer, in: Microplasticity (Advances in Materials Research, Vol. 2, 1967).
[8] D.O.Thompson, O.Buck, R.S.Barnes and H.B.Huntington, J. Appl. Phys. 38 (1967) 3051.
[9] D.O.Thompson, O.Buck, H.B.Huntington and R.S.Barnes, J. Appl. Phys. 38 (1967) 3057.
[10] D.O.Thompson and O.Buck, J. Appl. Phys. 38 (1967) 3068.
[11] O.S.Oen and D.K.Holmes, J. Appl. Phys. 30 (1959) 1289.
[12] A.Seeger, P.Schiller and H.Kronmüller, Phil. Mag. 5 (1960) 853.
[13] A.Seeger, E.Mann and R.von Jan, J. Phys. Chem. Solids 23 (1962) 639.
[14] J.Völkl and W.Schilling, Phys. Kondens. Materie 1 (1963) 296.
[15] A.Seeger and F.J.Wagner, Phys. Stat. Sol. 9 (1965) 583.
[16] L.V.Meisel and D.O.Thompson, J. Appl. Phys. 39 (1968) 3447.
[17] A.H.Cottrell and B.A.Bilby, Proc. Roy. Soc. 62 (1949) 49.
[18] G.Schöck, Phys. Rev. 102 (1956) 1458.
[19] G.Schöck and A.Seeger, Acta Met. 7 (1959) 469.
[20] P.Winterhager and K.Lücke, Symp. on the Interaction between Dislocations and Point Defects (Harwell, 1968).
[21] T.J.Queen, Phil. Mag. 16 (1967) 297.
[22] A.Sosin and L.L.Bienvenue, J. Appl. Phys. 31 (1960) 249.
[23] J.N.Lomer, E.W.J.Mitchell and D.H.Niblett, Symp. on Radiation Damage in Solids and Reactor Materials, Paper SM-25 (Venice 1962).
[24] A.D.N.Smith, Phil. Mag. 44 (1953) 453.
[25] A.Granato, A.Hikata and K.Lücke, Acta Met. 6 (1958) 470.
[26] J.B.Ward and J.W.Kauffman, Phys. Rev. 123 (1961) 90.
[27] W.Bauer, J.W.DeFord and J.S.Koehler, Phys. Rev. 128 (1962) 1497.
[28] R.R.Coltman Jr., C.E.Klabunde, J.K.Redman and A.L.Southern, Jül. Conf. 2 (Vol. II) 1968, p. 770.
[29] F.Dworschak and J.S.Koehler, Phys. Rev. 140 (1965) 941.
[30] W.Bauer and A.Sosin, Phys. Letters 24A (1967) 193.
[31] W.Bauer, A.Seeger and A.Sosin, Phys. Letters 24A (1967) 195.
[32] A.Sosin and L.H.Rachal, Phys. Rev. 130 (1963) 2238.
[33] G.Duesing and W.Schilling, private communication.
[34] G.P.Scheidler and G.Roth, Jül. Conf. 2 (Vol. I) 1968, p. 391.
[35] J.S.Koehler, this volume.
[36] A.Bourret, Jül. Conf. 2 (Vol. I) 1968, p. 377.
[37] A.Bourret and D.Dautreppe, Phys. Stat. Sol. 29 (1968) 283.
[38] G.Lück and R.Sizmann, Phys. Stat. Sol. 14 (1966) 507.
[39] J.M.Galligan, this volume.
[40] E.W.Müller, this volume.
[41] H.Diepers and J.Diehl, Phys. Stat. Sol. 16 (1966) K109.
[42] M.Rühle, Phys. Stat. Sol. 19 (1967) 263.

# PANEL DISCUSSION
## (EXTRACT OF TAPE RECORDING)

The subsequent discussion was first focussed on the *magnetic after effect* phenomenon associated with *stage* $I_E$ in irradiated nickel. More specifically, the question was whether it is associated with a diffusion or with a reorientation magnetic after effect (m.a.e.). Dautreppe emphasized that whenever a single relaxation process characterized by a single relaxation time is observed, one cannot confuse the orientation m.a.e. with the diffusion m.a.e. The only exception is the case that there is a spread in activation energies. In stage $I_E$ of nickel, however, the Grenoble group *does* observe a single relaxation time. Schilling pointed out that if the question "diffusion or orientation m.a.e." is decided from the small differences in the shapes of the relaxation curves, this is difficult when annealing takes place simultaneously. Dautreppe replied that at least in the *low* temperature part of the stage I m.a.e. zone there is *no* annealing during the experiment. Kronmüller compared theoretical relaxation curves with the experimental data of Peretto (Grenoble) [1]. He showed that from relaxation curves for small measuring times $t < \tau$ ($\tau$ = time constant) one cannot distinguish between orientation and diffusion after effect, whereas at large measuring times the relaxation curves of both types of after effects show significant differences (see fig. 19 of ref. [22]). The difficulties in the analysis of the relaxation at large measuring times but small annealing times are due to the recovery of the defects. This recovery modifies the observed curves and can simulate an orientation after effect. This difficulty does not exist if the specimen has been preannealed to such an extent that during the measuring time no appreciable further recovery takes place. After such a treatment, e.g., if 75% of the relaxation effect of stage $I_E$ has annealed out, Peretto's data fit the diffusion after effect completely. This suggests that the recovery affecting the relaxation curves measured immediately after irradiation conceals the true time dependence of the relaxation process. Dautreppe replied that Peretto found an *increase* in the spread of activation energy after the early annealing Kronmüller had talked about. Questioned about the physical nature of this spread, Dautreppe was of the opinion that a spread was rather natural because free interstitial migration is accompanied by pair annihilation and by di-interstitial (or cluster) formation. Finally, it was agreed upon that Peretto's original (before annealing) curve *can* be fitted by a reorientation process. If the measured activation energy is inserted, however, this fitting implies a frequency factor of $10^{10}-10^{11}$ s$^{-1}$, which is somewhat low for elementary jumps. If, on the other hand, the fitting is done for a diffusion process with a diffusion length of, say, 50Å, the frequency factor turns out to be of the order of $10^{13}$ s$^{-1}$, which is more reasonable.

The discussion turned then towards the determination of the *annealing kinetics* in this stage and the problems associated with electrical resistivity measurements. Schilling argued that in the case of stage $I_E$ any deduction of reaction kinetics is doubtful, since the reference line of complete recovery is not known exactly. More specifically, the radiation induced electrical resistivity increment $\Delta\rho$ is a direct measure of the concentration of mobile defects only in the beginning of the re- covery process. In the final part of the stage, the value of $\Delta\rho$ depends increasingly on the sink density or cluster concentration rather than on the mobile defect con- centration. Seeger added that experimentally determined recovery kinetics of stage $I_E$ are indeed reliable only if stages II and III are vanishing or amount to a very small fraction of the initial resistivity increment only. However, according to Oddou (Grenoble) [2] this is the case for electron-irradiated nickel. This question of reac- tion order $\gamma$ has an important bearing on the question as to whether the crowdion- type interstitial exists or not. For free (one-dimensional) migration of crowdions one expects $\gamma = 3$. For three-dimensional migration of interstitials, however, $\gamma$ should lie between 1 and 2 (Seeger [3]). In the case of nickel Oddou found $\gamma = 3$ in iso- thermal annealing runs of the electrical resistivity. Moser pointed out, however, that the temperature shift of the recovery stage with increasing dose observed by Oddou did *not* confirm Oddou's isothermal data. To illustrate the stage $I_E$ situation in elec- tron-irradiated copper, Corbett compared the Corbett-Smith-Walker [4,5] fit (fig. 1) of their resistivity data with the Frank-Seeger-Schottky [6] fit (fig. 2) of the same data, with the latter fit being based on crowdion kinetics.

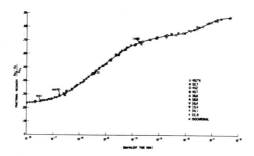

Fig. 1. Corbett-Smith-Walker fit [4] for stage-$I_D$ and -$I_E$ recovery in copper following electron irradiation.

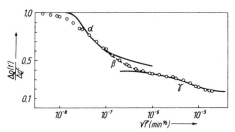

Fig. 2. Comparison between crowdion recovery kinetics [6] and the experiments of Corbett et al. [4] on stage-$I_D$ and -$I_E$ recovery in electron irradiated copper.

Further experimental difficulties were emphasized by Wenzl. Whenever one has different kinds of scattering centres (foreign atoms, clusters, etc.), one may have deviations from Matthiessen's rule, even in cases where the reference line of zero recovery is approximately reached at the end of stage $I_E$.

Quéré focussed the discussion on the *motion* of crowdion. He felt that it was difficult to have the crowdion move freely (thermally activated) along the ⟨110⟩-direction while around this path there are positions of lower energy which the crowdion could adopt. He considered this question of free crowdion migration as one of the weak points of the two-interstitial model. Irradiation experiments at subthreshold energies such as performed in Jülich might give an answer to this problem. In such experiments one may have a number of crowdions present in the freshly irradiated state, but in a long-time irradiation experiment they should be converted so that — within the two-interstitial model — essentially dumbbell interstitials would be present in the specimen. In defending the crowdion concept, Seeger drew attention to the experimental evidence for a conversion mechanism. The work of Thompson and Buck [7–9], for example, suggests an activation energy of 0.3–0.4 eV for thermal conversion of crowdions into dumbbell interstitials. Seeger felt that the cadmium data of Coltman et al. [10] could also be understood in terms of the two-interstitial model. The observation that for long irradiation times the high-temperature fraction of recovery increases at the expense of the low-temperature stages might in fact indicate that certain interstitial configurations could be wiped out by long time irradiation, implying that more than one interstitial configuration exist [11]. Corbett and Wollenberger interjected that according to the latter's [12, 13] experimental results on electron-irradiated copper there was no enormous thermal conversion taking place. If there were thermal conversion, one would expect a temperature dependence of the production rate. In reply to questions by Schilling and Corbett about the evidence for thermal conversion, Seeger outlined again the Thompson and Buck experiment [7–9]. In those experiments, high-purity copper was γ-irradiated at room temperature such that the defect concentration remained below $10^{-13}$. Therefore, all dimer formation and trapping could be excluded. They measured the dislocation pinning rate and drew the following conclusion:

1. Approximately one defect per displacement arrived at the dislocations.
2. The pinning defects had a migration energy of 0.65 eV.
3. There was no fast pinning component.
4. The pinning defects were not fast-moving defects that had been temporarily held up at traps.
5. Furthermore, as explained in ref. [3], the pinning defect gave rise to a Snoek effect, i.e., it was anisotropic. Therefore the defect cannot be a vacancy, and since the experiment involves only simple defects, it must be an interstitial.

In a discussion with Corbett, Seeger reemphasized that the Thompson-Buck experiments gave direct evidence for the thermal conversion of the $I_E$-defects. Corbett insisted that the resistivity experiments by Wollenberger just did *not* show a production mechanism for such stage-III interstitials. It turned out to be difficult to compare defect production rates for electron irradiations at $4.2°K$ with those for $\gamma$-irradiations at room temperature, since in the former experiments correlated (and to some extent spontaneous) close-pair recovery is predominant while in the latter experiments the chances for an interstitial to arrive at a dislocation is much larger than that to find a vacancy.

The discussion turned then to the *gold dilemma*. Venables drew attention to the observation of interstitial clustering reported by Koehler [14] and to his own studies [15], both of which — he claimed — suggest long-range migration at low temperatures. The absence of appreciable dislocation pinning at low temperatures in irradiated gold might not necessarily indicate absence of long-range migration, but may alternatively mean that interstitials can move along the dislocations without pinning. Seeger replied that defect motion along dislocations is accounted for in the interpretation of Thompson's and Buck's experiments, but that it cannot be a big effect for the low-temperature defect, since unpinning (reduction in modulus) occurs at fairly high temperatures only. Furthermore, he pointed out that for the two-interstitial model it is not essential whether in Au there is low-temperature migration or not. He emphasized that a detailed discussion of the gold problem remains difficult as long as the defenders of a low-temperature free migration in gold cannot present the temperature of the onset of free migration, the activation energy of free migration and a recovery stage which shifts to lower temperatures with increasing dose. Several speakers mentioned relevant experiments: Koehler said that the defect production rate at $110°K$ in a quenched specimen indicates some interstitial migration below this temperature. Corbett reminded the audience of Swanson's [16] similar experiments at $4.2°K$ and pointed out that impurity effects might play a larger role in "high-purity gold" than has been realized so far. Lomer said that she saw dislocation pinning in gold irradiated at $20°K$, which suggests defect migration below this temperature. Schilling contributed the essential results of his review paper [17] on this point, namely

1. Stage-I recovery is smaller in gold than in other f.c.c. metals.
2. The influence of vacancy doping on the production rate and recovery of gold is contradictory in literature.

3. Radiation doping decreases stage I of gold, while an increase is observed in other f.c.c. metals.

To Corbett this experimental situation looks as if what is called stage I in gold exhibits the same phenomenon as stage II in copper, implying that in gold interstitials would have to migrate below 1.8°K, as in silicon, for example. This raised the question of whether interstitials might migrate under the influence of zero point oscillations (Schilling). Seeger argued that if the migration energy for interstitials in gold was very low, the physical effects would not be essentially different from those of an athermal process, e.g., long-range propagation due to focussing. He emphasized that in all these cases one could not well understand the series of first-order annealing peaks above 10°K, which has been repeatedly verified and which then could not be explained in terms of close-pair stages. Koehler did not share Corbett's view that this substructure corresponds to stage II in dirty copper, i.e., to detrapping processes, but considered them intrinsic to gold. He felt that in gold close-pair recombination stages could in principle occur also *above* the long-range migration stage (trapped pair annihilation), but this would not well explain the difference between gold and the other f.c.c. metals. Quéré and Koehler mentioned the several years old proposal by Koehler and Leibfried [18] who postulated that in copper and silver interstitials are on octahedral sites whereas for gold the split ⟨100⟩-interstitial is considered to be the stable configuration. To Koehler this would be one possible way to explain the apparently more complicated situation in gold.

Concerning the focussing events in irradiated f.c.c. metals, Wollenberger pointed out the discrepancy which exists between experiment and theory. From the tail of the defect production rates in gold, a reaction volume of $\approx 10^4$ atomic volumes (corresponding to $10^3$ atomic distances) can be derived for the focussing event. This is considerably more than is found in the calculations by Duesing and Leibfried [19] (25 atomic distances) and in those of the Brookhaven group [20]. Wollenberger felt that this discrepancy was a strong indication for a mobile defect in gold at 7°K. Diehl questioned the validity of the theoretical estimates in view of the fact that in ion-bombarded thin foils of gold and copper the range of focussing collisions at room temperature and at liquid nitrogen temperature were found to lie between 150 and 250Å. Venables said that the interpretation of his experiments required ranges of up to 2000 Å. He emphasized that the temperature dependence of the focussing collision phenomenon is still unknown.

At this point the Chairman suggested to leave the low-temperature stages and to turn to the interpretation of *stage III*. Van den Beukel turned to "Seeger's opponents" by firstly asking whether there is an alternative explanation for the mechanical and magnetic after effects in stage III of nickel as reported by the Stuttgart group and compiled in Kronmüller's paper [22]. Corbett said that trapped interstititals and/or di-interstitials in various configurations provide multiple possibilities to give rise to such after effects, and Dautreppe pointed out that the stage III m.a.e. is several orders of magnitude smaller than the stage I m.a.e. and superimposed on a strong background. Both speakers felt that the Stuttgart peak is not particularly distinguished

from the other peaks occurring all over stages II, III, and IV. Seeger replied that
the peak *has* been shown to be a distinguished one. He recalled the essential features
of the mechanical measurements by Wagner [23]. The defect has a ⟨100⟩-orientation,
it is a *single* relaxation peak and is *not* due to impurity effects. Its absolute height is
consistent with modulus measurements and theoretical estimates of the relaxation
strength of the defect. Lücke presented his viewpoint that although nothing speaks
against the interpretation of Wagner's experiments in terms of a dumbbell interstitial, the published experimental data still leave room for doubts in view of the
large background of the measurements. He added that in his opinion the situation
in copper was not much better than in nickel.

Secondly, van den Beukel invited comments on the "stage-III dilemma" encountered by vacancy models for stage III. He quoted the evidence presented by Schilling [17], according to which stage III is due to a unique defect moving. In the cases
of gold, aluminium, and perhaps platinum a single vacancy mechanism might work.
In the case of copper, however, it would then be difficult to understand Koehler's
assignment of *di*vacancies to the 0.7-eV-process in stage III, since in van den Beukel's
opinion at defect concentrations of $10^{-6}$ such as employed in the electron irradiation
experiments divacancies can be neither produced during irradiation nor be formed by
migration of single vacancies. Consequently, 0.7 eV in stage III of Cu would have to
correspond to *single* vacancies. Koehler agreed that there is a problem in both Ag and
Cu how divacancies can be produced in stage III. He defended his view by proposing
that there might be more than one divacancy production mechanism. Firstly, he felt
that in the beginning of annealing vacancies start to move at a reduced activation
energy in the strain field of interstitial clusters and that association into divacancies
occurs at later stages of annealing. Secondly, he proposed that the strain field of
interstitial clusters might have a complicated geometry. Interstitials migrating into
this strain field may mop up vacancies that are in their paths, but may leave a supersaturation of vacancies in the repulsive directions. Such a region would then favour
divacancy formation. In referring to the analysis of self-diffusion and high-temperature data [24], Seeger compared the activation energies $E_{1V}^{M}$ obtained for single
vacancy migration with those given for stage III in gold and aluminium. Although
in Au the difference between the activation energy of migration of single vacancies
of 0.89 eV (which is in agreement with the extrapolation of the activation energies
to zero impurity content presented on a slide of Professor Koehler's lecture) and
the stage-III activation energy of about 0.81 eV is not very large, Seeger felt that
the two processes involved were of different natures (e.g., monovacancies and interstitials). He admitted that in Al the margin between the monovacancy migration
energy and the stage-III energy was so small that it is indeed hard to decide whether
the interstitial or the single vacancy is more mobile.

Lucasson tried to cast some light on the stage-III dilemma by looking at some
"more specific" experiments. He felt that Wollenberger's doping experiments
[12, 13] are not necessarily to be interpreted in terms of a third type of interstitial
(as discussed by Wollenberger), but may rather support the thermal conversion

model. The post-doping specimen (doping in stage III) would likely contain a different distribution of Frenkel pairs with a different spontaneous recombination volume and a different Frenkel pair resistivity as compared to the specimen freshly irradiated at 4.2°K [25]. Wollenberger explained his results in the following way: They measured the defect production rate by electrons in copper before and after stage-III annealing. The resistivity data are interpreted to indicate that in this stage either vacancies migrate or interstitials are converted into a configuration with a higher resistivity.

Koehler then turned to the theoreticians and asked them to present their view on interstitial configurations and mobilities, but the response was not very strong. Torrens suggested that a one-dimensional migration of an interstitial with a smaller activation energy than that for thermal migration in the lattice might be possible if following one jump the interstitial retains a little kinetic energy and the lattice ahead is relaxed.

At this time, the Chairman proposed to devote the final minutes to some *specific problems* on individual metals, which had not been discussed yet. Schilling recalled that in the case of platinum he considers the stage-III dilemma solved by relabelling the nomenclature (calling the old stage IV now stage III). Secondly, he considered it puzzling that in copper electron irradiated by Scheidler, Rühle found after stage-III annealing both interstitial *and* vacancy clusters [26]. He felt that this would either imply vacancy migration in stage III or direct generation of vacancy agglomerates by the low-temperature irradiation. The latter process appears, however, unlikely in view of the electron microscope experiments by Scheidler and Roth [27] who found that the cluster density increases proportional to the dose. Seeger emphasized the still preliminary character of the copper observations and drew attention to the more complete *nickel* study presented by Bourret [28]. The latter did find an incubation period in nickel. Seeger expressed the view that in these highly-irradiated materials, the formation of vacancy clusters may be easily understood in terms of multiple vacancies.

Holmes reminded the audience of the stage-$I_D$ and -$I_E$ copper experiments by Coltman et al. [29] which seemed to be in good agreement with the view now generally accepted.

Venables took up gold once again in stating that people who have been looking for interstitial evidence in stage III of gold do not find any now. So he claimed that the burden of proof *for* a stage-III interstitial should be taken over by those who proposed it. Seeger replied that for this kind of proof gold is an unsuitable metal (as would also be aluminium), since the activation energies of stage III and of vacancy migration differ by a few percent only. Venables felt that this was not a good argument.

Mughrabi emphasized the disagreement between high-temperature equilibrium data on formation energies and defect properties from irradiation recovery stages, which might arise if interstitial migration is assigned to temperatures below stage III and vacancies to stage III.

Koehler pointed out that in high-purity platinum, gold, and aluminium very little extra resistivity is left after stage III, and that preliminary experiments on silver in his laboratory [30] indicate the same phenomenon. Isebeck questioned him about the physical reason for assuming that in the case of vacancy annealing at interstitial clusters the reaction rate is proportional to the number of interstitials in the cluster. Koehler argued qualitatively that the strain field of a cluster is proportional to the number of defects and that vacancy motion towards the cluster is dependent on the strain field. He felt that in certain cases this effect may even lower the activation energy of the vacancies.

Blewitt suggested that simultaneous measurements of the change in lattice parameter $\Delta a/a$ and some other physical property might clarify the nature of stage III ($\Delta a/a$ increases for interstitials and decreases for vacancies). Preliminary experiments on copper by this technique are felt to favour vacancy migration. Wenzl replied that if interstitials or vacancies interact without condensing into dislocation loops, then length and lattice parameter change in the same way and the experiment is not decisive. In stage III of copper, he found from $\Delta l/l$ and $\Delta a/a$ measurements that interstitial agglomeration into Frank loops is predominant over vacancy agglomeration, although the experimental errors were quite large.

At this point the Chairman stopped the discussion because the time was over. He emphasized that it would not be easy to summarize the entire discussion. Nevertheless, there was general agreement on the nature of stages I and II, while residual problems of $I_E$ and the entire stage III had not been resolved by this panel discussion. He urged the audience to concentrate on experiments involving techniques other than electrical resistivity, and he suggested doping experiments as a powerful tool for future studies. Furthermore, he considered desirable more knowledge of the actual sink density in experiments and advocated studies of the variation of the defect jump numbers with the sink density. Such problems were amenable to attack by high-voltage transmission electron microscopy. There was still a need for more experiments which could be directly and unambiguously interpreted.

## References

[1] P.Peretto, P.Moser and D.Dautreppe, Phys. Stat. Sol. 13 (1966) 325.
[2] J.L.Oddou, Thesis, University of Grenoble, 1967.
[3] See A.Seeger's introductory remarks to the panel discussion, this volume, p. 999.
[4] J.W.Corbett, R.B.Smith and R.M.Walker, Phys. Rev. 114 (1959) 1460.
[5] See J.W.Corbett's introductory remarks to the panel discussion, this volume, p. 977.
[6] W.Frank, A.Seeger and G.Schottky, Phys. Stat. Sol. 8 (1965) 345.
[7] D.O.Thompson, O.Buck, R.S.Barnes and H.B.Huntington, J. Appl. Phys. 38 (1967) 3051.
[8] D.O.Thompson, O.Buck, H.B.Huntington and R.S.Barnes, J. Appl. Phys. 38 (1967) 3057.
[9] D.O.Thompson and O.Buck, J. Appl. Phys. 38 (1967) 3068.
[10] R.R.Coltman, C.E.Klabunde, J.K.Redman and A.L.Southern, Jül. Conf. 2 (Vol. II) 1968, p. 770.
[11] Cf.: A.Seeger's comment to the paper of D.Schmacher in this volume.
[12] F.Dworschak, H.Schuster, H.Wollenberger and J.Wurm, Phys. Stat. Sol. 29 (1968) 75.

[13] F.Dworschak, H.Schuster, H.Wollenberger and J.Wurm, Phys. Stat. Sol. 29 (1968) 81.

[14] J.S.Koehler, this volume.

[15] J.A.Venables and G.J.Thomas, this volume.

[16] M.L.Swanson and G.R.Piercy, Can. J. Phys. 42 (1964) 1605.

[17] W.Schilling, this volume.

[18] J.S.Koehler and G.Leibfried, J. Phys. Soc. Japan 18, suppl. III (1963) 266.

[19] G.Duesing and G.Leibfried, Phys. Stat. Sol. 9 (1965) 463.

[20] J.G.Gibson, A.N.Goland, M.Milgram and G.H.Vineyard, Phys. Rev. 120 (1960) 1229.

[21] J.Diehl, H.Diepers and B.Hertel, Can. J. Phys. 46 (1968) 647.

[22] H.Kronmüller, this volume.

[23] A.Seeger and F.J.Wagner, Phys. Stat. Sol. 9 (1965) 583.

[24] A.Seeger and H.Mehrer, this volume.

[25] Cf. P.Lucasson's comment to H.Wollenberger's contribution, this volume.

[26] F.Häussermann, M.Rühle, G.P.Scheidler and G.Roth, to be published.

[27] G.P.Scheidler and G.Roth, Jül. Conf. 2 (vol. I), 1968, p. 391.

[28] A.Bourret and D.Dautreppe, Phys. Stat. Sol. 29 (1968) 283.

[29] R.R.Coltman, Jr., C.E.Klabunde and J.K.Redman, Phys. Rev. 159 (1967) 521.

[30] J.S.Koehler, see his introductory remarks to the panel discussion, this volume, p. 989.

# PART 10


# APPENDIX

# TITLES OF CONTRIBUTED PAPERS

(Full papers have been published in the report Jül. Conf. 2 (Vol. I, II) 1968 *.
The indicated page numbers refer to that report.)

## I. Diffusion and equilibrium measurements

* Copies of this report may be obtained from Zentralbibliothek der Kernforschungsanlage
Jülich GmbH, Jülich, Germany.

# AUTHOR INDEX*

---

\* Numbers in italics refer to the references to the literature.

# SUBJECT INDEX